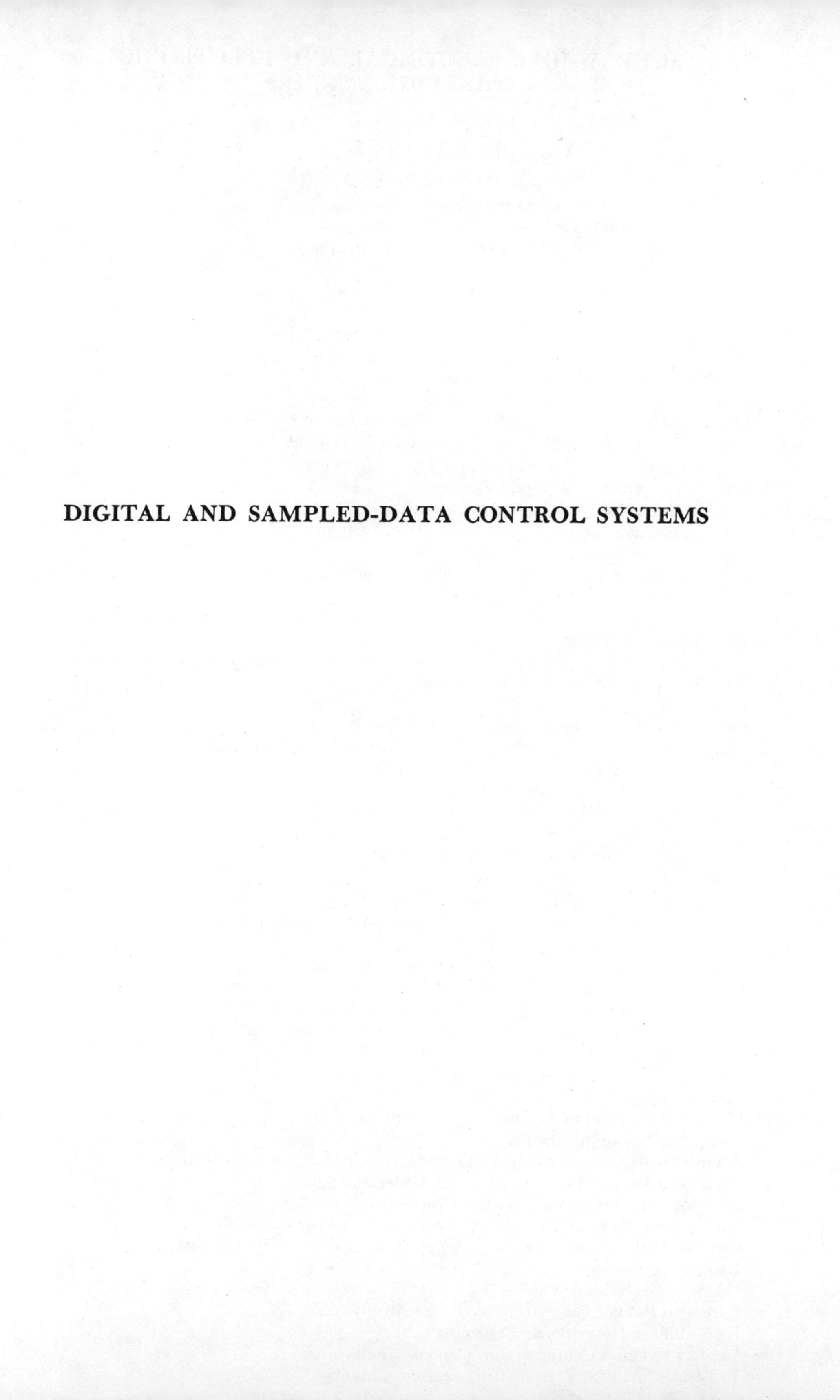

DIGITAL AND SAMPLED-DATA CONTROL SYSTEMS

McGRAW-HILL ELECTRICAL AND ELECTRONIC ENGINEERING SERIES

Frederick Emmons Terman, *Consulting Editor*
W. W. Harman and J. G. Truxal,
Associate Consulting Editors

Ahrendt and Savant · Servomechanism Practice
Angelo · Electronic Circuits
Aseltine · Transform Method in Linear System Analysis
Atwater · Introduction to Microwave Theory
Bailey and Gault · Alternating-current Machinery
Beranek · Acoustics
Bracewell · The Fourier Transform and Its Applications
Bracewell · Transform Methods in Linear Systems
Brenner and Javid · Analysis of Electric Circuits
Brown · Analysis of Linear Time-invariant Systems
Bruns and Saunders · Analysis of Feedback Control Systems
Cage · Theory and Application of Industrial Electronics
Cauer · Synthesis of Linear Communication Networks
Chen · The Analysis of Linear Systems
Chen · Linear Network Design and Synthesis
Chirlian · Analysis and Design of Electronic Circuits
Chirlian and Zemanian · Electronics
Clement and Johnson · Electrical Engineering Science
Cote and Oakes · Linear Vacuum-tube and Transistor Circuits
Cuccia · Harmonics, Sidebands, and Transients in Communication Engineering
Cunningham · Introduction to Nonlinear Analysis
D'Azzo and Houpis · Feedback Control System Analysis and Synthesis
Eastman · Fundamentals of Vacuum Tubes
Elgerd · Control Systems Theory
Feinstein · Foundations of Information Theory
Fitzgerald and Higginbotham · Basic Electrical Engineering
Fitzgerald and Kingsley · Electric Machinery
Frank · Electrical Measurement Analysis
Friedland, Wing, and Ash · Principles of Linear Networks
Ghausi · Principles and Design of Linear Active Circuits
Ghose · Microwave Circuit Theory and Analysis
Greiner · Semiconductor Devices and Applications
Hammond · Electrical Engineering
Hancock · An Introduction to the Principles of Communication Theory
Happell and Hesselberth · Engineering Electronics
Harman · Fundamentals of Electronic Motion
Harman · Principles of the Statistical Theory of Communication
Harman and Lytle · Electrical and Mechanical Networks
Harrington · Introduction to Electromagnetic Engineering
Harrington · Time-harmonic Electromagnetic Fields
Hayashi · Nonlinear Oscillations in Physical Systems
Hayt · Engineering Electromagnetics
Hayt and Kemmerly · Engineering Circuit Analysis
Hill · Electronics in Engineering
Javid and Brenner · Analysis, Transmission, and Filtering of Signals
Javid and Brown · Field Analysis and Electromagnetics
Johnson · Transmission Lines and Networks
Koenig and Blackwell · Electromechanical System Theory
Koenig, Tokad, and Kesavan · Analysis of Discrete Physical Systems
Kraus · Antennas
Kraus · Electromagnetics
Kuh and Pederson · Principles of Circuit Synthesis
Kuo · Linear Networks and Systems
Ledley · Digital Computer and Control Engineering
LePage · Analysis of Alternating-current Circuits

LePage · Complex Variables and the Laplace Transform for Engineering
LePage and Seely · General Network Analysis
Levi and Panzer · Electromechanical Power Conversion
Ley, Lutz, and Rehberg · Linear Circuit Analysis
Linvill and Gibbons · Transistors and Active Circuits
Littauer · Pulse Electronics
Lynch and Truxal · Introductory System Analysis
Lynch and Truxal · Principles of Electronic Instrumentation
Lynch and Truxal · Signals and Systems in Electrical Engineering
Manning · Electrical Circuits
McCluskey · Introduction to the Theory of Switching Circuits
Meisel · Principles of Electromechanical-energy Conversion
Millman · Vacuum-tube and Semiconductor Electronics
Millman and Seely · Electronics
Millman and Taub · Pulse and Digital Circuits
Millman and Taub · Pulse, Digital, and Switching Waveforms
Mishkin and Braun · Adaptive Control Systems
Moore · Traveling-wave Engineering
Nanavati · An Introduction to Semiconductor Electronics
Pettit · Electronic Switching, Timing, and Pulse Circuits
Pettit and McWhorter · Electronic Amplifier Circuits
Pfeiffer · Concepts of Probability Theory
Pfeiffer · Linear Systems Analysis
Reza · An Introduction to Information Theory
Reza and Seely · Modern Network Analysis
Rogers · Introduction to Electric Fields
Ruston and Bordogna · Electric Networks: Functions, Filters, Analysis
Ryder · Engineering Electronics
Schwartz · Information Transmission, Modulation, and Noise
Schwarz and Friedland · Linear Systems
Seely · Electromechanical Energy Conversion
Seely · Electron-tube Circuits
Seely · Electronic Engineering
Seely · Introduction to Electromagnetic Fields
Seely · Radio Electronics
Seifert and Steeg · Control Systems Engineering
Siskind · Direct-current Machinery
Skilling · Electric Transmission Lines
Skilling · Transient Electric Currents
Spangenberg · Fundamentals of Electron Devices
Spangenberg · Vacuum Tubes
Stevenson · Elements of Power System Analysis
Stewart · Fundamentals of Signal Theory
Storer · Passive Network Synthesis
Strauss · Wave Generation and Shaping
Su · Active Network Synthesis
Terman · Electronic and Radio Engineering
Terman and Pettit · Electronic Measurements
Thaler · Elements of Servomechanism Theory
Thaler and Brown · Analysis and Design of Feedback Control Systems
Thaler and Pastel · Analysis and Design of Nonlinear Feedback Control Systems
Thompson · Alternating-current and Transient Circuit Analysis
Tou · Digital and Sampled-data Control Systems
Tou · Modern Control Theory
Truxal · Automatic Feedback Control System Synthesis
Tuttle · Electric Networks: Analysis and Synthesis
Valdes · The Physical Theory of Transistors
Van Bladel · Electromagnetic Fields
Weinberg · Network Analysis and Synthesis
Williams and Young · Electrical Engineering Problems

Digital and Sampled-data Control Systems

JULIUS T. TOU
Associate Professor of Electrical Engineering
Purdue University

McGRAW-HILL BOOK COMPANY
New York Toronto London
1959

DIGITAL AND SAMPLED-DATA CONTROL SYSTEMS

 Library of Congress Catalog Card Number 59-8569

7 8 9 10 - MP - 9 8
65085

To My Grandfather
in honor of
his 80th birthday

PREFACE

This book was written to provide scientists, engineers, and system analysts with a comprehensive, well-organized, and up-to-date account of the basic theory and available techniques for the analysis and design of digital and sampled-data control systems and related problems. The material presented in this text is, in the main, the outgrowth of a set of lecture notes, first prepared in 1956, for a two-semester course offered by the author to graduate students at the Moore School of the University of Pennsylvania.

In recent years, the intense and widespread interest in digital and sampled-data control has resulted in great advances in the development of theory and techniques for the analysis and design of control systems involving digital equipment. The subject of digital and sampled-data control systems has become, in the past decade, an important phase of control engineering. The bulk of the material dealing with this subject, however, has been widely scattered in various technical journals or proceedings of conferences. Consequently, it is rather difficult for an engineer, particularly a newcomer to the field, to learn the state of the art of this subject when he has not been following it closely. This text attempts to put under one cover available techniques and fundamental principles and to organize them in a coherent and unified manner. A certain amount of original material has been included, although, as evidenced by the numbered references, most of the material has been derived from other sources in the literature.

The present volume is intended to be of use both as a textbook and as a reference. The material is so arranged that it progresses from the simpler to the more difficult problems. To the student, it presents in step-by-step fashion a discussion of basic theory and important techniques. For the practicing engineer, it provides in systematic form a ready source of reference material. In the preparation of the book, an attempt was made to make as many of the chapters as possible self-contained or partially independent. As a background to the text, it is assumed that the reader has adequate preparation in an introductory course on feedback control systems and has a sound knowledge of Laplace transforms and complex variable theory.

In presenting the material, emphasis is placed upon the development of basic theory. Many numerical examples are worked out in the text to clarify the development of the theory and to illustrate the discussion of the various methods. A feature of the book is the unified, concise, definitive mathematical treatment in the body of the text complemented by applications in the problem section. Some 70 problems of various types and complexity are included in Appendix 3. Nevertheless, in keeping the book at a reasonable length, it is necessary to ask the reader to use as additional illustrations examples from his own experience.

Citations are generally avoided in the text. However, a list of numbered references forms Appendix 2, which covers the contributions of many workers in the field. In view of the enormous literature on this subject published in the technical journals of many countries, the list of references in Appendix 2 must remain incomplete. To those contributors in the field whose publications are omitted from the list due to the author's oversight, he wishes to express his apology.

The subject matter may be divided into three main parts: (1) introductory material, (2) system analysis, (3) system design. Chapters 1 through 3 are introductory in nature and serve as a brief review of the background material. For those readers who have had a thorough training in basic control theory, Chapter 2 may be skipped. The second part is comprised of Chapters 4 through 7. Chapter 4 discusses the important aspects of system analysis from the frequency domain point of view through the extension of conventional techniques. In Chapter 5, the reader is introduced to the z-transform method and its variations, which form the basis for the development of the remaining chapters of the book. Chapters 6 and 7 emphasize system analysis by the z-transform techniques. The third part covers Chapters 8 through 10. Chapter 8 is concerned with analog-digital conversion techniques, and Chapters 9 and 10 are devoted to system-design techniques and principles. The book concludes with a discussion of the problem of finite sampling duration. In the last chapter, the τ-transform analysis is introduced and several approximation methods are discussed. Appended are a table of z transforms and modified z transforms, a list of over 200 references, and a section on problems.

The author wishes to express his deep appreciation for the intellectual stimulation he has received from his coworkers throughout the world. He owes a debt of gratitude to Dr. John G. Truxal, Head of the Electrical Engineering Department, Polytechnic Institute of Brooklyn, who read the manuscript and contributed many excellent ideas and innumerable constructive suggestions. The author is also indebted to his colleagues and students at the University of Pennsylvania and Purdue University, who assisted in the preparation of the manuscript. Discussions with Drs. J. G. Brainerd and Morris Rubinoff of the University of Pennsylvania were particularly helpful. Messrs. G. A. Austin, E. S. McVey, and R. Sridhar of Purdue University did most of the proofreading and deserve special mention. Something more than thanks is due the author's wife who typed the manuscript and assisted in its preparation. Without her help and patience the book could never have been completed.

Julius T. Tou

CONTENTS

Preface ix

Chapter 1. Introduction 1

1.1. Types of Feedback Control Systems 1
1.2. Definition of Digital and Sampled-data Systems 5
1.3. Importance of Sampling and Digital Techniques in Control Field . . . 6
1.4. Methods of Analysis and Synthesis for Sampled-data and Digital Control Systems 10
1.5. Examples of Digital and Sampled-data Control Systems 11

Chapter 2. Continuous-data Control Systems 14

2.1. Introduction 14
2.2. Block-diagram Reduction 17
2.3. Stability Criteria 20
2.4. Asymptotic Gain and Phase Plots 31
2.5. Control-system Compensation 36
2.6. Root-locus Method 45
2.7. Modulated Control Systems 60

Chapter 3. Basic Theory of Sampling and Quantizing 69

3.1. Sampling Process 69
3.2. Analysis of the Unit-sampling Function 70
3.3. Frequency Spectra of Sampled Signals 72
3.4. Effects of Clamping 76
3.5. Sampling Theorems 80
3.6. Amplitude Quantization 83

Chapter 4. Frequency Domain Analysis 93

4.1. Properties of the Sampler 93
4.2. Comparison between Continuous-data and Sampled-data Systems . . . 102
4.3. Frequency Response and Transfer Function of Sampled-data and Digital Control Systems 108
4.4. Construction of Frequency-characteristic Locus 117
4.5. Stability Considerations 125
4.6. Properties of Holding Devices 127
4.7. The Effects of External Disturbances and Nonlinearities 140
4.8. Conclusion 144

Chapter 5. Theory of the *z* Transformation 145

5.1. Definition of *z* Transform and Pulse-transfer Function 145
5.2. Evaluation of *z* Transforms and Pulse-transfer Functions 149

5.3. Basic z-transformation Theorems . . . 161
5.4. Properties of Pulse-transfer Functions . . . 166
5.5. z-Transform Loci . . . 169
5.6. Inverse z Transformations . . . 176
5.7. Modified z Transforms . . . 184
5.8. Numerical Integration; z Forms . . . 198
5.9. Conclusion . . . 212

Chapter 6. z-Transform Analysis . . . 214

6.1. Block Diagrams and Output Transforms of Sampled-data Control Systems 214
6.2. Graphical Stability Analysis; Schur-Cohn Criterion; Bilinear Transformation . . . 230
6.3. Evaluation of System Response at Sampling Instants . . . 249
6.4. System Response during Intersampling Periods . . . 255
6.5. Steady-state Error at the Sampling Instants . . . 265
6.6. Error Coefficients . . . 269
6.7. Multirate Sampled-data Control Systems . . . 281
6.8. Sampled-data Systems with Nonsynchronized Samplers . . . 304
6.9. Cyclic Variable-rate Sampled-data Systems . . . 308
6.10. Sampled-data Feedback Control Systems with Transport Lags . . . 318
6.11. Conclusion . . . 321

Chapter 7. Transient Response and System-error Analysis . . . 323

7.1. Effect of the Pole-zero Configurations in the z Plane upon the System Transient Behavior . . . 323
7.2. Maximum Transient Overshoot and Peak Time of the Output Sequence . 327
7.3. Analysis of System Error and Intersampling Ripples . . . 336
7.4. Determination of Sampling Frequency; Ripple Factor . . . 349
7.5. High-frequency Oscillations between Sampling Instants . . . 356
7.6. Conclusion . . . 367

Chapter 8. Analog-Digital Conversion Principles . . . 368

8.1. Introduction . . . 368
8.2. Number Systems for Digital Control . . . 369
8.3. Basic Conversion Requirements . . . 375
8.4. Encoding Techniques . . . 377
8.5. A High-speed Encoder Utilizing Operational Amplifiers . . . 390
8.6. Decoding Techniques . . . 394
8.7. Conclusion . . . 404

Chapter 9. General Design Principles . . . 405

9.1. Introduction . . . 405
9.2. Sinusoidal Sequences . . . 410
9.3. Reshaping of the Open-loop Frequency-characteristic Locus . . . 413
9.4. Cascade Compensation by Continuous-data Networks . . . 416
9.5. Cascade Compensation by Pulsed-data Networks . . . 430
9.6. Realization of Pulse-transfer Functions . . . 444
9.7. Synthesis in the w Plane by the Bode-diagram Technique . . . 465
9.8. Root-locus Method in the z Plane . . . 479
9.9. Conclusion . . . 499

Chapter 10. Optimum Control through Digital Compensation 501

10.1. Introduction 501
10.2. Systems Having Fastest Response and Zero Steady-state Error at the Sampling Instants 502
10.3. Suppression of Intersampling Ripples 512
10.4. Minimization of System Error 518
10.5. Systems with Multiple Inputs 525
10.6. Design of Multirate Compensators 531
10.7. Statistical Design Principles 534
10.8. Adaptive Control 552
10.9. Simulation 557
10.10. Conclusion 560

Chapter 11. Analysis of Sampled-data Control Systems with Finite Sampling Duration 562

11.1. Introduction 562
11.2. The Sampler and the Delayed z Transform 563
11.3. Sampler with Finite Sampling Duration and τ Transform 567
11.4. System Analysis 571
11.5. An Alternate Approach 580
11.6. Conclusion 585

Appendix 1. Table of z Transforms and Modified z Transforms 588

Appendix 2. References 593

Appendix 3. Problems 604

Index 625

CHAPTER 1

INTRODUCTION

1.1. Types of Feedback Control Systems. "A feedback control system is a control system comprising one or more feedback control loops, which combines functions of the controlled signals with functions of the commands to tend to maintain prescribed relationships between the commands and the controlled signals. . . . A servomechanism is a feedback control system in which one or more of the system signals represent mechanical motion."†

The importance of automatic control and servomechanisms to our modern civilization and particularly to national defense cannot be overemphasized. For instance, in modern houses, the temperature and humidity are automatically regulated for comfortable living; in industry, feedback control systems are employed for increasing the production as well as for improving the quality of the products; in aviation and navigation, airplanes and steamships are controlled by servomechanisms for safe and comfortable traveling; and in national defense, feedback controls are vitally needed in the guidance of missiles and for fast and accurate control of antiaircraft artillery and other weapons.

The main purposes of using feedback in a control system are to monitor or control a high-power, low-accuracy output element of the system with an accurate, sensitive measuring device in the feedback loop and to reduce unwanted output due to any disturbance in the forward path of the control system. When a disturbance occurs in a system and causes an undesired output, an actuating error signal will be generated, flowing down the forward path to make necessary corrections. In view of their importance, a considerable amount of work has been done during the past two decades in the analysis and synthesis of feedback control systems. Today, feedback control and servomechanisms have become one of the most fascinating fields of engineering.

Feedback control systems can be classified in a variety of ways. Their classification can be made with respect to the properties of the components constituting the control system; or they can be classified with regard to the nature of the signals flowing in the control system. According to the

† IRE Standards on Terminology for Feedback Control Systems, *Proc. IRE*, January, 1956.

properties of the system components, feedback control systems can be divided into two types:

1. Linear feedback control systems
2. Nonlinear feedback control systems

Linear and nonlinear control systems may be further subdivided into systems with constant parameters and systems with time-varying parameters.

In linear feedback control systems the relationships between the pertinent measures of the system signals are linear. A linear feedback control system with constant parameters is made up of linear components which can be described by linear differential equations with constant coefficients and by transfer functions. This type of linear feedback control problem is among the simplest and can usually be solved systematically by conventional techniques.

A feedback control system with variable coefficients which are explicit functions of time is called a time-varying feedback control system. For instance, feedback control systems for rocket-powered guided missiles, supersonic aircraft, and fast-running steel and paper mills are control systems of this type. In common practice, time-varying control systems often refer to linear systems with time-varying parameters, which can then be described by linear differential equations with variable coefficients.

The analysis of linear time-varying control systems is more difficult than that of linear control systems with constant coefficients. The response of a linear time-varying control system is a function of two independent variables, the time at which an input (or a disturbance) is applied and the time at which the response is measured, whereas, in a linear control system with constant coefficients, the response is a function of one variable which is simply the time difference between the application of the input (or the disturbance) and the measurement of the system response. Linear time-varying control systems usually behave quite differently from linear control systems with constant coefficients, and cannot be described by simple exponential functions.

Rigorously speaking, linear feedback control systems are idealized systems since most system components are linear only when the actuating signals are small. In any practical servomechanism there always exists some nonlinearity. The extent of its importance depends upon the violence of the disturbances to which the system is subjected. For instance, a servomotor is not always capable of supplying a torque proportional to the control signal. When the signal is increasing constantly the motor will eventually reach the limit of its possible power output due to magnetic saturation or other causes. Electronic amplifiers often introduce nonlinearity when the applied signal becomes large. A feedback control system consisting of components which are nonlinear within the operating range of the control signal is called a nonlinear feedback control system. In a nonlinear control system the relationships between the pertinent measures of the system input and output signals can be adequately described by nonlinear differential equations. A servo system employing relays is a nonlinear feedback control system. The friction associated with a servomotor and load introduces a different type of nonlinearity into the servo system. The backlash in gearing forms another type of nonlinear problem. The most widely used techniques for solving nonlinear control problems in engineering are:†

1. Differential equation approach
2. Method of harmonic balance or describing function
3. Phase-plane or topological approach
4. Numerical techniques

Feedback control systems which are made up of components with variable coefficients as well as nonlinear components are often referred to as nonlinear time-varying feedback control systems. The analysis of such control systems is quite complicated.

According to the nature of the control signals flowing in the system, feedback control systems can be classified as:

1. Continuous-data feedback control systems
2. Sampled-data feedback control systems

The continuous-data feedback control system is monitored *continuously* by some function of the actuating error. In this type of servo system control signals flow in the system continuously without interruption. This kind of control system can be further divided into:

1. Conventional-continuous or d-c feedback control systems
2. Modulated or carrier-type feedback control systems

In the conventional-continuous or d-c (data-signal) type of feedback system, the control signals are *continuous* but *unmodulated;* whereas in the second type, the control signals in a certain portion of the system are *modulated* functions. The d-c feedback control systems have been extensively used. Perhaps the most common type of modulated control system is an a-c servo system, in which the carrier is a low-frequency a-c signal. A synchro set serves as the error detector and modulator, and a two-phase induction motor functions as the demodulator. The dynamic characteristics of the motor and load behave as a low-pass filter following demodulation. Shown in Fig. 1.1-1 and Fig. 1.1-2 are the block diagrams

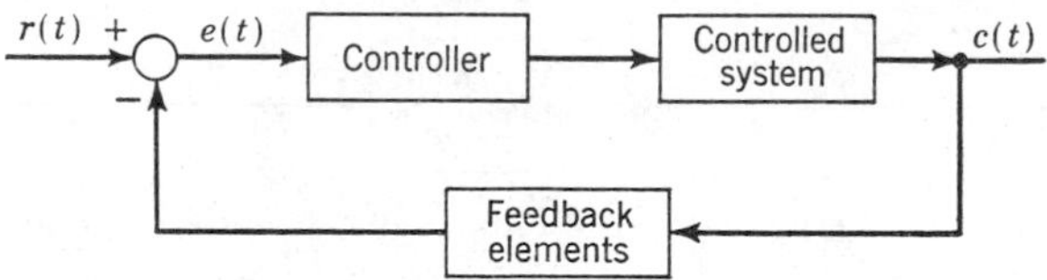

FIG. 1.1-1. Block diagram of a typical continuous-data feedback control system.

of a typical d-c servo system and modulated feedback control system. The most common carrier signals for modulated control systems are the

† Y. H. Ku, "Analysis and Control of Nonlinear Systems," The Ronald Press Company, New York, 1958.

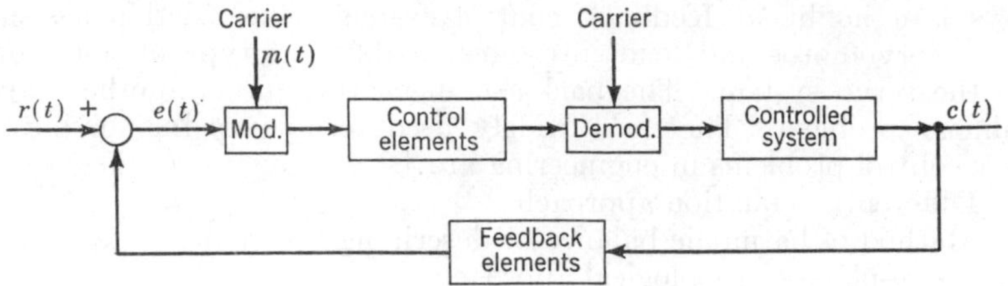

FIG. 1.1-2. A typical modulated feedback control system.

sinusoidal carrier signal, rectangular-wave carrier signal, and short-pulse carrier signal, as shown in Fig. 1.1-3.

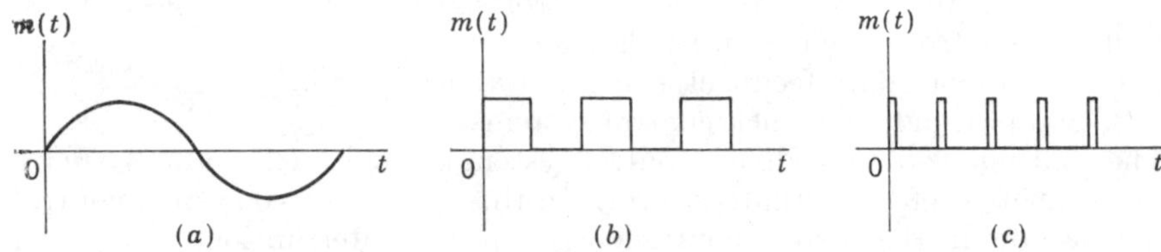

FIG. 1.1-3. Carriers for modulated control systems.

The sampled-data feedback control system is monitored by some function of the actuating error data which are transmitted intermittently at a constant rate. In this type of servo system the control signal in a certain section of the system is in the form of a pulse train. The block diagram of a typical sampled-data feedback control system is shown in Fig. 1.1-4, in which the sampler passes the control signal at discrete instants

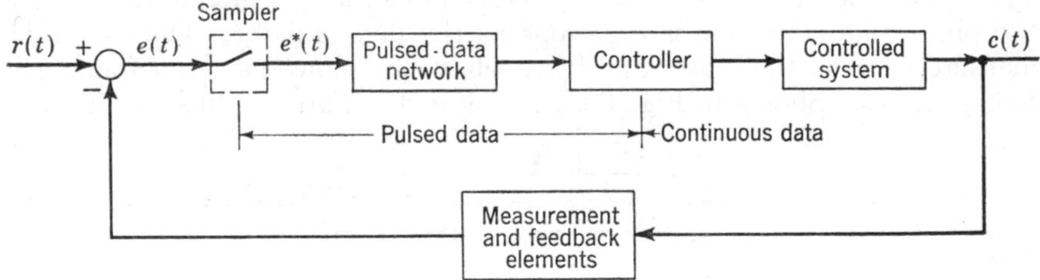

FIG. 1.1-4. A basic sampled-data feedback control system.

equally spaced in time. This book concerns itself with the pulsed-data type of servo system. The analysis and synthesis of this type of control system are discussed in detail in the following chapters.

From another point of view, control systems can also be classified as modulated (or carrier-type) control systems and unmodulated (or non-carrier) control systems. The sampled-data control system falls into the first category. In this respect, sampled-data control systems bear a resemblance to a-c control systems. In an a-c control system, the carrier signal is a sinusoidal wave, whereas, in a sampled-data control system, the carrier signal is a train of very narrow pulses of unit height which result from the sampling process.

In some sampled-data control systems, the sampling period or the duration between successive sampling pulses is not constant, but it is cyclic varying or it is controlled by a certain function of the input of the sampler. For instance, the sampler is sometimes made to operate at a speed proportional to the rate of fluctuation of the input signal. This type of system may be termed a variable-rate sampled-data control system.

1.2. Definition of Digital and Sampled-data Systems. A sampled-data control system is one in which the control signal in a certain portion of the system is supplied *intermittently* at a constant rate. In a sampled-data control system the data signal at one or more points is a sequence of pulses which are modulated in accordance with the continuous function of the signal from which the samples are taken. These pulses convey adequately all the essential information contained in the continuous function. Such control systems may have a variety of forms. Figure 1.1-4 illustrates a basic type of sampled-data control system in which the error is sampled. In Fig. 1.1-4, $r(t)$, $c(t)$, and $e(t)$ stand for the input signal, the output signal, and the actuating error respectively, and $e^*(t)$ denotes the sampled-error signal. For a given input, the error signal from the error detector is a continuous function of time which is then sampled by the sampler S at regular intervals of time, before it is used to actuate the controller and the controlled system. The relationships between the actuating error signal and the sampled-error signal are further explained in Fig. 1.2-1. At regular intervals the signal is measured by a device which is called the sampler. The time interval T is called the sampling period. As shown in Fig. 1.2-1*b*, the sampler output $e^*(t)$ is a train of very narrow pulses of which the amplitudes are determined by the magnitude of the sampler input $e(t)$ at the sampling instants, $O, T, 2T, 3T, \ldots$. The information contained in the continuous actuating-error signal is then carried in the amplitude of the pulses or the samples. A basic sampled-data feedback control system consists mainly of:

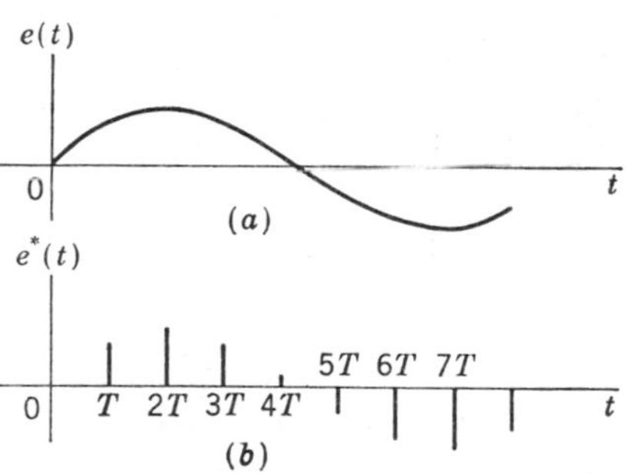

FIG. 1.2-1. Sampler input and output waveforms.

1. Controlled system
2. Error-sensing device
3. Controller and measuring device
4. Holding device
5. Sampler

A radar-tracking servomechanism is an example of a sampled-data feedback control system. The scanning operation of the radar performs the function of a sampler which converts both the azimuth and the elevation information into pulsed data.

In sampled-data control systems the control signal is sampled at equally spaced intervals. The signal values at the sampling instants are sometimes quantized and coded into pulse groups for adapting the available digital equipment to the transmission and processing of the desired information. Such a sampled-data control system is referred to as a digital control system. Thus, though a digital control system can be considered a variation of the sampled-data control system, yet it is the most important sampled-data system. A digital control system is defined as a control system in which the control signal in one or more sections of the system is expressed in a *numerical code* (such as the binary code) for the digital data-processing and decision-making equipment of the control system. A digital control system can be reduced to a basic sampled-data control system if the numerically coded data signal in the digital system is decoded into pulse-amplitude-modulated signals or sampled data, and the operation of the digital computer is represented by the transfer function of an equivalent pulsed-data network. The equivalent pulsed-data network or digital filter operates on the successive samples in precisely the same way as the computer operates on the numerically coded or digital-input data. The strength of the output samples of the equivalent pulsed-data network corresponds to the digital output of the control computer. The methods for solving sampled-data control problems are directly applicable to digital control systems. The major components of a basic digital control system are:

1. Controlled system
2. Control elements
3. Digital-to-analog converter
4. Analog-to-digital converter
5. Digital data-processing equipment or computer

The digital computer plays the important role of the central control unit for data processing and system compensation. In some cases it is the nerve center of the control system in making decisions. The digital-to-analog and analog-to-digital converters are used to interconnect the digital and analog quantities for control and instrumentation. Thus, three new operations occur in a digital control system, i.e., the encoding process at the input of the computer, the programming or data processing of the digital information in the computer, and the decoding process at the output of the computer. A closed-loop control system which operates on pulse-code-modulated signals or numerically coded data is called a digital feedback control system. The block diagram of a typical digital servo system is shown in Fig. 1.2-2. A numerically controlled machine-tool control system is an example of a digital servomechanism.

1.3. Importance of Sampling and Digital Techniques in Control Field. Since World War II the field of digital computers has experienced a period of remarkable growth primarily because its application to scientific compu-

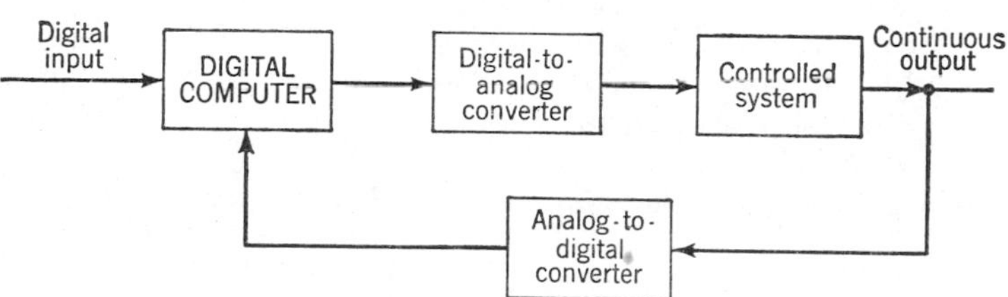

Fig. 1.2-2. A typical digital feedback control system.

tation provides high accuracy, computational speed as well as flexibility, and versatility which analog computation could not provide. As advantages over analog techniques became apparent, it seemed quite natural that control system engineers should also consider the application of digital techniques to control system design. By the use of sampling in control systems, simple, sensitive, and efficient power control devices can readily be built. Sampling permits the control of tremendous power by sensitive control elements without excessive power amplification, and also minimizes the loading effect upon sensitive instruments. Utilizing sampled-data and digital components in a control system allows time sharing of important parts of the system. This is a very significant advantage of digital control systems. Time sharing results in economy in the use of equipment so that one component may have several functions. It also facilitates the coordination of various parts of a system. Since sampled data can readily be coded, the data signals in digital control systems are received and transmitted in pulse-code form, and they will provide almost error-free channels for transmission through noisy media. Consequently, the only noise in the transmission of pulse-coded signals is the quantization error. Likewise, a digital computer in a control system allows data processing of control information so that the flexibility and versatility of the digital computer can be utilized to improve the performance of the control system. Furthermore, digital control techniques make feasible the system compensation by nonlinear programming and adaptive or self-optimizing control. This is, indeed, a significant advantage achievable with digital control.

The use of digital computers as elements in control systems is rapidly becoming an accepted and very effective practice. In view of the high accuracy and versatility of digital computers, the designers of airborne military systems have applied digital techniques to airborne control systems. The Digitac and Digitair airborne control systems designed by Hughes Aircraft Company and the Transac airborne control system developed by Philco Corporation are practical examples. In such systems, a small, compact, and versatile digital computer is used as the computational and control element of the flight and fire control system. For instance, the Digitair control computer, which occupies no more space than a 21-in. table-model TV set, can make a hundred decisions and can fly jet interceptors automatically from take-off to touchdown. It is conceivable that the flexibility of digital equipment can be exploited by using one type of general purpose digital computer for each class of airborne problem, such as navigation, flight control, weapons system control, etc.

Shown in Fig. 1.3-1 is the simplified block diagram of a basic digital

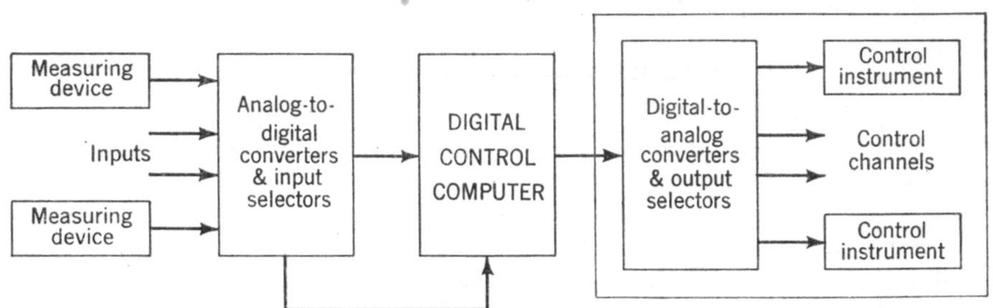

FIG. 1.3-1. Simplified block diagram of a basic digital airborne control system.

airborne control system. The system contains devices or instruments which measure the quantities defining the operating conditions of the aircraft and weapons system. Information obtained from these instruments is sent to a digital control computer which combines the results of these measurements with stored records of previous operating conditions to determine the current operating condition. The digital control computer compares this result with the condition in which the aircraft and the weapons system should be for the mission to be accomplished. The computer then determines the control operations which will change the course of the aircraft and improve the performance of the weapons system so that the mission will be successfully completed. The digital information required for the control operations is converted into continuous signals to actuate the control instruments.

Because of the urgent need for automatic equipment to perform the rather difficult machining operation for the manufacture of precision aircraft parts, the first industrial system using digital control probably appeared in the aircraft industry. The Servomechanisms Laboratory of the Massachusetts Institute of Technology and several major aircraft companies and leading machine-tool manufacturers have developed digital control systems for machine tools. Besides airborne control systems and machine-tool controls, the general principles of digital control also find significant applications in many other automatic control problems. The use of digital techniques in the field of process control appears quite attractive. In chemical industries, oil refineries, and pharmaceutical laboratories, a vast amount of data must be processed both manually and automatically. Due to the limitations of conventional techniques for solving control problems, combined with the increasing complexity of the problems in modern processing plants, the need for a better approach arises accordingly. To secure smooth, efficient operation of the processes and good quality of the products, digital control techniques will be employed extensively in these enterprises.

Digital control systems have the capacity for handling complete control of the operation of a processing plant. In process control work, the digital control computer is able to blend raw materials, to select the set of material for minimum material costs, to supplement analytical instruments in calculating material composition, to diagnose trouble in the control system and the plant, to determine optimum operating conditions, and the like. In a processing plant, a digital control system can generally be considered as an operator who follows a very complicated set of instructions which direct him to make arithmetic computations, to read process instruments, and to adjust intermediate variables automatically and continuously. The digital control system, however, can work with faster speed and higher efficiency than human operators, especially in some processes in which the control variables vary so fast and the relationships between control variables are so complicated that human operators can hardly manipulate these variables and control the process in the most efficient way. By means of its computational and logical operations, the digital control computer can analyze the situation, including the significance of previous operating conditions, can select the necessary control actions intelligently, and can optimize the process control. With the process run by digital control computer, a greater degree of automation can be accomplished than is possible with conventional control techniques. As a result, the manufacturers can achieve great improvements in the efficiency of the processes, in the quality as well as in the quantity of the products, and in their competitive position in the business world.

The first commercial digital computer designed for automatic control of industrial processes, for data logging, and for test-stand operation is the RW-300 Digital Control Computer built by Thompson Ramo Wooldridge Inc. The RW-300 has the features of flexibility and compatibility. The actions taken by the process-control computer are determined by a program of instructions stored in the memory unit. Any change in application does not affect the design of the computer, but will involve only a change in the program of the instructions. The input-output, buffering, selection, and analog-digital conversion equipments are built as an integral part of the computer, thus enabling the digital computer to be connected directly to process-measuring instruments and control devices. The available number of input and output connections ranges from 10 to more than 500. A typical analog input-output system of RW-300 can receive 96 pneumatic signals, 64 thermal signals, and 32 special electrical signals (including mass spectrometer, vapor-pressure analyzer, chromatograph, etc.), and yield 64 pneumatic signals and 32 electrical signals for the outputs.

In a nutshell, the usefulness of high-speed computers in scientific studies and in business is well established. With the advent of compact and versatile transistorized digital computers, digital techniques are making their way into the control field. In view of the many important advantages of digital and sampling techniques, it seems safe to predict that the use of digital control systems will be strongly emphasized in the future.

1.4. Methods of Analysis and Synthesis for Sampled-data and Digital Control Systems. Because of the increasing importance of sampled-data and digital control it has been the subject of considerable interest during the past few years. A large amount of work has been done in the analysis and synthesis of sampled-data control systems. The major approaches in treating of such control systems are:

1. Difference-equation approach
2. Conventional frequency-response approach
3. Impulse-response method
4. z-transform and modified z-transform methods
5. Synthesis in the w plane through bilinear transformation
6. Root-locus method.

The essential points of these major techniques for analysis and synthesis lie either in the extension of the analytical method of sequences to the continuous portion of the system or in the application of the conventional method for continuous data to the discrete part of the system. Without modification, the former idea suffers from several shortcomings because the output of most control systems is continuous and should be expressed as a continuous function of time; continuous signals flow in most parts of a sampled-data control system so that many components of the system can be readily described by conventional transfer functions.

The first approach lies in the solution of the difference equations describing a sampled-data control system by classical methods. The second technique is the extension of the conventional frequency-domain analysis and synthesis to sampled-data control systems. By this method, Nyquist diagrams for sampled-data systems are plotted, the Nyquist criterion is applied, and the conventional design procedures can be followed. The impulse-response method is based upon the evaluation of the response to an impulse and uniformly delayed impulses, and the system response is given by the sum of the weighted-impulse and delayed-impulse responses. In applying the z-transform and modified z-transform methods, the system components are described by pulse-transfer functions which are functions of z. The system stability is determined by the Nyquist criterion or by the Schur-Cohn criterion, and the system response is derived from the inverse modified z transform. Synthesis in the w plane requires the mapping of the system open-loop pulse-transfer function into the w plane through a bilinear transformation. In the w plane the much-used Bode method is applicable. The sixth approach is the direct application of the root-locus method, originally developed for conventional control systems, to sampled-data control systems. The location of the roots of the system characteristic equation in the z plane determines the performance of the sampled-data control system.

All of these approaches are based upon the assumption that sampling occurs instantaneously, and the sampling pulses are of infinitesimal or zero width. Thus, in the analysis the pulses in the control system are represented by ideal pulses or impulses of equivalent strength. However, this assumption is valid only when the sampling duration is very small in comparison with the time constants of the controlled system, or the sampler of the system is followed by a zero-order holding device. Yet, in practical sampled-data control systems, sampling does not occur momentarily, and the pulse width can be comparable to the time constants of the system. If the sampling duration is not negligible, the above-mentioned methods will lose much of their accuracy. This book introduces the τ-transform techniques for analyzing sampled-data control systems with finite sampling duration.

1.5. Examples of Digital and Sampled-data Control Systems. Digital and sampled-data controls find wide applications in both military and civilian industries. To obtain a general picture of digital control, several digital and sampled-data control systems in practice are considered for the purpose of illustration. An example of a sampled-data control system is the GCI (Ground Controlled Interceptor) system for air defense. In the GCI system, a number of target and interceptor aircraft are present in the area of the sky. These are being observed by a scanning radar which provides information about the location of all aircraft. These data are displayed to a ground crew who, in turn, detect the targets, assign interceptors to the targets, and send instructions to the interceptor pilot or crew who fly the interceptor as directed until contact is made with the target. This is a sampled-data system which involves human operators as components in the control loop. The ground crew plot aircraft motions from radar data, calculate the proper course of the interceptor, and send out instructions via radio.

The past decade has shown an increase in the air threat to this country to an extent that has outdated manually coordinated traffic handling techniques and manual data processing. At current aircraft speeds, the present GCI system is too slow and too inaccurate to solve the air-intercept problem, since the information is processed manually. As a result, the need for a better air-defense system has arisen. To solve the current air-defense problem, a system is required which can maintain a complete up-to-date picture of the air and ground situations over wide areas of the country; which can control modern weapons rapidly and accurately; which can present filtered pictures of the air and weapons situations to the air force personnel who conduct the air battle. To meet the above requirements the SAGE (Semi-Automatic Ground Environment) system was developed. The SAGE system is an example of a digital control system for air defense which utilizes a large-scale digital computer for data processing from a network of radar stations to provide flight-course instruction from the interceptors. The SAGE system is a large-scale electronic air-surveillance and weapon-control system which is comprised of three groups of facilities: (1) equipment to pick up and to transmit surveillance data from data-gathering sources to data-processing centers; (2) data-processing facilities to convert the collected data into an air situation and to generate weapon-guidance orders; (3) facilities to transmit processed data to weapons, to command levels, to adjacent centers, and to other users such as the Civil Aeronautics Administration and civil defense agencies. In the SAGE system, all data are digitized at the radar sites for transmission over telephone wires to the data-processing centers. The SAGE system is a closed-loop system because outputs from the digital computer are used via data links to direct the flight course of interceptors.

As a second example, the digital control of machine tools is considered. The digital control of machine motions, such as those of a tool, a work-table, etc., may be divided into two categories, contouring and point-to-point positioning. In contouring, the path taken by the machine member as it moves from place to place is vitally important. In point-to-point positioning, only the destination is critical and the path taken between starting point and set point is of no consequence. For instance, if a machine is to be used for drilling or boring, the setting of the axes of a machine to carry out an operation at fixed location must be accurately controlled, whereas accurate control of position while in motion is not required. A digitally controlled point-to-point positioning system for a machine such as the drill press involves four basic building blocks: input equipments, position transducers, comparison devices, and driving motors or positioning servos.

The block diagram of a digitally controlled drill-table positioning system is illustrated in Fig. 1.5-1 which comprises two control channels. The digital control is initiated with a command—to move a machine member (e.g., the drill table) to a new location; to start or stop some machine operation (e.g., drilling); etc. All such commands are expressed in digital codes stored on the input medium (punched tape or punched cards) and read into the control system when a machine operation is to be initiated. The digital control system requires sensing devices to measure data on the exact location of the machine member along its axis of movement. These measured data are fed back for comparison with the input data. The difference between the input signal and the feedback signal is used for starting, stopping, and adjusting the speed of the drive motors of the machine; for starting operation of the drill head; and for advancing the tape preparatory to the next step in the cycle. The driving motors or the positioning servos move the drill table and the drill head to the desired position.

In reference to Fig. 1.5-1, when input signals are applied to the system the drill head is moved in the X direction and the drill table is displaced in the Y direction until the desired location is reached. This location is indicated by zero output from the digital comparators. At this instant the digital comparator of the Y channel emits a signal to operate the drill. Upon the completion of the drill operation a signal is generated to advance the tape preparatory to the next step in the cycle.

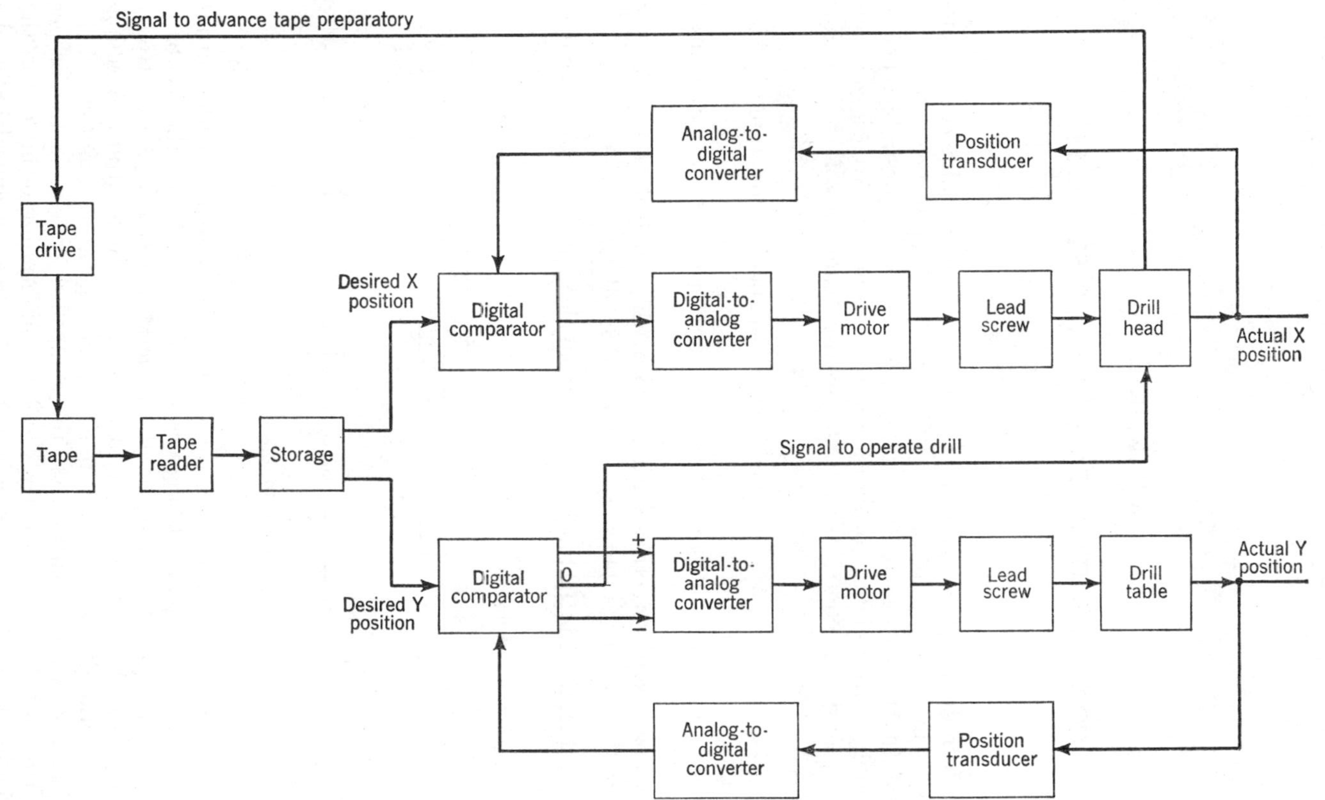

FIG. 1.5-1. Block diagram of a digitally controlled drill press.

CHAPTER 2

CONTINUOUS-DATA CONTROL SYSTEMS†

2.1. Introduction. Sampled-data control systems resemble continuous-data systems in many aspects. In view of this resemblance, a brief review of the theory of continuous-data controls seems desirable, before discussing sampled-data and digital control techniques. A basic continuous-data feedback control system is usually made up of three major parts:

1. A plant, process, or controlled system, the position or state of which is being regulated or monitored
2. The controller which consists of a measuring device and control elements
3. A comparator or error-sensing device which detects the difference between the reference input and the output signal

Shown in Fig. 2.1-1 is the block diagram of an elementary feedback control

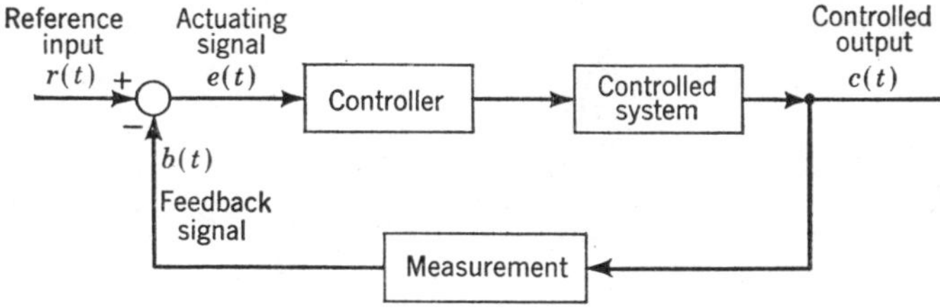

FIG. 2.1-1. Block diagram of a basic feedback control system.

system in which $r(t)$ is the reference input to the system; $c(t)$, the output of the system; $e(t)$, the actuating error or signal; and $b(t)$, the feedback signal. Upon receiving the order of the actuating signal, the controller operates upon the controlled system to yield a desired output. A simple example of a feedback control system is a man operating a motor vehicle. The driver wants to keep his car, the controlled system, in the proper lane. He does this by constantly watching the heading of his car in the direction of the road. The center line of his lane may be considered as the

† This chapter constitutes a brief review of the basic linear feedback control theory.

reference input. The heading of his car is the output of the system, which is measured by his eyes and is fed to his brain for judging any difference between the reference line and the measured value. His brain is then used as an error-sensing device. The detected deviations form the order by which his hands are instructed to move the steering wheel of his car to the proper direction. Thus, in this case the controller's position is taken by his hands. In brief, this operation may be explained by the block diagram of Fig. 2.1-2.

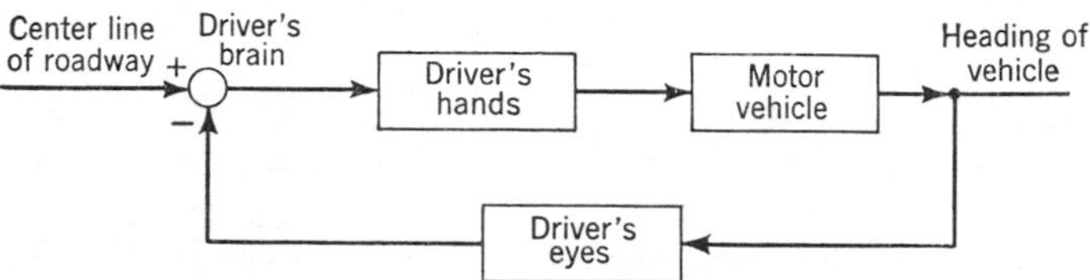

FIG. 2.1-2. Block diagram describing the steering of a motor vehicle.

The analysis and design of feedback control systems usually involve the determination of the stability of the system, the evaluation of the output of the system in response to impulse, step, ramp, or sinusoidal input function, and the compensation of the system to meet design specifications. The purpose of compensation is primarily to modify the performance of a system so that it will have satisfactory stability and the resulting error will fall within the specified value. One of the most popular methods for analyzing and synthesizing feedback control systems is the frequency-response approach. This is the method of investigating the steady-state response of the system to a sinusoidal input. In view of the fact that a periodic function can be expressed in a Fourier series and an aperiodic function may be represented by a Fourier integral, the steady-state response of a given linear system to a function of time which satisfies Dirichlet conditions can be determined by the principle of superposition, if the steady-state response to a sinusoidal input is known for all positive real frequencies.

In the analysis of feedback control systems, control engineers have found it convenient to employ the transfer-function concept and the block-diagram representation of the system. The transfer-function concept pervades the entire field of feedback controls and is basic in the application of the frequency-response method of analysis. The input-output signal relations for individual components of a control system are described by transfer functions, and the operations of the components are represented by noninteracting blocks which are interconnected to form the block diagram or signal-flow diagram of the over-all system. The blocks represent the functions that have to be performed by the components rather than the pieces of equipment. Thus, the block diagram, which describes the basic characteristic of a feedback control system, is a functional representation rather than a physical layout. To control engineers the block diagram of a system is much more meaningful than the equivalent set of simultaneous equations describing the system since it bears, to a certain extent, a schematic resemblance to the physical system from which the block diagram is derived, whereas a list of equations appears rather abstract. The block diagram indicates graphically the transfer of signals in a system and the interconnection of the building components of the system; on the other hand, the equivalent set of simultaneous equations expresses mathematically the relations among variables present in the physical system. Furthermore, the block-diagram representation enables the designer to see the effect of particular parameter variations upon the over-all system performance by looking at the block diagram, whereas a set of simultaneous differential equations tends to make such an investigation much more difficult. Thus, the block-diagram approach to the analysis of control systems has gained great popularity.

To analyze and design a feedback control system by the frequency-response method, the following basic procedures are usually followed:

1. Derive the transfer functions or transfer characteristics for all the components in use in the system from the differential equations describing the components or from physical measurements.

2. Formulate the block diagram from the system by connecting all like inputs and outputs of the various noninteracting blocks.

3. Reduce the complicated block diagram of the system to simple, basic, single-loop configuration having a transfer function in the forward and in the feedback branch.

4. Determine the open-loop transfer function and the output transform of the system from the simplified block diagram.

5. Sketch the Nyquist diagram or the Bode plot of the system.

6. Design the desired compensators by reshaping the Nyquist diagram or the Bode plot to meet the specifications.

In addition to the above basic steps, the designer has to investigate the effect of the variation of individual parameters, of corrupting disturbances coming into the system, of different types of compensating devices, and of element tolerances; and finally, he has to perform model testing or make use of analog simulation.

The transfer function of a device or a servo element is defined as the complex ratio of the output of the device to its input, or as the ratio of the output transform of the device to its input transform. Transfer functions are the basis for the analytical treatment of feedback control systems. In spite of the great variety of control-system components, the linear elements of control systems may be described by a combination of one or more of nine basic forms of the transfer functions listed in Table 2.1-1. These basic forms of the transfer functions represent a large number of the components commonly used in control systems, which are describable by linear ordinary or partial differential equations with constant coefficients. The first seven basic forms are very common and require no further explanation.

The transport lag is a dead time or delay during which the element yields no response to an applied input. Figure 2.1-3 depicts the block diagram of a transport-lag element of which the input is $e_i(t)$ and the output is $e_o(t)$. It is easily seen that the input and output are related by

$$e_o(t) = e_i(t - T) \qquad (2.1\text{-}1)$$

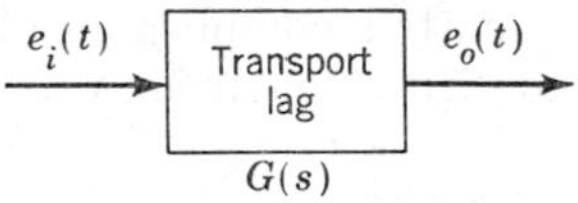

FIG. 2.1-3. An element with transport lag.

where T is the dead-time lag of the element, and both the input and the output functions are zero for negative values of t. Laplace transformation of Eq. (2.1-1) yields the relationship between the input and the output transforms:

$$E_o(s) = \epsilon^{-Ts}E_i(s) \qquad (2.1\text{-}2)$$

where $E_o(s)$ and $E_i(s)$ denote the Laplace transforms of the output and the input, respectively. Hence the transfer function of the transport-lag element is given by

$$G(s) = \frac{E_o(s)}{E_i(s)} = \epsilon^{-Ts} \qquad (2.1\text{-}3)$$

The distributed lag represents an element describable by a linear partial differential equation. Examples of such elements exist in heat

TABLE 2.1-1. NINE BASIC FORMS OF TRANSFER FUNCTIONS

Element	*Transfer function*
1. Gain or sensitivity	K (a constant)
2. Differentiator	Ts
3. Integrator	$\frac{1}{Ts}$
4. Simple lead	$1 + Ts$
5. Simple lag	$\frac{1}{1 + Ts}$
6. Complex lead	$1 + \frac{2\zeta}{\omega_n}s + \frac{1}{\omega_n^2}s^2$
7. Complex lag	$\frac{1}{1 + (2\zeta/\omega_n)s + (1/\omega_n^2)s^2}$
8. Transport lag	ϵ^{-Ts}
9. Distributed lag	$\epsilon^{-\sqrt{Ts}}$

conduction in a homogeneous continuous medium, in transmission of air through a long pneumatic line, and in electrical transmission lines. It can readily be shown that the transfer function of an element with pure distributed lag is $\epsilon^{-\sqrt{Ts}}$.

2.2. Block-diagram Reduction. The block diagrams of most feedback control systems in practice usually contain several loops, and consequently the open-loop transfer functions of the systems may not be recognized directly from the block diagrams. To facilitate evaluation of the open-loop transfer function and the output transform of a system, frequently a complicated block diagram is first reduced to a basic, single-loop configuration from which both the open-loop transfer function and the output transform can be derived by inspection. This section is concerned with the simplification of the block diagrams of control systems.

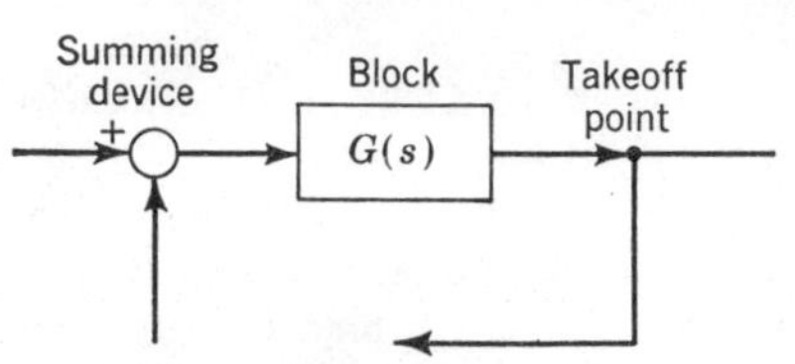

FIG. 2.2-1. Three basic elements forming a block diagram.

The block diagram is made up of three elements, namely, the building blocks, the summing devices, and the take-off points as illustrated in Fig. 2.2-1. The main point in simplifying a block diagram is to move the summing devices to the left-hand side of the major loop of the diagram and to shift the take-off points to the right. Basic rules for block-diagram reduction are presented below (sketch of the original diagram appears on the left, of the equivalent diagram, on the right):

Rule 1. Combining cascade elements—N elements with transfer functions $G_1(s)$, $G_2(s)$, . . . , $G_N(s)$ connected in cascade are equivalent to an element with transfer function $G(s) = \prod_{k=1}^{N} G_k(s)$.

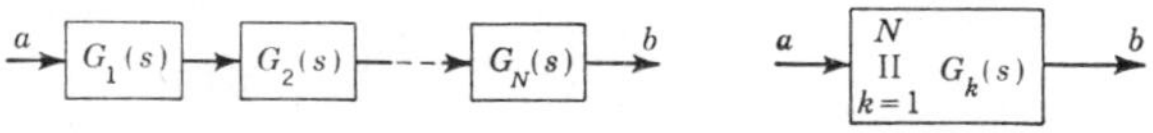

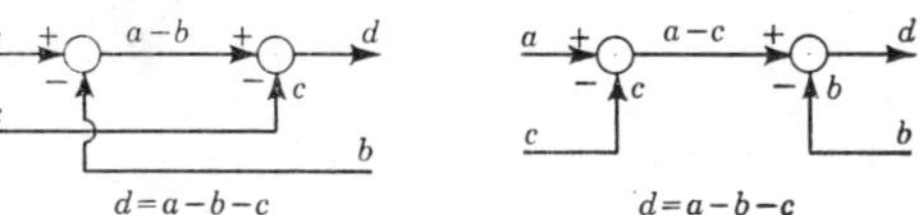

Rule 2. Interchange of summing devices.

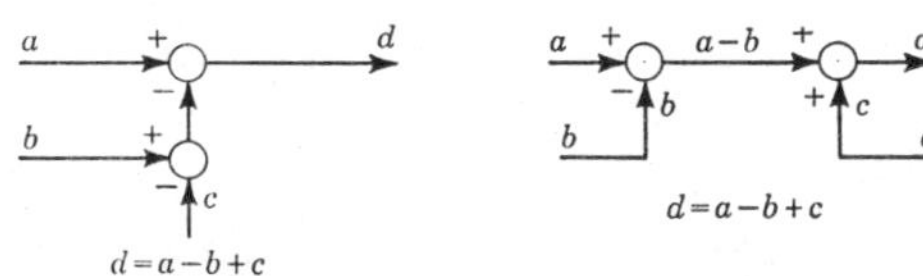

Rule 3. Rearrangement of summing devices.

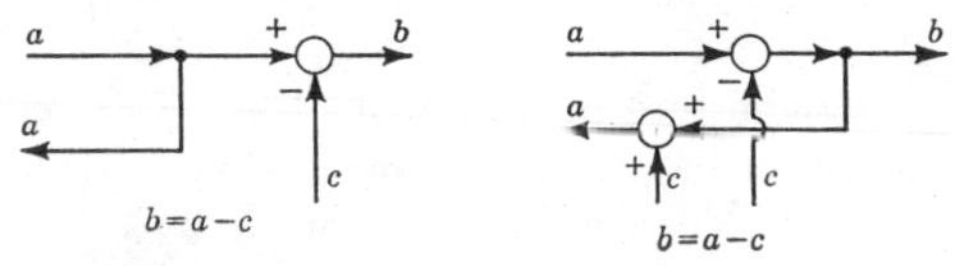

Rule 4. Moving a take-off point beyond a summing device.

Rule 5. Moving a take-off point ahead of an element.

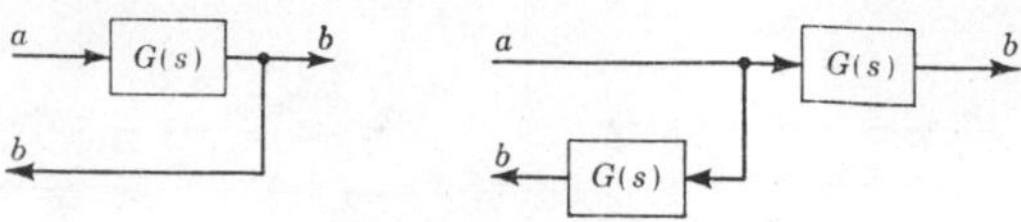

Rule 6. Moving a take-off point beyond an element.

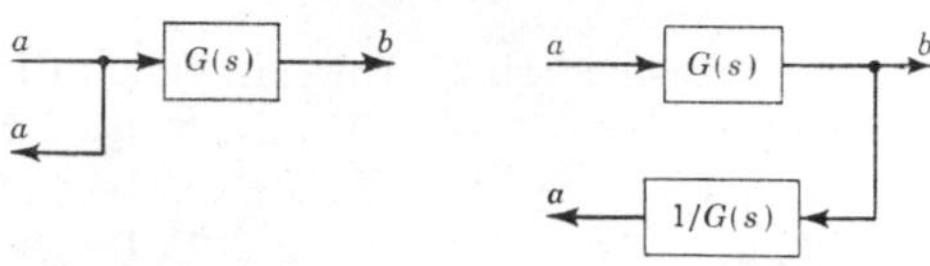

Rule 7. Moving a take-off point ahead of a summing device.

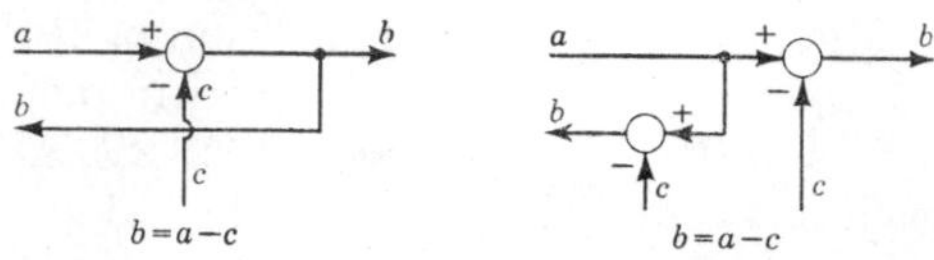

Rule 8. Moving a summing device ahead of an element.

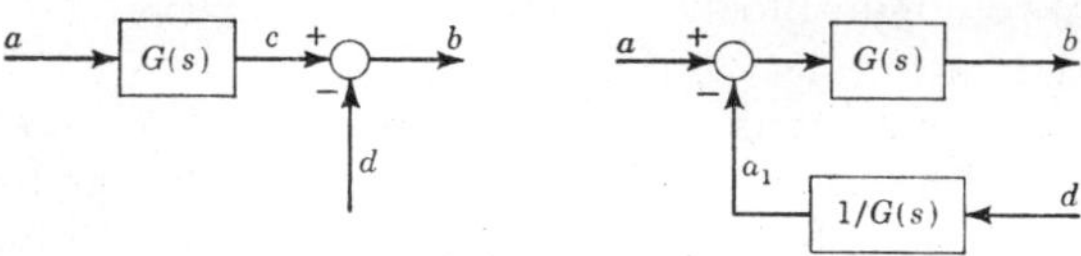

Rule 9. Moving a summing device beyond an element.

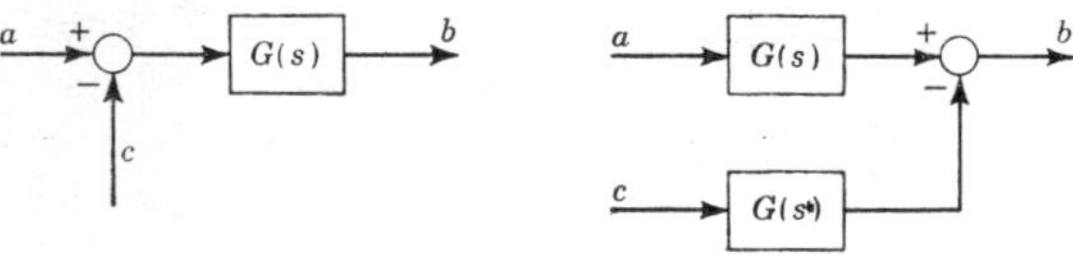

Rule 10. Removing an element from feedback path.

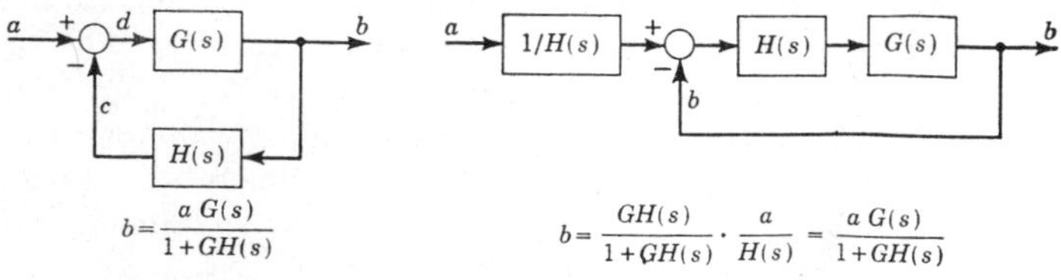

Rule 11. Eliminating a feedforward circuit.

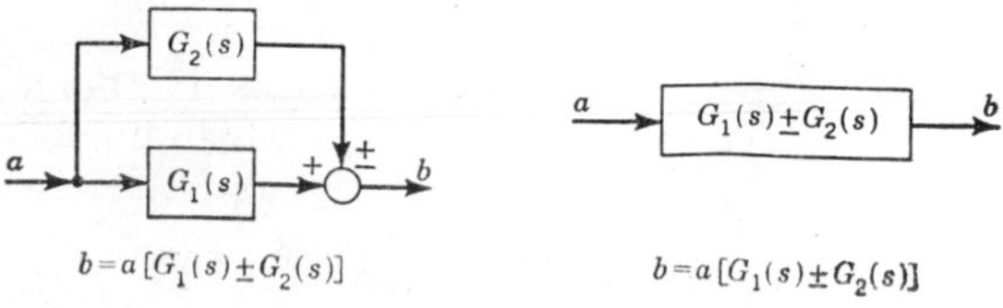

Rule 12. Over-all transfer function of a basic single-loop feedback control system.

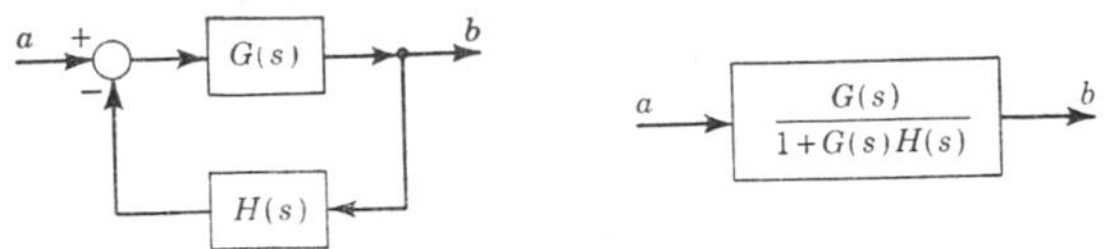

As an illustration of the use of these rules in block-diagram reduction, the system of Fig. 2.2-2*a* is considered. Application of Rules 8, 2, and 6 reduces the original block diagram of Fig. 2.2-2*a* to that of Fig. 2.2-2*b*. Rule 1 converts the block diagram of Fig. 2.2-2*b* to that of Fig. 2.2-2*c*, which is further simplified to Fig. 2.2-2*d* by making use of Rule 12. Then, the over-all transfer function of the system can readily be obtained from Fig. 2.2-2*d* by inspection or by further application of Rules 1 and 12. As can be seen, a great deal of labor has been saved in deriving the over-all transfer function by use of the above rules.

The basic approach in the reduction of the block diagram of a complex feedback control system generally involves the following steps:

1. To reduce the simple cascade, parallel, and feedback structures of a block diagram into single blocks. This step is effected by making use of Rules 1, 11, and 12.

2. To move the summing devices and to reshuffle the take-off points in such a way that all loops of the block diagram are freed from interconnection. Rules 2, 3, 4, 7, 8, and 9 are used to move the summing devices to desirable locations; and Rules 4, 5, 6, and 7 are used to reshuffle the take-off points.

3. To reduce successively the interconnection-free inner loops of the partially reduced block diagram into single blocks so as to end with a single-loop block diagram. This step can readily be accomplished by applying Rule 12. Rule 10 is used to convert a nonunity-feedback control system into a unity-feedback control system.

2.3. Stability Criteria. The analysis of feedback control systems usually covers three general topics, namely, system stability, transient behavior of the system, and steady-state performance of the system. The primary requirement of a feedback control system is stability. A system is defined as stable if the output of the system in response to any bounded input is finite. Assume that the input and output of the linear system are $e_i(t)$ and $e_o(t)$, respectively, and the impulse response (or weighting function) of the system is $w(t)$; then the system is stable if

$$\int_0^\infty |w(t)|\, dt < \infty \tag{2.3-1}$$

with the exception of a perfect integrator. This is the necessary and sufficient condition for the stability of a system, which has been proved by James and Weiss.[2]† Equation (2.3-1) states the stability condition in the

† Superscript numerals are keyed to references in Appendix 2.

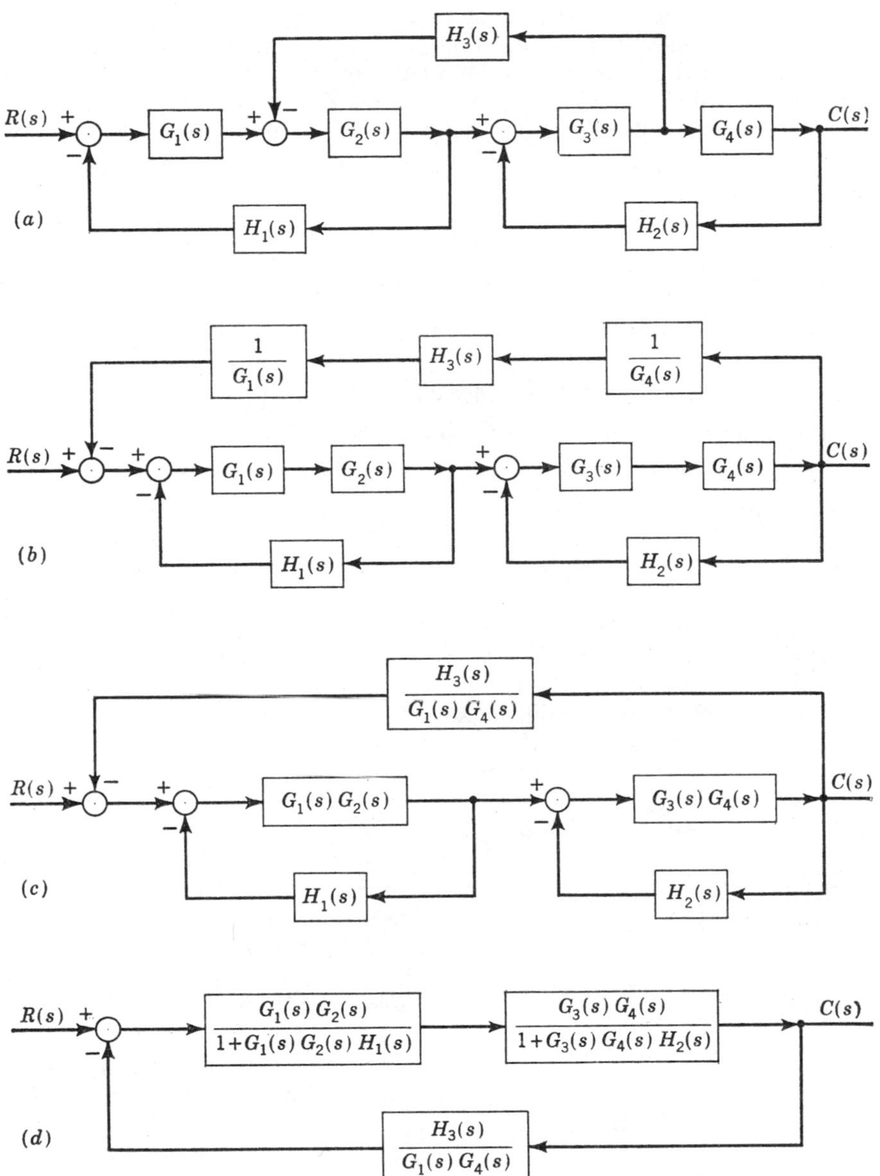

FIG. 2.2-2. An example illustrating the simplification of block diagrams.

time domain, and the stability is determined by the behavior of the weighting function $w(t)$ of the system.

In the frequency domain or s domain the system stability may be determined from the transfer function of the system, or simply system function, $W(s)$, which is defined as the ratio of the output transform to the input transform, $W(s) = E_o(s)/E_i(s)$. For an impulse input, $W(s) = E_o(s)$; hence $W(s)$ is the Laplace transform of the impulse response of the system:

$$W(s) = \int_0^\infty w(t)\epsilon^{-st}\,dt \tag{2.3-2}$$

By letting $s = c + j\omega$, $W(s)$ may be written as

$$W(s) = \int_0^\infty w(t)\epsilon^{-ct}\,(\cos \omega t - j \sin \omega t)\,dt$$

which is less than $\int_0^\infty |w(t)|\,dt$, since c is positive. It can readily be shown that $w(t)$ approaches zero when t approaches infinity, and that the integral $\int_0^\infty |w(t)|\,dt$ is finite, if the system function $W(s)$ contains no singularity in the right half of the s plane or on the imaginary axis. Thus, a system is said to be stable if all the poles of $W(s)$ are located in the left half of the s plane except for possibly a pole of order 1 at the origin. If the transfer function $W(s)$ involves the exponential factor ϵ^{-as}, this factor can be approximated by a rational polynomial in s.

As can be seen from the inverse Laplace transformation, a real pole of $W(s)$ in the right half of the s plane corresponds to an exponential rising function in the time domain, a pair of complex poles in the right half plane corresponds to a growing oscillation, a pair of conjugate poles of order 1 on the imaginary axis corresponds to a sustained oscillation of constant amplitude, and a pole of order 1 at the origin to a constant value of response. On the other hand, poles of $W(s)$ in the left half plane correspond to an exponential decaying function or damped oscillation in the time domain. Consequently, in the s domain the stability problem is the problem of determining whether or not all poles of $W(s)$ are in the left half of the s plane.

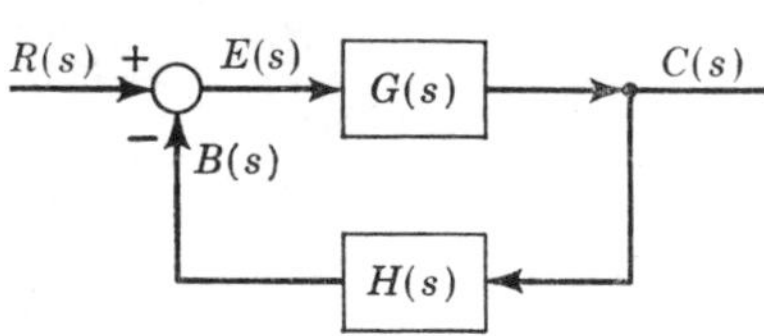

FIG. 2.3-1. Block diagram of a feedback control system.

For the feedback control system of the general form shown in Fig. 2.3-1, the over-all transfer function is given by

$$W(s) = \frac{C(s)}{R(s)} = \frac{G(s)}{1 + G(s)H(s)} = \frac{G(s)}{1 + A(s)} \tag{2.3-3}$$

where $R(s)$ and $C(s)$ are the input and output transforms; $G(s)$ and $H(s)$ are the transfer functions of the elements in the forward and feedback paths, respectively; and $A(s) = G(s)H(s)$ is called the open-loop transfer function of the system. Then the system is stable if all the poles of

$G(s)/[1 + A(s)]$ or the zeros of $1 + A(s)$ lie in the left half of the s plane. In other words, the stability condition requires that all the roots of the characteristic equation of the system

$$1 + A(s) = 0 \tag{2.3-4}$$

be located in the left half of the s plane. Methods for detecting the presence of any roots of the characteristic equation not in the left half of the s plane form stability criteria.

Routh's Stability Criterion.† This criterion describes a method of determining the stability of a system analytically. To apply Routh's test for stability determination the over-all transfer function (or the open-loop transfer function) of the system must first be obtained. The characteristic equation of the system is then given by the denominator of the over-all transfer function equated to zero, which will have the general polynomial form

$$a_n s^n + a_{n-1}s^{n-1} + a_{n-2}s^{n-2} + \cdots + a_1 s + a_0 = 0 \tag{2.3-5}$$

In view of the fact that Routh's criterion can be applied to rational polynomials only, any exponential factor involved in the open-loop transfer function must be approximated by a polynomial. The first procedure of Routh's test is to write the coefficients a_k of Eq. (2.3-5) in an array of the form

$$\begin{array}{l|lllll} s^n & a_n & a_{n-2} & a_{n-4} & a_{n-6} & \cdots \\ s^{n-1} & a_{n-1} & a_{n-3} & a_{n-5} & & \\ s^{n-2} & b_1 & b_2 & b_3 & & \\ s^{n-3} & c_1 & c_2 & & & \\ s^{n-4} & d_1 & d_2 & & & \end{array} \tag{2.3-6}$$

The coefficients of a third row are found by cross multiplication as follows:

$$\begin{aligned} b_1 &= \frac{a_{n-1}a_{n-2} - a_n a_{n-3}}{a_{n-1}} \\ b_2 &= \frac{a_{n-1}a_{n-4} - a_n a_{n-5}}{a_{n-1}} \\ &\cdots\cdots\cdots\cdots\cdots\cdots \end{aligned} \tag{2.3-7}$$

In like manner, the coefficients of a fourth row are determined from the second row and the third row by cross multiplication.

$$\begin{aligned} c_1 &= \frac{b_1 a_{n-3} - a_{n-1}b_2}{b_1} \\ c_2 &= \frac{b_1 a_{n-5} - a_{n-1}b_3}{b_1} \end{aligned} \tag{2.3-8}$$

† M. F. Gardner and J. L. Barnes, "Transients in Linear Systems," p. 197, John Wiley & Sons, Inc., New York, 1942.

New rows are formed in this way until the array of Eq. (2.3-6) contains $n + 1$ rows. In the course of obtaining the successive rows of the array, the coefficients in any row may be multiplied or divided by a positive number without altering the general nature of the array. This simplifies the numerical computation in determining the coefficients of the succeeding row.

With the array of Eq. (2.3-6) thus completely determined, Routh's criterion states that all the roots of Eq. (2.3-5) lie in the left half of the s plane provided that (1) the coefficients a_k of Eq. (2.3-5) are all present and positive, and (2) all the coefficients in the first column of the array are of one sign. The number of right half plane roots of Eq. (2.3-5) is given by the number of changes in sign of the coefficients in the first column of the array.

Two exceptions to this general process can arise and require special attention. The first exception arises when the term in the first element of any row is zero, but at least one of the remaining terms in that row is nonzero. Any attempt to determine the coefficients in the following row in the usual manner fails, because the coefficients will be infinite. To overcome this difficulty the first-column zero is replaced by an arbitrarily small real number ϵ, and the computation is then continued in the usual manner. The number of changes in sign in the first column will be the same whether ϵ is considered positive or negative. The second exception arises when all the coefficients in the second or any derived row are zero. This result reveals the existence of roots of equal order lying radially opposite each other and equidistant from the origin. The process can be continued by forming an auxiliary polynomial in descending power of s^2 of order $n - k + 1$, the coefficients of which are the coefficients of the last nonzero row, where n is the order of Eq. (2.3-5) and k the number of the last nonzero row. The zeros in the all-zero row are replaced by the coefficients of the derivative with respect to s of the auxiliary polynomial in s^2. With the all-zero row replaced by a new nonzero row, the coefficients of the succeeding rows can then be determined in the usual manner.

The stability conditions for third- and fourth-order control systems are relatively simple and are given below:

1. A third-order system. The characteristic equation of a third-order system takes the general form

$$a_3s^3 + a_2s^2 + a_1s + a_0 = 0 \tag{2.3-9}$$

Then the stability conditions become the following:

The coefficients of Eq. (2.3-9) are all positive and nonzero

$$a_1a_2 - a_0a_3 > 0 \tag{2.3-10}$$

2. A fourth-order system. The characteristic equation of a fourth-order system takes the general form

$$a_4s^4 + a_3s^3 + a_2s^2 + a_1s + a_0 = 0 \tag{2.3-11}$$

The stability conditions become the following:
The coefficients of Eq. (2.3-11) are all positive and nonzero.

$$a_1(a_3a_2 - a_4a_1) - a_3^2a_0 > 0 \tag{2.3-12}$$

To illustrate the application of Routh's criterion an example is given below.

EXAMPLE 2.3-1. Consider the feedback control system of Fig. 2.3-2.

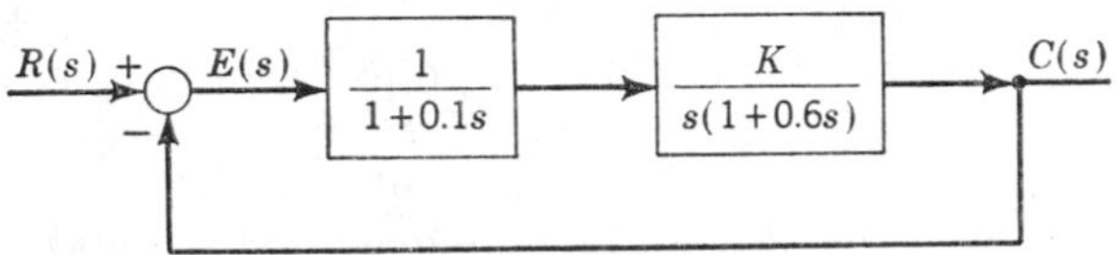

FIG. 2.3-2. Block diagram of the system illustrating the use of Routh's criterion.

It is required to determine the maximum value of the gain constant K for stable operation. The open-loop transfer function and the over-all transfer function of the system are obtained from inspection of the block diagram of Fig. 2.3-2.

$$A(s) = \frac{K}{s(1 + 0.1s)(1 + 0.6s)} \tag{2.3-13}$$

$$\frac{C(s)}{R(s)} = \frac{K}{s(1 + 0.1s)(1 + 0.6s) + K} \tag{2.3-14}$$

The characteristic equation is then given by

$$0.06s^3 + 0.7s^2 + s + K = 0 \tag{2.3-15}$$

The stability of the system may be determined by testing the presence of any roots of Eq. (2.3-15) in the right half of the s plane. Applying Routh's test procedure or Eq. (2.3-10) leads to

$$1 \times 0.7 - 0.06K > 0 \tag{2.3-16}$$

According to the first condition of (2.3-10), K must be greater than zero. Equation (2.3-16) gives

$$K < 11.65 \tag{2.3-17}$$

Hence the system would become unstable if the gain constant K is increased to 11.65.

The application of Routh's criterion is simple if the order of the system is low. For higher order systems the computations involved may become tedious. As can be noted, Routh's criterion provides a test for absolute stability of a system but it sheds little light upon the degree of stability. For most applications in control systems, a knowledge of whether the system is merely stable or unstable is not enough. The failure of Routh's test to indicate the degree of stability is certainly a shortcoming. Furthermore, Routh's test gives no indication of the effect of variations of particular parameters on the stability of the system.

Nyquist's Stability Criterion. This criterion furnishes a graphical method for determining the stability of a system. A feedback control system is stable if a plot of its open-loop transfer function $A(s)$ for a succession of values of s, encircling the entire right half of the s plane in the clockwise direction, makes a number of counterclockwise revolutions about the critical point $(-1 + j0)$ equal to the number of the poles of $A(s)$ in the right half of the s plane. Nyquist's stability criterion follows directly from the important theorem of complex-variable theory which states: If $f(s)$ is a meromorphic function of s, which is single valued on and within a simple closed contour C and is analytic and different from zero on the contour C, then

$$\frac{1}{2\pi j} \oint_C \frac{f'(s)}{f(s)}\, ds = P - N \tag{2.3-18}$$

where P is the number of poles and N is the number of zeros of $f(s)$ inside the contour C, and a pole or zero of order n is counted n times. To derive Nyquist's stability criterion by this theorem the function $f(s)$ is identified as $1 + A(s)$, where $A(s)$ is the open-loop transfer function of a feedback control system, and the contour C covers the entire right half of the s plane (Fig. 2.3-3). It can readily be shown that

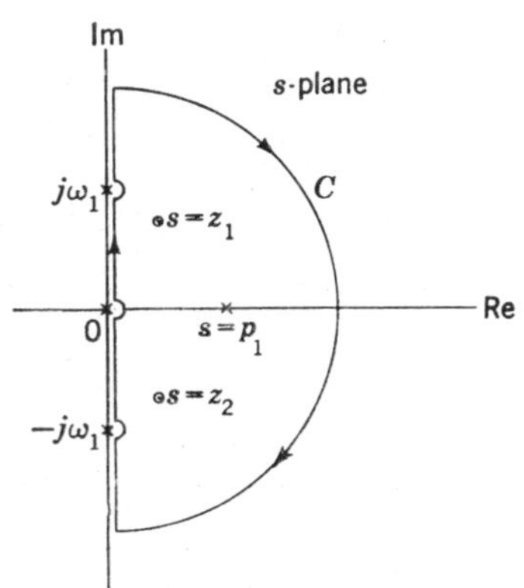

FIG. 2.3-3. Contour of integration.

$$\frac{1}{2\pi j} \oint_C \frac{f'(s)}{f(s)}\, ds = \frac{1}{2\pi} \Delta \{\arg [1 + A(s)]\} = \Omega \tag{2.3-19}$$

where Ω is the number of encirclements of the plot of $1 + A(s)$ about the origin as s traverses once around the closed contour C in the clockwise direction. Therefore, equating Eq. (2.3-19) with Eq. (2.3-18) yields

$$\Omega = P - N \tag{2.3-20}$$

Equation (2.3-20) may be applied directly to determine the stability of feedback control systems.

As can be seen, when s varies over the path C, encircling the entire right half of the s plane in the clockwise direction, the vector of $1 + A(s)$ swings once around the origin in the clockwise direction for each zero of $1 + A(s)$ in the right half plane and once around the origin in the counterclockwise direction for each pole of $1 + A(s)$ in the right half of the s plane. Since the stability condition requires that $1 + A(s)$ contain no zero in the right half plane (that is, $N = 0$), in a stable system the number of encirclements of the origin by $1 + A(s)$ in the counterclockwise direction must be equal to the number of poles of $1 + A(s)$ in the right half of the s plane. Now, if the plot of $A(s)$ is considered instead of $1 + A(s)$, the point to which the encirclements are referred becomes the point $(-1 + j0)$. Hence, for a stable system the number of encirclements of the point $(-1 + j0)$ by the plot of $A(s)$ in the counterclockwise direction must be equal to the number of poles of $A(s)$ in the right half plane. In symbols,

$$\Omega = P \tag{2.3-21}$$

Consequently, in applying the Nyquist criterion, the first step is to determine the number of right-half-plane poles of the open-loop transfer function $A(s)$; the second step is to plot $A(s)$ for a succession of values of s encircling the entire right half plane in the counterclockwise direction; and the third step is to count the number of counterclockwise encirclements of the critical point $(-1 + j0)$ by the plot of $A(s)$. Very often the first step is rather difficult. However, if the open-loop transfer function $A(s)$ can be expressed in accurate form, the number of right-half-plane poles of $A(s)$ can readily be determined. It becomes even more obvious if the open-loop transfer function $A(s)$ is expressed in factored form. The second step usually involves a great deal of labor especially if $A(s)$ is of higher order and contains transcendental terms. Clearly, the third step is quite simple.

In view of the fact that on the imaginary axis the real part of the complex variable s is zero, the imaginary part is $j\omega$, and $A(s)$ equals $A(j\omega)$, and that on the infinite semicircle, $s = j\omega$, $\omega = \infty$, and $A(s) = A(j\omega) =$ zero or a constant for all physical systems, $j\omega$ is usually used to substitute the complex variable s for practical plotting of the transfer function. The polar plot of the transfer function for $j\omega$ varying from $-j\infty$ to $+j\infty$ and back along the right-hand infinite semicircle is often referred to as the Nyquist diagram. As can be noted, a polar plot of frequency range $-\infty$ to 0 is the mirror image about the horizontal axis of the plot with frequency range 0 to $+\infty$. Thus, to evaluate the polar plot of a transfer function the only frequency range to be considered is from 0 to $+\infty$, and back along the infinite semicircle to the positive real axis.

It should be pointed out that in case the transfer function contains poles on the imaginary axis, the contour C must be modified to avoid the poles by using indentations as shown in Fig. 2.3-3; otherwise the conditions for Eq. (2.3-18) would be violated. The poles may be either excluded from contour C or included in C by the indentations of small semicircles (usually drawn to the right of the imaginary axis). For a pole at $s = j\omega_1$, the indentation about the pole is given by

$$s = j\omega_1 + r\epsilon^{j\theta} \tag{2.3-22}$$

where r is the radius of the semicircle which approaches zero as its limit, and the angle θ varies from $-\pi/2$ radians through zero to $\pi/2$ radians if the pole is excluded from the contour and varies from $-\pi/2$ radians through $-\pi$ radians to $\pi/2$ radians if the pole is enclosed in the contour.

When poles on the imaginary axis are included in contour C, they must be counted in calculating the value of P of Eqs. (2.3-20) and (2.3-21).

The form of the polar plot of $A(s)$ may be classified in three categories, depending upon the nature of the system:

1. The polar plot makes no encirclement of the critical point $(-1 + j0)$. The system is stable if $A(s)$ has no pole in the right half plane. However, if $A(s)$ has poles in the right half plane, the system is unstable.
2. The polar plot makes clockwise encirclements of the critical point. The system is unstable since there are zeros of $1 + A(s)$ in the right half plane. The number of clockwise encirclements measures the excess of the right-half-plane zeros over poles of $1 + A(s)$.
3. The polar plot makes counterclockwise encirclements of the critical point. The system is stable only if the number of the counterclockwise encirclements is equal to the number of the right-half-plane poles of $A(s)$.

Nyquist's criterion offers several advantages over Routh's criterion. Nyquist's criterion can be applied to control systems of which the open-loop transfer functions contain transcendental terms of specific forms, such as ϵ^{-Ts}, in addition to polynomials. Experimental open-loop frequency-response data of a linear system can be used to construct the Nyquist diagram without resorting to a mathematical model. Furthermore, the Nyquist diagram indicates not only the absolute stability of the system but also the relative stability. The degree of stability as measured by the resonant peak and resonant frequency is readily determined from the Nyquist diagram.

Example 2.3-2. By applying Nyquist's criterion, study the stability of a feedback control system having open-loop transfer function

$$A(s) = \frac{K(1 + s + 0.25s^2)}{s^3(1 + 0.81s + 0.21s^2 + 0.018s^3)} \tag{2.3-23}$$

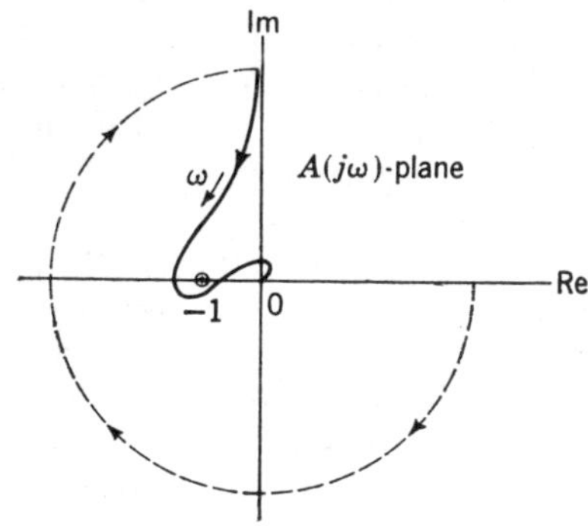

Fig. 2.3-4. Polar plot of Example 1 illustrating a conditionally stable system.

The extreme values of $A(s)$ can readily be determined from Eq. (2.3-23): At $\omega = \infty$, $A(s) = 0$. On the indentation, $\omega = r\epsilon^{j\theta}$ with $r \to 0$; various values are given below:

ω	$A(s)$
$r\epsilon^{j\theta}$	$\infty \underline{/0^\circ}$
$r\epsilon^{j\pi/6}$	$\infty \underline{/-90^\circ}$
$r\epsilon^{j\pi/3}$	$\infty \underline{/-180^\circ}$
$r\epsilon^{j\pi/2}$	$\infty \underline{/-270^\circ}$
$r\epsilon^{-j\pi/2}$	$\infty \underline{/270^\circ}$

For a certain value of the gain constant $K = K_1$, Fig. 2.3-4 sketches the polar plot of $A(s)$ for s varying over the contour C encircling the entire right half of the s plane in the clockwise direction. Since $A(s)$ contains no pole in the right half of the s plane and its polar plot makes no encirclement of the critical point $(-1 + j0)$, the system is stable at this gain level. When the gain is increased, the polar plot is shifted to the left and would encircle the critical point twice in the clockwise direction, thus indicating that $1 + A(s)$ contains two right-half-plane zeros and the system becomes unstable. On the other hand, if the gain is decreased, the polar plot is shifted to the right and also would encircle the critical point twice in the clockwise direction signifying an unstable operation. Control systems which are stable at a certain gain level and can be made unstable by an increase or a decrease in gain are defined as conditionally stable.

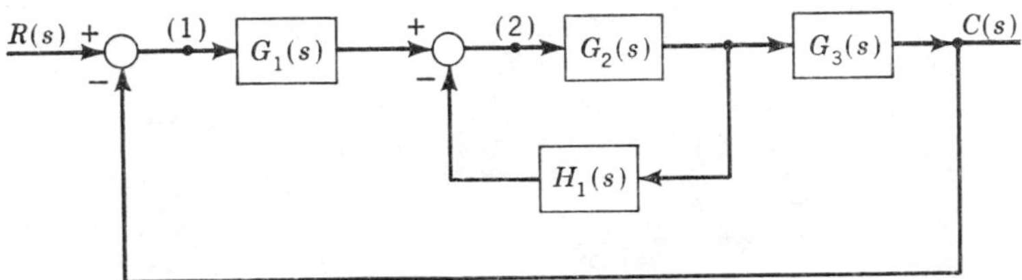

FIG. 2.3-5. Block diagram of Example 2 illustrating a multiple-loop system.

EXAMPLE 2.3-3. Investigate the stability of the multiple-loop system of Fig. 2.3-5, in which the transfer functions are

$$G_1(s) = 10 \tag{2.3-24}$$

$$G_2(s) = \frac{200}{s^2(1 + 0.1s)} \tag{2.3-25}$$

$$G_3(s) = 20s \tag{2.3-26}$$

$$H_1(s) = 5 \tag{2.3-27}$$

The open-loop transfer function of the system resulting from breaking the major loop only is found to be

$$A_1(s) = \frac{G_1(s)G_2(s)G_3(s)}{1 + A_m(s)} \tag{2.3-28}$$

$$= \frac{40{,}000s}{0.1s^3 + s^2 + 1{,}000} \tag{2.3-29}$$

where $A_m(s)$ is the open-loop transfer function of the minor loop and is equal to

$$A_m(s) = G_2(s)H_1(s) = \frac{1{,}000}{s^2(1 + 0.1s)} \tag{2.3-30}$$

From Fig. 2.3-6a, it is noted that the polar plot of $A_1(s)$ makes two counterclockwise encirclements of the critical point $(-1 + j0)$. Then, according to Eq. (2.3-20), the system would be stable if $A_1(s)$ possessed two poles in the right half of the s plane. The presence of right-half-plane poles of $A_1(s)$ may be detected from the polar plot of $A_m(s)$ or $1 + A_m(s)$ which forms the denominator of $A_1(s)$. The polar plot of $A_m(s)$ sketched in Fig. 2.3-6b reveals that $1 + A_m(s)$ has two right-half-plane zeros. This implies

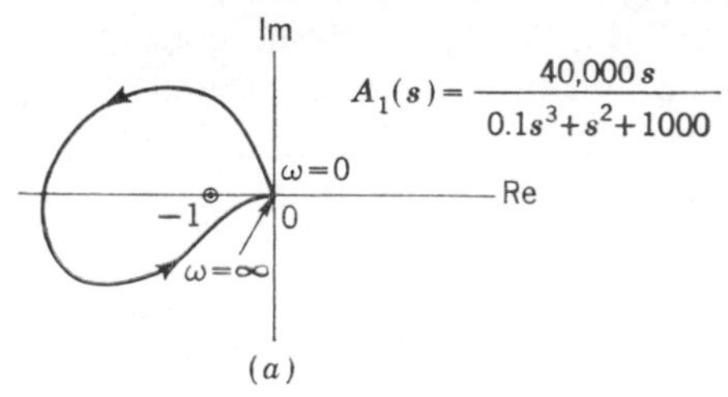

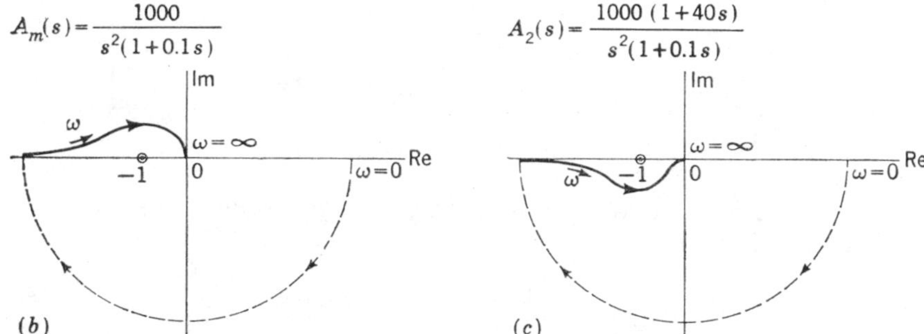

FIG. 2.3-6. (a) Polar plot of $A_1(j\omega)$; (b) polar plot of $A_m(j\omega)$; (c) polar plot of $A_2(j\omega)$.

that $A_1(s)$ contains two right-half-plane poles. Therefore, the stability condition of Eq. (2.3-20) is fulfilled and the system is stable.

Since this is a dual-loop system, the open-loop transfer function may have two possible forms depending upon how the loops are opened. If both the major and the minor loop are broken, as shown at position 2 of Fig. 2.3-5, the open-loop transfer function is then given by

$$A_2(s) = G_2(s)H_1(s) + G_1(s)G_2(s)G_3(s) \tag{2.3-31}$$

$$= \frac{1{,}000(1 + 40s)}{s^2(1 + 0.1s)} \tag{2.3-32}$$

Obviously, $A_2(s)$ of Eq. (2.3-32) is quite different from $A_1(s)$ of Eq. (2.3-29) which is derived by breaking the major loop alone; and $A_2(s)$ contains no right-half-plane pole. As can be seen from Fig. 2.3-6c the polar plot of $A_2(s)$ makes no encirclement of the critical point. Hence the system is stable. This conclusion is in agreement with the result of the first investigation. The above discussions reveal that the polar plot of $A_1(s)$ resulting from breaking the major loop alone fails to yield a direct indication of the system stability, whereas the polar plot of $A_2(s)$, obtained by breaking both loops, points out immediately whether the system is stable or not.

2.4. Asymptotic Gain and Phase Plots. In view of the fact that important performance characteristics of the control system can be determined from the frequency plots of the transfer function, the frequency response of a control system is one of the most convenient media to use for system analysis and design. The transfer functions may be plotted in different ways. The most popular graphical representations of the transfer functions of a control system are the polar plot (Nyquist diagram), the plots of magnitude and phase versus frequency in logarithmic units (Bode diagram), and the gain-phase plot.

Although the complex-plane representation of the transfer function is the most direct method for studying the frequency characteristic of a control system, the Bode diagram and the gain-phase plot are much more convenient to apply. As can readily be seen, to derive the polar plot of the equivalent transfer function of several transfer functions in cascade one must multiply the magnitudes of the polar plots of the original transfer functions at each frequency. This is a tedious job. However, if the logarithmic representation (Bode diagram and gain-phase plot) is employed, the magnitude of the equivalent transfer function at each frequency can be obtained from the corresponding magnitude of the original transfer function by simple addition because logarithmic operation converts multiplications into additions. Consequently, the use of the Bode diagram and the gain-phase plot in control-system design can save a tremendous amount of labor.

The Bode diagram of a transfer function consists of two curves; namely, the magnitude or gain plot and the phase plot. The former is a plot of the magnitude or gain in logarithmic units against the logarithm of the frequency, and the latter is a plot of the phase angle in degrees (or radians) versus the logarithm of the frequency. The Bode diagram possesses several important properties:

1. The gain plot of a complex rational transfer function may be constructed by a simple linear combination of the gain plots of its component factors.
2. The gain plot can easily be approximated in a simple manner by straight line asymptotes.
3. For most transfer functions, which belong to the minimum-phase class, the gain characteristic is completely determined when the phase characteristic is prescribed and vice versa.

With the first two properties the construction of the gain plots is greatly simplified even for very complex systems. In addition, the first property can be utilized to facilitate the evaluation of the required system compensation. The third property enables the designer to carry through a large portion of the design procedure using only the gain plots. On account of these properties the Bode-diagram approach has been extensively used in the analysis and design of control systems.

As discussed above, a rational transfer function may contain poles and zeros at the origin, real poles and zeros, and complex conjugate poles and zeros, and it can be factored into linear and quadratic factors of six basic forms:

1. s, a zero at origin
2. $\frac{1}{s}$, a pole at origin
3. $1 + Ts$, a real zero
4. $\frac{1}{1 + Ts}$, a real pole
5. $1 + 2\zeta \frac{s}{\omega_n} + \frac{s^2}{\omega_n{}^2}$, a pair of complex conjugate zeros
6. $\frac{1}{1 + 2\zeta s/\omega_n + s^2/\omega_n{}^2}$, a pair of complex conjugate poles

The Bode diagrams of these basic transfer functions can easily be sketched and are tabulated in Fig. 2.4-1. The frequency at which the asymptotes meet is often called the break frequency, ω_b. For the linear factor, $\omega_b = 1/T$; and for the quadratic factor, ω_b is the natural frequency, ω_n. Since the gain and phase plots of a composite transfer function may be constructed from the Bode diagrams of its component factors, with the aid of the basic Bode diagrams of Fig. 2.4-1 the construction of the gain and phase of the transfer function becomes a simple matter.

To design a feedback control system by means of the Bode-diagram technique, control engineers very often work with the asymptotic Bode plots. The *asymptotic gain plot* of a transfer function can be constructed by inspection, provided that the transfer function is expressed in linear and quadratic factors. However, the construction of the *asymptotic phase plot* is not so obvious and probably warrants clarification. In the case of nonminimum-phase transfer functions, the phase plot becomes quite important. The asymptotic phase plot of a rational transfer function can be constructed from the asymptotic phase plots of the linear and quadratic factors of the transfer function by superposition. The asymptotic phase plot of a linear or quadratic factor is readily sketched if the slopes and the break frequencies of the plot are determined.

Linear Factors

$$G_1(s) = (1 + Ts)^k \tag{2.4-1}$$

where k is a positive or negative integer. Clearly, the phase shift of $G_1(j\omega)$ is given by

$$\beta = k \tan^{-1} \omega T \tag{2.4-2}$$

As shown in Fig. 2.4-2, the phase plot approaches the line $\beta = 0$ as ω approaches zero, and it approaches the line $\beta = k\pi/2$ as ω approaches infinity. At $\omega = \omega_b = 1/T$, which is the break frequency of the asymptotic gain plot of $G_1(j\omega)$, the phase shift β is $k\pi/4$. The asymptotic phase

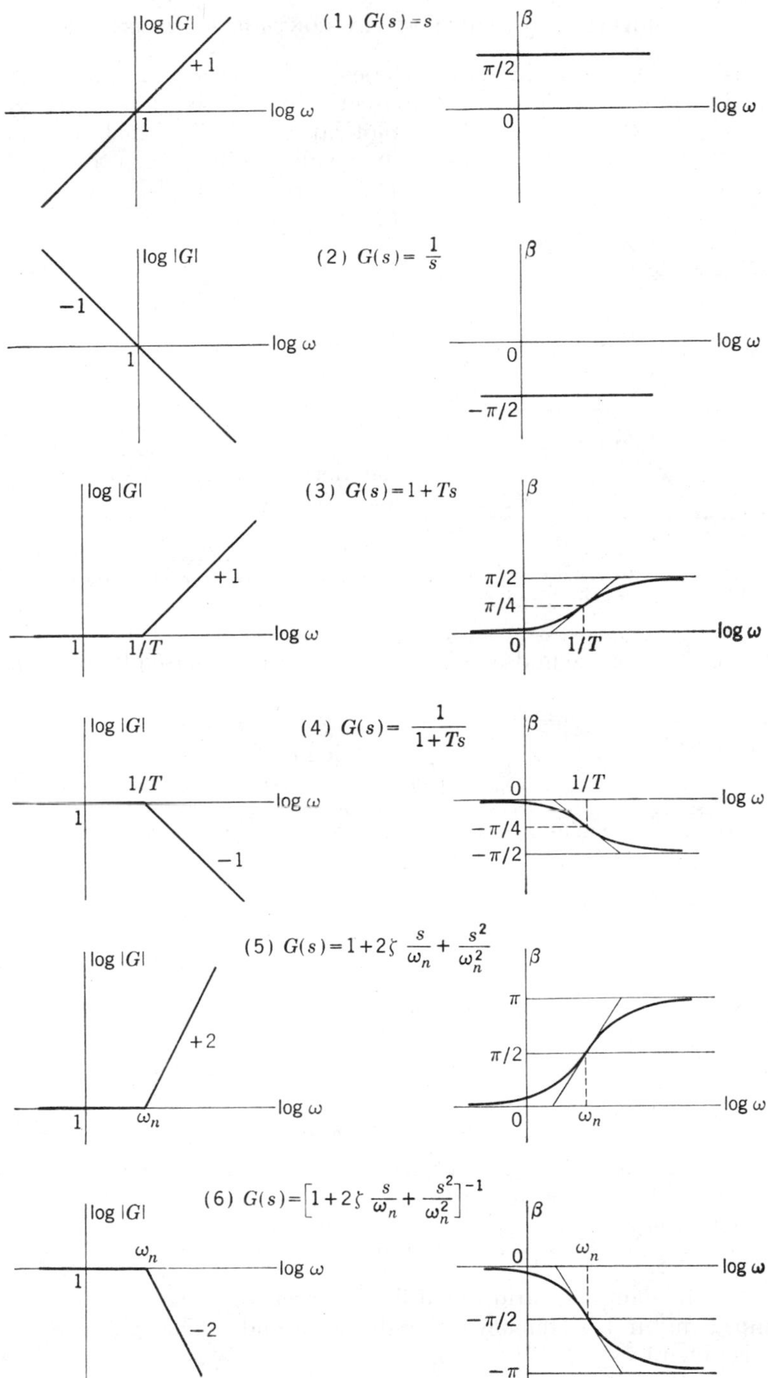

FIG. 2.4-1. Bode diagrams of the basic forms of transfer functions.

plot consists of three sections. The slopes of the lower and upper sections are equal to zero. The slope of the midsection equals the slope of the phase plot at $\omega = 1/T$, which can readily be determined from Eq. (2.4-2). Differentiating both sides of Eq. (2.4-2) yields

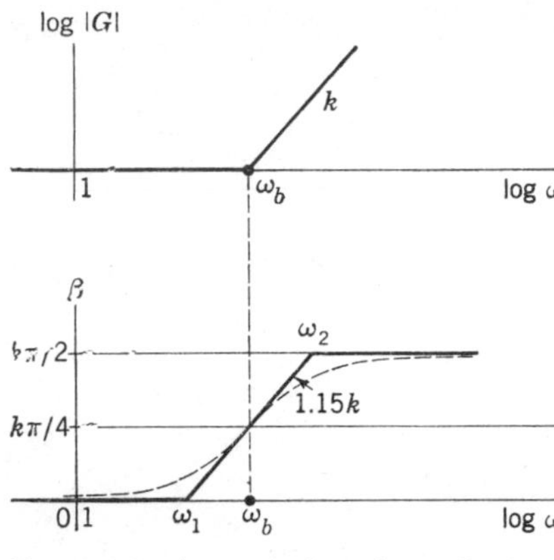

FIG. 2.4-2. Asymptotic gain and phase plots of the linear factor $G_1(s) = (1 + Ts)^k$.

$$\frac{d\beta}{d\omega} = \frac{kT}{1 + T^2\omega^2} \tag{2.4-3}$$

In view of the relationship

$$\frac{d\omega}{d(\log \omega)} = \frac{\omega}{\log \epsilon} \tag{2.4-4}$$

the derivative of β with respect to $\log \omega$ is

$$\frac{d\beta}{d(\log \omega)} = \frac{d\beta}{d\omega}\frac{d\omega}{d(\log \omega)} = \frac{\omega}{\log \epsilon}\frac{kT}{1 + T^2\omega^2} \tag{2.4-5}$$

Hence, the slope of the midsection of the asymptotic phase plot of $G_1(j\omega)$ is given by

$$\left.\frac{d\beta}{d(\log \omega)}\right|_{\omega = 1/T} = \frac{k}{2 \log \epsilon} = 1.15k \tag{2.4-6}$$

The break frequencies ω_1 and ω_2 of the asymptotic plot can be computed from the following relationships:

$$\frac{k\pi/4}{\log \omega_b - \log \omega_1} = \frac{k}{2 \log \epsilon} \tag{2.4-7}$$

$$\frac{k\pi/4}{\log \omega_2 - \log \omega_b} = \frac{k}{2 \log \epsilon} \tag{2.4-8}$$

Thus,

$$\omega_1 = \frac{\omega_b}{4.81} \tag{2.4-9}$$

$$\omega_2 = 4.81\omega_b \tag{2.4-10}$$

From Eqs. (2.4-6), (2.4-9), and (2.4-10), the asymptotic phase plot of $G_1(j\omega)$ can readily be constructed.

Quadratic Factors

$$G_2(s) = (s^2 + 2\zeta\omega_n s + \omega_n^2) \tag{2.4-11}$$

where ζ is the damping ratio which lies between zero and 1, and ω_n is the undamped natural frequency in radians/second. The phase shift of $G_2(j\omega)$ is given by

$$\beta = \tan^{-1} \frac{2\zeta\omega_n\omega}{\omega_n^2 - \omega^2} \tag{2.4-12}$$

As demonstrated in Fig. 2.4-3, for small frequencies the phase plot approaches the line $\beta = 0$ as an asymptote, and for high frequencies it approaches the line $\beta = \pi$ as an asymptote. At $\omega = \omega_n$, which is the break frequency of the asymptotic gain plot of $G_2(j\omega)$, the phase shift β equals $\pi/2$. The asymptotic phase plot consists of three sections. The lower and upper sections are of zero slope. The slope of the midsection can be determined by differentiating Eq. (2.4-12) with respect to log ω and evaluating the derivative at $\omega = \omega_n$. Thus,

$$\left.\frac{d\beta}{d(\log \omega)}\right|_{\omega = \omega_n} = \frac{1}{\zeta \log \epsilon} = \frac{2.3}{\zeta} \tag{2.4-13}$$

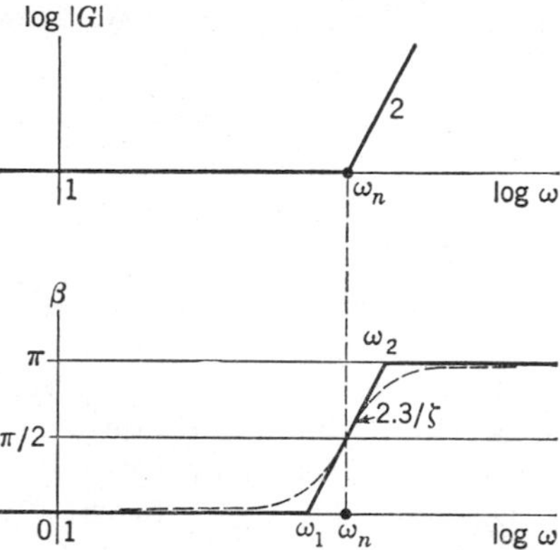

FIG. 2.4-3. Asymptotic gain and phase plots of the quadratic factor $G_2(s) = (s^2 + 2\zeta\omega_n s + \omega_n^2)$.

Equation (2.4-13) indicates that the slope of the midsection of the asymptotic phase plot of $G_2(j\omega)$ is inversely proportional to the damping ratio ζ.

Referring to Fig. 2.4-2, one obtains

$$\frac{\pi/2}{\log \omega_n - \log \omega_1} = \frac{1}{\zeta \log \epsilon} \tag{2.4-14}$$

$$\frac{\pi/2}{\log \omega_2 - \log \omega_n} = \frac{1}{\zeta \log \epsilon} \tag{2.4-15}$$

Equations (2.4-14) and (2.4-15) yield the break frequencies of the asymptotic phase plot as

$$\omega_1 = 4.81^{-\zeta}\omega_n \tag{2.4-16}$$

$$\omega_2 = 4.81^{\zeta}\omega_n \tag{2.4-17}$$

When the quadratic factor occurs in the denominator, the slope of the midsection of the asymptotic phase plot is equal to $-2.3/\zeta$ and the break frequencies are the same as that given by Eqs. (2.4-16) and (2.4-17) but the phase plot approaches the line $\beta = -\pi$ as ω approaches infinity.

The accuracy with which the asymptotes approximate the true phase plot is readily checked. The asymptotic phase plot for a term such as s is exact; but the asymptotic phase plots for terms such as $(1 + Ts)^{\pm 1}$ are not exact and have the greatest error at the break frequencies, $\omega_1 = 1/4.81T$ and $\omega_2 = 4.81/T$. At these frequencies, the error introduced by asymptotic representation is

$$\begin{aligned} \beta_\epsilon &= \tan^{-1} \omega_1 T = \tan^{-1} \frac{1}{4.81} \\ &= 11.8^\circ \text{ or } 0.205 \text{ radians} \end{aligned} \tag{2.4-18}$$

For terms such as $(s^2 + 2\zeta\omega_n s + \omega_n^2)^{\pm 1}$, the greatest error also occurs at the break frequencies, $\omega_1 = 4.81^{-\zeta}\omega_n$ and $\omega_2 = 4.81^{\zeta}\omega_n$. At these frequencies, the error introduced by asymptotic representation is readily computed from Eq. (2.4-12). Thus, the phase error is

$$\beta_\epsilon = \tan^{-1} \frac{2\zeta\omega_n(4.81)^{-\zeta}\omega_n}{\omega z^2 - (4.81)^{-2\zeta}\omega_n^2}$$

$$= \tan^{-1} \frac{2\zeta 4.81^{\zeta}}{4.81^{2\zeta} - 1} \tag{2.4-19}$$

which is dependent upon the value of ζ. Within the range of the damping ratio 0.4 to 0.9, the maximum error lies in the range 30 to 25°.

By use of the results derived in the preceding paragraphs, the construction of the asymptotic phase plot of a complex transfer function is illustrated in the following example.

EXAMPLE 2.4-1. Construct the asymptotic phase plot of the transfer function

$$G(s) = \frac{100s(1 + s/5)}{(s^2 + 6s + 25)(1 + s/50)} \tag{2.4-20}$$

Since the order of the denominator of $G(s)$ exceeds that of the numerator by 1, at the high-frequency end the asymptotic phase plot approaches the line $\beta = -\pi/2$. The s term of the numerator of $G(s)$ yields a phase shift $\beta = \pi/2$. Thus, at the low-frequency end the asymptotic phase plot approaches the line $\beta = \pi/2$.

For the $(1 + s/5)$ term, the slope of the midsection of the asymptotic phase plot is +1.15, and the break frequencies are

$$\omega_1 = \frac{5}{4.81} = 1.04 \text{ radians/sec} \qquad \omega_2 = 5 \times 4.81 = 24.05 \text{ radians/sec}$$

For the $(1 + s/50)^{-1}$ term, the slope of the midsection of the asymptotic phase plot is -1.15, and the break frequencies are 10.4 and 240.5 radians/sec.

For the $(s^2 + 6s + 25)^{-1}$ term, $\omega_n = 5$ radians/sec and $\zeta = 0.6$. The slope of the midsection of the asymptotic phase plot is $-2.3/0.6$, or -3.84, and the break frequencies are

$$\omega_1 = \frac{5}{4.81^{0.6}} = 1.95$$

$$\omega_2 = 5 \times 4.81^{0.6} = 12.8$$

To construct the asymptotic phase plot of the transfer function $G(s)$, the first step is to sketch the asymptotic phase plots of the factors of $G(s)$ (Fig. 2.4-4). The asymptotic phase plot of $G(s)$ is then obtained from the plots of those factors by simple addition, as illustrated in Fig. 2.4-4.

2.5. Control-System Compensation. The design of a control system generally involves four major steps. The first step is to obtain certain

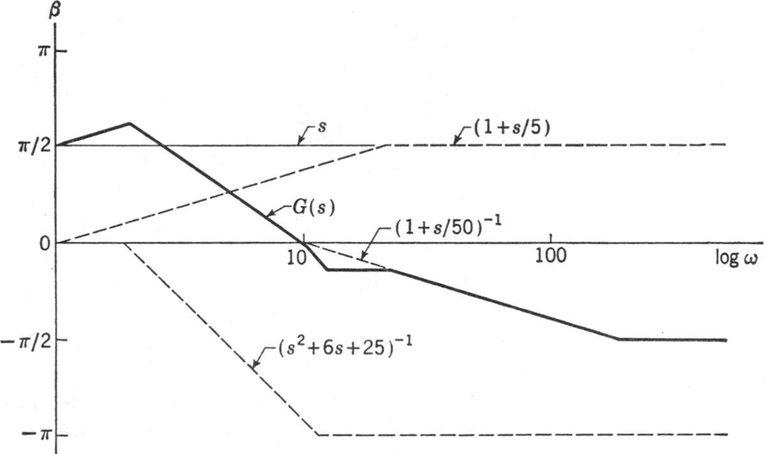

FIG. 2.4-4. Construction of the asymptotic phase plot of

$$G(s) = \frac{100s\,(1 + s/5)}{(1 + s/50)(s^2 + 6s + 25)}$$

information in the form of specifications concerning the system to be designed which describes, for example, the type of control, the desired accuracy, the nature of the load and external disturbances, the speed of response, the allowable transient overshoot, the rms error, the settling time of transient response, and the like. The second step is the interpretation of these specified data in terms of the design parameters of control system and the tentative selection of suitable components which are basic for building the system. In making the selection, reliability, power, cost, weight, and space limitations are taken into consideration. The basic components include the power elements of the controlled system, the actuating and amplifying elements, and the signal detecting and transmitting devices. The third step is the formulation of the transfer functions of all the components, the construction of a basic block diagram, and the preliminary analysis of this rudimentary system. The fourth step is to improve the performance of the preliminary system by appropriate compensation so as to meet the design specifications. In addition to these basic procedures the effects of tolerance and parameter variations must be investigated. Furthermore, any control system of reasonable complexity is usually designed with the aid of computer studies and model testing. A brief discussion of the control-system compensation is presented in the following paragraphs.

Control-system design can be carried out either in the frequency domain or in the time domain. The frequency-domain specifications generally include the steady-state error, the gain margin, the phase margin, the maximum output-input magnitude ratio M_p (sometimes called the resonance peak), the resonance frequency ω_r, the bandwidth B and the cutoff rate of the system. The steady-state error measures the accuracy of the system. The gain margin, phase margin, and M_p specify the relative stability which has been discussed in the previous section. The resonance frequency ω_r, being defined as the frequency at which the magnitude ratio M is maximum, is closely related to the speed of response of the system. High-resonance frequency reflects fast response and low-resonance frequency corresponds to slow response. The bandwidth B, being intimately related to system performance, design complexity, and cost, is a measure of the rise time, the filtering characteristic, and the noise-rejection properties of the system. Control systems with wide bandwidth generally have shorter rise time and higher speed of response; but large bandwidth may increase the transmitted noise and cause undesired saturation in the system by raising the signal levels. On the other hand, reducing the bandwidth can improve filtering and noise-rejection characteristics of the control system, and can simplify the desired compensation. The cutoff rate also has influence on the noise attenuation. A high cutoff rate of frequency can sufficiently attenuate the noise which enters the system with the input signal and possesses a large amount of energy at frequencies just beyond the end of the signal spectrum.

In the time domain the system specifications are usually expressed in terms of the characteristics of the step-function response of the system. The most common time-domain specifications are the damping factor ζ, the undamped natural frequency ω_n, the frequency of transient oscillation ω_t, the maximum transient overshoot M_m, the rise time T_r, the settling time T_s, and the time delay T_d. A typical step-function response of a feedback control system is depicted in Fig. 2.5-1. The damping factor

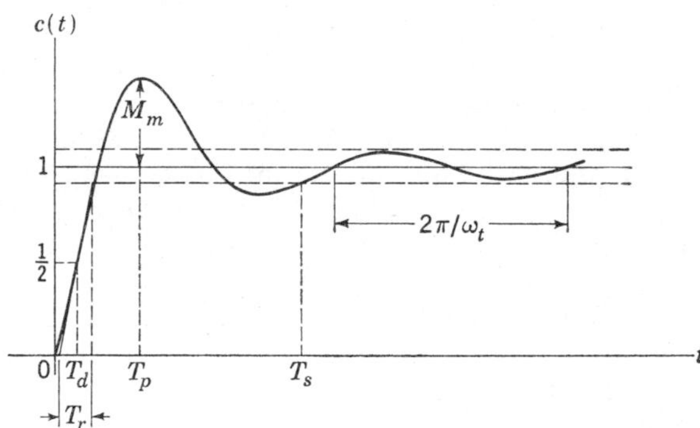

FIG. 2.5-1. Typical step-function response.

indicates how fast the transient dies out, and is often used as a measure of the relative stability of the system. The maximum transient overshoot which is expressed as a percentage of the steady-state value of the response provides another way of measuring the relative stability of control systems. The maximum overshoot depends upon the damping factor, and it increases as the damping factor decreases. The rise time is usually defined as the reciprocal of the slope of the response at the instant the response is half the steady-state value, or as the time required for the response to rise from 10 to 90 per cent of its steady-state value. The rise time is related to the signal distortion caused by the system. The settling time is often defined as the time required for the oscillation of the response to come to and thereafter remain within a specified percentage of the steady-state value. Common practice uses a specification of 5 or 2 per cent depending upon the application of the system. The settling time is related to the most significant time constant in the over-all transfer function of the control system. The time delay is sometimes defined as the required time for the response to reach half the steady-state value. The time delay depends upon the rate of change of the phase shift with respect to frequency.

Although no exact mathematical relationship has been derived between the design parameters in the frequency domain and those in the time domain, these parameters in both domains are related. The correlations between the transient response and the frequency response are briefly given below.

1. M_p versus M_m and ζ. $(1 + M_m)$ is generally less than M_p. The resonance peak increases as the damping factor decreases. A system with over-all damping factor of 0.5 to 0.8 usually exhibits a resonance peak under 1.35 in its closed-loop frequency response curve.

2. ω_r versus ω_t and T_d. Generally speaking, the resonance frequency is about the same as the base frequency of the transient oscillation which, for $\zeta < 1$, is given by $\omega_t = \omega_n\sqrt{1 - \zeta^2}$. The time delay increases as the resonance frequency decreases.

3. B versus T_r and T_s. The product of the rise time T_r and the bandwidth B is directly related to the maximum overshoot. In general, the value of the product T_rB becomes larger when the overshoot increases. Systems with negligible overshoot in the step-function response have the value of T_rB around 1.9, and systems with 10 per cent overshoot have the value of T_rB in the neighborhood of 2.8, where T_r is measured in seconds and B in radians per second. The settling time T_s usually decreases as the bandwidth increases.

Gain Adjustment. When the preliminary analysis of a control system in its primitive form indicates that the system is unstable or that the over-all performance is inadequate, it is necessary to improve the system performance. The most direct and simplest way of changing the performance is the adjustment of the system gain. However, for most control systems the design specifications cannot be met by gain adjustment alone, thus necessitating the introduction of compensating devices into the control loops.

The adequate gain setting for a control system can be determined either from the Nyquist diagram of the system and the constant-M circles, or from the gain-phase plot of the system and the Nichols charts, or from the Bode diagram of the system.

A change in system gain usually affects practically all of the system design parameters. For instance, an increase in system gain may cause a reduction of the system error, may increase the speed of response of the control system, and may make the system more oscillatory. The effects of gain variations upon the behavior of a control system become more obvious when the root locus of the control system is plotted. The root-locus method is discussed in Sec. 2.6.

Cascade Compensation. When the desired behavior of a control system cannot be obtained by the gain adjustment alone, compensation techniques must be used. Compensation means to improve the system performance by reshaping the open-loop transfer function plot of the system. The compensation of a control system can generally be accomplished either by an element in series with other components as shown in Fig. 2.5-2, or by an element in parallel with one or more components and form-

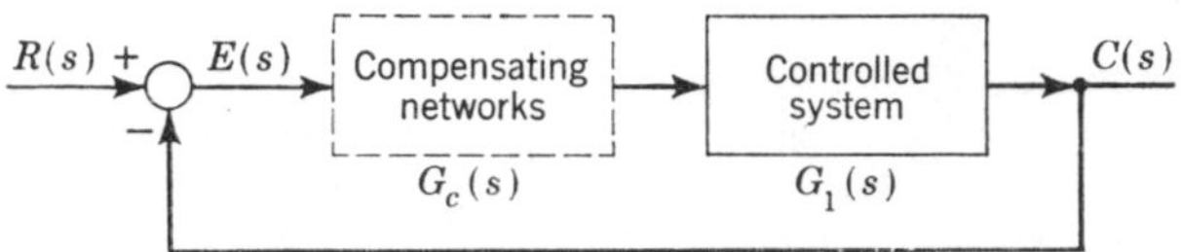

FIG. 2.5-2. Cascade compensation.

ing a subsidiary loop, as shown in Fig. 2.5-3. The former arrangement is referred to as cascade or series compensation and the latter is called feedback or minor-loop compensation. A compensator or compensating device can stabilize a system when it is unstable for all values of gain; it can

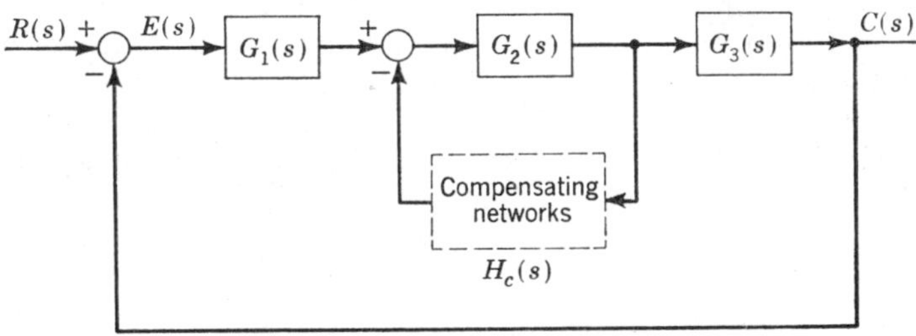

FIG. 2.5-3. Feedback compensation.

improve both the transient and the steady-state performance of a system; and it can reduce the system error. Compensators are classified according to their operating characteristics into lead-phase (differentiating) type, phase-lag (integrating) type, and lag-lead (integro-differentiating) type. The phase-lead type of compensator is generally used to modify the high-frequency portion of the open-loop transfer function plot and to improve the transient behavior of the system, whereas the phase-lag type of compensator is often used to alter the low-frequency portion of the open-loop plot and to improve the steady-state performance of the system.

Although the modification of the open-loop frequency characteristic may be worked out in the polar plane, the simplicity and ease with which the Bode diagrams and the gain-phase plots can be reshaped to meet performance specifications have made the Bode approach and gain-phase representation very attractive. An example illustrating the use of the Bode method to determine the cascade compensation is given below.

EXAMPLE 2.5-1. Design a d-c positioning servomechanism using two helipots as the error transducer between the input and the output shaft positions, a d-c amplifier to provide gain adjustment, and a d-c generator to drive the servomotor which is coupled to a load through a gear train. The specifications are that (1) the phase margin of the system should be larger than 40°, and (2) the allowable system error at 1 radian/sec be about 1 per cent of input.

A schematic diagram of this system is presented in Fig. 2.5-4*a*. The major time constants of the system are found to be 0.1 and 0.01 sec. Preliminary analysis yields the open-loop transfer function

$$A(s) = \frac{500}{s(1 + 0.1s)(1 + 0.01s)} \tag{2.5-1}$$

The block diagram of this system is shown in Fig. 2.5-4*b*. As can be seen

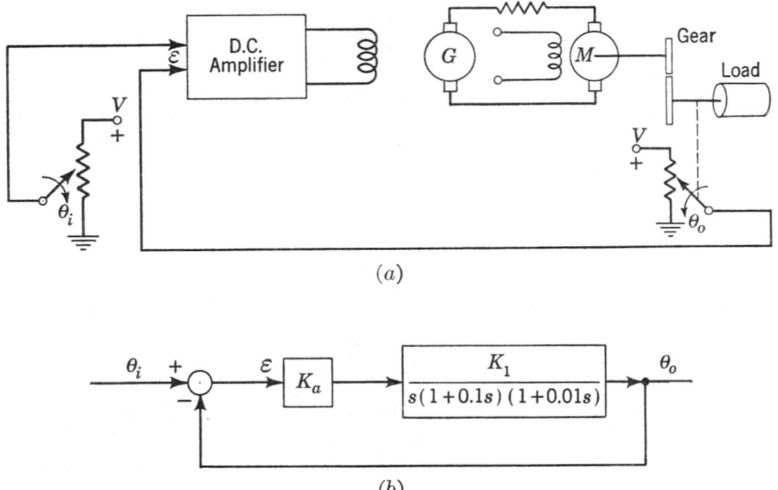

FIG. 2.5-4. (*a*) Schematic diagram of a simple positioning servo; (*b*) block diagram of the positioning servo.

from the Bode plot of the system shown in Fig. 2.5-5, the system specifications cannot be met by gain adjustment alone and a phase-lead compensator probably must be introduced into the system.

From the accuracy requirement it is found that the gain constant K

should be set at a value equal to or greater than 100. At this gain level the open-loop transfer function becomes

$$A(s) = \frac{100}{s(1 + 0.1s)(1 + 0.01s)} \tag{2.5-2}$$

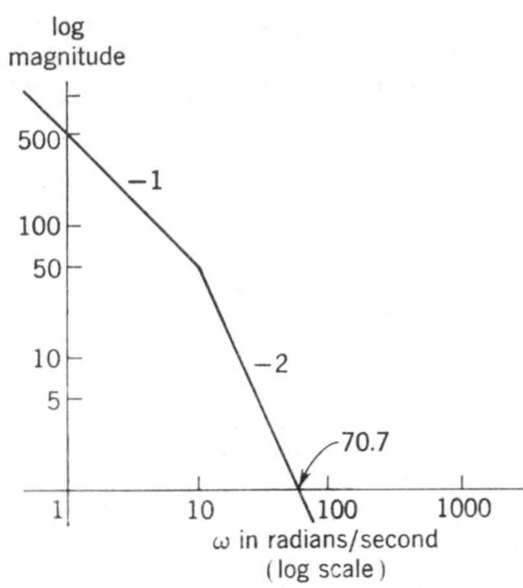

FIG. 2.5-5. Asymptotic log-magnitude vs. log-frequency plot (for $K = 500$).

From the asymptotic gain plot of $A(s)$ (Fig. 2.5-6), the crossover frequency is found to be 31.6 radians/sec and the computed phase margin is $-1.60°$. Additional phase shift of 38.4° is needed. Consequently, it is required to introduce a phase-lead compensator into the system so as to raise the phase margin and to meet the specified relative stability.

Let the transfer function of the required equalizer be

$$G_c(s) = \frac{1 + s/\omega_a}{1 + s/\omega_b} = \frac{1 + T_a s}{1 + T_b s} \tag{2.5-3}$$

Then the phase shift of the lead network at frequency ω_c is given by

$$\beta_{cc} = \tan^{-1}\frac{\omega_c}{\omega_a} - \tan^{-1}\frac{\omega_c}{\omega_b} \tag{2.5-4}$$

As can easily be shown, this network will provide maximum phase shift at

$$\omega_c = \sqrt{\omega_a \omega_b} \tag{2.5-5}$$

For most effective compensation, this frequency will be chosen as the crossover frequency of the compensated open-loop transfer function. The phase shift of the equalizer at ω_c is then obtained by substituting Eq. (2.5-5) into Eq. (2.5-4):

$$\beta_{cc} \approx \frac{\pi}{2} - 2\sqrt{\frac{\omega_a}{\omega_b}} \tag{2.5-6}$$

From the above calculation it is found that an additional phase shift (lead) of 38.4° or greater is required at crossover. This additional phase shift will be furnished by the compensator. By trying $\beta_{cc} = 69°$, Eq. (2.5-6) yields

$$\sqrt{\frac{\omega_a}{\omega_b}} \approx 0.183 \tag{2.5-7}$$

Then with the cascade compensation the phase shift of $A_c(s)$ at crossover frequency ω_c is given by

$$\beta_c \approx -\frac{\pi}{2} - \left(\frac{\pi}{2} - \frac{10}{\omega_c}\right) + \left(\frac{\pi}{2} - \frac{\omega_a}{\omega_c}\right) - \frac{\omega_c}{\omega_b} - \frac{\omega_c}{100} \tag{2.5-8}$$

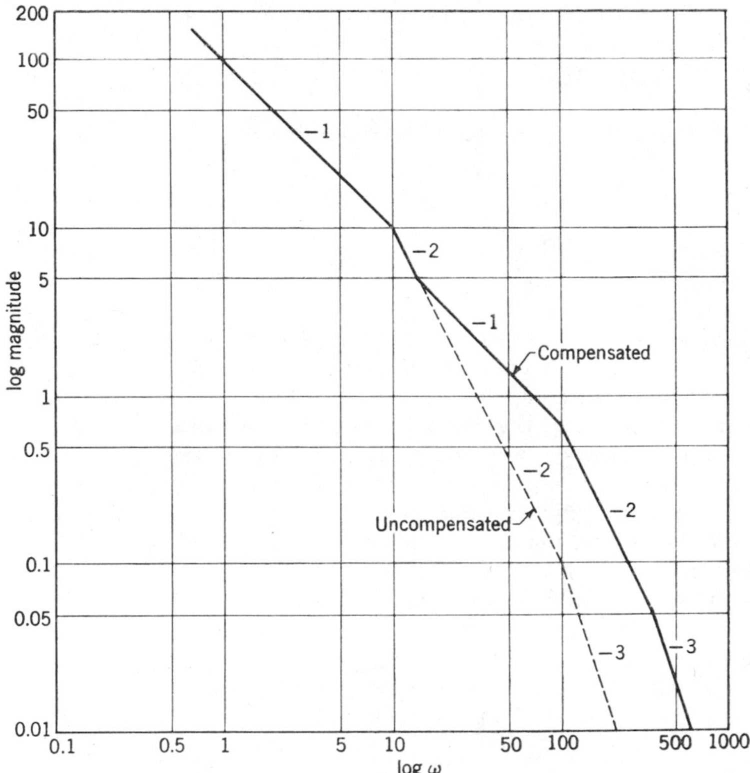

FIG. 2.5-6. Bode diagram of the control system of Fig. 2.5-4 with gain constant K equal to 100.

Setting $\beta_c = 40°$, the required phase margin, Eq. (2.5-8) becomes

$$\frac{10}{\omega_c} - \frac{\omega_c}{100} - \frac{\omega_a}{\omega_c} - \frac{\omega_c}{\omega_b} = \frac{\pi}{2} - \frac{14\pi}{18} = -\frac{5\pi}{18} \tag{2.5-9}$$

Since $\omega_c = \sqrt{\omega_a\omega_b}$, the above equation reduces to

$$\frac{10}{\omega_c} - \frac{\omega_c}{100} - 2\sqrt{\frac{\omega_a}{\omega_b}} = -\frac{5\pi}{18} \tag{2.5-10}$$

Substituting Eq. (2.5-7) into Eq. (2.5-10) and rearranging yields

$$\omega_c^2 - 50.7\omega_c - 1000 = 0 \tag{2.5-11}$$

The positive root of Eq. (2.5-11) gives the crossover frequency,

$$\omega_c = 66 \text{ radians/sec} \tag{2.5-11a}$$

The values of ω_a and ω_b can then be determined from Eqs. (2.5-5) and (2.5-7):

$$\omega_a = 12.1 \text{ radians/sec} \qquad \omega_b = 360 \text{ radians/sec} \tag{2.5-12}$$

Thus, the transfer function of the series equalizer is given by

$$G_c(s) = \frac{1 + s/12.1}{1 + s/360} = \frac{1 + 0.0826s}{1 + 0.00278s} \tag{2.5-13}$$

and the compensated open-loop transfer function is

$$A_c(s) = \frac{100(1 + 0.0826s)}{s(1 + 0.1s)(1 + 0.01s)(1 + 0.00278s)} \tag{2.5-14}$$

The log-gain plot of the compensated open-loop transfer function is then plotted from Eq. (2.5-14). The next step is to check whether the computed $A_c(s)$ meets the specification or not. The log-gain plot of $A_c(s)$ indicates a crossover frequency around 70 radians/sec, which is slightly higher than the estimated value of 66 radians/sec. From Eq. (2.5-14) the phase margin of the compensated system is found to be around 42°. Thus, both the accuracy and the relative stability requirements are fulfilled and the cascade compensation given by Eq. (2.5-13) is adequate. It is noticed that a preamplifier is always used with phase-lead compensators in order to maintain unity gain at d-c level.

Feedback Compensation. The choice of a method of compensation generally depends upon the specific system involved, the available components, economic reasons, and the designer's experience and judgment. The feedback compensation is sometimes advantageous over cascade compensation in that the variation of the parameters of the system components bridged by the feedback elements of the minor loop becomes less effective upon system performance if the minor-loop gain is made sufficiently large and if the parameters of the feedback compensator do not vary. Use is frequently made of this merit of feedback compensation to improve the performance of control systems which contain components with varying gain factor and time constants. The block diagram of a control system employing feedback compensation is shown in Fig. 2.5-7, where $G_1(s)$ and

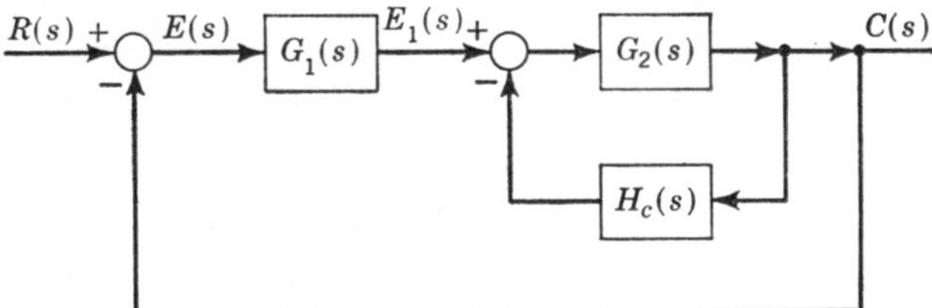

FIG. 2.5-7. A system employing feedback compensation.

$G_2(s)$ are the transfer functions of the system components and $H_c(s)$ is the transfer function of the compensator.

For the minor loop of Fig. 2.5-7 the open-loop transfer function is

$$A_m(s) = G_2(s)H_c(s) \tag{2.5-15}$$

and the input and the output are related by

$$\frac{C(s)}{E_1(s)} = \frac{G_2(s)}{1 + G_2(s)H_c(s)} \tag{2.5-16}$$

From these two equations it is noted that if the gain of the minor loop is much less than unity,

$$|A_m(j\omega)| \ll 1 \tag{2.5-17}$$

then

$$\frac{C(j\omega)}{E_1(j\omega)} \approx G_2(j\omega) \tag{2.5-18}$$

and the minor loop is ineffective; and if the minor-loop gain is much larger than unity,

$$|A_m(j\omega)| \gg 1 \tag{2.5-19}$$

then

$$\frac{C(j\omega)}{E_1(j\omega)} \approx \frac{1}{H_c(j\omega)} \tag{2.5-20}$$

and the system elements bridged by the compensator produce little effect. Thus, the variation of the gain factor and the time constants of these elements do not enter into the compensated frequency characteristic. Equation (2.5-20) further points out that for the frequency range that the minor loop is in control, that is, $|A_m(j\omega)| \gg 1$, a lead network in the feedback branch of the minor loop behaves as a lag network in the major loop of the compensated system and vice versa.

For the major loop the open-loop transfer function of the system with compensation is given by

$$A_c(s) = \frac{G_1(s)G_2(s)}{1 + A_m(s)} \tag{2.5-21}$$

Equation (2.5-21) indicates that for the frequency range in which the gain of the minor loop is much less than unity, the open-loop transfer function of the compensated system, $A_c(j\omega)$, is approximately equal to that of the original system, $A(j\omega)$, that is,

$$A_c(j\omega) \approx G_1(j\omega)G_2(j\omega) = A(j\omega) \tag{2.5-22}$$

Thus, for the frequency range of the Bode diagram in which the minor-loop gain is far below unity the log-gain plot undergoes no change by the introduction of feedback compensation. When the minor-loop gain is much greater than unity, Eq. (2.5-21) may be approximated by

$$A_c(s) \approx \frac{G_1(s)G_2(s)}{A_m(s)} = \frac{A(s)}{A_m(s)} \tag{2.5-23}$$

or in terms of ω,

$$A_c(j\omega) \approx \frac{A(j\omega)}{A_m(j\omega)} \tag{2.5-24}$$

Equation (2.5-24) reveals that for the frequency range of high minor-loop gain the log-gain plot of the compensated system may be derived by subtracting the log-gain plot of the minor loop from the log-gain plot of the original system. By making use of these properties the required feedback compensation can be determined from the Bode diagram of the control system with ease.

2.6. Root-locus Method. The preceding section presents a brief review of the basic design techniques using frequency response as the primary medium for representing the system behavior. In system design some performance specifications are usually expressed in terms of the transient response of the system. The time-domain design parameters, such as peak time, maximum overshoot, damping factor, and settling time, are intimately related to the roots of the characteristic equation of the control system, which are the poles of the closed-loop system function. Once these characteristic roots are determined, the different modes of the transient response are known. Consequently, to design a control system from time-domain specifications, the control engineer often needs a general knowledge of how the variation of the characteristic roots will influence the transient performance of the system. Such knowledge can be easily and conveniently derived from a plot of the locus of the characteristic roots of the control system with the system loop gain as a parameter. A plot of this nature is commonly known as the root locus. The root-locus method of system design is essentially based upon the study of the effects of shifting the characteristic roots upon the transient behavior from the root-locus plot of the system. With the aid of the root locus, control-system design can be accomplished by simply adjusting the zeros of the open-loop transfer function, the roots of the characteristic equation, and the loop gain of the system so as to end with an improved closed-loop system function with new pole-zero distributions which will yield the desired transient response. The root-locus method provides the control engineer with design techniques to take into account both the frequency response and the transient response, thus forming a bridge between the extensively used frequency-domain approach and the fairly difficult time-domain synthesis.

In view of the fact that the root-locus method, which was originally developed for continuous-data control systems, can be readily carried over to the analysis and design of sampled-data and digital control systems, a brief review of some important aspects of this method appears quite desirable. Since the basic rules for the construction of the root loci are covered in most standard textbooks on linear servo theory, they will not be repeated here. This section is primarily concerned with the discussions of the design aspects of the root-locus method. The concepts involved in these discussions will find much use when the design of sampled-data control systems by the root-locus method is studied in Sec. 9.8.

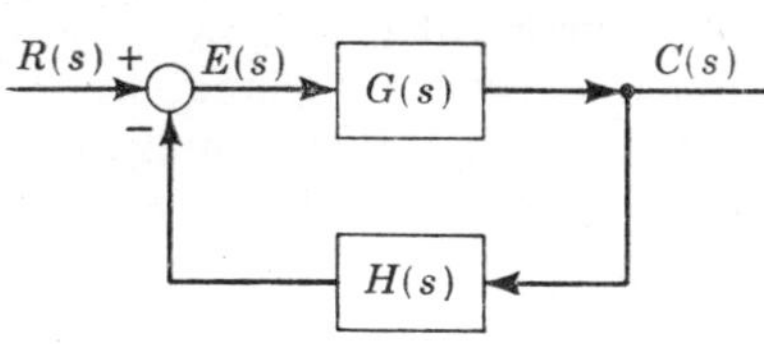

Fig. 2.6-1. Block diagram of a basic feedback control system.

Referring to the block diagram of a basic feedback control system shown in Fig. 2.6-1, the characteristic equation of the system is

$$1 + G(s)H(s) = 0 \tag{2.6-1}$$

or

$$1 + A(s) = 0 \tag{2.6-2}$$

where $A(s) = G(s)H(s)$ is the open-loop transfer function. The poles and zeros of $A(s)$ are referred to as the open-loop poles and zeros, respectively. Equation (2.6-2) may be written as

$$A(s) = -1 = \epsilon^{j(180 \pm n360°)} \tag{2.6-3}$$

in which n is an integer or zero. Since $A(s)$ is a function of complex variable s, Eq. (2.6-3) may be split into two equations by equating, respectively, the magnitude and the phase angle of both sides. They are the magnitude equation

$$|A(s)| = 1 \tag{2.6-4}$$

and the phase-angle equation

$$\underline{/A(s)} = 180 \pm n360° \tag{2.6-5}$$

The plot of the phase-angle equation in the complex plane with the gain factor as a parameter is called the root locus of the system. The magnitude equation determines the value of the gain of each point of the locus.

The design of feedback control systems by use of the root-locus method involves the reshaping of the root-locus plots by shifting or introducing open-loop poles and zeros. As a preliminary to the discussion of the design aspects, the effects of shifting open-loop poles and zeros are first studied with the aid of examples.

EXAMPLE 2.6-1. The effect of shifting an open-loop pole.

Consider a feedback control system with open-loop transfer function

$$A(s) = \frac{Ks^3}{(s+1)^2(s+p_1)} \tag{2.6-6}$$

Study the effect of the variation p_1 upon the root locus of the system and sketch the loci for several values of p_1.

Since the open-loop transfer function has three zeros and three poles, there are three branches ($n = 3$) in the root locus of which none terminates at infinity. These three branches of the locus start from poles $-1, -1, -p_1$ and terminate at zeros 0, 0, 0. The segment between $s = 0$ and $s = -1$ is a branch and the segment between $s = -1$ and $s = -p_1$ is a portion of the locus.

The real-axis intercept (or break-away point) is computed as follows: At a point on the root locus the phase angles are related by

$$\theta_{p1} + 2\theta_{p2} - 3\theta_{z1} = -180° \tag{2.6-7}$$

When this point is very close to the real axis,

$$\theta_{p1} \approx \frac{\Delta\omega}{p_1 - x_0} \qquad \theta_{p2} \approx 180° - \frac{\Delta\omega}{x_0 - 1} \qquad \theta_{z1} \approx 180° - \frac{\Delta\omega}{x_0} \tag{2.6-8}$$

and Eq. (2.6-7) reduces to

$$\frac{1}{p_1 - x_0} - \frac{2}{x_0 - 1} + \frac{3}{x_0} = 0 \tag{2.6-9}$$

The above relationships hold only for p_1 larger than unity. The intercept on the negative real axis is given by the root of Eq. (2.6-9):

$$x_0 = \frac{3p_1}{p_1 + 2} \tag{2.6-10}$$

That is, the root locus breaks away from the real axis at a distance $3p_1/(p_1 + 2)$ to the left of the origin of the s plane. The intercepts for several values of p_1 are given in Table 2.6-1.

The origin of the s plane is the junction point where the three branches of the root locus meet. At this point the tangents to the locus make an angle of 120° with each other or an angle of 60° with the real axis which is called the angle of arrival of the root locus.

The characteristic equation of the system is easily obtained from Eq. (2.6-6):

$$(1 + K)s^3 + (2 + p_1)s^2 + (1 + 2p_1)s + p_1 = 0 \tag{2.6-11}$$

from which the intercepts of the root locus on the imaginary axis can be determined. Replacing s by $j\omega$, Eq. (2.6-11) yields two simultaneous equations

$$(2 + p_1)\omega^2 - p_1 = 0 \tag{2.6-12}$$

$$(1 + K)\omega^2 - (1 + 2p_1) = 0 \tag{2.6-13}$$

The solutions of these two equations are

$$\omega = \pm\sqrt{\frac{p_1}{p_1 + 2}} \tag{2.6-14}$$

which gives the intercepts on the imaginary axis, and

$$K = \frac{2(p_1 + 1)^2}{p_1} \tag{2.6-15}$$

which is the value of the corresponding gain constant at which the system will exhibit sustained oscillation. Several values of the imaginary axis intercept y_i and the corresponding gain constant K_i are tabulated in Table 2.6-1.

TABLE 2.6-1

p_1	x_0	y_i	K_i
0	. . .	0	∞
1	1	0.578	8
2	1.5	0.707	9
3	1.8	0.774	10.7
5	2.14	0.845	14.4
10	2.5	0.913	24.2

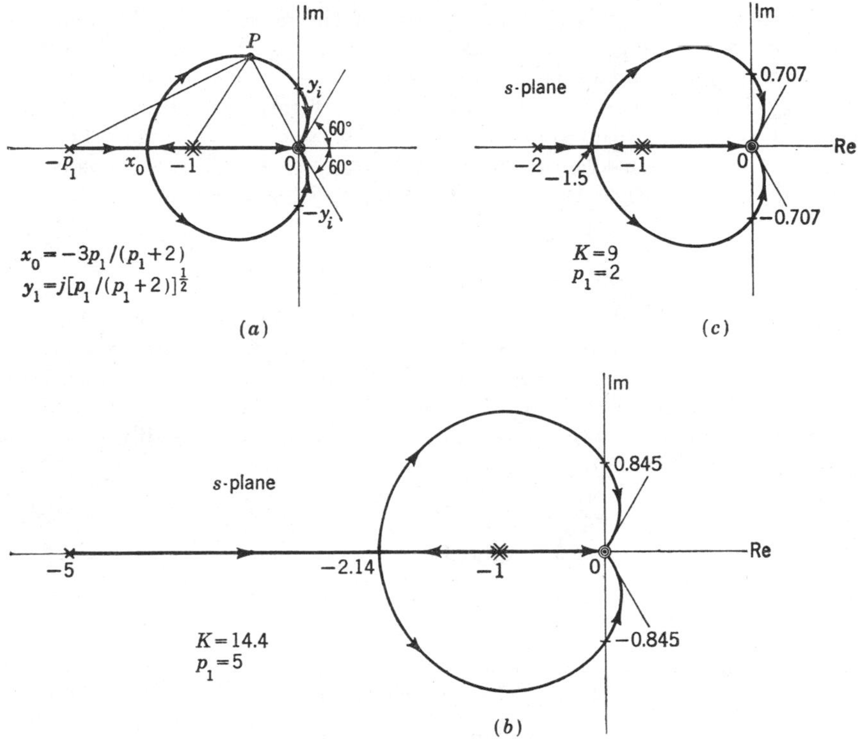

FIG. 2.6-2. Root locus of the system of Example 2.6-1 for various values of K and p_1.

The root locus of this system is sketched in Fig. 2.6-2. The locus is bounded since the system has equal number of open-loop poles and zeros. The three branches of the locus are the segment from $s = -1$ to $s = 0$, the curve from $s = -1$ through $s = -3p_1/(p_1 + 2)$ and $s = j\sqrt{p_1/(p_1 + 2)}$ to $s = 0$, and the curve from $s = -p_1$ through $s = -3p_1/(p_1 + 2)$ and $s = -j\sqrt{p_1/(p_1 + 2)}$ to $s = 0$. The loci corresponding to various values of p_1 indicate that, as the pole p_1 is pushed to the left of the origin, the root locus is also displaced to the left and it crosses the imaginary axis at a higher gain level, resulting in a more stable system. For instance, when $p_1 = 2$ the system would be in sustained oscillation if K is raised to 9, whereas when $p_1 = 10$ sustained oscillation will not occur until K is increased to 24.2.

EXAMPLE 2.6-2. The effect of shifting an open-loop zero.

Consider a feedback control system having open-loop transfer function

$$A(s) = \frac{K(s + z_1)}{s(s^2 + 4s + 20)} = \frac{K(s + z_1)}{s(s + 2 + j4)(s + 2 - j4)} \tag{2.6-16}$$

Study the effect of the variation of z_1 upon the root locus of the system and sketch the loci for several values of z_1.

The root locus of this system consists of three branches of which two terminate at infinity because the open-loop transfer function $A(s)$ contains three poles and one zero. These branches of the locus start from poles, $p_0 = 0$, $p_1 = -2 + j4$, and $p_2 = -2 - j4$. The branch on the negative real axis is the segment from $s = 0$ to $s = -z_1$. The other two branches tend toward the asymptotes at angles of $\pm 90°$ with respect to the real axis; and these two asymptotes intersect the real axis at

$$x_c = \frac{z_1 - 4}{2} \tag{2.6-17}$$

which is the centroid of the open-loop pole-zero configuration. When z_1 equals 4, x_c is zero and the locus approaches the imaginary axis as the asymptote. For $z_1 < 4$ the centroid falls on the negative real axis whereas for $z_1 > 4$ the centroid would be on the positive real axis.

The intercepts of the locus on the imaginary axis can readily be determined from the characteristic equation of the system:

$$s^3 + 4s^2 + (20 + K)s + Kz_1 = 0 \tag{2.6-18}$$

On the imaginary axis, $s = j\omega$ and Eq. (2.6-18) becomes

$$-j\omega^3 - 4\omega^2 + j(20 + K)\omega + Kz_1 = 0 \tag{2.6-19}$$

which yields two simultaneous equations

$$4\omega^2 - Kz_1 = 0 \tag{2.6-20}$$

$$\omega^2 - (20 + K) = 0 \tag{2.6-21}$$

The solutions of these two equations are

$$\omega = \pm \sqrt{\frac{20z_1}{z_1 - 4}} \tag{2.6-22}$$

$$K = \frac{80}{z_1 - 4} \tag{2.6-23}$$

which determine the intercepts on the imaginary axis and the value of the gain constant at the intercepts. If the gain factor K is increased to the value given by Eq. (2.6-23) the system would be put into sustained oscillation. Equation (2.6-22) indicates that the root locus crosses the imaginary axis only when $z_1 > 4$. For $z_1 = 4$, the locus will meet the imaginary axis at infinity; that is, the imaginary axis is the asymptote of the root locus. The centroid x_c, the imaginary-axis intercepts y_i, and the corresponding gain constant K_i for several values of z_1 are listed in Table 2.6-2. As can easily be seen the root locus of this system does not intersect with the real axis.

The angles at which the branches of the locus leave the complex poles are readily evaluated from the phase-angle equation of the system:

$$\theta_{p0} + \theta_{p1} + \theta_{p2} - \theta_{z1} = 180° \tag{2.6-24}$$

TABLE 2.6-2

z_1	x_c	y_i	K_i	θ_{p1}, deg
0	−2	. . .	. . .	90
2	−1	. . .	. . .	63.5
4	0	∞	∞	37
6	1	7.75	40	18.5
8	2	6.32	20	7.2

At a point of the locus very near the pole p_1, $\theta_{p2} \approx 90°$. Thus, the angle of departure of the locus from pole p_1 is given by

$$\theta_{p1} = 90° + \theta_{z1} - \theta_{p0} \tag{2.6-25}$$

where θ_{z1} and θ_{p0} are the angles of the phasors from zero z_1 to pole p_1 and from pole p_0 to pole p_1, respectively. From the geometry of pole-zero configurations in Fig. 2.6-3, it is found that

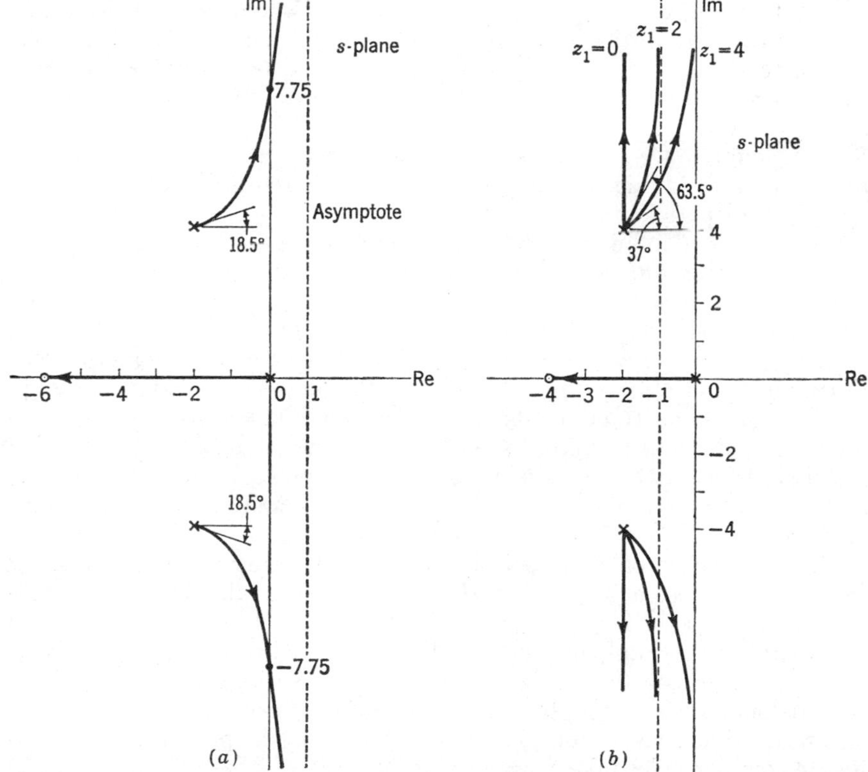

FIG. 2.6-3. (a) Root locus of the system of Example 2.6-2 for $z_1 = 6$; (b) root locus of the system of Example 2.6-2 for several values of z_1.

$$\theta_{z1} = \tan^{-1}\frac{4}{z_1 - 2} \qquad \theta_{p0} = 116.5° \tag{2.6-26}$$

Hence, the angle of departure θ_{p1} is given by

$$\theta_{p1} = \tan^{-1}\frac{4}{z_1 - 2} - 26.5° \tag{2.6-27}$$

The departure angle θ_{p1} for several values of z_1 is tabulated in Table 2.6-2. Because of the symmetry of the root locus with respect to the real axis, the angle of departure of the locus from the conjugate pole p_2 is then equal to $-\theta_{p1}$.

The root locus of this system is sketched in Fig. 2.6-3. The three branches of the locus are the segment from $s = 0$ to $s = -z_1$, the curve from $s = -2 + j4$ through $s = j\sqrt{\dfrac{20z_1}{z_1 - 4}}$ to infinity, and the curve from $s = -2 - j4$ through $s = -j\sqrt{\dfrac{20z_1}{z_1 - 4}}$ to minus infinity. It is observed that the two branches of the locus starting from the complex poles are moved to the left by decreasing z_1 (i.e., shifting the zero z_1 to the right) whereas they are displaced to the right by increasing z_1 (i.e., shifting the zero z_1 to the left). Obviously, the system would become more stable if the zero z_1 were pushed toward the right. When z_1 reaches 4, the system becomes stable at all finite values of K, since no imaginary-axis crossing is possible for $z_1 \leq 4$. In the special case of $z_1 = 0$, the open-loop transfer function $A(s)$ is reduced to second order and the root locus is made up of straight lines parallel to the imaginary axis extending from the conjugate complex poles to infinity in opposite directions.

Design Considerations. Because of the simplicity and ease with which the root locus of a feedback control system can be constructed from the open-loop poles and zeros, and the effects of changes in system parameters such as gain factor and time constants can be perceived from the root locus, the application of the root-locus method to control-system design has become very attractive. The root-locus method can be used to determine the gain constant from the time-domain specification of relative stability, to estimate the maximum overshoot of step-function response, and to evaluate the desired compensation for improving the system performance.

Since the effect of gain variation upon both transient and frequency responses becomes evident when the root locus is available, the determination of the gain constant from the root locus to meet performance specification is a simple matter. In the time domain the relative stability is often specified in terms of a damping ratio associated with the pair of the predominating conjugate complex poles (or in some cases by the most significant time constant of the system response). The predominating conjugate complex poles take the general form

$$s^2 + 2\zeta\omega_n s + \omega_n^2 = [s + (\zeta - j\sqrt{1 - \zeta^2})\omega_n][s + (\zeta + j\sqrt{1 - \zeta^2})\omega_n] \tag{2.6-28}$$

where ζ is the damping factor and ω_n is the undamped natural frequency of the mode of transient oscillation associated with the predominating pole pair. In the complex plane the locus of constant ζ is a semi-infinite straight line from the origin-making angle ψ with the negative real axis, and is given by

$$\psi = \cos^{-1} \zeta \tag{2.6-29}$$

This constant ζ locus is often called the damping line. The smaller the angle ψ, the higher the damping factor. When the damping factor ζ is specified, a damping line corresponding to the specified ζ can be drawn in the plane of the root locus (Fig. 2.6-5a). Assume this damping line intersects the root locus at point P. Then to meet the damping specification the characteristic roots of the system must lie to the left of the damping line, and the highest system gain to give a response with adequate damping is the gain constant corresponding to the intersecting point. Thus, the gain constant can readily be determined from the magnitude equation for the point P. As an illustration, consider the feedback system of Fig. 2.6-4. The root locus of this system is depicted in Fig. 2.6-5a. Measure

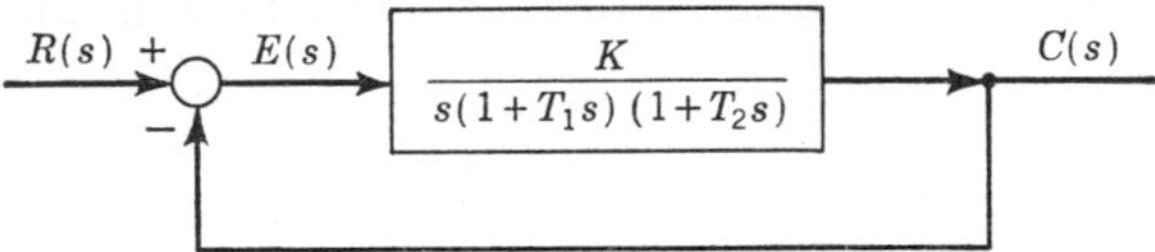

FIG. 2.6-4. Block diagram of the example illustrating the determination of the gain from the root locus.

the distances from the open-loop poles to the point P, and equate the product of the distances to K/T_1T_2:

$$a_0a_1a_2 = \frac{K}{T_1T_2} \tag{2.6-30}$$

Therefore, the required gain constant to meet the damping specification is

$$K = a_0a_1a_2T_1T_2 \tag{2.6-31}$$

With the gain set at a value given by the above equation, one of the characteristic roots of the system occurs at the point P. Assuming this root to be

$$r_1 = -\alpha_1 + j\omega_1 \tag{2.6-32}$$

then the conjugate root must be

$$r_2 = -\alpha_1 - j\omega_1 \tag{2.6-33}$$

The third root† r_3 can readily be determined from the closed-loop transfer function of the system:

$$\frac{C(s)}{R(s)} = \frac{K/T_1T_2}{s^3 + (1/T_1 + 1/T_2)s^2 + s/T_1T_2 + K/T_1T_2} \tag{2.6-34}$$

† This root can be estimated from the asymptotic Bode diagram of the system.

$$= \frac{-(r_1 r_2 r_3)}{(s - r_1)(s - r_2)(s - r_3)} \tag{2.6-35}$$

Since

$$r_1 + r_2 + r_3 = -\left(\frac{1}{T_1} + \frac{1}{T_2}\right) \qquad r_1 + r_2 = -2\alpha_1 \tag{2.6-36}$$

$$r_1 r_2 r_3 = \frac{-K}{T_1 T_2} \qquad r_1 r_2 = \alpha_1^2 + \omega_1^2 = a_0^2 \tag{2.6-37}$$

the third root is

$$r_3 = -\left(\frac{1}{T_1} + \frac{1}{T_2} - 2\alpha_1\right) \tag{2.6-38}$$

or

$$r_3 = \frac{-K}{T_1 T_2 a_0^2} = \frac{-a_1 a_2}{a_0} \tag{2.6-39}$$

When the three roots are determined from the root locus, the closed-loop frequency response is obtainable from the root-locus plot. The transient overshoot due to a unit step-function input can be quickly estimated from the configuration of the characteristic roots (Fig. 2.6-5*b*). The system out-

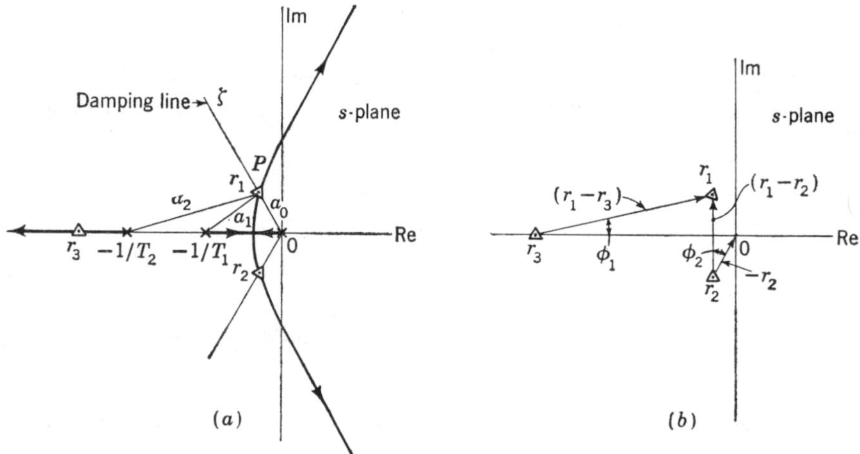

FIG. 2.6-5. (*a*) Root locus and damping line of the system of the illustrative example; (*b*) closed-loop poles of the system of the illustrative example.

put in response to a unit step-function input is

$$C(s) = \frac{-(r_1 r_2 r_3)}{s(s - r_1)(s - r_2)(s - r_3)} \tag{2.6-40}$$

By partial-fraction expansion, Eq. (2.6-40) may be written as

$$C(s) = \frac{K_0}{s} + \frac{K_1}{s - r_1} + \frac{K_2}{s - r_2} + \frac{K_3}{s - r_3} \tag{2.6-41}$$

where $K_0 = 1$, $K_1 = -r_2r_3/(r_1 - r_2)(r_1 - r_3)$, K_2 is the conjugate of K_1, and $K_3 = -r_1r_2/(r_3 - r_1)(r_3 - r_2)$. The transient response is then given by

$$c(t) = 1 + K_1\epsilon^{r_1t} + K_2\epsilon^{r_2t} + K_3\epsilon^{r_3t} \tag{2.6-42}$$

of which the terms $K_1\epsilon^{r_1t} + K_2\epsilon^{r_2t}$ represent the damped oscillation and determine the maximum overshoot. From the geometry of the characteristic-roots configuration in Fig. 2.6-5*b*, it is found that

$$-\frac{r_2}{r_1 - r_2} = \frac{1}{2\cos\phi_2}\epsilon^{-j\phi_2} \qquad -\frac{r_3}{r_1 - r_3} = \left|\frac{r_3}{r_1 - r_3}\right|\epsilon^{-j\phi_1} \tag{2.6-43}$$

Then

$$K_1 = -\frac{1}{2\cos\phi_2}\left|\frac{r_3}{r_1 - r_3}\right|\epsilon^{-j(\phi_1+\phi_2)} \tag{2.6-44}$$

and

$$K_2 = -\frac{1}{2\cos\phi_2}\left|\frac{r_3}{r_1 - r_3}\right|\epsilon^{j(\phi_1+\phi_2)} \tag{2.6-45}$$

Making use of Eqs. (2.6-44) and (2.6-45) yields the oscillatory part of $c(t)$ as

$$\begin{aligned} K_1\epsilon^{r_1t} + K_2\epsilon^{r_2t} &= \frac{1}{\cos\phi_2}\left|\frac{r_3}{r_1 - r_3}\right|\epsilon^{-\alpha_1t}\cos(\omega_1t - \pi - \phi_1 - \phi_2) \\ &= \frac{1}{\sqrt{1 - \zeta^2}}\left|\frac{r_3}{r_1 - r_3}\right|\epsilon^{-\alpha_1t}\cos(\omega_1t - \pi - \phi_1 - \phi_2) \end{aligned} \tag{2.6-46}$$

The peak of the first overshoot of Eq. (2.6-46), which occurs at $t = (\pi + \phi_1 + \phi_2)/\omega_1$, is then given by

$$\frac{1}{\sqrt{1 - \zeta^2}}\left|\frac{r_3}{r_1 - r_3}\right|\epsilon^{-\alpha_1(\pi+\phi_1+\phi_2)/\omega_1} \tag{2.6-47}$$

Since the term $K_3\epsilon^{r_3t}$ tends to decrease the transient overshoot of the system, the maximum overshoot of the transient response would be

$$M_m \le \frac{1}{\sqrt{1 - \zeta^2}}\left|\frac{r_3}{r_1 - r_3}\right|\epsilon^{-\alpha_1(\pi+\phi_1+\phi_2)/\omega_1} \tag{2.6-48}$$

In the above equation, the values of the roots and the phase angles are available from Fig. 2.6-5*b*; thus, the maximum overshoot can be quickly estimated.

The effects of introducing an open-loop pole and an open-loop zero into a control system are clearly illustrated by the root locus of a simple second-order system having open-loop transfer function

$$A(s) = \frac{K}{(s + \alpha_1 - j\omega_1)(s + \alpha_1 + j\omega_1)} \tag{2.6-49}$$

The root locus of this simple system consists of two straight lines parallel to the imaginary axis and extending from the complex poles to infinity, as shown in Fig. 2.6-6*a*. Evidently this system is stable at all finite values of the gain constant. When an open-loop pole is introduced the root locus is displaced to the right (Fig. 2.6-6*b*), thus making the system unstable at higher gain level. On the other hand, if an open-loop zero is inserted, the locus bends toward the left (Fig. 2.6-6*c*). As indicated by the loci and the damping line of Fig. 2.6-6 the addition of a zero would make the system

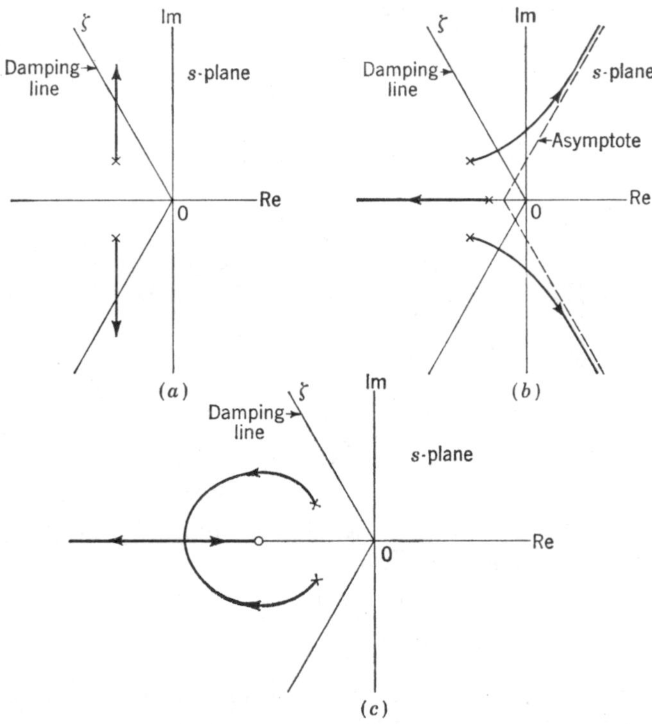

Fig. 2.6-6. (*a*) Root locus of a feedback control system having a pair of conjugate complex open-loop poles; (*b*) effect of introducing an additional open-loop pole upon the root-locus diagram; (*c*) effect of introducing an additional zero upon the root-locus diagram.

more stable. In general, by the introduction of appropriate pole-zero combinations the root locus is so modified that the characteristic roots may be shifted to the desired locations to result in improved transient as well as frequency response.

The transfer function of a desired cascade-compensating network can be determined from the root locus of the system. The commonly used basic types of system compensation are the integral, the derivative, and the pole-zero shifting compensation. The integral compensation may be used to increase the velocity constant without adversely affecting the relative stability; the derivative compensation provides a means of increasing the phase shift in the vicinity of crossover; and the pole-zero shifting compensation is a more general method of compensation which may alter the root locus completely. To illustrate the general principles of the evaluation of the system compensation from the root locus, a simple control system, shown in Fig. 2.6-7, having transfer function

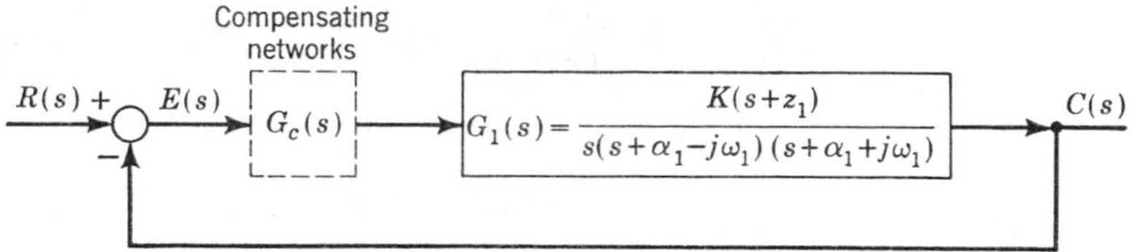

FIG. 2.6-7. Block diagram of the system of the illustrative example.

$$G_1(s) = \frac{K(s+z_1)}{s(s+\alpha_1-j\omega_1)(s+\alpha_1+j\omega_1)}$$
$$= \frac{z_1K}{\alpha_1^2+\omega_1^2}\,\frac{1+s/z_1}{s[1+s/(\alpha_1-j\omega_1)][1+s/(\alpha_1+j\omega_1)]} \qquad (2.6\text{-}50)$$

is considered. The root locus of this system without compensation is sketched in Fig. 2.6-8.

If a lag network is used as the compensator $G_c(s)$ in series with $G_1(s)$,

$$G_c(s) = \frac{s+k/T}{s+1/T} \qquad k > 1 \qquad (2.6\text{-}51)$$

the open-loop transfer function becomes

$$A_c(s) = \frac{K(s+z_1)(s+k/T)}{s(s+1/T)(s+\alpha_1-j\omega_1)(s+\alpha_1+j\omega_1)}$$
$$= \frac{kz_1K}{\alpha_1^2+\omega_1^2}\,\frac{(1+s/z_1)(1+Ts/k)}{s(1+Ts)[1+s/(\alpha_1-j\omega_1)][1+s/(\alpha_1+j\omega_1)]} \qquad (2.6\text{-}52)$$

From Eqs. (2.6-50) and (2.6-52) it is evident that the velocity constant of the system with compensation is increased by k times. The root locus is shifted toward the left by the lag network as shown in Fig. 2.6-8. The amount of shift depends upon the separation between the compensating pole and zero. When they are close to each other, the displacement of the locus is slight. Thus, to maintain a high velocity constant (i.e., large k) while avoiding excessive phase lag due to the lag network, both the compensating pole and the compensating zero are usually placed near the origin. (In other words, the lag network is often used to alter the low frequency portion of the open-loop frequency response.)

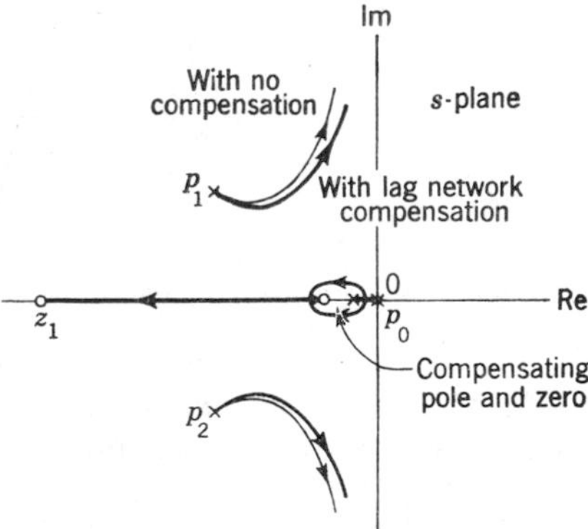

FIG. 2.6-8. Root locus of the control system of Fig. 2.6-7 with and without phase-lag compensation.

When phase-shift is needed in the vicinity of crossover, use is often made of derivative compensation. Referring to the system of Fig. 2.6-7, if a lead network is selected as the compensator,

$$G_c(s) = \frac{s + 1/T_1}{s + 1/T_2} \qquad T_1 > T_2 \tag{2.6-53}$$

the open-loop transfer function of the compensated system is

$$A_c(s) = \frac{K(s + z_1)(s + 1/T_1)}{s(s + 1/T_2)(s + \alpha_1 - j\omega_1)(s + \alpha_1 + j\omega_1)} \tag{2.6-54}$$

The root locus of the system which is sketched in Fig. 2.6-9 is pushed to

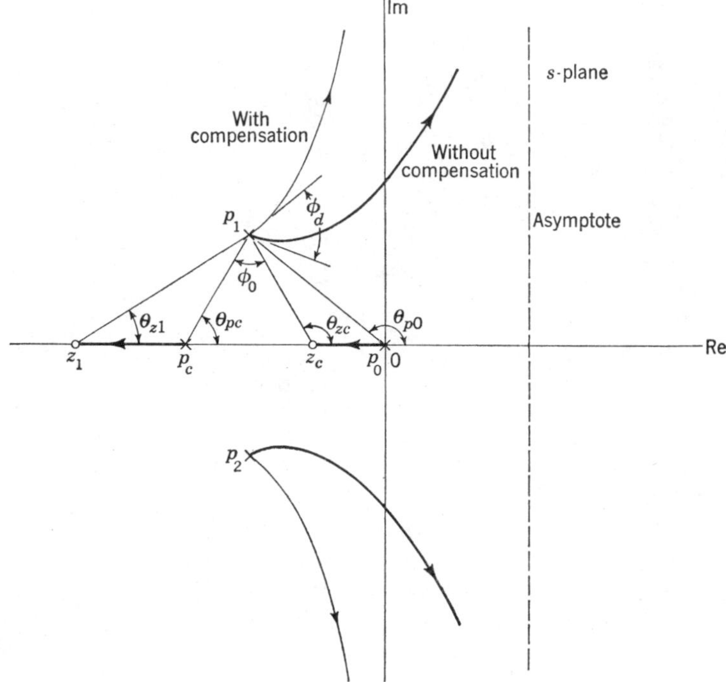

FIG. 2.6-9. Root locus of the system of Fig. 2.6-7 with and without phase-lead compensation.

the left by the lead network. The increase in the angle of departure ϕ_d of the locus is equal to the phase shift ϕ_0 introduced by the lead network.

$$\phi_d = \phi_0 \tag{2.6-55}$$

ϕ_0 is the angle between the phasors from pole p_1 to zero z_c and from pole p_1 to pole p_c. Without compensation, the angle of departure of the locus from pole p_1 is given by Eq. (2.6-25):

$$\theta_{p1} = 90° + \theta_{z1} - \theta_{p0} \tag{2.6-56}$$

With lead compensation, the phase-angle equation of the system is

$$\theta_{p1} + \theta_{p2} + \theta_{p0} + \theta_{pc} - \theta_{zc} - \theta_{z1} = 180° \tag{2.6-57}$$

At a point very near pole p_1,

$$\theta_{p2} \approx 90° \qquad \theta_{pc} - \theta_{zc} = -\phi_0 \tag{2.6-58}$$

The angle of departure of the new locus is then given by

$$\theta_{p1} = 90° + \theta_{z1} - \theta_{p0} + \phi_0 \tag{2.6-59}$$

Thus, the increase in the angle of departure is equal to the phase shift ϕ_0 due to the lead network. It is seen from Fig. 2.6-9 that ϕ_0 is increased by further separating the compensating pole and zero. When the gain is predetermined, the lead-network compensator required to meet damping specification may be evaluated from the root-locus plot. This can be done by estimating the desirable location of the new root locus and the angle of departure. The specified damping line should intersect the new root locus at such a point that the corresponding gain constant is higher than the predetermined value. The desired lead network is then evaluated from the estimated angle of departure of the new locus. A satisfactory result can usually be obtained through several trials. In case the damping specification cannot be fulfilled by the introduction of a simple practical lead network, more elaborate compensating networks have to be used. The transfer function of an elaborate network, which may be considered as consisting of several simple pole-zero pairs, can be determined from the root-locus diagram by applying the above procedure to each pole-zero pair in succession. Each pole-zero pair would shift the root locus to a better location. The combined effect of the pole-zero pairs would then make the system respond with appropriate dynamic performance. However, in some control systems, which contain a pair of conjugate complex open-loop poles close to the imaginary axis, phase-lead compensation fails to be an effective means. When phase-lead compensation proves ineffective, resort is made to pole-zero shifting compensation.

A more general method of compensation is the pole-zero shifting compensation, which is based upon the shifting of the poles and zeros to more desirable locations through cancellation of the original open-loop poles and zeros, either partially or completely. By means of this type of compensation the entire root locus may be moved to a new location where the characteristic roots of the system would give rise to satisfactory frequency and transient response. Consider the control system of Fig. 2.6-7. The transfer function of the controlled system is

$$G_1(s) = \frac{K(s + z_1)}{s(s + \alpha_1 - j\omega_1)(s + \alpha_1 + j\omega_1)} \tag{2.6-60}$$

When α_1 is small, the pair of conjugate complex poles of $G_1(s)$ is close to the imaginary axis and compensation by phase-lead networks of simple poles and zeros would be of little avail. However, as can easily be seen, if this pair of complex poles could be moved away from the imaginary axis the dynamic performance of the system would be greatly improved. The shifting of the complex poles can be accomplished by introducing a compensating network with transfer function

$$G_c(s) = \frac{(s + \alpha_1' - j\omega_1')(s + \alpha_1' + j\omega_1')}{(s + \alpha_c - j\omega_c)(s + \alpha_c + j\omega_c)} \tag{2.6-61}$$

such that $\alpha_1' = \alpha_1$ and $\omega_1' = \omega_1$. Then the pair of conjugate complex zeros of $G_c(s)$ will cancel the complex poles of $G_1(s)$, resulting in open-loop transfer function

$$\begin{aligned} A_c(s) &= G_1(s)G_c(s) \\ &= \frac{K(s + z_1)}{s(s + \alpha_c - j\omega_c)(s + \alpha_c + j\omega_c)} \end{aligned} \tag{2.6-62}$$

which contains a pair of new conjugate complex poles. The root loci of the original and the compensated system are sketched in Fig. 2.6-10*a*. Although perfect cancellation of the undesired open-loop complex poles by the zeros of a compensator can hardly be realized in common practice, it is always possible to place the zeros of the compensator in the proximity of the unwanted open-loop poles to obtain partial cancellation; meanwhile new poles are placed at some desirable locations. In this case, the open-loop transfer function would be

$$A_c(s) = \frac{K(s + z_1)(s + \alpha_1' - j\omega_1)(s + \alpha_1' + j\omega_1')}{s(s + \alpha_c - j\omega_c)(s + \alpha_c + j\omega_c)(s + \alpha_1 - j\omega_1)(s + \alpha_1 + j\omega_1)} \tag{2.6-63}$$

where $\alpha_1' \approx \alpha_1$ and $\omega_1' \approx \omega_1$. The root locus of the compensated system when the cancellation of the open-loop poles by compensator zeros is imperfect is illustrated in Fig. 2.7-10*c*. The values of α_c and ω_c of the new poles are determined in such a way that the specifications of the velocity constant, the closed-loop frequency response, the maximum overshoot and setting time of the step-function response, etc., can be fulfilled.

2.7. Modulated Control Systems. In many feedback control systems modulated signals are developed in and transmitted through a portion of a control loop. Such systems, which are often classified as *modulated* or *carrier-frequency* control systems, find very wide applications in control and instrumentation. The most common type of modulated control system is the a-c servo system, which is characterized by the transmission of the information as the envelope of a suppressed-carrier amplitude-modulated a-c signal. In industrial and military applications a carrier-frequency of 60 cps or 400 cps is frequently used.

Examples of a-c control systems are two-phase motor-driven feedback control systems, servomechanisms employing synchro generators and control transformers, and electronic servo systems using a-c amplifiers and detectors instead of d-c amplifiers. Through a sequence of modulation, a-c amplification and detection, the problems, such as amplifier drifts

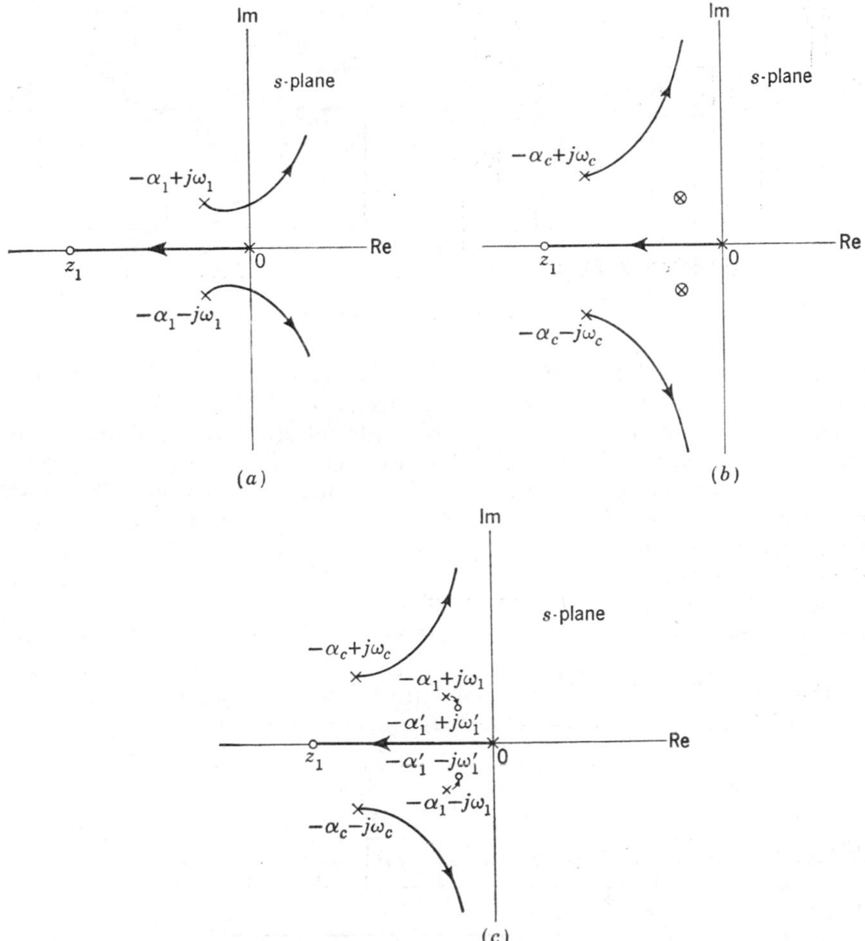

FIG. 2.6-10. (a) Root locus of the system without compensation; (b) root locus of the system with compensation (complete cancellation); (c) root locus of the system with compensation (partial cancellation).

which are peculiar to d-c servo systems, may be avoided. The schematic diagram of a simple a-c servo system is depicted in Fig. 2.7-1. In this system the synchro set serves as an error-sensing device and a modulator, and the two-phase servomotor performs the function of a demodulator. The modulator is a device for converting a data-signal input into the envelope of a sinusoidal carrier wave which bears a determinate phase relative to a given reference a-c voltage. In many a-c servo systems, modulation and error detection are often accomplished by one device. Since little extraneous noise or false-error signal can be tolerated, electromechanical modulators are sometimes considered more favorable than

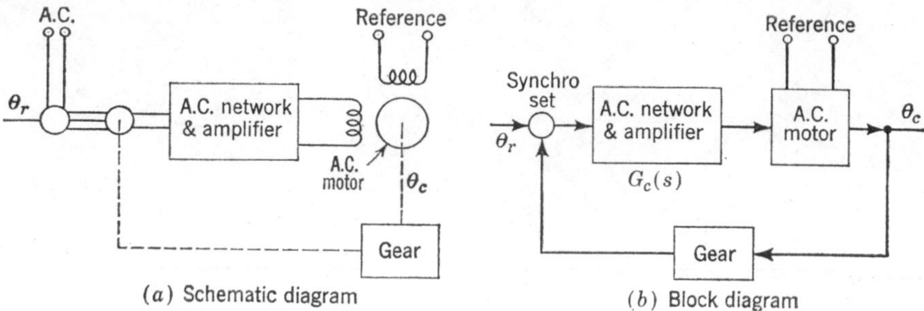

FIG. 2.7-1. A simple a-c servomechanism.

vacuum-tube modulating devices. The most commonly used modulators are the synchronous vibrators, the electromechanical choppers, the balanced potentiometers, the synchro sets, the electronic modulators, and the a-c tachometers. The demodulator or detector of an a-c servo system is used to extract the data signal from the modulated function. The most popular demodulators for control systems are the phase-sensitive detectors, synchronous detectors, the two-phase servomotors, and semiconductor diode demodulators.

Shown in Fig. 2.7-2*a* is the block diagram of a feedback control system which contains a carrier-frequency channel in the system. The transfer function of the carrier-frequency elements is denoted by $G_c(s)$, and those of the noncarrier (data-signal) elements by $G_1(s)$, $G_2(s)$, and $H(s)$. Because of the presence of the carrier-frequency signals in the loop, direct

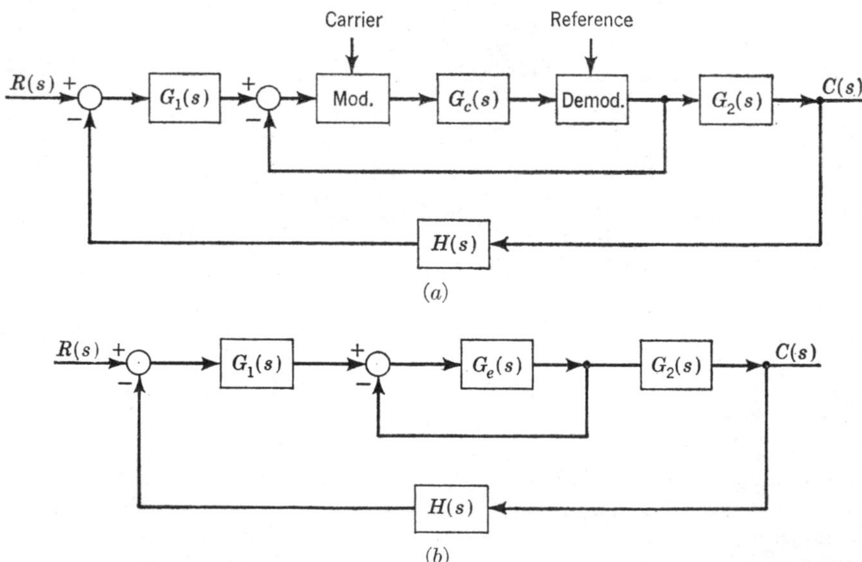

FIG. 2.7-2. (*a*) A modulated control system; (*b*) the equivalent d-c control system.

application of the conventional techniques for feedback-control-system analysis and synthesis does not seem feasible. However, if the carrier-frequency channel of the system is replaced by equivalent transfer functions the conventional techniques can effectively be employed to solve such control problems. The derivation of equivalent transfer functions is presented in the following paragraphs.

The carrier-frequency channel of the modulated control system is shown in Fig. 2.7-3, with the modulator denoted by M; the synchronous detector

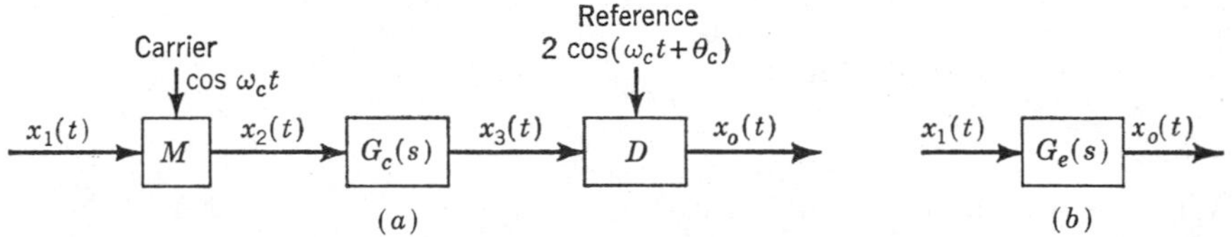

FIG. 2.7-3. (a) The block diagram of the carrier-frequency channel; (b) the equivalent block diagram.

by D; and the transfer function of the a-c amplifiers and networks in the carrier-frequency channel by $G_c(j\omega)$. In a-c servo systems the carrier signal is a sinusoidal function with frequency much higher than that of the data signal. The carrier signal of the modulator may be assumed to be $\cos \omega_c t$ without the loss of generality, and the reference signal of the demodulator is assumed to be $2 \cos (\omega_c t + \theta_c)$, where ω_c is the carrier frequency and θ_c is the phase angle which can be varied. The data-signal input $x_1(t)$ modulates the carrier in the modulator M to yield the modulated signal $x_2(t)$ which is given by

$$x_2(t) = x_1(t) \cos \omega_c t \tag{2.7-1}$$

This amplitude-modulated signal is then impressed on the carrier-frequency elements $G_c(s)$. Making use of the identity

$$\cos \omega_c t = \tfrac{1}{2}(\epsilon^{j\omega_c t} + \epsilon^{-j\omega_c t}) \tag{2.7-2}$$

Eq. (2.7-1) reduces to

$$x_2(t) = \tfrac{1}{2}(\epsilon^{j\omega_c t} + \epsilon^{-j\omega_c t})x_1(t) \tag{2.7-3}$$

Taking the Laplace transform of both sides of Eq. (2.7-3),

$$\begin{aligned} X_2(s) &= \tfrac{1}{2}[\mathfrak{L}\{\epsilon^{j\omega_c t}x_1(t)\} + \mathfrak{L}\{\epsilon^{-j\omega_c t}x_1(t)\}] \\ &= \tfrac{1}{2}[X_1(s - j\omega_c) + X_1(s + j\omega_c)] \end{aligned} \tag{2.7-4}$$

where $\quad X_1(s) \triangleq \mathfrak{L}\{x_1(t)\} \qquad X_2(s) \triangleq \mathfrak{L}\{x_2(t)\}$

By definition the input transform $X_2(s)$ and the response transform $X_3(s)$ of the carrier-frequency elements $G_c(s)$ are related by

$$\frac{X_3(s)}{X_2(s)} = G_c(s) \tag{2.7-5}$$

Substituting for $X_2(s)$ from Eq. (2.7-4) and simplifying, there is obtained the transform of the response of the carrier-frequency elements to the input $x_2(t)$:

$$X_3(s) = \tfrac{1}{2}[X_1(s - j\omega_c) + X_1(s + j\omega_c)]G_c(s) \tag{2.7-6}$$

Representing the inverse transform of $X_3(s)$ by $x_3(t)$, the inverse Laplace transformation of Eq. (2.7-6) yields

$$x_3(t) = \tfrac{1}{2}[\mathcal{L}^{-1}\{G_c(s)X_1(s - j\omega_c) + G_c(s)X_1(s + j\omega_c)\}] \tag{2.7-7}$$

Application of the theorem of complex translation enables Eq. (2.7-7) to be written as

$$x_3(t) = \tfrac{1}{2}[\mathcal{L}^{-1}\{G_c(s + j\omega_c)X_1(s)\}\epsilon^{-j\omega_c t} + \mathcal{L}^{-1}\{G_c(s - j\omega_c)X_1(s)\}\epsilon^{j\omega_c t}] \tag{2.7-8}$$

With the aid of Euler's equation,

$$\epsilon^{\pm j\omega_c t} = \cos \omega_c t \pm j \sin \omega_c t \tag{2.7-9}$$

Eq. (2.7-8) may be put into the form

$$x_3(t) = x_p(t) \cos \omega_c t + jx_q(t) \sin \omega_c t \tag{2.7-10}$$

in which $$x_p(t) = \tfrac{1}{2}\mathcal{L}^{-1}\{[G_c(s + j\omega_c) + G_c(s - j\omega_c)]X_1(s)\} \tag{2.7-11}$$

and $$x_q(t) = \tfrac{1}{2}\mathcal{L}^{-1}\{[G_c(s - j\omega_c) - G_c(s + j\omega_c)]X_1(s)\} \tag{2.7-12}$$

Both $x_p(t)$ and $x_q(t)$ are low-frequency signals. Equation (2.7-10) indicates that the response of the carrier-frequency elements $x_3(t)$ is a modulated signal consisting of two components which are 90° out of phase. The low-frequency signal $x_p(t)$, which is in phase with the carrier, is called the in-phase component, and the low-frequency signal $x_q(t)$, which is at quadrature with the carrier, is called the quadrature component. The output of the synchronous detector $x_0(t)$ is then given by the data signal contained in the function

$$2x_3(t) \cos (\omega_c t + \theta_c)$$

The data-signal output $x_0(t)$, which is extracted from the above function through detection and filtering, may have various forms depending upon the value of the phase angle θ_c.

In view of Eq. (2.7-10),

$$\begin{aligned} 2x_3(t) \cos (\omega_c t + \theta_c) = {} & [x_p(t) \cos \theta_c + jx_q(t) \sin \theta_c] \\ & + [\cos \theta_c \cos 2\omega_c t + \sin \theta_c \sin 2\omega_c t]x_p(t) \\ & + j[\cos \theta_c \sin 2\omega_c t - \sin \theta_c \cos 2\omega_c t]x_q(t) \end{aligned} \tag{2.7-13}$$

Since the synchronous detector passes only low-frequency signals and the carrier frequency ω_c is usually much higher than the largest frequency component of the data signal, the output of the detector is given by the first term of Eq. (2.7-13). That is,

$$x_0(t) = x_p(t) \cos \theta_c + jx_q(t) \sin \theta_c \tag{2.7-14}$$

Applying the Laplace transformation to both members of Eq. (2.7-14) there results

$$X_0(s) = X_p(s) \cos \theta_c + jX_q(s) \sin \theta_c \tag{2.7-15}$$

where

$$X_0(s) = \mathcal{L}\{x_0(t)\} \qquad X_p(s) = \mathcal{L}\{x_p(t)\} \qquad X_q(s) = \mathcal{L}\{x_q(t)\}$$

The transforms of the inphase and quadrature components are available from Eqs. (2.7-11) and (2.7-12):

$$X_p(s) = \tfrac{1}{2}[G_c(s + j\omega_c) + G_c(s - j\omega_c)]X_1(s) \tag{2.7-16}$$

$$X_q(s) = \tfrac{1}{2}[G_c(s - j\omega_c) - G_c(s + j\omega_c)]X_1(s) \tag{2.7-17}$$

By defining

$$G_p(s) = \tfrac{1}{2}[G_c(s + j\omega_c) + G_c(s - j\omega_c)] \cos \theta_c \tag{2.7-18}$$

and

$$G_q(s) = \tfrac{1}{2}[G_c(s - j\omega_c) - G_c(s + j\omega_c)] \sin \theta_c \tag{2.7-19}$$

and substituting the expressions of $X_p(s)$ and $X_q(s)$ into Eq. (2.7-15), one obtains the output transform of the carrier-frequency channel.

$$X_0(s) = [G_p(s) + jG_q(s)]X_1(s) \tag{2.7-20}$$

Now, dividing both sides of Eq. (2.7-20) by $X_1(s)$ and representing the ratio of the output transform to the input transform by $G_e(s)$, the result is

$$G_e(s) = \frac{X_0(s)}{X_1(s)} \tag{2.7-21}$$

$$= G_p(s) + jG_q(s) \tag{2.7-22}$$

$$= \tfrac{1}{2}[G_c(s + j\omega_c) + G_c(s - j\omega_c)] \cos \theta_c + j\tfrac{1}{2}[G_c(s - j\omega_c) - G_c(s + j\omega_c)] \sin \theta_c \tag{2.7-23}$$

$G_e(s)$ is defined as the equivalent transfer function of the carrier-frequency channel. The expression of Eq. (2.7-23) may be simplified if the frequeney characteristic of the a-c elements is symmetrical with respect to thc carrier frequency ω_c. In such cases,

$$G_c(s + j\omega_c) = G_c(s - j\omega_c) \tag{2.7-24}$$

Consequently, the quadrature component $x_q(t)$ is reduced to zero, and the equivalent transfer function becomes

$$G_e(s) = G_c(s + j\omega_c) \cos \theta_c \tag{2.7-25a}$$

or

$$G_e(s) = G_c(s - j\omega_c) \cos \theta_c \tag{2.7-25b}$$

As can be seen the phase angle θ_c of the reference of the detector would not only affect the gain of the system but also cause distortions in the signal and waste of power. Thus, for most efficient operation, θ_c is set at zero, i.e., the carrier of the modulator and the reference of the demodulator are in phase. The output signal from the detector is then equal to the inphase component $x_p(t)$ which is the desired data signal. The equivalent transfer function for $\theta_c = 0$ follows immediately from Eq. (2.7-23):

$$G_e(s) = \tfrac{1}{2}[G_c(s + j\omega_c) + G_c(s - j\omega_c)] \tag{2.7-26}$$

Furthermore, in the case of a carrier-frequency channel which has symmetrical frequency characteristic, the equivalent transfer function would be reduced to

$$G_e(s) = G_c(s + j\omega_c) \tag{2.7-27a}$$

or

$$G_e(s) = G_c(s - j\omega_c) \tag{2.7-27b}$$

These equations describe the operation of bandpass to low-pass conversion. By the above operation an a-c network is said to be converted into its low-pass equivalent.

Consequently, when the carrier-frequency channels of a modulated control system are described by equivalent transfer functions, the system is reduced to an equivalent all d-c (or data-signal) control system, and the conventional methods of analysis and synthesis can be used advantageously. Equations (2.7-27*a*) and (2.7-27*b*), which express the bandpass to low-pass conversion of an a-c network, are useful in system analysis. To design an a-c servo system by means of the conventional techniques an expression of the transfer function of the a-c elements in terms of the equivalent transfer function seems desirable. Through appropriate substitution, Eqs. (2.7-27*a*) and (2.7-27*b*) lead to

$$G_c(s) = G_e(s - j\omega_c) \tag{2.7-28a}$$

or

$$G_c(s) = G_e(s + j\omega_c) \tag{2.7-28b}$$

In terms of $j\omega$,

$$G_c(j\omega) = G_e(j\omega - \omega_c) \qquad \text{for} \qquad \omega > 0 \tag{2.7-29a}$$

or

$$G_c(j\omega) = G_e(j\omega + \omega_c) \qquad \text{for} \qquad \omega < 0 \tag{2.7-29b}$$

For instance, to design a system like that shown in Fig. 2.7-1 the procedures described in preceding sections can be followed to evaluate the equivalent transfer function $G_e(j\omega)$ of the desired a-c equalizer. Then by making use of Eq. (2.7-29*a*) and (2.7-29*b*) the transfer function $G_c(j\omega)$ of the desired a-c network is obtained.

Although the sinusoidal function has been extensively employed as the carrier of a modulated control system, the use of a train of very narrow uniform pulses as the carrier appears extremely attractive. The function of a modulator with pulse-train carrier can easily be performed by a sampler which is operated at a rate equal to the pulse frequency of the carrier signal. When a train of very narrow uniform pulses is used as the carrier, the modulator converts the data signal of a control system into a train of very narrow amplitude-modulated pulses. As discussed in Chap. 1, such an operation characterizes sampled-data control systems. Consequently, a sampled-data control system may be thought of as a special type of modulated control system (pulse-amplitude-modulated) in which the carrier is a train of very narrow uniform pulses and the transmission of information is intermittent. In such modulated control systems, modulation is accomplished by samplers and demodulation by holding devices, as shown in Fig. 2.7-4*b*. Furthermore, a digital control system may be considered as a pulse-code-modulated type of modulated control system, since in a control system utilizing a digital computer the operation of converting analog information into digital form is, in part, a modulation process. In these control systems the positions of the modulator and the demodulator are respectively taken by the analog-to-digital and the digital-to-analog converters, as shown in Fig. 2.7-4*c*.

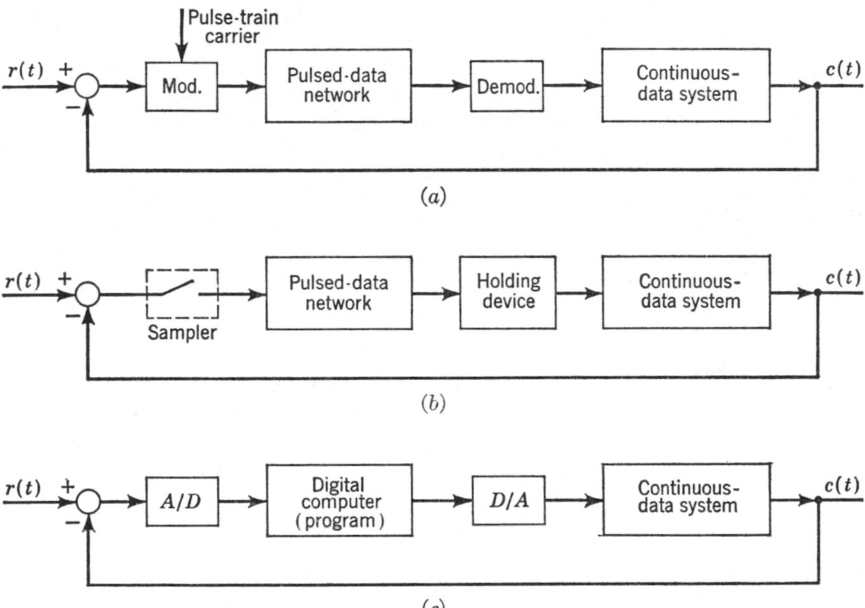

FIG. 2.7-4. (*a*) A modulated control system with pulse-train carrier; (*b*) a modulated control system using sampler and holding device as modulator and demodulator—sampled-data control system; (*c*) a modulated control system using analog-to-digital and digital-to-analog converters as modulator and demodulator—digital control system.

As has been discussed in this section, the analysis of the a-c type of modulated control system is greatly facilitated by the representation of the carrier-frequency channels by equivalent transfer functions. By analogy, the equivalent transfer-function concept may be applied to the analysis of the sampled-data type of modulated control systems, although the application to sampled-data systems is not so simple and straightforward as in the a-c modulated case. The essential point of the equivalent transfer-function approach is to describe the operation of the entire control system in terms of one kind of data, either modulated (sampled) or unmodulated (continuous), thus allowing a thorough investigation of the system performance by a unified method. The analysis and design principles of sampled-data and digital control systems are discussed in detail in the chapters to follow.

REFERENCES

Graybeal, T. D.: Block Diagram Network Transformation, *Elec. Eng.*, vol. 70, pp. 985–990, 1951.

Evans, W. R.: "Control System Dynamics," McGraw-Hill Book Company, Inc., New York, 1954.

Tou, J.: Analysis of Feedback Control Systems Containing Carrier-frequency Circuits, *Proc. Natl. Electronics Conf.*, vol. 11, pp. 1012–1016, 1955.

Truxal, J. G.: "Automatic Feedback Control System Synthesis," McGraw-Hill Book Company, Inc., New York, 1955.

Savant, C. J., Jr.: "Basic Feedback Control System Design," McGraw-Hill Book Company, Inc., New York, 1958.

Bower, J. L., and P. M. Schultheiss: "Introduction to the Design of Servomechanisms," John Wiley & Sons, Inc., New York, 1958.

CHAPTER 3

BASIC THEORY OF SAMPLING AND QUANTIZING

3.1. Sampling Process. Sampled-data and digital control systems differ from continuous-data control systems in a major aspect. In a sampled-data control system the signal at one or more points of the system undergoes a process of sampling which is sometimes referred to as quantizing of time. In a digital control system the signal at a certain portion of the system is quantized both in time of occurrence and in magnitude. By combining quantization of time and magnitude, control signals can be encoded into various numerical codes, such as the decimal number system, the binary number system, the binary-coded decimal number system, etc. The decimal system, which makes use of digits 0 through 9, has been traditionally used for arithmetic calculations. But, in the organization of a digital control and computing system, the binary number system, which uses only the digits 0 and 1, and the binary-coded decimal system are popular and in common use. The numerical codes and the encoding process for digital control systems will be studied in Chap. 8. As a preliminary to the study of the sampled-data and digital control systems, the sampling process and the basic theory of sampling and quantizing are briefly reviewed and discussed in this chapter.

Although the process of sampling can be performed at a constant rate or at a variable rate or at random, in the following analysis constant-rate, periodically operated sampling is assumed. Shown in Fig. 3.1-1 is a sam-

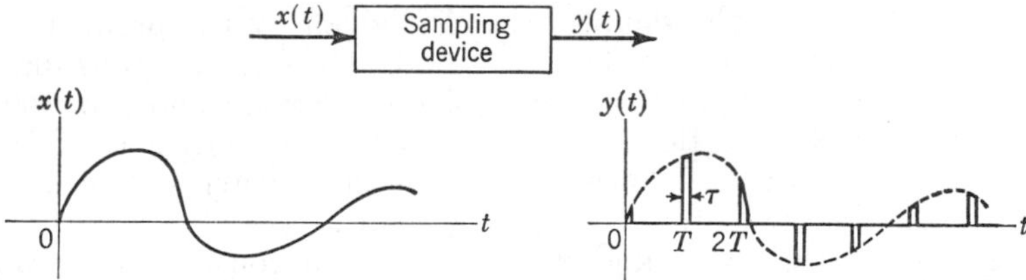

FIG. 3.1-1. The waveforms of the input and the output signal of a sampling device.

pling device which operates at a constant rate with a period equal to T sec. The sampling device permits the input signal to pass through only during the short interval τ of a sampling period, but it blocks the flow of the signal during the other portion of a sampling period. The signal transmission interval τ is very short in comparison to the sampling period T. It is clear that if the input signal to the sampling device is a continuous function $x(t)$, no signal is measured at the output except during the short interval τ of a sampling period. The measured quantities of the output function during the interval τ are equal to the corresponding values of the input function in that interval. In other words, the output function of a sampling device is a train of very narrow pulses, the envelope of which is identical to the input signal. Consequently, sampling may be thought of as a pulse-modulation process, which converts a continuous signal wave into a train of very narrow amplitude-modulated pulses; and a sampling device may be treated as a modulator, the carrier of which is a unit-sampling function.

As shown in Fig. 3.1-2*b*, the unit-sampling function consists of a train

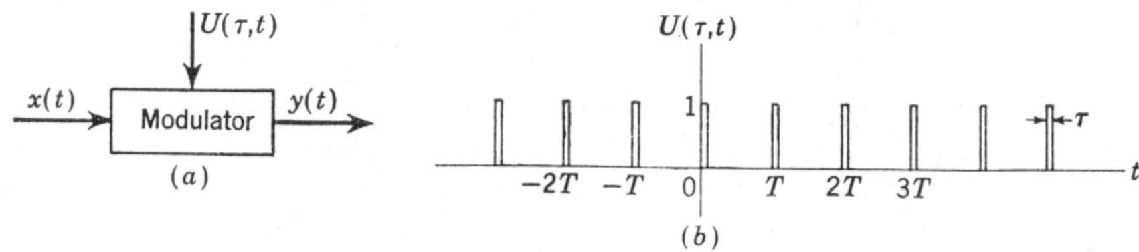

FIG. 3.1-2. (*a*) Sampling device behaves as a modulator; (*b*) waveform of unit-sampling function.

of uniform narrow pulses which are of unity height and are equally spaced. The time interval T between two consecutive pulses is called the sampling period, and the width of the pulses τ is referred to as the sampling duration. With sampling likened to pulse modulation, the output function $y(t)$ of a sampling device is related to its input signal $x(t)$ by

$$y(t) = U(\tau,t)x(t) \tag{3.1-1}$$

where $U(\tau,t)$ denotes the unit-sampling function of sampling period T and sampling duration τ. The waveform of $U(\tau,t)$ is plotted in Fig. 3.1-2*b*. In the following analysis the input of a sampling device will be referred to as the original signal and its output as the sampled signal.

3.2. Analysis of the Unit-sampling Function. As has been discussed in the preceding section, the sampled signal is given by the product of the unit-sampling function and the original signal. The unit-sampling function plays an important role in the process of sampling. A knowledge of the characteristics of this function appears essential in the study of the behavior of sampling devices and the operation of sampling systems. The analysis of the unit-sampling function is presented below.

Since the unit-sampling function $U(\tau,t)$, which consists of a train of uniform pulses with unity height as depicted in Fig. 3.1-2*b*, is a periodic function, it can be expanded in a Fourier series. Assuming that

$$\omega_s = 2\pi f_s \tag{3.2-1}$$

is the frequency of the sampling function in radians per second, and that

$$T = \frac{1}{f_s} \tag{3.2-2}$$

is the sampling period in seconds, and τ is the width of the sampling pulse in seconds, the Fourier series representation of the sampling function $U(\tau,t)$ is

$$U(\tau,t) = \sum_{n=-\infty}^{\infty} c_n \epsilon^{jn\omega_s t} \tag{3.2-3}$$

where c_n denotes the Fourier coefficients and is given by

$$c_n = \frac{1}{T} \int_0^T U(\tau,t)\epsilon^{-jn\omega_s t}\, dt \tag{3.2-4}$$

Since over a sampling period T, the unit-sampling function is described by

$$U(\tau,t) = \begin{cases} 1 & \text{for } kT \leq t < kT + \tau \\ 0 & \text{otherwise} \end{cases} \tag{3.2-5}$$

Eq. (3.2-4) reduces to

$$\begin{aligned} c_n &= \frac{1}{T} \int_0^\tau \epsilon^{-jn\omega_s t}\, dt \\ &= -\frac{\epsilon^{-jn\omega_s t}}{jn\omega_s T}\bigg|_0^\tau \\ &= \frac{1 - \epsilon^{-jn\omega_s \tau}}{jn\omega_s T} \end{aligned} \tag{3.2-6}$$

It can readily be shown that for $n = 0$,

$$c_0 = \frac{\tau}{T} \tag{3.2-7}$$

Substituting Eq. (3.2-6) into Eq. (3.2-3) gives

$$\begin{aligned} U(\tau,t) &= \sum_{n=-\infty}^{\infty} \frac{1 - \epsilon^{-jn\omega_s \tau}}{jn\omega_s T} \epsilon^{jn\omega_s t} \\ &= \frac{\tau}{T} + \sum_{n=1}^{\infty} \frac{\epsilon^{jn\omega_s t} - \epsilon^{-jn\omega_s t} - \epsilon^{jn\omega_s(t-\tau)} + \epsilon^{-jn\omega_s(t-\tau)}}{jn\omega_s T} \\ &= \frac{\tau}{T} + \sum_{n=1}^{\infty} \frac{2[\sin n\omega_s t - \sin n\omega_s(t-\tau)]}{n\omega_s T} \\ &= \frac{\tau}{T} + \sum_{n=1}^{\infty} \frac{4 \sin (n\omega_s \tau/2) \cos (n\omega_s t - n\omega_s \tau/2)}{n\omega_s T} \end{aligned} \tag{3.2-8}$$

Hence,

$$U(\tau,t) = \frac{\tau}{T} + \frac{2\tau}{T} \sum_{n=1}^{\infty} \frac{\sin (n\pi\tau/T)}{n\pi\tau/T} \cos n(\omega_s t - \phi) \tag{3.2-9}$$

where

$$\omega_s = \frac{2\pi}{T} \tag{3.2-10}$$

is the fundamental frequency of the pulse train which is called the sampling frequency, and

$$n\phi = n\omega_s \frac{\tau}{2} \tag{3.2-11}$$

is the phase angle of the nth harmonic of the unit-sampling function.

Equation (3.2-9) indicates that the unit-sampling function contains a d-c component as well as an infinite number of harmonics with decreasing amplitude. The amplitude of the kth harmonic component is

$$\frac{2\tau}{T} \frac{\sin (k\pi\tau/T)}{k\pi\tau/T} \tag{3.2-12}$$

which diminishes rapidly as k is increased. The above discussion implies that the sampled signal would contain not only the original signal but also the sinusoidal components as a result of the process of sampling. The effect of sampling can readily be visualized from the frequency spectra of the original and the sampled signals. The discussion of the frequency spectra of sampled signals is taken up in the following section.

3.3. Frequency Spectra of Sampled Signals. In view of Eqs. (3.1-1) and (3.2-9), the relationship between the sampled signal and the original signal may be written as

$$y(t) = \frac{\tau}{T} x(t) + \frac{2\tau}{T} \sum_{n=1}^{\infty} \frac{\sin (n\pi\tau/T)}{n\pi\tau/T} x(t) \cos n(\omega_s t - \phi) \tag{3.3-1}$$

The simplest way to study the frequency spectra of the sampled signal is to assume that the original signal contains only one frequency component. Such a signal might be described by

$$\begin{aligned} x(t) &= V \cos (\omega_0 t + \theta_0) \\ &= \frac{V\epsilon^{j\theta_0}}{2} \epsilon^{j\omega_0 t} + \frac{V\epsilon^{-j\theta_0}}{2} \epsilon^{-j\omega_0 t} \end{aligned} \tag{3.3-2}$$

where ω_0 is the angular frequency of the original signal and θ_0 is its phase angle. Since the frequency spectrum of a function is a representation of its frequency distributions, the frequency spectrum of a periodic signal is a plot of the magnitude of its sinusoidal components at the corresponding frequency. The amplitude-frequency spectrum of the original signal $x(t)$ given in Eq. (3.3-2) would then consist of two vertical lines at frequencies $\omega = \pm\omega_0$ with height equal to $V/2$ as shown in Fig. 3.3-1*a*.

It follows from Eqs. (3.3-1) and (3.3-2) that the sampled signal is given by

$$\begin{aligned} y(t) &= \frac{\tau V}{T} \cos (\omega_0 t + \theta_0) \\ &\quad + \frac{2\tau V}{T} \sum_{n=1}^{\infty} \frac{\sin (n\pi\tau/T)}{n\pi\tau/T} \cos (\omega_0 t + \theta_0) \cos n(\omega_s t - \phi) \\ &= \frac{\tau V}{T} \cos (\omega_0 t + \theta_0) + \frac{\tau V}{T} \sum_{n=1}^{\infty} \frac{\sin (n\pi\tau/T)}{n\pi\tau/T} \cos [(\omega_0 + n\omega_s)t + \theta_0 - n\phi] \end{aligned}$$

$$+ \frac{\tau V}{T} \sum_{n=1}^{\infty} \frac{\sin (n\pi\tau/T)}{n\pi\tau/T} \cos [(\omega_0 - n\omega_s)t + \theta_0 + n\phi] \quad (3.3\text{-}3)$$

To plot the frequency spectra of the sampled signal, $y(t)$ is usually expressed in terms of the complex form of the Fourier series. Thus,

$$y(t) = \frac{\tau V}{T} \sum_{n=-\infty}^{\infty} \frac{\sin (n\pi\tau/T)}{n\pi\tau/T} \cos [(\omega_0 + n\omega_s)t + \theta_0 - n\phi]$$

$$= \frac{\tau V}{2T} \epsilon^{j\theta_0} \sum_{n=-\infty}^{\infty} \frac{\sin (n\pi\tau/T)}{n\pi\tau/T} \epsilon^{-jn\phi} \epsilon^{j(\omega_0 + n\omega_s)t}$$

$$+ \frac{\tau V}{2T} \epsilon^{-j\theta_0} \sum_{n=-\infty}^{\infty} \frac{\sin (n\pi\tau/T)}{n\pi\tau/T} \epsilon^{jn\phi} \epsilon^{-j(\omega_0 + n\omega_s)t} \quad (3.3\text{-}4)$$

The coefficients of $\epsilon^{\pm j(\omega_0 + n\omega_s)t}$ of the above equation defined as

$$c_n = \frac{\tau V}{2T} \frac{\sin (n\pi\tau/T)}{n\pi\tau/T} \epsilon^{\pm j(\theta_0 - n\phi)}$$

$$= |c_n| \epsilon^{\pm j\alpha_n} \quad (3.3\text{-}5)$$

are sometimes referred to as the spectrum function from which the frequency spectra of the time function $y(t)$ are plotted. In Eq. (3.3-5), $|c_n|$

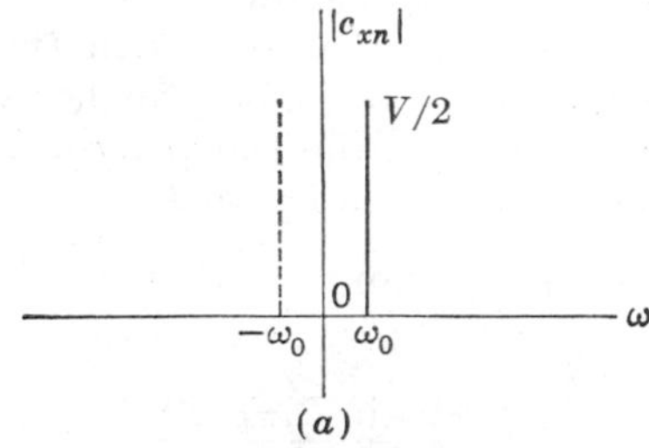

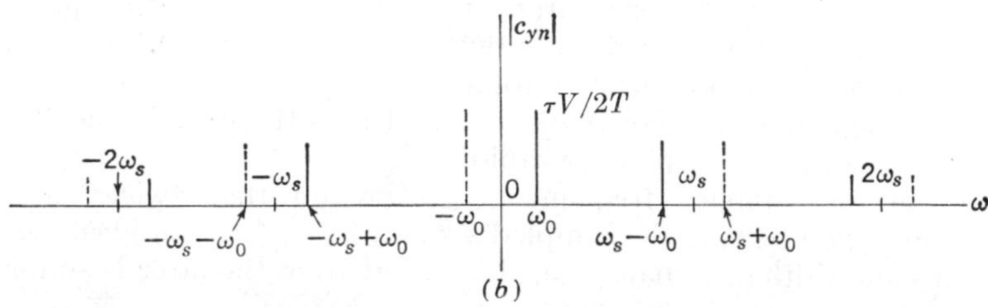

Fig. 3.3-1. (a) Line spectrum of a signal containing only one frequency component; (b) line spectrum of the sampled signal.

and α_n denote, respectively, the magnitude and phase angle of c_n and are given by

$$|c_n| = \frac{\tau V}{2T} \frac{\sin (n\pi\tau/T)}{n\pi\tau/T} \tag{3.3-6}$$

and

$$\alpha_n = \theta_0 - n\phi \tag{3.3-7}$$

Inasmuch as the coefficients c_n are complex, it is necessary to make two plots in order to describe the spectrum function completely. The ones usually chosen are the magnitude $|c_n|$ and the phase angle α_n. The plots of $|c_n|$ and α_n versus frequency are called, respectively, the amplitude and phase spectra of the time function $y(t)$. For instance, $|c_k|$ and α_k are the amplitude and phase of the spectrum function at frequencies $\omega = \pm(\omega_0 + k\omega_s)$. Since ω_0 and ω_s are constant, both $|c_n|$ and α_n are, in effect, functions of n. In view of the fact that n assumes only positive and negative integers, these plots are not in the form of continuous curves, but they consist merely of a series of vertical lines representing the values of $|c_n|$ and α_n corresponding to various values of n. Plotted in Fig. 3.3-1*b* is the amplitude spectrum of the sampled signal $y(t)$, which is a discrete function of frequency. A discrete frequency spectrum is sometimes referred to as *line spectrum* because it is made up of vertical lines. The energy contained in a periodic signal is concentrated at isolated frequencies. The line spectra of a periodic signal, which describe the amplitude and phase of the frequency components of the signal, form a convenient display of the information contained in that signal.

The effects of sampling are shown in Fig. 3.3-1 and Eq. (3.3-3). Examination of Fig. 3.3-1 reveals that sampling would bring about an infinite number of sideband frequencies $(\omega_0 \pm n\omega_s)$ in the frequency spectrum of the sampled signal. Equation (3.3-3) further points out that sampling would cause attenuation of the signal by a factor of τ/T and that sampling would result in the addition to the attenuated original signal $\frac{\tau V}{T} \cos (\omega_0 t + \theta_0)$ of an infinite number of sinusoidal components of amplitude

$$\frac{\tau V}{T} \frac{\sin (n\pi\tau/T)}{n\pi\tau/T} \tag{3.3-8}$$

differing in frequency and phase from the original signal by $\pm n\omega_s$ and $\mp n\phi$, respectively. The phase angle ϕ is defined in Eq. (3.2-11). These added sinusoidal components due to sampling are often referred to as the *sidebands* or *complementary signals*. It is noted that the high-frequency components of Eq. (3.3-3) attenuate rapidly.

Now, if the sampling frequency ω_s is greater than twice the signal frequency ω_0, on passing the sampled signal $y(t)$ through an ideal low-pass filter of bandwidth ω_s radians/sec, the output from the filter is simply

$$\frac{\tau V}{T} \cos (\omega_0 t + \theta_0) \tag{3.3-9}$$

which is practically the same as the original signal except by the difference

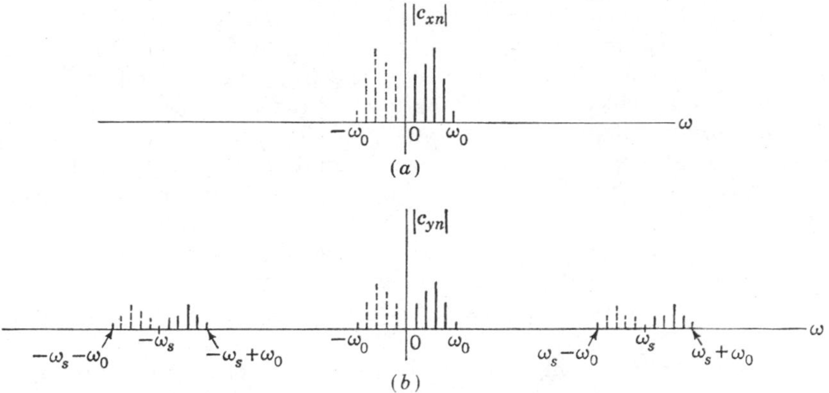

FIG. 3.3-2. (a) Line spectra of a signal containing a number of components within a frequency band; (b) line spectra of the sampled signal.

of an attenuation factor τ/T. Thus, under such conditions the original signal could readily be regained through amplification.

When the original signal $x(t)$ is a composite periodic wave consisting of m frequency components ranging from 0 to ω_0 radians/sec, the frequency spectrum of $x(t)$ would contain within its frequency range m vertical lines, as shown in Fig. 3.3-2a. The height of these spectral lines is equal to the magnitude of the corresponding frequency component. In view of Eq. (3.3-1), following the same reasoning as in the case of a single frequency signal, it can be seen that the frequency spectra of the sampled signal would contain not only the frequencies of the original signal but also the sideband frequencies which differ from the original frequencies by $\pm n\omega_s$. The line spectra of a sampled periodic signal are illustrated in Fig. 3.3-2b. Now, if the composite signal $x(t)$ contains an infinite number of frequency components within its frequency band, then in the limit the signal $x(t)$ becomes nonperiodic and its frequency spectrum would approach a continuous curve (Fig. 3.3-3a). In fact, the frequency spectrum of a non-

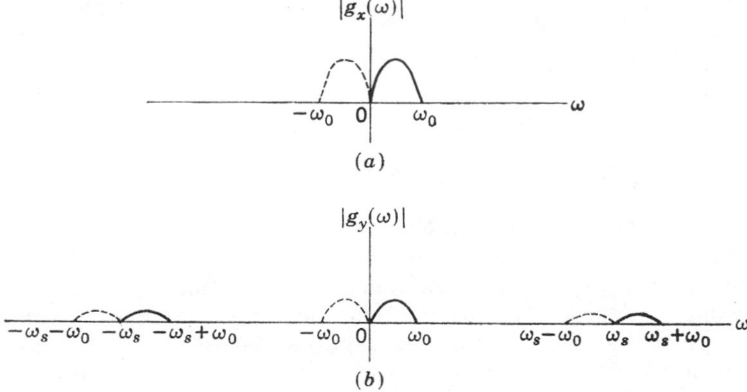

FIG. 3.3-3. (a) Frequency spectrum of an aperiodic signal of limited frequency band; (b) frequency spectrum of the sampled signal.

periodic signal is usually derived from the frequency plots of its Fourier transform which is a continuous function of frequency. Thus, when the original signal $x(t)$ with frequency spectrum extending from 0 to ω_0 radians/sec is specified, the spectrum function of the sampled signal is given by the Fourier integral of Eq. (3.3-1). Based upon the above reasoning, it is conceivable that the frequency spectrum of a sampled aperiodic signal would have a signal band as well as the sidebands. The amplitude spectra are illustrated in Fig. 3.3-3*b*, where the spectra in solid line are associated with the positive frequency spectrum of the original signal and those in dotted line are associated with the negative frequency spectrum of the original signal. Further discussions of the continuous spectra are presented in the following chapter.

3.4. Effects of Clamping. From the discussions of the preceding section it is learned that sampling causes the generation of sidebands or complementary signals in a sampled-data system. These spurious signals are not welcome, simply because they bring about undesirable ripples in the output of control systems. One way to get rid of these unwanted ripples is to make use of clamping. Here clamping refers to a process of holding the measured values of a signal at the sampling instants 0, T, $2T$, $3T$, . . . , constant for a fraction of or the entire sampling period. A signal undergoing the process of sampling followed by clamping is converted into a flat-topped pulse train (Fig. 3.4-1*b*) if clamping occurs only for a fraction

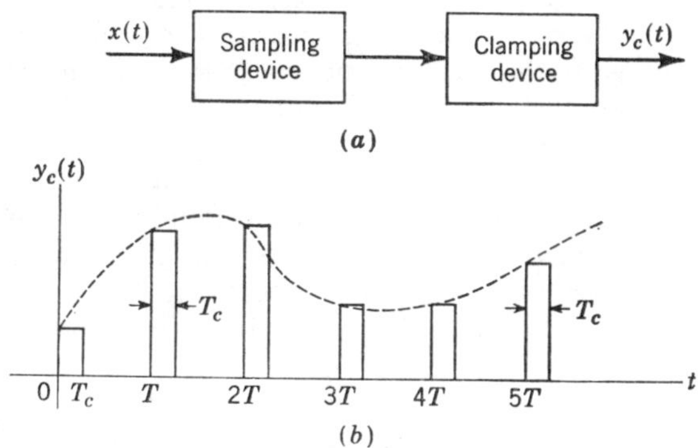

FIG. 3.4-1. (*a*) Process of sampling and clamping; (*b*) partial clamping yields a flat-topped pulse train.

of the sampling period (i.e., partial clamping), or it is converted into a staircase waveform (Fig. 3.4-2) provided that clamping extends over the whole sampling period (i.e., full clamping). This section is concerned with the study of the effects of clamping.

Shown in Fig. 3.4-1*a* is the block diagram of a sampling device followed by a clamping device. In order to make the analysis as simple as possible, it is assumed that the input to the sampling device is a sinusoidal signal of the form

$$x(t) = V \cos (\omega_0 t + \theta_0) \tag{3.4-1}$$

If a flat-topped pulse of width

$$T_c = aT \tag{3.4-2}$$

is subdivided into a number of elementary pulses of width $\Delta\xi$ (Fig. 3.4-3),

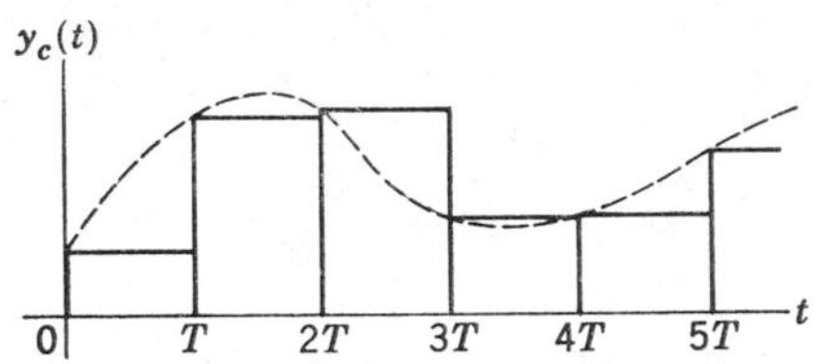

FIG. 3.4-2. Full clamping yields a *staircase* waveform.

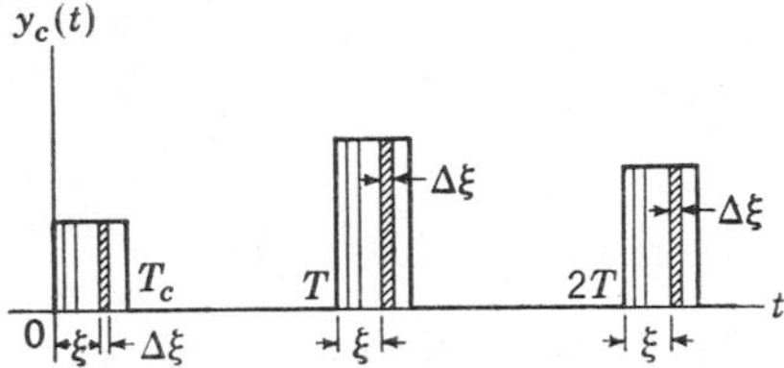

FIG. 3.4-3. The flat-topped pulse train is decomposed into a number of elementary pulse trains successively delayed in time by $\Delta\xi$.

a flat-topped pulse train may be thought of as the sum of a number of identical elementary pulse trains which are successively delayed in time by $\Delta\xi$. In Eq. (3.4-2), T_c stands for the clamping period in seconds; T, the sampling period in seconds; and a is a constant greater than zero and less than or equal to one, with $a < 1$ corresponding to partial clamping and $a = 1$ corresponding to full clamping. It has been shown in Sec. 3.3 that for a sinusoidal signal given by Eq. (3.4-1) the amplitude-modulated pulse train with pulse width τ can be described by

$$y(t) = \frac{\tau V}{T} \sum_{n=-\infty}^{\infty} \frac{\sin(n\pi\tau/T)}{n\pi\tau/T} \cos[(\omega_0 + n\omega_s)t + \theta_0 - n\phi] \tag{3.4-3}$$

where $\phi = \omega_s\tau/2$. In Fig. 3.4-3, the elementary pulse train occurring at $0, T, 2T, 3T, \ldots$, which may be considered as amplitude modulated since the pulse width $\Delta\xi$ is an infinitesimal, is then given by

$$\Delta y(0) = \frac{V\,\Delta\xi}{T} \sum_{n=-\infty}^{\infty} \frac{\sin n\pi\,\Delta\xi/T}{n\pi\,\Delta\xi/T} \cos[(\omega_0 + n\omega_s)t + \theta_0 - \tfrac{1}{2}n\omega_s\,\Delta\xi] \tag{3.4-4}$$

Since in the limit as $\Delta\xi$ approaches zero

$$\frac{\sin n\pi\,\Delta\xi/T}{n\pi\,\Delta\xi/T} = 1 \tag{3.4-5}$$

by ignoring high-order infinitesimals, Eq. (3.4-4) reduces to

$$\Delta y(0) = \frac{V}{T} \sum_{n=-\infty}^{\infty} \cos[(\omega_0 + n\omega_s)t + \theta_0]\,\Delta\xi \tag{3.4-6}$$

It can readily be shown that the elementary pulse train occurring at ξ, $T + \xi$, $2T + \xi$, $3T + \xi$, . . . , of Fig. 3.4-3 may be described by

$$\Delta y(\xi) = \frac{V}{T} \sum_{n=-\infty}^{\infty} \cos[(\omega_0 + n\omega_s)(t - \xi) + \theta_0]\,\Delta\xi \tag{3.4-7}$$

Hence, the flat-topped (or clamped) pulse train of Fig. 3.4-3, which may be derived by summing up all the elementary pulse trains within pulse width T_c, is given by

$$y_c(t) = \lim_{\Delta\xi \to 0} \sum_{\xi=0}^{aT} \Delta y(\xi)$$

$$= \int_0^{aT} \frac{V}{T} \sum_{n=-\infty}^{\infty} \cos\left[(\omega_0 + n\omega_s)(t - \xi) + \theta_0\right] d\xi \tag{3.4-8}$$

Interchanging the operation of summation and integration, Eq. (3.4-8) becomes

$$y_c(t) = \frac{V}{T} \sum_{n=-\infty}^{\infty} \int_0^{aT} \cos\left[(\omega_0 + n\omega_s)(t - \xi) + \theta_0\right] d\xi \tag{3.4-9}$$

Integrating,

$$y_c(t) = \frac{V}{T} \sum_{n=-\infty}^{\infty} \left. \frac{-\sin\left[(\omega_0 + n\omega_s)(t - \xi) + \theta_0\right]}{(\omega_0 + n\omega_s)} \right|_0^{aT}$$

$$= \frac{V}{T} \sum_{n=-\infty}^{\infty} \frac{\sin\left[(\omega_0 + n\omega_s)t + \theta_0\right] - \sin\left[(\omega_0 + n\omega_s)(t - aT) + \theta_0\right]}{(\omega_0 + n\omega_s)} \tag{3.4-10}$$

Simplifying, the output of the clamping device is then described by

$$y_c(t) = \frac{V}{T} \sum_{n=-\infty}^{\infty} \frac{2\sin\left[(\omega_0 + n\omega_s)aT/2\right] \cos\left[(\omega_0 + n\omega_s)(t - aT/2) + \theta_0\right]}{(\omega_0 + n\omega_s)}$$

$$= aV \sum_{n=-\infty}^{\infty} \frac{\sin\left[(\omega_0 + n\omega_s)T_c/2\right]}{(\omega_0 + n\omega_s)T_c/2} \cos\left[(\omega_0 + n\omega_s)(t - T_c/2) + \theta_0\right] \tag{3.4-11}$$

If the sampling frequency ω_s is greater than twice the signal frequency ω_0, passing the clamped sampled signal through an ideal low-pass filter of bandwidth ω_s radians/sec yields the output from the filter as

$$aV \frac{\sin(\omega_0 T_c/2)}{\omega_0 T_c/2} \cos\left[\omega_0(t - T_c/2) + \theta_0\right] \tag{3.4-12}$$

which is delayed by half the clamping period and is distorted by the factor

$$\frac{a \sin(\omega_0 T_c/2)}{(\omega_0 T_c/2)} \tag{3.4-13}$$

The distortion factor depends upon the frequency of the original signal as well as the clamping period. From the above discussions it is seen that the process of sampling followed by clamping causes a distortion of the signal and brings about an infinite number of complementary components of amplitude

$$\frac{aV \sin [(\omega_0 + n\omega_s)T_c/2]}{(\omega_0 + n\omega_s)T_c/2} \tag{3.4-14}$$

differing in frequency from the original signal by $n\omega_s$, and in addition introduces a fixed delay equal to half the clamping period. In the case of full clamping, the output function $y_c(t)$ is given by

$$y_c(t) = V \sum_{n=-\infty}^{\infty} \frac{\sin [(\omega_0 + n\omega_s)T/2]}{(\omega_0 + n\omega_s)T/2} \cos \left[(\omega_0 + n\omega_s)\left(t - \frac{T}{2}\right) + \theta_0 \right] \tag{3.4-15}$$

Apparently, the magnitude of the complementary components is reduced as a result of clamping. However, the use of a clamping device imposes a penalty of constant delay upon the system.

The effects of clamping can also be studied, in a simpler manner, by treating the clamping device as a linear network. The performance characteristics of a clamping device, which is essentially a type of the hold circuits used in sampled-data systems, can be derived from the transfer function describing the clamping device. Referring to Fig. 3.4-1a, the input to the clamping device $y(t)$ is a train of uniformly spaced very narrow pulses, and the output of the clamping device $y_c(t)$ is a train of uniformly spaced flat-topped pulses of width T_c. With the input pulse train represented by an equivalent impulse train, the Laplace transform of the input $y(t)$ is

$$Y(s) = \sum_{k=0}^{N} y_k \epsilon^{-kTs} \tag{3.4-16}$$

where y_k is the value of the kth sample (or the strength of the kth equivalent impulse). From the waveform of the clamped output $y_c(t)$, shown in Fig. 3.4-1b, the Laplace transform of the clamped signal is readily derived. Thus,

$$Y_c(s) = \frac{1 - \epsilon^{-T_c s}}{s} \sum_{k=0}^{N} y_k \epsilon^{-kTs} \tag{3.4-17}$$

Consequently, the transfer function of the clamping device is

$$G_h(s) = \frac{1 - \epsilon^{-T_c s}}{s} \tag{3.4-18}$$

Substituting $j\omega$ for s in Eq. (3.4-18) yields the frequency response as

$$G_h(j\omega) = \frac{1 - \epsilon^{-jT_c\omega}}{j\omega} = \frac{2 \sin (T_c\omega/2)}{\omega \epsilon^{jT_c\omega/2}} \tag{3.4-19}$$

The phase characteristic of the clamping device is then given by

$$\phi(\omega) = \frac{-T_c}{2} \omega \tag{3.4-20}$$

Clearly, the time delay introduced by the clamping (or holding) device is equal to half the clamping period. Further discussions of the performance characteristics of the holding devices are presented in the following chapter.

3.5. Sampling Theorems. *Fundamental Theorem of Sampling.* If a signal $f(t)$ has a frequency spectrum extending from zero to f_0 cps, it is completely determined by the values of the signal (i.e., the samples) taken at a series of instants separated by $T = 1/2f_0$ sec, where T is the sampling period.

This theorem implies that if a signal is sampled instantaneously at a constant rate equal to twice the highest signal frequency, the samples contain all of the information in the original signal. In view of this fundamental theorem, a signal can be transmitted in sampled form without the loss of any information as long as the sampling rate is equal to, or higher than, twice the highest frequency of the signal. Thus, a transmission medium capable of handling a wide band of frequencies can be used simultaneously by a group of channels without mutual interference. The technique of sampling, as justified by the above theorem, has found many applications in communication systems as a means of multiplexing transmission channels, and in control systems, as a means of time sharing important equipments.

To prove the fundamental sampling theorem, assume that the frequency spectral function of a signal $f(t)$ is $F(\omega)$. Then the Fourier integral of $f(t)$ is

$$f(t) = \frac{1}{2\pi} \int_{-\infty}^{\infty} F(\omega)\epsilon^{j\omega t}\, d\omega \tag{3.5-1}$$

in which the frequency spectral function $F(\omega)$ is given by

$$F(\omega) = \int_{-\infty}^{\infty} f(t)\epsilon^{-j\omega t}\, dt \tag{3.5-2}$$

Equations (3.5-1) and (3.5-2) form the Fourier transform pair of $f(t)$. Since it is assumed that $F(\omega)$ is zero outside the frequency band f_0, Eq. (3.5-1) reduces to

$$f(t) = \frac{1}{2\pi} \int_{-\omega_0}^{\omega_0} F(\omega)\epsilon^{j\omega t}\, d\omega \tag{3.5-3}$$

where

$$\omega_0 = 2\pi f_0 \tag{3.5-4}$$

Now, if the function $f(t)$ is sampled at a constant rate $f_s = 2f_0$, at any sampling instant

$$t = n/2f_0 = nT \tag{3.5-5}$$

the value of the signal is then given by

$$f(nT) = \frac{1}{2\pi} \int_{-\omega_0}^{\omega_0} F(\omega)\epsilon^{jn\omega T}\, d\omega \tag{3.5-6}$$

In Eqs. (3.5-5) and (3.5-6), n is any positive or negative integer.

The frequency spectral function $F(\omega)$ is defined in the interval

$$-\omega_0 \le \omega \le \omega_0 \tag{3.5-7}$$

and may be expanded in a Fourier series in this interval:

$$F(\omega) = \sum_{n=-\infty}^{\infty} c_n \epsilon^{-jn\omega T} \tag{3.5-8}$$

where the Fourier coefficients are given by

$$c_n = \frac{T}{2\pi} \int_{-\omega_0}^{\omega_0} F(\omega) \epsilon^{jn\omega T} \, d\omega \tag{3.5-9}$$

Comparison of Eq. (3.5-9) with Eq. (3.5-6) yields

$$c_n = Tf(nT) \tag{3.5-10}$$

Equation (3.5-10) places in evidence that once the values of the signal $f(t)$ at sampling instants nT are available, the Fourier coefficients c_n of the frequency spectral function $F(\omega)$ can readily be computed. In other words, the samples $f(nT)$ of the signal taken at instants nT completely determine the Fourier coefficients c_n, which in turn define the function $F(\omega)$. In view of the fact that once the frequency spectrum of a signal is known, the signal itself is specified, the samples $f(nT)$ of the signal taken at instants nT completely determine the signal $f(t)$. The above rather heuristic proof of the theorem, while not rigorous, is nevertheless sufficient to show the truth of this statement.

Furthermore, it can readily be shown that a signal, which has a frequency spectrum limited to frequency band f_0 cps, may be reconstructed from its samples taken at a series of instants with spacing $T = 1/2f_0$ sec. Substitution of Eq. (3.5-10) into Eq. (3.5-8) yields

$$F(\omega) = T \sum_{n=-\infty}^{\infty} f(nT) \epsilon^{-jn\omega T} \tag{3.5-11}$$

In view of Eq. (3.5-11), the Fourier integral of $f(t)$, Eq. (3.5-3), may be written as

$$f(t) = \frac{T}{2\pi} \int_{-\omega_0}^{\omega_0} \left[\sum_{n=-\infty}^{\infty} f(nT) \epsilon^{j\omega(t-nT)} \right] d\omega \tag{3.5-12}$$

Interchanging the operation of summation and integration,

$$\begin{aligned} f(t) &= \frac{T}{2\pi} \sum_{n=-\infty}^{\infty} f(nT) \int_{-\omega_0}^{\omega_0} \epsilon^{j\omega(t-nT)} \, d\omega \\ &= \frac{T}{2\pi} \sum_{n=-\infty}^{\infty} \frac{f(nT)[\epsilon^{j\omega_0(t-nT)} - \epsilon^{-j\omega_0(t-nT)}]}{j(t-nT)} \\ &= \frac{T}{\pi} \sum_{n=-\infty}^{\infty} f(nT) \frac{\sin \omega_0(t-nT)}{(t-nT)} \end{aligned} \tag{3.5-13}$$

Since

$$T = \frac{1}{2f_0} = \frac{\pi}{\omega_0} \tag{3.5-14}$$

Eq. (3.5-13) may be put into the form

$$f(t) = \sum_{n=-\infty}^{\infty} f(nT) \frac{\sin \omega_0(t - nT)}{\omega_0(t - nT)} \tag{3.5-15}$$

Equation (3.5-15) yields an expression of the signal $f(t)$ in terms of its values at the sampling instants and a known function

$$\frac{\sin \omega_0(t - nT)}{\omega_0(t - nT)} \tag{3.5-16}$$

which equals unity at the nth sampling instant $t = nT$ and zero at all other sampling instants. A graph of this function for $n = 0$ is plotted in Fig. 3.5-1*a*. Therefore, when the values of a signal at the sampling instants are known, by making use of Eq. (3.5-15) the signal itself can be reconstructed from these samples, as shown in Fig. 3.5-1*b*.

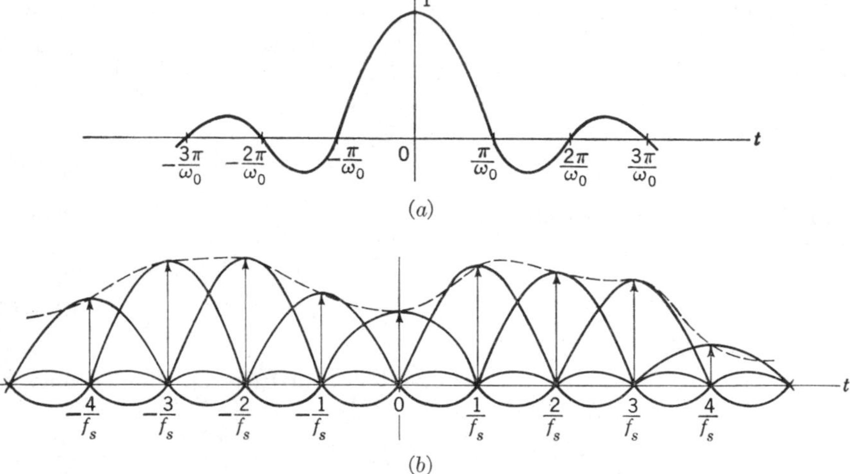

FIG. 3.5-1. (*a*) Plot of the function $(\sin \omega_0 t)/\omega_0 t$; (*b*) reconstruction of a function from its samples.

Mean-square Value of the Samples of a Signal. If a signal $f(t)$ does not contain a component of angular frequency $n\omega_s/2$, or two components of angular frequency ω_1 and ω_2, such that

$$|\omega_1 \pm \omega_2| = n\omega_s \tag{3.5-17}$$

the mean-square value of the samples $\overline{f^2(kT)}$ is equal to the mean square of the signal $\overline{f^2(t)}$, where ω_s is the sampling frequency in radians/second, $\overline{f^2(kT)}$ denotes the average of the squares of the instantaneous samples of the signal $f(t)$ over an infinite number of samples, and

$$n = 1, 2, 3, \ldots \tag{3.5-18}$$

In view of Eq. (3.2-9), the unit-sampling function in the case of instantaneous sampling is given by

$$U(t) = \lim_{\tau \to 0} \left[\frac{\tau}{T} + \frac{2\tau}{T} \sum_{n=1}^{\infty} \frac{\sin (n\pi\tau/T)}{n\pi\tau/T} \cos n(\omega_s t - \phi) \right] \qquad (3.5\text{-}19)$$

It is noted that the phase angle $\phi = \omega_s \tau/2$ of Eq. (3.5-19) becomes zero as τ approaches zero. The function describing the squared samples is given by the product of the square of the signal $f^2(t)$ and the sampling function defined in Eq. (3.5-19), that is,

$$f^2(t)U(t) = \lim_{\tau \to 0} \left[\frac{\tau}{T} f^2(t) + \frac{2\tau}{T} f^2(t) \sum_{n=1}^{\infty} \frac{\sin (n\pi\tau/T)}{n\pi\tau/T} \cos n\omega_s t \right] \qquad (3.5\text{-}20)$$

The mean value of the squared samples is the limit of the average value of $f^2(t)U(t)$ taken over the interval of sampling duration τ. As can readily be seen from Fig. 3.5-2, the average value of a pulse train taken over the interval of sampling duration (pulse width) τ is equal to T/τ times its average value taken over the whole repetition period T. Consequently, the mean-square value of the samples is given by

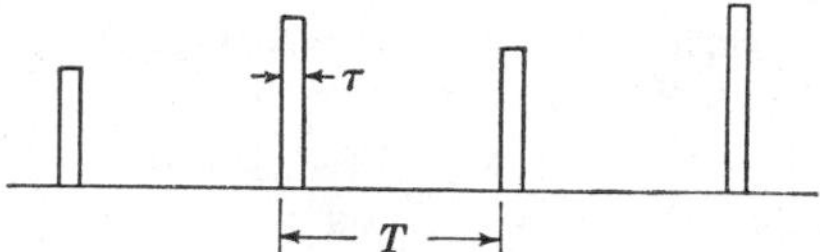

FIG. 3.5-2. A pulse train.

$$\overline{f^2(kT)} = \frac{T}{\tau} \overline{f^2(t)U(t)} \qquad (3.5\text{-}21)$$

Substituting Eq. (3.5-20) into Eq. (3.5-21) yields

$$\overline{f^2(kT)} = \lim_{\tau \to 0} \left[\overline{f^2(t)} + 2 \sum_{n=1}^{\infty} \overline{f^2(t) \cos n\omega_s t \frac{\sin (n\pi\tau/T)}{n\pi\tau/T}} \right]$$

$$= \overline{f^2(t)} + 2 \sum_{n=1}^{\infty} \overline{f^2(t) \cos n\omega_s t} \qquad (3.5\text{-}22)$$

It is clear that the average value of $f^2(t) \cos n\omega_s t$ taken over a very long time interval is zero unless $f^2(t)$ contains a component of angular frequency $n\omega_s$. However, this could occur only when the signal $f(t)$ itself contains a component of angular frequency $n\omega_s/2$ or two components of angular frequencies ω_1 and ω_2 related by Eq. (3.5-17). Thus, if the signal $f(t)$ does not contain such components, Eq. (3.5-22) reduces to

$$\overline{f^2(kT)} = \overline{f^2(t)} \qquad (3.5\text{-}23)$$

This proves the theorem.

3.6. Amplitude Quantization. In Chap. 1 it is explained that in sampled-data control systems the signal at one or more points of the system is pulse-amplitude modulated whereas in digital control systems the signal in certain parts of the system is pulse-code modulated. A signal can be converted into pulse-amplitude-modulated form through the process of sampling as discussed in previous sections. However, the conversion of a signal into pulse-code-modulated form generally involves the process of sampling and amplitude quantization. In a digital system, samples of the signal are obtained frequently enough so that the signal is completely specified by the samples, but only certain discrete levels of amplitude of the sample are allowed. Any sample falling between the allowed levels is converted into a sample of amplitude level nearest the actual value of the signal. This process of representing the signal by certain discrete amplitude levels is called amplitude quantization. The amplitude levels of a quantized sample are then described by a code group which consists of several pulses. A code group is transmitted for each sample of the signal. The process of describing a sample by a numerical code, such as a binary code, is called encoding.

In the binary number system, for example, a code group consists of several "on-off" pulses indicating *on* (1) or *off* (0). A code group of n "on-off" pulses can represent 2^n amplitude levels of the sample of a signal. The process of sampling, amplitude quantization, and encoding in digital systems is often referred to as analog-to-digital conversion. Through this conversion process a physical quantity or its analog is translated into a numerical code which is the kind of language that the digital equipment of a control system can understand. Both quantizing and sampling are of fundamental importance in the evaluation of the performance of digital control systems. While the details of the analog-digital conversion principles and techniques form the theme of Chap. 8, the process of amplitude quantization is discussed in the following paragraphs.

The quantizing process is a nonlinear operation in the sense that only a discrete set of amplitude levels are produced for a continuous range of amplitude levels of the input signal. Quantization generally occurs whenever a physical quantity is measured and represented numerically. The measured value is often designated by a number corresponding to the nearest number of amplitude levels or units contained in the physical quantity, which may be considered as quantizing levels or steps. Quantizing inherently introduces a distortion in the measured value, and the precision of measurement would depend upon the *fineness* of the quantizing steps. This distortion as a result of quantization is often called the quantization error. To determine the number of amplitude levels or quantizing steps required for the accurate measurement or representation of specific signals or physical quantities, a knowledge of the relationship between the size of the quantizing levels and the distortion is essential.

Shown in Fig. 3.6-1 is a quantizing device (or quantizer) together with its input-output characteristic. The output y of the quantizer is a single-valued function of the input x. An input falling somewhere within a quantizing level would yield an output corresponding to the center of that step. For example, the input $x = 57.468 \ldots$, which falls within the 57th quan-

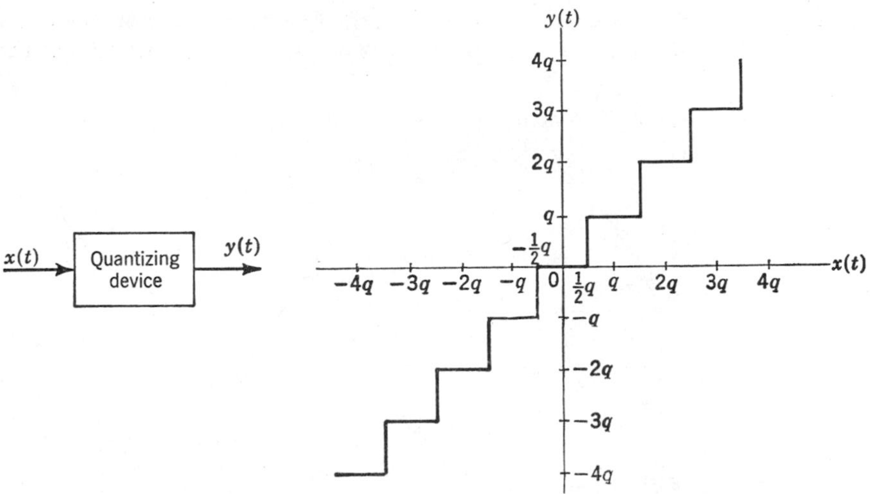

FIG. 3.6-1. The quantizing device and its input-output characteristics.

tized level, would yield an output $y = 57$; and the input $x = 56.895\ldots$, which also lies within the 57th quantized level, would yield an output $y = 57$. The input x could be any finite quantity, whereas the output y can take on only the integral number of quantizing levels (or quanta) which is nearest to the value of the input x. Inasmuch as quantizing is a process of approximating the value of an analog quantity by a number, it is a rounding-off process and the quantization error is equivalent to the round-off error in numerical analysis. A number is usually represented by writing a sequence of digits to the left and to the right of some reference point. The digits to the left of the reference point are finite in number, whereas the digits to the right of the reference may be infinite in number. In digital computations only a finite number of these digits can be enfolded. The error resulting from neglecting the other digits is called the round-off error. In a quantizing process the round-off error is produced because of the finite magnitude of the quantizing step. It is clear that the finer the quantizing steps, the smaller the round-off error.

When a continuous signal is impressed on the quantizing device, the quantized signal would be in the form of a *staircase* wave as depicted in Fig. 3.6-2*a*. The difference between the input signal and the quantized output forms the quantization error which is a function of the magnitude of a quantizing step and the input signal. Thus,

$$\varepsilon(q; x,t) = x(t) - y(t) \tag{3.6-1}$$

where q denotes the magnitude of the quantizing step, $\varepsilon(q; x,t)$ is the instantaneous deviation of the output signal from the input signal, and

$$0 \leq \varepsilon(q; x,t) \leq q \tag{3.6-2}$$

For the input signal shown in Fig. 3.6-2a, the quantization error as a function of time is sketched in Fig. 3.6-2b. It is noted that any variation of the

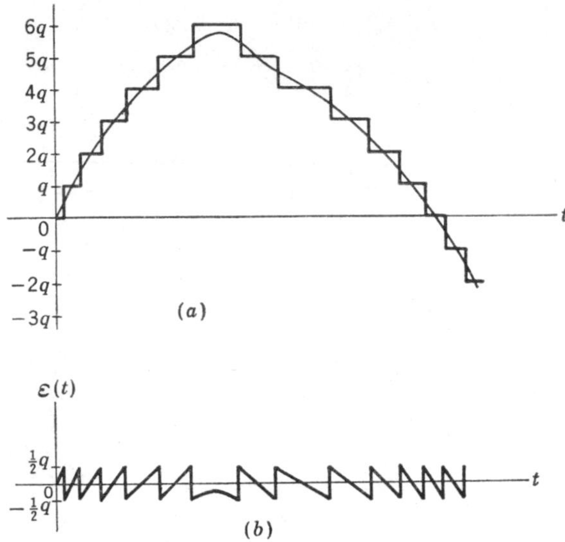

FIG. 3.6-2. (a) The waveform of a quantized signal; (b) waveform of quantization error.

input signal within a single quantization step does not change the output signal, and that distortion caused by quantization error brings about much the same sort of effects as a source of noise. In this respect quantization error may be looked upon as a noise which is introduced into the system as a result of quantizing. The frequency of this noise is dependent upon and higher than the frequency of the input signal to the quantizer. Since the peak-to-peak amplitude of this noise is equal to one quantizer step, in order to secure high accuracy in quantization the necessity of keeping the quantizing steps small becomes obvious.

Although the analytical expression of the quantization error $\varepsilon(q; x,t)$ is rather difficult to derive, the mean-square value of the error, which is frequently used for system evaluation and design, may be approximately determined in terms of the quantizing step q. Referring to Fig. 3.6-2b, it is seen that if there is a large number of closely spaced quantizing steps, the waveform of the quantization error may be approximated by a series of line segments with varying slopes, extending over the vertical interval between plus and minus half a quantizing step, except when the input signal reaches a maximum or minimum within a quantizing step. In this case the time function of the error signal would no longer take the form of a line segment during that interval as clearly indicated in Fig. 3.6-2b. Nevertheless, an approximate mean-square value of the quantization error[10] could be determined, provided that the quantizing steps are kept very small. Under such conditions, the mean-square error would be approximately given by the mean-square value of a typical line segment of the error signal extending from minus half a step to plus half a step with arbitrary slope m. For the time interval,

$$-\frac{q}{2m} < t < \frac{q}{2m} \tag{3.6-3}$$

the equation describing the typical line segment of the error signal is

$$\varepsilon = mt \tag{3.6-4}$$

In the above equations, the time variable t is counted from the middle point of the line segment. The mean-square error is, then, given by

$$\begin{aligned}\overline{\varepsilon^2} &= \frac{1}{q/m}\int_{-q/2m}^{q/2m}(mt)^2\,dt \\ &= \frac{q^2}{12}\end{aligned} \tag{3.6-5}$$

That is, the mean-square value of the quantization error is approximately one-twelfth the square of a quantum. Equation (3.6-5) also holds when the input to the quantizer is a sampled-data signal.

To illustrate the effect of quantization, consider the simple system of Fig. 3.6-3a, the output of which is quantized with fine steps. In response

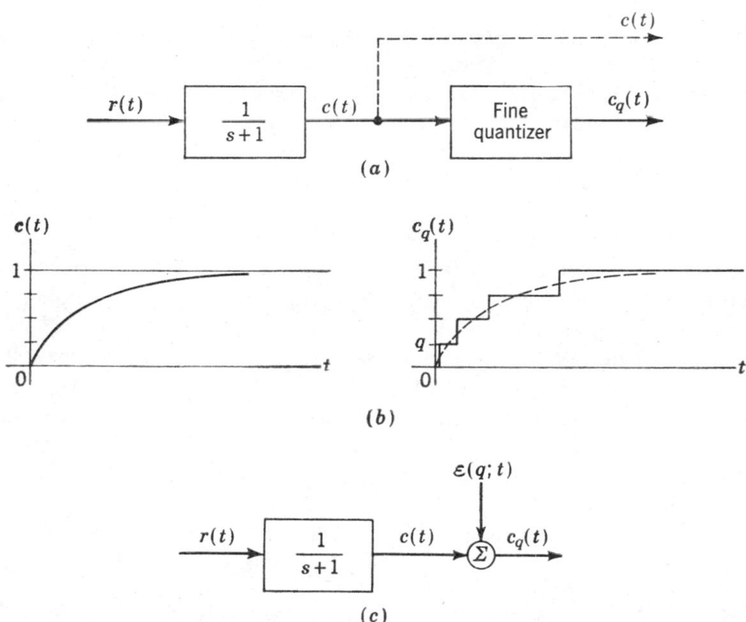

FIG. 3.6-3. (a) A simple system containing a fine quantizer; (b) waveforms of the system output before and after quantizing; (c) equivalent representation of the system in (a).

to a unit step-function input, the system outputs before and after quantizing are quite different in waveform, as demonstrated in Fig. 3.6-3*b*. The former describes a continuous, smooth curve, whereas the latter is in the form of a staircase. The effect of quantization is evidenced from the waveforms of the system outputs $c(t)$ and $c_q(t)$. The difference between these two functions represents the error or noise resulting from the process of quantization. When the quantizing steps are kept small, the quantization error is of the nature of an independent random noise. The quantizer behaves, in effect, as a source of random noise. Consequently, to analyze a system which contains a fine quantizer, the quantizer may be treated as a summing point, and uniformly distributed noise is introduced at that point, as shown in Fig. 3.6-3*c*.

Statistical Analysis. In view of the fact that quantization error is comparable to noise in electronic and control systems, statistical approach might be a convenient way of studying the process of amplitude quantization.† Statistical analysis yields only average results which, however, are adequate for the evaluation and design of most systems. Since, in digital control systems, the signal is first sampled and then quantized and encoded before it is fed to the digital equipment as discussed above, the following analysis is concerned with the amplitude quantization of sampled signals. The preceding discussion also points out that in order to reduce the quantization error the quantizing steps should be kept small. In the following investigation fine quantization is assumed. Under this assumption the quantizer can be treated as a source of independent random noise and the quantization error is uncorrelated to the quantizer input.

If the input signal to the quantizer is assumed to be the samples of some continuous variable which are random and statistically independent of each other, the input may be defined by its first probability distribution $P(x)$. Then the process of amplitude quantization would be statistically determined if the first probability distribution $W^*(x)$ of the quantized output could be derived from the input probability distribution. The probability distributions of the quantized output and the quantization error and their characteristic functions are determined in the following paragraphs.

Shown in Fig. 3.6-4 is the probability distribution of the quantizer input which is a continuous function of variable x, since the input variable can assume a continuous range of magnitudes. The characteristics of the quantized signal make it clear that the probability for the quantizer output taking on a value falling between allowable amplitude levels is zero. Referring to Fig. 3.6-4, the probability that the values of the input variable x lie within the range

$$-\frac{q}{2} < x < \frac{q}{2} \tag{3.6-6}$$

† H. Cramer, "Mathematical Methods of Statistics," Princeton University Press, Princeton, N.J., 1946.

W. B. Davenport and W. L. Root, "An Introduction to the Theory of Random Signals and Noise," McGraw-Hill Book Company, Inc., New York, 1958.

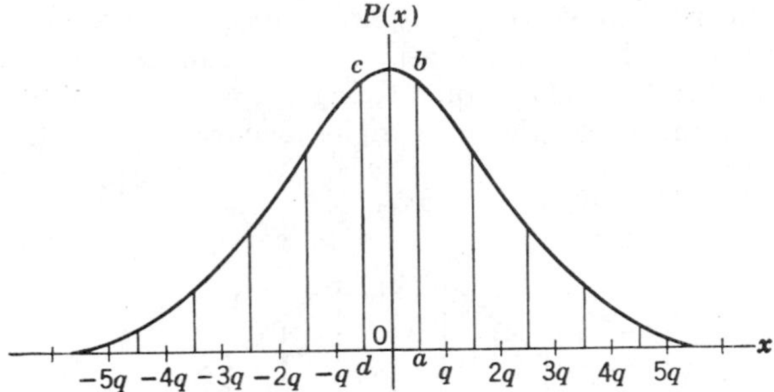

FIG. 3.6-4. Probability distribution of quantizer-input variables.

is, by definition, given by the area of the column *abcd* above the quantizing step centered at the origin. Since within this range of the input variable the quantizer output is zero, the area of the column *abcd* also represents the probability that the quantizer output is nil. This probability of occurrence is thus given by

$$W(0) = \int_{-q/2}^{q/2} P(x)\,dx \tag{3.6-7}$$

where the integration extends from minus half a quantizing step to plus half a quantizing step. In like manner, the probability that the values of the input variable lie within the range

$$\frac{q}{2} < x < q + \frac{q}{2} \tag{3.6-8}$$

is given by the area of the column centered at q (Fig. 3.6-4). Hence the probability that the quantized output contains one quantizing step is

$$W(q) = \int_{q-\frac{1}{2}q}^{q+\frac{1}{2}q} P(x)\,dx \tag{3.6-9}$$

Following the same reasoning, the probability that the quantized output contains two quantizing steps is found to be

$$W(2q) = \int_{2q-\frac{1}{2}q}^{2q+\frac{1}{2}q} P(x)\,dx \tag{3.6-10}$$

which equals the area of the column centered at $2q$. In general, the probability that the quantized output contains k quantizing steps is then given by

$$W(kq) = \int_{(k-\frac{1}{2})q}^{(k+\frac{1}{2})q} P(x)\,dx \tag{3.6-11}$$

which is equal to the area of the column centered at kq. Consequently, by assigning all positive and negative integers to k, Eq. (3.6-11) describes the probability distribution of the quantizer output. As depicted in Fig.

3.6-5 the output probability distribution is a discrete function of variable x. This is to be expected since a quantized signal can assume only a discrete number of amplitude levels or quantizing steps. The output probability distribution comprises a series of samples occurring at $x = 0, \pm q, \pm 2q,$

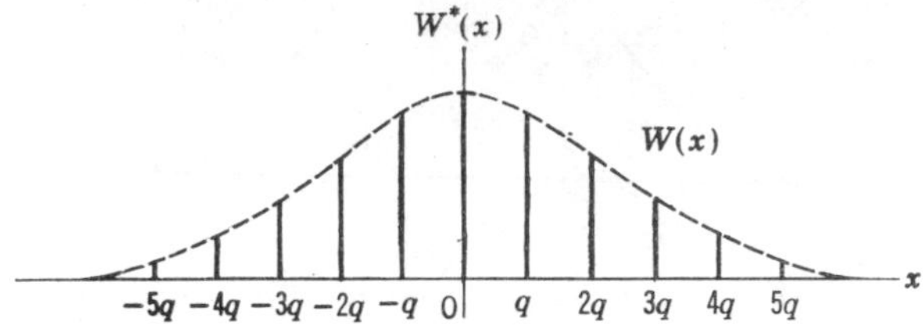

FIG. 3.6-5. Probability distribution of quantizer-output variables.

$\ldots, \pm kq, \ldots$. These samples may be represented by a sequence of equivalent impulses equal in strength to the values of the samples at the respective sampling points. Thus, the probability distribution of the quantizer output (Fig. 3.6-5) can be described by

$$\begin{aligned} W^*(x) &= W(0)\delta(x) + W(q)\delta(x-q) + W(2q)\delta(x-2q) + \cdots \\ &\quad + W(kq)\delta(x-kq) + \cdots \\ &\quad + W(q)\delta(x+q) + W(2q)\delta(x+2q) + \cdots \\ &\quad + W(kq)\delta(x+kq) + \cdots \\ &= \sum_{k=-N}^{N} W(kq)\delta(x-kq) \end{aligned} \tag{3.6-12}$$

where $W(kq)\delta(x - kq)$ is a Dirac delta function occurring at $x = kq$ with strength equal to $W(kq)$ which is the probability of occurrence defined in Eq. (3.6-11).

It is noted that Eq. (3.6-11) may be written as

$$W(kq) = \left[\int_0^{x+\frac{1}{2}q} P(x)\,dx - \int_0^{x-\frac{1}{2}q} P(x)\,dx\right]_{x=kq} \tag{3.6-13}$$

which is the value of the function

$$W(x) = \int_0^{x+\frac{1}{2}q} P(x)\,dx - \int_0^{x-\frac{1}{2}q} P(x)\,dx \tag{3.6-14}$$

evaluated at $x = kq$. As a result, the probability distribution of the quantizer output may be thought of as the samples taken from the function $W(x)$ of Eq. (3.6-14). Thus, according to the fundamental theorem of sampling, in order that the samples $W(kq)$ may contain all information in $W(x)$, the *sampling frequency* $1/q$ (i.e., the reciprocal of the size of the quantizing step) should be greater than twice the highest *frequency component* contained in the waveform of $W(x)$. By a suitable change of variable, Eq. (3.6-14) may be reduced to the form

$$W(x) = \int_{-q/2}^{x} P(x + \tfrac{1}{2}q)\,dx - \int_{q/2}^{x} P(x - \tfrac{1}{2}q)\,dx \tag{3.6-15}$$

Now, assuming that $F_i(u)$ and $F(u)$ be the respective characteristic functions of the probability distributions $P(x)$ and $W(x)$, they are related by

$$F_i(u) = \int_{-\infty}^{\infty} \epsilon^{-jux} P(x)\, dx \tag{3.6-16}$$

$$P(x) = \frac{1}{2\pi} \int_{-\infty}^{\infty} \epsilon^{jxu} F_i(u)\, du \tag{3.6-17}$$

and

$$F(u) = \int_{-\infty}^{\infty} \epsilon^{-jux} W(x)\, dx \tag{3.6-18}$$

$$W(x) = \frac{1}{2\pi} \int_{-\infty}^{\infty} \epsilon^{jxu} F(u)\, du \tag{3.6-19}$$

respectively. The characteristic function of a probability distribution is defined as its Fourier transform.

Taking the Fourier transform of both sides of Eq. (3.6-15) yields

$$\begin{aligned} F(u) &= \frac{\epsilon^{j\frac{1}{2}qu}}{ju} F_i(u) - \frac{\epsilon^{-j\frac{1}{2}qu}}{ju} F_i(u) \\ &= q \frac{\sin (qu/2)}{qu/2} F_i(u) \end{aligned} \tag{3.6-20}$$

By letting

$$F_n(u) = q \frac{\sin (qu/2)}{(qu/2)} \tag{3.6-21}$$

Eq. (3.6-20) may be written as

$$F(u) = F_n(u) F_i(u) \tag{3.6-22}$$

The above equation implies that the characteristic function of probability distribution $W(x)$ is equal to the product of the characteristic function of the probability distribution of the input variable, and the characteristic function $F_n(u)$ which depends upon the size of the quantizing step q. $F_n(u)$ can be taken as the characteristic function associated with the quantization error, since for fine quantization the quantizer is a source of independent random noise. In view of the statistical property that the characteristic function of the probability distribution of the sum of independent random variables is equal to the product of the characteristic functions of the individual variables, the probability distributions of the input variable and the quantization error, or noise, are related by

$$W(x) = Q(x) + P(x) \tag{3.6-23}$$

where $Q(x)$ is the probability distribution of the quantization error. $F_n(u)$ can then be identified as the characteristic function of $Q(x)$. Hence, by taking the Fourier transform of Eq. (3.6-21) the probability-distribution function of the quantization error is obtained:

$$\begin{aligned} Q(x) &= \frac{1}{2\pi} \int_{-\infty}^{\infty} \epsilon^{jxu} F_n(u)\, du \\ &= \frac{1}{2\pi} \int_{-\infty}^{\infty} q\epsilon^{jxu} \frac{\sin (qu/2)}{(qu/2)}\, du \end{aligned} \tag{3.6-24}$$

Integrating leads to

$$Q(x) = \begin{cases} 1 & \text{for } -q/2 \le x \le q/2 \\ 0 & \text{elsewhere} \end{cases} \tag{3.6-25}$$

which describes a uniform distribution. Both the characteristic function and the probability distribution of the quantization error are plotted in Fig. 3.6-6. For reasons which are obvious from the figure, $Q(x)$ is often referred to as the rectangular distribution.

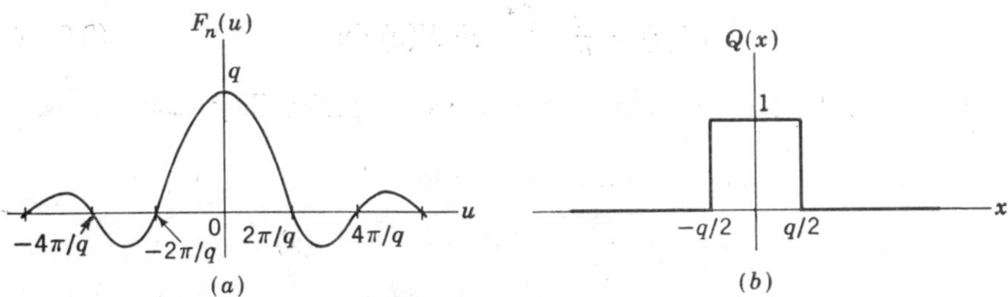

FIG. 3.6-6. (a) Characteristic function of the probability distribution of the quantization error; (b) probability distribution of the quantization error.

The above discussions lead to the idea that so far as the probability distributions of the independent random variables are concerned, the quantizer can be described by a device consisting of a summer and a sampler as shown in Fig. 3.6-7. This device may be called the equivalent *statistical sampler* of the quantizer. The probability distributions of the actual quantizer input and the quantization error form the input *signals* to the equivalent *sampler*, and the probability distribution of the quantizer output is the output signal of the equivalent sampler. This process is referred to as *area sampling* by Widrow.[122]

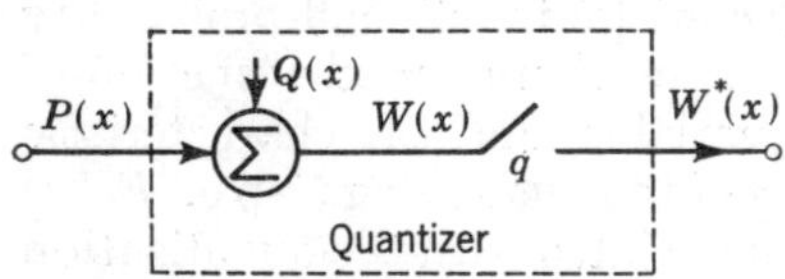

FIG. 3.6-7. *Statistical sampler* equivalent to quantizer.

The mean-square value of the quantization error is given by the second moment of its probability distribution $Q(x)$, which can be determined from the characteristic function $F_n(u)$ by evaluating its second derivative at the origin. Thus,

$$\overline{\varepsilon^2} = m_2 = \frac{d^2}{du^2} F_n(u) \bigg|_{u=0} \tag{3.6-26}$$

where $\overline{\varepsilon^2}$ is the mean square of the quantization error and m_2 denotes the second moment of $Q(x)$. Substituting Eq. (3.6-21) into Eq. (3.6-26) and evaluating yield the mean-square error

$$\overline{\varepsilon^2} = \frac{q^2}{12} \tag{3.6-27}$$

which agrees with the expression of Eq. (3.6-5) derived above.

CHAPTER 4

FREQUENCY DOMAIN ANALYSIS

4.1. Properties of the Sampler. The basic component of a sampled-data control system is the sampler, shown in Fig. 4.1-1, which converts the

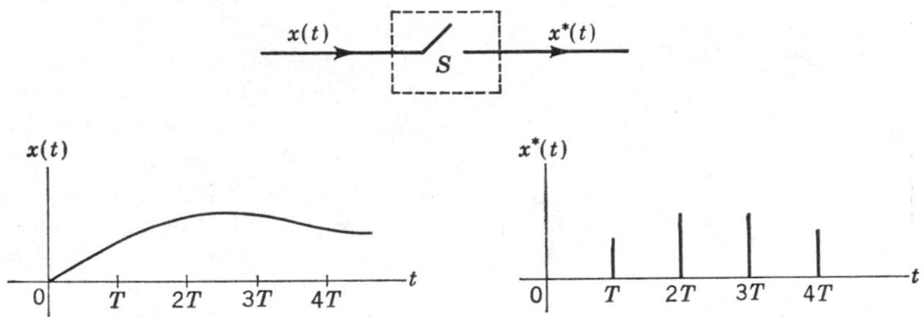

FIG. 4.1-1. The sampler and the waveforms of its input and output.

continuous signal applied to the sampler into a train of very narrow pulses occurring at the sampling instants 0, T, $2T$, $3T$, . . . kT, . . . , where T is the time interval between consecutive pulses and is called the sampling period. The quantity $f_s = 1/T$ is called the sampling frequency. The sampler transmits information intermittently at the sampling instants, and no data are passed between sampling instants. Since, in practice, in sampled-data control systems the sampling duration, or the width of the sampling pulse, is small in comparison with the most significant time constant of the control system, the sampler output can be considered as a train of impulses the strengths of which are equal to the values of the continuous time function at the respective sampling instants. Based upon this fundamental assumption the following analysis is carried out. The great advantage resulting from this assumption is that it simplifies considerably the analysis as well as synthesis of sampled-data control systems. Indeed, if the pulses are very narrow they carry little energy. In the limit, as the sampling duration approaches zero, the pulses of the sampler output carry no energy and cannot result in an output when applied to a physically realizable circuit. Consequently, in order to represent very narrow pulses by equivalent impulses it is assumed that energy is supplied by the sampler or by some subsequent holding device.

Let $x(t)$ be the continuous input signal and $x^*(t)$ be the sampler output, then the output and the input are related by

$$x^*(t) = \delta_T(t)x(t) \tag{4.1-1}$$

where $\delta_T(t)$ is the ideal sampling function which represents a train of unit impulses as shown in Fig. 4.1-2. From the waveform of $\delta_T(t)$ it follows that mathematically

$$\delta_T(t) = \sum_{n=-\infty}^{\infty} \delta(t - nT) \tag{4.1-2}$$

where $\delta(t)$ is the unit-impulse function occurring at $t = 0$ and $\delta(t - nT)$ is a delayed-impulse function occurring at $t = nT$. Equation (4.1-1) implies that the sampler output equals the product of the ideal sampling function and the continuous input. Thus, a sampler is equivalent to a modulator with the input $x(t)$ as the modulating signal and the ideal sampling function $\delta_T(t)$ as the carrier, and the operation of instantaneous sampling is analogous to the process of *impulse modulation*[21] (Fig. 4.1-3). The output from the impulse modulator is a train of impulses (or ideal pulses) the strengths (or the amplitude) of which bear a one-to-one

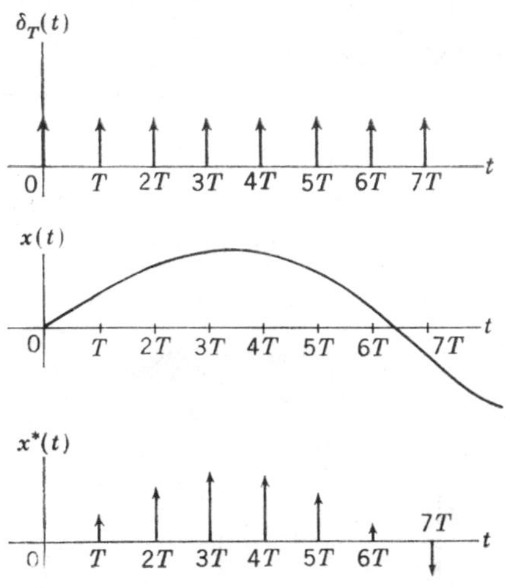

FIG. 4.1-2. Instantaneous sampling analogous to impulse modulation.

FIG. 4.1-3. Sampler equivalent to impulse modulator.

correspondence with the sequence $x(0)$, $x(T)$, $x(2T)$, $x(3T)$, . . . $x(kT)$, . . . The value of the kth sample $x(kT)$ is also given by

$$x(kT) = \int_{-\infty}^{\infty} x(t)\delta(t - kT)\, dt \tag{4.1-3}$$

which denotes the strength of the kth equivalent impulse.

Since $\delta_T(t)$ is periodic, as shown in Fig. 4.1-2, it can be expanded in a complex Fourier series:

$$\delta_T(t) = \sum_{n=-\infty}^{\infty} C_n \epsilon^{jn\omega_s t} \tag{4.1-4}$$

where $$\omega_s = \frac{2\pi}{T} = 2\pi f_s \tag{4.1-5}$$

is the sampling frequency in radians/second, and c_n's are the Fourier coefficients, which are given by

$$c_n = \frac{1}{T}\int_{-T/2}^{T/2} \delta_T(t)\epsilon^{-jn\omega_s t}\,dt \tag{4.1-6}$$

As $$\int_{-T/2}^{T/2} \delta_T(t)\epsilon^{-jn\omega_s t}\,dt = \int_{0^-}^{0^+} \delta(t)\,dt = 1 \tag{4.1-7}$$

then $$\delta_T(t) = \frac{1}{T}\sum_{n=-\infty}^{\infty} \epsilon^{jn\omega_s t} \tag{4.1-8}$$

and from Eq. (4.1-1) the sampler output is

$$x^*(t) = \frac{1}{T}\sum_{n=-\infty}^{\infty} x(t)\epsilon^{jn\omega_s t} \tag{4.1-9}$$

Equation (4.1-9) describes the relationship between the input and the output of an ideal sampler.

If the input to the sampler is a sinusoidal function of frequency ω_0 and amplitude V_i, which is described by

$$x(t) = V_i(\epsilon^{j\omega_0 t} + \epsilon^{-j\omega_0 t}) \tag{4.1-10}$$

then the response of the sampler to this input is

$$x^*(t) = \frac{V_i}{T}\sum_{n=-\infty}^{\infty} (\epsilon^{j(\omega_0+n\omega_s)t} + \epsilon^{-j(\omega_0+n\omega_s)t}) \tag{4.1-11}$$

Equation (4.1-11) implies that for an input signal of frequency ω and amplitude V_i, the output of the sampler contains the input signal attenuated by a factor $1/T$ and other component signals of amplitude V_i/T and frequencies differing from ω_0 by integer multiples of sampling frequency ω_s. When Eq. (4.1-11) is expanded, there results

$$\underbrace{x^*(t)}_{\text{Sampler output}} = \underbrace{\frac{V_i}{T}(\epsilon^{j\omega_0 t} + \epsilon^{-j\omega_0 t})}_{\text{Primary signal}}$$
$$+ \underbrace{\frac{V_i}{T}\sum_{n=1}^{\infty} (\epsilon^{j(\omega_0+n\omega_s)t} + \epsilon^{-j(\omega_0+n\omega_s)t} + \epsilon^{j(\omega_0-n\omega_s)t} + \epsilon^{-j(\omega_0-n\omega_s)t})}_{\text{Complementary signals}} \tag{4.1-12}$$

The first term of the right-hand side of Eq. (4.1-12) represents the primary signal which is an attenuated reproduction of the input signal, and the second term represents the complementary signals which are generated through the operation of sampling. The complementary signals have the same amplitude as that of the primary signal, but they are shifted in frequency from the primary signal by $n\omega_s$ units, as illustrated in Fig. 4.1-4.

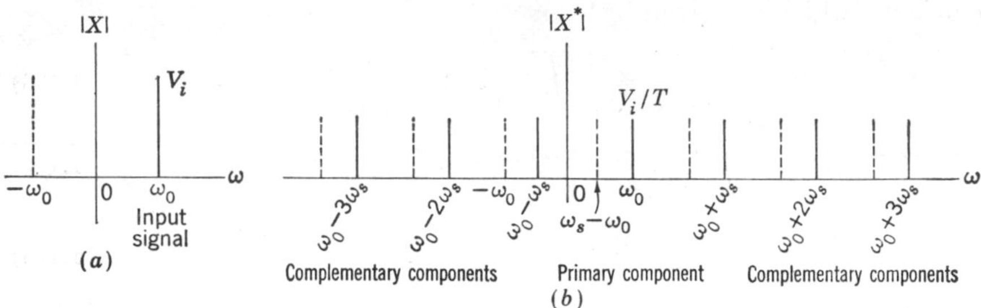

FIG. 4.1-4. Line spectra of the primary and complementary components.

Laplace transforming of Eq. (4.1-9) yields

$$X^*(s) = \frac{1}{T} \sum_{n=-\infty}^{\infty} \mathcal{L}\{x(t)\epsilon^{jn\omega_s t}\} \tag{4.1-13}$$

By the complex translation theorem,

$$X^*(s) = \frac{1}{T} \sum_{n=-\infty}^{\infty} X(s + jn\omega_s) \tag{4.1-14}$$

where $X(s)$ is the Laplace transform of the sampler input $x(t)$. If all the poles of $X^*(s)$ are located in the left half of the s plane, the Fourier transform of the output may be derived from Eq. (4.1-14) by substituting $j\omega$ for s. Thus,

$$X^*(j\omega) = \frac{1}{T} \sum_{n=-\infty}^{\infty} X[j(\omega + n\omega_s)] \tag{4.1-15}$$

Equation (4.1-14) implies that the $\mathcal{L}$ transform of the output of the sampler is a periodic function of s with period equal to $j\omega_s$. That is,

$$X^*(s) = X^*(s \pm jk\omega_s) \tag{4.1-16}$$

where k is an integer. The periodicity property of $X^*(s)$ is demonstrated by the frequency spectra plotted in Fig. 4.1-5. This is one of the fundamental properties of sampling. Generally speaking, periodic time functions have discrete frequency spectra, while discrete time functions resulting from periodic sampling processes possess periodic frequency spectra. A knowledge of the frequency spectrum is essentially equivalent to a knowledge of the time function. If the frequency spectrum of the sampler input is given, as shown in Fig. 4.1-5a, then the frequency spectra of the sampler output can readily be determined from Eq. (4.1-15). Figure 4.1-5b depicts

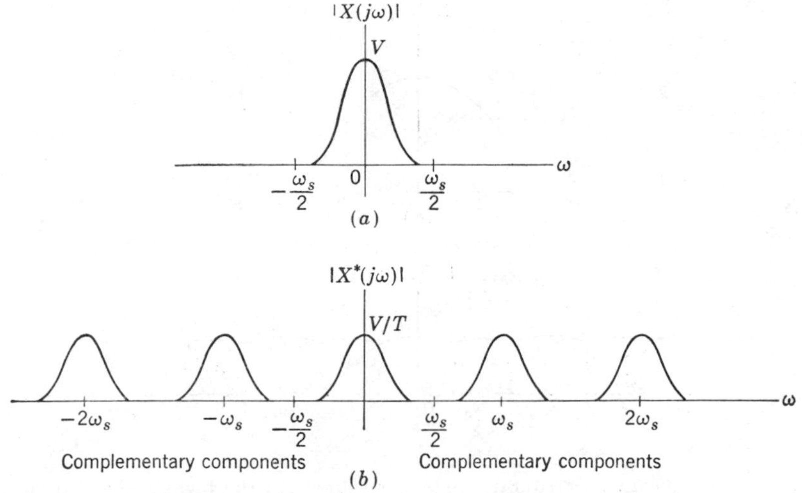

Fig. 4.1-5. Frequency spectra of the original and the sampled signal.

the frequency spectra of the sampler output, which consist of the spectrum of the primary signal and the spectra of the complementary signals. The spectrum of the primary signal is similar to that of the sampler input, except that it is attenuated by a factor $1/T$, and is centered at zero frequency. The spectra of the complementary signals are identical with those of the primary signal, but they are displaced from the primary component by $n\omega_s$ units.

The primary component is the desired signal, which can generally be recovered by filtering the unwanted complementary components. However, when the sampling frequency is less than twice the highest frequency of the input signal, the primary and the complementary signals will overlap as shown in Fig. 4.1-6, and thus the desired signal cannot be extracted from the sampler output by filtering. Hence, with the exception of a few special waveforms of signals, such as a piecewise-constant wave with breaks occurring only at integer multiples of T, signals of frequency equal to $\omega_s/2$ or higher cannot be transmitted by the sampling device. This was explained in Chap. 3. A fixed sampling rate generally imposes a limit upon the frequency band of the signals that can be transmitted. For transmitting signals of higher frequencies the sampling rate of the system needs to be increased.

Alternative Expressions Describing the Sampler.[26,149] Substituting Eq. (4.1-2) into Eq. (4.1-1) yields

$$x^*(t) = x(t) \sum_{n=-\infty}^{\infty} \delta(t - nT) \tag{4.1-17}$$

or

$$x^*(t) = \sum_{n=-\infty}^{\infty} x(nT)\delta(t - nT) \tag{4.1-18}$$

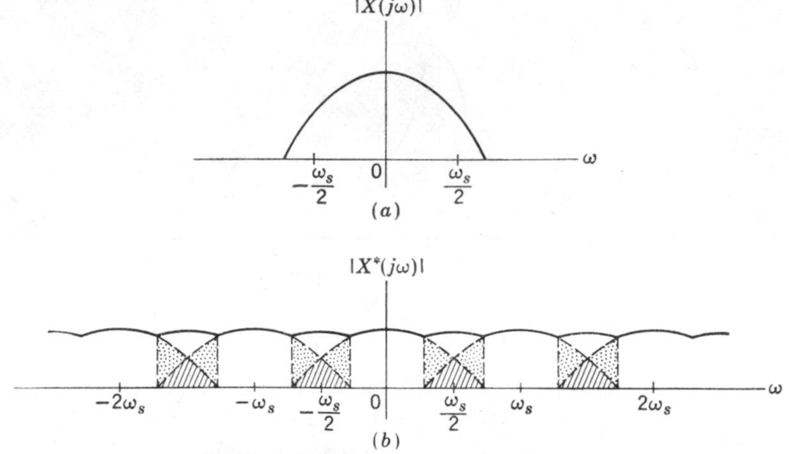

FIG. 4.1-6. Frequency spectrum of sampler output when the highest signal frequency is greater than half the sampling frequency.

where

$$x(nT) = \int_0^\infty x(t)\delta(t - nT)\,dt \tag{4.1-19}$$

represents the value of the nth sample. Since for physical systems $x(t) = 0$ when $t < 0$, the sampler output can be written as

$$x^*(t) = \sum_{n=0}^{\infty} x(nT)\delta(t - nT) \tag{4.1-20}$$

Taking the Laplace transform of Eq. (4.1-18) gives

$$X^*(s) = \mathcal{L}\{x^*(t)\} = \sum_{n=0}^{\infty} x(nT)\mathcal{L}\{\delta(t - nT)\} \tag{4.1-21}$$

or

$$X^*(s) = \sum_{n=0}^{\infty} x(nT)\epsilon^{-nTs} \tag{4.1-22}$$

In addition to Eq. (4.1-14), Eq. (4.1-22) is another way of describing the properties of the sampler. In Eq. (4.1-22), the Laplace transform of the sampler output is expressed in terms of the successive values of the input function at the sampling instants. This expression is particularly useful in the analysis of the over-all system containing a sampler.

Now let $X(s)$ and $\Delta_T(s)$ be the Laplace transforms of $x(t)$ and $\delta_T(t)$, respectively. The Laplace transform of Eq. (4.1-1), as given by the complex convolution, is

$$X^*(s) = X(s) * \Delta_T(s) \tag{4.1-23}$$

From Eq. (4.1-2),

$$\Delta_T(s) = \sum_{n=0}^{\infty} \epsilon^{-nTs} = 1 + \epsilon^{-Ts} + \epsilon^{-2Ts} + \cdots \tag{4.1-24}$$

which converges and is equal to

$$\Delta_T(s) = \frac{1}{1 - \epsilon^{-Ts}} \tag{4.1-25}$$

provided that

$$|\epsilon^{-Ts}| < 1 \tag{4.1-26}$$

Hence the Laplace transform of the sampler output is

$$X^*(s) = X(s) * \frac{1}{1 - \epsilon^{-Ts}} \tag{4.1-27}$$

It follows from the complex convolution theorem† that

$$X^*(s) = \frac{1}{2\pi j} \oint_{C_1} X(s - \chi) \frac{1}{1 - \epsilon^{-T\chi}} \, d\chi \tag{4.1-28}$$

where C_1 is the contour of integration which encloses all the poles of $\Delta_T(s)$, as shown in Fig. 4.1-7. The value of σ lies between $(c_1 - c_2)$ and 0, where

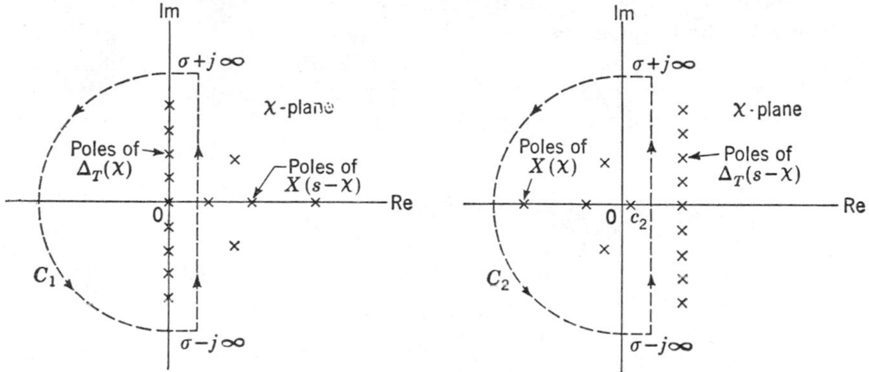

FIG. 4.1-7. Contour of integration for Eq. (4.1-28).

FIG. 4.1-8. Contour of integration for Eq. (4.1-36).

c_1 is the real part of the complex variable s ($s = c_1 + j\omega_1$), and c_2 is the largest real part of the poles of $X(s)$. The poles of $\Delta_T(s)$ can readily be determined by putting the denominator of Eq. (4.1-25) equal to zero and solving for s. Thus,

$$1 - \epsilon^{-Ts} = 0 \tag{4.1-29}$$

from which one obtains

$$s = \pm \frac{j2\pi n}{T} \tag{4.1-30}$$

where n is an integer. Since $\omega_s = 2\pi/T$, the poles of $\Delta_T(s)$ are

$$s = \pm jn\omega_s \tag{4.1-31}$$

† M. F. Gardner and J. L. Barnes, "Transients in Linear Systems," p. 275, John Wiley & Sons, Inc., New York, 1942.

The integral of Eq. (4.1-28) can readily be evaluated by the residue theorem,†

$$X^*(s) = \sum_k X(s - s_k) \,[\text{residue of } \Delta_T(\chi) \text{ at } \chi = s_k] \qquad (4.1\text{-}32)$$

where s_k is a pole of $\Delta_T(\chi)$ and the summation covers all the poles of $\Delta_T(\chi)$ inside the contour C_1. Equation (4.1-32) is true if $X(s - \chi)$ contains no poles on the imaginary axis of the χ plane. The residue of $\Delta_T(\chi)$ at $s_k = -jn\omega_s$ is

$$\lim_{\chi \to -jn\omega_s} \frac{\chi + jn\omega_s}{1 - \epsilon^{-T\chi}} = \lim_{\chi \to -jn\omega_s} \frac{1}{T\epsilon^{-T\chi}} = \frac{1}{T} \qquad (4.1\text{-}33)$$

Therefore, from Eq. (4.1-32) it follows that

$$X^*(s) = \frac{1}{T} \sum_{n=-\infty}^{\infty} X(s + jn\omega_s) \qquad (4.1\text{-}34)$$

This agrees with Eq. (4.1-14) derived above, which describes the sampler in terms of the frequency spectra of the input and the output signals, and indicates that sampling introduces complementary signals in addition to the desired primary signal. Combining Eq. (4.1-14) and Eq. (4.1-22) leads to a form of the Poisson summation rule:

$$\frac{1}{T} \sum_{n=-\infty}^{\infty} X(s + jn\omega) = \sum_{n=0}^{\infty} x(nT)\epsilon^{-nTs} \qquad (4.1\text{-}35)$$

According to the complex convolution theorem, Eq. (4.1-27) can also be written as

$$X^*(s) = \frac{1}{2\pi j} \oint_{C_2} X(\chi) \frac{1}{1 - \epsilon^{-T(s-\chi)}}\, d\chi \qquad (4.1\text{-}36)$$

where C_2 is the contour of integration which encloses all the poles of $X(\chi)$, as shown in Fig. 4.1-8. Applying the residue theorem yields

$$X^*(s) = \sum_k \text{residues} \left[\frac{1}{1 - \epsilon^{-(s-\chi)T}} X(\chi) \right] \text{at } \chi = s_k \qquad (4.1\text{-}37)$$

in which s_k is a pole of $X(\chi)$ and the summation covers all the poles of $X(\chi)$ inside the contour C_2 of the χ plane. In Fig. 4.1-8, $c_1 > \sigma > c_2$, $s = c_1 + j\omega_1$ and c_2 is the largest real part of the poles of $X(\chi)$. If $X(\chi)$ contains no multiple poles, Eq. (4.1-37) reduces to

$$X^*(s) = \sum_k \frac{1}{1 - \epsilon^{-(s-s_k)T}} \text{ residues of } X(\chi) \text{ at } \chi = s_k \qquad (4.1\text{-}38)$$

† L. A. Pipes, "Applied Mathematics for Engineers and Physicists," p. 525, McGraw-Hill Book Company, Inc., New York, 1958.

Furthermore, when $X(s)$ contains only simple poles and may be put in the form

$$X(s) = \frac{P(s)}{Q(s)} \tag{4.1-39}$$

where $P(s)$ and $Q(s)$ are rational polynomials in s with the order of $Q(s)$ higher than that of $P(s)$, the residue of $X(\chi)$ evaluated at $\chi = s_k$ is given by

$$\left.\frac{P(\chi)}{Q'(\chi)}\right|_{\chi=s_k} = \frac{P(s_k)}{Q'(s_k)} \tag{4.1-40}$$

in which

$$Q'(s_k) = \left.\frac{dQ(\chi)}{d\chi}\right|_{\chi=s_k} \tag{4.1-41}$$

is the derivative of $Q(\chi)$ evaluated at $\chi = s_k$. Hence it follows from Eqs. (4.1-38) and (4.1-40) that

$$X^*(s) = \sum_{k=1,2,3,\ldots n} \frac{P(s_k)}{Q'(s_k)} \frac{1}{1 - \epsilon^{Ts_k}\epsilon^{-Ts}} \tag{4.1-42}$$

where n is the number of poles of $X(\chi)$ inside the contour C_2. Since s_k and T are constants, Eq. (4.1-42) is a rational function of ϵ^{-Ts}.

A SPECIAL CASE. If $X(s)$ contains only an mth-order pole at $s = s_0$, and is of the form

$$X(s) = \frac{1}{(s - s_0)^m} \tag{4.1-43}$$

then from Eq. (4.1-37),

$$X^*(s) = \text{residue of } \left[\frac{1}{1 - \epsilon^{-(s-\chi)T}} \frac{1}{(\chi - s_0)^m}\right] \text{ at } \chi = s_0$$

$$= \frac{1}{(m-1)!} \frac{\partial^{m-1}}{\partial \chi^{m-1}} \left.\left(\frac{1}{1 - \epsilon^{-(s-\chi)T}}\right)\right|_{\chi=s_0} \tag{4.1-44}$$

Equation (4.1-37) together with Eqs. (4.1-14) and (4.1-22) are the three fundamental expressions describing a sampler and simple sampled-data systems. These equations provide three different ways of representing the relationship between the input and the output of a sampler. Once the input signal is known, the $\mathfrak{L}$ transform of the sampled output signal and the frequency characteristics can be computed. This facilitates the analysis of sampled-data control systems by frequency response and other related techniques. In fact, these three equations are of fundamental importance in the analysis of sampled-data and digital systems and will be applied frequently in the sections to follow. As an illustration, a simple example is presented below.

EXAMPLE 4.1-1. If the input signal to a sampler is

$$x(t) = \epsilon^{-at} \tag{4.1-45}$$

determine the $\mathcal{L}$ transform of the output signal of the sampler which operates with a sampling period T.

The $\mathcal{L}$ transform of Eq. (4.1-45) is

$$X(s) = \frac{1}{s + a} \tag{4.1-46}$$

Then, making use of Eq. (4.1-14) yields

$$X^*(s) = \frac{1}{T} \sum_{n=-\infty}^{\infty} \frac{1}{s + jn\omega_s + a}$$

$$= \frac{1}{T} \sum_{n=-\infty}^{\infty} \frac{1}{s + j2\pi n/T + a} \tag{4.1-47}$$

Since the value of the nth sample of $x(t)$ is $x(nT) = \epsilon^{-anT}$, from Eq. (4.1-22) it is obtained that

$$X^*(s) = \sum_{n=0}^{\infty} \epsilon^{-anT}\epsilon^{-nTs}$$

$$= 1 + \epsilon^{-(s+a)T} + \epsilon^{-2(s+a)T} + \cdots$$

$$= \frac{1}{1 - \epsilon^{-(s+a)T}} \tag{4.1-48}$$

provided that

$$|\epsilon^{-(s+a)T}| < 1$$

Application of Eq. (4.1-37) or (4.1-38) leads to

$$X^*(s) = \frac{1}{1 - \epsilon^{-(s-s_k)T}} \text{ residue of } X(\chi) \text{ at } \chi = s_k = -a$$

Since the residue of $X(\chi) = 1/(\chi + a)$ at $\chi = -a$ is unity, the $\mathcal{L}$ transform of the sampler output is given by

$$X^*(s) = \frac{1}{1 - \epsilon^{-(s+a)T}} \tag{4.1-49}$$

which is identical to the expression derived from Eq. (4.1-22).

4.2. Comparison between Continuous-data and Sampled-data Systems. In view of the fact that control engineers are quite familiar with the analysis of continuous-data systems, as an aid to the visualization and understanding of pulsed-data systems the similarities between these two types of control systems are reviewed and compared.

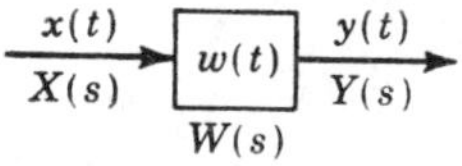

FIG. 4.2-1. Block diagram of a continuous-data system.

Continuous-data System.[2] To outline briefly some fundamental characteristics of continuous-data systems, reference is made to the system of Fig. 4.2-1, in which $x(t)$ and $y(t)$ are the input and the output signals and $w(t)$ is the weighting function (or the impulse response) of the system. Then the output and the input are related by the *convolution integral*

$$y(t) = \int_0^t x(\tau)w(t - \tau)\, d\tau \tag{4.2-1a}$$

or

$$y(t) = \int_0^t w(\tau)x(t - \tau)\, d\tau \tag{4.2-1b}$$

When the input is a unit-impulse function,

$$x(t) = \delta(t) \tag{4.2-2}$$

the output is equal to, by definition, the weighting function of the system, that is,

$$y(t) = w(t) \tag{4.2-3}$$

When the input is a unit-step function,

$$x(t) = u(t) \tag{4.2-4}$$

it follows from Eq. (4.2-1) that the system response is

$$y(t) = \int_0^t w(\tau)\, d\tau \tag{4.2-5}$$

A continuous-data system is stable, if $\int_0^\infty |w(t)|\, dt$ is finite. It should be pointed out that this definition of stability excludes the case that the weighting function is a constant and the system is a simple integrator.

For stable systems, the frequency function and the time function of a signal are related by

$$A(\omega) = \int_0^\infty y(t) \cos \omega t\, dt \tag{4.2-6}$$

and

$$B(\omega) = -\int_0^\infty y(t) \sin \omega t\, dt \tag{4.2-7}$$

in which $A(\omega)$ and $B(\omega)$ are, respectively, the real part and the imaginary part of the frequency function $Y(j\omega)$ of the signal $y(t)$. Equations (4.2-6) and (4.2-7) can readily be derived from the following expression:

$$Y(j\omega) = \int_0^\infty y(t)\epsilon^{-j\omega t}\, dt \tag{4.2-8}$$

In view of Euler's equation,

$$\epsilon^{-j\omega t} = \cos \omega t - j \sin \omega t \tag{4.2-9}$$

Equation (4.2-8) reduces to

$$Y(j\omega) = \int_0^\infty y(t) \cos \omega t\, dt - j \int_0^\infty y(t) \sin \omega t\, dt \tag{4.2-10}$$

of which the real part is given by Eq. (4.2-6) and the imaginary part by Eq. (4.2-7). Just as the signal $y(t)$ may be represented graphically by being plotted in the time domain, the equivalent functions $A(\omega)$ and $B(\omega)$ may be plotted in the frequency domain. The plots of $A(\omega)$ and $B(\omega)$ as functions of frequency are more commonly known as the spectrum representation of the signal $y(t)$. In fact, a knowledge of the frequency spectrum is essentially equivalent to a knowledge of the time function. When the frequency function is known, the time function of the signal $y(t)$ can be derived by taking the inverse Fourier transform of Eq. (4.2-6) or (4.2-7). Thus,

$$y(t) = \frac{1}{2\pi} \int_0^\infty A(\omega) \cos t\omega \, d\omega \tag{4.2-11}$$

As shown in the following paragraphs, in sampled-data systems there exist relationships similar to those for the continuous-data systems discussed above.

Sampled-data System. Various block-diagram representations of a simple, linear, sampled-data system are shown in Fig. 4.2-2, in which the input

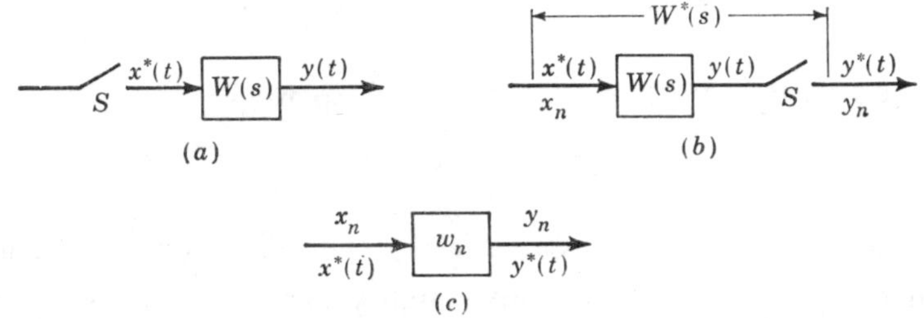

FIG. 4.2-2. Various block-diagram representations of a pulsed-data system.

data are intermittently supplied to the system at a uniform rate. The system parameters do not vary with time, and the system output $y(t)$ depends linearly upon the input data received previously. In Fig. 4.2-2, $x^*(t)$ and $y^*(t)$ are the pulsed input and output signals, and w_n is the weighting sequence of the sampled-data system. x_n and y_n are the values of the input and the output at the sampling instant nT such that

$$x_n = x(nT) \tag{4.2-12}$$

and

$$y_n = y(nT) \tag{4.2-13}$$

The pulsed input function $x^*(t)$ and its value at the nth-sampling instant $x(nT)$ are related by

$$x^*(t) = \sum_{n=0}^{\infty} x(nT)\delta(t - nT) \tag{4.2-14}$$

Similarly, $y^*(t)$ and $y(nT)$ are related by

$$y^*(t) = \sum_{n=0}^{\infty} y(nT)\delta(t - nT) \tag{4.2-15}$$

Referring to Fig. 4.2-2a, in contrast to Eqs. (4.2-1a) and (4.2-1b) the continuous output function of the pulsed-data system can be described by a *convolution summation*, since the input is a discrete function of time. Thus, for $0 \leq t \leq nT$, the output $y(t)$ is given by

$$y(t) = \sum_{k=0}^{n} w(t - kT)x(kT) \tag{4.2-16a}$$

but

$$y(t) \neq \sum_{k=0}^{n} x(t - kT)w(kT) \tag{4.2-16b}$$

In Fig. 4.2-2*a*, the pulsed-data input $x^*(t)$ is a train of ideal pulses with various amplitudes. Then the response to the input $x^*(t)$ is the sum of the individual impulse responses. That is, for $0 \leq t \leq nT$,

$$y(t) = w(t)x(0) + w(t - T)x(T) + w(t - 2T)x(2T) + \cdots + w(t - kT)x(kT) + \cdots + w(t - nT)x(nT) \tag{4.2-17}$$

which may be put in the form of Eq. (4.2-16*a*).

At the sampling instant nT, Eq. (4.2-16) yields

$$y(nT) = \sum_{k=0}^{n} w(nT - kT)x(kT) \tag{4.2-18a}$$

or

$$y(nT) = \sum_{k=0}^{n} x(nT - kT)w(kT) \tag{4.2-18b}$$

In view of Eqs. (4.2-12) and (4.2-13) the above two equations can also be written as

$$y_n = \sum_{k=0}^{n} x_k w_{n-k} \tag{4.2-19a}$$

or

$$y_n = \sum_{k=0}^{n} w_k x_{n-k} \tag{4.2-19b}$$

In comparison with Eqs. (4.2-1*a*) and (4.2-1*b*), w_n of the sampled-data system corresponds to $w(t)$ of the continuous-data system. So, w_n is often referred to as the *weighting sequence* of the sampled-data system. w_n and $w(t)$ are related by

$$w_n = w(nT) = w(t)\big|_{t=nT} \tag{4.2-20}$$

When the input is an ideal pulse of unit height which may be represented by an equivalent impulse of unit strength, it is seen that

$$x_{n-k} = \begin{cases} 1 & \text{for } k = n \\ 0 & \text{otherwise} \end{cases} \tag{4.2-21}$$

and Eq. (4.2-18*b*) leads to

$$y_n = w_n \tag{4.2-22}$$

that is, the pulsed-data output is equal to the weighting sequence of the system. If the input is a sampled unit-step function, then

$$x_{n-k} = \begin{cases} 1 & \text{for } 0 \leq k \leq n \\ 0 & \text{for } k > n \end{cases} \tag{4.2-23}$$

and Eq. (4.2-18b) yields

$$y_n = \sum_{k=0}^{n} w_k \tag{4.2-24}$$

Clearly, Eqs. (4.2-22) and (4.2-24) for the pulsed-data system bear a close resemblance to Eqs. (4.2-3) and (4.2-5) for the continuous-data system. Furthermore, with the exception of a simple pulsed-data integrator, a sampled-data system is stable, if $\sum_{n=0}^{\infty} |w_n|$ is finite.

The frequency characteristics of the pulsed-data output signal $y^*(t)$ are briefly discussed below. In view of Eq. (4.1-22),

$$Y^*(s) = \sum_{n=0}^{\infty} y(nT)\epsilon^{-nTs} \tag{4.2-25}$$

Substituting $j\omega$ for s in Eq. (4.2-25) yields

$$Y^*(j\omega) = \sum_{n=0}^{\infty} y(nT)\epsilon^{-jnT\omega} \tag{4.2-26}$$

Since $Y^*(j\omega)$ is a complex function in ω,

$$\sum_{n=0}^{\infty} y(nT)\epsilon^{-jnT\omega} = A^*(\omega) + jB^*(\omega) \tag{4.2-27}$$

where $A^*(\omega)$ is the real part of $Y^*(j\omega)$ and $B^*(\omega)$ is the imaginary part. In view of Euler's equation [Eq. (4.2-9)], Eq. (4.2-27) may be written as

$$A^*(\omega) + jB^*(\omega) = \sum_{n=0}^{\infty} y(nT)(\cos nT\omega - j \sin nT\omega) \tag{4.2-28}$$

Equating the real part and the imaginary part of Eq. (4.2-28) leads to

$$A^*(\omega) = \sum_{n=0}^{\infty} y(nT) \cos nT\omega \tag{4.2-29}$$

and

$$B^*(\omega) = -\sum_{n=0}^{\infty} y(nT) \sin nT\omega \tag{4.2-30}$$

These two equations resemble Eqs. (4.2-6) and (4.2-7) for the corresponding continuous-data system. Furthermore, Eqs. (4.2-29) and (4.2-30) reveal that both $A^*(\omega)$ and $B^*(\omega)$ are periodic functions of ω. This can be expected since, as shown in Sec. 4.1, $Y^*(j\omega)$ is a periodic function of ω. Equation (4.2-29) expresses the real part of $Y^*(j\omega)$ in a Fourier cosine series of ω, and Eq. (4.2-30) expands the imaginary part of $Y^*(j\omega)$ in a Fourier sine series. The coefficients of the Fourier series are the output of the sampled-data system at successive sampling instants. These Fourier coefficients are given by

$$y(nT) = \frac{4}{\omega_s} \int_0^{\omega_s/2} A^*(\omega) \cos nT\omega \, d\omega \tag{4.2-31}$$

or

$$y(nT) = -\frac{4}{\omega_s} \int_0^{\omega_s/2} B^*(\omega) \sin nT\omega \, d\omega \tag{4.2-32}$$

TABLE 4.2-1

	Continuous-data system	Pulsed-data system
1. Input and output:		
$\delta(t)$	$y(t) = w(t)$	$y_n = w_n$
$u(t)$	$y(t) = \int_0^t w(\tau)\, d\tau$	$y_n = \sum_{k=0}^{n} w_k$
$x(t)$	$y(t) = \int_0^t w(\tau)x(t-\tau)\, d\tau$	$y_n = \sum_{k=0}^{n} w_k x_{n-k}$
	$y(t) = \int_0^t x(\tau)w(t-\tau)\, d\tau$	$y_n = \sum_{k=0}^{n} x_k w_{n-k}$
2. Frequency functions	$Y(j\omega) = A(\omega) + jB(\omega)$	$Y^*(j\omega) = A^*(\omega) + jB^*(\omega)$
	$A(\omega) = \int_0^\infty y(t) \cos \omega t\, dt$	$A^*(\omega) = \sum_{n=0}^{\infty} y(nT) \cos nT\omega$
	$B(\omega) = -\int_0^\infty y(t) \sin \omega t\, dt$	$B^*(\omega) = -\sum_{n=0}^{\infty} y(nT) \sin nT\omega$
3. Time functions	$y(t) = \frac{1}{2\pi} \int_0^\infty A(\omega) \cos t\omega\, d\omega$	$y(nT) = \frac{2}{\pi} \int_0^\pi A^*(\theta/T) \cos n\theta\, d\theta$
		$y(nT) = -\frac{2}{\pi} \int_0^\pi B^*(\theta/T) \sin n\theta\, d\theta$
4. Stability condition	$\int_0^\infty \lvert w(t)\rvert\, dt < \infty$	$\sum_{n=0}^{\infty} \lvert w_n\rvert < \infty$
5. Described by	Differential equations	Difference equations

The substitution of θ for ωT reduces the above equations to

$$y(nT) = \frac{2}{\pi} \int_0^\pi A^*(\theta/T) \cos n\theta \, d\theta \tag{4.2-33}$$

and

$$y(nT) = -\frac{2}{\pi} \int_0^\pi B^*(\theta/T) \sin n\theta \, d\theta \tag{4.2-34}$$

Therefore, when the frequency function of the pulsed output of a sampled-data system is obtained either analytically or experimentally, one can calculate the output sequence as the coefficients of the expansion of the real part of the frequency function in a Fourier cosine series or the expansion of the imaginary part in a Fourier sine series. This provides one method for evaluating the transient response of sampled-data control systems at sampling instants. Equations (4.2-33) and (4.2-34) are particularly useful when the frequency functions $A^*(\omega)$ and $B^*(\omega)$ can only be obtained from experimental data. Examples illustrating the application of these two equations are presented in Sec. 4.4.

In summary, the similarities between continuous-data and sampled-data systems mentioned above are tabulated in Table 4.2-1 for further reference. Other properties of sampled-data systems are discussed in detail in the following sections.

4.3. Frequency Response and Transfer Function of Sampled-data and Digital Control Systems. Of the many approaches to the design of servomechanisms the frequency-response method is the most popular and widely used. A very large number of papers and books have been written on the subject of frequency-response techniques. The frequency-response approach has proved extremely effective in dealing with problems in continuous-data control systems. Control engineers are most familiar with this method of analyzing and designing control systems. Besides, the extension of the frequency-response method to digital and pulsed-data control systems is recommended by the fact that the continuous-data signal often occupies the larger portion of a digital or sampled-data control system and that linear digital programs of a computer can readily be described by transfer functions. In view of these reasons, the conventional frequency-response techniques are first applied to the analysis of pulsed-data control systems.

Open-loop Systems. Shown in Fig. 4.3-1 is an elementary open-loop sampled-data system, in which the output $y(t)$ is sampled synchronously with the input $x(t)$ at a constant rate to yield a pulsed time function $y^*(t)$.

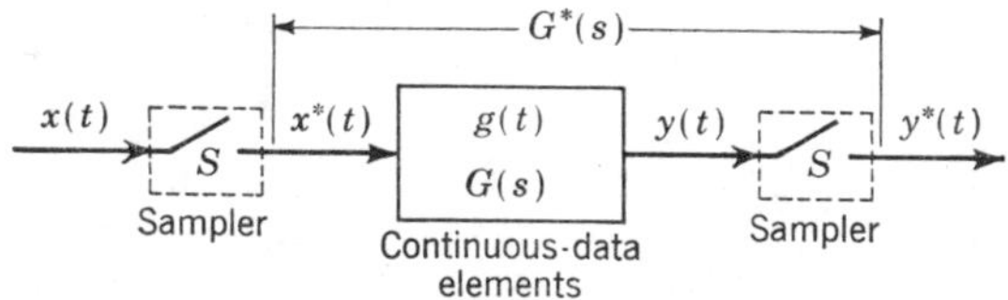

FIG. 4.3-1. An open-loop sampled-data system.

In Fig. 4.3-1 $G(s)$ is the transfer function of the continuous part of the system, $g(t)$ is the impulse response of system $G(s)$, and $x^*(t)$ is the output of the first sampler. Then, from Eq. (4.2-16a) the continuous output of $G(s)$ is given by

$$y(t) = \sum_{k=0}^{\infty} g(t - kT)x(kT) \tag{4.3-1}$$

Taking the Laplace transform of both sides of Eq. (4.3-1) yields

$$Y(s) = \int_0^\infty \left[\sum_{k=0}^{\infty} g(t - kT)x(kT) \right] \epsilon^{-st}\, dt \tag{4.3-2}$$

Rearranging and substituting $d(t - kT)$ for dt lead to

$$Y(s) = \sum_{k=0}^{\infty} x(kT)\epsilon^{-kTs} \int_0^\infty g(t - kT)\epsilon^{-s(t-kT)}\, d(t - kT) \tag{4.3-3}$$

The lower limit of the integral is 0 because $g(t - kT) = 0$ for $t < kT$. Making use of Eq. (4.1-22) and the definition of the Laplace transform gives the Laplace transform of the output $y(t)$ as

$$Y(s) = G(s)X^*(s) \tag{4.3-4}$$

Equation (4.3-4) implies that the Laplace transform of the system output $y(t)$ is equal to the product of the Laplace transform of the pulsed input and the transfer function of the system. The frequency response is obtained from Eq. (4.3-4) by substituting $j\omega$ for s, thus,

$$G(j\omega) = \frac{Y(j\omega)}{X^*(j\omega)} \tag{4.3-5}$$

It is interesting to note the similarity between Eq. (4.3-5) and the familiar relationship

$$G(j\omega) = \frac{Y(j\omega)}{X(j\omega)} \tag{4.3-6}$$

which would be the frequency response of the system if the samplers were absent.

THE STARRED TRANSFORM OF THE OUTPUT. By making use of Eq. (4.1-14), the pulsed output of the system can readily be derived. Applying the expression of Eq. (4.1-14) and Eq. (4.3-4) yields

$$Y^*(s) = \frac{1}{T} \sum_{n=-\infty}^{\infty} G(s + jn\omega_s)X^*(s + jn\omega_s) \tag{4.3-7}$$

The periodicity property of $X^*(s + jn\omega_s)$ enables Eq. (4.3-7) to be written as

$$Y^*(s) = X^*(s)\left[\frac{1}{T} \sum_{n=-\infty}^{\infty} G(s + jn\omega_s)\right] \tag{4.3-8}$$

According to Eq. (4.1-14), therefore, the Laplace transform of the system output $Y^*(s)$ is given by

$$Y^*(s) = G^*(s)X^*(s) \tag{4.3-9}$$

and the frequency function is

$$Y^*(j\omega) = G^*(j\omega)X^*(j\omega) \tag{4.3-10}$$

where $G^*(s)$ is the over-all transfer function of the sampled-data system and is defined as

$$G^*(s) = \frac{1}{T} \sum_{n=-\infty}^{\infty} G(s + jn\omega_s) \tag{4.3-11}$$

Equation (4.3-9) implies that the Laplace transform of the pulsed output $y^*(t)$ is equal to the product of the Laplace transform of the pulsed input and the over-all transfer function of the sampled-data system. The frequency-response function of the system follows immediately from Eq. (4.3-10),

$$G^*(j\omega) = \frac{Y^*(j\omega)}{X^*(j\omega)} \tag{4.3-12}$$

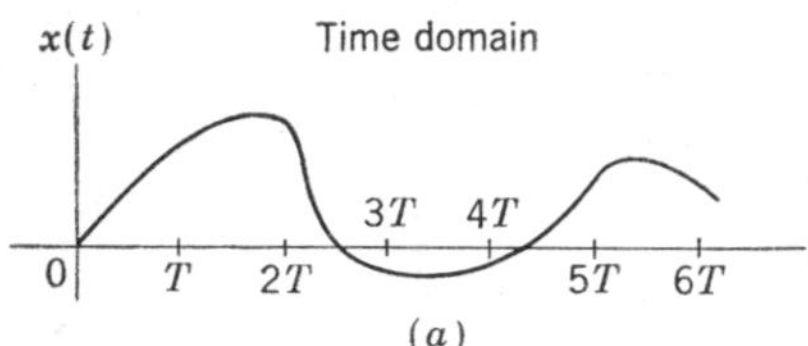

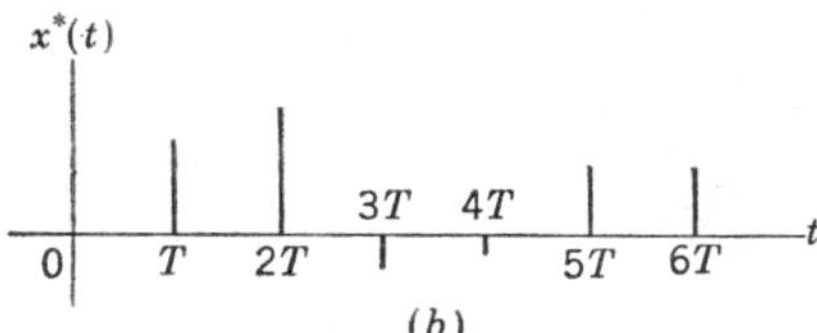

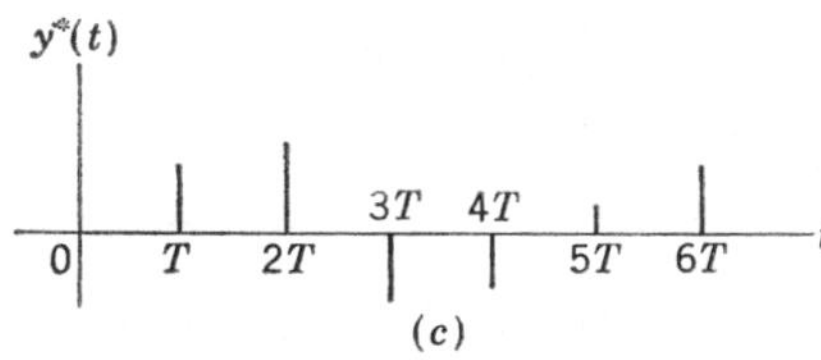

FIG. 4.3-2. Time functions.

In contrast, Eq. (4.3-12) is similar to the expression of Eq. (4.3-6) for the system without the samplers.

The significance of sampling in a system is further explained in Figs. 4.3-2 and 4.3-3 in terms of the time functions and the corresponding frequency spectra of the input and the output signals. The frequency spectrum of the system output, which is obtainable through the use of Eq. (4.3-10), comprises the desired signal spectrum centered at zero frequency, and sidebands composed of the primary component shifted by the sampling frequency and its multiples (Fig. 4.3-3*c*). The sidebands or complementary components can be removed by filtering, provided that the input signal contains no component of frequency greater than half the sampling frequency as demonstrated in Fig. 4.3-4.

Shown in Fig. 4.3-5*a* is an elementary digital control system which can be represented by the equivalent sampled-data system of Fig. 4.3-5*b*, if the quantization error is neglected. In Fig. 4.3-5*a*, A/D stands for the analog-to-digital converter and D/A denotes the digital-to-analog conversion device. The principles of analog-digital conversion are discussed in Chap. 8.

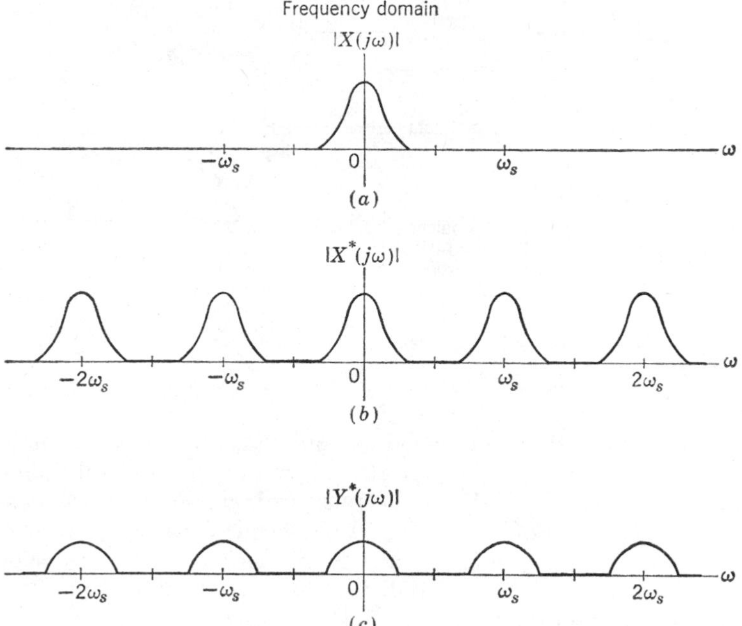

FIG. 4.3-3. Frequency spectra.

The pulsed-data network of Fig. 4.3-5*b* is equivalent to the program designed for the digital computer of Fig. 4.3-5*a*, including the time delay in encoding which is usually very small in comparison with the sampling period. In digital control systems, samples of the signal are obtained frequently enough so that the signal is completely specified by the samples, but only certain discrete levels of amplitude of the sample are allowed. Thus, the input and the output of the computer are in numerically coded form, whereas the signals flowing through the equivalent pulsed-data network are sampled data, but not coded. In other words, the signals flowing

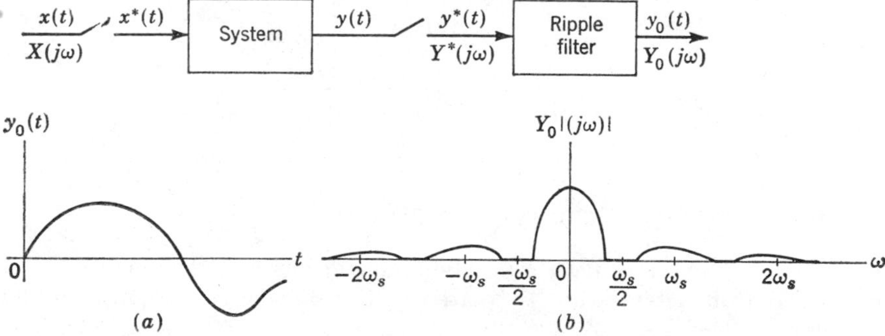

FIG. 4.3-4. Desired signal recovered by filtering.

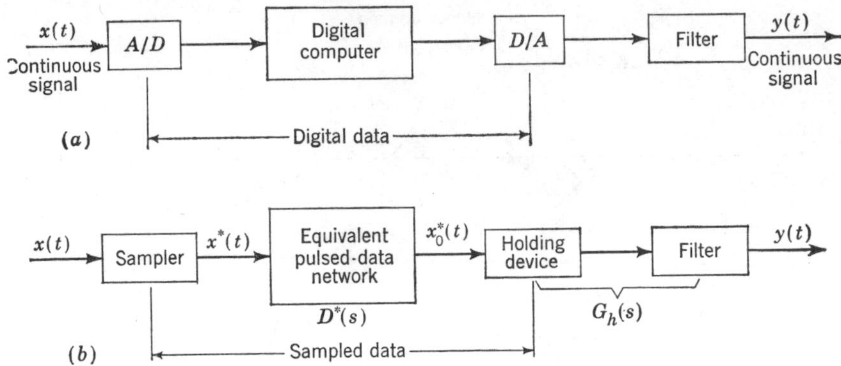

FIG. 4.3-5. Equivalent digital system (quantization error being ignored).

through the computer are pulse-code modulated, whereas the signals flowing through the equivalent pulsed-data network are pulse-amplitude modulated. The conversion of a signal into pulse-code-modulated form generally involves the processes of sampling and amplitude quantization. Both the sampling and the quantizing operations are performed by the analog-to-digital converter, which is essentially a combined sampler, quantizer, and encoder. Thus, the digital system of Fig. 4.3-5*a* is more precisely represented by the equivalent sampled-data system of Fig. 4.3-6*a*. The analog-to-digital converter is represented by a sampler followed by a quantizer; the program of the digital computer, by the equivalent pulsed-data network; and the digital-to-analog converter, by a hold circuit. As discussed in Chap. 3, the process of quantizing a signal introduces a quantization error into the system, and the quantizer behaves as a noise generator. Thus, the system of Fig. 4.3-6*a* may also be described by the block diagram of Fig. 4.3-6*b*, where quantization error is introduced to the input of the

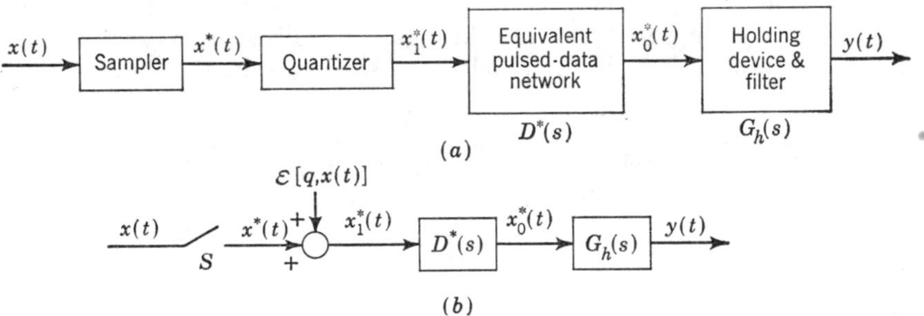

FIG. 4.3-6. Equivalent representation of a digital system.

equivalent pulsed-data network. The above discussions demonstrate that digital control systems can be treated in the same way as sampled-data systems.

With reference to Fig. 4.3-6*b*, the transfer function of the equivalent pulsed-data network is $D^*(s)$ and that of the holding device and the ripple filter is $G_h(s)$. The transfer function $D^*(s)$ includes the finite delay resulting from encoding and computation. Making use of Eqs. (4.3-4) and (4.3-9) yields the input-output relationship for the equivalent pulsed-data network (or the digital computer) as

$$X_0^*(s) = D^*(s)X_1^*(s) \tag{4.3-13}$$

and that for the holding device and ripple filter as

$$Y(s) = G_h(s)X_0^*(s) \tag{4.3-14}$$

Substituting Eq. (4.3-13) into Eq. (4.3-14) gives

$$Y(s) = D^*(s)G_h(s)X_1^*(s) \tag{4.3-15}$$

Moreover, if the quantization error in the digital computer may be ignored, Eq. (4.3-15) becomes

$$Y(s) = D^*(s)G_h(s)X^*(s) \tag{4.3-16}$$

Equation (4.3-16) describes the mathematical relationship between the input and the output of this digital control system with negligible quantization error.

Closed-loop Systems. Sampled-data feedback control systems have a variety of forms, a basic type of which is shown in Fig. 4.3-7. It illustrates

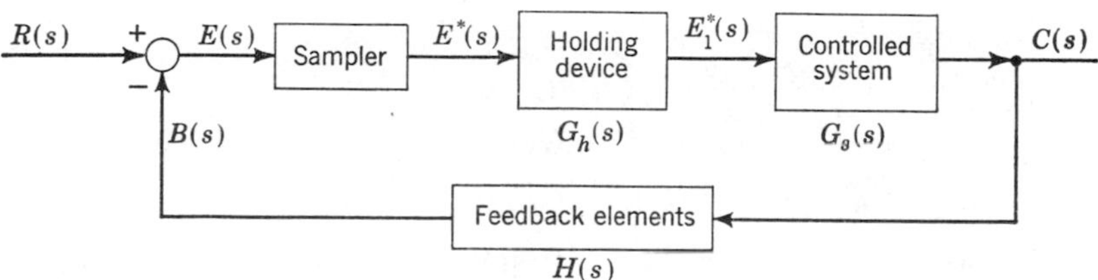

Fig. 4.3-7. Basic single-loop sampled-data system.

an error-sampled-data system in which the sampling is performed only upon the actuating error signals. $G_h(s)$, $G_s(s)$, and $H(s)$ are the transfer functions of the holding device, the controlled system, and the feedback elements, respectively. In most control systems the complementary signal components introduced by the operation of sampling must be removed before the control signal reaches the output stage of the controlled system. A large portion of these complementary signals is screened by components in the controlled system which behave as low-pass filters. For accomplishing better smoothing of the ripples, a holding device is often employed in sampled-data control systems to hold or to clamp the sampled values as illustrated in Fig. 4.3-7. The holding device converts the sampled control signal into continuous form which is an approximate reproduction of the desired actuating error signal before it is fed into the controlled system. One of the simplest holding devices is the zero-order holding circuit or boxcar generator, in which the value of an input pulse (i.e., the strength of its equivalent impulse) is held constant until the arrival of the next sampling pulse. The waveforms of the input and the output of a zero-order holding circuit are shown in Fig. 4.3-8.

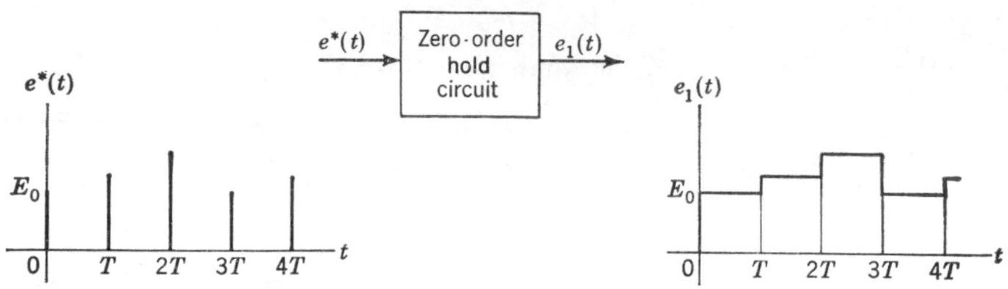

FIG. 4.3-8. Waveforms of the input and output of a zero-order hold circuit.

From Eq. (4.1-1), the sampled actuating error signal is given as

$$e^*(t) = \delta_T(t)e(t) \tag{4.3-17}$$

Making use of Eq. (4.1-14) yields the Laplace transform of the sampled actuating error signal as

$$E^*(s) = \frac{1}{T} \sum_{n=-\infty}^{\infty} E(s + jn\omega_s) \tag{4.3-18}$$

Reference to Fig. 4.3-7 indicates that

$$C(s) = G(s)E^*(s) \tag{4.3-19}$$

where

$$G(s) = G_h(s)G_s(s) \tag{4.3-20}$$

is the transfer function for the continuous-data elements in the forward path of the system. The block diagram of Fig. 4.3-7 can be redrawn as shown in Fig. 4.3-9 with the sampler in the forward path being replaced

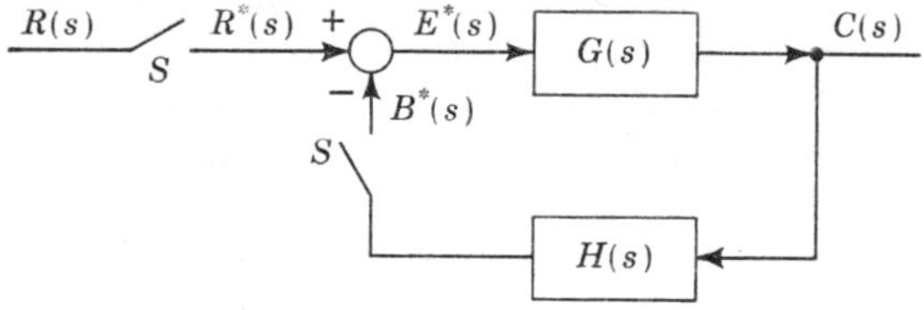

FIG. 4.3-9. Equivalent representation of the system of Fig. 4.3-7.

by a sampler in the feedback path and a sampler outside the control loop. An inspection of the block diagram of Fig. 4.3-9 reveals that

$$E^*(s) = R^*(s) - B^*(s) \tag{4.3-21}$$

$$B^*(s) = GH^*(s)E^*(s) \tag{4.3-22}$$

Substituting Eq. (4.3-22) into Eq. (4.3-21) and rearranging yield

$$E^*(s) = \frac{R^*(s)}{1 + GH^*(s)} \tag{4.3-23}$$

It follows from Eq. (4.3-18) that

$$E^*(s) = \frac{T^{-1} \sum_{n=-\infty}^{\infty} R(s + jn\omega_s)}{1 + T^{-1} \sum_{n=-\infty}^{\infty} GH(s + jn\omega_s)} \tag{4.3-24}$$

By substituting Eq. (4.3-24) into Eq. (4.3-19), one obtains the Laplace transform of the output of the sampled-data system as

$$C(s) = \frac{G(s)\, T^{-1} \sum_{n=-\infty}^{\infty} R(s + jn\omega_s)}{1 + T^{-1} \sum_{n=-\infty}^{\infty} GH(s + jn\omega_s)} \tag{4.3-25}$$

and the frequency function for the system output as

$$C(j\omega) = \frac{G(j\omega)\, T^{-1} \sum_{n=-\infty}^{\infty} R(\overline{j\omega + n\omega_s})}{1 + T^{-1} \sum_{n=-\infty}^{\infty} GH(\overline{j\omega + n\omega_s})} \tag{4.3-26}$$

The function

$$GH^*(s) = \frac{1}{T} \sum_{n=-\infty}^{\infty} GH(s + jn\omega_s) \tag{4.3-27}$$

is defined as the loop-gain function or the open-loop transfer function of a sampled-data control system. Equations (4.3-24) and (4.3-25) form the basic representations characterizing the sampled-data feedback control system of Fig. 4.3-7.

Clearly, Eqs. (4.3-24) and (4.3-25) for the sampled-data feedback control system bear a close resemblance to those equations which would describe the control system in the absence of the sampler. With a view to helping the visualizing and understanding of the behavior of sampled-data feedback systems and the significance of the transfer functions describing them, the similarities between these two types of feedback control systems are compared and tabulated in Fig. 4.3-10.

For sampled-data feedback control systems, it does not seem possible to express the ratios $E(s)/R(s)$ and $C(s)/R(s)$ in terms of the transfer functions of the system components, since the sampler is a multiplying device and sampling is a modulation process, and thus cannot be described by a

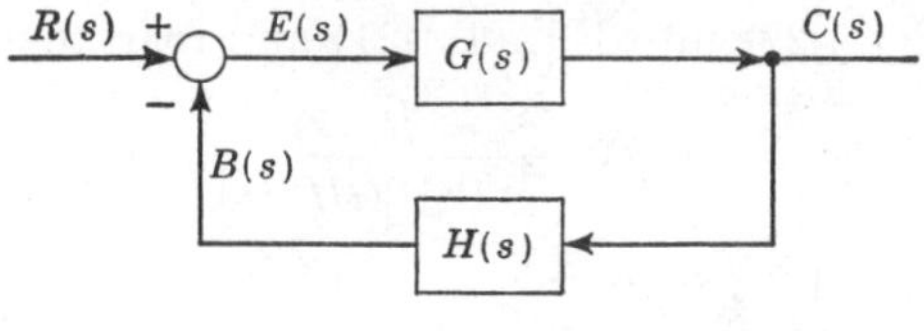

Equivalent block diagram

Transfer function

R(s) → $\frac{1}{1+GH(s)}$ → E(s)

$$\frac{E(s)}{R(s)} = \frac{1}{1+GH(s)}$$

R(s) → $\frac{1}{1+GH(s)}$ → G(s) → C(s)

$$\frac{C(s)}{R(s)} = \frac{G(s)}{1+GH(s)}$$

(a)

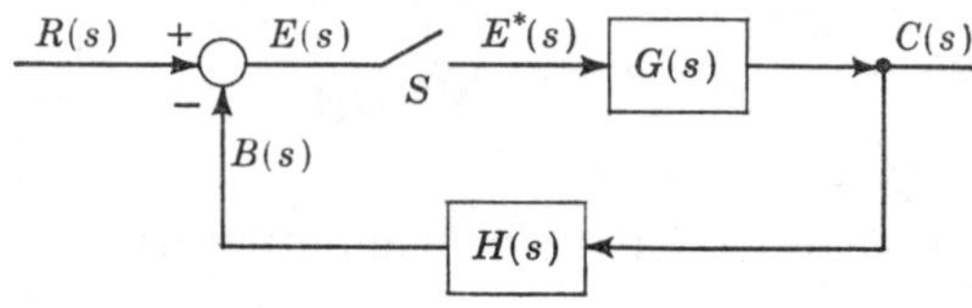

Equivalent block diagram

Transfer function

R(s) S R*(s) → $\frac{1}{1+T^{-1}\sum_{n=-\infty}^{\infty} GH(s+jn\omega_s)}$ → E*(s)

$$\frac{E^*(s)}{R^*(s)} = \frac{1}{1+T^{-1}\sum_{n=-\infty}^{\infty} GH(s+jn\omega_s)}$$

R(s) S R*(s) → $\frac{1}{1+T^{-1}\sum_{n=-\infty}^{\infty} GH(s+jn\omega_s)}$ → G(s) → C(s)

$$\frac{C(s)}{R^*(s)} = \frac{G(s)}{1+T^{-1}\sum_{n=-\infty}^{\infty} GH(s+jn\omega_s)}$$

(b)

FIG. 4.3-10. Block-diagram representations and transfer functions of continuous-data and sampled-data feedback control systems.

simple transfer function. Instead, for error-sampled systems the ratios

$$\frac{E^*(s)}{\sum_{n=-\infty}^{\infty} R(s+jn\omega_s)} \quad \text{and} \quad \frac{C(s)}{\sum_{n=-\infty}^{\infty} R(s+jn\omega_s)} \tag{4.3-28}$$

are found, which can be expressed in compact forms similar to those for the corresponding ratios $E(s)/R(s)$ and $C(s)/R(s)$ of a continuous-data feedback control system. In the analysis of such a system, its behavior is frequently described and interpreted by the polar plot of

$$GH(j\omega) \tag{4.3-29}$$

In contrast, the performance of a sampled-data feedback control system can be described by the polar plot of

$$\frac{1}{T} \sum_{n=-\infty}^{\infty} GH(\overline{j\omega + n\omega_s}) \tag{4.3-30}$$

which is given in Eq. (4.3-26). In most cases, in practice, these polar plots can readily be constructed, since the transfer function of the continuous part $GH(j\omega)$ has the properties of a low-pass filter and thus only a few terms of

$$GH^*(j\omega) = \frac{1}{T} \sum_{n=-\infty}^{\infty} GH(\overline{j\omega + n\omega_s}) \tag{4.3-31}$$

are enough for obtaining a useful picture describing the operation of the sampled-data system. In the right-hand member of Eq. (4.3-31) the function $GH(j\omega)$ would be the open-loop transfer function (or the loop-gain function) of the system if the sampler or the sampling operation were absent. A polar plot of Eq. (4.3-31) for various values of ω is commonly known as the frequency-characteristic locus or the Nyquist diagram for a sampled-data control system. The construction of the frequency-characteristic locus for a sampled-data system from the polar plot of $GH(j\omega)$ is explained in the next section.

4.4. Construction of Frequency-characteristic Locus. The polar plot of $GH(j\omega)$, which is the open-loop transfer function of the sampled-data feedback control system in the absence of the sampler, can readily be constructed according to well-known rules. The graphical representation of the frequency characteristic of the sampled-data control system can be plotted from the $T^{-1}GH(j\omega)$ locus of its continuous part, if the frequency-characteristic (or open-loop frequency-response) function is expressed in a series,

$$\begin{aligned}\frac{1}{T} \sum_{n=-\infty}^{\infty} & GH(\overline{j\omega + n\omega_s}) \\ &= \frac{1}{T}\left[GH(j\omega) + \sum_{n=1}^{\infty} GH(\overline{j\omega + n\omega_s}) + \sum_{n=1}^{\infty} GH(\overline{j\omega - n\omega_s})\right] \\ &= \frac{1}{T}[GH(j\omega) + GH(\overline{j\omega + \omega_s}) + GH(\overline{j\omega + 2\omega_s}) + \cdots \\ &\qquad + GH(\overline{j\omega - \omega_s}) + GH(\overline{j\omega - 2\omega_s}) + \cdots]\end{aligned} \tag{4.4-1}$$

and the frequency loci for the component functions are combined vectorially. The terms of the right-hand side of Eq. (4.4-1) represent the phasors drawn from the origin of the complex plane to points ω, $(\omega + \omega_s)$, $(\omega + 2\omega_s)$, . . . $(\omega - \omega_s)$, $(\omega - 2\omega_s)$, . . . , on the polar plot of $T^{-1}GH(j\omega)$, as shown in

Fig. 4.4-1. Equation (4.4-1) implies that the frequency-characteristic locus of

$$GH^*(j\omega) = \frac{1}{T} \sum_{n=-\infty}^{\infty} GH(\overline{j\omega + n\omega_s}) \tag{4.4-2}$$

can be derived from the sum of these phasors.

In view of the fact that $GH^*(j\omega)$ is a periodic function of frequency with a period $j\omega_s$, the polar plot of $GH^*(j\omega)$ repeats itself when the frequency ω is increased by ω_s. Thus, the polar plot of $GH^*(j\omega)$ for the frequency range from $-\infty$ to $+\infty$ is identical with that for the frequency

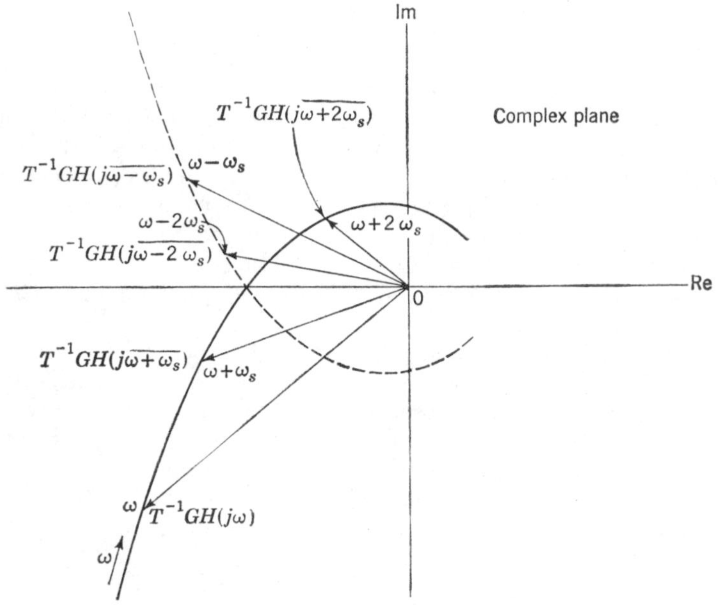

FIG. 4.4-1. Phasors of $T^{-1}GH(\overline{j\omega \pm n\omega_s})$.

range from 0 to ω_s. Furthermore, since the polar plot of $GH^*(j\omega)$ is symmetrical with respect to the real axis, the plot for the frequency range between $\omega_s/2$ and ω_s is the mirror image of the plot for the frequency range between 0 and $\omega_s/2$. As a result, in investigating the frequency characteristic of a sampled-data control system only the frequency range from 0 to $\omega_s/2$ is of interest. With the increase in frequency, the magnitude of $GH(j\omega)$ tends to zero, and consequently, for large values of n, $(\omega + n\omega_s)$ becomes large and the magnitude of $GH(\overline{j\omega + n\omega_s})$ is negligible. Here, ω lies in the range from 0 to $\omega_s/2$. When constructing the Nyquist diagram of a sampled-data control system from the polar plot of $T^{-1}GH(j\omega)$, it is, therefore, possible to limit the computation to the low-frequency section of the graph and usually to a small number of phasor components of Eq. (4.4-1). The number of phasors needed generally depends upon the bandwidth of the system and usually can be seen in the construction process. In most cases, several terms in the vectorial summation are sufficient. When the sampling frequency ω_s is high in comparison with the bandwidth of the system, Eq. (4.4-1) can be approximated by the first three terms, as given in Eq. (4.4-3), without much loss of accuracy.

$$\frac{1}{T}\sum_{n=-\infty}^{\infty} GH(j\overline{\omega + n\omega_s}) \approx \frac{1}{T}GH(j\omega) + \frac{1}{T}GH(j\overline{\omega - \omega_s}) + \frac{1}{T}GH(j\overline{\omega + \omega_s}) \qquad (4.4\text{-}3)$$

The first term of the right-hand member of Eq. (4.4-3) is the predominating term, the second term is the major correction term, and the third term is added for obtaining better accuracy. At higher frequencies the third term of the above equation is much smaller than the second term.

The construction process is explained in Fig. 4.4-2. First the polar plot

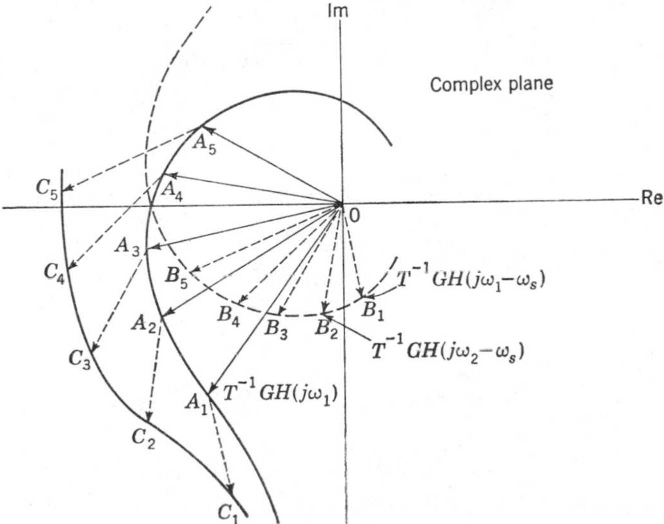

FIG. 4.4-2. Construction of frequency-characteristic locus.

of $T^{-1}GH(j\omega)$ for both positive and negative frequencies is constructed. Points $\omega_1, \omega_2, \omega_3, \ldots$ are marked on the positive-frequency plot and points $(\omega_1 - \omega_s), (\omega_2 - \omega_s), (\omega_3 - \omega_s), \ldots$, on the negative-frequency plot. Phasors $0A_1, 0A_2, 0A_3, \ldots$ and $0B_1, 0B_2, 0B_3, \ldots$ are drawn to these points. Then the phasors $A_1C_1, A_2C_2, A_3C_3, \ldots$ are added to the phasors $0A_1, 0A_2, 0A_3, \ldots$ It is noted that the phasors $A_1C_1, A_2C_2, A_3C_3, \ldots$ are identical to the phasors $0B_1, 0B_2, 0B_3, \ldots$, respectively. The points $C_1, C_2, C_3, \ldots$ are on the approximate frequency-characteristic locus of the sampled-data control system. A more accurate diagram can easily be plotted if the phasors of $T^{-1}GH(\overline{j\omega_1 + \omega_s})$, $T^{-1}GH(\overline{j\omega_2 + \omega_s})$, $T^{-1}GH(\overline{j\omega_3 + \omega_s})$, . . . corresponding to frequencies $(\omega_1 + \omega_s)$, $(\omega_2 + \omega_s)$, $(\omega_3 + \omega_s)$, . . . on the positive-frequency locus of $T^{-1}GH(j\omega)$ and the phasors of $T^{-1}GH(\overline{j\omega_1 - 2\omega_s})$, $T^{-1}GH(\overline{j\omega_2 - 2\omega_s})$, $T^{-1}GH(\overline{j\omega_3 - 2\omega_s})$, . . . corresponding to frequencies $(\omega_1 - 2\omega_s)$, $(\omega_2 - 2\omega_s)$, $(\omega_3 - 2\omega_s)$, . . . on the negative-frequency locus of $T^{-1}GH(j\omega)$ are added to the points C_1, C_2, C_3, . . . , respectively. Better accuracy is attained if this process is continued to cover more terms of the series of Eq. (4.4-1).

To facilitate the construction and interpretation of the Nyquist diagram for a sampled-data control system, some salient properties of the frequency-characteristic function $\sum_{n=-\infty}^{\infty} GH(\overline{j\omega + n\omega_s})$ and its polar plot are outlined below.

1. $\sum_{n=-\infty}^{\infty} GH(\overline{j\omega + n\omega_s})$ is a periodic function of frequency with period equal to $j\omega_s$.

2. The polar plot of $\sum_{n=-\infty}^{\infty} GH(\overline{j\omega + n\omega_s})$ for the frequency range $-\infty \leq \omega \leq +\infty$ is the same as that for the frequency range $0 \leq \omega \leq \omega_s$.

3. The value of $\sum_{n=-\infty}^{\infty} GH(\overline{j\omega + n\omega_s})$ at $\omega = \omega_s/2$ is real. At $\omega = \omega_s/2$,

$$\begin{aligned}\sum_{n=-\infty}^{\infty} GH(\overline{j\omega + n\omega_s}) &= GH\left(\frac{j\omega_s}{2}\right) + GH\left(\frac{j3\omega_s}{2}\right) + \cdots \\ &\quad + GH\left(\frac{-j\omega_s}{2}\right) + GH\left(\frac{-j3\omega_s}{2}\right) + \cdots \\ &= 2\left[\operatorname{Re} GH\left(\frac{j\omega_s}{2}\right) + \operatorname{Re} GH\left(\frac{j3\omega_s}{2}\right) + \cdots\right] \\ &= \text{a real quantity}\end{aligned}$$

4. If $GH(s)$ contains an integration (i.e., a factor $1/s$), the value of $\sum_{n=-\infty}^{\infty} GH(j\omega + n\omega_s)$ at $\omega = 0$ and $\omega = \omega_s$ is infinite. Since

$$\sum_{n=-\infty}^{\infty} GH[j(\omega + n\omega_s)] = GH(j\omega) + GH[j(\omega - \omega_s)] + \cdots$$

$GH(j\omega) = \infty$ at $\omega = 0$, and $GH(\overline{j\omega - \omega_s}) = \infty$ at $\omega = \omega_s$, the frequency-characteristic function is infinite at these two frequencies.

Example 4.4-1. Plot the Nyquist diagram for the open-loop transfer function of the sampled-data control system of Fig. 4.4-3. The sampling frequency is 8 radians/sec and the time constant of the controlled system is 0.5 sec.

Referring to Fig. 4.4-3, the open-loop transfer function for the continuous part of the system is

$$GH(j\omega) = \frac{K}{j\omega(1 + j0.5\omega)} \tag{4.4-4}$$

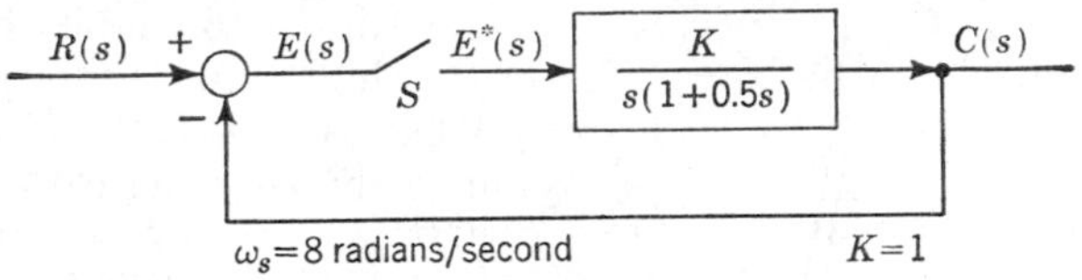

FIG. 4.4-3. Block diagram of the system of Example 4.4-1.

The polar plot of Eq. (4.4-4) with $K = 1$ is shown in curve a of Fig. 4.4-4. For the sampled-data system, the open-loop transfer function is given by

$$GH^*(j\omega) = \frac{1}{T} \sum_{n=-\infty}^{\infty} GH(\overline{j\omega + n\omega_s})$$

$$= \frac{1}{T} \sum_{n=-\infty}^{\infty} \frac{1}{j(\omega + n\omega_s)[1 + j0.5(\omega + n\omega_s)]} \tag{4.4-5}$$

where $T = 2\pi/\omega_s$ is the sampling period in seconds. As a first approximation, only two terms in the expansion of Eq. (4.4-5) are considered in plotting the Nyquist diagram. Thus,

$$GH^*(j\omega) = \frac{8/2\pi}{j\omega(1 + j0.5\omega)} + \frac{8/2\pi}{j(\omega - 8)[1 + j0.5(\omega - 8)]} \tag{4.4-6}$$

From Eq. (4.4-6) it is seen that at

$$\omega = 4 \text{ radians/sec} \qquad |GH^*(j\omega)| = 0.255$$

$$\omega = 0 \text{ radians/sec} \qquad |GH^*(j\omega)| = \infty$$

$$\omega = 8 \text{ radians/sec} \qquad |GH^*(j\omega)| = \infty$$

The construction of the frequency-characteristic plot is shown in Fig. 4.4-4. The value of $T^{-1} \sum_{n=-\infty}^{\infty} GH(\overline{j\omega + n\omega_s})$ is real at $\omega = \omega_s/2 = 4$ radians/sec. For frequencies greater than half the sampling frequency, the polar plot continues into the upper half of the complex plane. The section of the polar plot where frequencies are in the vicinity of $\omega_s/2$ is of primary interest, and in some cases is important in the study of system stability. As the sampling rate is increased, the value of $T^{-1} \sum_{n=1}^{\infty} GH(\overline{j\omega + n\omega_s})$ tends to zero, and the polar plot of $GH^*(j\omega)$ approaches the Nyquist diagram of $GH(j\omega)$.

From the above discussions it is seen that the construction of an accurate frequency-characteristic plot of a sampled-data system from the $T^{-1}GH(j\omega)$ locus of its continuous part is quite cumbersome, unless the transfer function $GH(s)$ is of sufficiently low-pass nature as to enable the omission of the higher order terms in Eq. (4.4-1). However, this method becomes more practical when the $T^{-1}GH(j\omega)$ locus for the system components can be determined only from the experimental data. A simpler and direct method of constructing the exact frequency-characteristic plot is presented in Chap. 5, after the z-transform techniques are discussed.

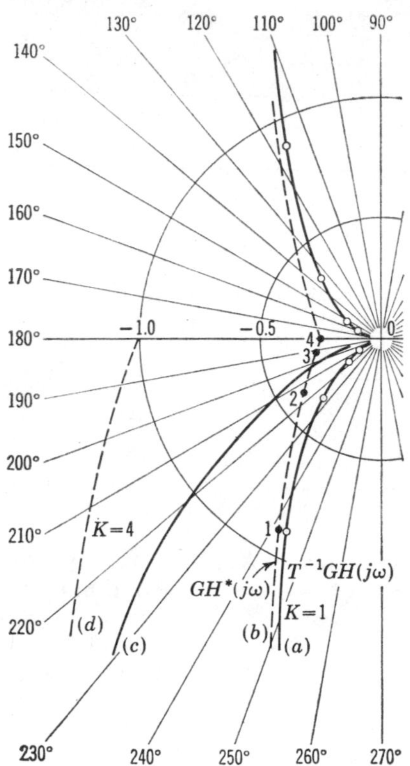

FIG. 4.4-4. Nyquist diagrams for Example 4.4-1.

Closed-loop Frequency Response. Referring to Fig. 4.4-5, the closed-loop (over-all) transfer function of the basic sampled-data feedback control system is given by

$$G_0^*(s) = \frac{C^*(s)}{R^*(s)} = \frac{G^*(s)}{1 + G^*(s)} \tag{4.4-7}$$

The closed-loop frequency-response function is obtained from Eq. (4.4-7) by substituting $j\omega$ for s. That is,

$$G_0^*(j\omega) = \frac{C^*(j\omega)}{R^*(j\omega)} = \frac{G^*(j\omega)}{1 + G^*(j\omega)} \tag{4.4-8}$$

Equation (4.4-8) may be written as

$$\frac{G^*(j\omega)}{1 + G^*(j\omega)} = |G_0^*(j\omega)|\epsilon^{j\phi(\omega)} \tag{4.4-9}$$

where $|G_0^*(j\omega)|$ denotes the magnitude of $G_0^*(j\omega)$, and $\phi(\omega)$, the phase angle. The closed-loop frequency-response curve can be determined graphically

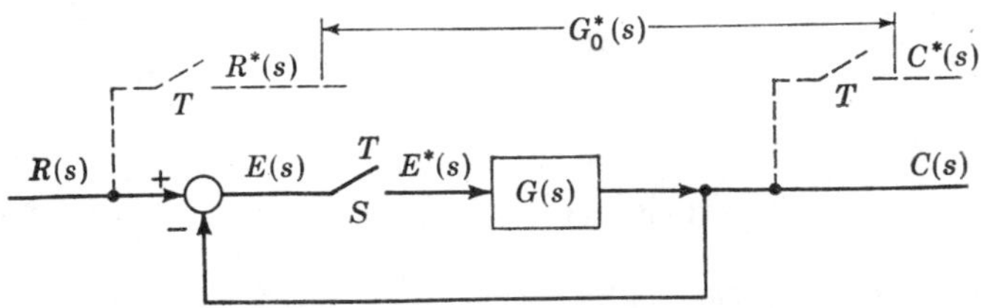

FIG. 4.4-5. Block diagram of a basic sampled-data feedback control system.

from the open-loop frequency-characteristic locus. Shown in Fig. 4.4-6 is the open-loop frequency-characteristic plot of the sampled-data system.

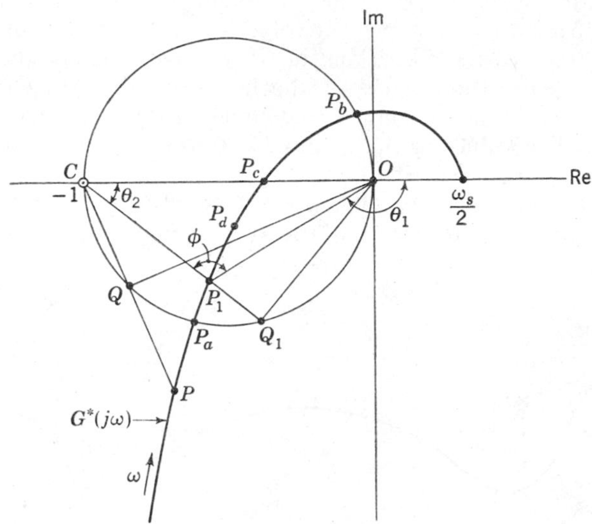

FIG. 4.4-6. Open-loop frequency-characteristic plot of a sampled-data feedback control system.

Point P_1 is a point on this frequency plot at which the frequency is ω_1. From Fig. 4.4-6 it is seen that the phasors OP_1 and CP_1 are

$$\overline{OP_1} = G^*(j\omega) = OP_1\epsilon^{j\theta_1} \tag{4.4-10}$$

$$\overline{CP_1} = 1 + G^*(j\omega) = CP_1\epsilon^{j\theta_2} \tag{4.4-11}$$

Thus,

$$G_0^*(j\omega) = \frac{\overline{OP_1}}{\overline{CP_1}} = \frac{OP_1}{CP_1}\,\epsilon^{j\phi} \tag{4.4-12}$$

where

$$\phi = \theta_1 - \theta_2 \tag{4.4-13}$$

Equation (4.4-12) may be written as

$$G_0^*(j\omega) = \frac{OP_1 \cos\phi + jOP_1 \sin\phi}{CP_1} \tag{4.4-14}$$

A circle with OC as diameter is constructed. Point C is the critical point $(-1,0)$. Then the real part of the closed-loop frequency-response function $G_0^*(j\omega)$ is

$$A_0^*(\omega) = \frac{OP_1 \cos\phi}{CP_1} = \frac{Q_1P_1}{CP_1} \tag{4.4-15}$$

and the imaginary part is

$$B_0^*(\omega) = \frac{OP_1 \sin\phi}{CP_1} = \frac{OQ_1}{CP_1} \tag{4.4-16}$$

Point Q_1 is the point of intersection of the circle with the line CP_1 (extended). Clearly, the real part and the imaginary part of $G_0^*(j\omega)$ can easily be determined graphically from the open-loop frequency plot by the use of Eqs. (4.4-15) and (4.4-16), respectively. To find the value of $A_0^*(\omega)$ at a frequency ω, first locate a point P on the $G^*(j\omega)$ plot at which the frequency is ω. Then measure the lengths of the line segments QP, CP, and OQ, where Q is the intersecting point of the circle with the line CP (extended, if necessary). The values of $A_0^*(\omega)$ and $B_0^*(\omega)$ at ω are given by the ratios QP/CP and OQ/CP, respectively.[103]

A typical frequency plot for $A_0^*(\omega)$, constructed from the $G^*(j\omega)$ plot of Fig. 4.4-6, is presented in Fig. 4.4-7a. At zero frequency, $A_0^*(\omega)$ is unity.

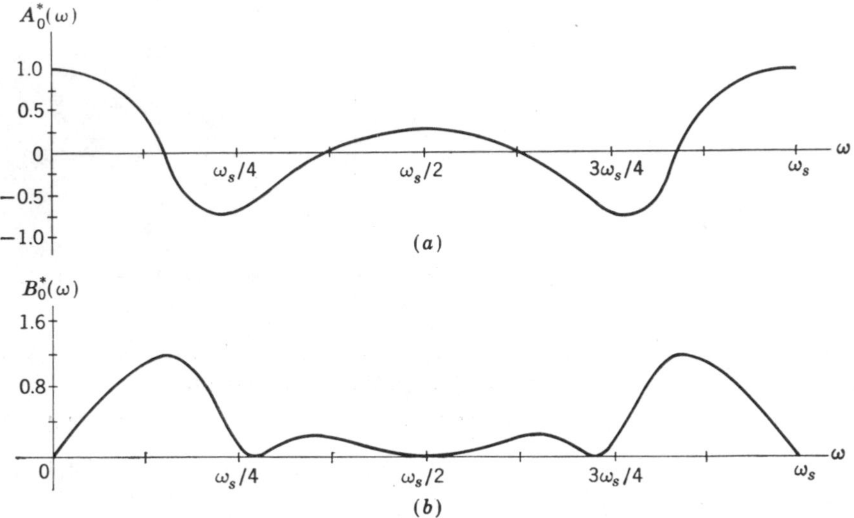

Fig. 4.4-7. (a) A typical frequency plot for $A_0^*(\omega)$; (b) a typical frequency plot for $B_0^*(\omega)$.

At the frequency corresponding to the intersecting point P_a of the $G^*(j\omega)$ plot with the circle, $A_0^*(\omega)$ is zero. With further increase in frequency, $A_0^*(\omega)$ becomes negative and reaches a minimum at the frequency corresponding to point P_d. Then $A_0^*(\omega)$ increases with frequency and becomes zero when the $G^*(j\omega)$ plot intersects the circle again (point P_b). The plot of $A_0^*(\omega)$ completes the first half period of the waveform at $\omega = \omega_s/2$. The frequency plot of $B_0^*(\omega)$ is sketched in Fig. 4.4-7b. $B_0^*(\omega)$ is zero at $\omega = 0$, and reaches a maximum at the frequency corresponding to the intersecting point P_a. It becomes zero again at the frequency corresponding to the crossover point P_c, and is maximum at the frequency corresponding to the intersecting point P_b. At half sampling frequency, $B_0^*(\omega)$ is zero. From the waveforms of Fig. 4.4-7 it is seen that $A_0^*(\omega)$ is an even function of frequency and $B_0^*(\omega)$ is an odd function. The Fourier series equivalent of the waveform of $A_0^*(\omega)$ may be found by graphical integration. According to the discussions of Sec. 4.2, the Fourier coefficients of $A_0^*(\omega)$ represent the weighting sequence of the closed-loop system.

4.5. Stability Considerations. One of the major problems involved in feedback control systems is the system stability. This section is concerned with some basic stability considerations of sampled-data control systems, which may be readily inferred from the frequency-characteristic locus. The discussions of the stability criteria for sampled-data systems are presented in great detail in Chap. 6.

In Sec. 4.3 it is shown that the Laplace transform of the output of a basic sampled-data feedback control system (Fig. 4.3-7) is given by

$$C(s) = \frac{G(s)T^{-1} \sum_{n=-\infty}^{\infty} R(s + jn\omega_s)}{1 + T^{-1} \sum_{n=-\infty}^{\infty} GH(s + jn\omega_s)} \tag{4.5-1}$$

where $G(s)$ is the transfer function of the linear elements in the forward path; $GH(s)$ the open-loop transfer function for the continuous part of the system; and $R(s)$ the Laplace transform of the input to the system. Referring to Fig. 4.3-10, the characteristic equation of the conventional continuous-data feedback control system is

$$1 + G(s)H(s) = 0 \tag{4.5-2}$$

and by analogy, the characteristic equation of the sampled-data feedback control system is

$$1 + \frac{1}{T} \sum_{n=-\infty}^{\infty} GH(s + jn\omega_s) = 0 \tag{4.5-3}$$

The performance of a continuous-data feedback control system is determined by the locations of the roots of Eq. (4.5-2) in the s plane. In the same way the behavior of a sampled-data feedback control system is characterized by the nature of the roots of Eq. (4.5-3).

The stability of a continuous-data feedback control system is often determined from the polar plot of the open-loop transfer function $GH(j\omega)$ for frequency varying from $-\infty$ to $+\infty$. As is briefly explained in Chap. 2, a stable system requires that the polar plot of $GH(j\omega)$ does not encircle the critical point $(-1,0)$, provided that the system is known to be open-loop stable. By analogy, the stability of a sampled-data feedback control system can be determined from the polar plot of the open-loop transfer function

$$GH^*(j\omega) = \frac{1}{T} \sum_{n=-\infty}^{\infty} GH(\overline{j\omega + n\omega_s}) \tag{4.5-4}$$

for the frequency range from zero to infinity. Since the frequency-characteristic function of Eq. (4.5-4) is periodic with period $j\omega_s$, an infinite number of identical polar plots can be drawn within this frequency range.

The plots for the frequency range $0 \leq \omega \leq \omega_s$, $\omega_s \leq \omega \leq 2\omega_s$, $2\omega_s \leq \omega \leq 3\omega_s$, . . . are all the same, and the polar plot for the frequency range between $\omega_s/2$ and ω_s is the mirror image of that for the frequency range between 0 and $\omega_s/2$. As a result, to study the stability and behavior of a sampled-data feedback control system, only the polar plot of $GH^*(j\omega)$ for the frequency range from 0 to $\omega_s/2$ is needed.

Like continuous-data feedback control systems, sampled-data feedback systems can be either open-loop stable or open-loop unstable. The stability condition for a sampled-data system which is open-loop stable is that the polar plot of its open-loop transfer function, Eq. (4.5-4), for the frequency increasing from 0 to ω_s does not encircle the critical point $(-1,0)$ of the complex plane. The stability criterion for a sampled-data system which is open-loop unstable is discussed in Sec. 6.2.

With the exception of conditionally stable systems, the degree of stability of a sampled-data control system is decreased with increase in the loop gain of the system. Referring to Example 4.4-1 of the previous section for $K = 1$, the value of the open-loop transfer function $GH^*(j\omega)$ is 0.255, when the polar plot of the system crosses the negative real axis. As shown in curve b of Fig. 4.4-4, the polar plot crosses the real axis only once, and does not enclose the critical point $(-1,0)$. Thus, the system at this gain level is stable. However, if the gain constant is increased fourfold, the polar plot of $GH^*(j\omega)$ crosses the negative real axis at -1.02, curve d of Fig. 4.4-4, which indicates that the system is unstable. Furthermore, as is to be seen from curve c of Fig. 4.4-4, in the absence of the sampler the system with $K = 4$ is stable. Hence the cause of instability may be attributed to the sampling process.

It would seem that intermittent and sampling control would generally result in an inferior performance of the system due to a loss of information in the control data. Curve b of Fig. 4.4-4 shows that the sampled-data control system is less stable in comparison to the corresponding system if the sampler is absent. If the sampling frequency ω_s is reduced, the phasor of $T^{-1}GH(\overline{j\omega \pm \omega_s})$ at a given frequency ω is increased in magnitude and is rotated slightly clockwise, and other terms in $T^{-1} \sum_{n=1}^{\infty} GH(\overline{j\omega \pm n\omega_s})$ which were previously neglected in the computation of the polar plot from Eq. (4.4-3) are no longer negligible and must be considered. In consequence, the effect of decreasing the sampling rate is to push the polar plot of the open-loop transfer function of the sampled-data system to the left. It is quite obvious from the curves in Fig. 4.4-4 that shifting the polar plot to the left would reduce the relative stability or even result in instability. The introduction of sampling into a feedback control system will, in general, lead to a decrease in the degree of stability; and the sampling frequency is an important factor in determining the degree of stability of the system. Further discussions of the stability of sampled-data control systems are presented in Chaps. 6 and 9.

Moreover, considered from another viewpoint, the insertion of the sampler into a feedback control system can be seen as a special method of reshaping the open-loop transfer function $T^{-1}GH(j\omega)$ by the addition of the term

$$T^{-1} \sum_{n=1}^{\infty} GH(\overline{j\omega \pm n\omega_s}) \tag{4.5-5}$$

which is dependent upon the characteristic of the original open-loop transfer function $GH(j\omega)$.

In most control systems, sampling would either introduce instability or cause a decrease in the degree of stability, as demonstrated in the above example. On the other hand, however, sampled-data control can improve the performance of, and provide stabilization to, certain systems with distributed constants and transport lags, such as the process control systems. Considerable difficulties are often encountered in the stabilization and compensation of such control systems by conventional means. Yet the use of sampling in such control systems sometimes improves the system performance and increases the system stability. As shown in Chap. 2, the transfer function of an element with pure transport lag is ϵ^{-T_ds}, where T_d stands for the transport lag or the dead-time delay. The open-loop transfer function for the continuous part of the system then contains ϵ^{-T_ds} as a factor (Fig. 4.5-1). The stabilization effect lies in the fact that by properly

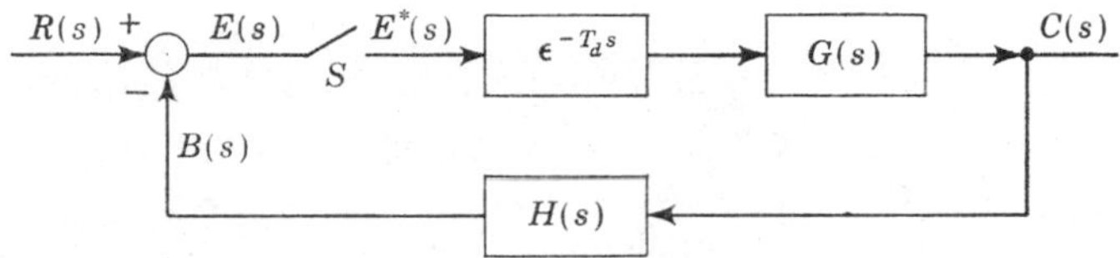

FIG. 4.5-1. Sampled-data control system with transport lag.

choosing the sampling rate the factor $\epsilon^{-jT_d\omega}$, which is introduced to the open-loop transfer function by the transport lag T_d, could shift the polar plot of $GH^*(j\omega)$ to the right of the $T^{-1}GH(j\omega)$ locus. This shifting of the polar plot would generally result in an increased stability. System stabilization by sampling is further discussed in Chap. 6.

4.6. Properties of Holding Devices. In most sampled-data control systems, the high-frequency complementary components resulting from the sampling process must be removed before the actuating signal reaches the output stage. Although a large portion of the unwanted complementary signals are removed by the system components, such as the servomotor between the sampler and the output, more complete smoothing is usually accomplished by the use of a holding device in the system. A holding device is a smoothing device which converts the pulsed-input signal into continuous form by interpolation or extrapolation of the input pulses, so that the envelope function of the input signal may be approximately reproduced. The smoothing of the pulsed data by a holding device is essentially an extrapolation problem. The extrapolated time function between two consecutive sampling instants nT and $(n + 1)T$ depends upon its values at the preceding sampling instants nT, $(n - 1)T$, $(n - 2)T$, . . . , and can generally be described by the Taylor series expansion[26] of the output between the interval $t = nT$ and $t = (n + 1)T$, as illustrated in Fig. 4.6-1. Let

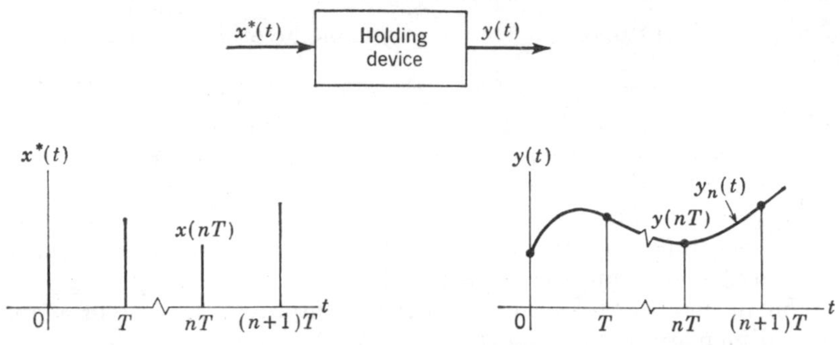

FIG. 4.6-1. High-order holding device.

$y(t)$ be the output function and $y_n(t)$ be the output between sampling instants nT and $(n + 1)T$, that is, $y_n(t) = y(t)$ for $nT \leq t \leq (n + 1)T$.

Then
$$y_n(t) = y(nT) + y^{(1)}(nT)(t - nT) + \frac{y^{(2)}(nT)}{2!}(t - nT)^2 + \cdots + \frac{y^{(k)}(nT)}{k!}(t - nT)^k \qquad (4.6\text{-}1)$$

where $y(nT)$ is the value of $y(t)$ at $t = nT$, and $y^{(1)}(nT)$, $y^{(2)}(nT)$, . . . , $y^{(k)}(nT)$ are the values of the derivatives $y^{(1)}(t)$, $y^{(2)}(t)$, . . . , $y^{(k)}(t)$ evaluated at $t = nT$.

When a holding device is designed to approximate the time function between two consecutive sampling instants by a zero-order polynomial or a constant equal to the value of the function at the beginning of the interval in question, that is,

$$y_n(t) = y(nT) \qquad \text{for } nT \leq t \leq (n + 1)T \qquad (4.6\text{-}2)$$

it is referred to as a perfect zero-order hold circuit. When the holding device approximates the time function between two consecutive sampling instants by a first-order polynomial,

$$y_n(t) = y(nT) + y'(nT)(t - nT) \qquad (4.6\text{-}3)$$

it forms a first-order holding device. When the time function is described by a kth-order polynomial, as given by Eq. (4.6-1), the holding device is commonly known as a kth-order holding device. It is conceivable that, in general, a high-order holding device can give rise to better reproduction of the desired time function from the input-data pulses.

Since the holding device receives information only at the sampling instants, the values of these derivatives can be estimated only from the sampled-input data. A simple expression for the estimate of the first derivative at $t = nT$ is given by

$$y^{(1)}(nT) = \frac{y(nT) - y[(n-1)T]}{T} \tag{4.6-4}$$

An approximated value of the second derivative at $t = nT$ is given by

$$y^{(2)}(nT) = \frac{y'(nT) - y'[(n-1)T]}{T} \tag{4.6-5}$$

and the approximated value of the kth derivative at $t = nT$ is given by

$$y^{(k)}(nT) = \frac{y^{(k-1)}(nT) - y^{(k-1)}[(n-1)T]}{T} \tag{4.6-6}$$

Substituting Eq. (4.6-4) into Eq. (4.6-5) yields

$$y^{(2)}(nT) = \frac{y(nT) - 2y[(n-1)T] + y[(n-2)T]}{T^2} \tag{4.6-7}$$

and, in general, the approximated value of the kth derivative at $t = nT$ may be obtained from

$$y^{(k)}(nT) = \frac{1}{T^k}\left\{y(nT) - ky[(n-1)T] + \frac{k(k-1)}{2!}y[(n-2)T] - \cdots + (-1)^k y[(n-k)T]\right\} \tag{4.6-8}$$

From Eqs. (4.6-4), (4.6-7), and (4.6-8), it is seen that to obtain an estimated value of a derivative of $y(t)$ the minimum number of the data pulses which are required is equal to the order of the derivative plus one. For instance, to obtain an estimate of the first derivative at a sampling instant requires the values of two consecutive data pulses, and to obtain an approximated value of the second derivative at a sampling instant requires the values of three consecutive data pulses. Thus, to estimate a higher-order derivative requires a greater delay before a reliable value of that derivative can be obtained. The delay introduced by a higher-order holding device is detrimental to system stability. On the other hand, in order to obtain a better reproduction of the desired time function from the input-data pulses and to reduce the ripple content, it is advisable to employ a higher-order holding device in the sampled-data control system. Consequently, to design a holding device for a pulsed-data system, it would seem necessary to compromise between the tolerable ripple content and the specified system stability and dynamic performance. Because of the high cost and constructional complexity involved in high-order holding devices and the large amount of lag phase shift introduced by them, the most common holding devices used in digital and sampled-data control systems are the zero-order holding devices, although the first-order holding devices are also occasionally used. The characteristics of these two types of holding devices are discussed in the following paragraphs.

Zero-order Holding Device. The basic operation of a simple zero-order holding device lies in the instantaneous charging and slow discharging of a capacitor. At the sampling instants, the storage capacitor of the holding device is fully charged; between two consecutive sampling instants, the capacitor discharges very slowly. The circuit diagram of a typical zero-order hold is illustrated in Fig. 4.6-2. The storage capacitor of this circuit

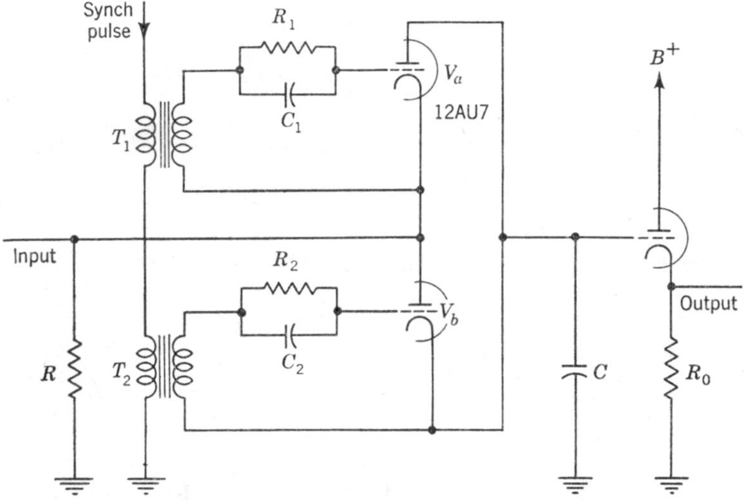

FIG. 4.6-2. A typical zero-order hold circuit.

is C. The input signal is normally disconnected from the output because of the bias developed across networks R_1C_1 and R_2C_2 by the previous synch pulse or sampling pulse. A positive synch pulse applied to the grids of tube V_a and tube V_b causes conduction for positive and negative input signals. The values of the resistors and capacitors of the bias networks are determined in such a way that the time constants are much greater than the sampling period. It is noted that when the input signal is in pulsed form, this device is a zero-order hold, whereas if the input is a continuous signal, this device performs both the sampling and the holding operation. Another zero-order holding device which makes use of an operational amplifier is shown in Fig. 4.6-3. The storage capacitor C is charged instantaneously at the sampling instant, and the voltage across the storage capacitor is held almost constant between the sampling instants.

The decay of the output voltage of the holding device generally follows some composite exponential curve. For simplicity, it is assumed that the

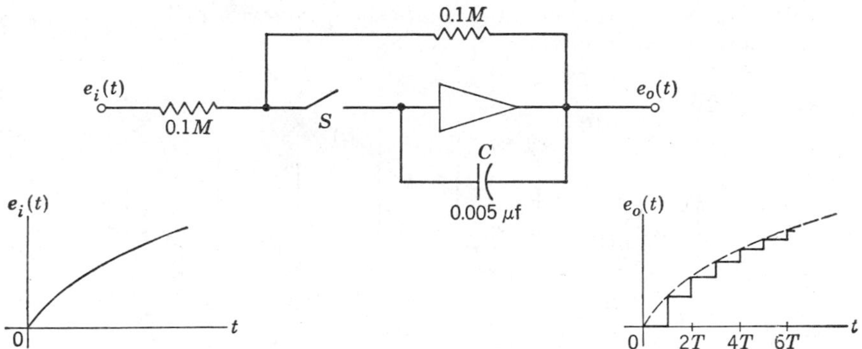

FIG. 4.6-3. A zero-order hold circuit utilizing an operational amplifier.

discharge time constant is T_0. The waveform of the output voltage during the first sampling interval is shown in Fig. 4.6-4. The input to the holding device is a train of very narrow pulses, which can be represented by equiva-

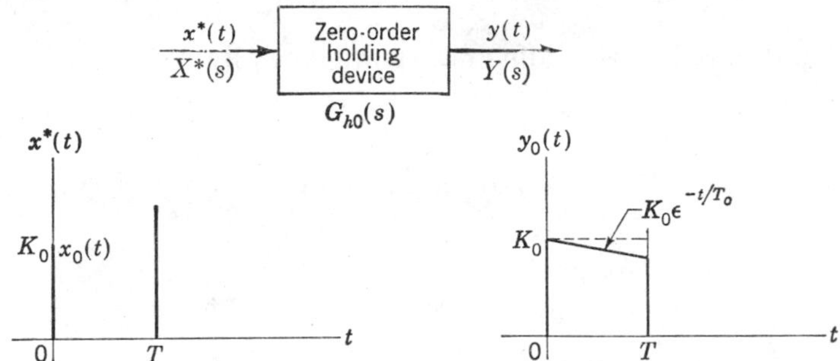

FIG. 4.6-4. An imperfect zero-order holding device and its output waveform.

lent impulses in the analysis. At the first sampling instant, $t = 0$, the input to the holding device is

$$x_0(t) = K_0\delta(t) \tag{4.6-9}$$

where K_0 is the strength of the equivalent impulse. During the first sampling interval, the output voltage is given by

$$y_0(t) = K_0\epsilon^{-t/T_0} \tag{4.6-10}$$

At the second sampling instant, $t = T$,

$$y_0(T) = K_0\epsilon^{-T/T_0} \tag{4.6-11}$$

where T is the sampling period of the input signal. The output from the holding circuit is also a pulse train, but the width of each pulse is equal to the sampling period. Figure 4.6-5 shows the waveforms of both the input and the output time functions.

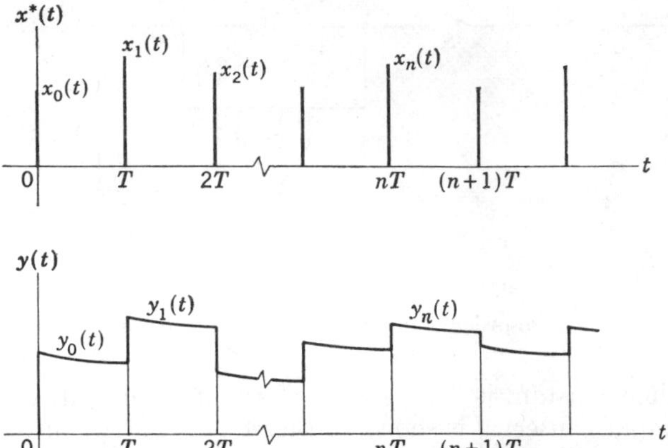

FIG. 4.6-5. Input and output waveforms of a zero-order holding device.

The input data to the holding device are given by

Time functions:

$$\begin{aligned} x_0(t) &= K_0\delta(t) \\ x_1(t) &= K_1\delta(t - T) \\ x_2(t) &= K_2\delta(t - 2T) \\ &\cdots\cdots \\ x_k(t) &= K_k\delta(t - kT) \end{aligned} \tag{4.6-12}$$

Laplace transforms:

$$\begin{aligned} X_0(s) &= K_0 \\ X_1(s) &= K_1\epsilon^{-Ts} \\ X_2(s) &= K_2\epsilon^{-2Ts} \\ &\cdots\cdots \\ X_k(s) &= K_k\epsilon^{-kTs} \end{aligned} \tag{4.6-13}$$

Then the input time function of the holding device is

$$\begin{aligned} x^*(t) &= x_0(t) + x_1(t) + x_2(t) + \cdots + x_k(t) + \cdots \\ &= \sum_{k=0}^{N} K_k\delta(t - kT) \end{aligned} \tag{4.6-14}$$

and the Laplace transform is

$$\begin{aligned} X^*(s) &= X_0(s) + X_1(s) + X_2(s) + \cdots + X_k(s) + \cdots \\ &= \sum_{k=0}^{N} K_k\epsilon^{-kTs} \end{aligned} \tag{4.6-15}$$

The output functions from the holding device during the successive sampling intervals are given by

Time functions:

$$\begin{aligned}
y_0(t) &= K_0\epsilon^{-t/T_0}[u(t) - u(t - T)] \\
y_1(t) &= K_1\epsilon^{-(t-T)/T_0}[u(t - T) - u(t - 2T)] \\
y_2(t) &= K_2\epsilon^{-(t-2T)/T_0}[u(t - 2T) - u(t - 3T)] \\
&\cdots\cdots\cdots\cdots\cdots\cdots\cdots\cdots \\
y_k(t) &= K_k\epsilon^{-(t-kT)/T_0}\{u(t - kT) - u[t - (k + 1)T]\}
\end{aligned} \tag{4.6-16}$$

Laplace transforms:

$$\begin{aligned}
Y_0(s) &= \frac{K_0T_0}{1 + T_0s}(1 - \epsilon^{-T/T_0}\epsilon^{-Ts}) \\
Y_1(s) &= \frac{K_1T_0}{1 + T_0s}(1 - \epsilon^{-T/T_0}\epsilon^{-Ts})\epsilon^{-Ts} \\
Y_2(s) &= \frac{K_2T_0}{1 + T_0s}(1 - \epsilon^{-T/T_0}\epsilon^{-Ts})\epsilon^{-2Ts} \\
&\cdots\cdots\cdots\cdots\cdots\cdots\cdots\cdots \\
Y_k(s) &= \frac{K_kT_0}{1 + T_0s}(1 - \epsilon^{-T/T_0}\epsilon^{-Ts})\epsilon^{-kTs}
\end{aligned} \tag{4.6-17}$$

Clearly, the output time function of the holding device is

$$\begin{aligned}
y(t) &= y_0(t) + y_1(t) + y_2(t) + \cdots + y_k(t) + \cdots \\
&= \sum_{k=0}^{N} K_k\epsilon^{-(t-kT)/T_0}\{u(t - kT) - u[t - (k + 1)T]\}
\end{aligned} \tag{4.6-18}$$

and the Laplace transform is

$$\begin{aligned}
Y(s) &= Y_0(s) + Y_1(s) + Y_2(s) + \cdots + Y_k(s) + \cdots \\
&= \frac{T_0}{1 + T_0s}(1 - \epsilon^{-T/T_0}\epsilon^{-Ts}) \sum_{k=0}^{N} K_k\epsilon^{-kTs}
\end{aligned} \tag{4.6-19}$$

Then, it follows from Eqs. (4.6-15) and (4.6-19) that the transfer function of a holding device, which is defined as the ratio $Y(s)/X^*(s)$, is given by

$$G_{h0}(s) = \frac{T_0s}{1 + T_0s} \frac{(1 - \epsilon^{-T/T_0}\epsilon^{-Ts})}{s} \tag{4.6-20}$$

Moreover, the transfer function of the zero-order hold may be derived in a simpler manner. It is seen from Fig. 4.6-5 that the impulse response of the zero-order hold is

$$g_{h0}(t) = \epsilon^{-t/T_0}[u(t) - u(t - T)] \tag{4.6-21}$$

The Laplace transform of Eq. (4.6-21) is given by

$$G_{h0}(s) = \frac{T_0}{1 + T_0 s} - \frac{T_0 \epsilon^{-T/T_0} \epsilon^{-Ts}}{1 + T_0 s} \tag{4.6-22}$$

which leads to Eq. (4.6-20) upon simplification.

However, in common practice the discharge time constant T_0 is so large that the following assumptions can be made. Thus,

$$\epsilon^{-T/T_0} \approx 1 \tag{4.6-23}$$

and

$$\frac{T_0 s}{1 + T_0 s} \approx 1 \tag{4.6-24}$$

Consequently, Eq. (4.6-20) reduces to

$$G_{h0}(s) \approx \frac{1 - \epsilon^{-Ts}}{s} \tag{4.6-25}$$

It is apparent that the transfer function of a perfect zero-order hold circuit can be derived directly from the input and the output waveforms, as illustrated in Fig. 4.3-8, by inspection. The Laplace transform of the input function, which consists of a train of equivalent impulses, is $\sum_{k=0}^{N} E_k \epsilon^{-kTs}$; and the Laplace transform of the output function is

$$\frac{1 - \epsilon^{-Ts}}{s} \sum_{k=0}^{N} E_k \epsilon^{-kTs}$$

Clearly, the transfer function of a perfect zero-order hold circuit is given by

$$G_{h0}(s) = \frac{1 - \epsilon^{-Ts}}{s} \tag{4.6-26}$$

A perfect zero-order hold circuit is commonly known as a boxcar generator. From the waveform of its output shown in Fig. 4.3-8, it is seen that the zero-order hold circuit yields no ripple at the output if the input is a pulse train of constant amplitude. Equation (4.6-26) implies that at high frequencies the zero-order hold circuit behaves as an imperfect integrating device. Replacing s by $j\omega$ and T by $2\pi/\omega_s$ in Eq. (4.6-26) yields the frequency response as

$$G_{h0}(j\omega) = \frac{1 - \epsilon^{-j2\pi\omega/\omega_s}}{j\omega} \tag{4.6-27}$$

Equation (4.6-27) may be simplified to

$$G_{h0}(j\omega) = \frac{2 \sin (\pi\omega/\omega_s)}{\omega \epsilon^{j\pi\omega/\omega_s}} \tag{4.6-28}$$

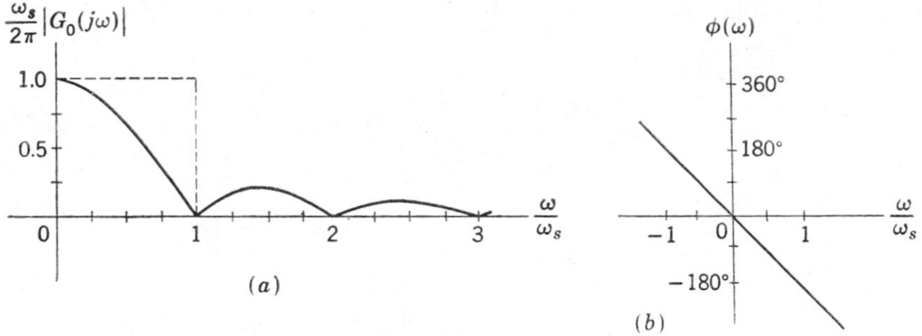

FIG. 4.6-6. Gain and phase characteristics of a zero-order hold. (a) Gain characteristic; (b) phase characteristic.

It follows from Eq. (4.6-28) that the phase characteristic and the gain or amplitude characteristic of the zero-order hold circuit are given by

$$\phi(\omega) = -\frac{\pi}{\omega_s}\,\omega \tag{4.6-29}$$

$$|G_{h0}(j\omega)| = \frac{2\pi}{\omega_s}\,\frac{|\sin(\pi\omega/\omega_s)|}{\pi\omega/\omega_s} \tag{4.6-30}$$

Equation (4.6-29) reveals that the zero-order hold circuit introduces a time delay of $T/2$ sec. The gain and phase characteristics are plotted in Figs. 4.6-6 and 4.6-7.

It is seen from Fig. 4.6-6 that the zero-order hold circuit is essentially a low-pass filter which transmits the low-frequency primary component and blocks the shifted high-frequency complementary components resulting

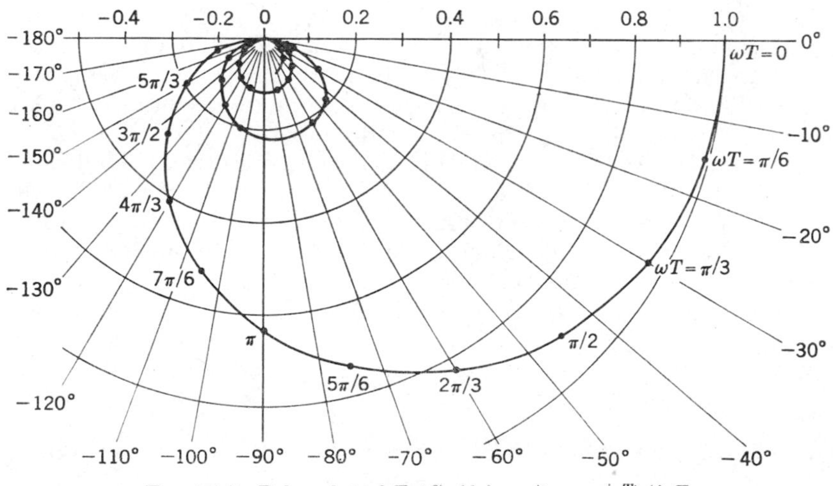

FIG. 4.6-7. Polar plot of $T^{-1}G_{h0}(j\omega) = (1 - \epsilon^{-j\omega T})/j\omega T$.

from the sampling process. A few values of the frequency response are tabulated below:

ω/ω_s	ϕ, deg	$\lvert G_{h0}(j\omega)\rvert$
0	0	$\frac{2\pi}{\omega_s}$
¼	−45	$0.901\,\frac{2\pi}{\omega_s}$
½	−90	$0.636\,\frac{2\pi}{\omega_s}$
¾	−135	$0.300\,\frac{2\pi}{\omega_s}$
1	−180	0

The percentage transmission at half sampling frequency is

$$\left|\frac{G_{h0}(j\tfrac{1}{2}\omega_s)}{G_h(j0)}\right| = \frac{2}{\pi} = 63.6\% \tag{4.6-31}$$

Apparently, this filter does not cut off sharply although the phase decreases rather rapidly as the frequency is increased. When the input signal is fairly steady, the zero-order hold circuit is an effective smoothing device. In most cases the holding circuit forms an integrated part of the sampling equipment, as shown in Fig. 4.6-3.

The effect of imperfect holding can be seen from Eq. (4.6-20). The discharge-time constant T_0 bears an influence over both the gain and the phase of the holding device. A slight imperfection of holding may cause an increase in phase shift by a small amount equal to $(90° - \tan^{-1}\omega T_0)$. Equation (4.6-20) further indicates that, if T_0 is finite, the magnitude of $G_{h0}(j\omega)$ approaches $T_0(1 - \epsilon^{-T/T_0})$ as a limit when ω is decreasing to zero. As a result, imperfect holding may introduce more attenuation on low-frequency signals, which is considered undesirable.

First-order Holding Device. The operation of a first-order holding device is explained in Fig. 4.6-8. The extrapolated time function $y_n(t)$ between two successive sampling instants nT and $(n + 1)T$ is a linear function given in Eq. (4.6-3), the slope of which is determined by the slope of the line passing through the points $[x_{n-1}, (n - 1)T]$ and (x_n, nT) as shown in Fig. 4.6-8. At $t = nT$, $x_n = K_n$ and $y(nT) = K_n$. During the interval $nT \le t \le (n + 1)T$,

$$y_n(t) = K_n + y'(nT)(t - nT) \tag{4.6-32}$$

and

$$y'(nT) = \frac{K_n - K_{n-1}}{T} \tag{4.6-33}$$

From Fig. 4.6-8 it is to be observed that the ripple at the output of a first-order holding device is nil, if the envelope of the input function has a constant slope. During the interval $0 \leq t \leq T$,

$$y_0(t) = K_0 + \frac{K_0 - y(-T)}{T} t \tag{4.6-34}$$

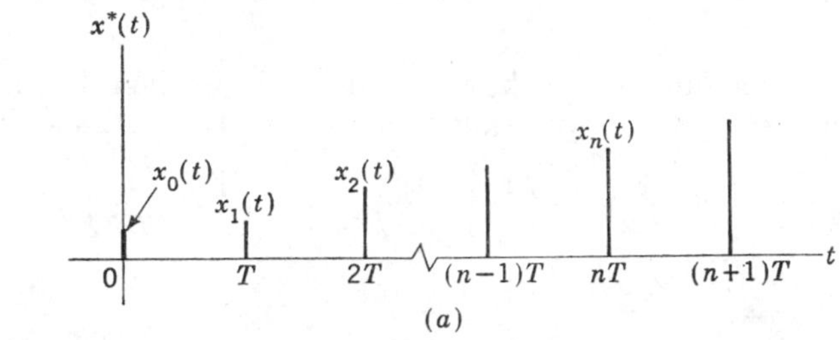

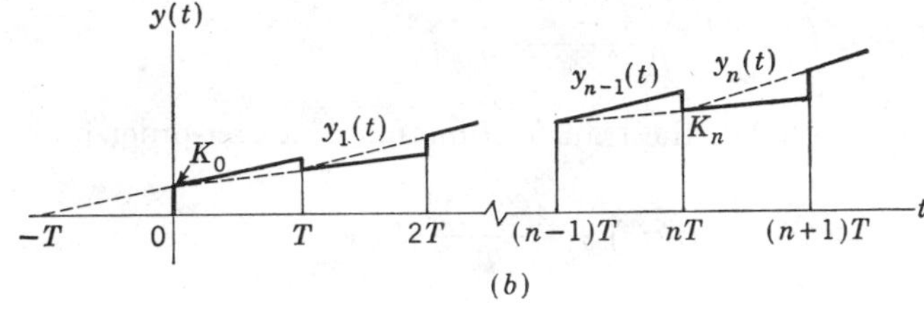

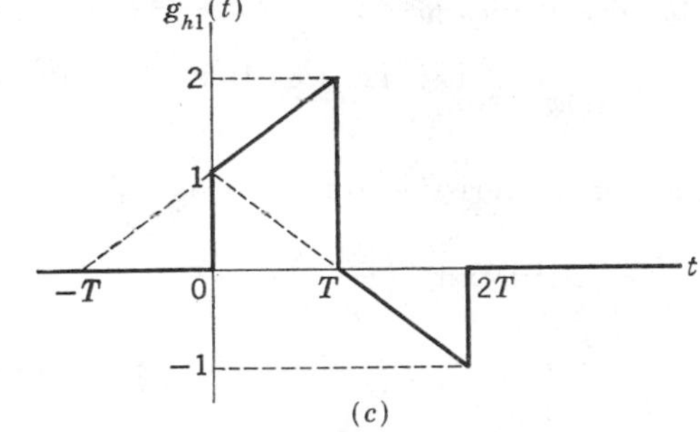

FIG. 4.6-8. Input and output waveforms of a first-order hold and the impulse response.

which is indeterminate, since the device could not determine what $y(t)$ was at $t = -T$. However, if sampling is assumed to be coincident with the start of the time function which is zero for $t < 0$, Eq. (4.6-34) reduces to

$$y_0(t) = K_0 + \frac{K_0}{T} t \tag{4.6-35}$$

where $0 \leq t \leq T$.

The impulse response $g_{h1}(t)$ of the first-order hold is shown in Fig. 4.6-8*c*. During the interval $0 \leq t \leq T$, $g_{h1}(t) = 1 + t/T$; during the interval

$T \le t \le 2T$, $g_{h1}(t) = 1 - t/T$; and for t less than zero and greater than $2T$, $g_{h1}(t) = 0$. Thus, the impulse response $g_{h1}(t)$ is given by

$$g_{h1}(t) = \left(1 + \frac{t}{T}\right) u(t) - 2\left(1 + \frac{t-T}{T}\right) u(t-T) + \left(1 + \frac{t-2T}{T}\right) u(t-2T) \qquad (4.6\text{-}36)$$

Since the transfer function of the first-order hold is given by the Laplace transform of its impulse response, it follows from Eq. (4.6-36) that

$$\begin{aligned} G_{h1}(s) &= \frac{1}{s} + \frac{1}{Ts^2} - 2\left(\frac{1}{s} + \frac{1}{Ts^2}\right)\epsilon^{-Ts} + \left(\frac{1}{s} + \frac{1}{Ts^2}\right)\epsilon^{-2Ts} \\ &= \frac{(1-\epsilon^{-Ts})^2}{s} + \frac{1}{T}\frac{(1-\epsilon^{-Ts})^2}{s^2} \\ &= \left(\frac{1+Ts}{T}\right)\left(\frac{1-\epsilon^{-Ts}}{s}\right)^2 \end{aligned} \qquad (4.6\text{-}37)$$

In view of Eq. (4.6-26), the transfer function of a first-order hold may be written as

$$G_{h1}(s) = \frac{1+Ts}{T}[G_{h0}(s)]^2 \qquad (4.6\text{-}38)$$

Substituting $j\omega$ for s and $2\pi/\omega_s$ for T in Eq. (4.6-38) yields the frequency response of this holding device as

$$G_{h1}(j\omega) = \frac{1 + j2\pi\omega/\omega_s}{2\pi/\omega_s} \frac{4(\sin \pi\omega/\omega_s)^2}{\omega^2 \epsilon^{j2\pi\omega/\omega_s}} \qquad (4.6\text{-}39)$$

The phase and gain characteristics are given by

$$\phi(j\omega) = \tan^{-1}\left(\frac{2\pi\omega}{\omega_s}\right) - \frac{2\pi\omega}{\omega_s} \qquad (4.6\text{-}40)$$

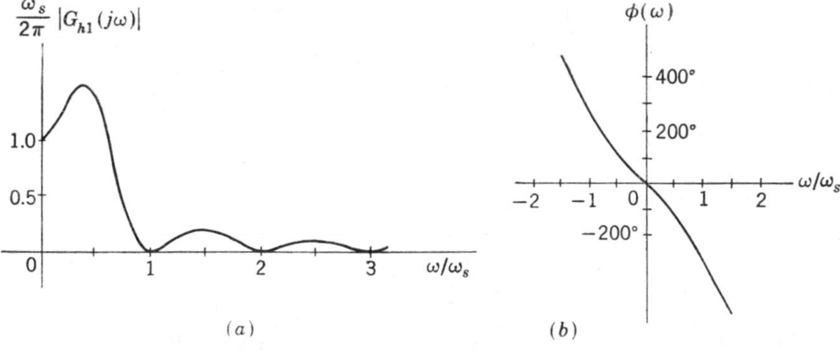

FIG. 4.6-9. Gain and phase characteristics of a first-order hold. (*a*) Gain characteristic; (*b*) Phase characteristic.

$$|G_{h1}(j\omega)| = \frac{2\pi}{\omega_s}\left(1 + \frac{4\pi^2\omega^2}{\omega_s^2}\right)^{1/2}\left(\frac{\sin \pi\omega/\omega_s}{\pi\omega/\omega_s}\right)^2 \qquad (4.6\text{-}41)$$

The frequency-response characteristics are plotted in Fig. 4.6-9. It is seen that the gain-characteristic curve cuts off sharply.

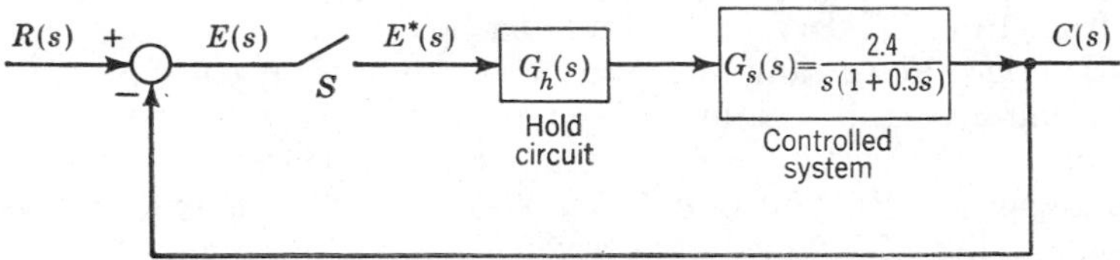

FIG. 4.6-10. The sampled-data feedback control system of the illustrative example.

The gain characteristics of these two types of holding devices show that the first-order hold, which cuts off much more sharply than the zero-order hold, provides better smoothing effect. However, the first-order introduces much more lagging phase shift than the zero-order hold. For instance, at a frequency of ω_s radians/sec, the former introduces a phase shift of $-279.1°$, while the latter causes a phase shift of $-180°$ only. The insertion of a first-order hold in a feedback control system generally complicates the problem of stabilization. Furthermore, the first-order holding device is more complicated in construction than the zero-order hold. Consequently, in practice, first-order hold is not commonly used in feedback control systems.

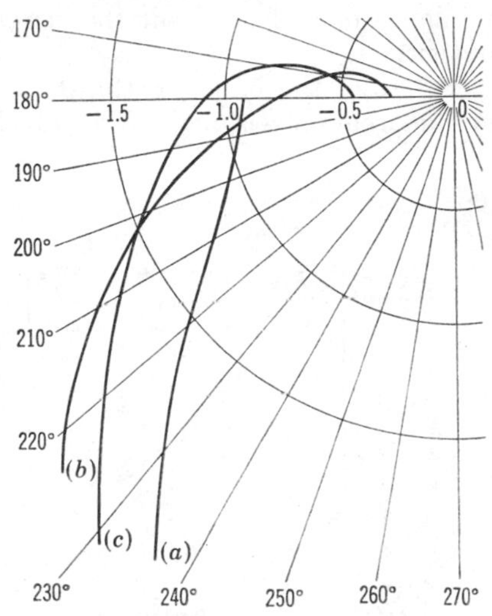

FIG. 4.6-11. Illustrations of the effects of the hold circuits upon the frequency characteristics. (a) With no hold; (b) with zero-order hold; (c) with first-order hold.

The effects of the hold circuits upon the frequency characteristics of sampled-data control systems are illustrated by an example. Shown in Fig. 4.6-10 is the block diagram of a sampled-data feedback control system. The sampling period is 1 sec, and the transfer function of the controlled system is

$$G_s(s) = \frac{2.4}{s(1 + 0.5s)} \qquad (4.6\text{-}42)$$

The open-loop frequency characteristic loci of the system with and without a hold circuit are plotted in Fig. 4.6-11. Curve a illustrates the frequency characteristic of the system with no hold circuit; curves b and c describe the frequency characteristics of the system with a zero-order and a first-order hold circuit, respectively. It is seen that the holding devices affect the stability of the system. Figure 4.6-11 reveals that without a hold circuit the system is stable, and that with the insertion of a first-order hold circuit the system becomes unstable. A zero-order hold circuit increases the gain margin of the system from 1.09 to 1.31, but it decreases the phase margin from 15 to 8°. In fact, a zero-order hold behaves as a lag network and, with appropriate sampling rate and system time constants, it can generally improve the stability of sampled-data control systems if the stabilization of the system requires phase-lag compensation. On account of the large phase shift it introduces, a first-order hold usually decreases the degree of stability of sampled-data feedback control systems.

4.7. The Effects of External Disturbances and Nonlinearities. In control systems, disturbing signals may enter into the system at points other than the input. The disturbances usually occur in the fixed elements of the system. The suppression of the adverse effect of the disturbances upon the output of the control system is one of the major requirements of feedback control. A well-designed feedback control system must be able to minimize or at least limit the effect of the disturbances upon the system output.

To study the effect of the disturbances upon the output of a control system, reference is made to the block diagram of Fig. 4.7-1. The disturbing

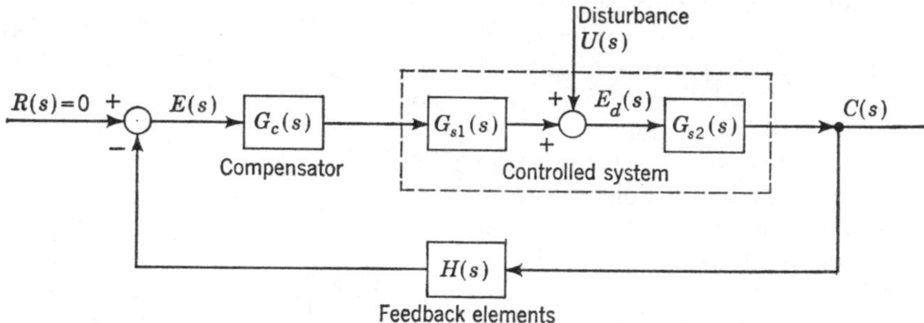

FIG. 4.7-1. A control system subjected to a disturbance.

signal $U(s)$ is introduced into the controlled system $G_s(s)$, which comprises fixed elements $G_{s1}(s)$ and $G_{s2}(s)$. In investigating the effectiveness of the system to suppress a disturbance the system is assumed to receive no input except the disturbing signal $u(t)$. Let $E_d(s)$ be the signal exerted on the output member $G_{s2}(s)$ as a result of the introduction of the disturbance $U(s)$ to the system. Then

$$E_d(s) = U(s) - G_c(s)G_s(s)H(s)E_d(s) \tag{4.7-1}$$

Transposing and simplifying yield

$$E_d(s) = \frac{U(s)}{1 + G_c(s)G_s(s)H(s)} \tag{4.7-2}$$

Equation (4.7-2) may be written as

$$E_d(s) = \left[1 - \frac{G_c(s)G_s(s)H(s)}{1 + G_c(s)G_s(s)H(s)}\right] U(s) \tag{4.7-3}$$

Evidently, the effect of the disturbance upon the output can be minimized, provided that

$$\frac{G_c(j\omega)G_s(j\omega)H(j\omega)}{1 + G_c(j\omega)G_s(j\omega)H(j\omega)} \approx 1 \tag{4.7-4}$$

or

$$G_c(j\omega)G_s(j\omega)H(j\omega) \gg 1 \tag{4.7-5}$$

for the frequency band of the disturbing signal $u(t)$. Thus, to suppress a disturbance, the loop gain over the frequency band of the disturbance must be made very high.

Now, turning to sampled-data feedback control systems, the effect of the disturbances upon the output may be investigated in much the same manner. Shown in Fig. 4.7-2 is the block diagram of a basic error-sampled

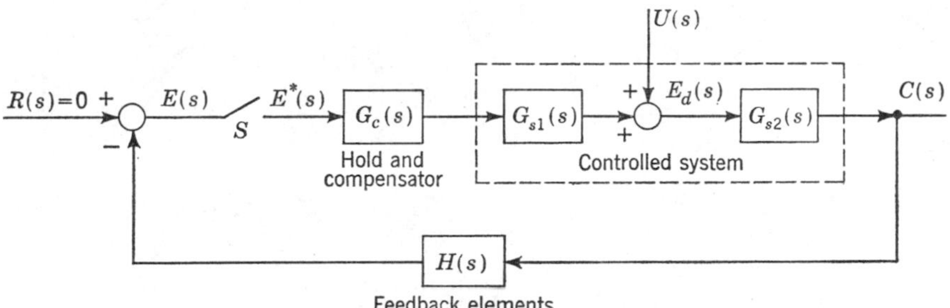

FIG. 4.7-2. A sampled-data control system subjected to a disturbance.

system. The system receives no input, except that a disturbance occurs in the controlled system $G_s(s)$. In response to the disturbance $u(t)$, an actuating error signal is generated through feedback action. This is the signal generated to counteract the disturbance. On account of the sampling process, the actuating error signal $e^*(t)$ contains both primary and complementary components with equal amplitudes. Only the primary component of the actuating signal is able to reduce the effect of the disturbance. The complementary components are merely ripples and produce no beneficial effect upon the system performance.[21]

The input to the sampler consists of two parts:

$$E(s) = E_a(s) + E_b(s) \tag{4.7-6}$$

in which

$$E_a(s) = -G_{s2}(s)H(s)U(s) \tag{4.7-7}$$

and

$$E_b(s) = -G_c(s)G_s(s)H(s)E^*(s) \tag{4.7-8}$$

$E_a(s)$ results from the introduction of the disturbing signal $u(t)$, and $E_b(s)$ is due to the sampled error signal $e^*(t)$. The output of the sampler is obtained by taking the starred transform of Eq. (4.7-6), thus,

$$E^*(s) = E_a^*(s) + E_b^*(s) \tag{4.7-9}$$

From Eqs. (4.7-7) and (4.7-8) it follows that

$$E_a^*(s) = -G_{s2}HU^*(s) \tag{4.7-10}$$

and

$$E_b^*(s) = -G_cG_sH^*(s)E^*(s) \tag{4.7-11}$$

Equation (4.7-9) can then be written as

$$E^*(s) = -G_{s2}HU^*(s) - G_cG_sH^*(s)E^*(s) \tag{4.7-12}$$

which is reduced to

$$E^*(s) = \frac{-G_{s2}HU^*(s)}{1 + G_cG_sH^*(s)} \tag{4.7-13}$$

Since the input exerted on the output member $G_{s2}(s)$ is given by

$$E_d(s) = U(s) + G_c(s)G_{s1}(s)E^*(s) \tag{4.7-14}$$

combining Eqs. (4.7-13) and (4.7-14) yields

$$E_d(s) = U(s) - \frac{G_c(s)G_{s1}(s)G_{s2}HU^*(s)}{1 + G_cG_sH^*(s)} \tag{4.7-15}$$

The corresponding frequency function is

$$E_d(j\omega) = U(j\omega) - \frac{G_c(j\omega)G_{s1}(j\omega)G_{s2}HU^*(j\omega)}{1 + G_cG_sH^*(j\omega)} \tag{4.7-16}$$

where

$$G_{s2}HU^*(j\omega) = \frac{1}{T} \sum_{n=-\infty}^{\infty} G_{s2}HU(s + jn\omega_s) \tag{4.7-17}$$

In many cases, Eq. (4.7-17) may be approximated as

$$G_{s2}HU^*(j\omega) \approx \frac{1}{T} G_{s2}(j\omega)H(j\omega)U(j\omega) \tag{4.7-18}$$

Then Eq. (4.7-16) reduces to

$$E_d(j\omega) \approx \left[1 - \frac{T^{-1}G_c(j\omega)G_s(j\omega)H(j\omega)}{1 + G_cG_sH^*(j\omega)}\right] U(j\omega) \tag{4.7-19}$$

Equation (4.7-19) places in evidence that the disturbance is suppressed, if the second term in the brackets is made unity over the frequency band of the disturbing signal. Clearly, the ratio

$$\frac{T^{-1}G_c(j\omega)G_s(j\omega)H(j\omega)}{1 + G_cG_sH^*(j\omega)} \tag{4.7-20}$$

may be used as a measure of how well the sampled-data feedback system can suppress a disturbing signal of certain frequency or frequency band.

The frequency ω_d of a disturbing signal may be either less than half the sampling frequency or greater than half the sampling frequency. Discussions of these two cases are presented below.

CASE 1. $$\omega_d < \frac{\omega_s}{2}$$

When the frequency of the disturbing signal is smaller than half the sampling frequency, the frequencies of the complementary components of the actuating error signal are greater than $\omega_s/2$ and thus can be removed by the elements of low-pass nature in the forward branch $G_c(s)G_s(s)$. Low-frequency disturbing signals generally cause little adverse effect.

CASE 2. $$\omega_d > \frac{\omega_s}{2}$$

When the frequency of the disturbing signal exceeds half the sampling frequency, the frequency of some complementary components of the actuating error signal is smaller than $\omega_s/2$. These low-frequency components resulting from sampling form a large-amplitude disturbing signal exerted on the output member $G_{s2}(s)$ of the system, which is more objectionable than the original disturbing signal. Consequently, in this case the feedback action impairs the system performance by introducing a low-frequency, large-amplitude disturbance in the output. One way of solving this problem is to prevent the high-frequency disturbing signal from reaching the sampler. This can be accomplished by making the system elements between the points where high-frequency disturbances occur and the input side of the sampler very effective low-pass filters. For instance, in the case of the system of Fig. 4.7-2, $G_{s2}(s)H(s)$ must be of very effective low-pass nature. Furthermore, in view of the fact that feedback fails to reduce the contamination of the output signal due to the high-frequency disturbance, the system elements between the point of occurrence of the high-frequency disturbance and the output terminal of the system [for example, $G_{s2}(s)$ of the system of Fig. 4.7-2] must behave as a very effective low-pass filter.

Effects of Nonlinearities. To study the effect of nonlinearities in the system components, reference is made to Fig. 4.7-3. If the controlled

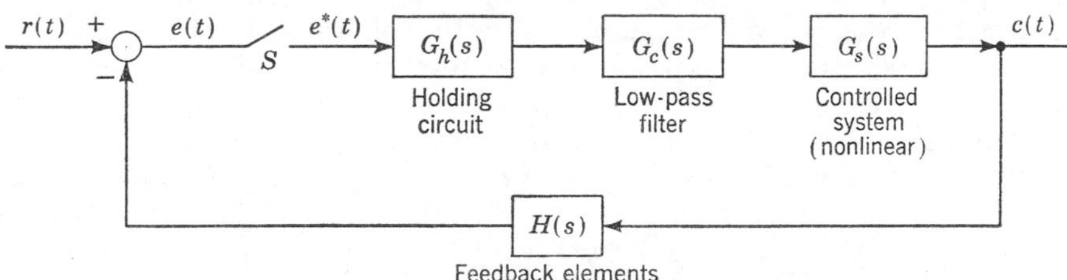

FIG. 4.7-3. A sampled-data system containing nonlinearities in the system components.

system $G_s(s)$ contains some nonlinearity (e.g., the saturation effects of the amplifier or the servomotor), the primary component of the actuating signal would beat with the complementary components in the nonlinear elements to produce new complementary components. These new components form the unwanted noise in the system. If the highest frequency of the input signal is much smaller than half the sampling frequency, the noise resulting from the intermodulation of the primary and complementary components in the nonlinear elements is of higher frequency and can readily be filtered in the output stage of the system. However, when the frequency spectrum of the input signal extends to frequencies near half sampling frequency, the intermodulation effect in the nonlinear elements becomes more troublesome. The intermodulation of the primary and complementary components would give rise to new complementary components, the frequency of which may be much lower than that of the primary component of the actuating signal. As a result, the low-frequency intermodulation noise cannot be removed by filtering without impairing the desired primary signal. Indeed, the intermodulation in nonlinear elements presents a rather troublesome problem. To solve this problem, the immediate remedy seems to be the elimination of the nonlinearities in the system. In case this cannot be done, effective low-pass filters should be introduced into the system to suppress the complementary components from the sampler before they reach the nonlinear elements. Another remedial measure is to increase the sampling frequency to a value much higher than twice the highest frequency of the input signal. However, it should be pointed out that sometimes nonlinear elements are deliberately introduced into control systems for improving the performance.

4.8. Conclusion. This chapter has presented the frequency domain analysis of digital and sampled-data control systems. The output of a sampling device may be described by three alternate expressions, which are given in Eqs. (4.1-14), (4.1-22), and (4.1-37), respectively. Based upon these relationships the (starred) transfer functions of pulsed-data networks and systems are derived. The first expression is particularly useful when the conventional frequency-response method is extended to the analysis and design of digital and sampled-data control systems. By making use of this expression the Nyquist diagram of a pulsed-data system may be constructed from the Nyquist diagram of the corresponding continuous-data system. The second and the third expressions form the basis of the z-transform theory, which is discussed in the following chapter.

The sampling operation produces unwanted complementary signals. Although a large portion of the unwanted signals may be removed by the system components, which are of low-pass nature, more complete smoothing is usually accomplished by the use of a hold circuit. The most commonly used holding device is the zero-order hold, but the first-order hold is also occasionally used. In spite of the fact that a hold adds to the phase lag of the control loop and thus decreases the system stability, the hold circuit is still necessary in practice in order to provide a finite drive to the continuous-data portion of the system.

CHAPTER 5

THEORY OF THE z TRANSFORMATION

5.1. Definition of z Transform and Pulse-transfer Function. It is a modern trend that engineering analysis and design rely heavily upon mathematical methods. Thus, use of the Laplace-transform method is a basic mode of analysis in designing continuous-data control systems. Correspondingly, the z-transform method seems to be the basic mode of analysis for use in solving sampled-data and digital control problems. The z-transform concept, first introduced by Hurewicz,[2] has been elaborated by a number of workers such as Barker[25] in England and Ragazzini and Zadeh[26] in the United States. At present, the z-transform techniques have become the most used method for the analysis and synthesis of sampled-data and digital control systems. In this chapter z-transformation theory is discussed in detail.

In Sec. 4.1 it is shown that a sampler (Fig. 4.1-1) can be described by Eq. (4.1-22) which, repeated here, is

$$X^*(s) = \mathcal{L}\{x^*(t)\} = \sum_{n=0}^{\infty} x(nT)\epsilon^{-nTs} \tag{5.1-1}$$

where $X^*(s)$ is the Laplace transform of the sampler output $x^*(t)$; $x(nT)$, the value of the input $x(t)$ at $t = nT$; T, the sampling period; and s, a complex variable. Equation (5.1-1) indicates that $X^*(s)$ is an infinite series in ϵ^{Ts}. Consequently, it is more convenient to make use of the substitution

$$z = \epsilon^{Ts} \tag{5.1-2}$$

and the abbreviated notation $X(z)$ for the resulting function of z; thus

$$X(z) \triangleq X^*\left(\frac{1}{T}\ln z\right) = \sum_{n=0}^{\infty} x(nT)z^{-n} \tag{5.1-3}$$

Equation (5.1-3) describes a mathematical operation commonly known as z transformation in the literature. $X(z)$ is defined as the z transform of $x(t)$ [or, perhaps more accurately, the z transform of $x^*(t)$]. It is also termed the sequence transform of x_n or $x(nT)$. The z transform of Eq. (5.1-3) is closely analogous to the Laplace transform

$$X(s) \triangleq \int_0^{\infty} x(t)\epsilon^{-st}\,dt \tag{5.1-4}$$

The z transformation is a summation process, because it deals with pulsed-data functions. Symbolically, it is common practice to write

$$X(z) = \mathfrak{z}\{x(t)\} \tag{5.1-5}$$

and

$$\mathfrak{z}\{x(t)\} = \mathfrak{L}\{x^*(t)\}|_{s=(1/T)\ln z} \tag{5.1-6}$$

as the z transform of function $x(t)$, where the symbol $\mathfrak{z}$ is used to denote the z-transform operator. Equation (5.1-6) implies that the z transform of a function is obtained by finding the Laplace transform of that function in pulsed-data form and replacing the complex variable s by $T^{-1} \ln z$. Indeed, the z transform of a function is a variant form of the Laplace transform of that function.

As shown in Sec. 4.1, the output of a sampler can also be described in terms of residues by Eq. (4.1-37) which, rewritten below, is

$$X^*(s) = \sum_k \text{residues of } \frac{1}{1 - \epsilon^{-T(s-\chi)}} X(\chi) \text{ at } \chi = s_k \tag{5.1-7}$$

where $X^*(s)$ and $X(s)$ are the Laplace transform of the output and the input respectively, and s_k is a pole of $X(\chi)$. $X(\chi)$ is equal to $X(s)$ with s replaced by χ. Substituting z for ϵ^{Ts} in Eq. (5.1-7) gives

$$X(z) \triangleq \sum_k \text{residues of } \frac{1}{1 - \epsilon^{T\chi}z^{-1}} X(\chi) \text{ at } \chi = s_k \tag{5.1-8}$$

which provides another definition of the z transform. Equations (5.1-3) and (5.1-8) form the two fundamental equations in z-transformation theory.

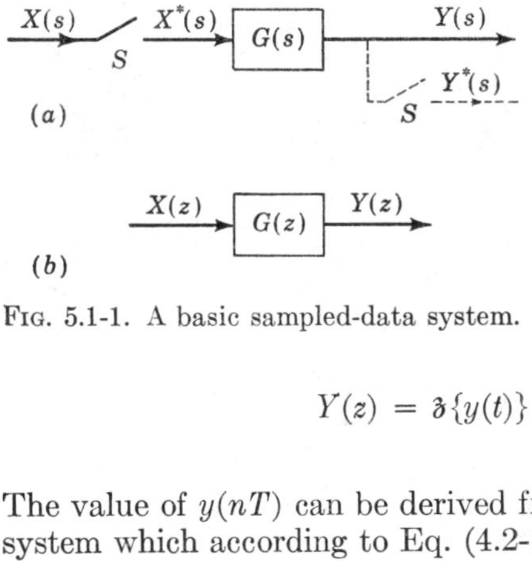

Now, consider a pulsed-data system with samplers which are synchronized in phase and operate at the same rate (Fig. 5.1-1). Making use of Eq. (5.1-3) the z transform of the output of the sampled-data system is given by

FIG. 5.1-1. A basic sampled-data system.

$$Y(z) = \mathfrak{z}\{y(t)\} = \sum_{n=0}^{\infty} y(nT)z^{-n} \tag{5.1-9}$$

The value of $y(nT)$ can be derived from the continuous output $y(t)$ of the system which according to Eq. (4.2-16) is

$$y(t) = \sum_{k=0}^{\infty} g(t - kT)x(kT) \tag{5.1-10}$$

where $g(t)$ is the impulse response or the weighting function of system $G(s)$.

Then, the value of the output at sampling instant nT is equal to

$$y(nT) = \sum_{k=0}^{\infty} g(nT - kT)x(kT) \tag{5.1-11}$$

Substituting Eq. (5.1-11) into Eq. (5.1-9) yields

$$Y(z) = \sum_{n=0}^{\infty} \sum_{k=0}^{\infty} g(nT - kT)x(kT)z^{-n} \tag{5.1-12}$$

Making the substitution $m = n - k$ and $n = m + k$ reduces Eq. (5.1-12) to

$$Y(z) = \sum_{n=0}^{\infty} \sum_{k=0}^{\infty} g(nT - kT)x(kT)z^{-n} \tag{5.1-12}$$

Rearranging Eq. (5.1-13) gives

$$Y(z) = \sum_{m=0}^{\infty} g(mT)z^{-m} \sum_{k=0}^{\infty} x(kT)z^{-k} \tag{5.1-14}$$

Since, from Eq. (5.1-3),

$$G(z) = \sum_{m=0}^{\infty} g(mT)z^{-m} \tag{5.1-15}$$

where $g(mT)$ is the weighting sequence of the system and Eq. (5.1-15) is by definition the z transform of time function $g(t)$, and

$$X(z) = \sum_{k=0}^{\infty} x(kT)z^{-k} \tag{5.1-16}$$

the z transform of the output, Eq. (5.1-14), can be written as

$$Y(z) = G(z)X(z) \tag{5.1-17}$$

This is an important equation which relates the pulsed output of the system to its pulsed input. Thus, as far as pulsed functions are concerned, the sampled-data system of Fig. 5.1-1*a* can be described in terms of the z transforms by the equivalent block diagram shown in Fig. 5.1-1*b*. Equation (5.1-17) applies to the output signal $y(t)$ at the sampling instants, since the z transformation is applicable only to discrete signals.

In Eq. (5.1-17), the function $G(z)$, which is the ratio of the output to the input,

$$G(z) = \frac{Y(z)}{X(z)} \tag{5.1-18}$$

is sometimes referred to as the *pulse-transfer function*[25] or the *z-transfer function* of the sampled-data system. Hence the pulse-transfer function of a sampled-data system (or device) may be defined as the ratio of the

z transforms of the pulsed output of the system (or device) to its pulsed input. It is interesting to note the similarity of Eq. (5.1-18) to the familiar expression

$$G(s) = \frac{Y(s)}{X(s)} \tag{5.1-19}$$

which would be the transfer function of the system if the samplers were removed. This important similarity makes possible the treatment and manipulation of z transforms and pulse-transfer functions in the same manner as the Laplace transform and conventional transfer functions, thus making the z transformation a very convenient mathematical technique in sampled-data system theory.

Now, for the sake of convenience, the z transform of a function $x(t)$ is also denoted by

$$X(z) = \mathfrak{z}\{X(s)\} \tag{5.1-20}$$

where $X(s)$ is the Laplace transform of $x(t)$. Of course, it is understood that the operation involved in Eq. (5.1-20) applies to the time function.

Reference to Fig. 5.1-1a indicates that the Laplace transform of the continuous output $y(t)$ and the pulsed output $y^*(t)$ are given by

$$Y(s) = G(s)X^*(s) \tag{5.1-21}$$

and

$$Y^*(s) = G^*(s)X^*(s) \tag{5.1-22}$$

which follow from Eqs. (4.3-4) and (4.3-9), respectively. The pulsed-data function $y^*(t)$ is obtained if a fictitious sampler, which operates in synchronism with the sampler of the system, is inserted at the output side of the system. The fictitious sampler is shown in dotted lines in Fig. 5.1-1a. Thus, Eq. (5.1-22) relates the sampled output to the sampled input of the system. Making the substitution $z = \epsilon^{Ts}$ and using the abbreviated notation $Y(z)$, $G(z)$, and $X(z)$ for the resulting functions of z, Eq. (5.1-22) may be written as

$$Y(z) = G(z)X(z) \tag{5.1-23}$$

where $Y(z)$ and $X(z)$ are the z transforms of $y^*(t)$ and $x^*(t)$ respectively, and $G(z)$ is the z transform associated with $G(s)$. According to the definition of the z transformation, Eqs. (5.1-3) and (5.1-20), the operation of passing from Eq. (5.1-21) to Eqs. (5.1-22) and (5.1-23) can thus be referred to as applying the z transformation to both members of Eq. (5.1-21). Taking the z transform associated with the function at the left-hand side of Eq. (5.1-21) yields

$$\mathfrak{z}\{Y(s)\} = Y(z) \tag{5.1-24}$$

In like manner, the z transform associated with the right-hand side of Eq. (5.1-21) is given by

$$\begin{aligned}\mathfrak{z}\{G(s)X^*(s)\} &= \mathfrak{z}\{G(s)\}X(z) \\ &= G(z)X(z)\end{aligned} \tag{5.1-25}$$

since

$$\mathfrak{z}\{G(s)\} = G(z) \tag{5.1-26}$$

That is, $G(s)$ is transformed to $G(z)$ and $X^*(s)$ is replaced by its equivalent function $X(z)$. Equation (5.1-25) describes a basic operation in the z-transform theory, which implies that the z transform associated with the product of a starred function of s and a nonstarred (conventional) function of s is equal to the product of the z transforms associated with these two functions.

5.2. Evaluation of z Transforms and Pulse-transfer Functions. The analysis and design of continuous-data feedback control systems is often carried out by the transfer-function method. In the analysis a servo system is represented by a block diagram connecting in proper sequence all the system building blocks which are described by transfer functions. The transfer function of a device is defined as the complex ratio of the output of the device to its input. From the block diagram the over-all system equation is derived. The transfer functions for each building block can readily be identified in the equation specifying the over-all system. The transfer-function method is advantageous over other methods, because it establishes for each building block a unique mathematical expression describing the effect of the individual component on the system behavior as a whole, thus enabling the effect of change or addition of building blocks upon the over-all system performance to be identified readily.

In view of these advantages of the transfer-function concept for analyzing continuous-data systems, it seems desirable to carry over this concept and technique to the analysis of sampled-data systems. As explained in the previous section, sampled-data and digital control systems can be described by pulse-transfer functions in the same manner that continuous-data systems are specified by conventional transfer functions. To analyze sampled-data systems by the transfer-function method, it is essential to know how to derive the z transforms from time functions, and the pulse-transfer functions (or the z-transfer functions) for the building blocks or the components of the system.

Having defined the z transform of a function and the pulse-transfer function of a sampled-data system, one is now in a position to illustrate the evaluation of the pulse-transfer functions of system components from their conventional transfer functions or the z transforms for their impulse responses. The z transform of a time function can readily be derived by the use of Eq. (5.1-3) which serves as a definition. Comparison of Eq. (5.1-15) with Eq. (5.1-26) brings out that the pulse-transfer function of a system is identical to the z transform of the impulse response of that system. This suggests a procedure for determining the pulse-transfer function of a sampled-data system. The following paragraphs illustrate the procedure for obtaining the z transforms and the pulse-transfer functions. A short list of z transform pairs of the most commonly encountered functions is given at the end of this section; and a more extensive table of important z transforms is presented in Appendix 1.

The evaluation of the z transforms of some basic functions by making use of the definition

$$G(z) \triangleq \sum_{n=0}^{\infty} g(nT)z^{-n} \tag{5.2-1}$$

is demonstrated below. When the function $g(t)$ is an impulsive function, $g(nT)$ of Eq. (5.2-1) represents the strength of the impulse at $t = nT$ rather than the value of $g(t)$ at that instant. In the following derivation an assumption is made that the sampling operation is coincident with the beginning of the time function.

1. IMPULSE FUNCTION

$$g(t) = K\delta(t) \tag{5.2-2}$$

$$G(s) = \mathfrak{L}\{g(t)\} = K \tag{5.2-3}$$

At $t = nT$, the strength of the impulse function $g(t)$ is given by

$$g(nT) = \int_{-\infty}^{\infty} K\delta(t)\,dt = \begin{cases} K & \text{for } n = 0 \\ 0 & \text{elsewhere} \end{cases} \tag{5.2-4}$$

Then it follows from Eq. (5.2-1) that the z transform of an impulse function of strength K is given by

$$G(z) = K \tag{5.2-5}$$

It is to be noted that the z transform of an impulse function is the same as its Laplace transform since an impulse function is a pulsed function itself.

2. STEP FUNCTION

$$g(t) = Ku(t) \tag{5.2-6}$$

$$G(s) = \mathfrak{L}\{g(t)\} = \frac{K}{s} \tag{5.2-7}$$

The substitution of nT for t in Eq. (5.2-6) yields the weighting sequence

$$g(nT) = Ku(nT) = K \tag{5.2-8}$$

It is assumed that the sampling operation is coincident with the beginning of the step function. Then, making use of Eq. (5.2-1) yields

$$\begin{aligned} G(z) &= \sum_{n=0}^{\infty} Kz^{-n} \\ &= K(1 + z^{-1} + z^{-2} + \cdots) \\ &= \frac{K}{1 - z^{-1}} \qquad \text{for } |z^{-1}| < 1 \end{aligned} \tag{5.2-9}$$

or

$$G(z) = \frac{Kz}{z - 1} \qquad \text{for } |z^{-1}| < 1 \tag{5.2-10}$$

which is the z transform of a step function (Fig. 5.2-1).

3. RAMP FUNCTION

$$g(t) = Kt \tag{5.2-11}$$

$$G(s) = \mathfrak{L}\{g(t)\} = \frac{K}{s^2} \tag{5.2-12}$$

From Eq. (5.2-11), at $t = nT$,

$$g(nT) = KnT \tag{5.2-13}$$

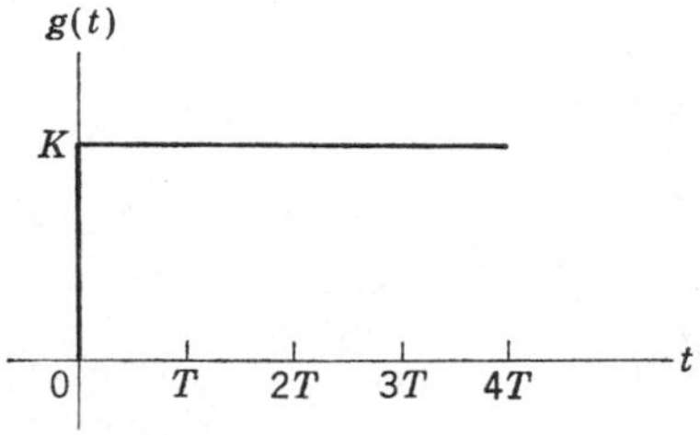

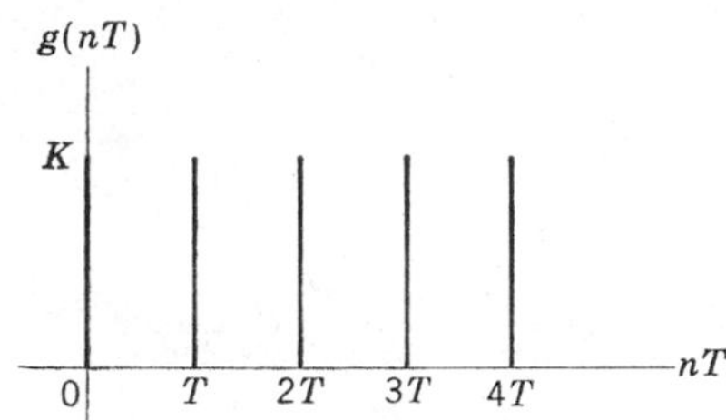

FIG. 5.2-1. Step function.

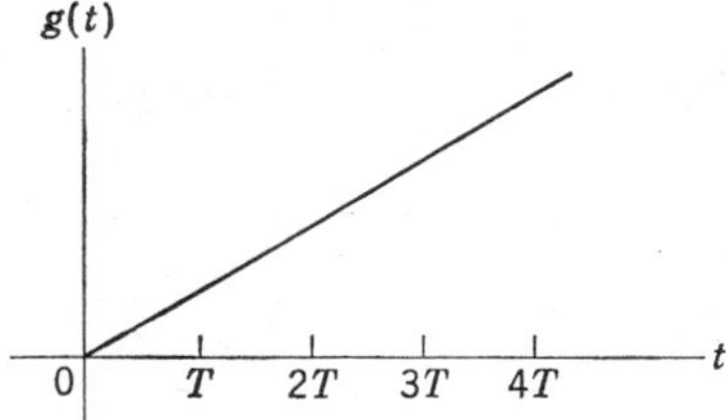

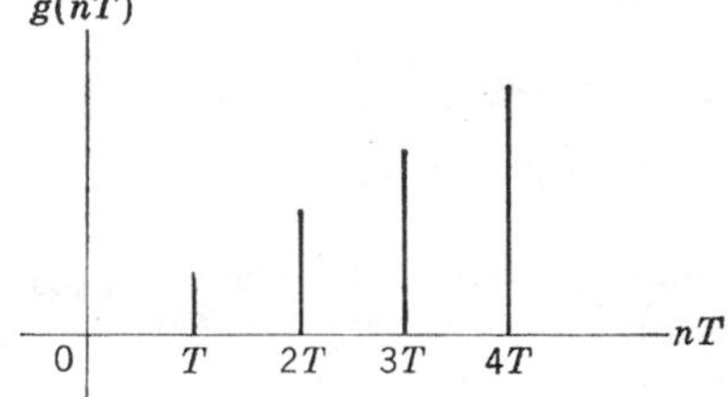

FIG. 5.2-2. Ramp function.

where n is an integer. By proper substitution, Eq. (5.2-1) yields the z transform of a ramp function (Fig. 5.2-2).

$$\begin{aligned} G(z) &= \sum_{n=0}^{\infty} KnTz^{-n} \\ &= KTz^{-1}[1 + 2z^{-1} + 3z^{-2} + \cdots + (k+1)z^{-k} + \cdots] \\ &= \frac{KTz^{-1}}{(1 - z^{-1})^2} \qquad \text{for } |z^{-1}| < 1 \end{aligned} \tag{5.2-14}$$

$$\text{or} \quad G(z) = \frac{KTz}{(z-1)^2} \qquad \text{for } |z^{-1}| < 1 \tag{5.2-15}$$

The right-hand side of Eq. (5.2-15) gives the z transform of a ramp function; also it is the pulse-transfer function for a system with the conventional transfer function $G(s) = K/s^2$.

4. SIMPLE HIGH-ORDER FUNCTION—POSITIVE POWERS OF t

$$g(t) = \frac{K}{k!} t^k \tag{5.2-16}$$

$$G(s) = \mathcal{L}\{g(t)\} = \frac{K}{s^{k+1}} \tag{5.2-17}$$

The weighting sequence is

$$g(nT) = \frac{K}{k!} (nT)^k \tag{5.2-18}$$

Then from Eq. (5.2-1), the z transform is given by

$$\begin{aligned} G(z) &= \sum_{n=0}^{\infty} \frac{K}{k!} (nT)^k z^{-n} \\ &= \frac{K}{k!} T^k [1^k z^{-1} + 2^k z^{-2} + 3^k z^{-3} + \cdots] \end{aligned} \tag{5.2-19}$$

The generating function for the series of Eq. (5.2-19) is

$$G(k+1,z) = -\frac{Tz}{k!} G'(k,z) \tag{5.2-20}$$

where $G'(k,z)$ is the derivative of $G(k,z)$ with respect to z. Equation (5.2-19) also represents the pulse-transfer function of the system $G(s) = K/s^{k+1}$. By the use of Eq. (5.1-8) a more compact expression is derived later.

5. DELAYED IMPULSE FUNCTION

$$g(t) = K\delta(t - kT) \tag{5.2-21}$$

$$G(s) = \mathcal{L}\{g(t)\} = K\epsilon^{-kTs} \tag{5.2-22}$$

where k is an integer. At $t = nT$, the strength of the given function $g(t)$ is given by

$$g(nT) = \int_{-\infty}^{\infty} K\delta(t - kT)\,dt = \begin{cases} K & \text{for } n = k \\ 0 & \text{elsewhere} \end{cases} \tag{5.2-23}$$

Substituting into Eq. (5.2-1) yields

$$\begin{aligned} G(z) &= \sum_{n=0}^{\infty} g(nT) z^{-n} \\ &= Kz^{-k} \end{aligned} \tag{5.2-24}$$

By comparing Eq. (5.2-24) with Eq. (5.2-5) it is seen that z^{-k} implies a time delay of kT units, where T is the sampling period.

6. EXPONENTIAL FUNCTION

$$g(t) = K\epsilon^{-at} \tag{5.2-25}$$

$$G(s) = \mathcal{L}\{g(t)\} = \frac{K}{s+a} \tag{5.2-26}$$

where a is a constant. The weighting sequence is

$$g(nT) = K\epsilon^{-anT} \tag{5.2-27}$$

Making use of Eq. (5.2-1) yields the z transform of the function which is given by Eq. (5.2-25) and is sketched in Fig. 5.2-3.

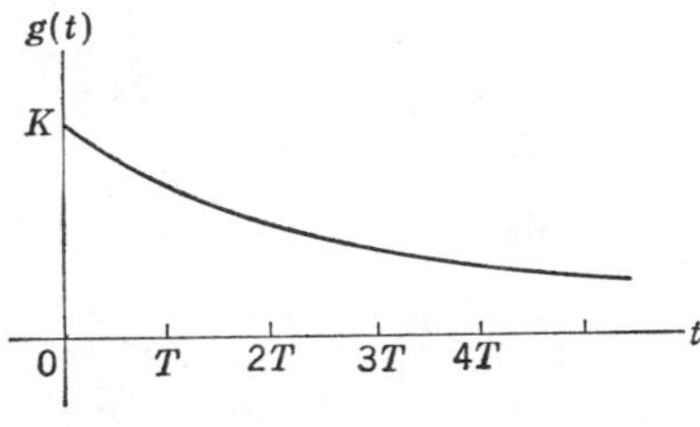

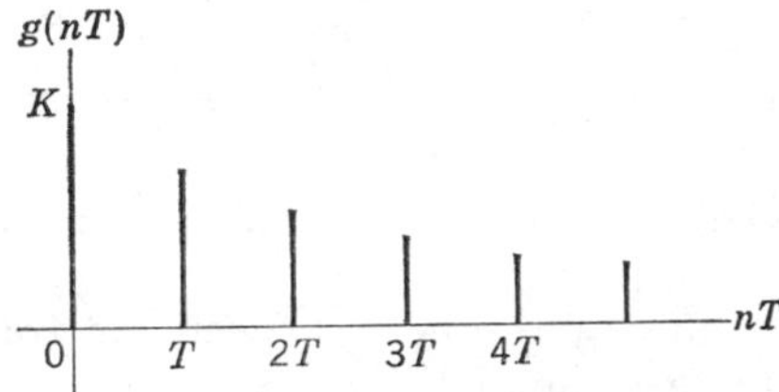

FIG. 5.2-3. Exponential function.

$$\begin{aligned} G(z) &= \sum_{n=0}^{\infty} K\epsilon^{\ anT} z^{-n} \\ &= K[1 + (\epsilon^{-aT}z^{-1}) + (\epsilon^{-aT}z^{-1})^2 + \cdots] \\ &= \frac{K}{1 - \epsilon^{-aT}z^{-1}} \end{aligned} \tag{5.2-28}$$

if $|\epsilon^{-aT}z^{-1}| < 1$; or

$$G(z) = \frac{Kz}{z - \epsilon^{-aT}} \tag{5.2-29}$$

for $|\epsilon^{-aT}z^{-1}| < 1$.

7. PRODUCT OF POSITIVE POWERS OF t AND EXPONENTIAL FUNCTION

$$g(t) = \frac{K}{r!} t^r \epsilon^{-at} \tag{5.2-30}$$

$$G(s) = \mathcal{L}\{g(t)\} = \frac{K}{(s+a)^{r+1}} \tag{5.2-31}$$

Since Eq. (5.2-30) can be written as

$$g(t) = (-1)^r \frac{K}{r!} \frac{\partial^r}{\partial a^r} \epsilon^{-at} \tag{5.2-32}$$

the weighting sequence is given by

$$g(nT) = (-1)^r \frac{K}{r!} \frac{\partial^r}{\partial a^r} \epsilon^{-anT} \tag{5.2-33}$$

Substituting into Eq. (5.2-1) yields

$$G(z) = \sum_{n=0}^{\infty} (-1)^r \frac{K}{r!} \frac{\partial^r}{\partial a^r} \epsilon^{-anT} z^{-n} \tag{5.2-34}$$

Rearranging Eq. (5.2-34) leads to

$$G(z) = (-1)^r \frac{K}{r!} \frac{\partial^r}{\partial a^r} \sum_{n=0}^{\infty} (z^{-1}\epsilon^{-aT})^n \tag{5.2-35}$$

Summation yields

$$G(z) = (-1)^r \frac{K}{r!} \frac{\partial^r}{\partial a^r} \left(\frac{1}{1 - \epsilon^{-aT} z^{-1}}\right) \tag{5.2-36}$$

which is the pulse-transfer function of a system whose conventional transfer function is given by Eq. (5.2-31).

8. RATIO OF TWO POLYNOMIALS IN s. When the transfer function of a system is a ratio of two polynomials in s,

$$G(s) = \frac{P(s)}{Q(s)} \tag{5.2-37}$$

and it can be represented by a partial fraction expansion

$$G(s) = \sum_{\mu,\nu} \frac{K_\mu}{(s + a_\mu)^\nu} \tag{5.2-38}$$

then the pulse-transfer function of the system is readily derived by making use of Eq. (5.2-36). Thus,

$$G(z) = \sum_{\mu,\nu} \frac{(-1)^{\nu-1}}{(\nu - 1)!} \frac{\partial^{\nu-1}}{\partial a_\mu{}^{\nu-1}} \left(\frac{K_\mu}{1 - \epsilon^{-a_\mu T} z^{-1}}\right) \tag{5.2-39}$$

9. SINE FUNCTION

$$g(t) = \sin \omega_0 t \tag{5.2-40}$$

$$G(s) = \frac{\omega_0}{s^2 + \omega_0{}^2} \tag{5.2-41}$$

At $t = nT$,

$$g(nT) = \sin \omega_0 nT = \frac{\epsilon^{jn\omega_0 T} - \epsilon^{-jn\omega_0 T}}{2j} \tag{5.2-42}$$

$g(t)$ and $g(nT)$ are sketched in Fig. 5.2-4. Substituting Eq. (5.2-42) into Eq. (5.2-1) yields

$$G(z) = \sum_{n=0}^{\infty} \frac{1}{2j} (\epsilon^{jn\omega_0 T} - \epsilon^{-jn\omega_0 T}) z^{-n}$$

$$= \frac{1}{2j} \left[\sum_{n=0}^{\infty} (\epsilon^{j\omega_0 T} z^{-1})^n - \sum_{n=0}^{\infty} (\epsilon^{-j\omega_0 T} z^{-1})^n \right] \qquad (5.2\text{-}43)$$

Summation yields

$$G(z) = \frac{1}{2j} \left(\frac{1}{1 - \epsilon^{j\omega_0 T} z^{-1}} - \frac{1}{1 - \epsilon^{-j\omega_0 T} z^{-1}} \right) \qquad (5.2\text{-}44)$$

Simplifying,

$$G(z) = \frac{z^{-1} \sin \omega_0 T}{1 - 2z^{-1} \cos \omega_0 T + z^{-2}} \qquad (5.2\text{-}45)$$

or

$$G(z) = \frac{z \sin \omega_0 T}{z^2 - 2z \cos \omega_0 T + 1} \qquad (5.2\text{-}46)$$

which is the z transform of $\sin \omega_0 t$.

10. COSINE FUNCTION

$$g(t) = \cos \omega_0 t \qquad (5.2\text{-}47)$$

$$G(s) = \frac{s}{s^2 + \omega_0^2} \qquad (5.2\text{-}48)$$

From Eq. (5.2-47), the replacing of t by nT yields the weighting sequence,

$$g(nT) = \cos \omega_0 nT = \tfrac{1}{2}(\epsilon^{jn\omega_0 T} + \epsilon^{-jn\omega_0 T}) \qquad (5.2\text{-}49)$$

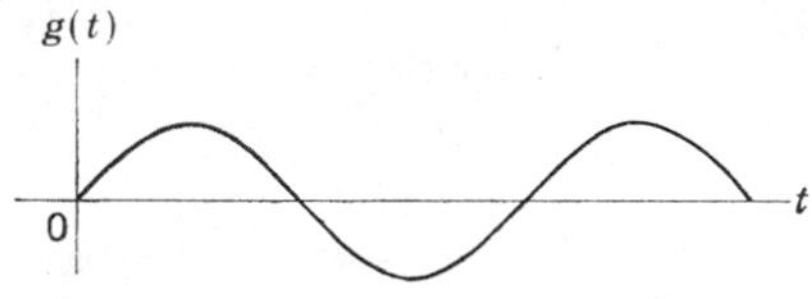

FIG. 5.2-4. Sinusoidal function.

Then the z transform of Eq. (5.2-47) is given by

$$G(z) = \sum_{n=0}^{\infty} \tfrac{1}{2}(\epsilon^{jn\omega_0 T} + \epsilon^{-jn\omega_0 T}) z^{-n}$$

$$= \tfrac{1}{2} \left(\frac{1}{1 - \epsilon^{j\omega_0 T} z^{-1}} + \frac{1}{1 - \epsilon^{-j\omega_0 T} z^{-1}} \right) \qquad (5.2\text{-}50)$$

Simplifying,

$$G(z) = \frac{z(z - \cos \omega_0 T)}{z^2 - 2z \cos \omega_0 T + 1} \qquad (5.2\text{-}51)$$

Suggested Rules for Calculating the Pulse-transfer Function of a System.

1. Derive the transfer function $G(s)$ of the system by conventional methods.

2. Determine the weighting function $g(t)$ (the impulse response) of the system by evaluating the inverse Laplace transform of $G(s)$.

3. Obtain the weighting sequence $g(nT)$ or g_n of the system by substituting nT for t in the weighting function $g(t)$.

4. Find the sum of the series

$$G(z) = \sum_{n=0}^{\infty} g(nT)z^{-n}$$

For a physically realizable system this series converges.

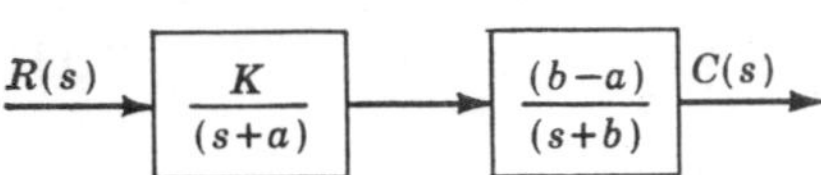

FIG. 5.2-5. Illustrative Example 5.2-1.

5. When the conventional transfer function $G(s)$ of the system is quite complicated, split $G(s)$ into partial fractions and apply Rules 2, 3, and 4 to these partial fractions.

EXAMPLE 5.2-1. Find the pulse-transfer function of the system shown in Fig. 5.2-5.

The over-all transfer function is

$$G(s) = \frac{K(b - a)}{(s + a)(s + b)} \tag{5.2-52}$$

which can be written as

$$G(s) = \frac{K}{s + a} - \frac{K}{s + b} \tag{5.2-53}$$

The weighting function and the weighting sequence are respectively given by

$$g(t) = K(\epsilon^{-at} - \epsilon^{-bt}) \tag{5.2-54}$$

and

$$g(nT) = K(\epsilon^{-anT} - \epsilon^{-bnT}) \tag{5.2-55}$$

By definition, the pulse-transfer function is

$$G(z) = \sum_{n=0}^{\infty} g(nT)z^{-n} = K \sum_{n=0}^{\infty} (\epsilon^{-anT} - \epsilon^{-bnT})z^{-n} \tag{5.2-56}$$

which can be put in the following compact form

$$G(z) = \frac{K}{1 - \epsilon^{-aT}z^{-1}} - \frac{K}{1 - \epsilon^{-bT}z^{-1}} \tag{5.2-57}$$

Simplifying, $G(z)$ becomes

$$G(z) = \frac{Kz(\epsilon^{-aT} - \epsilon^{-bT})}{(z - \epsilon^{-aT})(z - \epsilon^{-bT})} \tag{5.2-58}$$

The usefulness of the above rules depends upon the possibility and readiness of evaluating the summation of the infinite series in Rule 4. For most practical systems the sum of the series can readily be determined. However, when difficulty arises in expressing the infinite series in a compact form, it is then necessary to make use of other expressions defining the pulse-transfer function of a system.

In Chap. 4, three basic expressions describing a sampler are derived, that is,

$$X^*(s) = \frac{1}{T} \sum_{n=-\infty}^{\infty} X(s + jn\omega_s) \tag{5.2-59}$$

$$X^*(s) = \sum_{n=0}^{\infty} x(nT)\epsilon^{-nTs} \tag{5.2-60}$$

$$X^*(s) = \sum_k \text{residues of } \frac{1}{1 - \epsilon^{T\chi}\epsilon^{-Ts}} X(\chi) \text{ at } \chi = s_k \tag{5.2-61}$$

where s_k is a pole of $X(\chi)$ and the summation covers all the poles of $X(\chi)$ in the left half of the χ plane. In like manner the transfer function $G^*(s)$ of a pulsed-data system can also be expressed as

$$G^*(s) = \frac{1}{T} \sum_{n=-\infty}^{\infty} G(s + jn\omega_s) \tag{5.2-62}$$

$$G^*(s) = \sum_{n=0}^{\infty} g(nT)\epsilon^{-nTs} \tag{5.2-63}$$

$$G^*(s) = \sum_k \text{residues of } \frac{1}{1 - \epsilon^{T\chi}\epsilon^{-Ts}} G(\chi) \text{ at } \chi = s_k \tag{5.2-64}$$

where $g(nT)$ is the weighting sequence, $G(s)$ is the conventional transfer function, s_k is a pole of $G(\chi)$, and $G(\chi) = G(s)|_{s=\chi}$. Equations (5.2-62), (5.2-63), and (5.2-64) follow immediately from Eqs. (5.2-59), (5.2-60), and (5.2-61) respectively, if use is made of the duality between signals and impulse responses. A signal and an impulse response are said to be duals if they have identical Laplace transforms.

By substituting

$$z = \epsilon^{Ts} \tag{5.2-65}$$

and representing the new function by $G(z)$, Eqs. (5.2-63) and (5.2-64) become

$$G(z) = \sum_{n=0}^{\infty} g(nT)z^{-n} \tag{5.2-66}$$

$$G(z) = \sum_k \text{residues of } \frac{G(\chi)}{1 - z^{-1}\epsilon^{T\chi}} \text{ at } \chi = s_k \tag{5.2-67}$$

which represent the two most useful expressions defining the pulse-transfer function of a system. In Eq. (5.2-67), $G(\chi)$ is equal to $G(s)$ with s replaced by χ. When $G(s)$ contains only simple poles, Eq. (5.2-67) reduces to

$$G(z) = \sum_k \frac{1}{1 - \epsilon^{Ts_k} z^{-1}} \text{ residues of } G(\chi) \text{ at } \chi = s_k \tag{5.2-68}$$

Furthermore, if $G(s)$ is a ratio of two rational polynomials in s

$$G(s) = \frac{P(s)}{Q(s)} \tag{5.2-69}$$

with the order of the denominator higher than that of the numerator, Eq. (5.2-68) may be simplified to

$$G(z) = \sum_k \frac{P(s_k)}{Q'(s_k)} \frac{1}{1 - \epsilon^{Ts_k} z^{-1}} \tag{5.2-70}$$

Equations (5.2-67) and (5.2-68) provide the working definition of the pulse-transfer function of a system based upon residue evaluation. It should be pointed out that in many cases this is probably the simplest and the most powerful means for actual evaluation of z transforms and pulse-transfer functions in closed form. To emphasize this method, a few examples illustrating the evaluation of the pulse-transfer function by the use of Eqs. (5.2-67) and (5.2-68) are presented in the following:

1. A system with conventional transfer function

$$G(s) = \frac{K}{s + a} \tag{5.2-71}$$

where K and a are constants.

It is quite obvious that the residue of $G(s)$ at its pole $s = -a$ is K. Substitution into Eq. (5.2-68) yields the pulse-transfer function of the system as

$$G(z) = \mathfrak{z}\left\{\frac{K}{s + a}\right\} = \frac{K}{1 - \epsilon^{-aT} z^{-1}} \tag{5.2-72}$$

which is in agreement with Eq. (5.2-28) derived in a previous paragraph.

2. If the system transfer function contains a double pole at $s = -a$ and is given by

$$G(s) = \frac{K}{(s + a)^2} \tag{5.2-73}$$

then $G(s)$ can be written as

$$G(s) = -\frac{\partial}{\partial a}\left(\frac{K}{s + a}\right) \tag{5.2-74}$$

and the pulse-transfer function is given by

$$G(z) = \mathfrak{z}\left\{-\frac{\partial}{\partial a}\left(\frac{K}{s + a}\right)\right\} \tag{5.2-75}$$

Since a is a parameter independent of complex variable s, the z transformation can be performed before the partial derivative is taken, that is,

$$G(z) = -\frac{\partial}{\partial a}\left[\mathfrak{z}\left\{\frac{K}{s+a}\right\}\right] \qquad (5.2\text{-}76)$$

Making use of Eq. (5.2-72) yields the pulse-transfer function

$$G(z) = -\frac{\partial}{\partial a}\left(\frac{K}{1-\epsilon^{-aT}z^{-1}}\right) \qquad (5.2\text{-}77)$$

3. When the system transfer function contains a multiple pole such that

$$G(s) = \frac{K}{(s+a)^{k+1}} \qquad (5.2\text{-}78)$$

where k is an integer, $G(s)$ can be put into the following form

$$G(s) = (-1)^k \frac{K}{k!}\frac{\partial^k}{\partial a^k}\left(\frac{1}{s+a}\right) \qquad (5.2\text{-}79)$$

Taking the z transform of both sides of the above equation yields

$$G(z) = \mathfrak{z}\left\{(-1)^k \frac{K}{k!}\frac{\partial^k}{\partial a^k}\left(\frac{1}{s+a}\right)\right\}$$

$$= (-1)^k \frac{K}{k!}\,\mathfrak{z}\left\{\frac{\partial^k}{\partial a^k}\left(\frac{1}{s+a}\right)\right\} \qquad (5.2\text{-}80)$$

Inverting the order of partial differentiation and z transformation and making use of Eq. (5.2-72) yield the pulse-transfer function of the system:

$$G(z) = (-1)^k \frac{K}{k!}\frac{\partial^k}{\partial a^k}\left(\frac{1}{1-\epsilon^{-aT}z^{-1}}\right) \qquad (5.2\text{-}81)$$

4. In Eq. (5.2-19) the z transform associated with

$$G(s) = \frac{K}{s^{k+1}} \qquad (5.2\text{-}82)$$

is expressed in the form of a recurrent series which is rather clumsy when it is used in system analysis. Making use of the result of the preceding example, the z transform can readily be put into a compact form.

Since $1/s^{k+1}$ can be written as

$$\frac{1}{s^{k+1}} = \lim_{a\to 0}\frac{1}{(s+a)^{k+1}} \qquad (5.2\text{-}83)$$

then

$$\mathfrak{z}\left\{\frac{K}{s^{k+1}}\right\} = \mathfrak{z}\left\{\lim_{a\to 0}\frac{1}{(s+a)^{k+1}}\right\}$$

$$= \lim_{a\to 0}\mathfrak{z}\left\{\frac{1}{(s+a)^{k+1}}\right\} \qquad (5.2\text{-}84)$$

It follows from Eq. (5.2-81) that the z transform associated with K/s^{k+1} is given by

$$G(z) = (-1)^k \frac{K}{k!} \lim_{a\to 0} \frac{\partial^k}{\partial a^k} \left(\frac{1}{1 - \epsilon^{-aT} z^{-1}} \right) \tag{5.2-85}$$

The above illustrative examples demonstrate the simplicity and usefulness of the method of determining the pulse-transfer function of a system based upon residue evaluation.

A SHORT TABLE OF z TRANSFORMS AND THEIR INVERSE

$G(s)$	$g(t)$	$G(z)$	$g(nT)$
1. 1	$\delta(t)$	1 or z^{-0}	$\delta(nT)$
2. ϵ^{-kTs}	$\delta(t - kT)$	z^{-k}	$\delta(nT - kT)$
3. $\dfrac{1}{s - \frac{1}{T}\ln a}$	$a^{t/T}$	$\dfrac{z}{z-a}$	a^n
4. $\dfrac{1}{s}$	$u(t)$	$\dfrac{z}{z-1}$	$u(nT)$ or 1
5. $\dfrac{1}{s^2}$	t	$\dfrac{Tz}{(z-1)^2}$	nT
6. $\dfrac{1}{s^3}$	$\dfrac{1}{2!}t^2$	$\dfrac{T^2}{2}\dfrac{z(z+1)}{(z-1)^3}$	$\dfrac{1}{2}(nT)^2$
7. $\dfrac{1}{s^k}$	$\dfrac{1}{(k-1)!}t^{k-1}$	$\lim\limits_{a\to 0} \dfrac{(-1)^{k-1}}{(k-1)!}\dfrac{\partial^{k-1}}{\partial a^{k-1}}\left(\dfrac{z}{z-\epsilon^{-aT}}\right)$	$(-1)^{k-1}\lim\limits_{a\to 0}\dfrac{\partial^{k-1}}{\partial a^{k-1}}(\epsilon^{-aTn})$
8. $\dfrac{1}{s+a}$	ϵ^{-at}	$\dfrac{z}{z-\epsilon^{-aT}}$	ϵ^{-anT}
9. $\dfrac{1}{(s+a)^2}$	$t\epsilon^{-at}$	$\dfrac{Tz\epsilon^{-aT}}{(z-\epsilon^{-aT})^2}$	$(nT)\epsilon^{-anT}$
10. $\dfrac{1}{(s+a)^{k+1}}$	$\dfrac{t^k}{k!}\epsilon^{-at}$	$(-1)^k \dfrac{1}{k!}\dfrac{\partial^k}{\partial a^k}\left(\dfrac{z}{z-\epsilon^{-aT}}\right)$	$(-1)^k\dfrac{1}{k!}\dfrac{\partial^k}{\partial a^k}(\epsilon^{-anT})$
11. $\dfrac{a}{s(s+a)}$	$1 - \epsilon^{-at}$	$\dfrac{(1-\epsilon^{-aT})z}{(z-1)(z-\epsilon^{-aT})}$	$1 - \epsilon^{-anT}$
12. $\dfrac{a}{s^2(s+a)}$	$t - \dfrac{1-\epsilon^{-at}}{a}$	$\dfrac{Tz}{(z-1)^2} - \dfrac{(1-\epsilon^{-aT})z}{a(z-1)(z-\epsilon^{-aT})}$	$nT - \dfrac{1-\epsilon^{-anT}}{a}$
13. $\dfrac{\omega_0}{s^2+\omega_0^2}$	$\sin \omega_0 t$	$\dfrac{z \sin \omega_0 T}{z^2 - 2z\cos\omega_0 T + 1}$	$\sin n\,\omega_0 T$
14. $\dfrac{s}{s^2+\omega_0^2}$	$\cos \omega_0 t$	$\dfrac{z(z-\cos\omega_0 T)}{z^2 - 2z\cos\omega_0 T + 1}$	$\cos n\,\omega_0 T$
15. $\dfrac{\omega_0^2}{s(s^2+\omega_0^2)}$	$1 - \cos\omega_0 t$	$\dfrac{z(1-\cos\omega_0 T)(z+1)}{(z-1)(z^2-2z\cos\omega_0 T+1)}$	$1 - \cos n\,\omega_0 T$
16. $\dfrac{\omega_0}{(s+a)^2+\omega_0^2}$	$\epsilon^{-at}\sin\omega_0 t$	$\dfrac{z\epsilon^{-aT}\sin\omega_0 T}{z^2 - 2\epsilon^{-aT}z\cos\omega_0 T + \epsilon^{-2aT}}$	$\epsilon^{-anT}\sin n\omega_0 T$

5.3. Basic z-transformation Theorems. In Secs. 5.1 and 5.2 discussions of the z transforms and pulse-transfer functions have been presented. The z transform and the pulse-transfer function are defined either as an infinite series in terms of the weighting sequence, Eq. (5.2-66), or as the summation of the residues, Eq. (5.2-67). Section 5.2 gives a number of examples illustrating the derivation of z transforms and pulse-transfer functions. However, a better understanding of and insight into the z transformation can be obtained if certain fundamental theorems concerning these transformations are known and made part of its working principles. In the present section some basic z transformation theorems will be set forth, so more effective use may be made of concise mathematical expressions of fairly complicated physical relations in a pulsed-data control system. In the following discussions, sampling is assumed to be coincident with the start of the time functions, unless otherwise specified.

Theorem 1. *Linearity.* If the functions $g(t)$, $g_1(t)$, and $g_2(t)$ are z transformable and have z transforms $G(z)$, $G_1(z)$, and $G_2(z)$ respectively, and a is a constant or a variable independent of t and z, then

$$\mathfrak{z}\{ag(t)\} = aG(z) \tag{5.3-1a}$$

and

$$\mathfrak{z}\{g_1(t) \pm g_2(t)\} = G_1(z) \pm G_2(z) \tag{5.3-1b}$$

These two equations state the linear property of the z transformation. It is easily seen that the proof follows from the linear characteristics of the summation of Eq. (5.2-66) defining the z transform.

Theorem 2. *Real Translation.* If the function $g(t)$ is z transformable and has the z transform $G(z)$, then

$$\mathfrak{z}\{g(t - nT)\} = z^{-n}G(z) \tag{5.3-2}$$

$$\mathfrak{z}\{g(t + nT)\} = z^{n}G(z) \tag{5.3-3}$$

where n is a nonnegative integer, T is the sampling period of the hypothetical sampler which converts $g(t)$ into $g^*(t)$, and in taking the z transform it is assumed that sampling is coincident with the start of the time function. Equation (5.3-3) is valid, provided that $g(kT) = 0$ for $0 \leq k \leq (n - 1)$.

This theorem states that translation in the time domain goes over into multiplication by $z^{\pm n}$ in the z domain if the above conditions are fulfilled. Equation (5.3-2) follows from the summation definition of the z transform:

$$\mathfrak{z}\{g(t - nT)\} = \sum_{k=0}^{\infty} g(kT - nT)z^{-k} \tag{5.3-4}$$

which can be written as

$$\mathfrak{z}\{g(t - nT)\} = z^{-n} \sum_{k=0}^{\infty} g[(k - n)T]z^{-(k-n)} \tag{5.3-5}$$

Making use of the definition of $G(z)$, Eq. (5.3-5) is reduced to Eq. (5.3-2).

This equation implies that multiplication by z^{-n} means a time delay of nT seconds.

Equation (5.3-3) can be derived as follows: The z transform of $g(t + nT)$ is given by

$$\begin{aligned}\mathfrak{z}\{g(t + nT)\} &= g(nT) + g(nT + T)z^{-1} + g(nT + 2T)z^{-2} \\ &\quad + g(nT + 3T)z^{-3} + \cdots \\ &= z^n\{g(nT)z^{-n} + g[(n+1)T]z^{-(n+1)} + g[(n+2)T]z^{-(n+2)} \\ &\quad + g[(n+3)T]z^{-(n+3)} + \cdots\} \end{aligned} \tag{5.3-6}$$

If $g(kT) = 0$ for $0 \leq k \leq (n - 1)$, Eq. (5.3-6) may be written as

$$\begin{aligned}\mathfrak{z}\{g(t + nT)\} &= z^n\{g(0) + g(T)z^{-1} + g(2T)z^{-2} + \cdots \\ &\quad + g[(n-1)T]z^{-(n-1)} + g(nT)z^{-n} \\ &\quad + g[(n+1)T]z^{-(n+1)} + g[(n+2)T]z^{-(n+2)} \\ &\quad + g[(n+3)T]z^{-(n+3)} - \cdots\} \\ &= z^n \sum_{k=0}^{\infty} g(kT)z^{-k} \end{aligned} \tag{5.3-7}$$

In view of the definition of $G(z)$, Eq. (5.3-7) reduces to Eq. (5.3-3), which is stated in the theorem.

To illustrate the application of this theorem the following example is considered.

EXAMPLE 5.3-1. By use of theorem 2 determine the z transform of $(t - T)^2$.

From the short table of z transforms, it is found that

$$\mathfrak{z}\{t^2\} = T^2 \frac{z(z+1)}{(z-1)^3} \tag{5.3-8}$$

In view of Eq. (5.3-2),

$$\mathfrak{z}\{(t - T)^2\} = z^{-1}\mathfrak{z}\{t^2\} \tag{5.3-9}$$

Hence

$$\mathfrak{z}\{(t - T)^2\} = \frac{T^2(z+1)}{(z-1)^3} \tag{5.3-10}$$

Theorem 3. Scale Change in z Domain. If the function $g(t)$ is z transformable and has the z transform $G(z)$, then

$$\mathfrak{z}\{\epsilon^{at}g(t)\} = G(\epsilon^{-aT}z) \tag{5.3-11}$$

$$\mathfrak{z}\{\epsilon^{-at}g(t)\} = G(\epsilon^{aT}z) \tag{5.3-12}$$

where a is a nonnegative number.

This theorem states that multiplication by an exponential $\epsilon^{\pm at}$ in the time domain goes over into the z domain as a change of scale (i.e., the variable is multiplied by a constant $\epsilon^{\mp aT}$). It follows from the definition of the z transform that

$$\mathfrak{z}\{\epsilon^{\pm at}g(t)\} = \sum_{n=0}^{\infty} \epsilon^{\pm anT}g(nT)z^{-n} \tag{5.3-13}$$

Replacing z by ϵ^{sT}, Eq. (5.3-13) becomes

$$\mathfrak{z}\{\epsilon^{\pm at}g(t)\} = \sum_{n=0}^{\infty} \epsilon^{-(s\mp a)nT}g(nT) \tag{5.3-14}$$

Making the substitution

$$z_1 = \epsilon^{(s\mp a)T} = z\epsilon^{\mp aT} \tag{5.3-15}$$

Eq. (5.3-14) can be written as

$$\mathfrak{z}\{\epsilon^{\pm at}g(t)\} = \sum_{n=0}^{\infty} g(nT)z_1^{-n} = G(z_1) \tag{5.3-16}$$

Substituting Eq. (5.3-15) into Eq. (5.3-16) yields the relation

$$\mathfrak{z}\{\epsilon^{\pm at}g(t)\} = G(\epsilon^{\mp aT}z) \tag{5.3-17}$$

which is stated in the theorem.

EXAMPLE 5.3-2. Find the z transform of $t\epsilon^{-at}$ by means of this theorem. Since

$$\mathfrak{z}\{t\} = \frac{Tz}{(z-1)^2} \tag{5.3-18}$$

then by Eq. (5.3-12),

$$\mathfrak{z}\{t\epsilon^{-at}\} = \frac{Tz\epsilon^{aT}}{(z\epsilon^{aT}-1)^2} \tag{5.3-19}$$

Multiplying both numerator and denominator by ϵ^{-2aT} yields

$$\mathfrak{z}\{t\epsilon^{-at}\} = \frac{Tz\epsilon^{-aT}}{(z-\epsilon^{-aT})^2} \tag{5.3-20}$$

which agrees with formula 9 of the short table of z transforms.

Theorem 4. Final Value. If the function $g(t)$ has the z transform $G(z)$ which possesses no pole on or outside the unit circle, then

$$\lim_{z\to 1}\left\{\frac{z-1}{z}G(z)\right\} = \lim_{t\to\infty}\{g^*(t)\} \tag{5.3-21}$$

This theorem implies that the behavior of $g^*(t)$ as t becomes infinite corresponds to the behavior of $\frac{z-1}{z}G(z)$ in the vicinity of $z = 1$ in the z domain. To prove this theorem, let the function $g(t)$ be expressed as

$$g(t) = Ku(t) + \sum_{m} K_m\epsilon^{-a_m t} + \sum_{\mu,\nu} K_\mu t^\nu\epsilon^{-a_\mu t} \tag{5.3-22}$$

Then as t becomes infinite the limit of $g(t)$ approaches K, since

$$\lim_{t\to\infty} \epsilon^{-a_m t} = 0 \tag{5.3-23}$$

and

$$\lim_{t\to\infty} \frac{t^\nu}{\epsilon^{a_\mu t}} = \lim_{t\to\infty} \frac{\nu!}{(a_\mu)^\nu \epsilon^{a_\mu t}} = 0 \tag{5.3-24}$$

The z transform of Eq. (5.3-22) is given by

$$G(z) = \frac{Kz}{z-1} + \sum_m \left(\frac{K_m z}{z - \epsilon^{-a_m T}}\right) + \sum_{\mu,\nu} \frac{1}{\nu!} \frac{\partial^\nu}{\partial a_\mu{}^\nu} \left(\frac{K_\mu z}{z - \epsilon^{-a_\mu T}}\right) \tag{5.3-25}$$

Multiplying the above equation by $\frac{z-1}{z}$ and letting z approach 1 yields

$$\lim_{z\to 1} \left\{\frac{z-1}{z} G(z)\right\} = K \tag{5.3-26}$$

Thus,

$$\lim_{z\to 1} \left\{\frac{z-1}{z} G(z)\right\} = \lim_{t\to\infty} \{g^*(t)\} \tag{5.3-27}$$

It should be pointed out, in passing, that the final-value theorem is in no way a test for stability, but it provides a method of determining the steady-state value of a time function from its transform. For instance, the final-value theorem is often used to evaluate the steady-state error of a sampled-data system from the pulse-transfer functions, which is discussed in Sec. 6.5.

EXAMPLE 5.3-3. To illustrate the final-value theorem, consider the following z-transform pair

$$g(t) = b(1 - \epsilon^{-at}) \tag{5.3-28}$$

$$G(z) = \frac{bz(1 - \epsilon^{-aT})}{(z-1)(z - \epsilon^{-aT})} \tag{5.3-29}$$

The limit of $\frac{z-1}{z} G(z)$ as z approaches unity is given by

$$\lim_{z\to 1} \left\{\frac{z-1}{z} \frac{bz(1 - \epsilon^{-aT})}{(z-1)(z - \epsilon^{-aT})}\right\} = b \tag{5.3-30}$$

which indicates that the final value of $g(t)$ is b. This agrees with the limiting value given by

$$\lim_{t\to\infty} \{b(1 - \epsilon^{-at})\} = b \tag{5.3-31}$$

Theorem 5. *Initial Value.* If the function $g(t)$ has the z transform $G(z)$ and $\lim_{z\to\infty} \{G(z)\}$ exists, then

$$\lim_{z\to\infty} \{G(z)\} = \lim_{t\to 0} \{g(t)\} \tag{5.3-32}$$

In taking the z transforms, coincidence of the sampling and the starting of time functions is assumed.

This theorem implies that the behavior of $g(t)$ in the vicinity of zero in the time domain corresponds to the behavior of $G(z)$ in the vicinity of the point at infinity in the z domain. By definition,

$$G(z) = \sum_{n=0}^{\infty} g(nT)z^{-n}$$

$$= g(0) + g(T)z^{-1} + g(2T)z^{-2} + g(3T)z^{-3} + \cdots \qquad (5.3\text{-}33)$$

Clearly, when z approaches infinity $G(z)$ becomes $g(0)$, which is equal to the limit

$$\lim_{t\to 0} \{g(t)\} \qquad (5.3\text{-}34)$$

EXAMPLE 5.3-4. To illustrate the initial-value theorem, consider the following z-transform pair:

$$g(t) = \epsilon^{-at} \cos \omega_0 t \qquad (5.3\text{-}35)$$

$$G(z) = \frac{z^2 - z\epsilon^{-aT} \cos \omega_0 T}{z^2 - 2z\epsilon^{-aT} \cos \omega_0 T + \epsilon^{-2aT}} \qquad (5.3\text{-}36)$$

The initial value is shown to be

$$\lim_{z\to\infty} \{G(z)\} = 1 \qquad (5.3\text{-}37)$$

This is checked by

$$\lim_{t\to 0} \{g(t)\} = 1 \qquad (5.3\text{-}38)$$

EXAMPLE 5.3-5. Show that if $G(z) = \mathfrak{z}\{g(t)\}$ and $\lim_{t\to 0} \{g(t)\} = 0$, then

$$\lim_{t\to T} \{g(t)\} = \lim_{z\to\infty} \{zG(z)\} \qquad (5.3\text{-}39)$$

Since

$$G(z) = \mathfrak{z}\{g(t)\} \qquad (5.3\text{-}40)$$

it follows from theorem 2 that

$$zG(z) = \mathfrak{z}\{g(t + T)\} \qquad (5.3\text{-}41)$$

Making use of the initial value theorem yields

$$\lim_{t\to 0} \{g(t + T)\} = \lim_{z\to\infty} \{zG(z)\} \qquad (5.3\text{-}42)$$

Hence

$$\lim_{t\to T} \{g(t)\} = \lim_{z\to\infty} \{zG(z)\} \qquad (5.3\text{-}43)$$

It can readily be shown that, in general, if $g(kT) = 0$ for $0 \le k \le (n - 1)$,

$$g(nT) = \lim_{t\to nT} \{g(t)\} = \lim_{z\to\infty} \{z^nG(z)\} \qquad (5.3\text{-}44)$$

5.4. Properties of Pulse-transfer Functions. In the preceding sections information has been presented enabling the reader to derive the z transform and the pulse-transfer function of a system. Before discussing the details of the mapping of z-transform loci and the evaluation of inverse z transforms, certain important properties of pulse-transfer functions, which result from the previous discussions, should be summarized. These properties find much use in the analysis and synthesis of sampled-data control systems.

1. Periodicity: A pulse-transfer function $G^*(s) = G(z)|_{z=\epsilon^{Ts}}$ is a periodic function of s with imaginary period $j\omega_s$, where ω_s is the sampling frequency. The periodic property of pulse-transfer functions can readily be seen when reference is made to Eq. (4.1-14). Thus, the polar plot of a pulse-transfer function $G(z)$ with frequency range 0 to ω_s is the same as that with frequency range $k\omega_s$ to $(k+1)\omega_s$, where k is an integer.

2. The value of pulse-transfer function $G(z)$ is always real when $z = 1(\omega = 0)$ and $z = -1(\omega = n\omega_s/2)$; and it is finite at $z = 1$ if $G(s)$ has no pole at the origin. This implies that the polar plot of a pulse-transfer function intersects the real axis at zero frequency and at any multiple of the half sampling frequency. To illustrate this consider the following transfer functions:

a. $G(s)$ contains a pole at the origin.

$$G(s) = \frac{a}{s(s+a)} \tag{5.4-1}$$

The corresponding pulse-transfer function is

$$G(z) = \frac{(1-\epsilon^{-aT})z}{(z-1)(z-\epsilon^{-aT})} \tag{5.4-2}$$

At $z = 1$ ($\omega = 0$ or $n\omega_s$),

$$G(z) = \text{infinity}$$

At $z = -1$ ($\omega = n\omega_s/2$),

$$G(z) = -\frac{1-\epsilon^{-aT}}{2(1+\epsilon^{-aT})}$$

Evidently, the values of $G(z)$ are real at these two values of z, but $G(1)$ is not finite.

b. $G(s)$ possesses no pole at the origin.

$$G(s) = \frac{\omega_0}{s^2+\omega_0^2} \tag{5.4-3}$$

The corresponding pulse-transfer function is

$$G(z) = \frac{z \sin \omega_0 T}{z^2 - 2z \cos \omega_0 T + 1} \tag{5.4-4}$$

At $z = 1$ ($\omega = 0$ or $n\omega_s$),

$$G(z) = \frac{\sin \omega_0 T}{2(1 - \cos \omega_0 T)}$$

At $z = -1$ ($\omega = n\omega_s/2$),

$$G(z) = -\frac{\sin \omega_0 T}{2(1 + \cos \omega_0 T)}$$

The value of $G(z)$ is finite at $z = 1$.

3. The poles of the pulse-transfer function $G(z)$ in the z plane are related to the poles of $G(s)$ in the s plane by

$$z_k = \epsilon^{Ts_k} \tag{5.4-5}$$

where z_k and s_k are the poles of $G(z)$ and $G(s)$, respectively. $z = \epsilon^{Ts}$ is a mapping function or transformation function. The degree of the denominator of the pulse-transfer function $G(z)$ is equal to that of $G(s)$ in s, since $G(z)$ and $G(s)$ contain the same number of poles.

4. Addition or shifting of zeros in $G(s)$ will cause changes in the gain constants of the components of $G(z)$, but does not affect its poles. It has been shown that when $G(s)$ contains only simple poles, its pulse-transfer function is equal to

$$G(z) = \sum_k \frac{P(s_k)}{Q'(s_k)} \left(\frac{1}{1 - \epsilon^{Ts_k} z^{-1}} \right) \tag{5.4-6}$$

where it is assumed that

$$G(s) = \frac{P(s)}{Q(s)} \tag{5.4-7}$$

and $s = s_k$ is a pole of $G(s)$. Hence zeros of $G(s)$ will affect only the coefficient $P(s_k)/Q'(s_k)$ of the above expression.

Shifting the poles of $G(s)$ will bring about changes in the coefficient $P(s_k)/Q'(s_k)$ as well as the term $\dfrac{1}{1 - \epsilon^{Ts_k} z^{-1}}$ of Eq. (5.4-6), whereas introducing poles into $G(s)$ will increase the number of terms of the pulse-transfer function $G(z)$ as expressed in Eq. (5.4-6).

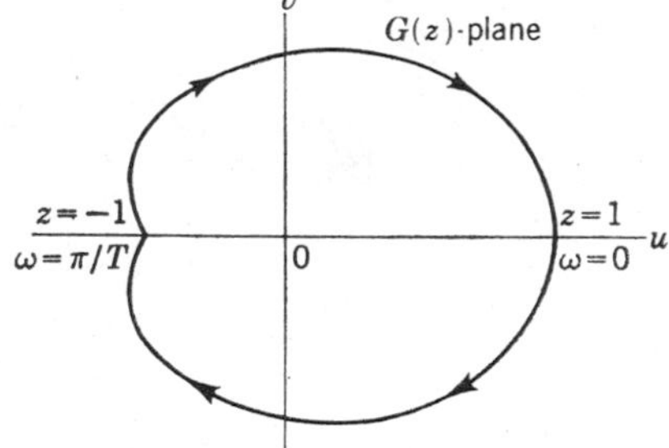

FIG. 5.4-1. The z-transform locus for $G(z)$ when the corresponding $G(s)$ has no pole at the origin.

5. If $G(s)$ has simple poles only and no pole at the origin, the locus of $G(z)$ describes a closed curve in the $G(z)$ plane, as shown in Fig. 5.4-1, when z traverses along the unit circle of the z plane.

If $G(s)$ has simple poles and a pole at the origin, the locus of $G(z)$ closes at infinity when z traverses along the unit circle of the z plane. However, the locus of $G(z)$ can close at infinity either in the left half of the $G(z)$ plane or in the right half. The determination of the direction of the locus at infinity is explained in the following: Assume that $G(s)$ is a ratio of two rational polynomials,

$$G(s) = \frac{P(s)}{Q(s)} \tag{5.4-8}$$

in which $Q(s)$ contains s as a factor. Then the z transform associated with $G(s)$ can be written as

$$G(z) = \frac{P(0)}{Q'(0)} \frac{1}{1 - z^{-1}} + \sum_{k=1,2,\ldots} \frac{P(s_k)}{Q'(s_k)} \frac{1}{1 - \epsilon^{Ts_k} z^{-1}} \tag{5.4-9}$$

where s_k is a pole of $G(s)$. The first term of the right-hand side of Eq. (5.4-9) is due to the pole at the origin, while the second term results from the other simple poles. The first term

$$G_1(z) = \frac{P(0)}{Q'(0)} \frac{z}{z - 1} \tag{5.4-10}$$

becomes infinite when z approaches one. That is, the point $z = 1$ of the z plane is mapped into infinity in the $G(z)$ plane. The second term

$$G_2(z) = \sum_{k=1,2,\ldots} \frac{P(s_k)}{Q'(s_k)} \frac{1}{1 - \epsilon^{Ts_k} z^{-1}} \tag{5.4-11}$$

is finite at $z = 1$.

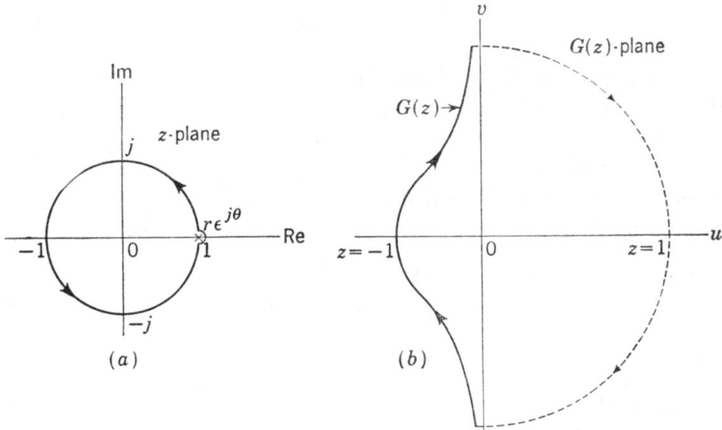

FIG. 5.4-2. (a) Unit circle of the z plane; (b) the z-transform locus for $G(z)$ when the corresponding $G(s)$ has a pole at the origin.

Referring to Fig. 5.4-2a, around the point $z = 1$ a small semicircle is drawn external to the unit circle to bypass the point $z = 1$. This semicircle is described by the equation

$$z = 1 + r\epsilon^{j\theta} \tag{5.4-12}$$

where r is an infinitesimal radius of the semicircle and θ is the angle of the radius vector r. When r approaches zero, z becomes 1. Then Eq. (5.4-10) can be written as

$$G_1(z) = \frac{P(0)}{Q'(0)} \frac{1 + r\epsilon^{j\theta}}{r\epsilon^{j\theta}} \tag{5.4-13}$$

and when z approaches 1,

$$\lim_{z \to 1} G_1(z) = \lim_{r \to 0} \frac{P(0)}{Q'(0)} \frac{1 + r\epsilon^{j\theta}}{r\epsilon^{j\theta}} \tag{5.4-14}$$

The amplitude and phase angle of $G_1(z)$ are calculated for several values of θ and are tabulated in the following:

θ	$\lvert G_1(z)\rvert$	Angle of $G_1(z)$
$-\pi/2$	∞	$\pi/2$
0	∞	0
$\pi/2$	∞	$-\pi/2$

The locus of $G(z)$ is shown in Fig. 5.4-2b. It is noted that the infinitesimal semicircle in the z plane is mapped into the semicircle with infinite radius in the $G(z)$ plane. From the computed values of the above table it is seen that when z moves along the infinitesimal semicircle in the counterclockwise direction, the locus of $G(z)$ traces a semicircle of infinite radius in the clockwise direction. This determines the locus of $G(z)$ at infinity.

5.5. z-transform Loci. The artifice of introducing a change of independent variable by substituting for the given one some function of a new variable usually implies the transformation of one region of the complex plane into another. A contour in one region is thereby mapped on the other. The substitution used in z transformation is

$$z = \epsilon^{Ts} \tag{5.5-1}$$

This is a mapping function by which the imaginary axis of the s plane is mapped into the unit circle of the z plane, as shown in Fig. 5.5-1.

For values on the imaginary axis, s is replaced by $j\omega$, resulting in $z = \epsilon^{j\omega T}$, which is a multivalued function of ω, with unity amplitude and phase angle equal to ωT. As ω is increased from 0 to $\omega_s/4$, z varies from $z = 1$ to $z = j$ along the unit circle in the first quadrant of the z plane. ω_s is the sampling frequency of the system. As ω increases from $\omega_s/4$ to $\omega_s/2$, z varies from $z = j$ to $z = -1$ along the unit circle in the second quadrant. When ω increases from $\omega_s/2$ to $3\omega_s/4$, z moves from $z = -1$ to $z = -j$ along the unit circle in the third quadrant. When ω increases

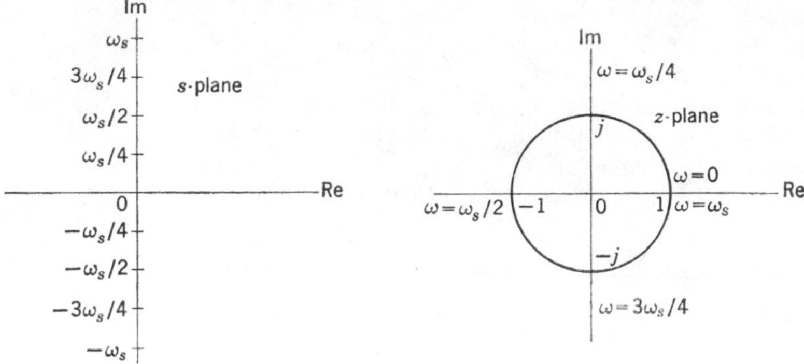

FIG. 5.5-1. Mapping of the imaginary axis of the s plane into the unit circle of the z plane.

from $3\omega_s/4$ to ω_s, z traverses from $z = -j$ to $z = 1$ along the unit circle in the fourth quadrant. A set of the corresponding points are:

ω	0	$\omega_s/4$	$\omega_s/2$	$3\omega_s/4$	ω_s
z	1	j	-1	$-j$	1

Thus, the section of the imaginary axis lying between $\omega = 0$ and $\omega = \omega_s$ is mapped into the unit circle of the z plane. As ω is increased from ω_s to $2\omega_s$, the values of z trace the unit circle once more. This process is repeated when ω increases or decreases through a range of ω_s.

At any point in the s plane,

$$s = \sigma + j\omega \tag{5.5-2}$$

If the substitution is made in Eq. (5.5-1), the result is

$$z = \epsilon^{\sigma T}\epsilon^{j\omega T} \tag{5.5-3}$$

At the point $(\sigma = -\infty, \omega = 0)$ of the s plane, the value of z is zero. This implies that a point at infinity on the negative real axis of the s plane is mapped into the origin of the z plane. For $\omega = 0$ and $\sigma \leq 0$, Eq. (5.5-3) yields $z = \epsilon^{\sigma T}$, which describes a line segment between 0 and 1. Thus, the negative real axis of the s plane is mapped into that section of the positive real axis of the z plane which falls inside the unit circle.

The magnitude of z is given by

$$|z| = |\epsilon^{\sigma T}\epsilon^{j\omega T}| = \epsilon^{\sigma T} \tag{5.5-4}$$

since $|\epsilon^{j\omega T}|$ is unity. For values of σ less than zero (i.e., any point in the left half of the s plane), $\epsilon^{\sigma T}$ is less than one and $|z| < 1$, which represents the region covering the interior of the unit circle. Hence the left half of the s plane is mapped into the area inside the unit circle of the z plane. On the other hand, since $|z| > 1$ for $\sigma > 0$, the right half of the s plane is mapped into the area outside the unit circle as shown by the unshaded area of Fig. 5.5-2.

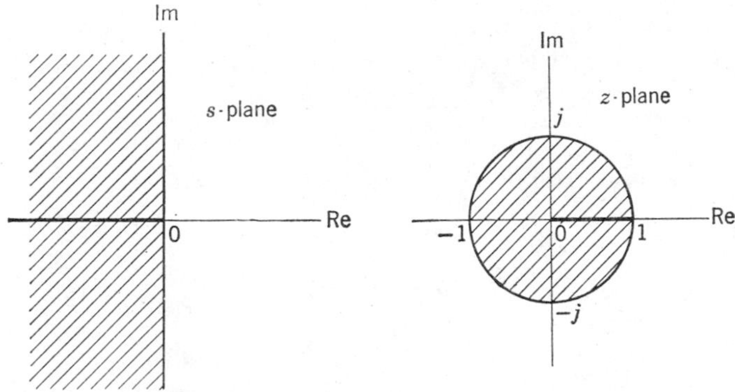

FIG. 5.5-2. The left half of the s plane is mapped into the interior of the unit circle of the z plane by $z = \epsilon^{Ts}$, and the negative real axis of the s plane is mapped into that section of the positive real axis of the z plane which falls inside the unit circle.

As the independent variable z traverses along the unit circle of the z plane, the z transform $G(z)$ traces out a locus, which is termed the z-transform locus. In the analysis and synthesis of sampled-data and digital control systems z-transform loci play an important role. For instance, the nature and location of the z-transform locus of a pulsed-data system determines its stability and performance, as will be discussed in detail in the following chapters.

The z transform of a complicated pulsed-data system can generally be considered as a combination of several basic z transforms, the loci of which are simple geometric figures and can readily be identified. Thus, it is instructive to study the construction and the characteristics of the loci of several basic z transforms which form the constituting components of more complicated z transforms.

The following basic z transforms are considered:

1.
$$G(z) = \frac{z}{z-1} \tag{5.5-5}$$

which is the z transform for $G(s) = 1/s$.

Confining the values of z on the unit circle of the z plane,

$$z = \epsilon^{j\omega T} = \cos \omega T + j \sin \omega T \tag{5.5-6}$$

Substituting into Eq. (5.5-5) yields

$$G(z) = \frac{\cos \omega T + j \sin \omega T}{\cos \omega T - 1 + j \sin \omega T} \tag{5.5-7}$$

which is a complex quantity and may be written as

$$G(z) = u + jv \tag{5.5-8}$$

It can readily be shown that the real part is

$$u = \frac{1}{2} \tag{5.5-9}$$

and the imaginary part is

$$v = \frac{1}{2} \frac{\sin \omega T}{\cos \omega T - 1} \tag{5.5-10}$$

for which a set of corresponding points are:

$\omega \ldots$	0	$\pi/2T$	π/T	$3\pi/2T$	$2\pi/T$
$u \ldots$	½	½	½	½	½
$v \ldots$	$-\infty$	$-$½	0	½	∞

Shown in Fig. 5.5-3 is the locus of $G(z) = z/(z-1)$ in the $G(z)$ plane,

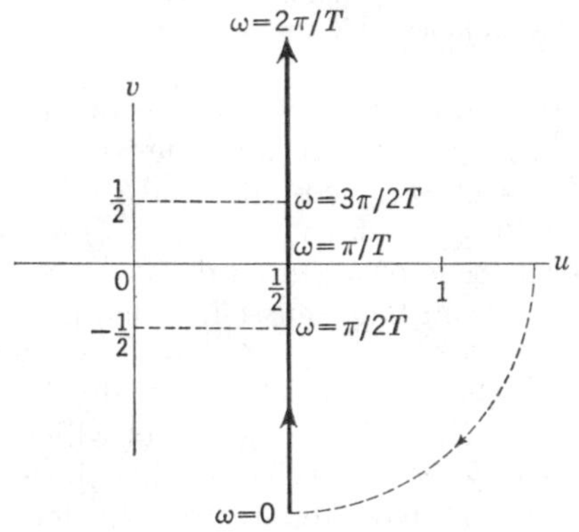

FIG. 5.5-3. The z-transform locus of $G(z) = z/(z-1)$.

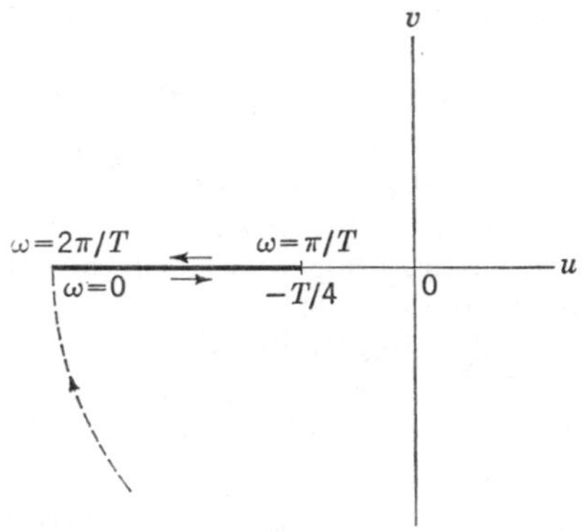

FIG. 5.5-4. The z-transform locus of $G(z) = \dfrac{Tz}{(z-1)^2}$.

which describes a straight line parallel to the imaginary axis and ½ unit to the right of the origin.

2.
$$G(z) = \frac{Tz}{(z-1)^2} \tag{5.5-11}$$

which is the z transform for $G(s) = \dfrac{1}{s^2}$.

Replacing z by $\cos \omega T + j \sin \omega T$, Eq. (5.5-11) becomes

$$G(z) = \frac{T(\cos \omega T + j \sin \omega T)}{(\cos \omega T - 1 + j \sin \omega T)^2} \tag{5.5-12}$$

Simplifying,

$$G(z) = \frac{T}{2(\cos \omega T - 1)} \tag{5.5-13}$$

A set of corresponding points are:

ω	0	$\pi/2T$	π/T	$3\pi/2T$	$2\pi/T$
$G(z)$ . . .	∞	$-T/2$	$-T/4$	$-T/2$	∞

The locus is a straight line on the negative real axis extending from $u = -T/4$ to minus infinity as shown in Fig. 5.5-4.

3.
$$G(z) = \frac{z}{z - \epsilon^{-\alpha T}} = \frac{z}{z - a} \tag{5.5-14}$$

which is the z transform for $G(s) = 1/(s + \alpha)$.

By proper substitution, Eq. (5.5-14) becomes

$$G(z) = \frac{\cos \omega T + j \sin \omega T}{(\cos \omega T - a) + j \sin \omega T} \tag{5.5-15}$$

which may be reduced to

$$G(z) = \frac{1}{1 - a^2}\left[1 + \frac{a(1 + a^2) \cos \omega T - 2a^2}{1 + a^2 - 2a \cos \omega T} - j\,\frac{a(1 - a^2) \sin \omega T}{1 + a^2 - 2a \cos \omega T}\right] \tag{5.5-16}$$

By letting
$$\frac{(1 + a^2) \cos \omega T - 2a}{1 + a^2 - 2a \cos \omega T} = \cos \theta \tag{5.5-17}$$

then
$$\frac{(1 - a^2) \sin \omega T}{1 + a^2 - 2a \cos \omega T} = \sin \theta \tag{5.5-18}$$

and $G(z)$ can be written as

$$G(z) = \frac{1}{1 - a^2} + \frac{a}{1 - a^2}\,\epsilon^{-j\theta} \tag{5.5-19}$$

which describes a family of circles with radii equal to

$$\left|\frac{a}{1 - a^2}\right| \tag{5.5-20}$$

and centers located at

$$u = \frac{1}{1 - a^2} \qquad v = 0 \tag{5.5-21}$$

Thus, as z traverses along the unit circle, the locus of $G(z) = \dfrac{z}{(z - a)}$ forms a family of circles, the radii and centers of which depend upon the location of the pole of $G(s) = \dfrac{1}{(s + \alpha)}$, as shown in Fig. 5.5-5.

When α is positive, the value of a is less than 1. The circles are located in the right half of the $G(z)$ plane. When α is complex and equals $(\sigma + j\omega_s/2)$,

$a = -\epsilon^{-\sigma T}$, and the circles also lie in the right half of the $G(z)$ plane. When α equals zero or $\pm j\omega_s$, the value of a is 1 and the locus of $G(z)$ degenerates into a straight line or a circle with infinite radius, as shown in Fig. 5.5-5. This agrees with the case discussed in item 1. When $a = 0$, $G(z) = 1$

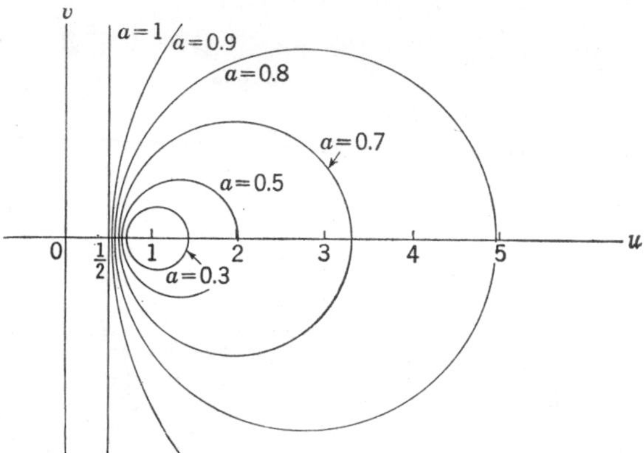

FIG. 5.5-5. The z-transform locus of $G(z) = z/(z - a)$.

and the locus becomes a point at (1,0). This is an extreme case. In fact, $G(z) = 1$ is the z transform of a unit-impulse function.

4.
$$G(z) = \frac{b}{z - a} \tag{5.5-22}$$

This equation may be written as

$$G(z) = \frac{b}{a}\left(\frac{z}{z - a} - 1\right) \tag{5.5-23}$$

Making use of the results derived in the preceding paragraph, Eq. (5.5-23) is reduced to

$$G(z) = \frac{ab}{1 - a^2} + \frac{b}{1 - a^2}\epsilon^{-j\theta} \tag{5.5-24}$$

This is the equation describing a family of circles with radii equal to

$$\left|\frac{b}{1 - a^2}\right| \tag{5.5-25}$$

and centers located at

$$u = \frac{ab}{1 - a^2} \qquad v = 0 \tag{5.5-26}$$

Hence the locus of $G(z) = b/(z - a)$ for z traversing on the unit circle is a family of circles, the radii and centers of which are determined by the values of a and b. For a given value of b, the circles are similar to those plotted in Fig. 5.5-5.

EXAMPLE 5.5-1. For the sampled-data feedback control system shown in Fig. 5.5-6, determine the open-loop pulse-transfer function and its locus.

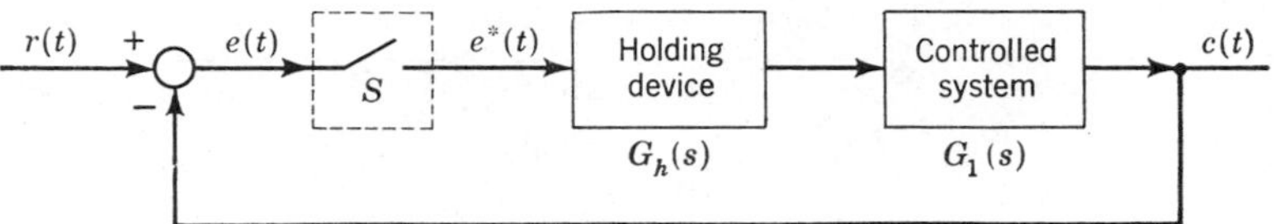

FIG. 5.5-6. A simple sampled-data feedback control system of Example 5.5-1.

In Fig. 5.5-6 it is assumed that a zero-order holding device is employed and the controlled system is of second order. Their transfer functions are

$$G_h(s) = \frac{1 - \epsilon^{-Ts}}{s} \tag{5.5-27}$$

and

$$G_1(s) = \frac{K}{s(s + a)} \tag{5.5-28}$$

where T is the sampling period; K, the system gain constant; and $1/a$, the time constant.

The open-loop transfer function is

$$G(s) = G_h(s)G_1(s) = \frac{K(1 - \epsilon^{-Ts})}{s^2(s + a)} \tag{5.5-29}$$

The corresponding z transform is

$$G(z) = \mathfrak{z}\left\{\frac{K(1 - \epsilon^{-Ts})}{s^2(s + a)}\right\} = K(1 - z^{-1})\,\mathfrak{z}\left\{\frac{1}{s^2(s + a)}\right\} \tag{5.5-30}$$

Since

$$\frac{1}{s^2(s + a)} = \frac{1}{as^2} - \frac{1}{a^2 s} + \frac{1}{a^2(s + a)} \tag{5.5-31}$$

from the short table of z transforms

$$\mathfrak{z}\left\{\frac{1}{s^2(s + a)}\right\} = \frac{Tz}{a(z - 1)^2} - \frac{z}{a^2(z - 1)} + \frac{z}{a^2(z - \epsilon^{-aT})} \tag{5.5-32}$$

Substituting Eq. (5.5-32) into Eq. (5.5-30) yields the open-loop pulse-transfer function:

$$G(z) = \frac{KT}{a(z - 1)} - \frac{K(1 - \epsilon^{-aT})}{a^2(z - \epsilon^{-aT})} \tag{5.5-33}$$

It is evident that the locus of $G(z)$ may be plotted from the vector sum of the loci of

$$\frac{KT}{a(z - 1)} \quad \text{and} \quad \frac{K(\epsilon^{-aT} - 1)}{a^2(z - \epsilon^{-aT})}$$

which describe, respectively, a straight line and a circle in the $G(z)$ plane.

5.6. Inverse z Transformations. Shown in Fig. 5.6-1 is a simple pulsed-

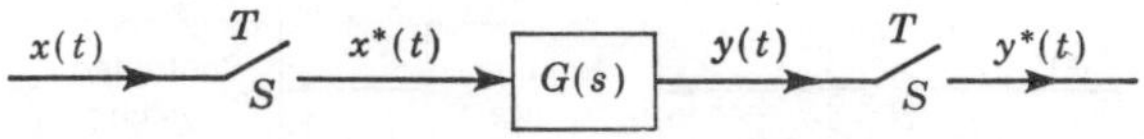

$x(t)$ — T, S — $x^*(t)$ — $G(s)$ — $y(t)$ — T, S — $y^*(t)$

FIG. 5.6-1. A simple sampled-data system.

data system, the input $x(t)$ and the output $y(t)$ of which are sampled synchronously. In terms of z the output of the system is given by

$$Y(z) = G(z)X(z) \tag{5.6-1}$$

where $X(z)$ and $Y(z)$ are the z transforms of $x(t)$ and $y(t)$ respectively, and $G(z)$ is the pulse-transfer function of the system. One way of evaluating the transient behavior of the system is to transform Eq. (5.6-1) into the time domain. The mathematical process of passing from the complex variable expression in the z domain to that of time is known as the *inverse z transformation.*[25] Through the real inversion, the z-transform method gives the time function which yields correct values only at the sampling instants.

It is seen from the discussions of the preceding sections that the transformation of a function from time domain or s domain to z domain is unique. However, the transformation from z domain to time domain or s domain is not so. An infinite number of inverse transforms in terms of t (or s) can be derived from a given z transform, because the transformation function

$$z = \epsilon^{Ts} \tag{5.6-2}$$

is multivalued in going from the z plane to the s plane. All possible values of s differing by $j\omega_s$ will yield the same value of z. If the s plane is sliced horizontally into a number of equal strips, as shown in Fig. 5.6-2, with the

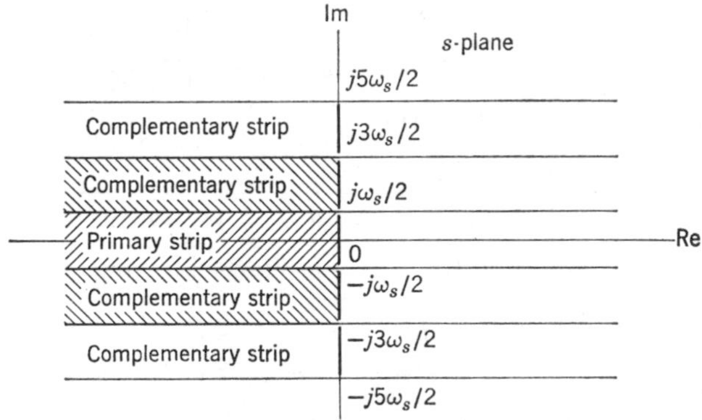

FIG. 5.6-2. The s plane is subdivided into a number of strips.

width of the strip equal to the sampling frequency ω_s, each strip is mapped into the entire region of the z plane by the transformation function of

Eq. (5.6-2). The strip containing the real axis is often called the primary or principal strip. Of the many $\mathcal{L}$ transforms $G(s)$, derivable from the corresponding z transform $G(z)$, the one which has its poles located in the primary strip of the s plane may be referred to as the principal $\mathcal{L}$ transform.

The z-transform pair is

$$G(z) = \sum_{n=0}^{\infty} g(nT)z^{-n} \tag{5.6-3}$$

and

$$g(nT) = \frac{1}{2\pi j} \oint_{\Gamma} G(z)z^{n-1}\, dz \tag{5.6-4}$$

where Γ is the path of integration in the z plane which encloses all the singularities of the integrand $G(z)z^{n-1}$. The transformation of Eq. (5.6-3) is called the *direct z transformation* which results in the *direct z transform*, whereas the transformation of Eq. (5.6-4) is called the *inverse z transformation*, the result of which is the *inverse z transform*. The inverse z-transformation formula, Eq. (5.6-4), may be derived from the inverse Laplace transform as follows:

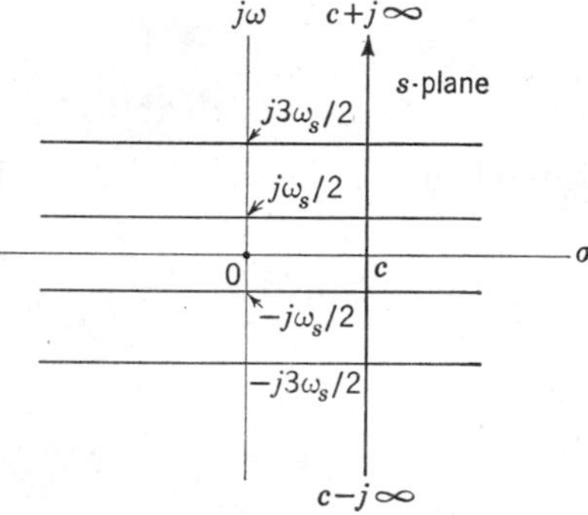

Fig. 5.6-3. The path of integration in the s plane.

Derivation of Inverse z-transform Integral. The Laplace-transform pair is

Direct transform:

$$G(s) = \int_0^{\infty} g(t)\epsilon^{-st}\, dt \tag{5.6-5}$$

Inverse transform:

$$g(t) = \frac{1}{2\pi j} \int_{c-j\infty}^{c+j\infty} G(s)\epsilon^{ts}\, ds \tag{5.6-6}$$

From the inverse Laplace-transform integral, Eq. (5.6-6), it follows that at $t = nT$, $g(t)$ is given by

$$g(nT) = \frac{1}{2\pi j} \int_{c-j\infty}^{c+j\infty} G(\xi)\epsilon^{nT\xi}\, d\xi \tag{5.6-7}$$

where the complex variable ξ replaces s in Eq. (5.6-6) for convenience. The integration is taken along the line parallel to the imaginary axis and c units from the origin, where c is the abscissa of convergence. If the path of integration is divided into a number of equal segments of width ω_s, as shown in Fig. 5.6-3, corresponding to the primary and complementary strips described in the preceding paragraph, then Eq. (5.6-7) may be written as

$$g(nT) = \frac{1}{2\pi j}\left[\int_{c-j\frac{1}{2}\omega_s}^{c+j\frac{1}{2}\omega_s} G(\xi)\epsilon^{nT\xi}\,d\xi + \int_{c-j\frac{3}{2}\omega_s}^{c-j\frac{1}{2}\omega_s} G(\xi)\epsilon^{nT\xi}\,d\xi + \int_{c+j\frac{1}{2}\omega_s}^{c+j\frac{3}{2}\omega_s} G(\xi)\epsilon^{nT\xi}\,d\xi + \cdots\right]$$

$$= \frac{1}{2\pi j}\sum_{k=-\infty}^{\infty}\int_{c+j(k-\frac{1}{2})\omega_s}^{c+j(k+\frac{1}{2})\omega_s} G(\xi)\epsilon^{nT\xi}\,d\xi \qquad (5.6\text{-}8)$$

By the substitution of

$$\xi = s + jk\omega_s \qquad (5.6\text{-}9)$$

where k is an integer, Eq. (5.5-8) becomes

$$g(nT) = \frac{1}{2\pi j}\sum_{k=-\infty}^{\infty}\int_{c-j\frac{1}{2}\omega_s}^{c+j\frac{1}{2}\omega_s} G(s + jk\omega_s)\epsilon^{nTs}\,ds \qquad (5.6\text{-}10)$$

Interchanging the summation and integration yields

$$g(nT) = \frac{T}{2\pi j}\int_{c-j\frac{1}{2}\omega_s}^{c+j\frac{1}{2}\omega_s} \frac{1}{T}\sum_{k=-\infty}^{\infty} G(s + jk\omega_s)\epsilon^{nTs}\,ds \qquad (5.6\text{-}11)$$

Making use of Eq. (4.1-14),

$$g(nT) = \frac{1}{2\pi j}\int_{c-j\frac{1}{2}\omega_s}^{c+j\frac{1}{2}\omega_s} G^*(s)\epsilon^{nTs}T\,ds \qquad (5.6\text{-}12)$$

Replacing ϵ^{Ts} by z,

$$\epsilon^{nTs} = z^n \qquad (5.6\text{-}13)$$

$$T\,ds = z^{-1}\,dz \qquad (5.6\text{-}14)$$

$$G^*(s) \to G(z) \qquad (5.6\text{-}15)$$

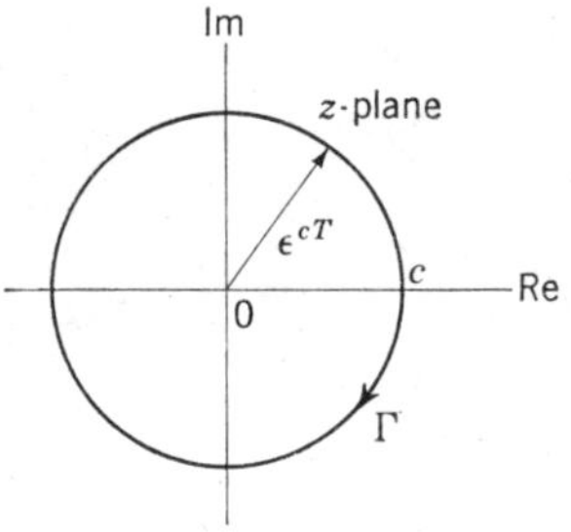

FIG. 5.6-4. The contour of integration in the z plane.

and the path of integration is converted into a circle of radius ϵ^{cT} with center located at the origin of the z plane (Fig. 5.6-4). Then Eq. (5.6-12) reduces to

$$g(nT) = \frac{1}{2\pi j}\oint_\Gamma G(z)z^{n-1}\,dz \qquad (5.6\text{-}16)$$

which is the inverse z-transform formula given in Eq. (5.6-4). The path of integration can be any closed contour enclosing all the poles of $G(z)$, since no singularity of $G(s)$ exists to the right of the line $\sigma = c$ (Fig. 5.6-3) and the path Γ encloses all the poles of $G(z)$. For physical systems the poles lie inside the left half of the s plane; so the contour of integration can be the unit circle of the z plane.

Methods of Evaluating Inverse z Transform. *a.* FROM THE REAL INVER-

SION FORMULA. This method requires the evaluation of the inversion integral of Eq. (5.6-4). By applying Cauchy's residue theorem, the value of the integral is given by the sum of all the residues of $G(z)z^{n-1}$ inside the contour Γ, thus,

$$g(nT) = \sum_{\text{all } z_k} \text{residues of } G(z)z^{n-1} \text{ at } z_k \tag{5.6-17}$$

where $G(z)z^{n-1}$ is a rational function of z, which is finite on the path of integration, and the contour Γ is a circle with center at the origin of the z plane (or any closed contour) enclosing all the poles z_k of $G(z)z^{n-1}$.

EXAMPLE 5.6-1. Find the inverse z transform of

$$G(z) = \frac{z^2(z^2 + z + 1)}{(z - 0.8)(z - 1)(z^2 - z + 0.8)} \tag{5.6-18}$$

To evaluate the inverse by this method, the residues of $G(z)z^{n-1}$ at all the poles are first determined. They are:

Pole	*Residue*
$z = 0.8$	$-19.1 \times 0.8^{n+1}$
$z = 1$	18.75
$z = 0.5 + j0.74$	$(0.89 \angle +56.5°)^{n+1}(1.75 \angle +85°)$
$z = 0.5 - j0.74$	$(0.89 \angle -56.5°)^{n+1}(1.75 \angle -85°)$

The inverse z transform follows from Eq. (5.6-17); that is,

$$\begin{aligned} g(nT) = -19.1 \times 0.8^{n+1} + 18.75 &+ (0.89 \angle 56.5°)^{n+1}(1.75 \angle 85°) \\ &+ (0.89 \angle -56.5°)^{n+1}(1.75 \angle -85°) \end{aligned} \tag{5.6-19}$$

From this expression the values of $g(nT)$ at various sampling instants can readily be computed. A few values of $g(nT)$ corresponding to the first several sampling instants are:

n	0	1	2	3	4	5
$g(nT)$ ...	1	3.80	8.20	12.4	14.68	16.62

b. BY PARTIAL-FRACTION EXPANSION. This method requires the expansion of $\frac{G(z)}{z}$ into partial fractions such that the inverse z transform of each component term multiplied by z is recognizable from the z-transform table.

EXAMPLE 5.6-2. Determine the inverse transform of Eq. (5.6-18) by partial-fraction-expansion method.

Let
$$G(z) = \frac{z^2(z^2 + z + 1)}{(z - 0.8)(z - 1)(z^2 - z + 0.8)} = zG_1(z) \tag{5.6-20}$$

where
$$G_1(z) = \frac{z(z^2 + z + 1)}{(z - 0.8)(z - 1)(z^2 - z + 0.8)} \tag{5.6-21}$$

which may be expanded into

$$G_1(z) = \frac{18.75}{z - 1} - \frac{15.3}{z - 0.8} + \frac{-1.2 + j}{z - (0.5 + j0.74)} + \frac{-1.2 - j}{z - (0.5 - j0.74)} \tag{5.6-22}$$

It is noted that the value in the numerator of the above equation is the residue of $G_1(z)$ at the corresponding pole. By proper substitution and putting

$$0.5 \pm j0.74 = \epsilon^{-0.12 \pm j} \qquad 0.8 = \epsilon^{-0.22} \tag{5.6-23}$$

Eq. (5.6-20) becomes

$$G(z) = 18.75 \frac{z}{z - 1} - 15.3 \frac{z}{z - \epsilon^{-0.22}} + (-1.2 + j) \frac{z}{z - \epsilon^{-0.12+j}} + (-1.2 - j) \frac{z}{z - \epsilon^{-0.12-j}} \tag{5.6-24}$$

From the table of z transforms, the inverse transforms of all the terms of the right-hand side of the above equation can easily be recognized. Thus, the time function is

$$g(t) = 18.75u(t) - 15.3\epsilon^{-0.22t/T} + (-1.2 + j)\epsilon^{(-0.12+j)t/T} + (-1.2 - j)\epsilon^{(-0.12-j)t/T} \tag{5.6-25}$$

which reduces to

$$g(t) = 18\ 75u(t) - 15.3\epsilon^{-0.22t/T} - \epsilon^{-0.12t/T}\left(2.4 \cos \frac{t}{T} + 2 \sin \frac{t}{T}\right) \tag{5.6-26}$$

Howeveı, Eq. (5.6-26) is valid only at the sampling instants. Several values of $g(t)$ are given below:

t	0	T	$2T$	$3T$	$4T$	$5T$
$g(t)$ ...	1	3.8	8.2	12.4	14.55	14.64

which check with the solution obtained through the first method.

c. BY POWER-SERIES EXPANSION (OR LONG DIVISION). By this method $G(z)$ is expanded into a power series of z^{-1} by long division. The coefficient of the z^{-n} term corresponds to the value of the time function $g(t)$ at the nth sampling instant. By definition,

$$
\begin{aligned}
g^*(t) &= \sum_{n=0}^{\infty} g(nT)\delta(t - nT) \\
&= g(0)\delta(t) + g(T)\delta(t - T) + g(2T)\delta(t - 2T) + \cdots \\
&\qquad + g(nT)\delta(t - nT) + \cdots
\end{aligned} \tag{5.6-27}
$$

Taking the z transforms of both sides of Eq. (5.6-27) yields

$$G(z) = g(0) + g(T)z^{-1} + g(2T)z^{-2} + \cdots + g(nT)z^{-n} + \cdots \tag{5.6-28}$$

Thus, by comparison, the coefficient of z^{-n} is equal to $g(nT)$ which is the value of $g(t)$ at the nth sampling instant.

In performing the long division, the polynomials are arranged in descending powers of z, such as

$$G(z) = \frac{b_m z^m + b_{m-1}z^{m-1} + b_{m-2}z^{m-2} + \cdots + b_0}{c_n z^n + c_{n-1}z^{n-1} + c_{n-2}z^{n-2} + \cdots + c_0} \qquad n \geq m \tag{5.6-29}$$

An expansion for $G(z)$ then results in the form

$$G(z) = a_0 + a_1 z^{-1} + a_2 z^{-2} + a_3 z^{-3} + \cdots \tag{5.6-30}$$

EXAMPLE 5.6-3. Evaluate the inverse transform of Eq. (5.6-18) by this method.

$$
\begin{aligned}
G(z) &= \frac{z^2(z^2 + z + 1)}{(z - 0.8)(z - 1)(z^2 - z + 0.8)} \\
&= \frac{z^4 + z^3 + z^2}{z^4 - 2.8z^3 + 3.4z^2 - 2.24z + 0.64}
\end{aligned} \tag{5.6-31}
$$

The division is carried out as follows:

$$
\begin{array}{r|rrrrrrr}
 & z^0 & z^{-1} & z^{-2} & z^{-3} & z^{-4} & & \\
 & 1 & +3.80 & +8.20 & +12.40 & +14.68 & +\cdots & \\
\hline
1-2.80+3.40 & & & & & & & \\
-2.24+0.64 & 1 & +1 & +1 & & & & \\
 & 1 & -2.80 & +3.40 & -2.24 & +0.64 & & \\
\cline{2-6}
 & & 3.80 & -2.40 & +2.24 & -0.64 & & \\
 & & 3.80 & -10.60 & +12.91 & -8.52 & +2.44 & \\
\cline{3-7}
 & & & 8.20 & -10.67 & +7.88 & -2.44 & \\
 & & & 8.20 & -23.07 & +27.90 & -18.36 & +5.25 \\
\cline{4-8}
 & & & & 12.40 & -20.02 & +15.92 & -5.25 \\
 & & & & 12.40 & -34.70 & +40.30 & -27.80 \; +7.94 \\
\cline{5-8}
 & & & & & 14.68 & -24.38 & +22.55 \; -7.94
\end{array}
$$

Then Eq. (5.6-31) expands into

$$G(z) = 1 + 3.8z^{-1} + 8.2z^{-2} + 12.4z^{-3} + 14.55^{-4} + \cdots \tag{5.6-32}$$

Therefore,

$$g^*(t) = \delta(t) + 3.8\delta(t - T) + 8.2\delta(t - 2T) + 12.4\delta(t - 3T) + 14.68\delta(t - 4T) + \cdots \quad (5.6\text{-}33)$$

This is in agreement with the values computed by the preceding methods.

EXAMPLE 5.6-4. Find the transient response of the sampled-data system of Fig. 5.6-5a to a unit step-function input. It is assumed that the sampling

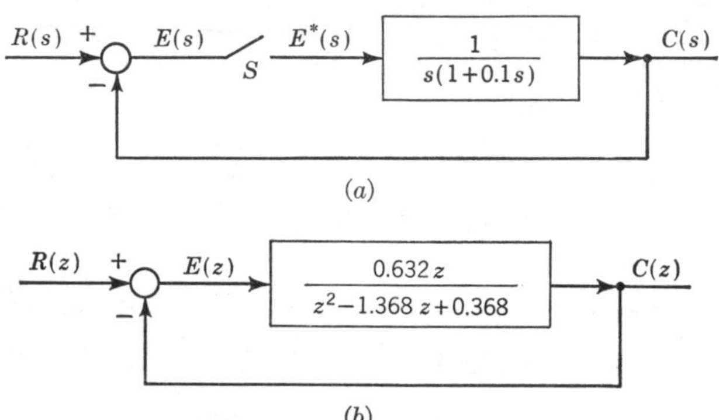

FIG. 5.6-5. (a) The block diagram of the sampled-data feedback control system of Example 5.6-4; (b) the block diagram of the system of Example 5.6-4 in terms of z.

period T is 0.1 sec and that the transfer function of the controlled system is

$$G(s) = \frac{1}{s(1 + 0.1s)} \quad (5.6\text{-}34)$$

For determining the transient behavior, the pulse-transfer function of the controlled system $G(s)$ is first calculated. To do this, transfer function $G(s)$ is expanded into its partial fractions,

$$G(s) = \frac{1}{s} - \frac{1}{s + 10} \quad (5.6\text{-}35)$$

The pulse-transfer function is

$$G(z) = \frac{z}{z - 1} - \frac{z}{z - \epsilon^{-1}}$$

$$= \frac{0.632z}{z^2 - 1.368z + 0.368} \quad (5.6\text{-}36)$$

In terms of z the system block diagram of Fig. 5.6-5a is reduced to that of Fig. 5.6-5b. It can readily be shown that the z transforms of the error and the output are given by

$$E(z) = \frac{R(z)}{1 + G(z)} \quad (5.6\text{-}37)$$

and
$$C(z) = \frac{G(z)R(z)}{1 + G(z)} \tag{5.6-38}$$

Substituting the value of $G(z)$ into Eq. (5.6-38) yields

$$C(z) = \frac{0.632z}{z^2 - 0.736z + 0.368} R(z) \tag{5.6-39}$$

For a unit step-function input, $r(t) = u(t)$, $R(s) = 1/s$, and

$$R(z) = \frac{z}{z - 1} \tag{5.6-40}$$

Then the z transform of the system output becomes

$$C(z) = \frac{0.632z^2}{(z - 1)(z^2 - 0.736z + 0.368)} \tag{5.6-41}$$

By long division, Eq. (5.6-41) expands into

$$C(z) = 0.632z^{-1} + 1.10z^{-2} + 1.22z^{-3} + 1.14z^{-4} + 1.04z^{-5} + \cdots \tag{5.6-42}$$

The inverse transform of the above expression is

$$c^*(t) = 0.632\delta(t - T) + 1.10\delta(t - 2T) + 1.22\delta(t - 3T) + 1.14\delta(t - 4T) + 1.04\delta(t - 5T) + \cdots \tag{5.6-43}$$

which describes the transient response of the system at the sampling instants to a unit step-function input. The system response at sampling instants, sometimes referred to as the output sequence, is plotted in Fig. 5.6-6.

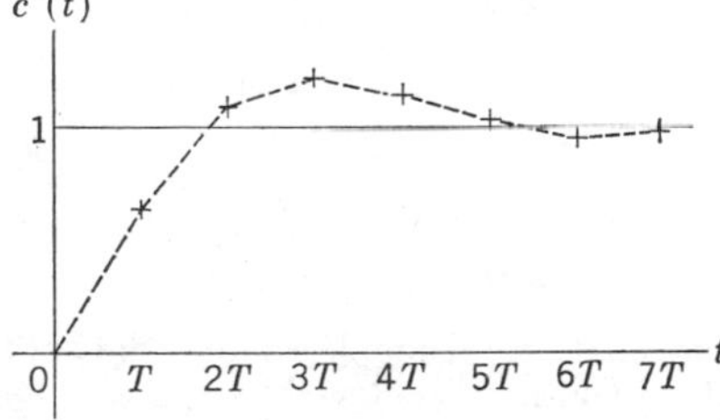

FIG. 5.6-6. The output sequence of the system of Example 5.6-4 in response to a unit step-function input.

In this section, three commonly used methods of evaluating the inverse z transform are presented. The first method yields the value of the inverse z transform at any instant $t = nT$. This method is particularly useful, when a general expression of the time sequence is required. The second method can provide not only the values of the time function at the sampling instants but also, in some cases, the approximate time function itself. This method can generally be used to determine the approximate transient response of a sampled-data system, provided that the sampling frequency of the system is much higher than the bandwidth of the system. The third method is probably the simplest and the most convenient of the three. This method is always used when only the first several values of the time sequence are needed. Although it is unable to yield a general expression of the time sequence, yet this method with the aid of a digital computer makes the calculation of the value of the time sequence at any instant a simple matter.

The previous discussions point out that the inverse z transformation fails to provide the correct information between sampling instants. In consequence, the complete transient response of a sampled-data control system cannot be determined by the z-transform method, unless the system output is a pulsed-data signal. This is a shortcoming of the method. A remedy is presented in the following section.

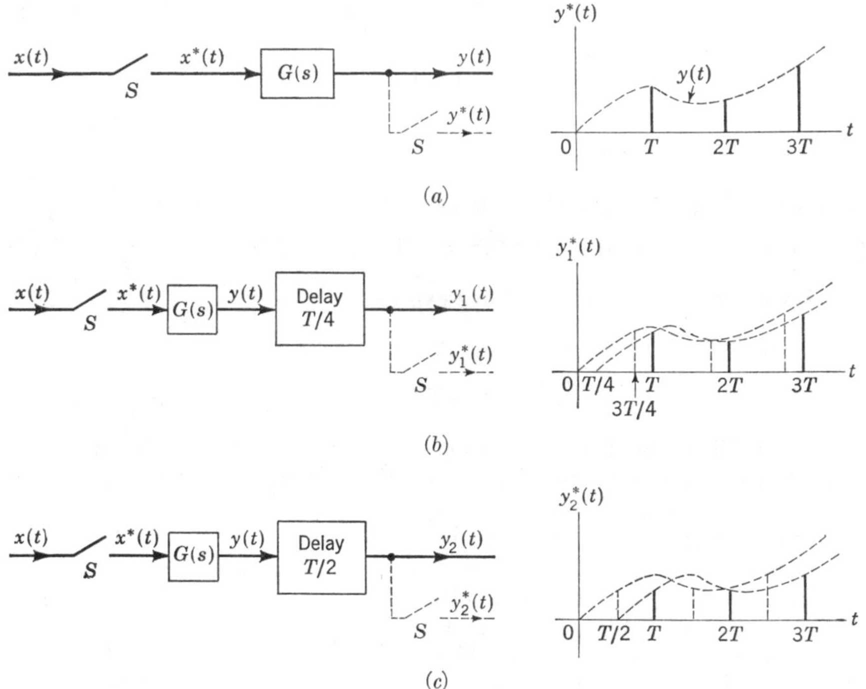

FIG. 5.7-1. (a) A simple sampled-data system (without delay) and the output waveform; (b) the output is delayed by $T/4$ sec; (c) the output is delayed by $T/2$ sec.

5.7. Modified z Transforms. The z-transform method, introduced by Hurewicz, has gained great popularity in the control engineering field as a convenient and powerful means for analyzing sampled-data and digital control systems. By use of the z-transform techniques the transfer-function concept and the block-diagram analysis can readily be carried over to solve pulsed-data control problems, enabling such control systems to be analyzed and synthesized in a systematic manner. However, it has been pointed out that the z-transform method suffers from a serious limitation: The inverse z transformation yields correct information only at the sampling instants, as explained and illustrated by the examples of Sec. 5.6. No doubt this would limit the practical applications of the frequently used z-transform method. But this shortcoming can be removed and the complete transient behavior can be derived through real inversion, if a modification is imposed upon the z-transform technique. This section is concerned with the modification of the z-transform method so that its application can be extended to the determination of the values between sampling instants.[25,107]

Referring to Fig. 5.7-1a, in terms of z transforms the input and the output are related by

$$Y(z) = G(z)X(z) \tag{5.7-1}$$

where $G(z)$ is the pulse-transfer function of the system. In spite of the fact that the output of this system is a continuous function $y(t)$, only the values of the output signal at sampling instants can be determined through real inversion of the above equation. This is because the z-transform method deals with discrete-data functions. A train of these sampled values represented by the starred time function $y^*(t)$ is taken from the output signal $y(t)$ by a fictitious sampler shown in dotted line in Fig. 5.7-1a. If the output of the system, $y(t)$, were delayed by one-quarter of the sampling period T (Fig. 5.7-1b), the samples taken by the fictitious sampler would be the values of the output signal at $t = 3T/4, 3T/4 + T, 3T/4 + 2T, 3T/4 + 3T, \ldots$; if delayed by one-half of the sampling period as shown in Fig. 5.7-1c, the fictitious sampler would yield values of the output at $t = T/2, T/2 + T, T/2 + 2T, T/2 + 3T, \ldots$; and if delayed by three-quarters of the sampling period, the fictitious sampler would pick up values of the output signal at $t = T/4, T/4 + T, T/4 + 2T, T/4 + 3T, \ldots$. In general, any value of the output between two consecutive sampling instants could be computed, if the output signal $y(t)$ were delayed by a proper interval of time in making the calculation. Based upon the above reasoning the modified z transforms† are derived.

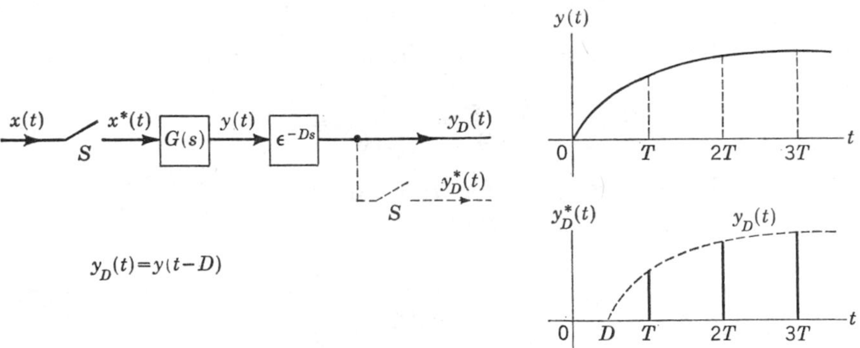

FIG. 5.7-2. A sampled-data system with the output delayed by D sec, and the output sequence.

When a sampled-data control system contains a transport lag or distance-velocity delay $D = \lambda T$, as shown in Fig. 5.7-2, the output of the

† The modified z-transform method was first developed by Barker.

system is given by

$$y_D(t) = y(t - D) = y(t - \lambda T) \qquad (5.7\text{-}2)$$

the values of the output signal $y_D(t)$ at sampling instants are given by the following sequence:

$$0, \quad y(T - \lambda T), \quad y(2T - \lambda T), \quad y(3T - \lambda T), \quad \ldots y(kT - \lambda T), \quad \ldots$$

and the output of the fictitious sampler is

$$\begin{aligned} y_D^*(t) &= y(T - \lambda T)\delta(t - T) + y(2T - \lambda T)\delta(t - 2T) \\ &\quad + y(3T - \lambda T)\delta(t - 3T) + \cdots + y(kT - \lambda T)\delta(t - kT) + \cdots \\ &= \sum_{k=0}^{\infty} y(kT - \lambda T)\delta(t - kT) \end{aligned} \qquad (5.7\text{-}3)$$

The z transform of Eq. (5.7-2) is

$$Y_D(z) = \sum_{k=0}^{\infty} y(kT - \lambda T)z^{-k} \qquad (5.7\text{-}4)$$

In Fig. 5.7-2, $G(s)$ is the system transfer function, ϵ^{-Ds} is the transfer function for the transport lag, and $x(t)$ and $y_D(t)$ are the input and the output, respectively. The delay factor $\lambda = D/T$ can be an integer, a fraction, or an integer plus a fraction. These three cases are discussed here.

CASE A. λ is an integer.

If the z transforms of $x(t)$ and $y(t)$ are $X(z)$ and $Y(z)$, then the z transform of $y_D(t)$ is

$$Y_D(z) = \mathfrak{z}\{y(t - \lambda T)\} = z^{-\lambda}Y(z) \qquad (5.7\text{-}5)$$

and the pulse-transfer function of the system with delay is given by

$$G_D(z) = \frac{Y_D(z)}{X(z)} = z^{-\lambda}\frac{Y(z)}{X(z)} = z^{-\lambda}G(z) \qquad (5.7\text{-}6)$$

where $G(z)$ is the z transform for $G(s)$. Making use of the definition of $G(z)$, Eq. (5.7-6) may be written as

$$G_D(z) = z^{-\lambda} \sum_{k=0}^{\infty} g(kT)z^{-k} \qquad (5.7\text{-}7)$$

From the above discussion it is seen that the effect of a delay of λT sec is to multiply the pulse-transfer function of the system without delay by $z^{-\lambda}$.

CASE B. λ is a fraction.

Let $mT + \lambda T = T$, $\lambda = 1 - m$, m being a number lying between 0 and

1, then Eq. (5.7-3) becomes

$$y_D^*(t) = \sum_{k=0}^{\infty} y[kT + (m - 1)T]\delta(t - kT) \tag{5.7-8}$$

and the z transform reduces to

$$Y_D(z) = z^{-1} \sum_{k=0}^{\infty} y(kT + mT)z^{-k} \tag{5.7-9}$$

The right-hand side of both Eq. (5.7-8) and Eq. (5.7-9) contains the parameter m.

Referring to Fig. 5.7-3, it is seen that the values taken from the delayed output signal $y_D(t)$ at the sampling instants are equal to the correspond-

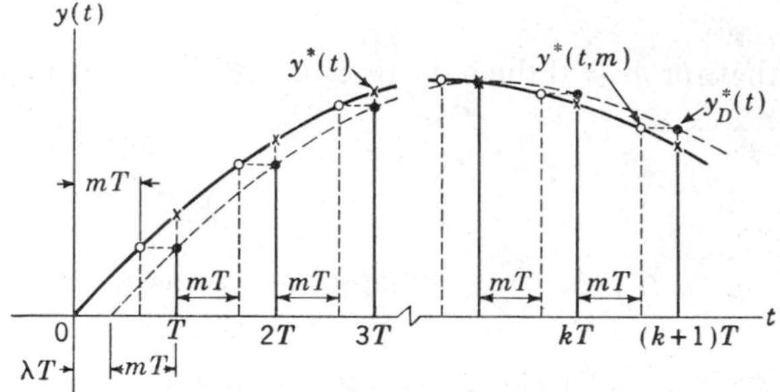

Fig. 5.7-3. Samples of the output function and the delayed output function.

ing values of the output $y(t)$ at the instants mT, $mT + T$, $mT + 2T$, $mT + 3T$, . . . , which are represented by $y^*(t,m)$. In symbol,

$$y_D(kT) = y(kT,m) \tag{5.7-10}$$

and $$y_D^*(t) = y^*(t,m) \qquad \text{in amplitude} \tag{5.7-11}$$

$y(kT,m)$ denotes a value of $y(t)$ at the instant $t = kT + mT$ which lies between the sampling intervals kT and $(k + 1)T$, and $y^*(t,m)$ describes a train of such values. By the substitution of Eq. (5.7-11) into Eq. (5.7-8), the train of values of $y(t)$ at corresponding points between successive sampling instants is obtained.

$$y^*(t,m) = \sum_{k=0}^{\infty} y[(k + m)T - T]\delta(t - kT) \tag{5.7-12}$$

Thus, if the value of m is varied from 0 to 1, Eq. (5.7-12) yields all the values of the output signal between sampling instants. The z transform of Eq. (5.7-12)

$$Y(z,m) = z^{-1} \sum_{k=0}^{\infty} y(kT + mT)z^{-k} \tag{5.7-13}$$

is referred to as the modified z transform of $y(t)$. Equation (5.7-12) and Eq. (5.7-13) form the modified z-transform pair in which m is a parameter. Symbolically it is written as

$$Y(z,m) = \mathfrak{Z}_m\{y(t)\} \tag{5.7-14}$$

The two extreme values of m are:

$m = 0$

$$y^*(t,0) = \sum_{k=0}^{\infty} y(kT - T)\delta(t - kT) \tag{5.7-15}$$

and

$$Y(z,0) = z^{-1} \sum_{k=0}^{\infty} y(kT)z^{-k} = z^{-1}Y(z) \tag{5.7-16}$$

This implies that for $m = 0$ the output signal $y(t)$ is delayed by a sampling period.

$m = 1$

$$y^*(t,1) = \sum_{k=0}^{\infty} y(kT)\delta(t - kT) = y^*(t) \tag{5.7-17}$$

and

$$Y(z,1) = z^{-1} \sum_{k=0}^{\infty} y(kT + T)z^{-k} = Y(z) \tag{5.7-18}$$

This means that for $m = 1$ the modified z transform becomes the z transform. The above statements can easily be seen from Fig. 5.7-3. It is to be noted that Eq. (5.7-17) and Eq. (5.7-18) hold providing that the output signal $y(t)$ contains no discontinuity at the sampling instants. In other words, $y(t)$ has a unique value at every sampling instant.

In the sampled-data system of Fig. 5.7-1a, if the z transform of the input $x(t)$ is $X(z)$ and the modified z transform of the output $y(t)$ is $Y(z,m)$, then the ratio of the output to the input,

$$\frac{Y(z,m)}{X(z)} = G(z,m) \tag{5.7-19}$$

is called the modified pulse-transfer function of the system or the modified z transform of $g(t)$. For a unit impulse-function input, $x(t) = \delta(t)$, $y(t) = g(t)$, $X(z) = 1$, and $Y(z,m) = G(z,m)$. Therefore, the modified pulse-transfer function $G(z,m)$ is given by

$$G(z,m) = z^{-1} \sum_{k=0}^{\infty} g(kT + mT)z^{-k} \tag{5.7-20}$$

Which is also the modified z transform of the impulse response $g(t)$.

CASE C. λ is an integer plus a fraction.

Assuming

$$(n-1) < \lambda < n \qquad \lambda = n - m \tag{5.7-21}$$

where n is an integer and m is a fraction, then the delayed output signal $y_D(t)$ becomes

$$y_D(t) = y[(t + mT) - nT] \tag{5.7-22}$$

and the train of values of $y(t)$ at the instants $t = nT - mT$, $(n+1)T - mT$, $(n+2)T - mT$, . . . is described by

$$y^*(t,m) = \sum_{k=0}^{\infty} y[(k+m)T - nT]\delta(t - kT) \tag{5.7-23}$$

The modified z transform of $y(t)$ is then given by

$$Y(z,m) = z^{-n} \sum_{k=0}^{\infty} y(kT + mT)z^{-k} \tag{5.7-24}$$

It is noted that when $n = 1$, Eq. (5.7-24) reduces to Eq. (5.7-13).

Alternate Definition of Modified z Transform. In the above discussion, the modified z transform is expressed as the summation of an infinite series. The usefulness of the above expression depends upon the possibility and readiness of finding the sum of the series. In most cases, in practice, the summation of the series can easily be performed. However, when difficulties arise in expressing the infinite series in a compact form, it would be necessary to make use of an alternate expression defining the modified z transform of a function or the modified pulse-transfer function of a system.

As has been shown in Sec. 5.2, the definition of the z transform (or the pulse-transfer function) can be expressed in either of the two forms given by Eqs. (5.2-66) and (5.2-67). Because of its close relationship to the z transform, the modified z transform may be defined by two different expressions following the same reasoning. Reference to Fig. 5.7-2 indicates that for the sampled-data system with the fictitious delay

$$G_D(s) = \epsilon^{-Ds}G(s) \tag{5.7-25}$$

$$G_D^*(s) = [\epsilon^{-Ds}G(s)]^* \tag{5.7-26}$$

where [ ]* implies *taking the starred transform of*, $D = \lambda T$ and λ is a fraction, $G(s)$, $G_D(s)$, and $G_D^*(s)$ are the Laplace transforms of the impulse responses $g(t)$, $g(t - D)$, and $g^*(t - D)$, respectively. Since

$$g^*(t - D) = g(t - D)\delta_T(t) \tag{5.7-27}$$

the corresponding starred transform is

$$G_D^*(s) = \mathcal{L}\{g^*(t - D)\} = \mathcal{L}\{g(t - D)\delta_T(t)\} \tag{5.7-28}$$

which may be written as

$$G_D^*(s) = G_D(s) * \Delta_T(s) \tag{5.7-29}$$

where $\Delta_T(s)$ is the Laplace transform of $\delta_T(t)$. It has been shown that

$$\Delta_T(s) = \frac{1}{1 - \epsilon^{-Ts}} \tag{5.7-30}$$

In view of Eq. (5.7-25), Eq. (5.7-29) can be put into the form

$$G_D^*(s) = \epsilon^{-Ds}G(s) * \Delta_T(s) \tag{5.7-31}$$

Making use of the theorem of complex convolution, Eq. (5.7-31) reduces to

$$G_D^*(s) = \frac{1}{2\pi j} \oint_C G(\chi)\epsilon^{-D\chi} \frac{1}{1 - \epsilon^{-T(s-\chi)}}\, d\chi \tag{5.7-32}$$

where the contour of integration C encloses all the poles of $G(\chi)\epsilon^{-D\chi}$ in the left half of the χ plane, as shown in Fig. 5.7-4. However, because of the

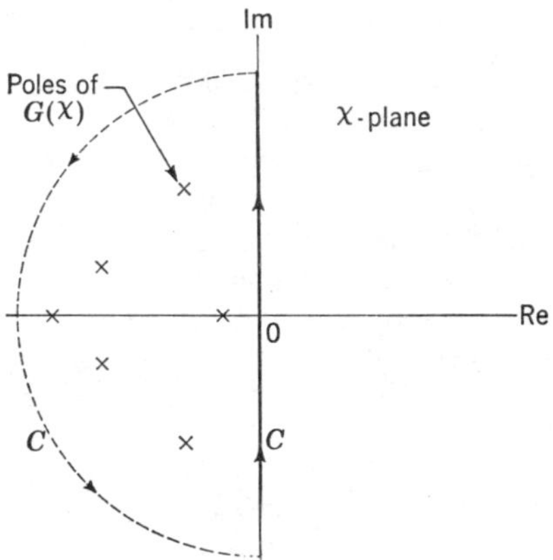

FIG. 5.7-4. Path of integration.

factor $\epsilon^{-D\chi}$ in the integrand, difficulties are encountered in the evaluation of the above contour integral. To overcome such difficulties, the expression of the modified z transform is derived as follows:

Let $$m = 1 - \lambda \qquad D = \lambda T = (1 - m)T \tag{5.7-33}$$

where m is a number lying between 0 and 1. Then it follows that

$$\mathcal{L}\{g(t - D)\} = \epsilon^{-Ts}\,\mathcal{L}\{g(t + mT)\} \tag{5.7-34}$$

$$\mathcal{L}\{g^*(t - D)\} = \epsilon^{-Ts}\,\mathcal{L}\{g^*(t + mT)\} = G^*(s,m) \tag{5.7-35}$$

Since
$$\begin{aligned}\mathcal{L}\{g^*(t + mT)\} &= \mathcal{L}\{g(t + mT)\delta_T(t)\} \\ &= \epsilon^{mTs}G(s) * \Delta_T(s) \\ &= \frac{1}{2\pi j} \oint_C \frac{G(\chi)\epsilon^{mT\chi}}{1 - \epsilon^{-T(s-\chi)}}\, d\chi \end{aligned} \tag{5.7-36}$$

it follows from Eq. (5.7-35) that

$$G^*(s,m) = \frac{\epsilon^{-Ts}}{2\pi j} \oint_C \frac{G(\chi)\epsilon^{mT\chi}}{1 - \epsilon^{-T(s-\chi)}} d\chi \tag{5.7-37}$$

By applying the residue theorem, Eq. (5.7-37) is reduced to

$$G^*(s,m) = \epsilon^{-Ts} \sum_k \text{residues of } \frac{G(\chi)\epsilon^{mT\chi}}{1 - \epsilon^{T\chi}\epsilon^{-Ts}} \text{ at } \chi = s_k \tag{5.7-38}$$

where s_k are the poles of $G(\chi)$ and $G(\chi) = G(s)|_{s=\chi}$.

In case $G(s)$ contains no multiple pole, Eq. (5.7-38) may be written as

$$G^*(s,m) = \epsilon^{-Ts} \sum_k \frac{\epsilon^{mTs_k}}{1 - \epsilon^{Ts_k}\epsilon^{-Ts}} \text{ residues of } G(\chi) \text{ at } \chi = s_k \tag{5.7-39}$$

Making use of the substitution $z = \epsilon^{Ts}$, Eqs. (5.7-38) and (5.7-39) become

$$G(z,m) = z^{-1} \sum_k \text{residues } \frac{G(\chi)\epsilon^{mT\chi}}{1 - \epsilon^{T\chi}z^{-1}} \text{ at } \chi = s_k \tag{5.7-40}$$

and

$$G(z,m) = z^{-1} \sum_k \frac{\epsilon^{mTs_k}}{1 - \epsilon^{Ts_k}z^{-1}} \text{ residues of } G(\chi) \text{ at } \chi = s_k \tag{5.7-41}$$

Equation (5.7-40) represents an alternate expression defining the modified pulse-transfer function of a system $G(s)$ or the modified z transform of its impulse response function $g(t)$.

Evaluation of Modified z Transforms. The modified z transform of a function can readily be derived by making use of Eq. (5.7-20) or Eq. (5.7-40). A table of commonly used modified z transforms is given in Appendix 1. In the following paragraph the evaluation of modified z transforms is illustrated by a few examples.

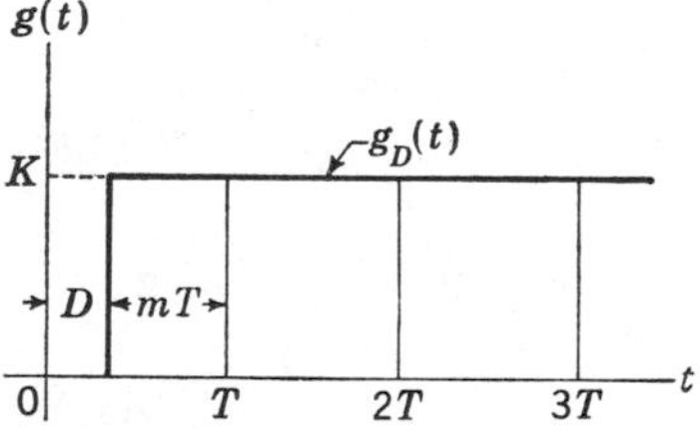

FIG. 5.7-5. Delayed step function.

1. STEP FUNCTION

$$g(t) = Ku(t) \qquad \text{and} \qquad g(kT + mT) = K \qquad \text{for } k = 0, 1, 2, \ldots \tag{5.7-42}$$

From Eq. (5.7-20), the modified z transform is given by

$$G(z,m) = z^{-1} \sum_{k=0}^{\infty} g(kT + mT)z^{-k}$$

$$= z^{-1}K(1 + z^{-1} + z^{-2} + \cdots) \tag{5.7-43}$$

or

$$G(z,m) = \frac{K}{z - 1} \tag{5.7-44}$$

The modified z transform of a step function is independent of the parameter m, because the weighting sequence is a train of pulses of equal magnitude and the first sample of the delayed function $g_D(t)$ is zero (Fig. 5.7-5). It is interesting to note that for a step function,

$$G(z,m) = z^{-1}G(z) \tag{5.7-45}$$

where $G(z)$ is its z transform.

2. RAMP FUNCTION

$$g(t) = Ktu(t) \qquad g(kT + mT) = (k + m)KT \tag{5.7-46}$$

The modified z transform is

$$\begin{aligned} G(z,m) &= z^{-1} \sum_{k=0}^{\infty} KT(k + m)z^{-k} \\ &= z^{-1}[mKT + (m + 1)KTz^{-1} + (m + 2)KTz^{-2} + \cdots \\ &\qquad + (m + k)KTz^{-k} + \cdots] \\ &= KTz^{-1}[m(1 + z^{-1} + z^{-2} + \cdots + z^{-k} + \cdots) \\ &\qquad + z^{-1}(1 + 2z^{-1} + 3z^{-2} + \cdots + kz^{-(k-1)} + \cdots)] \\ &= KTz^{-1}\left[\frac{m}{1 - z^{-1}} + \frac{z^{-1}}{(1 - z^{-1})^2}\right] \end{aligned} \tag{5.7-47}$$

or

$$G(z,m) = \frac{KmT}{z - 1} + \frac{KT}{(z - 1)^2} \tag{5.7-48}$$

It is observed that for $m = 0$, $\lambda = 1$,

$$G(z,0) = \frac{KT}{(z - 1)^2} = z^{-1}G(z) \tag{5.7-49}$$

where

$$G(z) = \frac{KTz}{(z - 1)^2} \tag{5.7-50}$$

is the z transform of the ramp function. If m is equal to unity, the modified z transform becomes the z transform:

$$G(z,1) = \frac{KTz}{(z - 1)^2} = G(z) \tag{5.7-51}$$

3. EXPONENTIAL FUNCTION

$$g(t) = \epsilon^{-at}u(t) \qquad g(kT + mT) = \epsilon^{-a(k+m)T} \tag{5.7-52}$$

Making use of Eq. (5.7-20), the modified z transform is found to be

$$G(z,m) = z^{-1} \sum_{k=0}^{\infty} \epsilon^{-a(k+m)T} z^{-k}$$
$$= z^{-1}[\epsilon^{-amT} + \epsilon^{-a(1+m)T} z^{-1} + \epsilon^{-a(2+m)T} z^{-2} + \cdots]$$
$$= z^{-1}\epsilon^{-amT}[1 + \epsilon^{-aT} z^{-1} + \epsilon^{-2aT} z^{-2} + \cdots]$$
$$= \frac{z^{-1}\epsilon^{-amT}}{1 - \epsilon^{-aT} z^{-1}} \tag{5.7-53}$$

or

$$G(z,m) = \frac{\epsilon^{-amT}}{z - \epsilon^{-aT}} \tag{5.7-54}$$

The modified z transform can also be derived from Eq. (5.7-41). Since $G(s) = 1/(s + a)$ with a pole at $s = -a$, the residue of $G(s)$ at this pole is equal to unity. Hence

$$G(z,m) = z^{-1} \frac{\epsilon^{-amT}}{1 - \epsilon^{-aT} z^{-1}} = \frac{\epsilon^{-amT}}{z - \epsilon^{-aT}} \tag{5.7-55}$$

which checks with the above result.

From the short table of z transforms, the z transform of the exponential function ϵ^{-at} is

$$G(z) = \frac{z}{z - \epsilon^{-aT}} \tag{5.7-56}$$

Then it follows that for $m = 0$, $G(z,0)$ is equal to $z^{-1}G(z)$; however, for $m = 1$, $G(z,1)$ is not equal to $G(z)$. This is due to the discontinuity of $g(t)$ at sampling instant $t = 0$. In fact,

$$G(z,1) = \frac{\epsilon^{-aT}}{z - \epsilon^{-aT}} \tag{5.7-57}$$

is the z transform of the function $\epsilon^{-at}u(t - T)$ which is depicted in Fig. 5.7-6. Making use of Eq. (5.2-1), the z transform of $\epsilon^{-at}u(t - T)$ is found to be

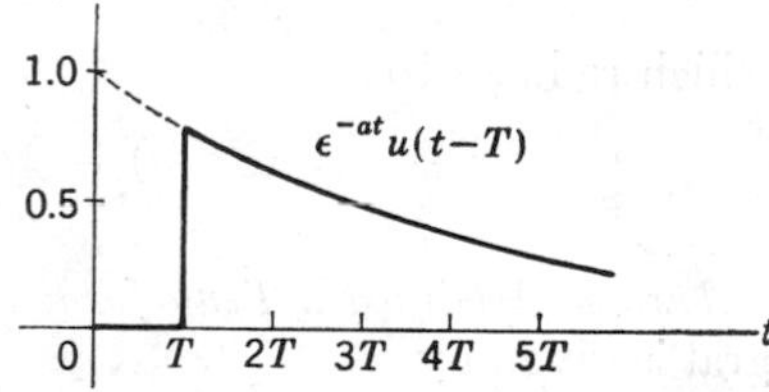

FIG. 5.7-6. Plot of $\epsilon^{-at}u(t - T)$.

$$\mathfrak{z}\{\epsilon^{-at}u(t - T)\} = \sum_{k=1}^{\infty} \epsilon^{-akT} z^{-k} \tag{5.7-58}$$

In Eq. (5.7-58) the lower limit of the summation is unity, because the time function is zero at $t = 0$. Equation (5.7-58) may be written as

$$\mathfrak{z}\{\epsilon^{-at}u(t - T)\} = \epsilon^{-aT} z^{-1}(1 + \epsilon^{-aT} z^{-1} + \epsilon^{-2aT} z^{-2} + \cdots)$$
$$= \frac{\epsilon^{-aT} z^{-1}}{1 - \epsilon^{-aT} z^{-1}}$$
$$= \frac{\epsilon^{-aT}}{z - \epsilon^{-aT}} \tag{5.7-59}$$

which is equal to $G(z,1)$. It is to be noted that in taking the modified z transform of a time function the value of the sample at $t = 0$ is zero, whereas in evaluating the z transform of a time function the value of the sample at $t = 0$ is equal to the actual value of the time function at that instant. Consequently, unless the time function is continuous and is zero at the start of the function, its modified z transform for $m = 1$ is different from its z transform.

4. PRODUCT OF POSITIVE POWERS OF t AND EXPONENTIAL FUNCTION

$$g(t) = \frac{1}{r!} t^r \epsilon^{-at} \qquad (t \geq 0) \tag{5.7-60}$$

which may be written as

$$g(t) = \frac{(-1)^r}{r!} \frac{\partial^r \epsilon^{-at}}{\partial a^r} \tag{5.7-61}$$

Then

$$g(kT + mT) = \frac{(-1)^r}{r!} \frac{\partial^r}{\partial a^r} \epsilon^{-a(k+m)T} \tag{5.7-62}$$

From Eq. (5.7-20) the modified z transform reads

$$G(z,m) = z^{-1} \sum_{k=0}^{\infty} \frac{(-1)^r}{r!} \frac{\partial^r \epsilon^{-a(k+m)T}}{\partial a^r} z^{-k}$$

$$= z^{-1} \frac{(-1)^r}{r!} \frac{\partial^r}{\partial a^r} \left[\epsilon^{-amT} \sum_{k=0}^{\infty} (\epsilon^{-aT} z^{-1})^k\right] \tag{5.7-63}$$

which reduces to

$$G(z,m) = \frac{(-1)^r}{r!} \frac{\partial^r}{\partial a^r} \left(\frac{\epsilon^{-amT}}{z - \epsilon^{-aT}}\right) \tag{5.7-64}$$

Inverse Modified z Transforms. The inverse modified z-transform integral is given by

$$g(nT,m) = \frac{1}{2\pi j} \oint_\Gamma G(z,m) z^{n-1}\, dz \tag{5.7-65}$$

where the contour Γ encloses all the singularities of $G(z,m)z^{n-1}$. Equation (5.7-65) may be derived in the same way as the inverse z-transform integral:

$$g(nT,m) = \frac{1}{2\pi j} \int_{c-j\infty}^{c+j\infty} G_D(\xi) \epsilon^{nT\xi}\, d\xi$$

$$= \frac{1}{2\pi j} \sum_{k=-\infty}^{\infty} \int_{c+j(k-\frac{1}{2})\omega_s}^{c+j(k+\frac{1}{2})\omega_s} G_D(\xi) \epsilon^{nT\xi}\, d\xi \tag{5.7-66}$$

By letting

$$\xi = s + jk\omega_s \tag{5.7-67}$$

Eq. (5.7-66) becomes

$$g(nT,m) = \frac{T}{2\pi j}\int_{c-j\frac{1}{2}\omega_s}^{c+j\frac{1}{2}\omega_s} \frac{1}{T}\sum_{k=-\infty}^{\infty} G_D(s + jk\omega_s)\epsilon^{nTs}\,ds \tag{5.7-68}$$

Making the substitution $z = \epsilon^{Ts}$, the function

$$\frac{1}{T}\sum_{k=-\infty}^{\infty} G_D(s + jk\omega_s) = G_D^*(s) \tag{5.7-69}$$

becomes $G(z,m)$, and Eq. (5.7-68) reduces to

$$g(nT,m) = \frac{1}{2\pi j}\oint_\Gamma G(z,m)z^{n-1}\,dz \tag{5.7-70}$$

which is the inverse modified z-transform integral.

EXAMPLE 5.7-1. Evaluate the inverse modified z transform of

$$G(z,m) = \frac{\epsilon^{-amT}}{z - \epsilon^{-aT}} \tag{5.7-71}$$

From Eq. (5.7-70), the inverse modified z transform is given by

$$g(nT,m) = \frac{1}{2\pi j}\oint_\Gamma \frac{\epsilon^{-amT}z^{n-1}}{z - \epsilon^{-aT}}\,dz \tag{5.7-72}$$

The integral can be evaluated by applying the residue theorem:

$$g(nT,m) = \text{residue of } \frac{\epsilon^{-amT}z^{n-1}}{z - \epsilon^{-aT}} \text{ at } z = \epsilon^{-aT}$$

$$= \epsilon^{-(n+m-1)aT} \tag{5.7-73}$$

At the first sampling instant, $n = 0$, $m = 1$, and $g(nT,m) = 1$. During the first sampling period, $n = 1$ and $g(T,m) = \epsilon^{-amT}$; during the second sampling period, $n = 2$ and $g(2T,m) = \epsilon^{-a(m+1)T}$; and during the kth sampling interval, $n = k$ and $g(kT,m) = \epsilon^{-a(m+k-1)T}$. Thus, as m varies between 0 and 1, $g(nT,m)$ will describe the exponential function ϵ^{-at}, as shown in Fig. 5.7-7.

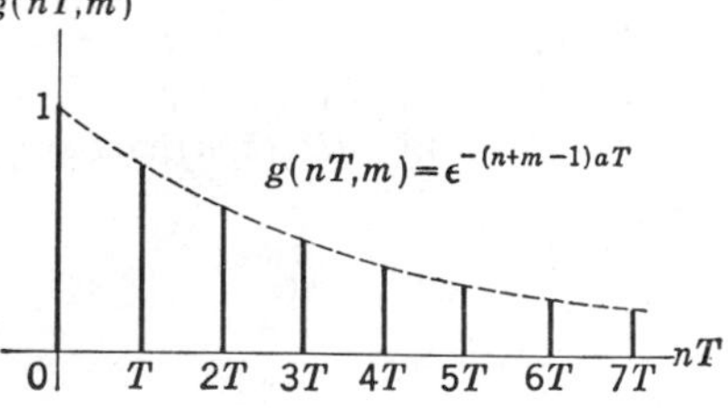

FIG. 5.7-7. Plot of $\epsilon^{-(n+m-1)aT}$ of Example 5.7-1.

EXAMPLE 5.7-2. Find the inverse modified z transform of

$$G(z,m) = \frac{1}{z-1} - \frac{z\cos m\omega_0 T - \cos(1-m)\omega_0 T}{z^2 - 2z\cos\omega_0 T + 1} \tag{5.7-74}$$

The inverse transform is given by

$$g(nT,m) = \sum \text{residues of } G(z,m)z^{n-1} \text{ inside } \Gamma \tag{5.7-75}$$

The residue at $z = 1$ is 1. Since

$$\frac{z \cos m\omega_0 T - \cos (1 - m)\omega_0 T}{z^2 - 2z \cos \omega_0 T + 1} = \frac{1}{2}\left(\frac{\epsilon^{-jm\omega_0 T}}{z - \epsilon^{-j\omega_0 T}} + \frac{\epsilon^{jm\omega_0 T}}{z - \epsilon^{j\omega_0 T}}\right) \tag{5.7-76}$$

the residues of $G(z,m)z^{n-1}$ at $z = \epsilon^{\pm j\omega_0 T}$ are

$$-\tfrac{1}{2}\epsilon^{j(n+m-1)\omega_0 T} \qquad -\tfrac{1}{2}\epsilon^{-j(n+m-1)\omega_0 T}$$

Hence

$$\begin{aligned} g(nT,m) &= 1 - \tfrac{1}{2}(\epsilon^{j(n+m-1)\omega_0 T} + \epsilon^{-j(n+m-1)\omega_0 T}) \\ &= 1 - \cos (n + m - 1)\omega_0 T \end{aligned} \tag{5.7-77}$$

A second method of evaluating the inverse modified z transform is the method of power-series expansion. By this method, $G(z,m)$ is expanded into a power series in z^{-1} by long division, assuming m to be constant. The coefficient of the z^{-n} term is a function of m which describes the corresponding time function $g(nT,m)$ during the nth sampling period as m varies from 0 to 1. As an illustration, the inverse modified z transform of Eq. (5.7-71) is evaluated by means of this method:

Expanding the right-hand member of Eq. (5.7-71) into a power series in z^{-1} yields

$$\begin{aligned} G(z,m) &= \epsilon^{-amT}z^{-1}[1 + \epsilon^{-aT}z^{-1} + (\epsilon^{-aT}z^{-1})^2 + \cdots + (\epsilon^{-aT}z^{-1})^k + \cdots] \\ &= \epsilon^{-amT}z^{-1} + \epsilon^{-a(m+1)T}z^{-2} + \epsilon^{-a(m+2)T}z^{-3} + \cdots \\ &\qquad + \epsilon^{-a(m+k-1)T}z^{-k} + \cdots \end{aligned} \tag{5.7-78}$$

From the above series, it is seen that during the first sampling period the time function is given by $g(T,m) = \epsilon^{-amT}$; during the second sampling period, the time function is $g(2T,m) = \epsilon^{-a(m+1)T}$; and during the kth sampling period, the time function is given by $g(kT,m) = \epsilon^{-a(m+k-1)T}$. Clearly, this agrees with the result computed above.

Initial and Final Value Determined from Modified z Transform. INITIAL-VALUE THEOREM. If the function $g(t)$ has the modified z transform $G(z,m)$ and the limit $\lim_{\substack{m=0 \\ z\to\infty}} \{zG(z,m)\}$ exists, then

$$\lim_{\substack{m=0 \\ z\to\infty}} \{zG(z,m)\} = \lim_{\substack{n=1 \\ m=0}} \{g(nT,m)\} = \lim_{t\to 0} \{g(t)\} \tag{5.7-79}$$

This theorem follows from the fact that

$$zG(z,0) = G(z), \qquad \lim_{z\to\infty} \{G(z)\} = \lim_{t\to 0} \{g(t)\} \tag{5.7-80}$$

It is interesting to note that from the initial value theorem the response during the first sampling period may be determined without taking the inverse modified z transforms. Since the limit of $zG(z,m)$ as z approaches infinity yields the value of $g(t)$ at $t = mT$,

$$\lim_{\substack{z\to\infty \\ 0\le m\le 1}} \{zG(z,m)\} = g(t) \qquad \text{for } 0 \le t \le T \tag{5.7-81}$$

In fact, it can be shown that Eq. (5.7-81) may be used to determine the complete time function by letting m vary from zero to infinity, if the modified z transform is derived from the time function directly.

EXAMPLE 5.7-3. Consider the following modified z transform pair:

$$\begin{cases} g(t) = \epsilon^{-at} & (5.7\text{-}82a) \\ g(nT,m) = \epsilon^{-(n+m-1)aT} & (5.7\text{-}82b) \end{cases}$$

$$G(z,m) = \frac{\epsilon^{-amT}}{z - \epsilon^{-aT}} \tag{5.7-83}$$

The initial value is shown to be

$$\lim_{\substack{m=0 \\ z\to\infty}} \{zG(z,m)\} = 1 \tag{5.7-84}$$

This is checked by

$$\lim_{t\to 0} \{g(t)\} = 1 \qquad \lim_{\substack{n=1 \\ m=0}} \{g(nT,m)\} = 1 \tag{5.7-85}$$

As z becomes infinite the limit of $zG(z,m)$ approaches ϵ^{-amT}, which describes the time function during the first sampling period when m is varied from 0 to 1. Furthermore, it is seen that

$$\lim_{z\to\infty} \{zG(z,m)\} = \epsilon^{-amT} \tag{5.7-86}$$

also describes the complete time function provided that m is allowed to vary from zero to infinity.

FINAL-VALUE THEOREM. If the function $g(t)$ has the modified z transform $G(z,m)$ which possesses no polc on or outside the unit circle of the z plane, then

$$\lim_{\substack{z\to 1 \\ 0\le m\le 1}} \left\{\frac{z-1}{z} G(z,m)\right\} = \lim_{\substack{n\to\infty \\ 0\le m\le 1}} \{g(nT,m)\} = \lim_{t\to\infty} \{g(t)\} \tag{5.7-87}$$

EXAMPLE 5.7-4. Consider the following modified z-transform pair:

$$\begin{cases} g(t) = 1 - \epsilon^{-at} & (5.7\text{-}88a) \\ g(nT,m) = 1 - \epsilon^{-(n+m-1)aT} & (5.7\text{-}88b) \end{cases}$$

$$G(z,m) = \frac{1}{z-1} - \frac{\epsilon^{-amT}}{z - \epsilon^{-aT}} \tag{5.7-89}$$

The limit of $(z - 1)z^{-1}G(z,m)$ as z approaches unity is 1. This checks with the limiting value

$$\lim_{t\to\infty} \{1 - \epsilon^{-at}\} = 1 \tag{5.7-90}$$

and

$$\lim_{\substack{n\to\infty \\ 0\le m\le 1}} \{1 - \epsilon^{-(n+m-1)aT}\} = 1 \tag{5.7-91}$$

By applying these two theorems the initial and the final value of a continuous response may be determined without evaluating the inverse transform.

5.8. Numerical Integration; *z* Forms. The evaluation of a definite integral may be carried out either by the rules of integral calculus or by the numerical-integration methods.† To evaluate a definite integral one usually turns to numerical methods when the corresponding indefinite integral is not expressible in a closed form or is so complicated that its evaluation is very laborious. In digital control systems, when the pulsed-data information needs to be processed by integration, the data processing is performed by a procedure of numerical integration. This section is concerned with the determination of the z transforms[59,118] associated with various numerical-integration methods and the discussion of the quality and accuracy of these methods as compared with ideal integration.

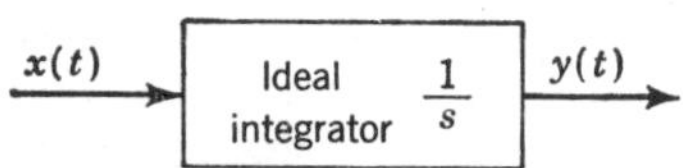

FIG. 5.8-1. An ideal integrator.

Shown in Fig. 5.8-1 is the block diagram of an ideal integrator. The output $y(t)$ and the input $x(t)$ are related by

$$y(t) = \int_0^t x(t)\,dt \tag{5.8-1}$$

Taking the Laplace transform of both sides of Eq. (5.8-1) yields

$$Y(s) = \frac{1}{s} X(s) \tag{5.8-2}$$

Thus, the integration operator or the transfer function of an ideal integrator is simply

$$D_0(s) = \frac{Y(s)}{X(s)} = \frac{1}{s} \tag{5.8-3}$$

The integration operators for numerical integration are derived in the following: Numerical integration is a process of evaluating a definite integral from a set of numerical values of the integrand. The basis of numerical integration lies in the principle of functional substitution or interpolation. The general problem of interpolation consists in representing a function, the analytical form of which is either totally unknown or else is of a very complicated nature, in a form chosen in advance with the aid of the given values of the function taken at regular intervals of the independent variable. Referring to Fig. 5.8-2, $x(t)$ denotes a rational function of t; and $x_0, x_1, x_2, \ldots x_n$ are the values of $x(t)$ taken at instants $t_0, t_1, t_2, \ldots t_n$, respectively. Then the given function $x(t)$ may be approximately represented by a simpler function or polynomial $P(t)$ which takes the same values as $x(t)$ for the instants $t_0, t_1, t_2, \ldots t_n$. The process of representing

† J. B. Scarborough, "Numerical Mathematical Analysis," chap. 7, The Johns Hopkins Press, Baltimore, 1958.

$x(t)$ by $P(t)$ over a given interval of the independent variable is commonly known as interpolation; and the function $P(t)$ is referred to as a formula of interpolation. The function $P(t)$ can have a variety of forms. When $P(t)$ is a polynomial, the process of replacing $x(t)$ by $P(t)$ is termed polynomial interpolation. The most important interpolation formulas are Newton's formula, Stirling's formula, and Bessel's formula. In this section Newton's formula is applied in performing numerical integration.

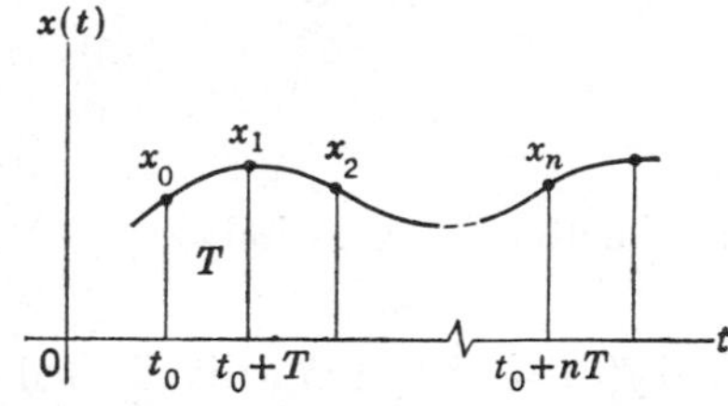

FIG. 5.8-2. Samples of the function $x(t)$.

The basic idea in numerical integration is to approximate a given function $x(t)$ over a short interval of t by a function or polynomial $P(t)$ and then to integrate that polynomial rather than the function $x(t)$. The advantage of this procedure lies in that, while $x(t)$ may be difficult or practically impossible to integrate, one can always integrate the polynomial $P(t)$. According to Newton's formula, between the interval $t_0 \leq t \leq t_0 + nT$ the function $x(t)$ may be represented by the polynomial $P(t)$ such that

$$\begin{aligned} P(t) &= P(t_0 + Tu) = f(u) \\ &= x_0 + u\Delta x_0 + \frac{u(u-1)}{2!}\Delta^2 x_0 + \frac{u(u-1)(u-2)}{3!}\Delta^3 x_0 \\ &\quad + \frac{u(u-1)(u-2)(u-3)}{4!}\Delta^4 x_0 \\ &\quad + \frac{u(u-1)(u-2)(u-3)(u-4)}{5!}\Delta^5 x_0 \\ &\quad + \frac{u(u-1)(u-2)(u-3)(u-4)(u-5)}{6!}\Delta^6 x_0 + \cdots \end{aligned} \tag{5.8-4}$$

in which

$$u = \frac{t - t_0}{T} \qquad t = t_0 + Tu \tag{5.8-5}$$

$$\Delta x_0 = x_1 - x_0 \tag{5.8-6}$$

$$\Delta^2 x_0 = \Delta x_1 - \Delta x_0 = x_2 - 2x_1 + x_0 \tag{5.8-7}$$

$$\Delta^3 x_0 = \Delta^2 x_1 - \Delta^2 x_0 = x_3 - 3x_2 + 3x_1 - x_0 \tag{5.8-8}$$

. . . .

and $x_0, x_1, x_2, \ldots x_n$ are the values of $x(t)$ at $t_0, t_0 + T, t_0 + 2T, \ldots t_0 + nT$. Then the value of the integral

$$\int_{t_0}^{t_0+nT} x(t)\, dt$$

may be obtained from the following approximation:

$$\int_{t_0}^{t_0+nT} x(t)\,dt \approx \int_{t_0}^{t_0+nT} P(t)\,dt$$
$$= T\int_0^n P(t_0+Tu)\,du$$
$$= T\int_0^n f(u)\,du \tag{5.8-9}$$

In the above expression,

$$dt = T\,du \tag{5.8-10}$$

and $f(u) = P(t_0 + Tu)$ is defined in Eq. (5.8-4). Substituting Eq. (5.8-4) into Eq. (5.8-9) and integrating term by term yield

$$\int_{t_0}^{t_0+nT} x(t)\,dt \approx T\left[nx_0 + \frac{n^2}{2}\Delta x_0 + \left(\frac{n^3}{3} - \frac{n^2}{2}\right)\frac{\Delta^2 x_0}{2!} + \left(\frac{n^4}{4} - n^3 + n^2\right)\frac{\Delta^3 x_0}{3!} + \left(\frac{n^5}{5} - \frac{3n^4}{2} + \frac{11n^3}{3} - 3n^2\right)\frac{\Delta^4 x_0}{4!} + \left(\frac{n^6}{6} - 2n^5 + \frac{35n^4}{4} - \frac{50n^3}{3} + 12n^2\right)\frac{\Delta^5 x_0}{5!} + \left(\frac{n^7}{7} - \frac{15n^6}{6} + 17n^5 - \frac{225n^4}{4} + \frac{274n^3}{3} - 60n^2\right)\frac{\Delta^6 x_0}{6!} + \cdots\right] \tag{5.8-11}$$

Equation (5.8-11) provides a general formula for numerical integration from which various quadrature formulas may be derived by putting $n = 1, 2, 3, \ldots$, etc.

The process of numerical integration is readily performed by a digital computer. When a definite integral is evaluated by numerical methods, the integration operator (or the transfer function of the digital integrator) may take a variety of forms depending upon the numerical integration rules and quadrature formulas applied. Some of the simplest and the most useful of the numerical integration rules and quadrature formulas[59] are discussed in the following paragraphs and the corresponding z transforms are derived.

a. Integration by the Rectangular Rule. A continuous curve can be approximated by a staircase waveform, and the area under the curve can be approximated by rectangles as shown in Fig. 5.8-3. The value of the integral or the area is brought up to date by adding the value of the latest rectangle to the value of the integral already computed. Referring to Fig. 5.8-3, let x_k be the value of $x(t)$ at $t = kT$ and y_{k-1} be the area under the curve of $x(t)$ between the interval $t = 0$ and $t = (k-1)T$. Then the area under the curve of $x(t)$ between $t = 0$ and $t = kT$ is given approximately by the sum of y_{k-1} and the area of the shaded rectangle; that is

$$y_k = y_{k-1} + Tx_k \tag{5.8-12}$$

Equation (5.8-12) leads to the simplest quadrature formula based upon the rectangular rule:

$$y^*(t) = y^*(t - T) + Tx^*(t) \tag{5.8-13}$$

where, at $t = kT$, $y^*(t) = y_k$, $y^*(t - T) = y_{k-1}$, and $x^*(t) = x_k$.

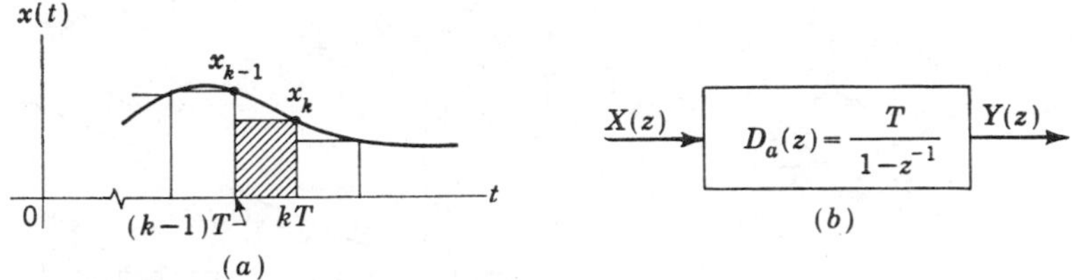

FIG. 5.8-3. (a) Integration by the rectangular rule; (b) the digital integrator based upon the rectangular rule.

Taking the z transform of both sides of Eq. (5.8-13) gives

$$Y(z) = z^{-1}Y(z) + TX(z) \tag{5.8-14}$$

Transposing and simplifying yield the pulse-transfer function of this digital integrator or the numerical integration operator as

$$D_a(z) = \frac{Y(z)}{X(z)} = \frac{T}{1 - z^{-1}} \tag{5.8-15}$$

The corresponding starred transform is

$$D_a^*(s) = \frac{T}{1 - \epsilon^{-Ts}} \tag{5.8-16}$$

Replacing s by $j\omega$ in Eq. (5.8-16) gives the frequency-characteristic function of this digital integrator as

$$D_a^*(j\omega) = \frac{T}{1 - \epsilon^{-j\omega T}} = \frac{T}{2}\left(1 - j \cot \frac{\omega T}{2}\right) \tag{5.8-17}$$

Then, the amplitude and phase characteristics are given by

$$|D_a^*(j\omega)| = \frac{T}{2}\left|\csc \frac{\omega T}{2}\right| \tag{5.8-18}$$

$$\phi_a(\omega) = -\frac{\pi}{2} + \frac{\omega T}{2} \tag{5.8-19}$$

The frequency characteristics are plotted in Fig. 5.8-4. At low frequencies the amplitude-characteristic curve is very close to that of an ideal integrator.

b. Integration by the Trapezoidal Rule. The area under a continuous curve can be approximated by trapezoids as shown in Fig. 5.8-5. By this approximation, the area under the curve of $x(t)$ between $t = 0$ and $t = kT$

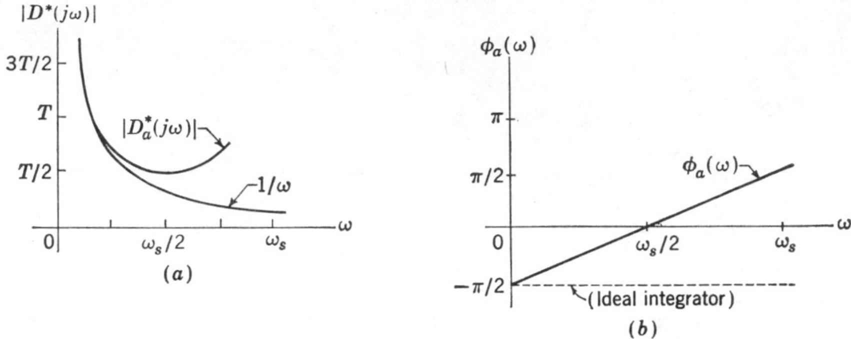

FIG. 5.8-4. (a) Amplitude characteristic and (b) phase characteristic of the digital integrator based upon the rectangular rule.

is given by the sum of y_{k-1} and the area of the shaded trapezoid; that is

$$y_k = y_{k-1} + \frac{T}{2}(x_k + x_{k-1}) \tag{5.8-20}$$

which leads to the quadrature formula based upon the trapezoidal rule as

$$y^*(t) = y^*(t - T) + \frac{T}{2}[x^*(t) + x^*(t - T)] \tag{5.8-21}$$

In fact, Eq. (5.8-21) can also be derived from the general formula given in Eq. (5.8-11) by having $n = 1$. Since the interval of integration extends only from t_0 to $t_0 + T$, only x_0 and x_1 of the function $x(t)$ are obtained.

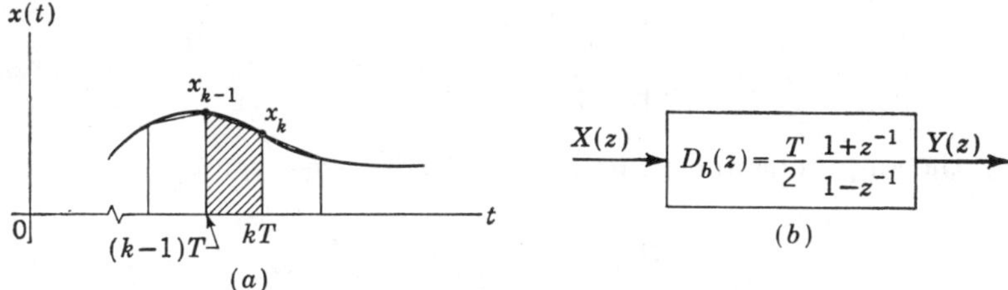

FIG. 5.8-5. (a) Integration by the trapezoidal rule; (b) the digital integrator based upon the trapezoidal rule.

With only two values of $x(t)$, there can be no differences higher than the first. Thus,

$$\int_{t_0}^{t_0+T} x(t)\,dt = y_1 - y_0 = T(x_0 + \tfrac{1}{2}\Delta x_0) \tag{5.8-22}$$

In view of Eq. (5.8-6) defining the first difference, the above equation reduces to

$$y_1 = y_0 + \frac{T}{2}(x_1 + x_0) \tag{5.8-23}$$

from which the quadrature formula of Eq. (5.8-21) follows.

Taking the z transform of both sides of Eq. (5.8-21) and transposing yield

$$(1 - z^{-1})Y(z) = \frac{T}{2}(1 + z^{-1})X(z) \tag{5.8-24}$$

Thus, the pulse-transfer function of the digital integrator performing the manipulations involved in Eq. (5.8-2) is given by

$$D_b(z) = \frac{Y(z)}{X(z)} = \frac{T}{2}\frac{1 + z^{-1}}{1 - z^{-1}} \tag{5.8-25}$$

which is sometimes referred to as the numerical integration operator based upon the trapezoidal rule. The corresponding starred transform is

$$D_b^*(s) = \frac{T}{2}\frac{1 + \epsilon^{-Ts}}{1 - \epsilon^{-Ts}} \tag{5.8-26}$$

The frequency-characteristic function of this digital integrator is obtained from Eq. (5.8-26) by the substitution of $s = j\omega$; that is

$$D_b^*(j\omega) = \frac{T}{2}\frac{1 + \epsilon^{-j\omega T}}{1 - \epsilon^{-j\omega T}} = -j\frac{T}{2}\cot\frac{\omega T}{2} \tag{5.8-27}$$

The amplitude and phase characteristics are

$$|D_b^*(j\omega)| = \frac{T}{2}\left|\cot\frac{\omega T}{2}\right| \tag{5.8-28}$$

$$\phi_b(\omega) = -\frac{\pi}{2} \tag{5.8-29}$$

From the frequency characteristics plotted in Fig. 5.8-6, it is observed that although the integration operator based upon the trapezoidal rule has ideal phase characteristic, its amplitude characteristic differs from the ideal curve appreciably.

c. Integration by Simpson's One-third Rule. The quadrature formula based upon Simpson's one-third rule can readily be derived from Eq. (5.8-11) by having $n = 2$. Since during the interval of integration from t_0 to $t_0 + 2T$ only x_0, x_1, and x_2 of the function $x(t)$ are known, there can exist no differences higher than the second. Thus,

$$\int_{t_0}^{t_0+2T} x(t)\,dt = y_2 - y_0 = T(2x_0 + 2\Delta x_0 + \tfrac{1}{3}\Delta^2 x_0) \tag{5.8-30}$$

Replacing all differences by the values of $x(t)$ defined in Eqs. (5.8-6) and

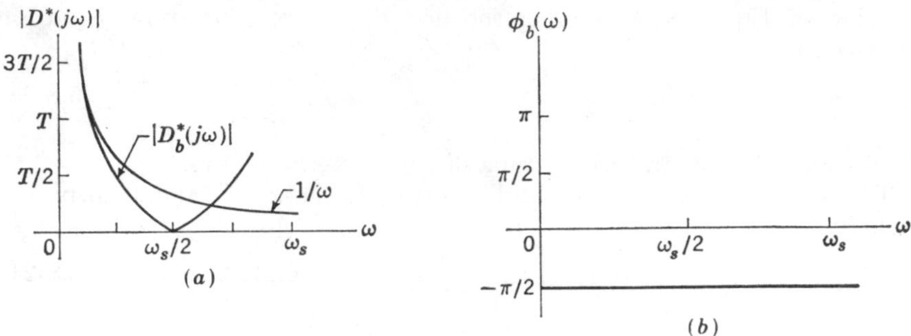

FIG. 5.8-6. (a) Amplitude characteristic and (b) phase characteristic of the digital integrator based upon the trapezoidal rule.

(5.8-7) yields

$$y_2 = y_0 + \frac{T}{3}(x_2 + 4x_1 + x_0) \tag{5.8-31}$$

which leads to the quadrature formula based upon Simpson's one-third rule:

$$y^*(t) = y^*(t - 2T) + \frac{T}{3}[x^*(t) + 4x^*(t - T) + x^*(t - 2T)] \tag{5.8-32}$$

As can readily be seen, the derivation of the above quadrature formula is essentially based upon fitting a parabola through three points of $x(t)$ at equal time increments during the interval of integration.

Taking the z transform of both sides of Eq. (5.8-32) and transposing yield

$$(1 - z^{-2})Y(z) = \frac{T}{3}(1 + 4z^{-1} + z^{-2})X(z) \tag{5.8-33}$$

Hence, the pulse-transfer function of this digital integrator is given by

$$D_c(z) = \frac{Y(z)}{X(z)} = \frac{T}{3}\frac{1 + 4z^{-1} + z^{-2}}{1 - z^{-2}} \tag{5.8-34}$$

Substituting $\epsilon^{j\omega T}$ for z in the Eq. (5.8-34) yields the frequency-characteristic function of this digital integrator as

$$\begin{aligned} D_c^*(j\omega) &= \frac{T}{3}\frac{1 + 4\epsilon^{-j\omega T} + \epsilon^{-j2\omega T}}{1 - \epsilon^{-j2\omega T}} \\ &= -j\frac{T}{3}\frac{2 + \cos\omega T}{\sin\omega T} \end{aligned} \tag{5.8-35}$$

Thus, the amplitude and phase characteristics are

$$|D_c^*(j\omega)| = \frac{T}{3}\left|\frac{2 + \cos\omega T}{\sin\omega T}\right| \tag{5.8-36}$$

$$\phi_c(\omega) = -\frac{\pi}{2} \tag{5.8-37}$$

which are plotted in Fig. 5.8-7. It is interesting to note that the numerical integration operator based upon Simpson's one-third rule also has ideal phase characteristic.

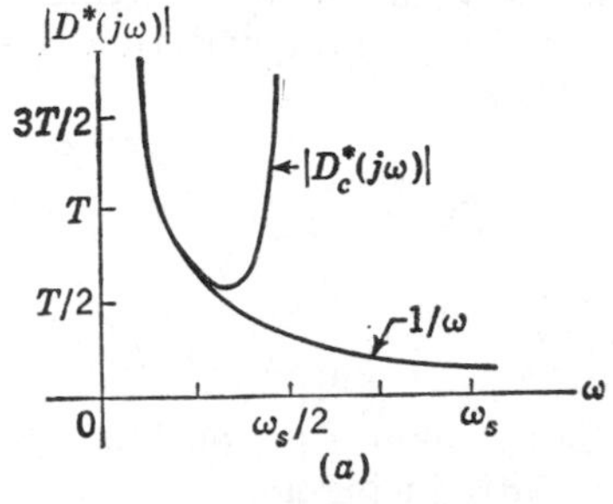

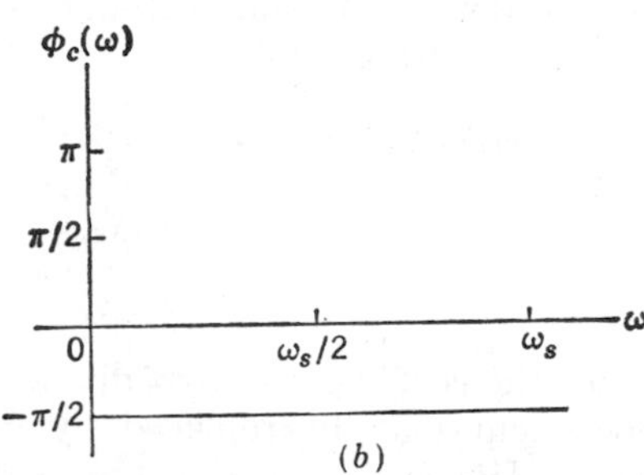

FIG. 5.8-7. (a) Amplitude characteristic and (b) phase characteristic of the digital integrator based upon Simpson's one-third rule.

d. Integration by Simpson's Three-eighth Rule. The quadrature formula based upon Simpson's three-eighth rule can be derived from Eq. (5.8-11) by having $n = 3$ and ignoring all differences above the third. This is equivalent to fitting a third-order polynomial through four points of $x(t)$ at equal time increments during the interval of integration. Thus,

$$\int_{t_0}^{t_0+3T} x(t)\,dt = y_3 - y_0 = T(3x_0 + \tfrac{9}{2}\Delta x_0 + \tfrac{9}{4}\Delta^2 x_0 + \tfrac{3}{8}\Delta^3 x_0) \tag{5.8-38}$$

Replacing all differences by the values of $x(t)$ defined in Eqs. (5.8-6), (5.8-7), and (5.8-8) and simplifying yields

$$y_3 = y_0 + \frac{3T}{8}(x_3 + 3x_2 + 3x_1 + x_0) \tag{5.8-39}$$

from which the quadrature formula based upon Simpson's three-eighth rule is obtained:

$$y^*(t) = y^*(t - 3T) + \frac{3T}{8}[x^*(t) + 3x^*(t - T) + 3x^*(t - 2T) + x^*(t - 3T)] \tag{5.8-40}$$

Taking the z transform of both sides of Eq. (5.8-40) and transposing gives

$$(1 - z^{-3})Y(z) = \frac{3T}{8}(1 + 3z^{-1} + 3z^{-2} + z^{-3})X(z) \tag{5.8-41}$$

Hence, the pulse-transfer function of the digital integrator performing the manipulations involved in Eq. (5.8-40) is

$$D_d(z) = \frac{3T}{8} \frac{1 + 3z^{-1} + 3z^{-2} + z^{-3}}{1 - z^{-3}} \tag{5.8-42}$$

e. Integration by Weddle's Rule. The quadrature formula based upon Weddle's rule can be derived from Eq. (5.8-11) by having $n = 6$ and ignoring all differences above the sixth. This is equivalent to fitting a sixth-order polynomial through seven points of $x(t)$ at equal time increments during the interval of integration. Thus,

$$\begin{aligned}\int_{t_0}^{t_0+6T} x(t)\,dt &= y_6 - y_0 \\ &= T(6x_0 + 18\Delta x_0 + 27\Delta^2 x_0 + 24\Delta^3 x_0 \\ &\qquad + {}^{123}\!/_{10}\Delta^4 x_0 + {}^{23}\!/_{10}\Delta^5 x_0 + {}^{41}\!/_{140}\Delta^6 x_0)\end{aligned} \tag{5.8-43}$$

Since the coefficient of $\Delta^6 x_0$ differs from $3/10$ by the small fraction $1/140$, this coefficient may be replaced by $3/10$ without introducing an appreciable error. Hence substituting $(3/10)\Delta^6 x_0$ for the last term of Eq. (5.8-43) and replacing all differences by their values in terms of the given quantities $x_0, x_1, x_2, \ldots x_6$, reduce Eq. (5.8-43) to

$$y_6 = y_0 + \frac{3T}{10}(x_6 + 5x_5 + x_4 + 6x_3 + x_2 + 5x_1 + x_0) \tag{5.8-44}$$

Equation (5.8-44) yields the quadrature formula based upon Weddle's rule as

$$\begin{aligned}y^*(t) = y^*(t - 6T) + \frac{3T}{10}[x^*(t) + 5x^*(t - T) + x^*(t - 2T) + 6x^*(t - 3T) \\ + x^*(t - 4T) + 5x^*(t - 5T) + x^*(t - 6T)]\end{aligned} \tag{5.8-45}$$

Taking the z transform of Eq. (5.8-45) gives

$$(1 - z^{-6})Y(z) = \frac{3T}{10}(1 + 5z^{-1} + z^{-2} + 6z^{-3} + z^{-4} + 5z^{-5} + z^{-6})X(z) \tag{5.8-46}$$

Hence, the pulse-transfer function of this digital integrator performing the manipulations involved in Eq. (5.8-45) is

$$D_e(z) = \frac{3T}{10} \frac{1 + 5z^{-1} + z^{-2} + 6z^{-3} + z^{-4} + 5z^{-5} + z^{-6}}{1 - z^{-6}} \tag{5.8-47}$$

It can be shown that the numerical integration operators based upon the above two integration rules also have ideal phase characteristics in their useful ranges of frequency.

In view of the fact that the numerical integration operators discussed above (b through e) have ideal phase characteristics at least in their useful ranges of frequency, the quality of approximation of the various numerical integration rules can be compared from their amplitude characteristics. Plotted in Fig. 5.8-8 are the amplitude characteristics of these

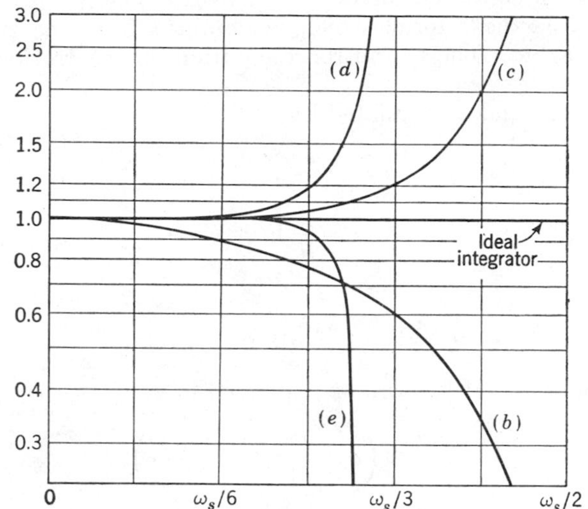

FIG. 5.8-8. Relative amplitude-characteristic curves of the four classical numerical-integration operators. (*From J. M. Salzer, Frequency Analysis of Digital Computer Operating in Real Time, Proc. IRE, vol.* 42, *p.* 463, *February,* 1954.)

four numerical integration operators relative to the amplitude characteristic of the ideal integration operator. Examination of Fig. 5.8-8 reveals that Simpson's one-third rule is superior to his more complicated three-eighth rule, and that up to a certain frequency Weddle's rule offers the highest precision although it is the most complicated among these four methods. Figure 5.8-8 further brings out that the trapezoidal rule is inferior to all others at low frequencies, but is inferior to the Simpson's one-third rule only at the high end of the frequency range. On the other hand, numerical integration based upon the trapezoidal rule not only has the feature of simplicity in programming but also introduces attenuation at higher frequencies, thus alleviating the effect of external disturbances. The quality of approximation to ideal integration in the frequency range from $\omega = 0$ to $\omega = \omega_s/2$ is further illustrated by a specific example: Assume a sine wave of frequency ω_0 radians/sec is to be integrated by using six samples in each cycle. Then at $\omega_0 = \omega_s/4$, Fig. 5.8-8 indicates that the percentage errors are -5.0 per cent for Weddle's rule, $+4.71$ per cent for Simpson's one-third rule, $+18.8$ per cent for Simpson's three-eighth rule, and -21.4 per cent for the trapezoidal rule. The above discussions lead to the conclusion that Weddle's rule is best, Simpson's one-third rule is next, the trapezoidal rule is poor, and Simpson's three-eighth rule is usually unacceptable.

The z-form Representation for Integration. In the preceding paragraphs, various z transforms for numerical integration are discussed. The derivation of these z transforms is based upon the formulas for interpolation. However, in addition to the z-transform representations discussed above, the integration process may be described by another function of z, commonly known as the z form, which is obtained from the power series expansion of $T/\ln z$. The z-form representation for integration is derived as follows:

By definition, z and s are related by

$$z = \epsilon^{Ts} \tag{5.8-48}$$

Solving for s yields

$$s = \frac{1}{T} \ln z \tag{5.8-49}$$

Thus,

$$s^{-1} = \frac{T}{\ln z} \tag{5.8-50}$$

In view of the fact that $\ln z$ can be expressed in a power series as

$$\ln z = 2\left(v + \frac{v^3}{3} + \frac{v^5}{5} + \cdots\right) \tag{5.8-51}$$

where

$$v = \frac{1 - z^{-1}}{1 + z^{-1}} \tag{5.8-52}$$

Eq. (5.8-50) may be written as

$$s^{-1} = \frac{T/2}{v + v^3/3 + v^5/5 + \cdots} \tag{5.8-53}$$

Long division yields the Laurent series as

$$s^{-1} = \frac{T}{2}\left(\frac{1}{v} - \frac{v}{3} - \frac{4v^3}{45} - \frac{44v^5}{945} - \cdots\right) \tag{5.8-54}$$

Since the above series converges relatively rapidly, it may be approximated by the principal part;[118] thus

$$s^{-1} \approx \frac{T}{2v} = \frac{T}{2}\frac{1 + z^{-1}}{1 - z^{-1}} \tag{5.8-55}$$

The right-hand member of Eq. (5.8-55) is referred to as the z form associated with s^{-1}.

Squaring both sides of Eq. (5.8-54),

$$\begin{aligned} s^{-2} &= \frac{T^2}{4}\left[\frac{1}{v^2} - \frac{2}{v}\left(\frac{v}{3} + \frac{4v^3}{45} + \frac{44v^5}{945} + \cdots\right) + \cdots\right] \\ &= \frac{T^2}{4}\left(\frac{1}{v^2} - \frac{2}{3} - \frac{8v^2}{45} - \cdots\right) \end{aligned} \tag{5.8-56}$$

Approximating the above series by the principal part and the constant term yields

$$s^{-2} \approx \frac{T^2}{4}\left(\frac{1}{v^2} - \frac{2}{3}\right) \tag{5.8-57}$$

In view of Eq. (5.8-52), one obtains

$$s^{-2} \approx \frac{T^2}{12} \frac{1 + 10z^{-1} + z^{-2}}{(1 - z^{-1})^2} \tag{5.8-58}$$

The right-hand member of Eq. (5.8-58) is referred to as the z form associated with s^{-2}.

In like manner, series expansions for s^{-k} can be obtained by raising both sides of Eq. (5.8-54) to the kth power. The z form associated with s^{-k} may be evaluated by taking the principal part and the constant term of the power series expansion for s^{-k}. A short table of z forms is given in Table 5.8-1.[118]

TABLE 5.8-1

s^{-k}	z form
s^{-1}	$\frac{T}{2}\frac{1+z^{-1}}{1-z^{-1}}$
s^{-2}	$\frac{T^2}{12}\frac{1+10z^{-1}+z^{-2}}{(1-z^{-1})^2}$
s^{-3}	$\frac{T^3}{2}\frac{z^{-1}+z^{-2}}{(1-z^{-1})^3}$
s^{-4}	$\frac{T^4}{6}\frac{z^{-1}+4z^{-2}+z^{-3}}{(1-z^{-1})^4} - \frac{T^4}{720}$
s^{-5}	$\frac{T^5}{24}\frac{z^{-1}+11z^{-2}+11z^{-3}+z^{-4}}{(1-z^{-1})^5}$

The z form may be utilized to find an approximation to the inverse Laplace transform. Assume that $G(s)$ is the Laplace transform of $g(t)$. Then the inverse Laplace integral is given by

$$g(t) = \frac{1}{2\pi j}\int_{c-j\infty}^{c+j\infty} G(s)\epsilon^{ts}\, ds \tag{5.8-59}$$

Since for stable systems the poles of $G(s)$ are confined in the left half of the s plane, the imaginary axis may be chosen as the path of integration, which implies that c equals zero. By splitting the path of integration into three sections as shown in Fig. 5.8-9a, Eq. (5.8-59) may be written as

$$g(t) = \frac{1}{2\pi j}\int_{-j\pi/T}^{j\pi/T} G(s)\epsilon^{ts}\, ds + \frac{1}{2\pi j}\int_{j\pi/T}^{j\infty} [G(s)\epsilon^{ts} + G(-s)\epsilon^{-ts}]\, ds \tag{5.8-60}$$

The first integral of Eq. (5.8-60) is for the midsection of the contour, $-j\pi/T \leq s \leq j\pi/T$; and the second integral covers the remaining portion of the contour, $s > j\pi/T$ and $s < -j\pi/T$. If the period T is chosen sufficiently small so as to make π/T much larger than the imaginary part of the poles of $G(s)$, the first integral of Eq. (5.8-60) will yield a good approximation to $g(t)$, and the contribution of the second integral may be

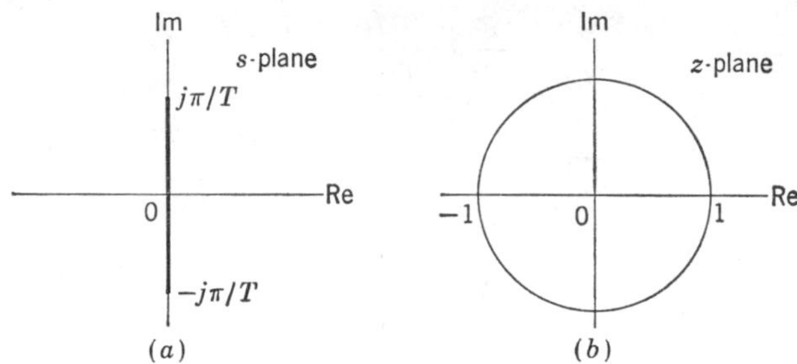

FIG. 5.8-9. (a) Path of integration in the s plane; (b) contour of integration in the z plane.

ignored. Consequently, Eq. (5.8-60) may be approximated by

$$g(t) \approx g_a(t) = \frac{1}{2\pi j} \int_{-j\pi/T}^{j\pi/T} G(s)\epsilon^{ts}\, ds \tag{5.8-61}$$

provided that the period T is properly chosen. In Eq. (5.8-61), $g_a(t)$ is defined as an approximation to $g(t)$.

Substituting nT for t in Eq. (5.8-61) gives the values of the approximate time function at the sampling instants as

$$g_a(nT) = \frac{1}{2\pi j} \int_{-j\pi/T}^{j\pi/T} G(s)\epsilon^{nTs}\, ds \tag{5.8-62}$$

In order to utilize the z-form representation discussed above, a change of variable from s to z is made in Eq. (5.8-62). Making use of Eq. (5.8-49) and simplifying yields

$$g_a(nT) = \frac{1}{2\pi j} \oint_{\Gamma} \frac{1}{T} G\left(\frac{1}{T} \ln z\right) z^{n-1}\, dz \tag{5.8-63}$$

where the contour is the unit circle in the z plane, as shown in Fig. 5.8-9b.

A comparison of Eq. (5.8-63) with Eq. (5.6-4) reveals that the integral of Eq. (5.8-63) has the form of an inverse z transform except for the constant multiplier $1/T$. Since $G[(1/T) \ln z]$ is a transcendental function of z, the evaluation of the inverse integral of Eq. (5.8-63) becomes fairly difficult. However, this difficulty may be overcome if use is made of the z forms discussed above. Since $G(s)$ can be expressed as the ratio of two rational polynomials in s^{-1} (or it can be expanded in a power series in s^{-1}), by making use of the z forms for s^{-k} the function $G[(1/T) \ln z]$ may be written as the ratio of two rational polynomials in z^{-1} (or a power series in z^{-1}). By doing so, the evaluation of the inverse transform given in

Eq. (5.8-63) may be readily carried out by means of the methods discussed in Sec. 5.6. As an illustration of the application of the z-form representation, a simple example is given below.[118]

EXAMPLE 5.8-1. Consider the feedback control system shown in Fig. 5.8-10. The transfer function of the controlled system is given by

$$G(s) = \frac{1}{s(1+s)} \qquad (5.8\text{-}64)$$

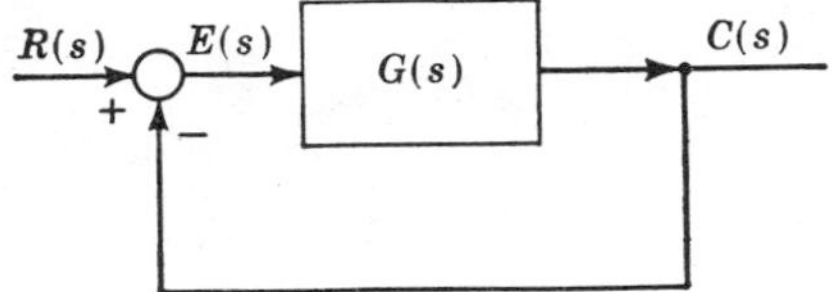

FIG. 5.8-10. Feedback system used in Example 5.8-1.

Evaluate the output of this system in response to a unit step-function input.

It is easy to show that the over-all transfer function of this system is

$$G_0(s) = \frac{1}{s^2 + s + 1} \qquad (5.8\text{-}65)$$

With a unit step-function input, the Laplace transform of the output is then given by

$$C(s) = \frac{1}{s^3 + s^2 + s} \qquad (5.8\text{-}66)$$

In order to use the z forms given in Table 5.8-1, $C(s)$ is first expressed as the ratio of two polynomials in s^{-1}; thus,

$$C(s) = \frac{s^{-3}}{1 + s^{-1} + s^{-2}} \qquad (5.8\text{-}67)$$

Substituting the corresponding z forms from Table 5.8-1 and dividing the result by T yields the equivalent z transform of the output as

$$C_a(z) = \frac{6T^2(z^{-1}+z^{-2})}{(12+6T+T^2) - (36+6T-9T^2)z^{-1} + (36-6T-9T^2)z^{-2} - (12-6T+T^2)z^{-3}} \qquad (5.8\text{-}68)$$

The solution is obtained by choosing T and dividing the denominator of Eq. (5.8-68) into the numerator. Thus, for $T = 1$ sec,

$$C_a(z) = 0.316z^{-1} + 0.864z^{-2} + 1.15z^{-3} + 1.06z^{-4} + 0.987z^{-5} + \cdots \qquad (5.8\text{-}69)$$

and for $T = 0.5$ sec,

$$C_a(z) = 0.0984z^{-1} + 0.335z^{-2} + 0.610z^{-3} + 0.853z^{-4} + \cdots \qquad (5.8\text{-}70)$$

The computed system response at sampling instants is given by the coefficients of the above series. The output sequence is plotted in Fig. 5.8-11 for $T = 1$ sec and $T = 0.5$ sec, together with the exact time response. From Fig. 5.8-11, it is seen that when T is taken as 1 sec the approximate solution is quite good. The accuracy improves if smaller values of T are chosen. For further discussions of the applications of the z form and the choice of T, see Ref. 118.

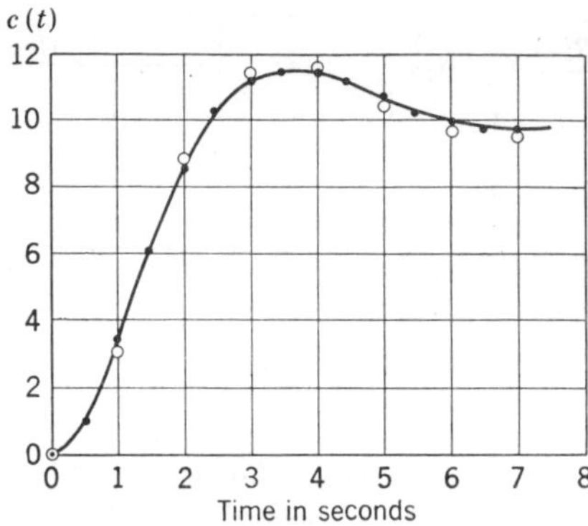

FIG. 5.8-11. Exact and approximate response of the system used for illustration. (*From Boxer and Thaler, A Simplified Method of Solving Linear and Nonlinear Systems, Proc. IRE, vol.* 44, *no.* 1, p. 93, *January*, 1956.)

5.9. Conclusion. This chapter introduces the theory of the z transformation. In the z domain, pulsed-data networks and systems can be described by pulse-transfer functions. The treatment and manipulation of the z transforms and pulse-transfer functions may be performed in the same manner as the Laplace transforms and conventional transfer functions for continuous-data systems. The z transform of a function can be determined either from the summation of an infinite series, given in Eq. (5.2-66), or from the integral expression based upon residue evaluation, as given in Eq. (5.2-67). However, in many cases the latter is the simplest means for actual determination of z transforms in closed form.

The evaluation of the inverse z transforms may be carried out in three different ways: (*a*) from the real inversion integral, (*b*) by partial-fraction expansion, and (*c*) by power-series expansion. The first method is used to find the time sequence in a closed form. The second method can provide not only the values of the time function at the sampling instants but also, in some cases, the approximate time function itself. This method may be used to determine the approximate transient response of a sampled-data system, provided that the sampling frequency is much higher than the system bandwidth. The third method is the most convenient of the three. This method is always used when only the first several values of the time sequence are needed.

In order to determine the complete transient response of a sampled-data control system, a modification is imposed upon the z-transform technique. However, compared to the basic concept of z transformation, the modified z transform is of secondary importance. The inverse modified z transforms can be evaluated either from the inversion integral given in Eq. (5.7-70) or by means of power-series expansion. The former method can provide a general expression of the time function, whereas the latter method is used to determine the time function during the first several sampling periods. Although the z-transform technique is developed primarily for solving linear difference equations and problems in the analysis and synthesis of linear pulsed-data systems, it may also be used to analyze continuous-data systems provided that the continuous-data system is represented by a pulsed-data model.

This chapter concludes with discussions of numerical integration, quadrature formulas and the z-form method. The pulse-transfer function for numerical integration may take a number of forms depending upon the integration rules followed. Some of the simplest and the most useful numerical integration rules are discussed. The successive integration process may be expressed as functions of z, which are referred to as the z forms. The z-form method enables the evaluation of the time response of continuous-data systems by means of the rules of z-transform technique. Furthermore, the z-form method may be used to solve ordinary differential equations with slowly varying coefficients. The use of the z-form method facilitates the solution of such problems on a digital computer.

CHAPTER 6

z-TRANSFORM ANALYSIS

6.1. Block Diagrams and Output Transforms of Sampled-data Control Systems. One of the basic concepts in the analysis of feedback control systems is the block-diagram approach. By this approach the control system is described by the interconnection of the constituent components which are represented by noninteracting blocks. Each block is characterized by a transfer function or a pulse-transfer function. Thus, block diagrams indicate graphically the transfer of signals in a system and the interconnection of the building components of the system. If the analysis of sampled-data and digital control systems is carried through with the z-transform techniques, the systems are first represented by block diagrams indicating the flow of information in the system and the interconnection of system components. From the block diagram the z transform or the modified z transform of the system output is determined and the system characteristic equation in terms of z is derived. The system response to a given input is obtainable from the output transform, and the system stability can readily be determined from the characteristic equation in z either by analytical methods or by graphical techniques. This section is concerned with the algebraic manipulation of block diagrams representing sampled-data and digital control systems and the determination of over-all pulse-transfer functions and the output transforms of the systems.[25,26,166]

To illustrate the derivation of the output transforms of sampled-data systems and the manipulation of block diagrams, a few examples are considered in the following paragraphs.

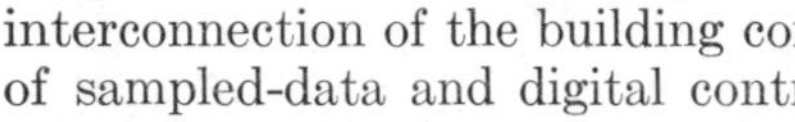

a. Open-loop Systems. A SIMPLE PULSED-DATA SYSTEM WITH INPUT SAMPLED. It is seen from Fig. 6.1-1 that the Laplace transform of the output $c(t)$ is given by

$r(t)$ —S— $r^*(t)$ → [$G(s)$] → $c(t)$

FIG. 6.1-1. A basic sampled-data system.

$$C(s) = G(s)R^*(s) \tag{6.1-1}$$

Making use of the definition of starred transform,

$$C^*(s) = \frac{1}{T} \sum_{n=-\infty}^{\infty} C(s + jn\omega_s) \tag{6.1-2}$$

Equation (6.1-1) reduces to

$$C^*(s) = \frac{1}{T} \sum_{n=-\infty}^{\infty} G(s + jn\omega_s)R^*(s + jn\omega_s) \tag{6.1-3}$$

The periodic property of the starred transfer function enables the above equation to be written as

$$C^*(s) = R^*(s)\left[\frac{1}{T} \sum_{n=-\infty}^{\infty} G(s + jn\omega_s)\right] \tag{6.1-4}$$

or simply

$$C^*(s) = G^*(s)R^*(s) \tag{6.1-5}$$

Replacing s by $(1/T) \ln z$, Eq. (6.1-5) becomes

$$C(z) = G(z)R(z) \tag{6.1-6}$$

which implies that the z transform of the output is equal to the product of the z transform of the input and the pulse-transfer function of the system. It is noted that Eq. (6.1-6) can be derived directly from Eq. (6.1-1) by taking the z transforms of both sides of that equation as has been explained in Sec. 5.1.

In terms of the modified z transforms, the system output is given by

$$C(z,m) = G(z,m)R(z) \tag{6.1-7}$$

where $C(z,m)$ is the modified z transform of the output $c(t)$; $R(z)$, the z transform of the input $r(t)$; and $G(z,m)$, the modified z transform for the system transfer function $G(s)$. Equation (6.1-7) can be derived by taking the modified z transforms of both sides of Eq. (6.1-1). It is to be noted that the modified z transform for a transfer function or a signal followed by a sampler has no significance, because no information is transmitted between the sampling instants.

TWO LINEAR SYSTEMS CONNECTED IN CASCADE BUT SEPARATED BY A SAMPLER WITH THE INPUT SAMPLED.

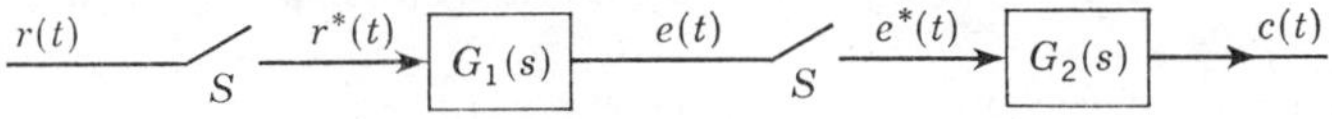

FIG. 6.1-2. Two linear systems in cascade separated by a sampler (sampled-data input).

Reference to Fig. 6.1-2 indicates that the outputs of the first system $G_1(s)$ and the second system $G_2(s)$ are given respectively by

$$E(s) = G_1(s)R^*(s) \tag{6.1-8}$$

and

$$C(s) = G_2(s)E^*(s) \tag{6.1-9}$$

Following the same reasoning as the above paragraph, the starred transfer function associated with Eq. (6.1-8) is obtained:

$$E^*(s) = G_1^*(s)R^*(s) \tag{6.1-10}$$

By substitution, Eq. (6.1-9) becomes

$$C(s) = R^*(s)G_1^*(s)G_2(s) \tag{6.1-11}$$

The corresponding starred transfer function is then given by

$$C^*(s) = R^*(s)G_1^*(s)\left[\frac{1}{T}\sum_{n=-\infty}^{\infty} G_2(s + jn\omega_s)\right] \tag{6.1-12}$$

or

$$C^*(s) = G_1^*(s)G_2^*(s)R^*(s) \tag{6.1-13}$$

The substitution of $z = \epsilon^{Ts}$ reduces Eq. (6.1-13) to

$$C(z) = G_1(z)G_2(z)R(z) \tag{6.1-14}$$

This equation implies that the z transform of the output $c(t)$ is equal to the product of the z transform of the input and the pulse-transfer functions of systems $G_1(s)$ and $G_2(s)$. Since the over-all pulse-transfer function is defined as the ratio

$$G(z) = \frac{C(z)}{R(z)} \tag{6.1-15}$$

it follows from Eq. (6.1-14) that the over-all pulse-transfer function is equal to the product of the pulse-transfer functions associated with the systems $G_1(s)$ and $G_2(s)$, that is,

$$G(z) = G_1(z)G_2(z) \tag{6.1-16}$$

It can readily be shown that the modified z transform of the system output is given by

$$C(z,m) = G_1(z)G_2(z,m)R(z) \tag{6.1-17}$$

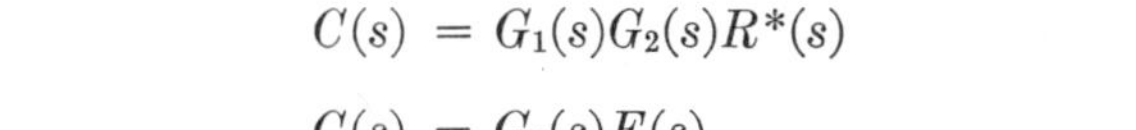

FIG. 6.1-3. Two linear systems in cascade with sampled-data input.

TWO LINEAR SYSTEMS CONNECTED IN CASCADE WITH THE INPUT SAMPLED. It follows from Fig. 6.1-3 that

$$C(s) = G_1(s)G_2(s)R^*(s) \tag{6.1-18}$$

since

$$C(s) = G_2(s)E(s) \tag{6.1-19}$$

and

$$E(s) = G_1(s)R^*(s) \tag{6.1-20}$$

Taking the starred transform of Eq. (6.1-18) yields

$$C^*(s) = G_1G_2^*(s)R^*(s) \tag{6.1-21}$$

in which $G_1G_2^*(s)$ is defined as the starred transform associated with

$G_1(s)G_2(s)$ and is given by

$$G_1G_2^*(s) = \frac{1}{T}\sum_{n=-\infty}^{\infty} G_1G_2(s + jn\omega_s) \tag{6.1-22}$$

The z transform and the modified z transform of the system output are then given by

$$C(z) = G_1G_2(z)R(z) \tag{6.1-23}$$

and

$$C(z,m) = G_1G_2(z,m)R(z) \tag{6.1-24}$$

respectively. From Eq. (6.1-23) it is seen that if two linear systems are not separated by a sampler, the over-all pulse-transfer function $G(z)$ would not be equal to the product of the pulse-transfer functions of these two linear systems but equal to the z transform corresponding to the product of the transfer functions $G_1(s)G_2(s)$. In symbols,

$$G(z) = G_1G_2(z) = \mathfrak{z}\{G_1(s)G_2(s)\} \tag{6.1-25}$$

It is noted that $G_1G_2(z)$ is entirely different from $G_1(z)G_2(z)$. The former denotes the z transform corresponding to $G_1(s)G_2(s)$, whereas the latter represents the product of the z transforms corresponding to $G_1(s)$ and $G_2(s)$.

EXAMPLE 6.1-1. Two linear systems $G_1(s)$ and $G_2(s)$ are connected in tandem, as shown in Fig. 6.1-2 and Fig. 6.1-3, with

$$G_1(s) = \frac{1}{s} \qquad G_2(s) = \frac{a}{s + a} \tag{6.1-26}$$

Determine the over-all pulse-transfer functions for these two connections.

For the systems in cascade as shown in Fig. 6.1-2, the over-all pulse-transfer function is given by

$$G(z) = G_1(z)G_2(z) \tag{6.1-27}$$

where

$$G_1(z) = \mathfrak{z}\left\{\frac{1}{s}\right\} = \frac{z}{z - 1} \tag{6.1-28}$$

and

$$G_2(z) = \mathfrak{z}\left\{\frac{a}{s + a}\right\} = \frac{az}{z - \epsilon^{-aT}} \tag{6.1-29}$$

Thus

$$G(z) = \frac{az^2}{(z - 1)(z - \epsilon^{-aT})} \tag{6.1-30}$$

For the configuration shown in Fig. 6.1-3, the over-all pulse-transfer function is found to be

$$G(z) = \mathfrak{z}\left\{\frac{a}{s(s + a)}\right\} \tag{6.1-31}$$

From formula 11 of the short table of z transforms on page 160 one obtains

$$G(z) = \frac{(1 - \epsilon^{-aT})z}{(z - 1)(z - \epsilon^{-aT})} \tag{6.1-32}$$

Comparison between Eq. (6.1-30) and Eq. (6.1-32) shows that the over-all pulse-transfer functions for these two configurations are quite different. This illustrates the statement made in the previous paragraph that $G_1G_2(z)$ is quite different from $G_1(z)G_2(z)$. Furthermore, the fact that a sampler between two networks makes so much difference is evident from the waveforms of the input signal of the second network $G_2(s)$ in these two cases. For a given input to the first network $G_1(s)$, the signal fed to the second network of Fig. 6.1-2 is a pulsed-data function, whereas the signal applied to the second network of Fig. 6.1-3 is a continuous-data function. Consequently, the over-all pulse-transfer functions are different in these two configurations.

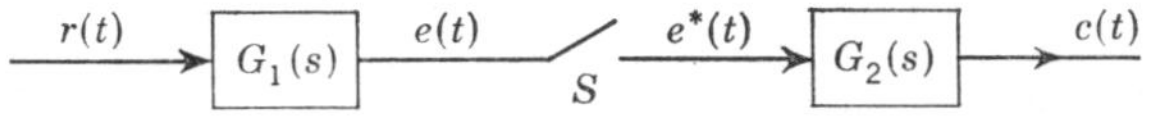

FIG. 6.1-4. Two linear systems in cascade separated by a sampler (continuous-data input).

TWO LINEAR SYSTEMS CONNECTED IN CASCADE BUT SEPARATED BY A SAMPLER. From Fig. 6.1-4 the following relationships are derived:

$$E(s) = G_1(s)R(s) \tag{6.1-33}$$

and

$$C(s) = G_2(s)E^*(s) \tag{6.1-34}$$

Taking the starred transform of Eq. (6.1-33) yields

$$E^*(s) = G_1R^*(s) \tag{6.1-35}$$

The Laplace transform of the output $c(t)$ follows from Eqs. (6.1-34) and (6.1-35).

$$C(s) = G_2(s)G_1R^*(s) \tag{6.1-36}$$

If the output were further sampled, the starred transform of the system output would be

$$C^*(s) = G_2^*(s)G_1R^*(s) \tag{6.1-37}$$

In terms of z, Eq. (6.1-37) can be written as

$$C(z) = G_2(z)G_1R(z) \tag{6.1-38}$$

which is the z transform of the system output. The modified z transform of the system output is readily derived from Eq. (6.1-36) by inspection, that is,

$$C(z,m) = G_2(z,m)G_1R(z) \tag{6.1-39}$$

b. Closed-loop Systems. SYSTEM WITH ACTUATING ERROR SAMPLED. Figure 6.1-5 describes a typical error-sampled feedback control system in which $G(s)$ denotes the transfer function of the elements in the forward path; $H(s)$, the transfer of the elements in the feedback path; and $r(t)$, $e(t)$, and $c(t)$ are the input, actuating signal, and the output, respectively. Reference to Fig. 6.1-5 indicates that the Laplace transform of the actuating signal is related to the input and the output by

$$E(s) = R(s) - H(s)C(s) \tag{6.1-40}$$

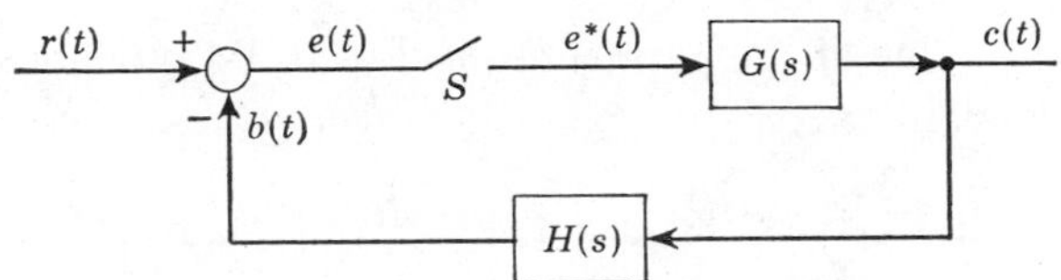

FIG. 6.1-5. System with actuating signal sampled.

Since the system output and the output of the sampler are related by

$$C(s) = G(s)E^*(s) \tag{6.1-41}$$

Equation (6.1-40) may be written as

$$E(s) = R(s) - G(s)H(s)E^*(s) \tag{6.1-42}$$

The starred transform of Eq. (6.1-42) is

$$E^*(s) = R^*(s) - GH^*(s)E^*(s) \tag{6.1-43}$$

Rearranging and simplifying yields the starred transform of the actuating signal as

$$E^*(s) = \frac{R^*(s)}{1 + GH^*(s)} \tag{6.1-44}$$

which also represents the Laplace transform of the output of the sampler. From Eqs. (6.1-41) and (6.1-44) the relationship between the system output and the sampled system input is obtained:

$$C(s) = \frac{G(s)R^*(s)}{1 + GH^*(s)} \tag{6.1-45}$$

Because of the presence of the sampler an explicit relation between $C(s)$ and $R(s)$ cannot be found. Since from Eq. (6.1-41),

$$C^*(s) = G^*(s)E^*(s) \tag{6.1-46}$$

the output $C^*(s)$ is related to the input $R^*(s)$ by

$$C^*(s) = \frac{G^*(s)R^*(s)}{1 + GH^*(s)} \tag{6.1-47}$$

In terms of the z transforms, the output transform is

$$C(z) = \frac{G(z)R(z)}{1 + GH(z)} \tag{6.1-48}$$

which describes the values of the output at the sampling instants. The modified z transform of the system output can be derived from Eq. (6.1-45) by inspection, thus,

$$C(z,m) = \frac{G(z,m)R(z)}{1 + GH(z)} \tag{6.1-49}$$

By varying the value of the parameter m, Eq. (6.1-49) defines the system output completely.

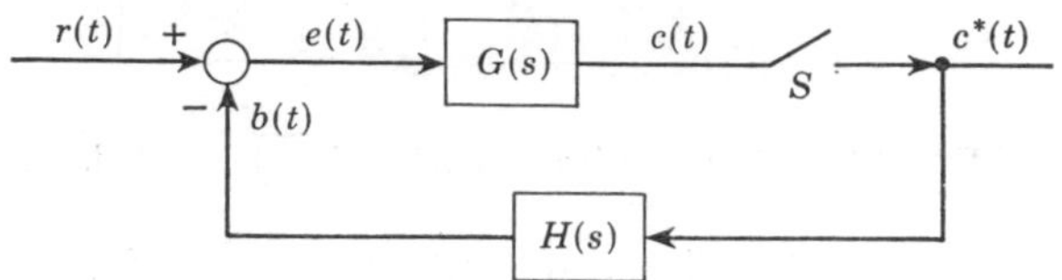

FIG. 6.1-6. System with output sampled.

SYSTEM WITH OUTPUT SAMPLED. An output-sampled feedback control system is illustrated in Fig. 6.1-6, from which the following relationships are derived:

$$E(s) = R(s) - H(s)C^*(s) \tag{6.1-50}$$

and

$$C(s) = G(s)E(s) \tag{6.1-51}$$

Substituting Eq. (6.1-50) into Eq. (6.1-51) yields

$$C(s) = G(s)R(s) - G(s)H(s)C^*(s) \tag{6.1-52}$$

Taking the starred transforms of Eq. (6.1-52) and rearranging, the Laplace transform of the system output results:

$$C^*(s) = \frac{GR^*(s)}{1 + GH^*(s)} \tag{6.1-53}$$

Then the z transform of the system output is given by

$$C(z) = \frac{GR(z)}{1 + GH(z)} \tag{6.1-54}$$

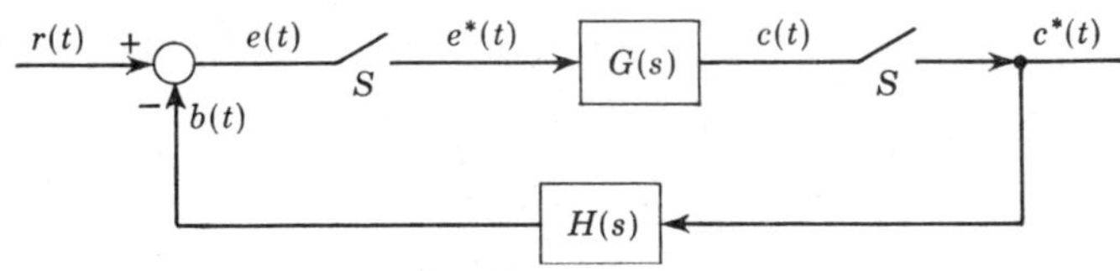

FIG. 6.1-7. System with both actuating signal and output sampled.

SYSTEM WITH BOTH OUTPUT AND ACTUATING SIGNAL SAMPLED. Referring to the error- and output-sampled feedback control system of Fig. 6.1-7, one obtains

$$E(s) = R(s) - H(s)C^*(s) \tag{6.1-55}$$

and

$$C(s) = G(s)E^*(s) \tag{6.1-56}$$

Taking the starred transforms reduces Eqs. (6.1-55) and (6.1-56) to

$$E^*(s) = R^*(s) - H^*(s)C^*(s) \tag{6.1-57}$$

and

$$C^*(s) = G^*(s)E^*(s) \tag{6.1-58}$$

Elimination of $E^*(s)$ between Eqs. (6.1-57) and (6.1-58) yields the Laplace transform of the system output

$$C^*(s) = \frac{G^*(s)R^*(s)}{1 + G^*(s)H^*(s)} \tag{6.1-59}$$

The corresponding z transform is

$$C(z) = \frac{G(z)R(z)}{1 + G(z)H(z)} \tag{6.1-60}$$

SYSTEM WITH FEEDBACK SIGNAL SAMPLED. Shown in Fig. 6.1-8 is a sampled-data control system in which the signal fed to the elements in the

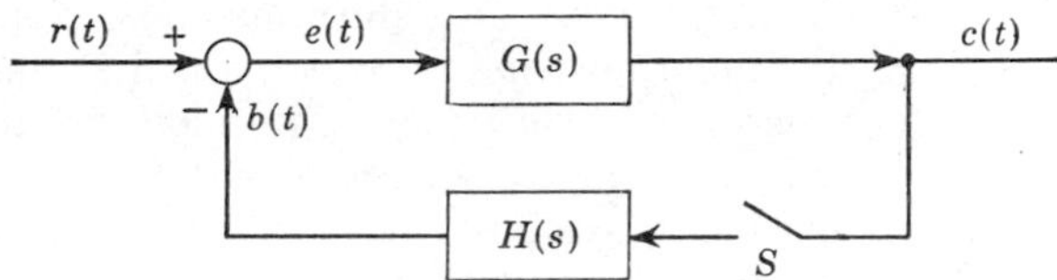

FIG. 6.1-8. System with feedback signal sampled.

feedback path is sampled. The Laplace transform of the actuating signal $e(t)$ is given by

$$E(s) = R(s) - H(s)C^*(s) \tag{6.1-61}$$

Since the transform $C(s)$ of the system output is related to $E(s)$ by the transfer function $G(s)$, the output transform $C(s)$ is given by

$$C(s) = GR(s) - GH(s)C^*(s) \tag{6.1-62}$$

Taking the starred transform reduces Eq. (6.1-62) to

$$C^*(s) = GR^*(s) - GH^*(s)C^*(s) \tag{6.1-63}$$

Rearranging,

$$C^*(s) = \frac{GR^*(s)}{1 + GH^*(s)} \tag{6.1-64}$$

In terms of the z transforms, the output transform is

$$C(z) = \frac{GR(z)}{1 + GH(z)} \tag{6.1-65}$$

which describes the values of the system output at the sampling instants.

Now, if the modified starred transform of Eq. (6.1-62) is taken, the modified transform of the output results:

$$C^*(s,m) = GR^*(s,m) - GH^*(s,m)C^*(s) \tag{6.1-66}$$

where $GR^*(s,m)$ is the modified starred transform of $G(s)R(s)$; and $GH^*(s,m)$ is that of $G(s)H(s)$. Substitution of Eq. (6.1-64) into Eq. (6.1-66) leads to

$$C^*(s,m) = GR^*(s,m) - \frac{GH^*(s,m)GR^*(s)}{1 + GH^*(s)} \tag{6.1-67}$$

In terms of z, Eq. (6.1-67) becomes

$$C(z,m) = GR(z,m) - \frac{GH(z,m)GR(z)}{1 + GH(z)} \tag{6.1-68}$$

which is the modified z transform of the system output.

From the above analysis it is seen that the location of the sampler in a sampled-data control system would cause a significant change in the expression of the output transform of the system. The procedures of system analysis and algebraic manipulation of block diagrams for sampled-data systems, as explained in the above discussions, can be applied to the study of more complicated configurations. To determine the output transform of a multiloop system, the innermost loop (or loops) is first replaced by its over-all pulse-transfer function and the other minor loops are then replaced by their over-all pulse-transfer functions successively.

Basic sampled-data feedback systems may be classified according to the location of the sampler (or samplers) as error-sampled systems and nonerror-sampled systems. The former refer to systems in which the actuating error is sampled; in other words, a sampler is placed immediately following the error-sensing device of the major loop. The latter refer to systems in which the control signal (or signals) other than the actuating error is sampled, i.e., no sampler is placed in the error channel of the sampled-data system. For instance, the systems of Figs. 6.1-5 and 6.1-7 are error-sampled systems, and those of Figs. 6.1-6 and 6.1-8 are not error-sampled systems. Although it is always possible to determine the output-input ratio $C(z)/R(z)$ of an error-sampled system, it seems impossible to determine that of a nonerror-sampled system. Referring to Fig. 6.1-5, the output-input ratio of the error-sampled system as obtained from Eq. (6.1-48) is

$$\frac{C(z)}{R(z)} = \frac{G(z)}{1 + GH(z)} \tag{6.1-69}$$

But the output-input ratio of the nonerror-sampled system of Fig. 6.1-6 does not exist. Instead, only the ratio $C(z)/GR(z)$ can be found.

A nonerror-sampled system can generally be reduced to an error-sampled configuration from which the output transform may be derived by inspection. To illustrate the reduction of a nonerror-sampled system to an error-sampled configuration, consider the system of Fig. 6.1-9*a*. Applying Rule 9 of Sec. 2.2 reduces the block diagram of Fig. 6.1-9*a* to that of Fig. 6.1-9*b* which is of the error-sampled configuration. From Fig. 6.1-9*b* it is seen that

$$\frac{C(z)}{R_1(z)} = \frac{G_2(z)}{1 + G_1G_2(z)} \tag{6.1-70}$$

and

$$R_1(z) = G_1R(z) \tag{6.1-71}$$

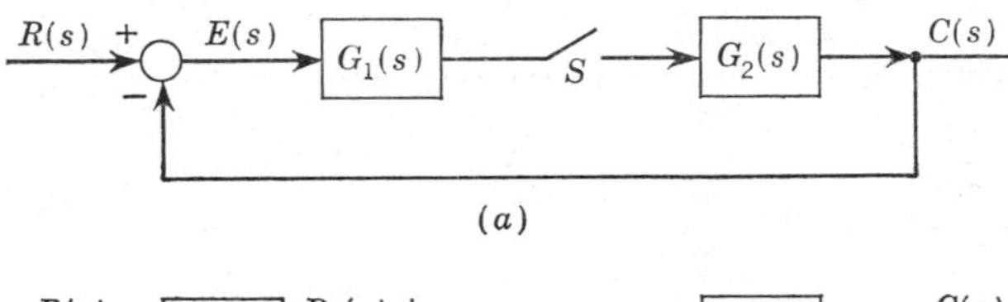

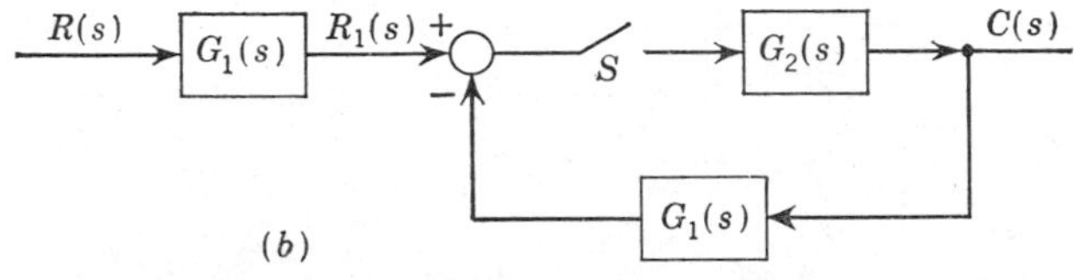

FIG. 6.1-9. (*a*) A nonerror-sampled system; (*b*) the error-sampled configuration of the system of (*a*).

Thus, the output transform is given by

$$C(z) = \frac{G_2(z)}{1 + G_1G_2(z)} G_1R(z) \tag{6.1-72}$$

As a second illustration, consider the system of Fig. 6.1-8. The z transform and the modified z transform of the output of the system can be derived by inspection, if the block diagram of Fig. 6.1-8 is reduced to an error-sampled configuration. By making use of Rule 9 of Sec. 2.2, the block

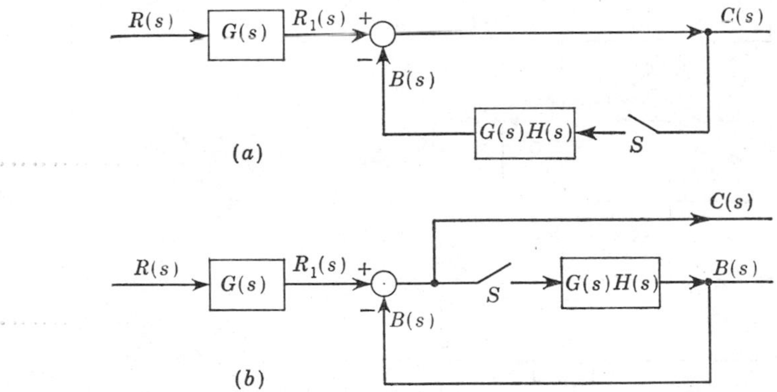

FIG. 6.1-10. The reduction of the system of Fig. 6.1-8 to the error-sampled configuration.

diagram of Fig. 6.1-8 is converted to that of Fig. 6.1-10*a*, which can further be redrawn in the form shown in Fig. 6.1-10*b*. Clearly, the block diagram

TABLE 6.1-1. OUTPUT TRANSFORMS OF SOME

	Systems	
1.	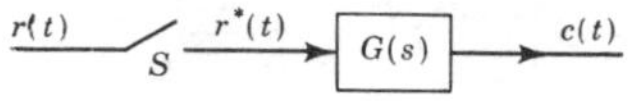 $r(t)$ S $r^*(t)$ $G(s)$ $c(t)$	....
2.	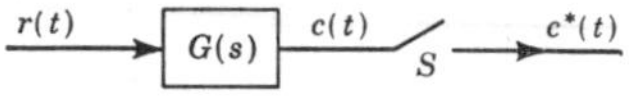 $r(t)$ $G(s)$ $c(t)$ S $c^*(t)$	....
3.	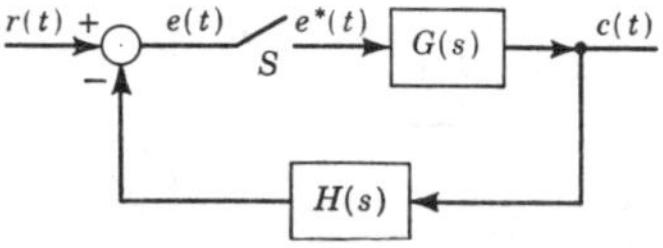 $r(t)$ + − $e(t)$ S $e^*(t)$ $G(s)$ $c(t)$ $H(s)$	....
4.	$r(t)$ + − $e(t)$ $G_1(s)$ $c_1(t)$ S $c_1^*(t)$ $G_2(s)$ $c(t)$ $H(s)$	....
5.	$r(t)$ + − $e(t)$ S $e^*(t)$ $G_1(s)$ S $G_2(s)$ $c(t)$ $H(s)$	....
6.	$r(t)$ + − $e(t)$ $G_1(s)$ S $G_2(s)$ S $G_3(s)$ $c(t)$ $H(s)$	....
7.	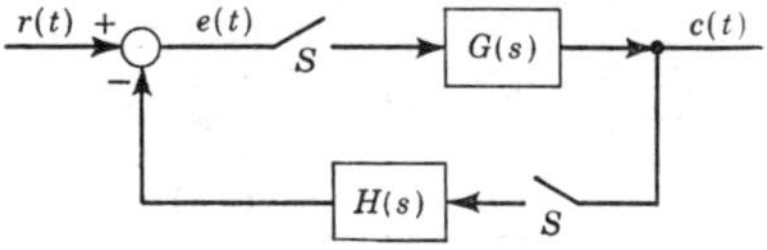 $r(t)$ + − $e(t)$ S $G(s)$ $c(t)$ $H(s)$ S	....
8.	$r(t)$ + − $e(t)$ S $G_1(s)$ S $G_2(s)$ $c(t)$ $H(s)$ S	....
9.	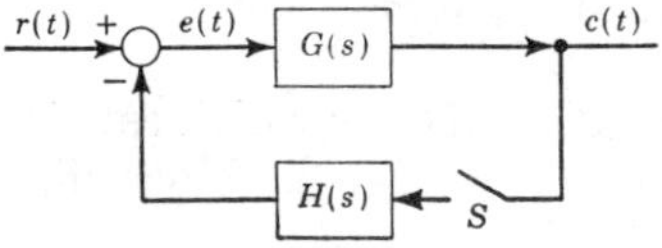 $r(t)$ + − $e(t)$ $G(s)$ $c(t)$ $H(s)$ S	....

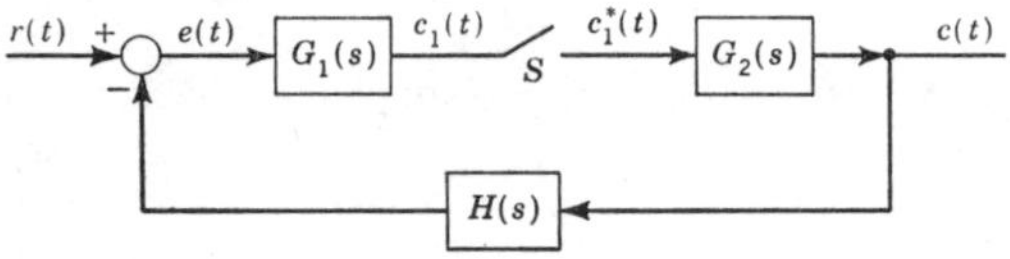

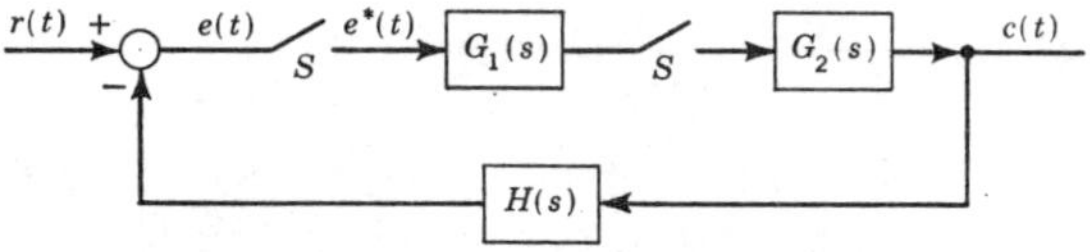

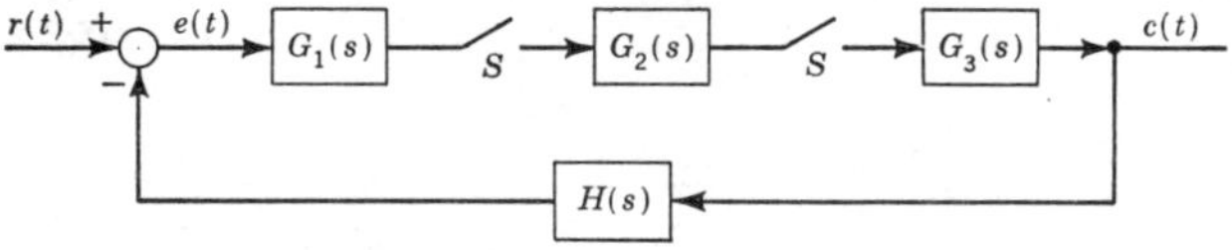

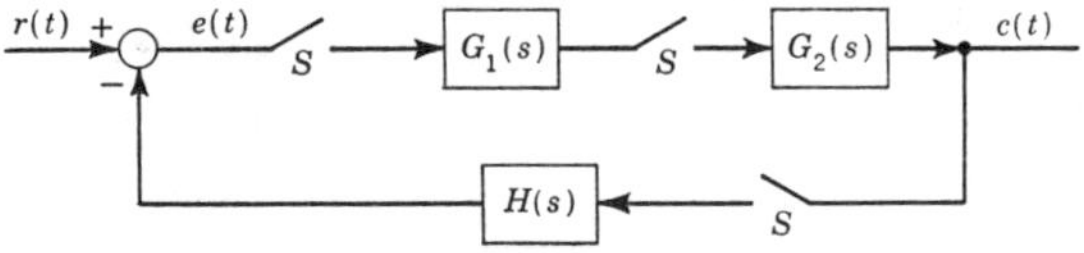

SIMPLE SAMPLED-DATA CONTROL SYSTEMS

Output Transforms

Laplace transform $C(s)$ or $C^*(s)$	z transform $C(z)$	Modified z transform $C(z,m)$
$G(s)R^*(s)$	$G(z)R(z)$	$G(z,m)R(z)$
$GR^*(s)$	$GR(z)$	$GR(z)$
$\dfrac{G(s)R^*(s)}{1 + GH^*(s)}$	$\dfrac{G(z)R(z)}{1 + GH(z)}$	$\dfrac{G(z,m)R(z)}{1 + GH(z)}$
$\dfrac{G_2(s)G_1R^*(s)}{1 + G_1G_2H^*(s)}$	$\dfrac{G_2(z)G_1R(z)}{1 + G_1G_2H(z)}$	$\dfrac{G_2(z,m)G_1R(z)}{1 + G_1G_2H(z)}$
$\dfrac{G_1^*(s)G_2(s)R^*(s)}{1 + G_1^*(s)G_2H^*(s)}$	$\dfrac{G_1(z)G_2(z)R(z)}{1 + G_1(z)G_2H(z)}$	$\dfrac{G_1(z)G_2(z,m)R(z)}{1 + G_1(z)G_2H(z)}$
$\dfrac{G_2^*(s)G_3(s)G_1R^*(s)}{1 + G_2^*(s)G_1G_3H^*(s)}$	$\dfrac{G_2(z)G_3(z)G_1R(z)}{1 + G_2(z)G_1G_3H(z)}$	$\dfrac{G_2(z)G_3(z,m)G_1R(z)}{1 + G_2(z)G_1G_3H(z)}$
$\dfrac{G(s)R^*(s)}{1 + G^*(s)H^*(s)}$	$\dfrac{G(z)R(z)}{1 + G(z)H(z)}$	$\dfrac{G(z,m)R(z)}{1 + G(z)H(z)}$
$\dfrac{G_1^*(s)G_2(s)R^*(s)}{1 + G_1^*(s)G_2^*(s)H^*(s)}$	$\dfrac{G_1(z)G_2(z)R(z)}{1 + G_1(z)G_2(z)H(z)}$	$\dfrac{G_1(z)G_2(z,m)R(z)}{1 + G_1(z)G_2(z)H(z)}$
$GR(s) - \dfrac{GH(s)GR^*(s)}{1 + GH^*(s)}$	$\dfrac{GR(z)}{1 + GH(z)}$	$RG(z,m) - \dfrac{GH(z,m)RG(z)}{1 + GH(z)}$

of Fig. 6.1-10*b* is of the error-sampled configuration, from which it is seen that

$$B(s) = \frac{GH(s)}{1 + GH^*(s)} R_1^*(s)$$

$$= \frac{GH(s)}{1 + GH^*(s)} GR^*(s) \qquad (6.1\text{-}73)$$

and
$$C(s) = GR(s) - \frac{GH(s)}{1 + GH^*(s)} GR^*(s) \qquad (6.1\text{-}74)$$

Taking the z transform of both sides of Eq. (6.1-74) yields the output transform as

$$C(z) = \frac{GR(z)}{1 + GH(z)} \qquad (6.1\text{-}75)$$

The modified z transform of the system output follows immediately from Eq. (6.1-74), that is,

$$C(z,m) = GR(z,m) - \frac{GH(z,m)GR(z)}{1 + GH(z)} \qquad (6.1\text{-}76)$$

To determine the z transform and the modified z transform of the output of a sampled-data control system, the simplified procedures suggested can be followed: (1) Derive the Laplace transform of the system output. (2) Obtain the z transform of the output by replacing the s function by the corresponding z transform, for example, $G^*(s)$ or $G(s)$ is replaced by $G(z)$, and $G(s)H(s)$, by $GH(z)$. (3) Obtain the modified z transform of the output by replacing the starred s function by the corresponding z transform and the s function by the corresponding modified z transform, for example, $G^*(s)$ is replaced by $G(z)$, and $G(s)$, by $G(z,m)$. The transforms of the output of several basic sampled-data systems are given in Table 6.1-1 for reference. In this table the Laplace transform (starred or nonstarred), the z transform, and the modified z transform of the system output for each case are listed.

EXAMPLE 6.1-2. In the system of Fig. 6.1-8, if

$$G(s) = \frac{10}{(s + 5)} \qquad H(s) = \frac{5}{s} \qquad (6.1\text{-}77)$$

the input is a unit step function and the sampling period is 0.2 sec, determine the z transform and the modified z transform of the system output.

From the given data the following transfer functions are obtained:

$$GR(s) = G(s)R(s) = \frac{10}{s(s + 5)} \qquad (6.1\text{-}78)$$

and
$$GH(s) = G(s)H(s) = \frac{50}{s(s + 5)} \qquad (6.1\text{-}79)$$

For sampling period equal to 0.2 sec, the z transforms corresponding to the above transfer functions are given by

$$GR(z) = \frac{1.26z}{(z-1)(z-0.368)} \tag{6.1-80}$$

and

$$GH(z) = \frac{6.32z}{(z-1)(z-0.368)} \tag{6.1-81}$$

Substituting these two z transforms into Eq. (6.1-65) and simplifying yields the z transform of the system output as

$$C(z) = \frac{1.26z}{z^2 + 4.95z + 0.368} \tag{6.1-82}$$

By use of the rules described in Chap. 5 or by inspection of the modified z-transform table of Appendix 1, the modified z transforms for $GR(s)$ and $GH(s)$ are found. They are

$$GR(z,m) = 2\left(\frac{1}{z-1} - \frac{0.368^m}{z-0.368}\right) \tag{6.1-83}$$

and

$$GH(z,m) = 10\left(\frac{1}{z-1} - \frac{0.368^m}{z-0.368}\right) \tag{6.1-84}$$

Then the modified z transform of the system output is obtained from Eq. (6.1-68), that is,

$$C(z,m) = \frac{2(z^2 + 4.95z - 5.95)[(1 - 0.368^m)z + 0.368^m - 0.368]}{(z-1)(z-0.368)(z^2 + 4.95z + 0.368)} \tag{6.1-85}$$

More Complicated Systems. To illustrate the derivation of the output transforms and the manipulation of the block diagrams of more complicated pulsed-data control systems, two examples are presented below.

SAMPLED-DATA FEEDBACK SYSTEM WITH FEEDFORWARD CONTROL. Figure 6.1-11 illustrates a typical error-sampled system with feedforward control. Applying Rules 9 and 7 of Sec. 2.2 reduces the block diagram of Fig. 6.1-11

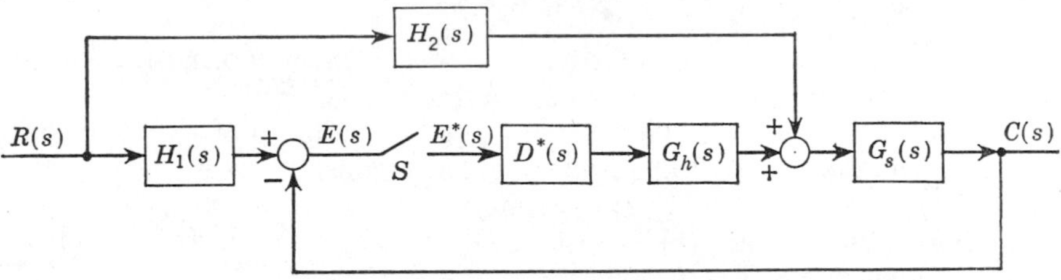

FIG. 6.1-11. Block diagram of a typical sampled-data feedback system with feedforward control.

to that of Fig. 6.1-12a, from which the output transform may be derived by inspection. Clearly, the closed-loop system of Fig. 6.1-12a can be readily reduced to the equivalent open-loop representation of Fig. 6.1-12*b*. Thus, the Laplace transform of the system output is given by

$$C(s) = G_sH_2(s)R(s) + \frac{D^*(s)G_hG_s(s)}{1 + D^*(s)G_hG_S^*(s)} [H_1R^*(s) - G_sH_2R^*(s)] \quad (6.1\text{-}86)$$

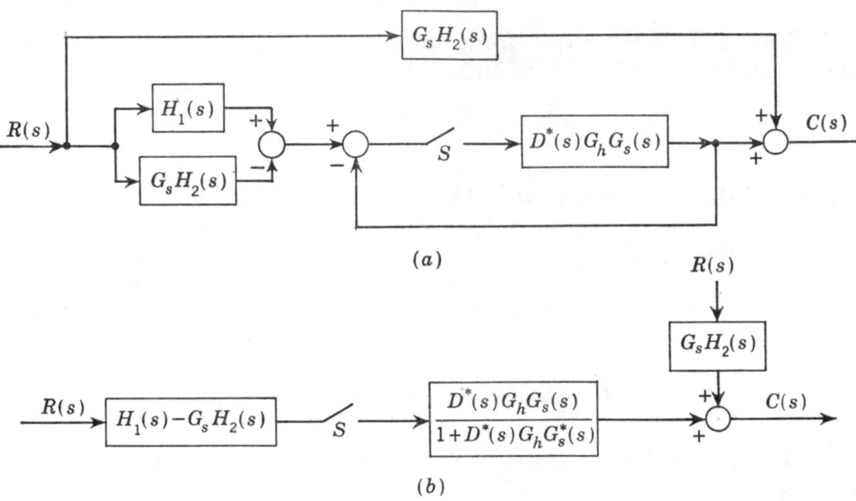

FIG. 6.1-12. (*a*) Block diagram of the system reduced from Fig. 6.1-11; (*b*) equivalent open-loop representation.

The z transform and the modified z transform of the system output follow immediately from the above equation, that is,

$$C(z) = G_sH_2R(z) + \frac{D(z)G_hG_s(z)}{1 + D(z)G_hG_s(z)} [H_1R(z) - G_sH_2R(z)] \quad (6.1\text{-}87)$$

$$C(z,m) = G_sH_2R(z,m) + \frac{D(z)G_hG_s(z,m)}{1 + D(z)G_hG_s(z)} [H_1R(z) - G_sH_2R(z)] \quad (6.1\text{-}88)$$

CLOSED-LOOP SYSTEM HAVING PULSED-DATA AND CONTINUOUS-DATA BRANCHES CONNECTED IN PARALLEL. A typical system of this nature is illustrated in Fig. 6.1-13. The forward path is made up of two branches, one of which contains a sampler operating at a constant rate. This system may be treated as a system with two inputs, $R(s)$ and $E^*(s)$. The output $C_1(s)$ due to $R(s)$ is obtained by setting $E^*(s)$ equal to zero. It is seen from the block diagram of Fig. 6.1-13 that

$$C_1(s) = \frac{G(s)R(s)}{1 + GH(s)} \quad (6.1\text{-}89)$$

The output $C_2(s)$ due to $E^*(s)$ can be readily derived from the block diagram of Fig. 6.1-14, which is reduced from the block diagram of Fig. 6.1-13 by setting $R(s)$ equal to zero. It follows from Fig. 6.1-14 that

$$C_2(s) = \frac{D^*(s)G_h(s)}{1 + GH(s)} E^*(s) \tag{6.1-90}$$

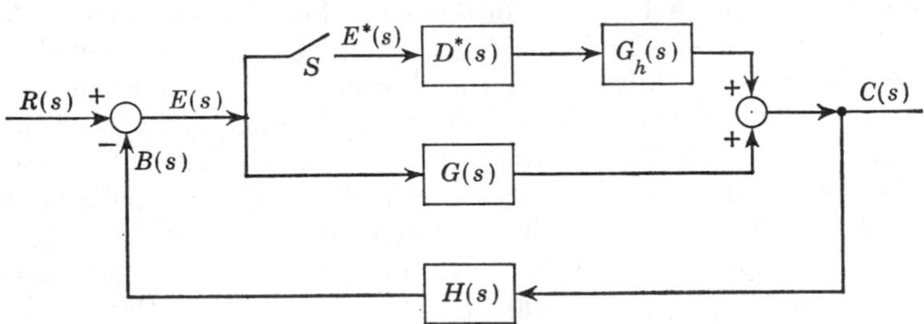

FIG. 6.1-13. System containing pulsed-data and continuous-data branches connected in parallel.

Combining Eqs. (6.1-89) and (6.1-90) yields the Laplace transform of the system output as

$$\begin{aligned} C(s) &= C_1(s) + C_2(s) \\ &= \frac{G(s)R(s)}{1 + GH(s)} + \frac{D^*(s)G_h(s)}{1 + GH(s)} E^*(s) \end{aligned} \tag{6.1-91}$$

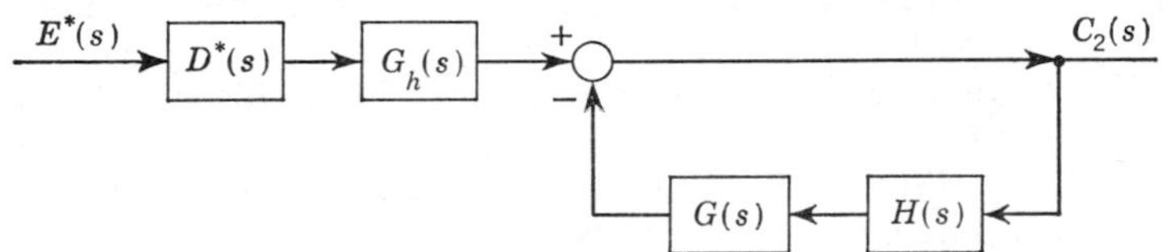

FIG. 6.1-14. Block diagram indicating the relationship between $E^*(s)$ and the corresponding output.

Inspection of Fig. 6.1-13 reveals that

$$E(s) = R(s) - [GH(s)E(s) + D^*(s)G_hH(s)E^*(s)] \tag{6.1-92}$$

Transposing and rearranging reduce Eq. (6.1-92) to

$$E(s) = \frac{R(s)}{1 + GH(s)} - \frac{D^*(s)G_hH(s)}{1 + GH(s)} E^*(s) \tag{6.1-93}$$

Taking the starred transform of both sides and simplifying yield

$$E^*(s) = \frac{\{R(s)/[1 + GH(s)]\}^*}{1 + D^*(s)\{G_hH(s)/[1 + GH(s)]\}^*} \tag{6.1-94}$$

Substituting Eq. (6.1-94) into Eq. (6.1-91) gives the Laplace transform of the system output in terms of the transfer functions of the system components and the input, from which the z transform and the modified z transform of the system output follow immediately. It is to be noted that this system is not reducible to the error-sampled configuration.

6.2. Graphical Stability Analysis; Schur-Cohn Criterion; Bilinear Transformation. The major problems involved in feedback control systems are the stability and the effectiveness of the control system to process information and its ability to alleviate external disturbances. A control-system engineer would like to have the actual output of his system the same as the desired output and the effect of disturbing signals introduced into the system at other points than at the input minimized. The problems of information processing and disturbance reduction in a control system are connected with the transient performance of the system and can generally be analyzed by studying the behavior of the system responding to transient or random input signals. The data-processing aspects of the control system problem may be treated as problems in information theory. The stability problem arises when the system error is reduced by increasing the gain or sensitivity of the control system. If the gain is increased beyond a certain allowable maximum value, sustained oscillations will result in the output of the system even though the input is quiescent. This control system is then considered unstable. An unstable system is generally undesirable. Consequently, stability forms a very important factor in control-system design, and the stability problem has received the foremost consideration.

This section is concerned with the study of the stability problem in sampled-data and digital feedback control systems. As in continuous-data systems, the stability for sampled-data systems may be determined either graphically or analytically. The stability criteria are discussed in the following paragraphs.

a. Nyquist Stability Criterion for Sampled-data Systems.[112] The stability of a linear continuous-data feedback control system is frequently determined by the location of the roots of the characteristic equation of the system in the s plane. A stable system requires that the characteristic roots be located in the left half of the s plane. Based upon this, the Nyquist stability criterion was derived, which describes a graphical method of determining the location of the roots and the stability of the system. Consider the typical feedback control system of Fig. 6.2-1, the open-loop transfer function of which is

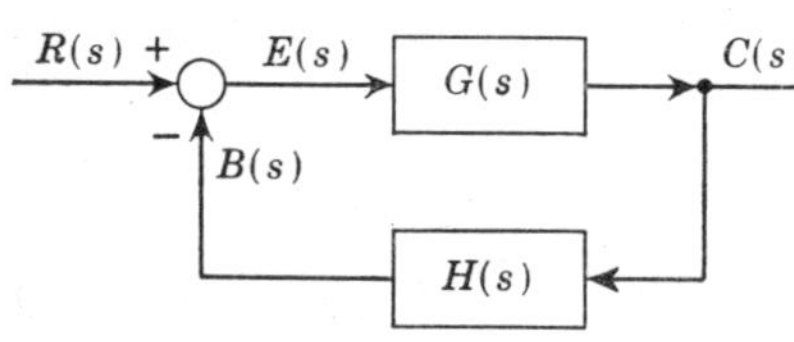

FIG. 6.2-1. Block diagram of a basic feedback control system.

$$A(s) = G(s)H(s) \tag{6.2-1}$$

It has been shown that stability is determined by the relative orientation of the polar plot of $A(j\omega)$ and a critical point or locus in the complex plane. This concept can readily be extended to the determination of the stability of sampled-data and digital feedback control systems, when the systems are analyzed by the method of z transforms. From the discussions of Sec. 6.1 it is seen that the denominator of the output transform of the system is either $1 + GH(z)$ or $1 + G(z)H(z)$, depending upon the location of the samplers in the control system. The terms $GH(z)$ and $G(z)H(z)$, referred to as the open-loop pulse-transfer functions, will be denoted by $A(z)$. Referring to Figs. 6.1-5, -6, -7, -8, the open-loop pulse-transfer function is derived from the transfer functions around the loop through z transformation. For instance, the open-loop pulse-transfer function of the system shown in Fig. 6.1-5 is

$$A(z) = \mathfrak{z}\{GH(s)\} = GH(z) \tag{6.2-2}$$

and that for system of Fig. 6.1-7 is

$$A(z) = \mathfrak{z}\{G(s)\}\mathfrak{z}\{H(s)\} = G(z)H(z) \tag{6.2-3}$$

where $$G(z) = \mathfrak{z}\{G(s)\} \qquad \text{and} \qquad H(z) = \mathfrak{z}\{H(s)\} \tag{6.2-4}$$

In general, the open-loop pulse-transfer function of a basic sampled-data feedback control system can be derived by opening the loop at the point where the signal is sampled. The pulse-transfer function of this open-loop system represents the open-loop pulse-transfer function of the given feedback system.

The characteristic equation of a sampled-data or digital control system may be derived by putting the denominator of the system output transform equal to zero. For example, the characteristic equation for the system of Fig. 6.1-5 is

$$1 + GH(z) = 0 \tag{6.2-5}$$

and that for the system of Fig. 6.1-7 is

$$1 + G(z)H(z) = 0 \tag{6.2-6}$$

In general, the characteristic equation is given by

$$1 + A(z) = 0 \tag{6.2-7}$$

The nature of the roots of Eq. (6.2-7) determines the stability and the transient behavior of the system. As has been discussed in Chap. 5, the z transformation can be considered as a process of mapping. $z = \epsilon^{Ts}$ is the mapping function which maps the imaginary axis of the s plane into the unit circle about the origin of the z plane and the left half of the s plane into the interior of the unit circle (Fig. 5.5-2). Consequently, a sampled-data or digital control system is stable if all the roots of the characteristic equation in z [Eq. (6.2-7)] lie inside the unit circle about the origin of the z plane.

The open-loop pulse-transfer function $A(z)$ can generally be expressed as a ratio of two polynomials in z:

$$A(z) = \frac{P(z)}{Q(z)} \tag{6.2-8}$$

Assume that the order of $P(z)$ is m and that of $Q(z)$ is n with $n \geq m$, and

$$A(z) = \frac{c_0 + c_1z + c_2z^2 + \cdots + c_kz^k + \cdots + c_mz^m}{b_0 + b_1z + b_2z^2 + \cdots + b_kz^k + \cdots + b_nz^n} \qquad (6.2\text{-}9)$$

Then $$1 + A(z) = \frac{a_0 + a_1z + a_2z^2 + \cdots + a_kz^k + \cdots + a_nz^n}{b_0 + b_1z + b_2z^2 + \cdots + b_kz^k + \cdots + b_nz^n} \qquad (6.2\text{-}10)$$

Equation (6.2-10) may be put into the form

$$1 + A(z) = \frac{K_0(z - z_1)(z - z_2) \cdots (z - z_k) \cdots (z - z_n)}{(z - p_1)(z - p_2) \cdots (z - p_k) \cdots (z - p_n)} = W(z) \qquad (6.2\text{-}11)$$

where z_k's are the zeros of $W(z)$ and p_k's are the poles. The function $W(z) = 1 + A(z)$ has n zeros and n poles of which p poles are assumed to be located in the unit circle about the origin of the z plane. The system is stable if the polar plot of $A(z)$ for a frequency range from 0 radian/sec to $2\pi/T$ radians/sec (or for z moving once around the unit circle of the z plane) makes $(n - p)$ encirclements of the critical point $(-1 + j0)$ in the counterclockwise direction, T being the sampling period of the system. This statement is explained and illustrated in the following paragraph.

Shown in Fig. 6.2-2 is a plot of the pole-zero configurations in the z plane, where $p_1, p_2, \ldots$ are the poles and $z_1, z_2, \ldots$ are the zeros of $W(z)$ inside

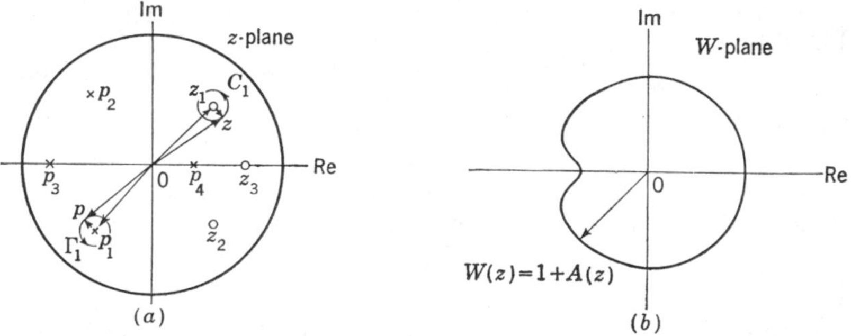

FIG. 6.2-2. (a) Pole-zero distribution diagram and (b) the polar plot in the W plane.

the unit circle. A pole is denoted by a cross and a zero is represented by a dot. In Fig. 6.2-2a, arbitrary closed curves Γ_1 and C_1 are drawn about the pole p_1 and the zero z_1, respectively. It is readily seen that as z moves in the counterclockwise direction around the contour C_1 about the zero $z = z_1$, the vector $(z - z_1)$ describes one complete counterclockwise revolution about the zero, and the locus of $W(z)$ makes one encirclement of the origin of the W plane in the same direction (Fig. 6.2-2b). Similarly as z moves in the counterclockwise direction around a closed contour enclosing two zeros, the locus of $W(z)$ makes two encirclements of the origin in the counterclockwise direction. Following the same reasoning it is conceivable that as z traverses in the counterclockwise direction around the unit circle which encloses N zeros, the function $W(z)$ describes a locus encircling the origin in the counterclockwise direction N times. In like manner, as z moves around the contour Γ_1, in the direction as indicated, the vector $(z - p_1)$ sweeps through one complete counterclockwise revolution whereas the locus of $W(z)$ describes one encirclement of the origin in the clockwise direction. Furthermore, when z moves in the counterclockwise direction around the unit circle which encloses p poles, the z-transform locus of $W(z)$ would make p encirclements of the origin in the clockwise direction. Thus it follows from the above discussion that if there are N zeros and p poles of the function $W(z)$ inside the unit circle, the z-transform locus of $W(z) = 1 + A(z)$ would encircle the origin $(N - p)$ times for z traversing once around the unit circle in the counterclockwise direction (or for the frequency increasing from 0 radian/sec to $2\pi/T$ radians/sec).

The plotting of the z-transform locus of a function $W(z)$ is a mapping process to pass from the z plane to the W plane. From the characteristic equation

$$W(z) = 1 + A(z) = 0 \tag{6.2-12}$$

it is observed that the mapping function for transforming a figure from the z plane to the W plane is

$$W(z) \tag{6.2-13}$$

and that for passing from the z plane to the A plane is

$$A(z) \tag{6.2-14}$$

The origin of the A plane is mapped into the point $W = 1$ in the W plane and the roots of $W(z) = 0$ are mapped into the origin of the W plane. In other words, the point $W = 1$ in the W plane corresponds to the origin of the A plane, and the point $W = 0$ in the W plane corresponds to the point $A = -1$ in the A plane, as shown in Fig. 6.2-3. Thus, if the

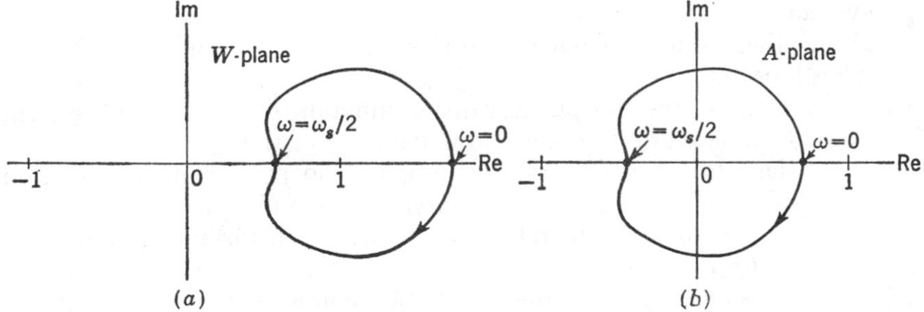

FIG. 6.2-3. (a) Mapping of the unit circle of the z plane into the W plane; (b) mapping of the unit circle of the z plane into the A plane.

z-transform locus of $A(z)$ is plotted, the encirclement of the plot should be referred to the point $(-1 + j0)$ of the A plane.

Now, let Ω be the number of encirclements of the z-transform locus of

$A(z)$ about the critical point $(-1 + j0)$ for increasing frequencies, Ω being considered positive for counterclockwise revolution and negative for clockwise rotation, then the above conclusion can be expressed by the following equation:

$$\Omega = N - p \tag{6.2-15}$$

Since the condition for stability requires that all the zeros of $1 + A(z)$ be located inside the unit circle, the number of zeros of $1 + A(z)$ must be equal to the order of $Q(z)$, that is,

$$N = n \tag{6.2-16}$$

Therefore, the system is stable provided that

$$\Omega = n - p \tag{6.2-17}$$

OPEN-LOOP STABLE SYSTEM. If the sampled-data feedback control system is open-loop stable, all the poles of $1 + A(z)$ will lie inside the unit circle, that is,

$$p = n \tag{6.2-18}$$

Then the system is stable, provided that

$$\Omega = 0 \tag{6.2-19}$$

That is, the z-transform locus of $A(z)$ for a frequency range from 0 radian/sec to $2\pi/T$ radians/sec makes no encirclement of the critical point $(-1 + j0)$.

OPEN-LOOP UNSTABLE SYSTEM. If the sampled-data system were open-loop unstable, there would be only p poles of $A(z)$ lying inside the unit circle with $p < n$. Then the system is stable, providing that

$$\Omega = n - p \tag{6.2-20}$$

which is the stability criterion for sampled-data and digital feedback control systems.

In brief, the stability of pulsed-data systems can be determined by the following procedures:

1. Derive the open-loop pulse-transfer function of the control system from the block diagram (or signal-flow diagram) of the system.
2. Plot the z-transform locus of the open-loop pulse-transfer function for z traversing once around the unit circle of the z plane.
3. Count the number of encirclements of the z-transform locus about the critical point $(-1 + j0)$.
4. If the open-loop pulse-transfer function contains no pole outside the unit circle of the z plane, Eq. (6.2-19) should be applied to test for stability; otherwise Eq. (6.2-20) should be used.

A few simple examples are given below to illustrate the determination of stability in the z domain by means of the Nyquist stability criterion for pulsed-data systems.

EXAMPLE 6.2-1. Consider a simple unity-feedback system with open-loop pulse-transfer function

$$A(z) = \frac{0.5z}{(z-1)(z+0.5)} \tag{6.2-21}$$

If the pole $z = 1$ of the pulse-transfer function $A(z)$ is enclosed inside the unit circle as indicated in Fig. 6.2-4a, the system is considered as open-

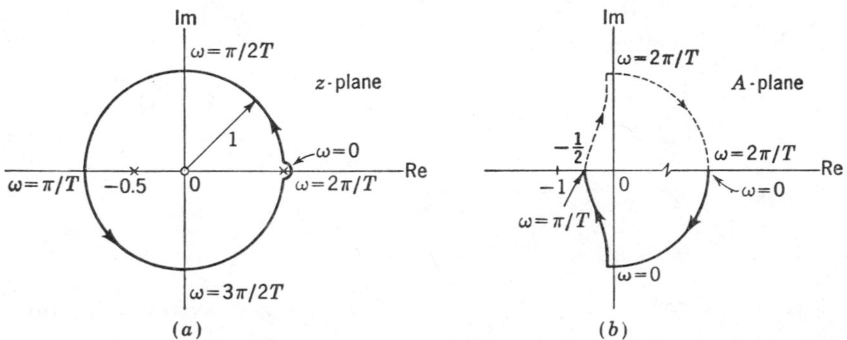

FIG. 6.2-4. (a) The unit circle of the z plane with indentation to include the pole at $z = 1$; (b) the z-transform locus for $A(z)$ of Example 6.2-1.

loop stable. Then $n = 2$ and $p = 2$. Inspection of the z-transform locus of $A(z)$ shown in Fig. 6.2-4b reveals that $\Omega = 0$. Equation (6.2-19) is satisfied and the system is stable.

All the zeros of the function $1 + A(z)$ lie inside the unit circle as pointed out by Eq. (6.2-22):

$$N = \Omega + p = 0 + 2 = 2 \tag{6.2-22}$$

The system characteristic equation is given by

$$1 + A(z) = 1 + \frac{0.5z}{(z-1)(z+0.5)} = 0 \tag{6.2-23}$$

or

$$z^2 - 0.5 = 0 \tag{6.2-24}$$

which confirms that the system is stable since its zeros are located at ± 0.707.

Since the pole $z = 1$ is on the unit circle, it may be excluded from the unit circle by an indentation shown in Fig. 6.2-5a. This would indicate that the system is open-loop unstable. The z-transform locus of $A(z)$ is sketched in Fig. 6.2-5b which is slightly different from the plot of Fig. 6.2-4b because a different indentation about the point $z = 1$ is chosen. The locus of Fig. 6.2-5b closes at infinity in the left half plane while that of Fig. 6.2-4b closes at infinity in the right half plane. From Fig. 6.2-5b it is seen that the z-transform locus of $A(z)$ makes one counterclockwise encirclement about the critical point $(-1 + j0)$, and hence $\Omega = 1$. The system is stable, since $n = 2$, $p = 1$, $\Omega = 1$ and Eq. (6.2-20) is satisfied.

This is in agreement with the conclusion derived from the analysis of the preceding paragraph by considering the pole $z = 1$ inside the unit circle.

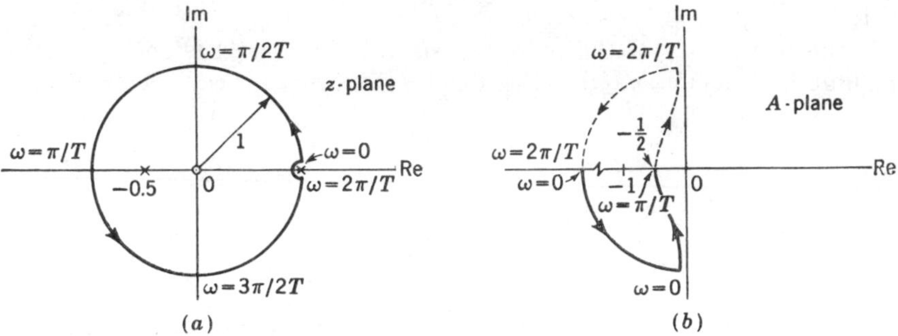

FIG. 6.2-5. (a) The unit circle with indentation to exclude the pole; (b) the z-transform locus for $A(z)$ of Example 6.2-1.

EXAMPLE 6.2-2. Consider a simple unity feedback system with open-loop pulse-transfer function

$$A(z) = \frac{0.5z}{(z+1)(z-0.5)} \tag{6.2-25}$$

By choosing the indentation as shown in Fig. 6.2-6a, all the poles of $A(z)$ lie inside the unit circle. Then

$$p = 2 \qquad n = 2 \tag{6.2-26}$$

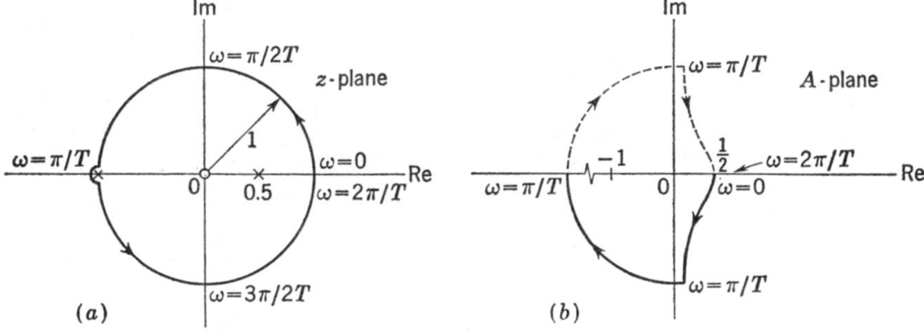

FIG. 6.2-6. (a) The unit circle of the z plane with indentation to enclose the pole at $z = -1$; (b) the z-transform locus for $A(z)$ of Example 6.2-2.

The z-transform locus of $A(z)$, plotted in Fig. 6.2-6b, encircles the critical point $(-1 + j0)$ once in the clockwise direction.

$$\Omega = -1 \qquad \Omega \neq n - p \tag{6.2-27}$$

Thus, the stability condition of Eq. (6.2-20) is not fulfilled and the system is unstable.

The fact that only one zero of $1 + A(z)$ lies inside the unit circle is demonstrated by the following calculation:

$$N = \Omega + p = -1 + 2 = 1 \tag{6.2-28}$$

The characteristic equation of the system is derived from Eqs. (6.2-7) and (6.2-25), that is,

$$z^2 + z - 0.5 = 0 \tag{6.2-29}$$

which possesses a root outside the unit circle, thus indicating an unstable system.

EXAMPLE 6.2-3. The block diagram of a sampled-data feedback control system is shown in Fig. 6.2-7a. This system employs a zero-order hold

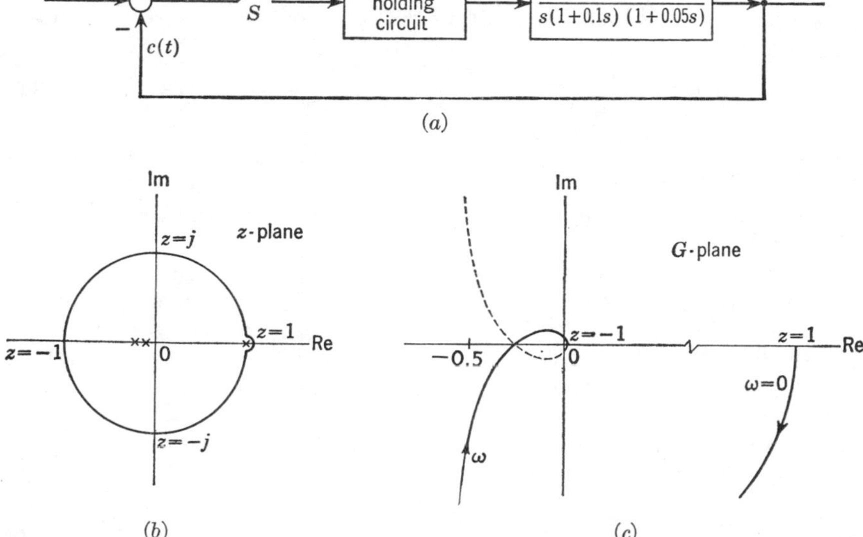

FIG. 6.2-7. (a) Block diagram of a third-order sampled-data system with a zero-order hold (Example 6.2-3); (b) the unit circle and the location of the poles of $G(z)$; (c) the z-transform locus for $G(z)$ of Example 6.2-3.

circuit as the smoothing device, and the controlled system is of the third order with the transfer function given as

$$G_s(s) = \frac{2}{s(1 + 0.1s)(1 + 0.05s)} \tag{6.2-30}$$

The sampling period is 0.2 sec. Determine the stability of the system.

The transfer function of a zero-order hold circuit, as derived in Sec. 4.6, is

$$G_h(s) = \frac{1 - \epsilon^{-Ts}}{s} \tag{6.2-31}$$

where T denotes the sampling period. The transfer function of the holding device and the controlled system is given by

$$G(s) = G_h(s)G_s(s) = \frac{1 - \epsilon^{-Ts}}{s} \frac{2}{s(1 + 0.1s)(1 + 0.05s)} \tag{6.2-32}$$

The z transform corresponding to $G(s)$ is

$$G(z) = (1 - z^{-1})\, \mathfrak{z} \left\{\frac{400}{s^2(s + 10)(s + 20)}\right\} = (1 - z^{-1})\, \mathfrak{z} \left\{\frac{2}{s^2} - \frac{0.3}{s} + \frac{0.4}{s + 10} - \frac{0.1}{s + 20}\right\} \tag{6.2-33}$$

The z transforms corresponding to the terms in the braces of the above equation are available in the table of Sec. 5.2, from which $G(z)$ is readily determined:

$$G(z) = \frac{0.4}{z - 1} + \frac{0.4(z - 1)}{z - 0.135} - \frac{0.1(z - 1)}{z - 0.0185} - 0.3 \tag{6.2-34}$$

Equation (6.2-34) also represents the open-loop pulse-transfer function $A(z)$, since this system is of unity feedback. To investigate the system stability, the polar plot of $G(z)$ for z traversing once around the unit circle is sketched in Fig. 6.2-7*c*.

From Fig. 6.2-7*c*, it is seen that the polar plot makes no encirclement about the critical point $(-1 + j0)$, that is, $\Omega = 0$. Since, in sketching the plot, the pole at $z = 1$ of $G(z)$ is included in the unit circle by the indentation (Fig. 6.2-7*b*) all the poles of $1 + G(z)$ lie inside the unit circle. Thus, Eq. (6.2-19) is satisfied and the system is stable.

b. Schur-Cohn Stability Criterion.[12] In linear continuous-data feedback control systems, stability can be determined analytically by means of the Routh and Hurwitz stability criteria. The stability of a system may be determined from the coefficients of the characteristic equation of the system according to the Routh test procedures. In like manner, the stability of sampled-data and digital feedback control systems may be determined analytically by the Schur-Cohn criterion. In applying the Schur-Cohn criterion, the characteristic equation in terms of z for the control system must first be obtained. As has been discussed in the preceding paragraphs, the stability of a system is dependent upon the location of the roots of the characteristic equation, with all the roots inside the unit circle corresponding to a stable system and with one or more roots outside the unit circle corresponding to an unstable system. The Schur-Cohn criterion comprises an elegant test for determining the presence of any root of the characteristic equation outside the unit circle of the z plane.

The characteristic equation will have the general polynomial form:

$$F(z) = a_0 + a_1 z + a_2 z^2 + \cdots + a_n z^n = 0 \tag{6.2-35}$$

where $F(z)$ stands for the numerator of $1 + A(z)$.

The first step in making a Schur-Cohn test is to write the coefficients a_k in the form of a determinant:

$$\Delta_k = \begin{vmatrix} a_0 & 0 & 0 & \cdots & 0 & a_n & a_{n-1} & \cdots & a_{n-k+1} \\ a_1 & a_0 & 0 & \cdots & 0 & 0 & a_n & \cdots & a_{n-k+2} \\ \cdots & \cdots & a_0 & \cdots & \cdots & \cdots & \cdots & \cdots & \cdots \\ \cdots & \cdots & \cdots & \cdots & \cdots & \cdots & \cdots & \cdots & \cdots \\ a_{k-1} & a_{k-2} & a_{k-3} & \cdots & a_0 & 0 & 0 & \cdots & a_n \\ \bar{a}_n & 0 & 0 & \cdots & 0 & \bar{a}_0 & \bar{a}_1 & \cdots & \bar{a}_{k-1} \\ \bar{a}_{n-1} & \bar{a}_n & 0 & \cdots & 0 & 0 & \bar{a}_0 & \cdots & \bar{a}_{k-2} \\ \cdots & \cdots & \bar{a}_n & \cdots & \cdots & \cdots & \cdots & \cdots & \cdots \\ \cdots & \cdots & \cdots & \cdots & \cdots & \cdots & \cdots & \cdots & \cdots \\ \bar{a}_{n-k+1} & \bar{a}_{n-k+2} & \bar{a}_{n-k+3} & \cdots & \bar{a}_n & 0 & 0 & \cdots & \bar{a}_0 \end{vmatrix} \qquad (6.2\text{-}36)$$

where $k = 1, 2, 3, 4, \ldots n$; n is the order of the characteristic equation; and $\bar{a}_n$ is the conjugate of a_n. Δ_k is a determinant of $2k$ rows and $2k$ columns. Then all the roots of the characteristic equation fall inside the unit circle and the system is stable provided that the coefficients of Eq. (6.2-35) satisfy the following conditions:

$$\Delta_k < 0 \qquad \text{for } k \text{ odd}$$

$$\Delta_k > 0 \qquad \text{for } k \text{ even}$$

For $k = 1$, $a_{k-1} = a_0$ and $a_{n-k+1} = a_n$. Hence

$$\Delta_1 = \begin{vmatrix} a_0 & a_n \\ \bar{a}_n & \bar{a}_0 \end{vmatrix} = a_0\bar{a}_0 - a_n\bar{a}_n \qquad (6.2\text{-}37)$$

For $k = 2$, $a_{k-1} = a_1$, $a_{k-2} = a_0$, $a_{n-k+1} = a_{n-1}$, and $a_{n-k+2} = a_n$. Δ_2 is a determinant of four rows and four columns:

$$\Delta_2 = \begin{vmatrix} a_0 & 0 & a_n & a_{n-1} \\ a_1 & a_0 & 0 & a_n \\ \bar{a}_n & 0 & \bar{a}_0 & \bar{a}_1 \\ \bar{a}_{n-1} & \bar{a}_n & 0 & \bar{a}_0 \end{vmatrix} \qquad (6.2\text{-}38)$$

In like manner, for $k = 3$,

$$\Delta_3 = \begin{vmatrix} a_0 & 0 & 0 & a_n & a_{n-1} & a_{n-2} \\ a_1 & a_0 & 0 & 0 & a_n & a_{n-1} \\ a_2 & a_1 & a_0 & 0 & 0 & a_n \\ \bar{a}_n & 0 & 0 & \bar{a}_0 & \bar{a}_1 & \bar{a}_2 \\ \bar{a}_{n-1} & \bar{a}_n & 0 & 0 & \bar{a}_0 & \bar{a}_1 \\ \bar{a}_{n-2} & \bar{a}_{n-1} & \bar{a}_n & 0 & 0 & \bar{a}_0 \end{vmatrix} \qquad (6.2\text{-}39)$$

The application of the Schur-Cohn criterion is illustrated by a few simple examples.

EXAMPLE 6.2-4. Consider a system with the open-loop pulse-transfer function given by

$$A(z) = \frac{z}{(2.45z + 1)(2.45z - 1)} \tag{6.2-40}$$

The characteristic equation of the system is given by

$$F(z) = 6z^2 + z - 1 = 0 \tag{6.2-41}$$

Substituting proper values for the coefficients of Eq. (6.2-36) yields

$$\Delta_1 = \begin{vmatrix} -1 & 6 \\ 6 & -1 \end{vmatrix} = 1 - 36 = -35 \tag{6.2-42}$$

which is less than zero, and

$$\Delta t = \begin{vmatrix} -1 & 0 & 6 & 1 \\ 1 & -1 & 0 & 6 \\ 6 & 0 & -1 & 1 \\ 1 & 6 & 0 & -1 \end{vmatrix} = 1176 \tag{6.2-43}$$

Hence all the roots of the above equation lie inside the unit circle and the system is stable.

Since the characteristic equation is quite simple the roots can be found by inspection.

$$F(z) = (2z + 1)(3z - 1) = 0 \tag{6.2-44}$$

$$z = -\tfrac{1}{2} \qquad z = \tfrac{1}{3} \tag{6.2-45}$$

This agrees with the conclusion derived from the Schur-Cohn criterion.

EXAMPLE 6.2-5. Consider a system with open-loop pulse-transfer function

$$A(z) = \frac{1.5z}{(z + 1)(z - 1)} \tag{6.2-46}$$

The system characteristic equation is found to be

$$F(z) = 2z^2 + 3z - 2 = 0 \tag{6.2-47}$$

Then the values of the Schur-Cohn determinants are given by

$$\Delta_1 = \begin{vmatrix} -2 & 2 \\ 2 & -2 \end{vmatrix} = 0 \tag{6.2-48}$$

and

$$\Delta_2 = \begin{vmatrix} -2 & 0 & 2 & 3 \\ 3 & -2 & 0 & 2 \\ 2 & 0 & -2 & 3 \\ 3 & 2 & 0 & -2 \end{vmatrix} = -144 \tag{6.2-49}$$

The Schur-Cohn criterion indicates that at least one root of the characteristic equation falls outside the unit circle. Hence the system is unstable.

Inspection of the characteristic equation yields the roots:

$$z = \tfrac{1}{2} \qquad z = -2 \tag{6.2-50}$$

which agrees with the result from the Schur-Cohn test.

EXAMPLE 6.2-6. Consider a system with open-loop pulse-transfer function

$$A(z) = \frac{3z}{(2z^2 + 1)} \tag{6.2-51}$$

The system characteristic equation is

$$F(z) = 2z^2 + 3z + 1 = 0 \tag{6.2-52}$$

The Schur-Cohn determinants are

$$\Delta_1 = \begin{vmatrix} 1 & 2 \\ 2 & 1 \end{vmatrix} = -3 \tag{6.2-53}$$

and

$$\Delta_2 = \begin{vmatrix} 1 & 0 & 2 & 3 \\ 3 & 1 & 0 & 2 \\ 2 & 0 & 1 & 3 \\ 3 & 2 & 0 & 1 \end{vmatrix} = 0 \tag{6.2-54}$$

This example illustrates an unstable system. One root of the characteristic equation lies inside the unit circle and the other is right on the unit circle. By inspection, the two roots are

$$z = -\tfrac{1}{2} \qquad z = -1 \tag{6.2-55}$$

The Schur-Cohn criterion provides a nice analytical method of determining the absolute stability of sampled-data and digital control systems. It can also be used to determine the stability boundary of a sampled-data system. However, in view of the fact that to make the Schur-Cohn test it is necessary to evaluate high-order determinants, the application of this criterion is mostly limited to simple systems.

SIMPLIFIED CRITERION FOR QUADRATIC POLYNOMIAL. The general Schur-Cohn stability criterion can be simplified if $F(z)$, the numerator of $1 + A(z)$, is a quadratic polynomial with real coefficients and the coefficient of z^2 unity. In such cases, the necessary and sufficient conditions for the roots of $F(z) = 0$ lying inside the unit circle are reduced to

1. $$|F(0)| < 1 \tag{6.2-56a}$$
2. $$F(1) > 0 \tag{6.2-56b}$$
3. $$F(-1) > 0 \tag{6.2-56c}$$

Condition 1 is necessary but not sufficient. Assuming that the characteristic equation

$$F(z) = z^2 + az + b = 0 \tag{6.2-57}$$

has roots z_1 and z_2, which are either complex or real,

$$F(0) = b = z_1 z_2 \tag{6.2-58}$$

If these two roots lie inside the unit circle,

$$|z_1| < 1 \qquad |z_2| < 1 \tag{6.2-59}$$

Equation (6.2-56*a*) is satisfied. However, in the case of two real roots this condition is not sufficient. The values of z_1 and z_2 could be such that $|z_1 z_2|$ is less than unity with either z_1 or z_2 falling outside the unit circle. Consequently, conditions 2 and 3 are introduced to make the criterion sufficient.

Condition 2 removes the possible existence of one positive real root greater than unity. If $|F(0)|$ is less than 1, at least one root is inside the unit circle, say z_1. Figure 6.2-8 indicates that z_2 is outside the unit circle,

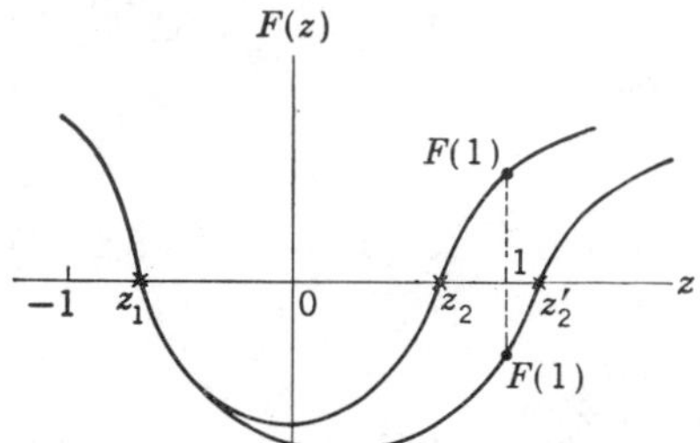

FIG. 6.2-8. The relationship between $F(1)$ and z_2.

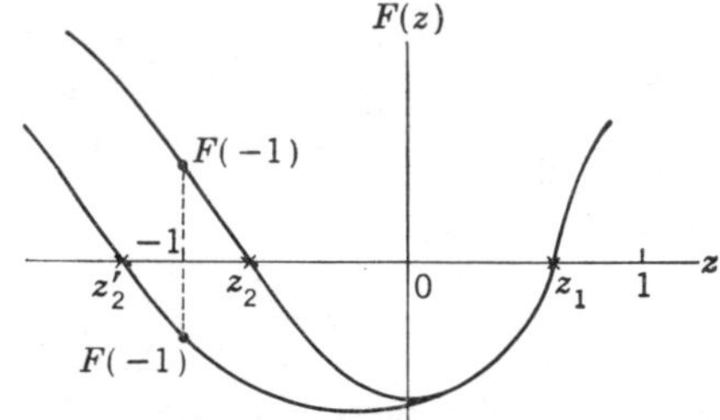

FIG. 6.2-9. The relationship between $F(-1)$ and z_2.

if $F(1) < 0$; z_2 is on the unit circle, if $F(1) = 0$; and z_2 is inside the unit circle, if $F(1) > 0$.

Condition 3 excludes the possibility that a negative real root may fall outside the unit circle. Since $|F(0)|$ is less than 1, it can be assumed that one root, say z_1, lies inside the unit circle. Then, as shown in Fig. 6.2-9, z_2 lies outside the unit circle, if $F(-1) < 0$; z_2 lies on the unit circle, if $F(-1) = 0$; and z_2 lies inside the unit circle, if $F(-1) > 0$.

EXAMPLE 6.2-7. A simple example is used to illustrate the analytical determination of stability. Figure 6.2-10 depicts the block diagram of a second-order sampled-data feedback control system in which T_m is the motor-time constant and K is the gain constant. It is well known that a

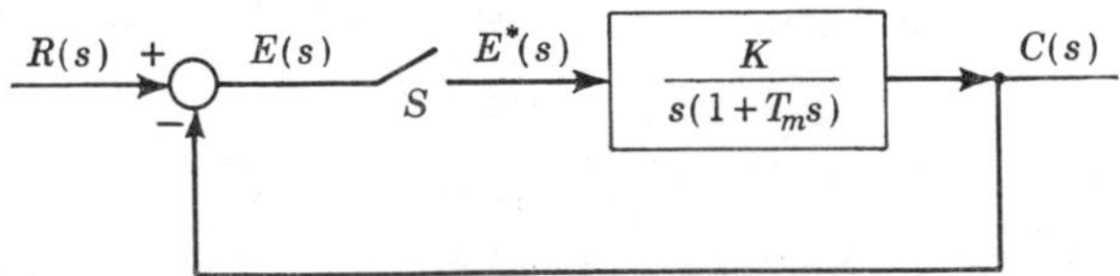

FIG. 6.2-10. Block diagram of a second-order sampled-data feedback control system (Example 6.2-7).

continuous-data second-order feedback control system is stable regardless of the value of the gain constant. However, with the introduction of the sampler, the second-order system becomes unstable when the gain is increased beyond a certain limit. The maximum allowable gain without causing instability is to be determined.

The transfer function of the controlled system is

$$G(s) = \frac{K}{s(1 + T_m s)} \tag{6.2-60}$$

Since this is a unity-feedback system, the open-loop transfer function is

$$A(s) = G(s) = \frac{K}{s(1 + T_m s)} \tag{6.2-61}$$

The open-loop pulse-transfer function is given by the z transform of Eq. (6.2-61). Referring to the table of z transforms of Sec. 5.2, the z transform associated with $A(s)$ is obtained:

$$A(z) = \frac{K(1 - \epsilon^{-T/T_m})z}{(z - 1)(z - \epsilon^{-T/T_m})} \tag{6.2-62}$$

where T is the sampling period. The characteristic equation of this system derived from $1 + A(z) = 0$ is given by

$$F(z) = z^2 + [K(1 - e)^{-T/T_m} - (1 + \epsilon^{-T/T_m})]z + \epsilon^{-T/T_m} = 0 \tag{6.2-63}$$

Applying the stability conditions of Eq. (6.2-56) leads to the following inequalities:

$$|F(0)| = |\epsilon^{-T/T_m}| < 1 \tag{6.2-64}$$

$$F(1) = K(1 - \epsilon^{-T/T_m}) > 0 \tag{6.2-65}$$

$$F(-1) = 1 - K(1 - \epsilon^{-T/T_m}) + (1 + \epsilon^{-T/T_m}) + \epsilon^{-T/T_m} > 0 \tag{6.2-66}$$

The system is stable, if the system constants satisfy the above inequalities. Obviously the first two conditions are fulfilled for any value of K and T/T_m. The third condition imposes a limit upon the gain constant, if both the sampling period and the motor-time constant are specified. Equation (6.2-66) shows that the system remains stable only if

$$K < \frac{2(1 + \epsilon^{-T/T_m})}{1 - \epsilon^{-T/T_m}} \tag{6.2-67}$$

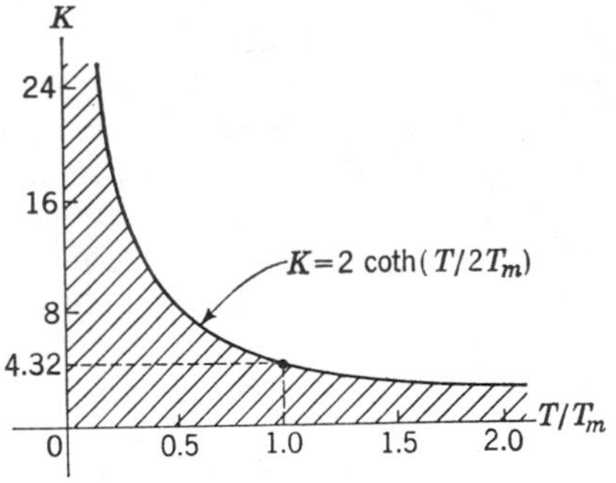

FIG. 6.2-11. Maximum allowable gain for a stable system.

The stability region is indicated by the shaded area under the curve of Fig. 6.2-11. For instance, if the sampling period is equal to the motor-time constant, the maximum gain for the system remaining to be stable is

$$K_m = 4.32 \tag{6.2-68}$$

It is seen from Fig. 6.2-11 that a lower sampling rate (or longer sampling period) would make the stabilization problem more difficult. When the sampling rate is kept very low, the system would turn out unstable even for a relatively small gain constant. This may readily be figured out from intuition. When the sampling period is infinitesimally small, Eq. (6.2-67) would allow an infinitely large gain constant, which implies that a continuous-data second-order system is always stable regardless of the amount of the gain. In fact, the introduction of sampling into a feedback control system usually causes instability or leads to a decrease in the degree of stability.

c. System Stability Determined through Bilinear Transformation.[6,24,87] The main reason which makes the well-known Routh criterion inapplicable to the analysis of a sampled-data control system in the s domain is that the characteristic equation of the system,

$$1 + GH^*(s) = 0 \tag{6.2-69}$$

or

$$1 + G^*(s)H^*(s) = 0 \tag{6.2-70}$$

is not a polynomial in s but a transcendental function of s. As discussed in previous chapters, the s plane may be considered as being made up of a number of horizontal strips with width equal to ω_s, the angular sampling frequency (Fig. 6.2-12). The strip containing the origin of the s plane is referred to as the primary strip. On account of the periodic property, the starred transform, such as $GH^*(s)$, takes on the same value at congruent points in the various strips of the s plane. If any strip can be mapped into the entire plane, say the w plane, the mapping function will convert the multivalued transcendental function in s of Eq. (6.2-69) into a single-valued polynomial in w. Such transformation will make possible the application of the Routh criterion and simplify the application of the extensively used Bode method to sampled-data systems.

The z transformation converts the transcendental function in s [for example, $1 + GH^*(s)$] into a polynomial function in z [for example, $1 + GH(z)$]; however, this process maps the primary and the complementary strips to the left of the imaginary axis of the s plane into the unit circle about the origin of the z plane, which fails to conform with the requirements of the Routh and the Bode methods. A review of complex variable theory reveals that the *bilinear transformation*

$$z = \frac{1 + w}{1 - w} \tag{6.2-71}$$

maps the unit circle of the z plane into the entire left half of the w plane (Fig. 6.2-12) and the polynomial in z is then converted into the ratio of two polynomials in w of the same order. Thus, the z transformation together with the bilinear transformation of Eq. (6.2-71) would map a strip to the left of the imaginary axis of the s plane into the entire left half of the w plane, and convert the transcendental function in s into a polynomial function in w. In the w domain, the condition for stability becomes the absence of the zeros of the polynomial function in the right half plane, and

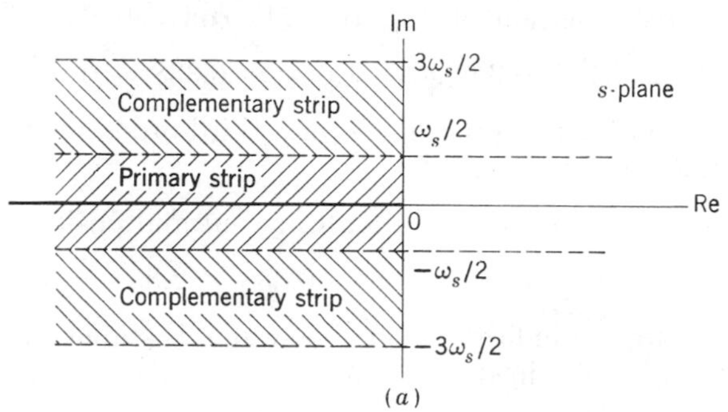

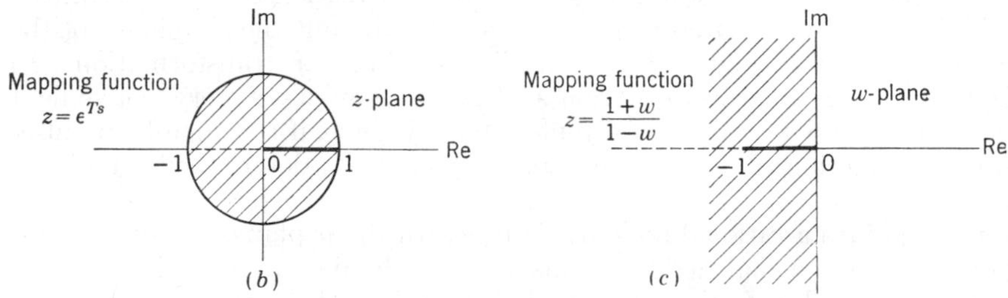

FIG. 6.2-12. (a) The primary and complementary strips of the s plane; (b) the primary and complementary strips of the s plane are mapped into the unit circle of the z plane; (c) the unit circle of the z plane is mapped into the left half of the w plane through bilinear transformation.

the methods, often employed to determine the stability of continuous-data control systems, may be applied in the study of sampled-data control systems. The determination of the system stability through bilinear transformation is illustrated by an example as follows:

EXAMPLE 6.2-8. Shown in Fig. 6.2-7a is a sampled-data feedback control system with a zero-order hold circuit. The sampling period is 0.2 sec, and the transfer function of the elements in the forward path is

$$G(s) = \frac{1 - \epsilon^{-0.2s}}{s} \frac{2}{s(1 + 0.1s)(1 + 0.05s)} \tag{6.2-72}$$

The z transform corresponding to $G(s)$ is given in Eq. (6.2-34), and repeated below:

$$G(z) = \frac{0.4}{z - 1} + \frac{0.4(z - 1)}{z - 0.135} - \frac{0.1(z - 1)}{z - 0.0185} - 0.3 \tag{6.2-73}$$

The characteristic equation of the system in terms of z is given by

$$1 + G(z) = 0 \tag{6.2-74}$$

which leads to

$$z^3 - 1.002z^2 - 0.336z + 0.00535 = 0 \tag{6.2-75}$$

The bilinear transformation of Eq. (6.2-71) converts Eq. (6.2-75) into

$$2.334w^3 + 3.68w^2 + 1.65w + 0.338 = 0 \tag{6.2-76}$$

Now, applying Routh's test procedures for a third-order system, which are given in Eq. (2.3-10):

1. The coefficients of Eq. (6.2-76) are all present and positive.
2. $$a_1a_2 - a_0a_3 = 1.65 \times 3.68 - 0.338 \times 2.334 = 5.27 \tag{6.2-77}$$

Thus, Routh's criterion indicates that the system is stable. This conforms with the conclusion obtained from the Nyquist diagram of the system shown in Fig. 6.2-7*b*.

Comparing the above analysis with the analysis based upon Nyquist's criterion as demonstrated in Example 6.2-3 bears out the simplicity of the method of stability determination through bilinear transformation. In fact, the bilinear transformation technique provides a very convenient means of stability analysis of sampled-data systems, if the open-loop pulse-transfer function of the system can be accurately determined. Through the bilinear transformation, the open-loop pulse-transfer function in z is converted into a rational polynomial in w. In the w plane, the system stability can also be analyzed by means of the Bode-diagram techniques which have been used so extensively in the analysis and design of continuous-data control systems. Performance criteria such as the gain margin and the phase margin can then be used to measure the relative stability of sampled-data systems.

As an illustration, consider the sampled-data system of the above example. The open-loop pulse-transfer function of this system, given in Eq. (6.2-73), can be written as

$$G(z) = \frac{0.152(z + 0.046)(z + 1.134)}{(z - 1)(z - 0.135)(z - 0.0185)} \tag{6.2-78}$$

Transforming into the w plane by means of the bilinear transformation of Eq. (6.2-71) yields

$$G(w) = \frac{0.200(1 - w)(1 + w/1.098)(1 - w/15.9)}{w(1 + w/0.764)(1 + w/0.965)} \tag{6.2-79}$$

In terms of the fictitious frequency v, Eq. (6.2-79) becomes

$$G(jv) = \frac{0.200(1 - jv)(1 + jv/1.098)(1 - jv/15.9)}{jv(1 + jv/0.764)(1 + jv/0.965)} \tag{6.2-80}$$

The asymptotic gain diagram is plotted in Fig. 6.2-13. It is seen that the crossover frequency is around 0.190 radian/sec. The asymptotic phase diagram is plotted in Fig. 6.2-14. It is observed that the 180°-phase shift occurs at a frequency of 0.78 radian/sec. From these two plots, the phase margin is found to be 65°, and the gain margin is found to be 4.75. The maximum allowable gain for stability is 2×4.75 or 9.50.

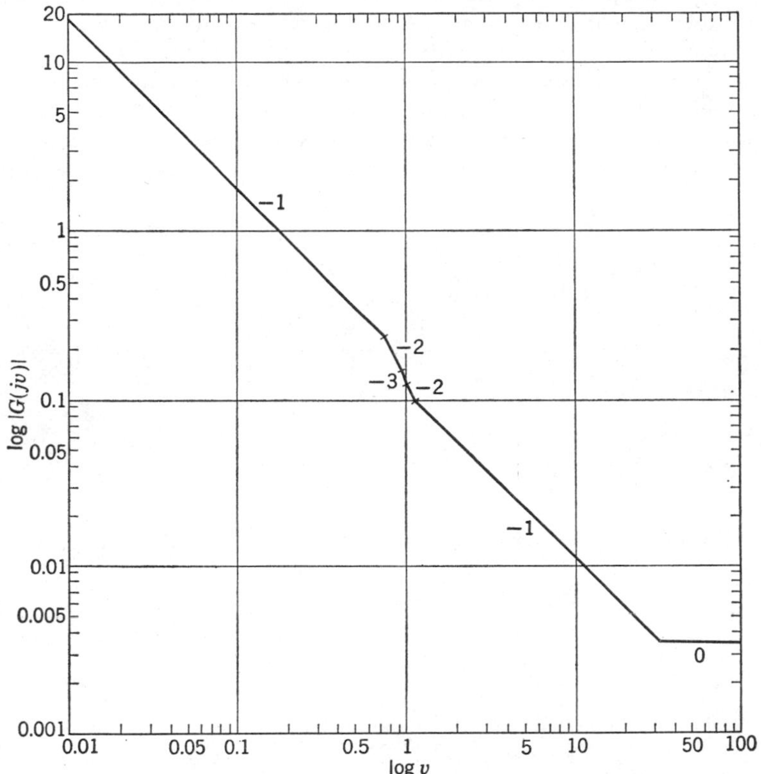

FIG. 6.2-13. Asymptotic gain plot of the system of Example 6.2-8.

In addition to stability analysis, the bilinear transformation technique enables the synthesis of sampled-data systems to be carried out in the w plane by use of the Bode method. The open-loop transfer function in w of a sampled-data system is of nonminimum-phase type. Thus, to evaluate the system behavior from the Bode diagrams, it is necessary to sketch both the gain plot and the phase plot of the open-loop transfer function. Further discussions of the bilinear transformation technique and the synthesis of sampled-data feedback control systems in the w plane are presented in Sec. 9.7.

Comparison of the Three Methods of Stability Determination. In this section, three methods of determining the stability of sampled-data and digital feedback control systems are presented. The Schur-Cohn criterion indicates the presence of the zeros of the characteristic equation outside or on the unit circle of the z plane. This criterion provides an analytical tool for testing the system stability. The results of this criterion offer little insight into the problem of compensation to improve performance and yield no indication of the degree of stability. In case several literal coefficients are present in the pulse-transfer functions, application of the Schur-Cohn criterion will generally result in a series of relationships which must be fulfilled by the variable coefficients for a stable system. The Schur-Cohn criterion is generally useful in the determination of the stability boundaries of sampled-data systems. However, in this method of stability analysis, the amount of labor involved in evaluating high-order determinants discourages the application of this criterion in any but very simple systems.

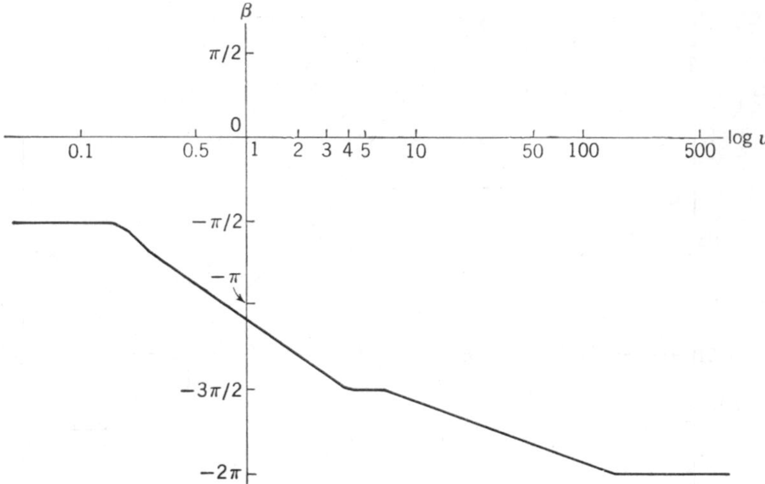

FIG. 6.2-14. Asymptotic phase plot of the system of Example 6.2-8.

The Nyquist criterion provides a graphical means of analyzing the stability of sampled-data and digital control systems. To apply this method, it is necessary to plot the z-transform locus of the open-loop pulse-transfer function of the system. A new locus must be plotted each time that a parameter or time constant is changed. If the pulse-transfer function is in simple factored form, the z-transform locus may often be sketched by inspection. However, if the pulse-transfer function is fairly complicated, the construction of the z-transform locus is by no means an easy task. Nyquist's criterion has the advantage that measured open-loop frequency-response data can generally be used to construct the z-transform locus or Nyquist diagram without resort to a mathematical model. Furthermore, the z-transform locus can indicate not only the absolute stability of the system but also the relative stability. In spite of the difficulty caused by the construction of the z-transform loci of complicated pulse-transfer functions, Nyquist's criterion is commonly used when sampled-data and digital control systems are analyzed by means of the z-transform techniques.

The bilinear transformation technique offers a simplified way of analyzing the stability of sampled-data and digital control systems. This technique allows the use of the Routh and Hurwitz criteria and facilitates the application of the Bode diagrams to pulsed-data systems. Consequently, through bilinear transformation, the designer can utilize the simplicity of the Routh and Hurwitz criteria and the great convenience of the Bode-diagram techniques in the analysis and synthesis of sampled-data and digital control systems.

6.3. Evaluation of System Response at Sampling Instants. The analysis of sampled-data and digital feedback control systems usually covers three general topics as in continuous-data systems:

1. System stability
2. Transient behavior
3. Steady-state performance

The methods for determining the stability of sampled-data feedback control systems have been discussed in the preceding section. At this point, it seems desirable and logical to turn our attention to the study of the transient behavior of sampled-data systems. The basic and useful criteria specifying the transient performance are the peak overshoot, the time to reach the first peak, the settling time, the number of overshoots before settling, and the speed of response. These response characteristics are best interpreted from the system response to a step-function input. Generally speaking, a feedback control system will have acceptable response characteristics if the transients are short and well damped. The details of transient response analysis are the subject matter of Chap. 7. In this and the following section only the evaluation of the system response to step-function input is treated.[25,107]

A discussion of the nature of typical responses of sampled-data control systems to representative inputs requires a general definition of the functions characterizing the systems. A sampled-data control system is often characterized by the over-all pulse-transfer function which can be readily derived from the block diagram of the system. From the over-all pulse-transfer function, which is defined as the ratio of the z transform of the system output to that of the system input, the system-output transform is obtained. For the open-loop sampled-data system shown in Fig. 6.1-1, the relationship between the output and the input is given by

$$\frac{C(z)}{R(z)} = G(z) \tag{6.3-1}$$

and obviously the output transform of the system is

$$C(z) = G(z)R(z) \tag{6.3-2}$$

Referring to the closed-loop sampled-data system of Fig. 6.1-5, the output transform of the system as derived from the block diagram is

$$C(z) = \frac{G(z)}{1 + GH(z)} R(z) \tag{6.3-3}$$

Then, the inverse z transforms of Eqs. (6.3-2) and (6.3-3) yield the system response to a given input. However, it should be emphasized that the inverse z transformation gives correct values only at the sampling instants. The system response at the sampling instants is often referred to as the output sequence. The evaluation of system response to a step function input is illustrated by the following examples.

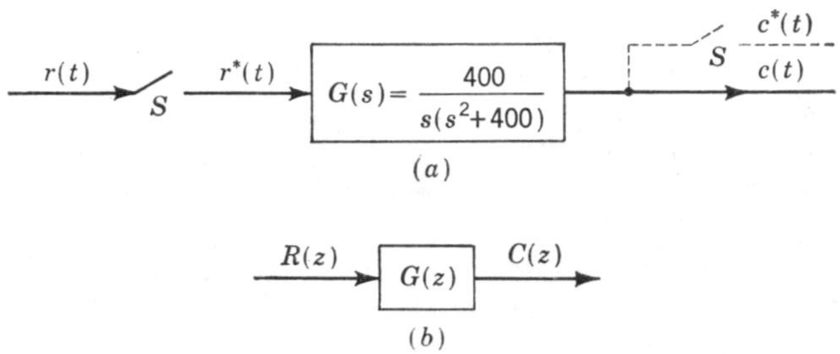

FIG. 6.3-1. (*a*) Block diagram of the open-loop sampled-data system of Example 6.3-1; (*b*) block diagram of Example 6.3-1 in terms of z transforms.

EXAMPLE 6.3-1. Consider a simple open-loop sampled-data system as shown in Fig. 6.3-1*a*. The transfer function of the system is

$$G(s) = \frac{400}{s(s^2 + 400)} \tag{6.3-4}$$

and the sampling period T is 0.1 sec. Determine the output sequence of the system in response to a unit step-function input.

In terms of the z transforms, the system can be represented by the block diagram of Fig. 6.3-1*b*. The over-all pulse-transfer function of the system is given by the z transform corresponding to Eq. (6.3-4):

$$G(z) = \frac{z(z + 1)(1 - \cos 20T)}{(z - 1)(z^2 - 2z \cos 20T + 1)} \tag{6.3-5}$$

For a unit step-function input,

$$r(t) = u(t) \qquad R(z) = \frac{z}{z - 1} \tag{6.3-6}$$

Then, Eq. (6.3-2) yields the output transform of the system as

$$C(z) = \frac{z^2(z + 1)(1 - \cos 20T)}{(z - 1)^2(z^2 - 2z \cos 20T + 1)} \tag{6.3-7}$$

By partial-fraction expansion, Eq. (6.3-7) is reduced to

$$C(z) = z\left[\frac{1}{(z-1)^2} + \frac{1}{2}\frac{1}{z-1} - \frac{1}{2}\frac{z+1}{z^2 - 2z\cos 20T + 1}\right] \qquad (6.3\text{-}8)$$

Furthermore, $C(z)$ can be put into the following form:

$$C(z) = \frac{z}{(z-1)^2} + \frac{1}{2}\frac{z}{z-1} - \frac{1}{2}\left(\frac{z^2 - z\cos 20T}{z^2 - 2z\cos 20T + 1}\right) - \frac{1}{2}\frac{1+\cos 20T}{\sin 20T}\left(\frac{z\sin 20T}{z^2 - 2z\cos 20T + 1}\right) \qquad (6.3\text{-}9)$$

The inverse z transforms of the terms on the right-hand side of Eq. (6.3-9) are available from the z-transform table of Sec. 5.2. The first term corresponds to a ramp function, the second term represents a step function, and the third and fourth terms are the z transforms of a cosine and a sine function, respectively. Thus, the inverse transform of Eq. (6.3-9) is

$$c_f(t) = \frac{t}{T} + \frac{1}{2} - \frac{1}{2}\cos 20t - \frac{1}{2}\frac{1+\cos 20T}{\sin 20T}\sin 20t \qquad (6.3\text{-}10)$$

Substituting 0.1 sec for T, the time function becomes

$$c_f(t) = 10t + 0.5 - 0.5\cos 20t - 0.321\sin 20t \qquad (6.3\text{-}11)$$

The values of $c_f(t)$ at several sampling instants are tabulated in Table 6.3-1.

TABLE 6.3-1

t	0	0.1	0.2	0.3	0.4	0.5	0.6	0.7
$c_f(t)$	0	1.415	3.07	3.12	4.25	6.13	6.31	7.21

and the curve of $c_f(t)$ is plotted in Fig. 6.3-2. It should be pointed out that $c_f(t)$ of Eq. (6.3-10) is not the only time function corresponding to the output transform $C(z)$. Several forms of the time function are obtainable from Eq. (6.3-7) through inverse transformation, yet all of them indicate correct output values only at the sampling instants. The complete time response can be determined by the modified z-transform method, which is discussed in the next section.

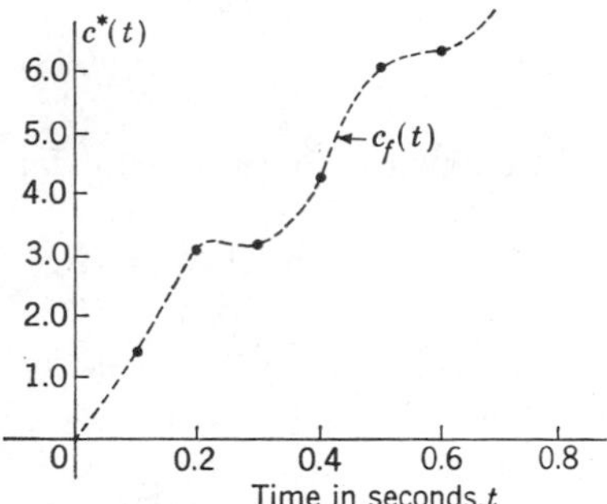

FIG. 6.3-2. System output of Example 6.3-1 computed from z transforms.

The above computations illustrate the evaluation of the system response by use of the z-transform table. In fact, the system response at sampling instants may be found in a much quicker way by the method of power series expansion. By this method, Eq. (6.3-7) is expanded into a series in z^{-1}:

For $T = 0.1$ sec,

$$C(z) = 1.415z^{-1} + 3.07z^{-2} + 3.12z^{-3} + 4.25z^{-4} + 6.13z^{-5} + 6.31z^{-6} + 7.21z^{-7} + \cdots \qquad (6.3\text{-}12)$$

As it has been explained in Chap. 5, the coefficients of the power series expansion of $C(z)$ represent the values of the corresponding time function $c(t)$ at the sampling instants. Then the system response at sampling instants may be written as

$$\begin{aligned} c^*(t) = 1.415\delta(t - T) &+ 3.07\delta(t - 2T) + 3.12\delta(t - 3T) \\ &+ 4.25\delta(t - 4T) + 6.13\delta(t - 5T) \\ &+ 6.31\delta(t - 6T) + 7.21\delta(t - 7T) + \cdots \end{aligned} \qquad (6.3\text{-}13)$$

This equation is obtained by taking the inverse z transform of Eq. (6.3-12) term by term. Table 6.3-1 and Fig. 6.3-2 indicate clearly that the output sequence of this system given by Eq. (6.3-13) matches perfectly the time function of Eq. (6.3-11) at the sampling instants.

EXAMPLE 6.3-2. Determine the response at the sampling instants of the sampled-data feedback control system of Fig. 6.3-3 to a unit step-

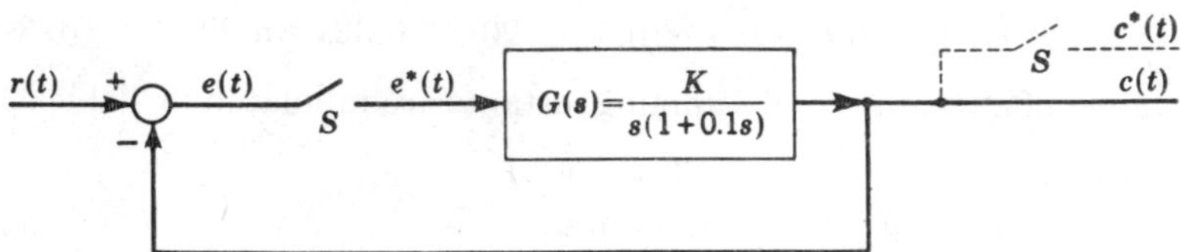

FIG. 6.3-3. Block diagram of the sampled-data control system of Example 6.3-2.

function input. The sampling period is 0.1 sec, and the transfer function of the controlled system is

$$G(s) = \frac{K}{s(1 + 0.1s)} \qquad (6.3\text{-}14)$$

The open-loop pulse-transfer function of the system is found to be

$$A(z) = G(z) = \frac{0.632Kz}{z^2 - 1.368z + 0.368} \qquad (6.3\text{-}15)$$

Since this is a unity-feedback system, the open-loop pulse-transfer function is given by the z transform of Eq. (6.3-14). The characteristic equation of this system is

$$F(z) = z^2 + (0.632K - 1.368)z + 0.368 = 0 \qquad (6.3\text{-}16)$$

It has been shown that when the value of gain constant K is increased to a certain value, a second-order sampled-data feedback control system would become unstable. This limiting value of the gain can readily be determined analytically from the Schur-Cohn criterion or from Eqs. (6.2-56). This control system is stable if the conditions of Eqs. (6.2-56) are fulfilled. The application of these conditions to Eq. (6.3-16) leads to

1. $$|F(0)| = 0.368 < 1 \tag{6.3-17a}$$

2. $$F(1) = 0.632K > 0 \tag{6.3-17b}$$

3. $$F(-1) = 2.736 - 0.632K > 0 \tag{6.3-17c}$$

The first two conditions are satisfied for any positive values of the gain constant. In order to fulfill the third condition, it is found that K should be less than 4.32. This limiting value of the gain constant may also be obtained from Fig. 6.2-11. When the gain of this system is raised to this value the system would become unstable.

The over-all pulse-transfer function of the system is given by

$$\frac{C(z)}{R(z)} = \frac{G(z)}{1 + A(z)} \tag{6.3-18}$$

With the system gain constant set at 2 and by proper substitution, Eq. (6.3-18) is reduced to

$$\frac{C(z)}{R(z)} = \frac{1.264z}{z^2 - 0.104z + 0.368} \tag{6.3-19}$$

For a unit step-function input, the output transform of the system is

$$C(z) = \frac{1.264z^2}{(z-1)(z^2 - 0.104z + 0.368)} \tag{6.3-20}$$

Then the system response may be obtained by taking the inverse z transform of the above equation. Thus, by partial-fraction expansion, Eq. (6.3-20) can be written as

$$C(z) = z\left[\frac{1}{z-1} - \frac{0.5 + j0.265}{z - (0.052 + j0.605)} - \frac{0.5 - j0.265}{z - (0.052 - j0.605)}\right] \tag{6.3-21}$$

To find the inverse z transform by use of the table, the second and third terms in the right-hand side of Eq. (6.3-21) are to be expressed in a form the inverse of which is available from the table.

Let $$\epsilon^{-(x+jy)T} = 0.052 - j0.605 \tag{6.3-22}$$

Then $$\epsilon^{-Tx}\cos(Ty) = 0.052 \qquad \epsilon^{-Tx}\sin(Ty) = 0.605 \tag{6.3-23}$$

Solving for Tx and Ty,

$$Tx = 0.5 \qquad Ty = 1.487 \tag{6.3-24}$$

Thus, $$z - (0.052 - j0.605) = z - \epsilon^{-0.1(5+j14.87)} \tag{6.3-25}$$

Similarly, $$z - (0.052 + j0.605) = z - \epsilon^{-0.1(5-j14.87)} \tag{6.3-26}$$

Substituting these two quantities in Eq. (6.3-21) yields an expression of the output transform, and the inverse of its terms is recognizable from the table:

$$C(z) = \frac{z}{z-1} - \frac{(0.5 + j0.265)z}{z - \epsilon^{-0.1(5-j14.87)}} - \frac{(0.5 - j0.265)z}{z - \epsilon^{-0.1(5+j14.87)}} \qquad (6.3\text{-}27)$$

By inspection of the z-transform table of Sec. 5.2, the time function corresponding to $C(z)$ is obtained:

$$c_f(t) = 1 - (0.5 + j0.265)\epsilon^{-(5-j14.87)t} - (0.5 - j0.265)\epsilon^{-(5+j14.87)t} \qquad (6.3\text{-}28a)$$

This equation may be simplified into

$$c_f(t) = 1 - \epsilon^{-5t}\,(\cos 14.87t - 0.53 \sin 14.87t) \qquad (6.3\text{-}28b)$$

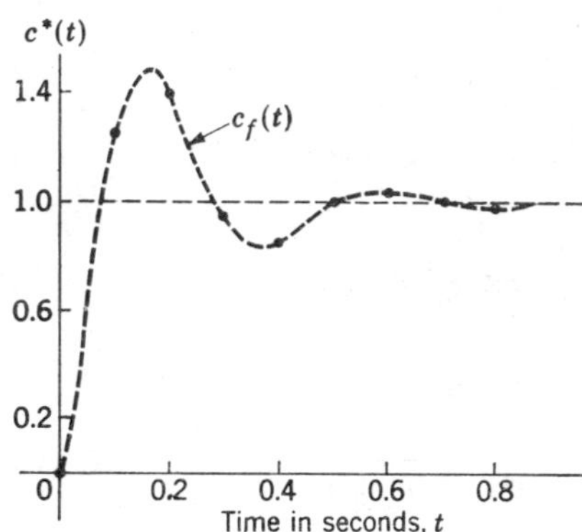

FIG. 6.3-4. System response of Example 6.3-2 computed from z transforms.

The time function $c_f(t)$ describes approximately the system response to a unit step-function input and is plotted in Fig. 6.3-4. Although calculations based upon the z transform yield correct values only at the sampling instants, for this particular case Eq. (6.3-28b) represents a very good approximation of the time response of the system. This is justified and discussed in Sec. 6.4.

Furthermore, the values of the system output at the sampling instants can quickly be determined from the power series expansion of the output transform. By long division, Eq. (6.3-20) is converted into a series:

$$\begin{aligned} C(z) = {} & 1.264z^{-1} + 1.396z^{-2} + 0.945z^{-3} + 0.851z^{-4} \\ & + 1.008z^{-5} + 1.05\ z^{-6} + 1.00\ z^{-7} \\ & + 0.976z^{-8} + \cdots \end{aligned} \qquad (6.3\text{-}29)$$

The coefficients of the above series represent the values of the system output at successive sampling instants. For instance, at $t = 0$, the output is zero, and at $t = T$, the output is 1.264. Taking the inverse z transform of Eq. (6.3-29) term by term yields

$$\begin{aligned} c^*(t) = {} & 1.264\delta(t - T) + 1.396\delta(t - 2T) + 0.945\delta(t - 3T) \\ & + 0.851\delta(t - 4T) + 1.008\delta(t - 5T) \\ & + 1.05\ \delta(t - 6T) + 1.00\ \delta(t - 7T) \\ & + 0.976\delta(t - 8T) + \cdots \end{aligned} \qquad (6.3\text{-}30)$$

This equation describes the output sequence of the system in response to a unit step-function input, i.e., the coefficients are values of $c(t)$ at the sampling instants $t = T, 2T, \ldots$.

In this section the evaluation of the output sequence of sampled-data systems in response to a specified input is discussed and illustrated by two numerical examples, an open-loop and a closed-loop sampled-data system. It is noted that the simplest method of evaluating the first several values of the output sequence is the method of power series expansion or long division. This is the method commonly used in practice. However, in some cases, such as Example 6.3-2, the approximate time response of the sampled-data control system can be derived by taking the inverse of the output transform with the aid of the z-transform table. This point is further discussed in the following section.

6.4. System Response during Intersampling Periods. In the evaluation of the time response of sampled-data systems by means of the z-transform method, the time function obtained through the inverse z transformation does not yield correct information between sampling instants. This is because the real inversion process is not unique. Different forms of time function $c(t)$ corresponding to an output transform $C(z)$ may be derived through inversion. All of these possible forms of the time function have identical values at the sampling instants, but generally they differ remarkably between these instants. As a result, $c(t)$ thus obtained fails to define the system output during intersampling periods. However, the time function $c(t)$ evaluated by this method would describe the true response of the system to a high degree of approximation, provided that the system were well behaved.

The complete transient response of a sampled-data system can be derived from its output transform through real inversion if the modified z-transform technique discussed in Sec. 5.7 is applied. To determine the time response by this technique, the first step is to obtain the output transform of the system in terms of the modified z transforms.[25,86,107] For the open-loop

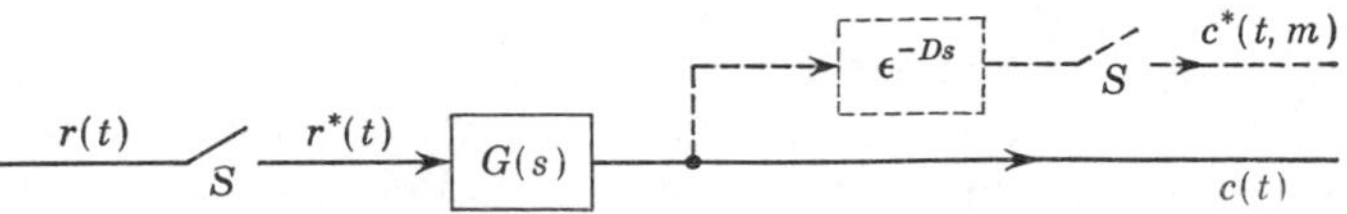

FIG. 6.4-1. Block diagram of an open-loop sampled-data system (with a variable delay introduced in the output stage).

sampled-data system of Fig. 6.4-1, the system output in terms of the modified z transforms is given by Eq. (6.1-7), and is repeated below

$$C(z,m) = G(z,m)R(z) \tag{6.4-1}$$

In the above equation, $G(z,m)$, defined as the modified pulse-transfer function of the system, is the modified z transform corresponding to $G(s)$; $R(z)$, the z transform of input $r(t)$; and $C(z,m)$, the modified z transform of output $c(t)$ or the z transform of $c^*(t,m)$.

Symbolically, $$C(z,m) = \mathfrak{Z}_m\{c(t)\} = \mathfrak{Z}\{c^*(t,m)\} \tag{6.4-2}$$

Closed-loop System. In reference to the sampled-data feedback control system of Fig. 6.4-2*a*, if a variable artificial delay of D sec were introduced in the forward path following $G(s)$ and a variable artificial advance of D sec were inserted in the feedback path, the signal in the forward path would be delayed by D sec, whereas the feedback signal would remain unchanged. D is a fraction of sampling period T such that

$$D = \lambda T, \qquad \lambda = 1 - m \tag{6.4-3}$$

and m is a parameter which may vary between 0 and 1. With these modifications in the system, the block diagram of Fig. 6.4-2*a* may be re-

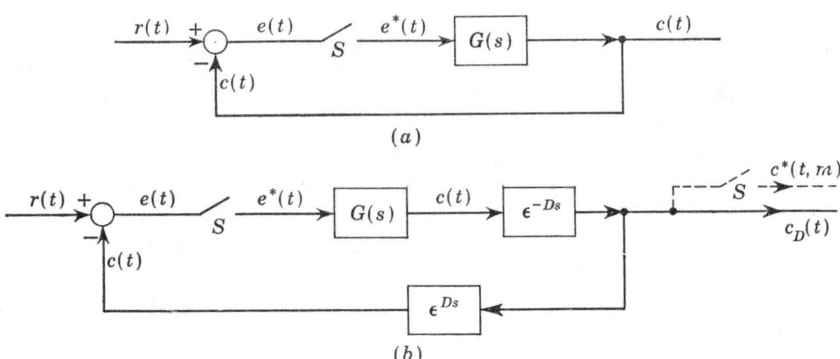

FIG. 6.4-2. (*a*) Block diagram of a basic sampled-data feedback control system; (*b*) block diagram of the basic system of (*a*) with a variable delay introduced in the forward branch and a variable advance in the feedback branch.

placed by that of Fig. 6.4-2*b*. In Fig. 6.4-2*b*, ϵ^{-Ds} and ϵ^{Ds} stand for the transfer functions of the delay and advance device, respectively. The behavior of the modified version of the system would be identical with that of the original form except that the sampled output $c_D^*[(k+1)T]$ of Fig. 6.4-2*b* at any instant $t = (k+1)T$ would correspond to the value of the output $c(t)$ at instant $t = kT + mT$. In other words, to compute the output function $c(t)$ from the block diagram of Fig. 6.4-2*b* the reference time should be shifted.

Inspection of the block diagram of Fig. 6.4-2*b* reveals that

$$C(s) = G(s)E^*(s) \tag{6.4-4}$$

$$\epsilon^{-Ds}C(s) = \epsilon^{-Ds}G(s)E^*(s) \tag{6.4-5}$$

Replacing $\epsilon^{-Ds}C(s)$ by $C_D(s)$ and $\epsilon^{-Ds}G(s)$ by $G_D(s)$, Eq. (6.4-5) becomes

$$C_D(s) = G_D(s)E^*(s) \tag{6.4-6}$$

The z transform of Eq. (6.4-6) is

$$C_D(z) = G_D(z)E(z) \tag{6.4-7}$$

Making use of the definition of the modified z transform given in Sec. 5.7, Eq. (6.4-7) may be written as

$$C(z,m) = G(z,m)E(z) \tag{6.4-8}$$

Since from Fig. 6.4-2*b*,

$$E(s) = R(s) - C(s) = R(s) - G(s)E^*(s) \tag{6.4-9}$$

the corresponding z transform is

$$E(z) = R(z) - C(z) = R(z) - G(z)E(z) \tag{6.4-10}$$

Then the modified z transform of the system output is obtained by eliminating $E(z)$ between Eqs. (6.4-8) and (6.4-10):

$$C(z,m) = \frac{G(z,m)}{1 + G(z)} R(z) \tag{6.4-11}$$

In fact, by applying the simplified procedures stated in Sec. 6.1, Eq. (6.4-11) follows immediately from the Laplace transform of the system output of the original block diagram shown in Fig. 6.4-2, which is given by

$$C(s) = \frac{G(s)}{1 + G^*(s)} R^*(s) \tag{6.4-12}$$

In the above discussions of the closed-loop systems, it is noted that the analysis is essentially based upon the conversion of the closed-loop system to an equivalent open-loop system, the output response of which is then calculated. Examination of Fig. 6.4-2 reveals that

$$E^*(s) = \frac{1}{1 + G^*(s)} R^*(s) \tag{6.4-13}$$

$$E(z) = \frac{1}{1 + G(z)} R(z) \tag{6.4-14}$$

The block diagram of the closed-loop system can be reduced to the open-loop structure as shown in Fig. 6.4-3, from which the Laplace transform

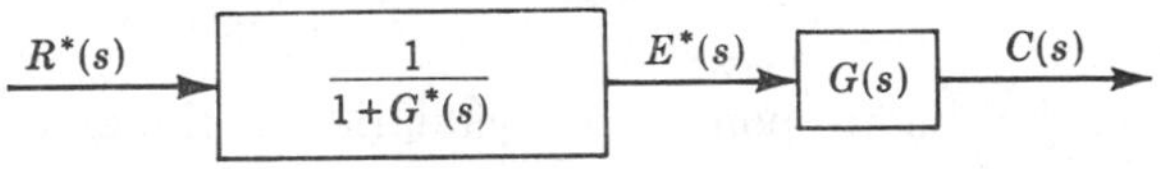

Fig. 6.4-3. Equivalent block-diagram representation of the system of Fig. 6.4-2(*a*).

of the system output given in Eq. (6.4-12) can be written by inspection. In fairly complicated sampled-data feedback control systems, the problem of evaluating the intersample response can generally be worked out in two steps: (1) convert the closed-loop system into an open-loop structure, and

(2) determine the intersample response of the equivalent open-loop system.

The value of the system output at any instant $(nT - T + mT)$ is given by the inverse transform of Eq. (6.4-11), that is,

$$c(nT,m) = \frac{1}{2\pi j} \oint_{\Gamma} \frac{G(z,m)}{1 + G(z)} R(z) z^{n-1}\, dz \tag{6.4-15}$$

where m is a parameter lying between 0 and 1. Consequently, by varying m from 0 to 1, $c(nT,m)$ of Eq. (6.4-15) describes the complete time response of the sampled-data feedback control system which is subjected to an arbitrary input $r(t)$. The response curve between sampling instants 0 and T is obtained from $c(T,m)$ and, in general, the response during the kth intersampling period is given by $c(kT,m)$.

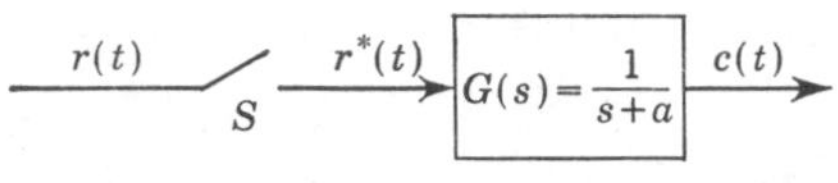

A few illustrative examples are given below.

FIG. 6.4-4. Block diagram of the system of Example 6.4-1.

EXAMPLE 6.4-1. Find the time response of the open-loop sampled-data system of Fig. 6.4-4 to a unit step-function input.

Referring to the block diagram of Fig. 6.4-4, the over-all pulse-transfer function of the system is found to be

$$G(z) = \frac{z}{z - \epsilon^{-aT}} \tag{6.4-16}$$

and the corresponding modified pulse-transfer function is

$$G(z,m) = \frac{\epsilon^{-amT}}{z - \epsilon^{-aT}} \tag{6.4-17}$$

where T denotes the sampling period of the system. For a unit step-function input, the z transform of the system output is

$$C(z) = G(z)R(z) = \frac{z^2}{(z - 1)(z - \epsilon^{-aT})} \tag{6.4-18}$$

and its modified z transform is

$$C(z,m) = G(z,m)R(z) = \frac{z\epsilon^{-amT}}{(z - 1)(z - \epsilon^{-aT})} \tag{6.4-19}$$

In determining the time response, the evaluation of the inverse transform of Eq. (6.4-19) is required:

$$c(nT,m) = \frac{1}{2\pi j} \oint_{\Gamma} \frac{z\epsilon^{-amT}}{(z - 1)(z - \epsilon^{-aT})} z^{n-1}\, dz \tag{6.4-20}$$

Applying Cauchy's residue theorem yields

$$c(nT,m) = \sum \text{residues of } \frac{z^n \epsilon^{-amT}}{(z-1)(z-\epsilon^{-aT})} \qquad \text{at } z = 1 \text{ and } z = \epsilon^{-aT}$$

$$= \frac{\epsilon^{-amT}}{1-\epsilon^{-aT}} + \frac{\epsilon^{-amT}\epsilon^{-anT}}{\epsilon^{-aT}-1} \tag{6.4-21}$$

Simplifying,

$$c(nT,m) = \frac{(1-\epsilon^{-anT})\epsilon^{-amT}}{1-\epsilon^{-aT}} \qquad 0 \le m < 1 \tag{6.4-22}$$

By assigning various values to m within the limits 0 and 1, Eq. (6.4-22) would describe the required time response of the system. Under steady-state condition, the system response is given by

$$c_{ss} = \lim_{n\to\infty} c(nT,m) = \frac{\epsilon^{-amT}}{1-\epsilon^{-aT}} \tag{6.4-23}$$

which determines the ripples in the system output.

Partial-fraction expansion reduces Eq. (6.4-18) to

$$C(z) = \frac{1}{1-\epsilon^{-aT}}\left(\frac{z}{z-1} - \frac{\epsilon^{-aT}z}{z-\epsilon^{-aT}}\right) \tag{6.4-24}$$

The time function corresponding to Eq. (6.4-24) can easily be derived by inspection of the z-transform table:

$$c_f(t) = \frac{1}{1-\epsilon^{-aT}}(1-\epsilon^{-aT}\epsilon^{-at}) \tag{6.4-25}$$

As t approaches infinity, $c_f(t)$ becomes

$$c_{ss} = \lim_{t\to\infty} c_f(t) = \frac{1}{1-\epsilon^{-aT}} \tag{6.4-26}$$

This is the final value which the system output at the sampling instants would reach.

Assuming that $a = 5$ and $T = 0.1$ sec, the curves of $c(nT,m)$ and $c_f(t)$ are plotted in Fig. 6.4-5. It is noted that although the plot of $c_f(t)$ matches that of $c(nT,m)$ at the sampling instants, they differ appreciably between these instants. The function $c(nT,m)$ describes the true time response of the system, whereas the function $c_f(t)$ represents a false response which yields correct information about the system output only at the sampling instants. It should be pointed out that Eq. (6.4-22) does not hold for m equal to unity, because the system response is not continuous at the sampling instants as indicated by the curve of Fig. 6.4-5.

Indeed, the above example is quite simple. Because of the simplicity of this example, the results for intersample response can be written by inspection. Nevertheless, this example illustrates clearly the evaluation of the response of an open-loop sampled-data system during the intersampling periods by use of the modified z-transform technique. In this system, it is noted that the time function derived from the z transform of the system output through inverse transformation is inadequate.

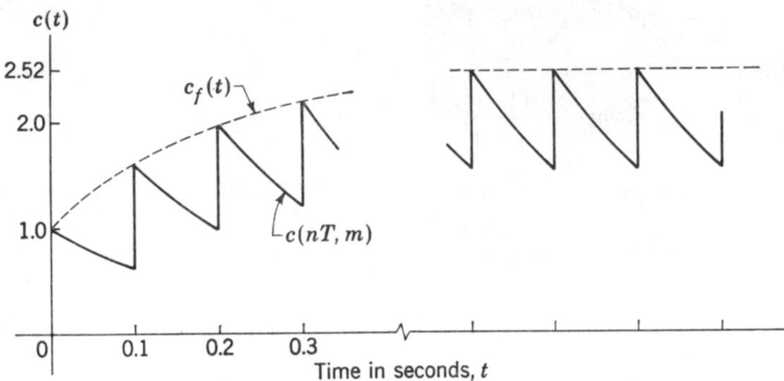

FIG. 6.4-5. System response of Example 6.4-1 computed from modified z transforms.

EXAMPLE 6.4-2. Determine the complete time response of the system of Fig. 6.3-1a to a unit step-function input.

The transfer function of the system is

$$G(s) = \frac{400}{s(s^2 + 400)} = \frac{1}{s} - \frac{1}{2}\left(\frac{1}{s + j20} + \frac{1}{s - j20}\right) \tag{6.4-27}$$

The modified z transform corresponding to the above equation is found to be

$$G(z,m) = \frac{1}{z - 1} - \frac{1}{2}\left(\frac{\epsilon^{-j20mT}}{z - \epsilon^{-j20T}} + \frac{\epsilon^{j20mT}}{z - \epsilon^{j20T}}\right) \tag{6.4-28}$$

For a unit step-function input, the output transform is given by

$$C(z,m) = \frac{z}{(z - 1)^2} - \frac{z}{2(z - 1)}\left(\frac{\epsilon^{-j20mT}}{z - \epsilon^{-j20T}} + \frac{\epsilon^{j20mT}}{z - \epsilon^{j20T}}\right) \tag{6.4-29a}$$

or

$$C(z,m) = \frac{z}{(z - 1)^2} - \frac{z^2 \cos 20mT - z \cos 20(1 - m)T}{(z - 1)(z^2 - 2z \cos 20T + 1)} \tag{6.4-29b}$$

Taking the inverse transform of Eq. (6.4-29a),

$$c(nT,m) = \frac{1}{2\pi j} \oint_\Gamma C(z,m)z^{n-1}\, dz$$

$$= \sum \text{residues of } C(z,m)z^{n-1} \tag{6.4-30}$$

The residue of $C(z,m)z^{n-1}$ at $z = 1$ is

$$n - \frac{1}{2}\left(\frac{\epsilon^{-j20mT}}{1 - \epsilon^{-j20T}} + \frac{\epsilon^{j20mT}}{1 - \epsilon^{j20T}}\right) \tag{6.4-31}$$

which may be reduced to

$$n - \frac{1}{2}\left(\cos 20mT - \frac{\sin 20T}{1 - \cos 20T} \sin 20mT\right) \qquad (6.4\text{-}32)$$

The sum of residues of $C(z,m)z^{n-1}$ at $z = \epsilon^{\pm j20T}$ is

$$\frac{1}{2}\left(\frac{\epsilon^{j20(m+n)T}}{1 - \epsilon^{j20T}} + \frac{\epsilon^{-j20(m+n)T}}{1 - \epsilon^{-j20T}}\right) \qquad (6.4\text{-}33)$$

which can be written as

$$\frac{1}{2}\left[\cos 20(m-n)T - \frac{\sin 20T}{1 - \cos 20T} \sin 20(m+n)T\right] \qquad (6.4\text{-}34)$$

Therefore, the inverse transform is given by

$$c(nT,m) = n - \frac{1}{2}[\cos 20mT - \cos 20(m+n)T]$$
$$+ \frac{1}{2}\frac{\sin 20T}{1 - \cos 20T}[\sin 20mT - \sin 20(m+n)T] \qquad (6.4\text{-}35)$$

This equation describes the response of the system subjected to a unit step-function input. With a sampling period T equal to 0.1 sec,

$$c(nT,m) = n - \frac{1}{2}[\cos 2m - \cos 2(m+n)]$$
$$+ 0.321 [\sin 2m - \sin 2(m+n)] \qquad (6.4\text{-}36)$$

The curves of Eqs. (6.4-36) and (6.3-11) are sketched in Fig. 6.4-6, showing

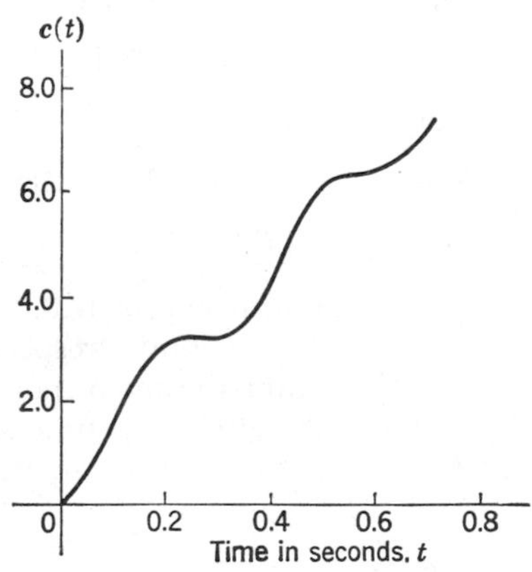

FIG. 6.4-6. System response of Example 6.4-2 computed from modified z transforms.

that the false response given by Eq. (6.3-11) differs slightly from the true response of Eq. (6.4-36) during the intersampling periods.

The functions describing the system response may also be derived from Eq. (6.4-29*b*) by power series expansion. With $T = 0.1$ sec, Eq. (6.4-29*b*) reduces to

$$C(z,m) = \frac{z}{(z-1)^2} - \frac{z^2 \cos 2m - z \cos 2(1-m)}{(z-1)(z^2 + 0.832z + 1)} \tag{6.4-37}$$

When $C(z,m)$ is expanded into a power series in z^{-1}, the coefficient of the z^{-1} term of the series is the value of the system response at the instant $t = mT$ and, in general, the coefficient of the $z^{-(k+1)}$ term is the value at $t = (k + m)T$. Consequently, by varying the value of parameter m from 0 to 1, the coefficients of the power series would trace out the system response.

To illustrate the determination of the system response by this method, sample computations are carried out in the following:

For $m = 1$, the power series of $C(z,m)$ is given by

$$C(z,1) = 1.415z^{-1} + 3.07z^{-2} + 3.12z^{-3} + 4.25z^{-4} + 6.13z^{-5} + \cdots \tag{6.4-38}$$

and the corresponding time function is

$$c^*(t,1) = 1.415\delta(t - T) + 3.07\delta(t - 2T) + 3.12\delta(t - 3T) + 4.25\delta(t - 4T) + 6.13\delta(t - 5T) + \cdots \tag{6.4-39}$$

It is noted that Eq. (6.4-39) is identical with Eq. (6.3-13), which describes the system reponse at the sampling instants. Similarly, for $m = 0.75$, 0.50, and 0.25,

$$c^*(t,0.75) = 0.93\delta(t - T) + 2.87\delta(t - 2T) + 3.16\delta(t - 3T) + 3.81\delta(t - 4T) + 5.81\delta(t - 5T) + \cdots \tag{6.4-40}$$

$$c^*(t,0.50) = 0.46\delta(t - T) + 2.45\delta(t - 2T) + 3.17\delta(t - 3T) + 3.42\delta(t - 4T) + 5.32\delta(t - 5T) + \cdots \tag{6.4-41}$$

$$c^*(t,0.25) = 0.123\delta(t - T) + 1.92\delta(t - 2T) + 3.13\delta(t - 3T) + 3.16\delta(t - 4T) + 4.76\delta(t - 5T) + \cdots \tag{6.4-42}$$

These equations determine the system response at 0.075 sec, 0.05 sec, and 0.025 sec from the successive sampling instants, respectively.

EXAMPLE 6.4-3. Compute the complete time response of the closed-loop system of Fig. 6.3-3 when it is subjected to a unit step-function input.

With the gain constant K set at 2, the transfer function of the controlled system is

$$G(s) = \frac{2}{s(1 + 0.1s)} \tag{6.4-43}$$

The corresponding modified z transform is found to be

$$G(z,m) = \frac{2(1 - \epsilon^{-m})z + (2\epsilon^{-m} - 0.736)}{z^2 - 1.368z + 0.368} \tag{6.4-44}$$

Substituting Eqs. (6.3-15) and (6.4-44) into Eq. (6.4-11) yields the output transform of the system as

$$C(z,m) = \frac{[2(1 - \epsilon^{-m})z + (2\epsilon^{-m} - 0.736)]\,R(z)}{z^2 - 0.104z + 0.368} \qquad (6.4\text{-}45)$$

For a unit step-function input, Eq. (6.4-45) becomes

$$C(z,m) = \frac{z[2(1 - \epsilon^{-m})z + (2\epsilon^{-m} - 0.736)]}{(z - 1)(z^2 - 0.104z + 0.368)} \qquad (6.4\text{-}46)$$

Expanding the above equation into a power series in z^{-1},

$$\begin{aligned} C(z,m) = (2 - 2\epsilon^{-m})z^{-1} &+ (1.472 - 0.208\epsilon^{-m})z^{-2} + (0.683 + 0.712\epsilon^{-m})z^{-3} \\ &+ (0.796 + 0.15\epsilon^{-m})z^{-4} + (1.1 - 0.248\epsilon^{-m})z^{-5} \\ &+ (1.07 - 0.062\epsilon^{-m})z^{-6} + \cdots \qquad (6.4\text{-}47) \end{aligned}$$

Then the time response of the system is given by the inverse transform of Eq. (6.4-47):

$$\begin{aligned} c^*(t,m) = {} & (2 - 2\epsilon^{-m})\delta(t - T) + (1.472 - 0.208\epsilon^{-m})\delta(t - 2T) \\ & + (0.683 + 0.712\epsilon^{-m})\delta(t - 3T) + (0.796 + 0.15\epsilon^{-m})\delta(t - 4T) \\ & + (1.1 - 0.248\epsilon^{-m})\delta(t - 5T) + (1.07 - 0.062\epsilon^{-m})\delta(t - 6T) + \cdots \end{aligned} \qquad (6.4\text{-}48)$$

For $m = 1$,

$$\begin{aligned} c^*(t,1) = c^*(t) = 1.264\delta(t - T) &+ 1.396\delta(t - 2T) + 0.945\delta(t - 3T) \\ &+ 0.851\delta(t - 4T) + 1.008\delta(t - 5T) \\ &+ 1.05\ \delta(t - 6T) + \cdots \qquad (6.4\text{-}49) \end{aligned}$$

which is identical with Eq. (6.3-30).

For $m = 0.75$,

$$\begin{aligned} c^*(t,0.75) = 1.056\delta(t - T) &+ 1.372\delta(t - 2T) + 1.019\delta(t - 3T) \\ &+ 0.867\delta(t - 4T) + 0.983\delta(t - 5T) \\ &+ 1.04\ \delta(t - 6T) + \cdots \qquad (6.4\text{-}50) \end{aligned}$$

For $m = 0.50$,

$$\begin{aligned} c^*(t,0.50) = 0.786\delta(t - T) &+ 1.346\delta(t - 2T) + 1.115\delta(t - 3T) \\ &+ 0.887\delta(t - 4T) + 0.949\delta(t - 5T) \\ &+ 1.034\delta(t - 6T) + \cdots \qquad (6.4\text{-}51) \end{aligned}$$

For $m = 0.25$,

$$\begin{aligned} c^*(t,0.25) = 0.442\delta(t - T) &+ 1.310\delta(t - 2T) + 1.238\delta(t - 3T) \\ &+ 0.913\delta(t - 4T) + 0.907\delta(t - 5T) \\ &+ 1.022\delta(t - 6T) + \cdots \qquad (6.4\text{-}52) \end{aligned}$$

From the plottings of Eqs. (6.4-48) and (6.3-28) shown in Fig. 6.4-7, little difference between $c^*(t,m)$ and $c_f(t)$ is noticeable. Consequently, the time function $c_f(t)$ given by Eq. (6.3-28) may be used to represent the step-function response of the system within reasonable accuracy.

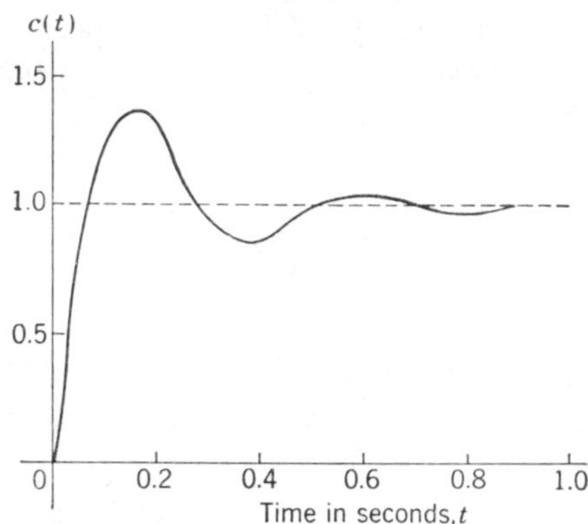

Fig. 6.4-7. System response of Example 6.4-3 computed from modified z transforms.

This section presents a discussion of the evaluation of intersample response of sampled-data control systems by means of the modified z-transform technique. The discussions of this section and the previous one point out that while the analysis based upon the z transforms generally fails to yield complete information, the use of the modified z transforms can provide all pertinent data. However, in some cases the z-transform analysis of system response can lead to an approximate solution. The uncertainty of the z-transform method is indicated by the value of the sampling frequency, the smoothing effect of $G(s)$, and the magnitudes of the imaginary parts of the complex poles of $G(s)$.

In the first example, because the system $G(s)$ is not a very effective low-pass filter, the time response calculated from the z transform of the system output is inadequate. However, if a zero-order hold is inserted between the sampler and the system $G(s)$, the time response resulting from the z-transform analysis would describe the actual output of the sampled-data system in response to a unit step-function input. With a zero-order hold, the Laplace transform of the system output is then given by

$$C(s) = \frac{1 - \epsilon^{-Ts}}{s} \frac{1}{s + a} R^*(s) \tag{6.4-53}$$

where $R^*(s)$ is the starred transform associated with $R(s) = 1/s$. The corresponding z transform is

$$C(z) = \frac{(1 - \epsilon^{-aT})z}{a(z - 1)(z - \epsilon^{-aT})} \tag{6.4-54}$$

Inspection of the table of z transforms yields the corresponding time function as

$$c_f(t) = 1 - \epsilon^{-at} \tag{6.4-55}$$

The above equation describes the actual step-function response of the sampled-data system with a zero-order hold. This is substantiated by the fact that the zero-order hold converts the pulsed step function into a continuous step function and Eq. (6.4-55) is the step-function response of the system $G(s) = 1/(s + a)$.

From the second example, it is seen that when the system $G(s)$ is a good low-pass filter and the imaginary parts of the poles of $G(s)$ are much smaller than the sampling frequency, the z-transform method may be used to calculate an approximate time response. The third example illustrates the case that when the sampling frequency is very high and $G(s)$ is an effective low-pass filter, the time response resulting from the z-transform analysis represents a very good approximation of the actual system response.

6.5. Steady-state Error at the Sampling Instants. Up to this point, the analysis of system stability and the evaluation of system response have been discussed. In addition to stability requirements other factors, which are important in determining the performance of a sampled-data or digital control system, include the effectiveness of the control system in processing information and its ability to alleviate external disturbances. The competence of a control system to keep the system error to a minimum is measured by its accuracy. Accuracy is one of the major items in judging a control system. The higher the accuracy of the system, the lower the system error necessary to obtain the desired output signal.

In the analysis of continuous-data feedback control systems, the performance of a given system to a certain input is often characterized by system parameters which are commonly known as the *error coefficients* or error constants. To obtain an approximate picture of the response characteristics of a feedback control system, the designer often specifies that the system should have a fast transient response and suitable error coefficients or error constants. The most common error constants are the position-, velocity-, and acceleration-error constants, which are measures of the steady-state errors if the input is a unit step function, a unit ramp function, and a unit parabolic function, respectively. The concept of error constants may be carried over to the analysis of sampled-data and digital control systems.[86] The definitions and interpretations of these basic error constants of sampled-data systems are discussed in this section.

The steady-state error of a sampled-data feedback control system which is subjected to an input $r(t)$ can be evaluated by making use of the final-value theorem described in Sec. 5.3. Referring to the unity-feedback system shown in Fig. 6.5-1, the system error and the system input are related by

$$\varepsilon(z) = R(z) - C(z) = \frac{R(z)}{1 + G(z)} \tag{6.5-1}$$

It is assumed that $\varepsilon(z)$ possesses no pole outside or on the unit circle of the z plane. By applying the final-value theorem, the steady-state error results as

$$\varepsilon_{ss} = \lim_{t\to\infty} \varepsilon(t) = \lim_{z\to 1} \frac{(z-1)R(z)}{z[1+G(z)]} \tag{6.5-2}$$

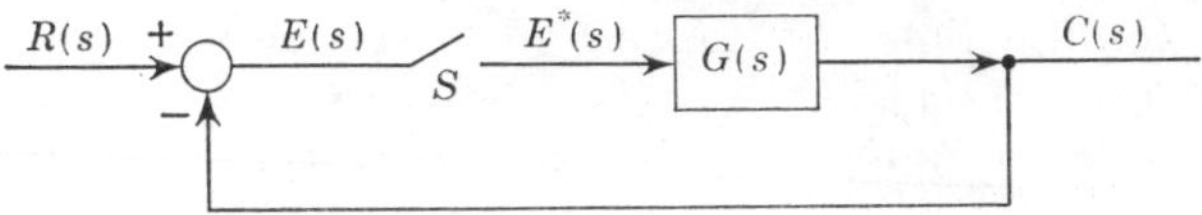

FIG. 6.5-1. Block diagram of a basic sampled-data unity-feedback control system.

Equation (6.5-2) yields the error at sampling instants only. The discussion of the system error between sampling instants and the intersampling ripples in the output is covered in the following chapter. The steady-state errors at the sampling instants of the system of Fig. 6.5-1 resulting from the application of three basic aperiodic inputs are evaluated as follows:

When the system is subjected to a unit step-function input,

$$R(z) = \frac{z}{(z-1)} \tag{6.5-3}$$

the steady-state error at sampling instants is given by

$$\varepsilon_{ss} = \lim_{z\to 1} \frac{1}{1+G(z)} = \frac{1}{1+G(1)} = \frac{1}{K_p} \tag{6.5-4}$$

which is referred to as the *position error* of the system. If the system is well behaved and does not contain objectionable intersampling ripples in the output, the value given by Eq. (6.5-4) is a good approximation of the steady-state error of the system. In Eq. (6.5-4), the constant K_p, defined as the reciprocal of the steady-state error of the system subjected to a unit step-function input, is referred to as the *position-error constant.* It follows from Eq. (6.5-4) that the position-error constant can be determined from the pulse-transfer function $G(z)$. That is,

$$K_p = \lim_{z\to 1} \{1 + G(z)\} \tag{6.5-5}$$

Inspection of Eq. (6.5-4) further reveals that the position error of the system would be zero, if $\lim_{z\to 1} G(z)$ is not finite, that is, if $G(z)$ contains a pole at $z = 1$.

For a unit ramp-function input (constant-velocity input),

$$r(t) = t \qquad R(z) = \frac{Tz}{(z-1)^2} \tag{6.5-6}$$

The sampled-data system would have a steady-state error given by

$$\varepsilon_{ss} = \lim_{z\to 1} \frac{T}{(z - 1)[1 + G(z)]}$$

$$= \frac{T}{\lim\limits_{z\to 1} \{(z - 1)G(z)\}} \tag{6.5-7}$$

which is called the *velocity error* of the system. This equation makes evident that the velocity error would be infinite if $\lim\limits_{z\to 1} G(z)$ were finite.

If a parabolic input (constant-acceleration input) $r(t) = \frac{1}{2}t^2$ is applied to this sampled-data control system, then from the table of z transforms in Sec. 5.2 the z transform of the input is

$$R(z) = \frac{T^2}{2} \frac{z(z + 1)}{(z - 1)^3} \tag{6.5-8}$$

and the steady-state error is given by

$$\varepsilon_{ss} = \frac{T^2}{2} \lim_{z\to 1} \frac{z + 1}{(z - 1)^2[1 + G(z)]}$$

$$= \frac{T^2}{\lim\limits_{z\to 1} \{(z - 1)^2 G(z)\}} \tag{6.5-9}$$

which is referred to as the *acceleration error* of the sampled-data system. It is easily seen from the above equation that if $\lim\limits_{z\to 1} G(z)$ were finite, the acceleration error would be infinite.

The above discussions for these three particular forms of input $r(t)$ indicate that the steady-state error of the sampled-data feedback control system depends upon the location of the poles of the pulse-transfer function $G(z)$. With the presence of poles of $G(z)$ at $z = 1$ the steady-state error could be made finite, which would be infinite otherwise.

Continuous-data feedback control systems are often classified in various types according to the number of poles of the open-loop transfer function of the system at the origin of the s plane. Thus, if the open-loop transfer function of a system is written in the standard form

$$G(s) = \frac{P(s)}{s^n Q(s)} \tag{6.5-10}$$

in which both $P(s)$ and $Q(s)$ do not contain s as a factor, then the value of the index n in the above equation is equal numerically to the type of the control system. For instance, when the index n is zero, the system is called a *type* 0 system; and when the index n is one, it is classified as a *type* 1 system. In like manner, sampled-data feedback control systems may be classified according to the number of poles at $z = 1$ contained in $G(z)$.

For example, a system with $G(z)$ possessing no pole at $z = 1$ may be called a *type* 0 sampled-data system, whereas a system with $G(z)$ containing a pole at $z = 1$ may be classified as a *type* 1 sampled-data system.

In reference to the sampled-data system of Fig. 6.5-1:

1. If the pulse-transfer function $G(z)$ possesses *no* pole at $z = 1$, $\lim_{z \to 1} G(z)$ is finite and is equal to $G(1)$. This corresponds to a type 0 sampled-data system. Examination of Eqs. (6.5-4), (6.5-7), and (6.5-9) reveals that

$$\text{Position error} = \frac{1}{1 + G(1)} \tag{6.5-11}$$

$$\text{Velocity error} = \infty \tag{6.5-12}$$

$$\text{Acceleration error} = \infty \tag{6.5-13}$$

2. If the pulse-transfer function $G(z)$ possesses only *one* pole at $z = 1$, this system is classified as type 1. Assuming

$$G(z) = \frac{G_1(z)}{z - 1} \tag{6.5-14}$$

where $G_1(z)$ does not contain $z - 1$ as a factor, it is seen that $\lim_{z \to 1} G(z)$ is infinite and $\lim_{z \to 1} G_1(z)$ is equal to $G_1(1)$, which is finite. From Eqs. (6.5-4), (6.5-7), and (6.5-9), the steady-state errors are obtained:

$$\text{Position error} = 0 \tag{6.5-15}$$

$$\text{Velocity error} = \frac{T}{G_1(1)} = \frac{T}{K_v} \tag{6.5-16}$$

$$\text{Acceleration error} = \infty \tag{6.5-17}$$

In Eq. (6.5-16), the constant K_v, defined as the ratio of the sampling period to the steady-state error of the system subjected to a unit velocity input, is referred to as the *velocity-error constant*. It is seen from Eq. (6.5-16) that the velocity-error constant can be computed from the pulse-transfer function $G(z)$ as follows:

$$K_v = \lim_{z \to 1} G_1(z) = \lim_{z \to 1} \{(z - 1)G(z)\} \tag{6.5-18}$$

3. If $G(z)$ contains *two* poles at $z = 1$, this system is of type 2. By letting

$$G(z) = \frac{G_1(z)}{z - 1} = \frac{G_2(z)}{(z - 1)^2} \tag{6.5-19}$$

it is noted that both $\lim_{z \to 1} G(z)$ and $\lim_{z \to 1} G_1(z)$ are infinite, but $\lim_{z \to 1} G_2(z)$ is equal to $G_2(1)$. Substitution of these values into Eqs. (6.5-4), (6.5-7), and

(6.5-9) yields the steady-state errors as

$$\text{Position error} = 0 \tag{6.5-20}$$

$$\text{Velocity error} = 0 \tag{6.5-21}$$

$$\text{Acceleration error} = \frac{T^2}{G_2(1)} = \frac{T^2}{K_a} \tag{6.5-22}$$

In Eq. (6.5-22), the constant K_a, defined as the ratio of the square of the sampling period to the steady-state error of the system subjected to a parabolic input, is referred to as the *acceleration-error constant.* Equation (6.5-22) makes evident that the acceleration-error constant can be evaluated from the pulse-transfer function $G(z)$. That is,

$$K_a = \lim_{z \to 1} G_2(z) = \lim_{z \to 1} \{(z-1)^2 G(z)\} \tag{6.5-23}$$

4. If $G(z)$ has *three* poles at $z = 1$, this describes a type 3 sampled-data system. As z approaches unity, the limits of $G(z)$, $G_1(z)$, and $G_2(z)$ become infinite. Thus, the three steady-state errors are all zero.

In summary, the results of the above discussions are tabulated in Table 6.5-1 to provide a comparison of the steady-state errors of the four *types* of sampled-data control systems.

TABLE 6.5-1

Type	Position error	Velocity error	Acceleration error
0	$\frac{1}{K_p}$	∞	∞
1	0	$\frac{T}{K_v}$	∞
2	0	0	$\frac{T^2}{K_a}$
3	0	0	0

In the above table, K_p, K_v, and K_a are the position-, velocity-, and acceleration-error constants, which are given in Eqs. (6.5-5), (6.5-18), and (6.5-23), respectively.

6.6. Error Coefficients. The discussions in the preceding section lead to the definitions of certain system parameters commonly known as the error coefficients or error constants, which characterize the performance of a sampled-data control system subjected to some specified input. The primary disadvantage of the above definitions lies in the limited amount of information available from the specification of the error constants, since only one constant is significant. However, the concept of error coefficients can be considerably generalized. Such a generalization provides a simple and useful way of considering the nature of the response of a control system to almost any arbitrary input. This section is concerned with the generalization of the concept of error coefficients for sampled-data and digital control systems.

The error coefficients have the same meaning for a sampled-data or digital feedback control system as they do for a continuous-data feedback control system.[2] In continuous-data systems the generalized error coefficients are defined in terms of the low-frequency behavior of the system-error transfer function $W_e(s) = E(s)/R(s)$. In like manner, for sampled-data systems the error coefficients can be evaluated from the system-error pulse-transfer function $W_e(z) = E(z)/R(z)$. To facilitate the transfer of the concept of error coefficients to sampled-data systems, a brief review of the characterization of a continuous-data control system by error coefficients is given in the following paragraphs.

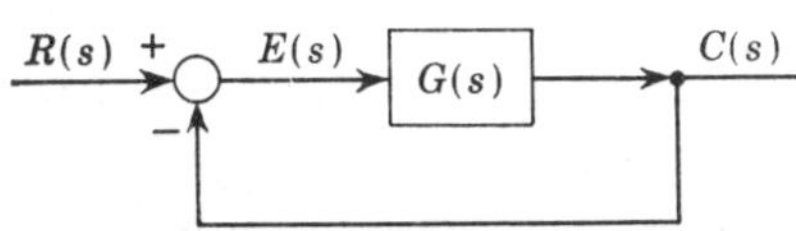

FIG. 6.6-1. Block diagram of a basic continuous-data feedback control system.

Shown in Fig. 6.6-1 is a basic feedback control system in which $G(s)$ is the transfer function of the controlled system, and $R(s)$, $E(s)$, and $C(s)$ denote the Laplace transform of the system input, the actuating signal, and the system output, respectively. The Laplace transform of the system error $E(s)$, which is defined as

$$E(s) = R(s) - C(s) \tag{6.6-1}$$

and that of the system input $R(s)$ are related by

$$\frac{E(s)}{R(s)} = \frac{1}{1 + G(s)} = W_e(s), \text{ say} \tag{6.6-2}$$

or

$$E(s) = W_e(s)R(s) \tag{6.6-3}$$

where $W_e(s)$, the ratio of the Laplace transform of the system error to the Laplace transform of the system input, may be referred to as the system-error transfer function. Then, from the theorem of real convolution, that part of the system error due to the input $r(t)$ is

$$\varepsilon(t) = \int_0^t w_e(\tau)r(t - \tau)\,d\tau \tag{6.6-4}$$

in which

$$w_e(t) = \mathcal{L}^{-1}\{W_e(s)\}$$

is the system-error response to a unit-impulse input and may be called the system-error weighting function. The system is assumed to be initially at rest. If the first $n + 1$ derivatives of $r(t)$ exist for all values of τ, the function $r(t - \tau)$ can be expanded in a Taylor series as a function of τ:

$$r(t - \tau) = r(t) - \tau r'(t) + \frac{\tau^2}{2!}r''(t) - \frac{\tau^3}{3!}r'''(t) + \cdots + (-1)^n \frac{\tau^n}{n!} r^{(n)}(t) + R_m \tag{6.6-5}$$

where $r^{(n)}(t)$ stands for the nth derivative of $r(t)$ with respect to the variable t, and R_m is the remainder which is given by

$$R_m = \frac{(-\tau)^{n+1}}{(n+1)!} r^{(n+1)}(t - \Delta\tau) \qquad 0 < \Delta\tau < 1 \tag{6.6-6}$$

It can readily be shown that the remainder becomes zero as n approaches infinity. Substituting Eq. (6.6-5) into Eq. (6.6-4) and rearranging yields

$$\begin{aligned} \varepsilon(t) = \left[\int_0^t w_e(\tau)\,d\tau\right] r(t) - \left[\int_0^t \tau w_e(\tau)\,d\tau\right] r'(t) \\ + \frac{1}{2!}\left[\int_0^t \tau^2 w_e(\tau)\,d\tau\right] r''(t) + \cdots \\ + \frac{(-1)^n}{n!}\left[\int_0^t \tau^n w_e(\tau)\,d\tau\right] r^{(n)}(t) + \cdots \end{aligned} \tag{6.6-7}$$

Now, Eq. (6.6-7) gives the error at any time t greater than $t = 0^+$. Suppose one is interested in the error under steady-state conditions, if such exists. Thus, one desires

$$\lim_{t\to\infty} \varepsilon(t) = \varepsilon_{ss}(t) \tag{6.6-8}$$

Then all the upper limits of the integrals become infinity, and all the $r^{(n)}(t)$ become the steady-state expressions. By defining

$$C_n = (-1)^n \int_0^\infty \tau^n w_e(\tau)\,d\tau \tag{6.6-9}$$

which implies

$$C_0 = \int_0^\infty w_e(\tau)\,d\tau \tag{6.6-10}$$

$$C_1 = -\int_0^\infty \tau w_e(\tau)\,d\tau \tag{6.6-11}$$

$$C_2 = \int_0^\infty \tau^2 w_e(\tau)\,d\tau \tag{6.6-12}$$

and so forth, the steady-state system error may be expressed by the following series:

$$\varepsilon_{ss}(t) = C_0 r(t) + C_1 r'(t) + \frac{C_2}{2!} r''(t) + \cdots + \frac{C_n}{n!} r^{(n)}(t) + \cdots \tag{6.6-13}$$

where $\varepsilon_{ss}(t)$ is the steady-state error, and $r(t)$, $r'(t)$, etc., are steady-state expressions. This is referred to as the steady-state error series by control engineers. The system error is seen to consist of terms proportional to the input, the input velocity, the input acceleration, and in general, still higher derivatives of the input signal. The constants $C_0, C_1, C_2, \ldots C_n, \ldots$ are referred to as the *error coefficients* which can be used to calculate the steady-state error of the feedback control system. These error coefficients give direct indication of the steady-state error when the input is a polynomial.

The error series of Eq. (6.6-13) is, in fact, derived from Eq. (6.6-3) through inverse transformation with the transient terms, generated by the poles of $W_e(s)$, discarded. Thus, Eq. (6.6-13) is a valid description of the system error only after sufficient time has elapsed to allow those terms in $\varepsilon(t)$ generated by the poles of $W_e(s)$ to decay to insignificant amplitudes. For instance, when the input $r(t)$ is the sum of exponentials, the error series is valid providing that a time constant of $r(t)$ is much larger than any of the time constants associated with $W_e(s)$. On the other hand, if a time constant associated with $W_e(s)$ is larger than any of the time constants of the input $r(t)$, Eq. (6.6-13) can never be a valid description of the system error, since the steady state is never reached. When $r(t)$ is a general input, the validity of Eq. (6.6-13) and the significance of the error coefficients must be investigated in more detail. Furthermore, the usefulness of Eq. (6.6-13) depends upon the rapidity of convergence of the series.

The error coefficients may readily be evaluated from the system-error transfer function. By definition,

$$W_e(s) = \int_0^\infty w_e(\tau)\epsilon^{-s\tau}\,d\tau \tag{6.6-14}$$

Successive differentiation with respect to s yields

$$\frac{dW_e(s)}{ds} = -\int_0^\infty \tau w_e(\tau)\epsilon^{-s\tau}\,d\tau \tag{6.6-15}$$

$$\frac{d^2W_e(s)}{ds^2} = \int_0^\infty \tau^2 w_e(\tau)\epsilon^{-s\tau}\,d\tau \tag{6.6-16}$$

$$\frac{d^3W_e(s)}{ds^3} = -\int_0^\infty \tau^3 w_e(\tau)\epsilon^{-s\tau}\,d\tau \tag{6.6-17}$$

$$\cdots\cdots\cdots\cdots\cdots\cdots$$

and

$$\frac{d^nW_e(s)}{ds^n} = (-1)^n\int_0^\infty \tau^n w_e(\tau)\epsilon^{-s\tau}\,d\tau \tag{6.6-18}$$

From Eq. (6.6-18) it is seen that the limit of

$$\frac{d^nW_e(s)}{ds^n} \tag{6.6-19}$$

as s approaches zero is

$$(-1)^n\int_0^\infty \tau^n w_e(\tau)\,d\tau \tag{6.6-20}$$

which is equal to the error coefficient of Eq. (6.6-9). Consequently, the error coefficients are given by

$$C_n = \left.\frac{d^nW_e(s)}{ds^n}\right|_{s=0} = W_e^{(n)}(0) \qquad n = 0, 1, 2, \ldots \tag{6.6-21}$$

Moreover, the error coefficients may be determined from the Taylor series expansion of the system-error transfer function $W_e(s)$ about the origin, that is,

$$W_e(s) = W_e(0) + W'(0)s + \frac{W_e''(0)}{2!}s^2 + \cdots + \frac{W_e^{(k)}(0)}{k!}s^k + \cdots \tag{6.6-22}$$

Therefore, the coefficients of the Taylor series expansion of $W_e(s)$ about the origin also represent the error coefficients.

EXAMPLE 6.6-1. A simple example is used to illustrate the evaluation of the steady-state system error from the error coefficients. Referring to Fig. 6.6-1, assume that the transfer function of the controlled system is

$$G(s) = \frac{K}{s(1+Ts)} \tag{6.6-23}$$

Then, it follows from Eq. (6.6-2) that the system-error transfer function is

$$W_e(s) = \frac{s(1+Ts)}{s^2T + s + K} \tag{6.6-24}$$

Making use of Eq. (6.6-21), the error coefficients are derived:

$$C_0 = W_e(0) = 0$$

$$C_1 = W_e'(0) = \frac{1}{K}$$

$$C_2 = W_e''(0) \approx \frac{2T}{K} \tag{6.6-25}$$

and

$$C_3 = W_e'''(0) \approx -\frac{12T}{K^2}$$

Substitution of the above values into Eq. (6.6-13) yields the error series of the system:

$$\varepsilon_{ss}(t) = \frac{1}{K}r'(t) + \frac{T}{K}r''(t) - \frac{2T}{K^2}r'''(t) + \cdots \tag{6.6-26}$$

For a system with a large gain constant, the error series converges rapidly, and the system error is given essentially by the first few terms of the above series, if the derivatives change slowly. With $K = 500$, $T = 0.1$ sec, and a single-frequency sinusoidal input $r(t) = \sin \omega t$, the error series of the system becomes

$$\varepsilon_{ss}(t) = \frac{\omega}{500}\cos \omega t - \frac{\omega^2}{5{,}000}\sin \omega t - \frac{2\omega^3}{2{,}500{,}000}\cos \omega t + \cdots \tag{6.6-27}$$

which is also sinusoidal. For small values of ω, the series converges rapidly and the error $\varepsilon(t)$ can be approximated by

$$\varepsilon_{ss}(t) \approx \frac{\omega}{500}(\cos \omega t - 0.1\omega \sin \omega t) \tag{6.6-28}$$

The peak amplitude of the steady-state error is then given by

$$\varepsilon_{ss} \approx \frac{\omega\sqrt{1 + (\omega/10)^2}}{500} \tag{6.6-29}$$

For instance, at a frequency of 5 radians/sec, the peak amplitude of the steady-state error of the system is 0.0112. Thus, as a percentage, it is 1.12 per cent of the peak amplitude of the input signal.

The discussion and evaluation in the preceding paragraphs of the error series and the error coefficients for continuous-data control systems can easily be extended to the study of the error series of sampled-data control systems. The error coefficients for a sampled-data control system have the same meaning as those for a continuous-data control system. The latter can be used to calculate the steady-state error of continuous-data systems, whereas the former can be used to determine the steady-state error at the sampling instants of sampled-data systems. In the analysis of sampled-data control systems an error series similar to Eq. (6.6-13) can be derived, and the error coefficients can be evaluated from the system-error pulse-transfer function. The evaluation and interpretation of the error coefficients of sampled-data and digital control systems are presented in the following paragraphs.

A basic pulsed-data feedback control system with the actuating error sampled is shown in Fig. 6.6-2, in which $G(s)$ is the transfer function of the elements in the forward path and $H(s)$ is that of the elements in the feedback path. Let the z transform of the system error and the system input be denoted by $E(z)$ and $R(z)$ respectively, and their ratio by

$$\frac{E(z)}{R(z)} = W_e(z) \tag{6.6-30}$$

The function $W_e(z)$, defined as the system-error pulse-transfer function, can easily be derived from the block diagram of Fig. 6.6-2 by use of the prin-

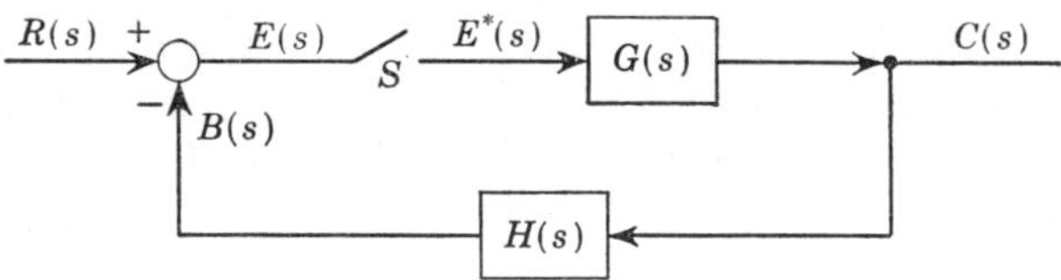

Fig. 6.6-2. Block diagram of a basic sampled-data feedback control system.

ciples and the procedures described in Sec. 6.1. Rearranging, Eq. (6.6-30) becomes

$$E(z) = W_e(z)R(z) \tag{6.6-31}$$

Let $r(kT)$ be the value of the input at sampling instant kT, and $w_e(kT)$ be the error weighting sequence, then at any sampling instant nT, that part of the system error due to $r(t)$ is given by

$$\varepsilon(nT) = \sum_{k=0}^{\infty} w_e(kT)r[(n-k)T] \tag{6.6-32}$$

where T is the sampling period. The value of $r[(n-k)T]$, resulting from Eq. (6.6-5) by the substitution of nT for t and kT for τ, is

$$r[(n-k)T] = r(nT) - kTr'(nT) + \frac{(kT)^2}{2!} r''(nT) + \cdots + (-1)^m \frac{(kT)^m}{m!} r^{(m)}(nT) + \cdots \tag{6.6-33}$$

Then Eq. (6.6-32) can be written as

$$\varepsilon(nT) = \sum_{k=0}^{\infty} \left\{ w_e(kT)r(nT) - kTw_e(kT)r'(nT) + \frac{(kT)^2}{2!} w_e(kT)r''(nT) + \cdots + (-1)^m \frac{(kT)^m}{m!} w_e(kT)r^{(m)}(nT) + \cdots \right\} \tag{6.6-34}$$

If the coefficient of the term of mth derivative in the above series is defined by

$$\sum_{k=0}^{\infty} (-1)^m (kT)^m w_e(kT) = C_m \tag{6.6-35}$$

the series of Eq. (6.6-34) becomes

$$\varepsilon(nT) = C_0 r(nT) + C_1 r'(nT) + \frac{C_2}{2!} r''(nT) + \cdots + \frac{C_m}{m!} r^{(m)}(nT) + \cdots \tag{6.6-36}$$

From the above equation, it is seen that the system steady-state error at any sampling instant nT consists of terms proportional to the input, the input velocity, the input acceleration, and in general, still higher derivatives of the input signal at the sampling instant nT. Equation (6.6-36) defines the error series of a sampled-data feedback control system, and the constants $C_0, C_1, C_2, \ldots, C_m, \ldots$, are referred to as the steady-state *error coefficients* which can be used to compute the steady-state error of the system at sampling instants. The error series given by Eq. (6.6-36) is a valid description of the system error only after sufficient time has elapsed to allow those transient terms generated by the poles of $W_e(z)$ to decay to insignificant amplitudes. The usefulness of Eq. (6.6-36) depends upon the rapidity with which the series converges. It is shown in the following paragraph that the error coefficients can be computed from

$$C_m = \left. \frac{d^m W_e^*(s)}{ds^m} \right|_{s=0} = W_e^{*(m)}(0) \qquad m = 0, 1, 2, \ldots \tag{6.6-37}$$

where $W_e^*(s)$ is the system-error pulse-transfer function in terms of the starred transform, which is obtainable from $W_e(z)$ by the substitution $z = \epsilon^{Ts}$.

Referring to the basic sampled-data feedback control system of Fig. 6.6-2, since the pulse-transfer function $G(z)$ and $GH(z)$ are functions of z, the system-error pulse-transfer function $W_e(z)$ may be expressed as a series in z^{-1}:

$$W_e(z) = a_0 + a_1z^{-1} + a_2z^{-2} + a_3z^{-3} + a_4z^{-4} + \cdots + a_kz^{-k} + \cdots \tag{6.6-38}$$

Taking the inverse transform of Eq. (6.6-38) yields

$$w_e^*(t) = a_0\delta(t) + a_1\delta(t - T) + a_2\delta(t - 2T) + a_3\delta(t - 3T) + \cdots + a_k\delta(t - kT) + \cdots \tag{6.6-39}$$

The function $w_e^*(t)$ represents the system error due to a unit-impulse input, and the coefficients $a_0, a_1, a_2, a_3, \ldots$ form the error weighting sequence. In symbols, it may be written as

$$w_e(kT) = a_k \tag{6.6-40}$$

By substituting ϵ^{Ts} for z, Eq. (6.6-38) becomes

$$W_e^*(s) = W_e(\epsilon^{Ts}) = a_0 + a_1\epsilon^{-Ts} + a_2\epsilon^{-2Ts} + a_3\epsilon^{-3Ts} + \cdots + a_k\epsilon^{-kTs} + \cdots \tag{6.6-41}$$

Successive differentiation yields

$$\frac{dW_e^*(s)}{ds} = -T(a_1\epsilon^{-Ts} + 2a_2\epsilon^{-2Ts} + 3a_3\epsilon^{-3Ts} + \cdots + ka_k\epsilon^{-kTs} + \cdots) \tag{6.6-42}$$

$$\frac{d^2W_e^*(s)}{ds^2} = T^2(a_1\epsilon^{-Ts} + 2^2a_2\epsilon^{-2Ts} + 3^2a_3\epsilon^{-3Ts} + \cdots + k^2a_k\epsilon^{-kTs} + \cdots) \tag{6.6-43}$$

$$\frac{d^mW_e^*(s)}{ds^m} = (-1)^mT^m(a_1\epsilon^{-Ts} + 2^ma_2\epsilon^{-2Ts} + 3^ma_3\epsilon^{-3Ts} + \cdots + k^ma_k\epsilon^{-kTs} + \cdots) \tag{6.6-44}$$

At $s = 0$, one obtains

$$W_e^*(0) = a_0 + a_1 + a_2 + a_3 + \cdots + a_k + \cdots \tag{6.6-45}$$

Making use of Eq. (6.6-40), Eq. (6.6-45) may be written

$$W_e^*(0) = \sum_{k=0}^{\infty} w_e(kT) \tag{6.6-46}$$

Similarly, the following is derived:

$$\left.\frac{dW_e^*(s)}{ds}\right|_{s=0} = -(Ta_1 + 2Ta_2 + 3Ta_3 + \cdots + kTa_k + \cdots) = -\sum_{k=0}^{\infty} kTw_e(kT) \tag{6.6-47}$$

$$\left.\frac{d^2W_e^*(s)}{ds^2}\right|_{s=0} = T^2a_1 + (2T)^2a_2 + (3T)^2a_3 + \cdots + (kT)^2a_k + \cdots$$
$$= \sum_{k=0}^{\infty} (kT)^2w_e(kT) \tag{6.6-48}$$

and

$$\left.\frac{d^mW_e^*(s)}{ds^m}\right|_{s=0} = (-1)^m[T^ma_1 + (2T)^ma_2 + (3T)^ma_3 + \cdots + (kT)^ma_k + \cdots]$$
$$= \sum_{k=0}^{\infty} (-1)^m(kT)^mw_e(kT) \tag{6.6-49}$$

From the definition of the error coefficients given in Eq. (6.6-35), it is seen that the right-hand side of Eq. (6.6-49) is equal to the error coefficient C_m. Thus, the error coefficients may be evaluated from the system-error pulse-transfer function $W_e^*(s)$, by successive differentiation and by finding the values of the derivatives at $s = 0$. Equating Eq. (6.6-49) to Eq. (6.6-35), the expression of Eq. (6.6-37) results, which determines the error coefficients. Comparing Eq. (6.6-21) with Eq. (6.6-37) reveals the similarity between the expression of the error coefficients for sampled-data systems and that for continuous-data systems.

In general, an error series similar to Eq. (6.6-36) can be derived to describe that part of the system error at sampling instants due to a disturbance that occurred in the sampled-data feedback control system. If the disturbance that occurred in the system is $n(t)$, the system error due to this disturbance would be given by

$$\varepsilon(kT) = C_0'n(kT) + C_1'n'(kT) + \frac{C_2'}{2!}n''(kT) + \cdots + \frac{C_m'}{m!}n^{(m)}(kT) + \cdots \tag{6.6-50}$$

However, the error coefficients of Eq. (6.6-50) generally differ from those of Eq. (6.6-36). The coefficients of Eq. (6.6-50) are derived from the system-error pulse-transfer function relating the system output to the disturbance. For instance, for a disturbance $n(t)$, the error coefficients would be determined from $W_{en}(z) = C(z)/N(z)$, where $C(z)$ and $N(z)$ are the z transforms of $c(t)$ and $n(t)$ respectively, and $c(t)$ represents the system output due to the disturbance.

The system-error pulse-transfer function $W_e(z)$ generally gives much information concerning the system performance. The poles of the pulse-transfer function $W_e(z)$ are also the poles of the system, and thus determine the nature and the time constants of the transient response of the pulsed-data system. When the pulse-transfer function $W_e(z)$ contains k zeros at $z = 1$ in the z plane, the first k error coefficients of the sampled-data control system are zero and the first nonzero error coefficients will be C_k. This can readily be shown. Since $W_e(z)$ has k zeros at $z = 1$, it may be written as

$$W_e(z) = (z - 1)^kP(z) \tag{6.6-51}$$

The corresponding expression in terms of the starred transform is

$$W_e^*(s) = (\epsilon^{Ts} - 1)^k P^*(s) \tag{6.6-52}$$

It is observed that at $s = 0$,

$$W_e^*(0) = 0 \tag{6.6-53}$$

and the first $(k - 1)$ derivatives of $W_e^*(s)$ are zero:

$$\left.\frac{d^n W_e^*(s)}{ds^n}\right|_{s=0} = 0 \qquad \text{for } n = 1, 2, \ldots (k-1) \tag{6.6-54}$$

This implies that the first k error coefficients are zero. The first nonzero error coefficient is then given by

$$C_k = k!\,(T)^k P^*(0) \tag{6.6-55}$$

It is interesting to note that the first nonzero error coefficient of a sampled-data control system can be greatly diminished by keeping the zeros of $W_e(z)$ closer to the point (1,0) in the z plane and by pushing the poles of $W_e(z)$ farther from that point.

Furthermore, the error coefficients may be determined from the power series expansion of $W_e(z)$ in $(1 - z^{-1})$. The error series of Eq. (6.6-36) may be written as

$$\varepsilon^*(t) = C_0 r^*(t) + C_1 r^{*\prime}(t) + \frac{C_2}{2!} r^{*\prime\prime}(t) + \frac{C_3}{3!} r^{*\prime\prime\prime}(t) + \cdots + \frac{C_m}{m!} r^{*(m)}(t) + \cdots \tag{6.6-56}$$

Taking the z transform of both sides of Eq. (6.6-56) yields

$$E(z) = \left[C_0 + C_1 \frac{1 - z^{-1}}{T} + \frac{C_2}{2!}\left(\frac{1 - z^{-1}}{T}\right)^2 + \frac{C_3}{3!}\left(\frac{1 - z^{-1}}{T}\right)^3 + \cdots + \frac{C_m}{m!}\left(\frac{1 - z^{-1}}{T}\right)^m + \cdots\right] R(z) \tag{6.6-57}$$

In view of Eq. (6.6-30),

$$W_e(z) = C_0 + \frac{C_1}{T}(1 - z^{-1}) + \frac{C_2}{2!T^2}(1 - z^{-1})^2 + \frac{C_3}{3!T^3}(1 - z^{-1})^3 + \cdots + \frac{C_m}{m!T^m}(1 - z^{-1})^m + \cdots \tag{6.6-58}$$

If the power series expansion of $W_e(z)$ in $(1 - z^{-1})$ is expressed as

$$W_e(z) = b_0 + b_1(1 - z^{-1}) + b_2(1 - z^{-1})^2 + b_3(1 - z^{-1})^3 + \cdots + b_m(1 - z^{-1})^m + \cdots \tag{6.6-59}$$

the error coefficients C_m are related to the coefficients b_m of the series by

$$C_m = m!\,b_m T^m \tag{6.6-60}$$

The relationships between the generalized error coefficients and the three basic error constants defined in Sec. 6.5 are derived as follows: Consider the unity-feedback error-sampled system of Fig. 6.5-1. The system-error pulse-transfer function is given by

$$W_e(z) = \frac{1}{1 + G(z)} \tag{6.6-61}$$

Substituting Eq. (6.6-61) into Eq. (6.6-58) yields

$$\frac{1}{1 + G(z)} = C_0 + \frac{C_1}{T}(1 - z^{-1}) + \frac{C_2}{2!T^2}(1 - z^{-1})^2 + \frac{C_3}{3!T^3}(1 - z^{-1})^3 + \cdots + \frac{C_m}{m!T^m}(1 - z^{-1})^m + \cdots \tag{6.6-62}$$

It follows from Eq. (6.6-62) that

$$C_0 = \lim_{z \to 1} \frac{1}{1 + G(z)} = \frac{1}{\lim\limits_{z \to 1} \{1 + G(z)\}} \tag{6.6-63}$$

In view of Eq. (6.5-5), one obtains the relationship

$$C_0 = \frac{1}{K_p} \tag{6.6-64}$$

For a type 1 system, C_0 is zero and Eq. (6.6-62) becomes

$$\frac{1}{1 + G(z)} = \frac{C_1}{T}(1 - z^{-1}) + \frac{C_2}{2!T^2}(1 - z^{-1})^2 + \cdots + \frac{C_m}{m!T^m}(1 - z^{-1})^m + \cdots \tag{6.6-65}$$

Then,

$$C_1 = \lim_{z \to 1} \frac{T}{(1 - z^{-1})[1 + G(z)]} = \frac{T}{\lim\limits_{z \to 1} \{(z - 1)G(z)\}} \tag{6.6-66}$$

Making use of Eq. (6.5-18) yields

$$C_1 = \frac{T}{K_v} \tag{6.6-67}$$

For a type 2 system, both C_0 and C_1 are zero and Eq. (6.6-62) reduces to

$$\frac{1}{1 + G(z)} = \frac{C_2}{2!T^2}(1 - z^{-1})^2 + \frac{C_3}{3!T^3}(1 - z^{-1})^3 + \cdots + \frac{C_m}{m!T^m}(1 - z^{-1})^m + \cdots \tag{6.6-68}$$

From Eq. (6.6-68) it is readily seen that

$$C_2 = \lim_{z \to 1} \frac{2!T^2}{(1 - z^{-1})^2[1 + G(z)]} = \frac{2!T^2}{\lim\limits_{z \to 1} \{(z - 1)^2 G(z)\}} \tag{6.6-69}$$

Making use of Eq. (6.6-23) yields

$$\frac{C_2}{2!} = \frac{T^2}{K_a} \tag{6.6-70}$$

Consequently, the error series for a unity-feedback sampled-data system is given by

$$z(nT) = \frac{1}{K_p} r(nT) + \frac{T}{K_v} r'(nT) + \frac{T^2}{K_a} r''(nT) + \cdots \tag{6.6-71}$$

EXAMPLE 6.6-2. Determine the error coefficients and the error series resulting from the input $r(t)$ of the sampled-data feedback control system shown in Fig. 6.6-3.

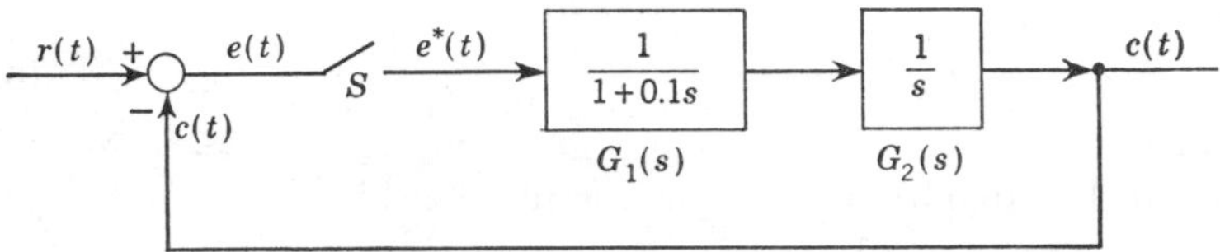

FIG. 6.6-3. Block diagram of the system of Example 6.6-2.

The control system of Fig. 6.6-3 is a unity-feedback error-sampled system with the transfer function of the elements in the forward path given by

$$G(s) = G_1(s)G_2(s) = \frac{1}{s(1 + 0.1s)} \tag{6.6-72}$$

The corresponding pulse-transfer function is

$$G(z) = \frac{0.632z}{z^2 - 1.368z + 0.368} \tag{6.6-73}$$

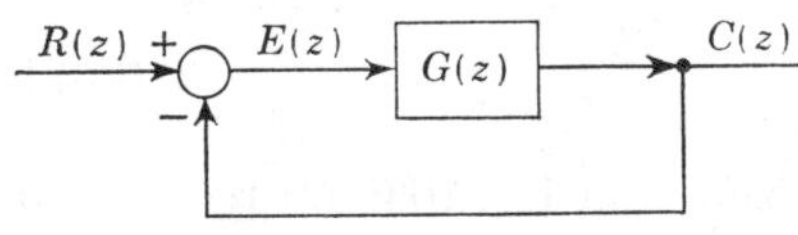

FIG. 6.6-4. Block diagram of the system of Example 6.6-2 in terms of z transforms.

In terms of the z transforms, the system is described by the block diagram of Fig. 6.6-4. For a unity-feedback system, the actuating signal is equal to the system error. Thus,

$$W_e(z) = \frac{E(z)}{R(z)} = \frac{1}{1 + G(z)} = \frac{(z-1)(z-0.368)}{z^2 - 0.736z + 0.368} \tag{6.6-74}$$

Since $W_e(z)$ contains a zero at $z = 1$, the first error coefficient C_0 is zero. In terms of the starred transforms, Eq. (6.6-74) may be written as

$$W_e^*(s) = (\epsilon^{Ts} - 1)P^*(s) \tag{6.6-75}$$

where

$$P^*(s) = \frac{\epsilon^{Ts} - 0.368}{\epsilon^{2Ts} - 0.736\epsilon^{Ts} + 0.368} \tag{6.6-76}$$

Then it can be shown that

$$\left.\frac{dW_e^*(s)}{ds}\right|_{s=0} = TP^*(0) \tag{6.6-77}$$

$$\left.\frac{d^2W_e^*(s)}{ds^2}\right|_{s=0} = T[TP^*(0) + 2P^{*\prime}(0)] \tag{6.6-78}$$

$$\left.\frac{d^3W_e^*(s)}{ds^3}\right|_{s=0} = T\{T[TP^*(0) + P^{*\prime}(0)] + [TP^{*\prime}(0) + P^{*\prime\prime}(0)]\} \tag{6.6-79}$$

From Eq. (6.6-76), the values of $P^*(s)$ and its derivatives at $s = 0$ are obtained. They are

$$P^*(0) = 1, \qquad P^{*\prime}(0) = -0.418T, \qquad P^{*\prime\prime}(0) = -1.9T^2 \tag{6.6-80}$$

The substituting of these values into Eqs. (6.6-77), (6.6-78), and (6.6-79) gives the error coefficients

$$C_1 = T = 0.1 \tag{6.6-81}$$

$$C_2 = 0.582T^2 = 0.00582 \tag{6.6-82}$$

$$C_3 = -1.736T^3 = -0.001736 \tag{6.6-83}$$

Hence the error series is

$$\varepsilon(nT) = 0.1r'(nT) + \frac{0.00582}{2!}r''(nT) - \frac{0.00174}{3!}r'''(nT) + \cdots \tag{6.6-84}$$

Inspection of the above equation reveals that for a unit step-function input the steady-state error at the sampling instants is zero; whereas if a unit-ramp function is applied to the system, the steady-state error at the sampling instants would be 0.1.

6.7. Multirate Sampled-data Control Systems. Up to this point in the analysis of sampled-data control systems, the samplers of the system are assumed to operate in synchronism, with the same sampling rate. Such systems may be called, for convenience, single-rate sampled-data systems. Although single-rate sampling occurs in the great majority of sampled-data control systems, there exist systems which contain two or more synchronized samplers operating with different sampling rates. In contrast to the single-rate sampled-data systems, such systems are often referred to as multirate sampled-data systems.[160] Multirate sampling either occurs inherently in the control system, as in flight control systems with a data-link computer operating at a rate different from the speed of the radar antenna, or is introduced deliberately into the system, as in sampled-data systems employing multirate digital controller or compensator to improve system performance. Multirate sampling technique is a means of reducing the ripple content in the system output and of increasing the system-response speed. This section is concerned with the analysis of multirate sampled-data control systems.

The block diagram of an open-loop multirate sampled-data system is shown in Fig. 6.7-1. The system contains two synchronized samplers, one

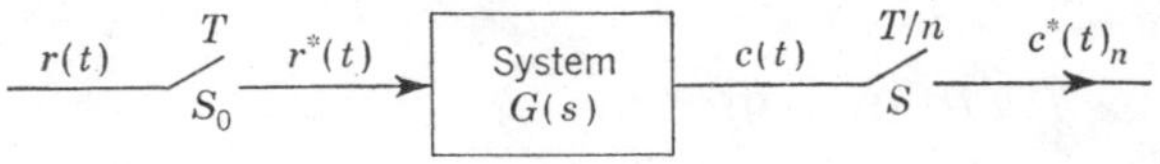

FIG. 6.7-1. A simple open-loop multirate sampled-data system.

operating at a rate $1/T$ and the other being n times as fast. n is assumed to be an integer. Because of the presence of the second sampler which operates with a period different from the first one, the analysis of such a system would appear to be more involved if not actually too unwieldy to effect. A close examination of the operation of the high-speed sampler of the system reveals that the sampler may be represented by n nonsynchronized samplers connected in parallel and operating with the same sampling period T, as shown in Fig. 6.7-2. The equivalent samplers, S_0, S_1, S_2,

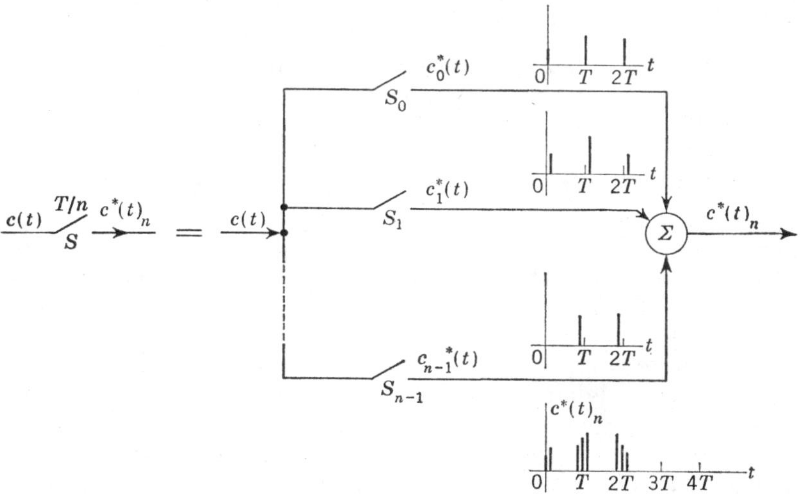

FIG. 6.7-2. Sampler S is represented by n delayed samplers.

$S_3, \ldots, S_{n-1}$, are not synchronized in phase. Sampler S_0 operates at instants kT, k being an integer; sampler S_1 switches at instants $(k + 1/n)T$; sampler S_2 operates at instants $(k + 2/n)T$; and so forth. In other words, the switching time of the equivalent samplers is successively delayed by T/n sec so that the total output from the equivalent samplers will be identical to the output of the high-speed sampler S. Since the switching time of S_1 falls behind that of S_0 by T/n sec, the values of its output would be the same as those of S_0 if the input signal to S_0 were advanced by T/n sec. Furthermore, if this output signal of S_0 is then delayed by T/n sec, it would be identical to the output of S_1 both in magnitude and in phase.

Consequently, the delayed sampler S_1 may be represented by the basic sampler S_0 preceded by an advance of T/n sec and followed by a delay of T/n sec as shown in Fig. 6.7-3a. In like manner, the delayed sampler S_2 is equivalent to the sampler S_0 preceded by an advance of $2T/n$ sec and followed by a delay of $2T/n$ sec. Based upon this argument, the other delayed samplers, S_3, S_4, S_5, . . . , S_{n-1}, may be similarly represented as shown in Fig. 6.7-3b, thus enabling the block diagram of the system of Fig. 6.7-1 to be redrawn in Fig. 6.7-4. It is noted that with the high-speed sampler replaced by its equivalent of Fig. 6.7-3b, the multirate sampled-data system is reduced to an equivalent single-rate sampled-data system of Fig. 6.7-4, and as a result, the system may be analyzed by the z-transform technique in a systematic manner.

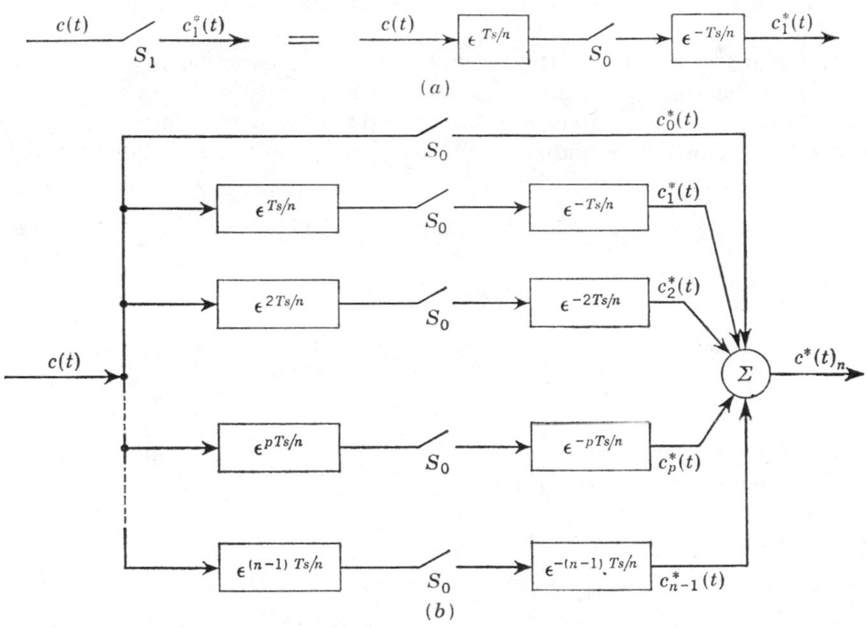

FIG. 6.7-3. (a) The delayed sampler and its equivalent; (b) the delayed samplers are represented by basic samplers together with advance and delay elements.

The z transform of a function $c(t)$, which is sampled with period T, is defined in Sec. 5.1 as

$$C(z) = \mathfrak{z}\{c(t)\} = \mathfrak{z}\{c^*(t)\} = \sum_{k=0}^{\infty} c(kT)z^{-k} \tag{6.7-1}$$

By analogy, the z transform of function $c(t)$ being sampled with period T/n may be defined by

$$C(z)_n = \mathfrak{z}_n\{c(t)\} = \mathfrak{z}\{c^*(t)_n\} = \sum_{k=0}^{\infty} c\left(\frac{kT}{n}\right)(z^{1/n})^{-k} \tag{6.7-2}$$

where the subscript n signifies that the z transform is taken with reference to sampling period T/n. Equation (6.7-2) describes the z transform of the output of the high-speed sampler S, which operates at a rate of n/T samples/sec. With a view to distinguishing from the basic z-transform operation with respect to sampling period T as defined in Eq. (6.7-1), the z-transform operator $\mathfrak{z}_n$ is introduced for samplers with sampling period T/n. By letting $z_n = z^{1/n}$, Eq. (6.7-2) may be written as

$$\mathfrak{z}_n\{c(t)\} = C(z_n) = \sum_{k=0}^{\infty} c\left(\frac{kT}{n}\right) z_n^{-k} \tag{6.7-3}$$

It should be pointed out that $C(z_n)$ is obtained by the substitution of $z = z_n^n$ in $C(z)_n$, not in $C(z)$, unless $C(z)$ is independent of the sampling period T.

Referring to Fig. 6.7-2, the output $c^*(t)_n$ of the sampler S with period T/n may be considered as comprising n outputs $c_0^*(t)$, $c_1^*(t)$, $c_2^*(t)$, . . . , $c_{n-1}^*(t)$, of the basic sampler and the $(n - 1)$ delayed samplers. Thus, the output $c^*(t)_n$, which is sampled with sampling period T/n, is given by

$$c^*(t)_n = c_0^*(t) + \sum_{p=1}^{n-1} c_p^*(t) \tag{6.7-4}$$

and the z transform of the output is

$$C(z)_n = C_0(z) + \sum_{p=1}^{n-1} \mathfrak{z}\{c_p^*(t)\} \tag{6.7-5}$$

where $C_0(z)$ is the z transform of the output of the basic sampler S_0, and $\mathfrak{z}\{c_p^*(t)\}$ denotes the z transform of the output from the pth delayed sampler S_p. Reference to Fig. 6.7-3 indicates that the z transform of the output of the sampler S_1 is given by

$$\mathfrak{z}\{c_1^*(t)\} = z^{-1/n}\mathfrak{z}\{\epsilon^{Ts/n}C(s)\} \tag{6.7-6}$$

Similarly, for sampler S_p the output transform is

$$\mathfrak{z}\{c_p^*(t)\} = z^{-p/n}\mathfrak{z}\{\epsilon^{Tsp/n}C(s)\} \tag{6.7-7}$$

Substituting Eq. (6.7-7) into Eq. (6.7-5) gives the output transform of the sampler S as

$$C(z)_n = C_0(z) + \sum_{p=1}^{n-1} z^{-p/n}\mathfrak{z}\{\epsilon^{Tsp/n}C(s)\} \tag{6.7-8}$$

This is a key equation, upon which is based the analysis of multirate sampled-data systems carried out in the following pages. It is noted that the z transform of $\epsilon^{Tsp/n}C(s)$ can readily be derived from the modified z transform $C(z,m)$ corresponding to $C(s)$, since

$$\mathfrak{Z}\{\epsilon^{\lambda Ts}C(s)\} = z\mathfrak{Z}_m\{C(s)\}\Big|_{m=\lambda} = zC(z,m)\Big|_{m=\lambda} = zC(z,\lambda) \tag{6.7-9}$$

provided that $C(s)$ is a rational polynomial of s. In case the function $C(s)$ contains a factor of the form $\epsilon^{-T_d s}$, Eq. (6.7-9) is still applicable if this exponential factor is absorbed in the factor $\epsilon^{\lambda Ts}$ when applying this equation. For instance, if $C(s) = \epsilon^{-aTs}C_1(s)$ and $C_1(s)$ is a rational polynomial of s, then

$$\mathfrak{Z}\{\epsilon^{\lambda Ts}C(s)\} = \mathfrak{Z}\{\epsilon^{(\lambda-a)Ts}C_1(s)\} = zC_1(z,m)\Big|_{m=\lambda-a} = zC_1(z, \lambda - a) \tag{6.7-10}$$

Open-loop Systems. The open-loop multirate sampled-data system of Fig. 6.7-1 is considered. The input-output relationship of the system $G(s)$ is given by

$$C(s) = G(s)R^*(s) \tag{6.7-11}$$

From the equivalent block diagram of Fig. 6.7-4a, the z transform of the

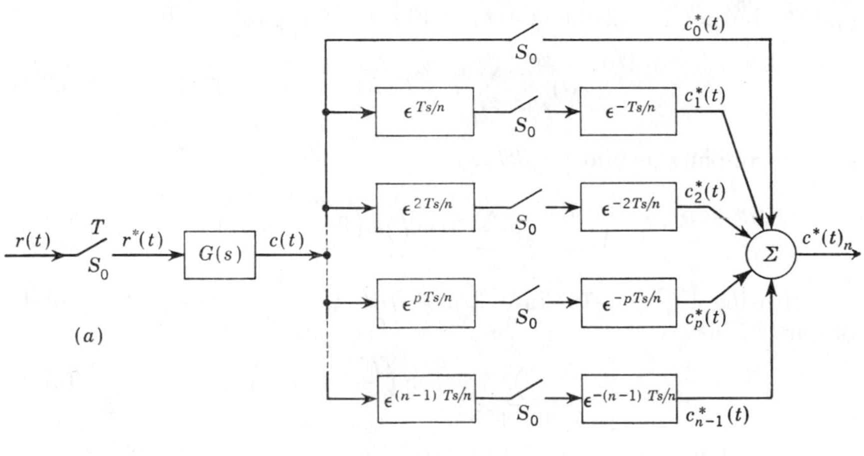

FIG. 6.7-4. (a) Equivalent single-rate system of the multirate system of Fig. 6.7-1; (b) equivalent block-diagram representation of the system of Fig. 6.7-1 (with the insertion of a fictitious sampler S_f).

output of the basic sampler S_0 is found to be

$$C_0(z) = G(z)R(z) \tag{6.7-12}$$

Substituting Eqs. (6.7-11) and (6.7-12) into Eq. (6.7-8) and simplifying yields the system output transform as

$$C(z)_n = \left[G(z) + \sum_{p=1}^{n-1} z^{-p/n} \mathfrak{z}\{\epsilon^{Tsp/n} G(s)\} \right] R(z) \tag{6.7-13}$$

Making use of Eq. (6.7-9), $C(z)_n$ may be put into the form

$$C(z)_n = \left[G(z) + \sum_{p=1}^{n-1} z^{1-p/n} G\left(z, \frac{p}{n}\right) \right] R(z) \tag{6.7-14a}$$

provided that $G(s)$ is a rational polynomial of s. By the substitution of $z = z_n{}^n$ in Eq. (6.7-14a), the system-output transform reduces to

$$C(z_n) = \left[G(z_n{}^n) + \sum_{p=1}^{n-1} z_n{}^{n-p} G\left(z_n{}^n, \frac{p}{n}\right) \right] R(z_n{}^n) \tag{6.7-14b}$$

The inverse z transform of Eq. (6.7-14a) or Eq. (6.7-14b) describes the transient response of the system at the instants $t = kT/n$ to an arbitrary input $r(t)$, the z transform of which is $R(z)$.

The z_n transform of the output $c(t)$, that is, the z transform with respect to sampling period T/n, can also be derived from the impulse-response concept. Assuming that $g(t)$ is the impulse response of $G(s)$, the input $r(t)$ and the output $c(t)$ of the system of Fig. 6.7-1 are related by

$$c(t) = \sum_{m=0}^{\infty} r(mT) g(t - mT) \tag{6.7-15}$$

and at sampling instant $t = kT/n$,

$$c\left(\frac{kT}{n}\right) = \sum_{m=0}^{\infty} r(mT) g\left(\frac{kT}{n} - mT\right) \tag{6.7-16}$$

Substituting Eq. (6.7-16) into Eq. (6.7-2) gives the z_n transform of the output $c(t)$ as

$$C(z)_n = \sum_{k=0}^{\infty} \sum_{m=0}^{\infty} r(mT) g\left(\frac{kT}{n} - mT\right) (z^{-k/n}) \tag{6.7-17}$$

Letting $k/n = m + v/n$ and rearranging reduces Eq. (6.7-17) to

$$C(z)_n = \sum_{v=0}^{\infty} g\left(\frac{vT}{n}\right) z^{-v/n} \sum_{m=0}^{\infty} r(mT) z^{-m} \tag{6.7-18}$$

Making use of the definitions of the z transform and z_n transform, $C(z)_n$ may be put into the form

$$C(z)_n = G(z)_n R(z) \tag{6.7-19}$$

or

$$C(z_n) = G(z_n) R(z_n{}^n) \tag{6.7-20}$$

where $G(z_n) = G(z)_n$ is the z_n transform of $g(t)$ and can be derived from the z-transform table by considering z_n as the complex variable and T/n as the sampling period.

Equation (6.7-19) may be derived from the equivalent block diagram shown in Fig. 6.7-4*b* by inspection. In Fig. 6.7-4*b*, a fictitious high-speed sampler S_f is inserted between the low-speed sampler S_0 and the system $G(s)$. This does not affect the system performance, since the input to $G(s)$ remains unchanged. Then it follows immediately from the equivalent block diagram that the z_n transform of $c(t)$ is given by

$$C(z)_n = \mathfrak{z}_n\{c(t)\} = \mathfrak{z}_n\{g(t)\}\mathfrak{z}_n\{r^*(t)\} \tag{6.7-21}$$

or

$$C(z)_n = G(z)_n R(z) \tag{6.7-22}$$

which is identical to Eq. (6.7-19).

By the substitution of $z = z_n{}^n$, Eq. (6.7-22) may be expressed as a function of z_n, namely,

$$C(z_n) = G(z_n)R(z_n{}^n) \tag{6.7-23}$$

from which the system output $c^*(t)_n$ at instants $t = kT/n$ in response to input $r(t)$ can be determined through real inversion. When $n = 1$, that is, both samplers operate with the same sampling period T, Eq. (6.7-14) and Eq. (6.7-20) reduce to

$$C(z) = G(z)R(z) \tag{6.7-24}$$

which is the output transform for the corresponding single-rate sampled-data system derived in Sec. 6.1*a*.

Comparing Eq. (6.7-14) with Eq. (6.7-23) reveals the discrepancy between these two expressions. Nevertheless, these two expressions are actually identical, since

$$G(z_n) = G(z_n{}^n) + \sum_{p=1}^{n-1} z_n{}^{n-p} G\left(z_n{}^n, \frac{p}{n}\right) \tag{6.7-25}$$

or

$$G(z)_n = G(z) + \sum_{p=1}^{n-1} z^{1-p/n} G\left(z, \frac{p}{n}\right) \tag{6.7-26}$$

The above equation provides an interesting relationship between the z transform $G(z)$ and the z_n transform $G(z_n)$. To verify consider

$$G(s) = \frac{1}{s+a} \tag{6.7-27}$$

Since the z transform and the modified z transform associated with $G(s)$ are

$$G(z) = \frac{z}{z - \epsilon^{-aT}} \tag{6.7-28}$$

and

$$G(z,m) = \frac{\epsilon^{-amT}}{z - \epsilon^{-aT}} \tag{6.7-29}$$

where T is the sampling period, then the right-hand side of Eq. (6.7-26) is equal to

$$G(z) + z^{2/3}G(z,\tfrac{1}{3}) + z^{1/3}G(z,\tfrac{2}{3}) = \frac{z}{z - \epsilon^{-aT}} + \frac{z^{2/3}\epsilon^{-aT/3}}{z - \epsilon^{-aT}} + \frac{z^{1/3}\epsilon^{-2aT/3}}{z - \epsilon^{-aT}}$$

$$= \frac{z^{1/3}(z^{2/3} + z^{1/3}\epsilon^{-aT/3} + \epsilon^{-2aT/3})}{z - \epsilon^{-aT}}$$

$$= \frac{z^{1/3}}{z^{1/3} - \epsilon^{-aT/3}} \tag{6.7-30}$$

Substituting z_3 for $z^{1/3}$ in Eq. (6.7-30) yields

$$\frac{z_3}{z_3 - \epsilon^{-aT/3}} \tag{6.7-31}$$

which is obviously the z transform of $G(s)$ with respect to sampling period $T/3$. This verifies the identity of Eq. (6.7-25).

It should be pointed out in passing that the simple multirate system of Fig. 6.7-1 can be easily analyzed by means of the modified z-transform method. However, in analyzing closed-loop systems as well as more complicated open-loop systems, such as the system of Fig. 6.7-6, Eq. (6.7-22) will be of great avail. Application of Eq. (6.7-22) yields the output transform of the cascaded system of Fig. 6.7-6 as

$$C(z)_n = G_1(z)_n G_2(z)_n R(z) \tag{6.7-32}$$

from which the system output in response to the input $r(t)$ can readily be computed.

Now let us consider the multirate sampled-data system of Fig. 6.7-5*a*. The input to the system $G(s)$ is sampled with a rate of n/T samples/sec, whereas the output of the system is sampled with a sampling rate of $1/T$. Representing the high-speed sampler S by its equivalent delayed samplers, the analysis may proceed as above. Reference to the equivalent block diagram of the system shown in Fig. 6.7-5*b* indicates that

$$c(t) = c_0(t) + \sum_{p=1}^{n-1} c_p(t) \tag{6.7-33}$$

and the z transform is

$$C(z) = C_0(z) + \sum_{p=1}^{n-1} C_p(z) \tag{6.7-34}$$

Since
$$C_p(z) = \mathfrak{z}\{\epsilon^{Tsp/n}R(s)\}\mathfrak{z}\{\epsilon^{-Tsp/n}G(s)\} \tag{6.7-35}$$

and
$$C_0(z) = G(z)R(z) \tag{6.7-36}$$

the z transform of $c(t)$ becomes

$$C(z) = G(z)R(z) + \sum_{p=1}^{n-1} \mathfrak{z}\{\epsilon^{Tsp/n}R(s)\}\mathfrak{z}\{\epsilon^{-Tsp/n}G(s)\} \tag{6.7-37}$$

In the above equation, both $\mathfrak{z}\{\epsilon^{Tsp/n}R(s)\}$ and $\mathfrak{z}\{\epsilon^{-Tsp/n}G(s)\}$ may be evaluated from the modified z transforms $R(z,m)$ and $G(z,m)$ respectively. It

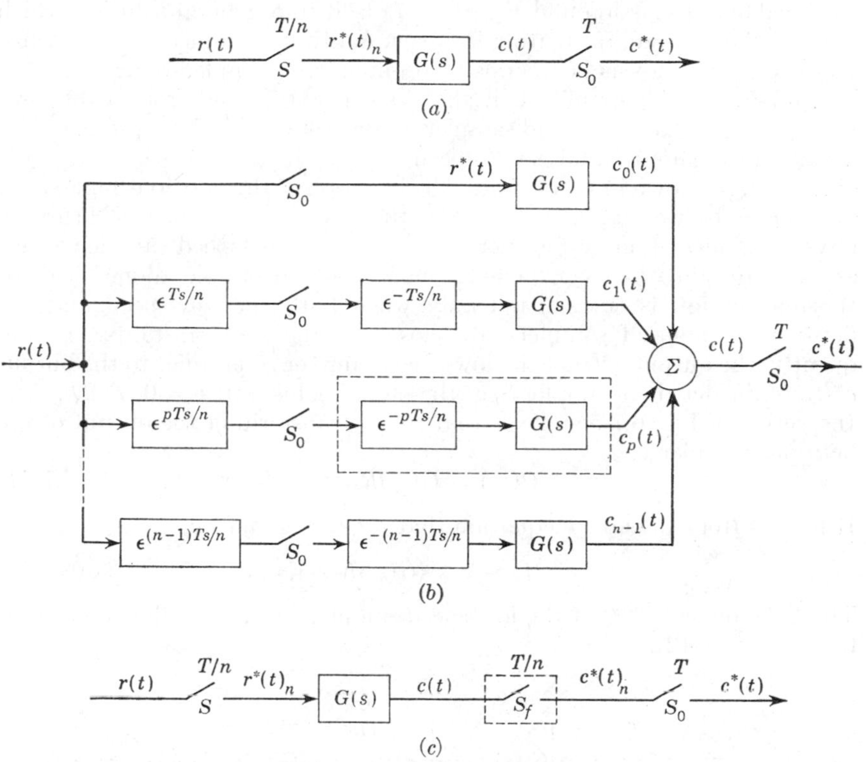

FIG. 6.7-5. (a) A sampled-data system with the input sampled n times as fast as the output; (b) equivalent single-rate system of the multirate system of (a); (c) equivalent block-diagram representation of the system of (a) (with the insertion of a fictitious sampler S_f).

follows from Eq. (6.7-9) that, if $R(s)$ and $G(s)$ are rational polynomials in s,

$$\mathfrak{z}\{\epsilon^{Tsp/n}R(s)\} = zR\left(z, \frac{p}{n}\right) \tag{6.7-38}$$

and the z transform of $\epsilon^{-Tsp/n}G(s)$ can be found from $G(z,m)$ by substituting $(1 - p/n)$ for m, namely,

$$\mathfrak{z}\{\epsilon^{-Tsp/n}G(s)\} = G(z,m)\big|_{m=1-p/n} = G\left(z, 1 - \frac{p}{n}\right) \tag{6.7-39}$$

Consequently, the output transform of the system is given by

$$C(z) = G(z)R(z) + \sum_{p=1}^{n-1} zR\left(z, \frac{p}{n}\right) G\left(z, 1 - \frac{p}{n}\right) \tag{6.7-40}$$

which will be reduced to Eq. (6.7-24) when n is equal to one.

The above discussion and Eq. (6.7-37) lead to a general solution which is particularly useful in treating feedback multirate sampled-data systems. However, the analysis of the open-loop multirate sampled-data system of Fig. 6.7-5*a* can be simplified, if the system is analyzed from a different point of view. The low-speed sampler of the system may be represented by a high-speed sampler and a low-speed sampler in cascade which are synchronized, as shown in Fig. 6.7-5*c*. The insertion of the fictitious high-speed sampler S_f between system $G(s)$ and the low-speed sampler S_0 bears no physical influence on system performance. The low-speed sampler generates zero output whenever the fictitious high-speed sampler alone is closed; the information is transmitted only when both the low-speed and the fictitious high-speed samplers are closed at the same instants. Consequently, the output $c^*(t)$ of the low-speed sampler S_0 is equal to the output $c^*(t)_n$ of the fictitious sampler S_f at the sampling instants $t = 0, T, 2T, \ldots$. Inspection of Fig. 6.7-5*c* reveals that the z_n transform of the output of the fictitious sampler is

$$C(z_n) = G(z_n)R(z_n) \tag{6.7-41}$$

It follows from the above equation that $c^*(t)_n$ is given by

$$c^*(t)_n = \mathfrak{z}_n^{-1}\{G(z_n)R(z_n)\} \tag{6.7-42}$$

Thus, the output $c^*(t)$ of the low-speed sampler can readily be determined from Eq. (6.7-42).

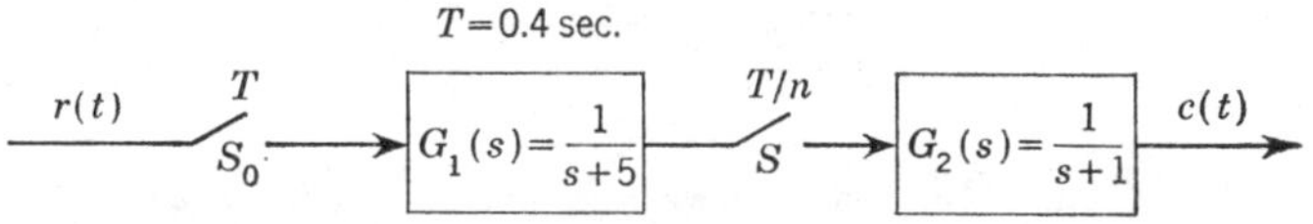

FIG. 6.7-6. Block diagram of the multirate sampled-data system of Example 6.7-1.

EXAMPLE 6.7-1. Consider the multirate sampled-data system shown in Fig. 6.7-6. The transfer functions $G_1(s)$ and $G_2(s)$ are

$$G_1(s) = \frac{1}{s+5} \qquad G_2(s) = \frac{1}{s+1} \tag{6.7-43}$$

The sampling period of the low-speed sampler is 0.4 sec, and that of the high-speed sampler is $0.4/n$ sec. Determine the unit step-function response of the system for $n = 1$, 2, and 3.

The z_n transform of the system output is given by

$$C(z_n) = G_1(z_n)G_2(z_n)R(z_n{}^n) \tag{6.7-44}$$

Since $r(t) = u(t)$ and $R(z) = z/(z - 1)$, substituting z_n^n for z yields

$$R(z_n^n) = \frac{z_n^n}{z_n^n - 1} \tag{6.7-45}$$

The z_n transforms associated with $G_1(s)$ and $G_2(s)$ are

$$G_1(z_n) = \frac{z_n}{z_n - \epsilon^{-5T/n}} \tag{6.7-46}$$

and

$$G_2(z_n) = \frac{z_n}{z_n - \epsilon^{-T/n}} \tag{6.7-47}$$

Substituting Eqs. (6.7-45), (6.7-46), and (6.7-47) into Eq. (6.7-44) yields

$$C(z_n) = \frac{z_n^{n+2}}{(z_n^n - 1)(z_n - \epsilon^{-5T/n})(z_n - \epsilon^{-T/n})} \tag{6.7-48}$$

When $n = 1$, the given system becomes a single-rate sampled-data system, the output transform of which is given by

$$C(z) = \frac{z^3}{(z - 1)(z - \epsilon^{-5T})(z - \epsilon^{-T})} \tag{6.7-49}$$

By the substitution of $T = 0.4$ sec, Eq. (6.7-49) is reduced to

$$C(z) = \frac{z^3}{z^3 - 1.805z^2 + 0.896z - 0.0905} \tag{6.7-50}$$

Long division yields

$$C(z) = 1 + 1.81z^{-1} + 2.36z^{-2} + 2.74z^{-3} + 2.99z^{-4} + \cdots \tag{6.7-51}$$

Thus, the output sequence is

$$c^*(t) = \delta(t) + 1.81\delta(t - T) + 2.36\delta(t - 2T) + 2.74\delta(t - 3T) + 2.99\delta(t - 4T) + \cdots \tag{6.7-52}$$

Equation (6.7-52) gives the values of system output at the sampling instants only. It is to be noted that between sampling instants the system output decays exponentially with a time constant of 1 sec.

For $n = 2$, the z_n transform of the system output is

$$C(z_2) = \frac{z_2^4}{(z_2^2 - 1)(z_2 - \epsilon^{-5T/2})(z_2 - \epsilon^{-T/2})} = \frac{z_2^4}{z_2^4 - 1.187z_2^3 - 0.7z_2^2 + 1.187z_2 - 0.301} \tag{6.7-53}$$

Long division reduces Eq. (6.7-53) to the following power series:

$$C(z_2) = 1 + 1.187z_2^{-1} + 2.11z_2^{-2} + 2.14z_2^{-3} + 2.91z_2^{-4} + 2.81z_2^{-5} + 3.46z_2^{-6} + \cdots \tag{6.7-54}$$

Thus, the output sequence is

$$c^*(t)_2 = \delta(t) + 1.187\delta\left(t - \frac{T}{2}\right) + 2.11\delta(t - T) + 2.14\delta\left(t - \frac{3T}{2}\right) + 2.91\delta(t - 2T) + 2.81\delta\left(t - \frac{5T}{2}\right) + \cdots \tag{6.7-55}$$

which yields the values of the system output at the sampling instants of the high-speed sampler. The system response during the intersampling periods are exponential curves, decaying with a time constant of 1 sec.

For $n = 3$, the z_n transform of the system output is

$$C(z_3) = \frac{z_3^5}{(z_3^3 - 1)(z_3 - \epsilon^{-5T/3})(z_3 - \epsilon^{-T/3})} = \frac{z_3^5}{z_3^5 - 1.394z_3^4 + 0.452z_3^3 - z_3^2 + 1.394z_3 - 0.452} \tag{6.7-56}$$

which expands into the power series

$$C(z_3) = 1 + 1.39z_3^{-1} + 1.49z_3^{-2} + 2.46z_3^{-3} + 2.75z_3^{-4} + 2.73z_3^{-5} + 3.56z_3^{-6} + 3.74z_3^{-7} + 3.61z_3^{-8} + 4.34z_3^{-9} + 4.42z_3^{-10} + \cdots \tag{6.7-57}$$

Thus, the output sequence is

$$c^*(t)_3 = \delta(t) + 1.39\delta\left(t - \frac{T}{3}\right) + 1.49\delta\left(t - \frac{2T}{3}\right) + 2.46\delta(t - T) + 2.75\delta\left(t - \frac{4T}{3}\right) + 2.73\delta\left(t - \frac{5T}{3}\right) + 3.56\delta(t - 2T) + 3.74\delta\left(t - \frac{7T}{3}\right) + \cdots \tag{6.7-58}$$

which describes the system output at the sampling instants of the high-speed sampler. The system responses during the intersampling periods are exponentially decaying curves with a time constant of 1 sec.

The unit step-function responses of the system for $n = 1$, 2, and 3 are sketched in Fig. 6.7-7, which illustrates the effect of the high-speed sampler upon the system behavior.

If the samplers S_0 and S of the system of Fig. 6.7-1 operate with sampling periods T_1 and T_2, respectively, and the ratio of T_2 to T_1 is not an integer, the techniques described above are also applicable. By assuming that $T_1 = T/n_1$ and $T_2 = T/n_2$, where n_1 and n_2 are integers and T is the least common multiple of T_1 and T_2, the sampler S_0 may be represented by n_1 nonsynchronized basic samplers connected in parallel, each of them operating with sampling period T and successively delayed by T/n_1 sec, and the sampler S may be similarly represented by n_2 equivalent samplers as shown in Fig. 6.7-8. With both S_0 and S replaced by their equivalent samplers operating with the same sampling rate, the multirate sampled-data system is reduced to an equivalent single-rate sampled-data system, and the techniques discussed in the preceding paragraphs may be employed to analyze the system.

Closed-loop Systems. The block diagram of a basic multirate feedback sampled-data control system is depicted in Fig. 6.7-9. The transfer functions for the elements in the forward branch and the feedback branch are $G(s)$ and $H(s)$, respectively. The system contains two samplers operating with different rates. Sampler S_0 operates with sampling period T, whereas sampler S operates n times as fast. To facilitate the analysis, this system of multirate sampling is first reduced to an equivalent single-rate sampled-data system. The high-speed sampler S is supplanted by its equivalent, which consists of n basic samplers of sampling period T together with various advance and delay elements, as shown in Fig. 6.7-10, thus enabling the z-transform technique to be applied to the analysis of this system.

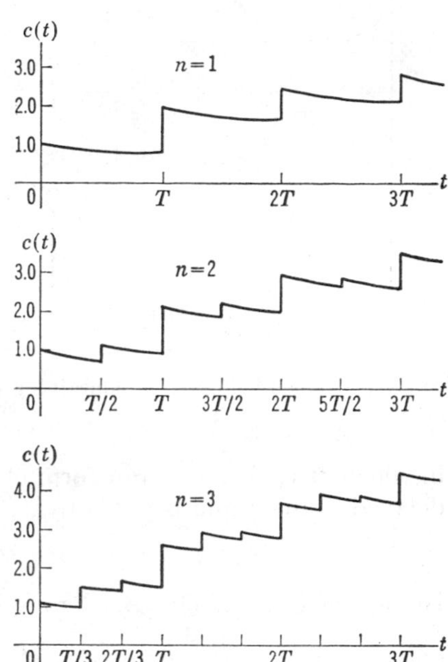

FIG. 6.7-7. The unit step-function responses of the system of Example 6.7-1 for various values of n.

With reference to the equivalent block diagram of Fig. 6.7-10 the following relationships are derived:

$$E(z) = R(z) - B(z) \tag{6.7-59}$$

$$C(s) = G(s)E^*(s) \tag{6.7-60}$$

$$C(z) = G(z)E(z) \tag{6.7-61}$$

$$B_0(z) = H(z)C(z) \tag{6.7-62}$$

and

$$b(t) = b_0(t) + \sum_{p=1}^{n-1} b_p(t) \tag{6.7-63}$$

The z transform of the feedback signal $b(t)$ follows from Eq. (6.7-63):

$$B(z) = B_0(z) + \sum_{p=1}^{n-1} B_p(z) \tag{6.7-64}$$

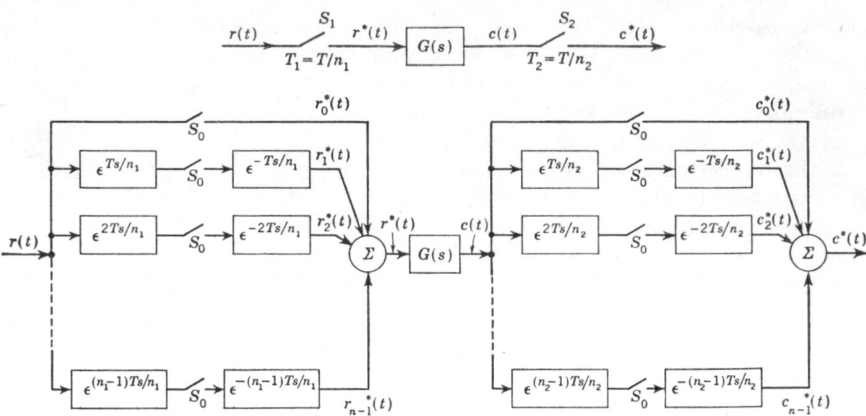

FIG. 6.7-8. Open-loop system containing two samplers with periods not related by an integer.

in which $B_p(z)$ is the z transform of the feedback signal $b_p(t)$ from the pth delayed sampler and is given by

$$B_p(z) = \mathfrak{z}\{\epsilon^{Tsp/n}C(s)\}\mathfrak{z}\{\epsilon^{-Tsp/n}H(s)\} \tag{6.7-65}$$

In view of Eq. (6.7-60), $B_p(z)$ may be written as

$$B_p(z) = E(z)\mathfrak{z}\{\epsilon^{Tsp/n}G(s)\}\mathfrak{z}\{\epsilon^{-Tsp/n}H(s)\} \tag{6.7-66}$$

Substituting Eqs. (6.7-66), (6.7-62), and (6.7-61) into Eq. (6.7-64) yields

$$B(z) = \left[G(z)H(z) + \sum_{p=1}^{n-1} \mathfrak{z}\{\epsilon^{Tsp/n}G(s)\}\mathfrak{z}\{\epsilon^{-Tsp/n}H(s)\}\right]E(z) \tag{6.7-67}$$

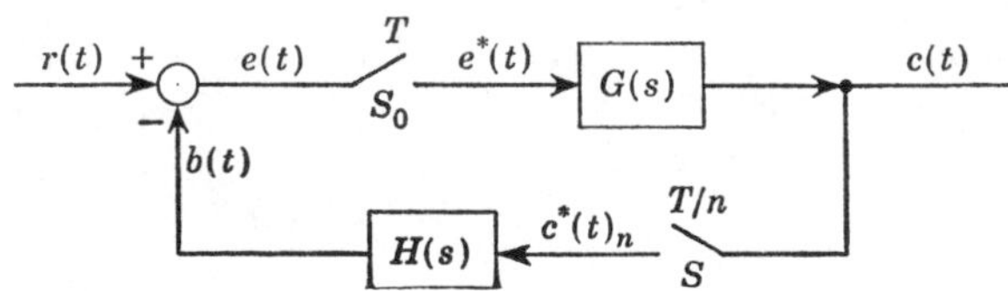

FIG. 6.7-9. Block diagram of a basic multirate feedback sampled-data system.

Then the z transform of the actuating signal resulting from the elimination of $B(z)$ between Eqs. (6.7-59) and (6.7-67) is

$$E(z) = \frac{R(z)}{1 + G(z)H(z) + \sum_{p=1}^{n-1} \mathfrak{z}\{\epsilon^{Tsp/n}G(s)\}\mathfrak{z}\{\epsilon^{-Tsp/n}H(s)\}} \tag{6.7-68}$$

where $R(z)$ is the z transform of the input $r(t)$.

The characteristic equation of the system is obtained by setting the denominator of the above equation equal to zero. Thus,

$$1 + G(z)H(z) + \sum_{p=1}^{n-1} \mathfrak{z}\{\epsilon^{Tsp/n}G(s)\}\mathfrak{z}\{\epsilon^{-Tsp/n}H(s)\} = 0 \qquad (6.7\text{-}69)$$

The stability condition requires that all the roots of Eq. (6.7-69) must lie inside the unit circle of the z plane. The procedures described in Sec. 6.2

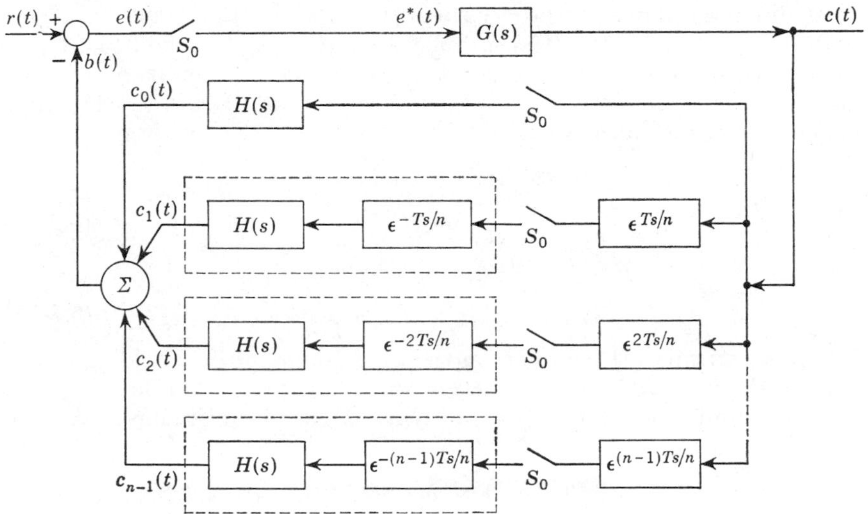

FIG. 6.7-10. Equivalent block diagram for the system of Fig. 6.7-9.

can be used to test for the absence of the characteristic roots outside the unit circle. It is interesting to note that if the sampler S were operating with the sampling period T also (that is, $n = 1$) the summation term of Eq. (6.7-69) would vanish and the characteristic equation would become

$$1 + G(z)H(z) = 0 \qquad (6.7\text{-}70)$$

which is, evidently, the characteristic equation of the corresponding single-rate sampled-data system derived in Sec. 6.1*b*.

From Eqs. (6.7-61) and (6.7-68) one obtains the z transform of the system output:

$$C(z) = \frac{G(z)R(z)}{1 + G(z)H(z) + \sum_{p=1}^{n-1} \mathfrak{z}\{\epsilon^{Tsp/n}G(s)\}\mathfrak{z}\{\epsilon^{-Tsp/n}H(s)\}} \qquad (6.7\text{-}71)$$

Since the modified z transform of the system output $C(z,m)$ is related to the z transform of the actuating error $E(z)$ by

$$C(z,m) = G(z,m)E(z) \qquad (6.7\text{-}72)$$

substituting Eq. (6.7-68) into Eq. (6.7-72) yields

$$C(z,m) = \frac{G(z,m)R(z)}{1 + G(z)H(z) + \sum_{p=1}^{n-1} \mathfrak{z}\{\epsilon^{Tsp/n}G(s)\}\mathfrak{z}\{\epsilon^{-Tsp/n}H(s)\}} \tag{6.7-73}$$

from which the transient response of the system to an arbitrary input $r(t)$ can readily be evaluated.

As discussed above, by proper substitution the z transforms associated with $\epsilon^{Tsp/n}G(s)$ and $\epsilon^{-Tsp/n}H(s)$ may be derived from the modified z transforms corresponding to $G(s)$ and $H(s)$, respectively. When $G(s)$ and $H(s)$ are rational polynomials in s, it follows from Eq. (6.7-9) and the definition of the modified z transform that

$$\begin{aligned} \mathfrak{z}\{\epsilon^{Tsp/n}G(s)\} &= zG(z,m)|_{m=p/n} \\ &= zG(z,p/n) \end{aligned} \tag{6.7-74}$$

and

$$\begin{aligned} \mathfrak{z}\{\epsilon^{-Tsp/n}H(s)\} &= H(z,m)|_{m=1-p/n} \\ &= H(z, 1 - p/n) \end{aligned} \tag{6.7-75}$$

Whenever a transport lag exists in the forward circuit or a holding device is used, the forward transfer function will contain ϵ^{-aTs} as a factor and it may be put into the form $G(s) = \epsilon^{-aTs}G_1(s)$. Under such circumstances, the z transform associated with $\epsilon^{Tsp/n}G(s)$ is given by

$$\begin{aligned} \mathfrak{z}\{\epsilon^{Tsp/n}G(s)\} &= \mathfrak{z}\{\epsilon^{(p/n-a)Ts}G_1(s)\} \\ &= zG_1(z,m)|_{m=p/n-a} \end{aligned} \tag{6.7-76}$$

where $G_1(z,m)$ is the modified z transform associated with $G_1(s)$. In like manner, when $H(s)$ is given as $H(s) = \epsilon^{-aTs}H_1(s)$,

$$\begin{aligned} \mathfrak{z}\{\epsilon^{-Tsp/n}H(s)\} &= \mathfrak{z}\{\epsilon^{-(p/n+a)Ts}H_1(s)\} \\ &= H_1(z,m)|_{m=1-(p/n+a)} \end{aligned} \tag{6.7-77}$$

where $H_1(z,m)$ is the modified z transform associated with $H_1(s)$.

To illustrate the analysis of multirate sampled-data feedback control systems and to study the effects of the high-speed sampler upon the system performance, a numerical example is presented below.

EXAMPLE 6.7-2. Consider the multirate feedback system of Fig. 6.7-11. The sampling period of the low-speed sampler is 1 sec. The high-speed sampler operates three times as fast. Zero-order holds are used in both the forward circuit and the feedback circuit. The transfer functions are

$$G(s) = \frac{1 - \epsilon^{-Ts}}{s} \frac{K}{s + 1} \tag{6.7-78}$$

and

$$H(s) = \frac{1 - \epsilon^{-Ts/3}}{s} \frac{1}{s} \tag{6.7-79}$$

Investigate the system stability and determine the system response to a unit step-function input for $K = 0.5$.

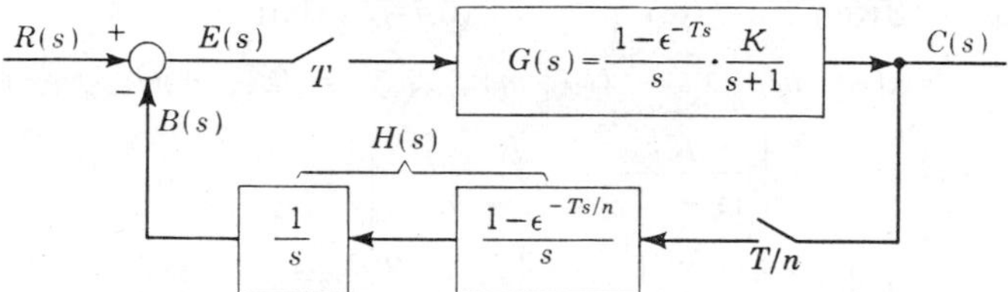

FIG. 6.7-11. Block diagram of the multirate sampled-data system of Example 6.7-2.

Since $n = 3$, the z transform of the system output is

$$C(z) = \frac{G(z)R(z)}{1 + G(z)H(z) + \mathfrak{z}\{\epsilon^{Ts/3}G(s)\}\mathfrak{z}\{\epsilon^{-Ts/3}H(s)\} + \mathfrak{z}\{\epsilon^{2Ts/3}G(s)\}\mathfrak{z}\{\epsilon^{-2Ts/3}H(s)\}} \tag{6.7-80}$$

The z transform and the modified z transform associated with $G(s)$ are found to be

$$G(z) = \frac{K(1 - \epsilon^{-T})}{(z - \epsilon^{-T})} = \frac{0.632K}{z - 0.368} \tag{6.7-81}$$

$$G(z,m) = \frac{K[(1 - \epsilon^{-m})z + (\epsilon^{-m} - 0.368)]}{(z - 0.368)} \tag{6.7-82}$$

The z transform associated with $H(s)$ is

$$H(z) = \mathfrak{z}\left\{\frac{1 - \epsilon^{-Ts/3}}{s^2}\right\} = \mathfrak{z}\left\{\frac{1}{s^2}\right\} - \mathfrak{z}\left\{\frac{\epsilon^{-Ts/3}}{s^2}\right\} \tag{6.7-83}$$

Letting $H_1(s) = 1/s^2$ and making use of Eq. (6.7-75) yields

$$\mathfrak{z}\left\{\frac{\epsilon^{-Ts/3}}{s^2}\right\} = H_1(z,m)\Big|_{m=1-\frac{1}{3}} = \left[\frac{mT}{z-1} + \frac{T}{(z-1)^2}\right]\Bigg|_{m=\frac{2}{3}}$$

$$= \frac{2T/3}{(z-1)} + \frac{T}{(z-1)^2} \tag{6.7-84}$$

Since
$$H_1(z) = \mathfrak{z}\left\{\frac{1}{s^2}\right\} = \frac{Tz}{(z-1)^2} \tag{6.7-85}$$

$$H(z) = \frac{T}{3(z-1)} = \frac{1}{3(z-1)} \tag{6.7-86}$$

The z transform associated with $\epsilon^{Ts/3}G(s)$ is

$$\mathfrak{z}\{\epsilon^{Ts/3}G(s)\} = \mathfrak{z}\left\{\frac{K\epsilon^{Ts/3}}{s(s+1)} - \frac{K\epsilon^{-2Ts/3}}{s(s+1)}\right\} \tag{6.7-87}$$

Assuming that $$G_1(s) = \frac{K}{s(s+1)}$$

then it follows from Eqs. (6.7-74) and (6.7-75) that

$$\begin{aligned}\mathfrak{z}\{\epsilon^{Ts/3}G(s)\} &= zG_1(z,m)|_{m=\frac{1}{3}} - G_1(z,m)|_{m=1-\frac{2}{3}} = (z-1)G_1(z,m)|_{m=\frac{1}{3}} \\ &= (z-1)\left[\frac{K}{(z-1)} - \frac{K\epsilon^{-mT}}{(z-\epsilon^{-T})}\right]\Bigg|_{m=\frac{1}{3}} \\ &= K\left[1 - \frac{(z-1)\epsilon^{-T/3}}{z-\epsilon^{-T}}\right] = \frac{0.286Kz + 0.348K}{z-0.368}\end{aligned} \tag{6.7-88}$$

In like manner, it is found that

$$\mathfrak{z}\{\epsilon^{2Ts/3}G(s)\} = (z-1)G_1(z,m)|_{m=\frac{2}{3}} = \frac{0.486Kz + 0.146K}{z-0.368} \tag{6.7-89}$$

$$\begin{aligned}\mathfrak{z}\{\epsilon^{-Ts/3}H(s)\} &= \mathfrak{z}\left\{\frac{\epsilon^{-Ts/3}}{s^2} - \frac{\epsilon^{-2Ts/3}}{s^2}\right\} \\ &= H_1(z,m)|_{m=\frac{2}{3}} - H_1(z,m)|_{m=\frac{1}{3}} = \frac{1}{3(z-1)}\end{aligned} \tag{6.7-90}$$

$$\begin{aligned}\mathfrak{z}\{\epsilon^{-2Ts/3}H(s)\} &= \mathfrak{z}\left\{\frac{\epsilon^{-2Ts/3}}{s^2} - \frac{\epsilon^{-Ts}}{s^2}\right\} \\ &= H_1(z,m)|_{m=\frac{1}{3}} - z^{-1}H_1(z) = \frac{1}{3(z-1)}\end{aligned} \tag{6.7-91}$$

Substituting the z transforms computed above into Eq. (6.7-80) yields the z transform of the system output as

$$C(z) = \frac{0.632K(z-1)R(z)}{z^2 + (0.258K - 1.368)z + (0.376K + 0.368)} \tag{6.7-92}$$

The characteristic equation of this system is

$$z^2 + (0.258K - 1.368)z + (0.376K + 0.368) = 0 \tag{6.7-93}$$

To determine the maximum allowable gain for stability, the simplified criterion given in Eq. (6.2-56) is applied. The conditions for the system to be stable are

1. $$0.376K + 0.368 < 1 \tag{6.7-94a}$$

2. $$0.634K > 0 \tag{6.7-94b}$$

3. $$0.118K + 2.736 > 0 \tag{6.7-94c}$$

Conditions 2 and 3 are satisfied for all positive values of K. From condition 1 it is found that the maximum allowable gain for stability is

$$K_m = 1.68 \tag{6.7-95}$$

In order to study the effect of the high-speed sampler, the output transform of the corresponding single-rate sampled-data system is derived. Setting n equal to one reduces Eq. (6.7-71) into

$$C(z) = \frac{G(z)R(z)}{1 + G(z)H(z)} \tag{6.7-96}$$

The z transform $G(z)$ is given by Eq. (6.7-81) but the z transform $H(z)$ is different from the expression of Eq. (6.7-86) since the holding device now clamps the samplers throughout the sampling period T. $H(z)$ is found to be

$$H(z) = \mathfrak{z}\left\{\frac{1 - \epsilon^{-Ts}}{s^2}\right\} = \frac{1}{z - 1} \tag{6.7-97}$$

Substituting Eqs. (6.7-81) and (6.7-97) into Eq. (6.7-96) and simplifying yields

$$C(z) = \frac{0.632K(z - 1)R(z)}{z^2 - 1.368z + (0.632K + 0.368)} \tag{6.7-98}$$

The characteristic equation is

$$z^2 - 1.368z + (0.632K + 0.368) = 0 \tag{6.7-99}$$

and the maximum allowable gain for stability is

$$K_m = 1 \tag{6.7-100}$$

The above analysis points out that the multirate system has a maximum allowable gain higher than the corresponding single-rate system, and that the high-speed sampler tends to make the system more stable.

When the gain constant is set at 0.5 and the input is a unit step function, the output transform of the multirate system becomes

$$C(z) = \frac{0.316z}{z^2 - 1.24z + 0.556} \tag{6.7-101}$$

Expanding the right-hand side of Eq. (6.7-101) into a power series in z^{-1} gives

$$C(z) = 0.316z^{-1} + 0.392z^{-2} + 0.311z^{-3} + 0.168z^{-4} + 0.0348z^{-5} - 0.0503z^{-6} - 0.0817z^{-7} - 0.0736z^{-8} - 0.0458z^{-9} - \cdots \tag{6.7-102}$$

The coefficients of the above equation represent the values of the unit step-function response at the sampling instants.

The system response during the intersampling periods can readily be derived from the modified z transform of the system output, which is found to be

$$C(z,m) = \frac{0.5(1 - \epsilon^{-m})z^2 + 0.5(\epsilon^{-m} - 0.368)z}{z^2 - 1.24z + 0.556} \tag{6.7-103}$$

For $m = 0.5$, Eq. (6.7-103) reduces to

$$C(z,0.5) = \frac{0.197z^2 + 0.119z}{z^2 - 1.24z + 0.556} \tag{6.7-104}$$

Expanding the right-hand member of Eq. (6.7-104) into a power series in z^{-1} yields

$$C(z,0.5) = 0.197 + 0.363z^{-1} + 0.34z^{-2} + 0.22z^{-3} + 0.084z^{-4} - 0.018z^{-5} - 0.0692z^{-6} - 0.0758z^{-7} - 0.0556z^{-8} - \cdots \tag{6.7-105}$$

The coefficients of the above equation represent the values of the system output at the midpoint between consecutive sampling instants. Other output values may be computed in the same manner.

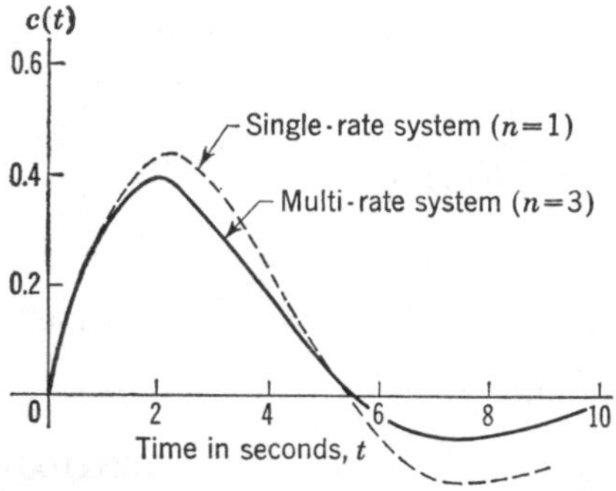

FIG. 6.7-12. The unit step-function responses of the multirate system of Example 6.7-2 and the corresponding single-rate system.

Plotted in Fig. 6.7-12 are the unit step-function responses of the multirate system and the corresponding single-rate system with the gain constant set at 0.5. These two plottings illustrate the effect of the high-speed sampler upon the transient behavior of the system.

System with Multirate Controller.[160] A feedback control system employing a multirate controller or compensator shown in Fig. 6.7-13 is considered. The Laplace transform of the controlled system is $G(s)$. The input to the multirate controller $D(z)_n$ is sampled with a sampling rate $1/T$, whereas the output of $D(z)_n$ is sampled n times as fast. The multirate system of Fig. 6.7-13 is represented by its equivalent single-rate system, the block diagram of which

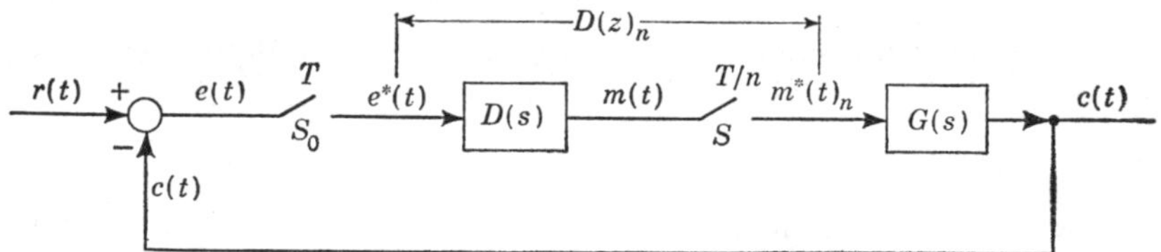

FIG. 6.7-13. Block diagram of a feedback control system employing a multirate compensator $D(z)_n$.

is sketched in Fig. 6.7-14. Examination of the equivalent block diagram indicates that

$$E(z) = R(z) - C(z) \tag{6.7-106}$$

$$M(s) = D(s)E^*(s) \tag{6.7-107}$$

$$M(z) = D(z)E(z) \tag{6.7-108}$$

$$C_0(z) = G(z)M(z) \tag{6.7-109}$$

$$C(z) = C_0(z) + \sum_{p=1}^{n-1} C_p(z) \tag{6.7-110}$$

and

$$C_p(z) = \mathfrak{z}\{\epsilon^{Tsp/n}M(s)\}\mathfrak{z}\{\epsilon^{-Tsp/n}G(s)\} \tag{6.7-111}$$

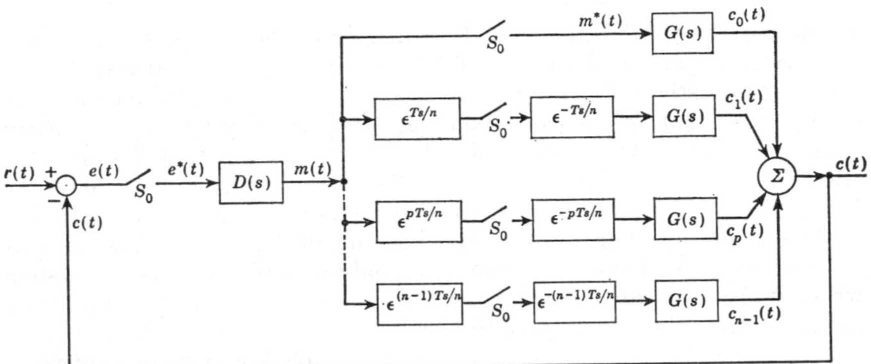

FIG. 6.7-14. Equivalent block diagram for the system of Fig. 6.7-13.

Substituting Eq. (6.7-107) into Eq. (6.7-111) and simplifying yields

$$C_p(z) = E(z)\mathfrak{z}\{\epsilon^{Tsp/n}D(s)\}\mathfrak{z}\{\epsilon^{-Tsp/n}G(s)\} \tag{6.7-112}$$

Algebraic manipulation converts Eq. (6.7-110) into:

$$C(z) = \left[D(z)G(z) + \sum_{p=1}^{n-1} \mathfrak{z}\{\epsilon^{Tsp/n}D(s)\}\mathfrak{z}\{\epsilon^{-Tsp/n}G(s)\}\right]E(z) \tag{6.7-113}$$

Eliminating $C(z)$ between Eqs. (6.7-106) and (6.7-113) yields the relationship between the z transforms of the actuating error and the input as

$$E(z) = \frac{R(z)}{1 + D(z)G(z) + \sum_{p=1}^{n-1} \mathfrak{z}\{\epsilon^{Tsp/n}D(s)\}\mathfrak{z}\{\epsilon^{-Tsp/n}G(s)\}} \tag{6.7-114}$$

Clearly, the z transform of the system output follows immediately from Eqs. (6.7-113) and (6.7-114).

Since

$$C(z)_n = G(z)_n M(z)_n = D(z)_n G(z)_n E(z) \tag{6.7-115}$$

and

$$C(z,m)_n = G(z,m)_n M(z)_n = D(z)_n G(z,m)_n E(z) \tag{6.7-116}$$

substituting Eq. (6.7-114) into Eqs. (6.7-115) and (6.7-116) yields the z_n transform and the modified z_n transform of the output of the multirate sampled-data system.

Setting the denominator of Eq. (6.7-114) equal to zero yields the characteristic equation of the system as

$$1 + D(z)G(z) + \sum_{p=1}^{n-1} \mathfrak{z}\{\epsilon^{Tsp/n}D(s)\}\mathfrak{z}\{\epsilon^{-Tsp/n}G(s)\} = 0 \qquad (6.7\text{-}117)$$

It is easily seen that in the case of $n = 1$ Eq. (6.7-117) reduces to

$$1 + D(z)G(z) = 0 \qquad (6.7\text{-}118)$$

which is evidently the characteristic equation of the corresponding single-rate system. Comparison of Eq. (6.7-117) with Eq. (6.7-118) reveals that the characteristic equation of a multirate feedback sampled-data system differs from that of the corresponding single-rate system by the extra summation term. On account of this extra term, the stability and the transient performance of the system could be improved. Furthermore, use can be made of the multirate controller to smooth the intersampling ripples in the output and to improve the settling time of the system. The numerical example given below illustrates the analysis of a sampled-data system with a multirate controller and affords discussion of the effects of multirate sampling upon the system performance.

EXAMPLE 6.7-3. Consider the multirate sampled-data system shown in Fig. 6.7-15. The sampling period of the low-speed sampler is 1 sec; the

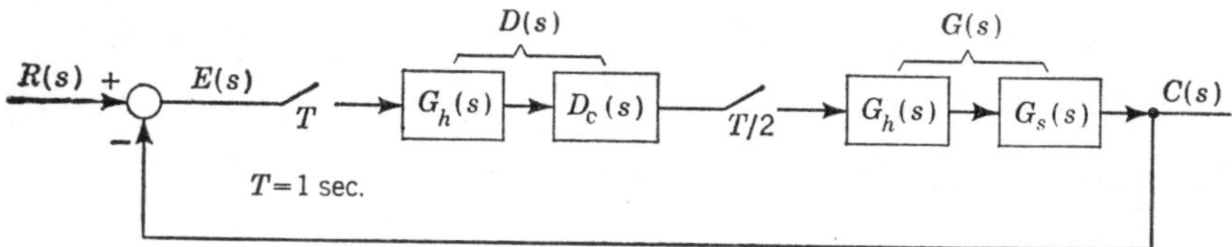

FIG. 6.7-15. Block diagram of the multirate system of Example 6.7-3.

high-speed sampler operates twice as fast. Each sampler is followed by a zero-order hold. The transfer functions of the controlled system and the control element are $G_s(s) = K/s$ and $D_c(s) = 1/(s + 1)$. Investigate the system stability and determine the system response to a unit step-function input for $K = 0.5$.

From the block diagram of Fig. 6.7-15 it is seen that the transfer functions $D(s)$ and $G(s)$ are

$$D(s) = \frac{1 - \epsilon^{-Ts}}{s} \frac{1}{s + 1} \qquad (6.7\text{-}119)$$

$$G(s) = \frac{1 - \epsilon^{-Ts/2}}{s} \frac{K}{s} \qquad (6.7\text{-}120)$$

Since $n = 2$, the z transform of the actuating error is given by

$$E(z) = \frac{R(z)}{1 + D(z)G(z) + \mathfrak{z}\{\epsilon^{Ts/2}D(s)\}\mathfrak{z}\{\epsilon^{-Ts/2}G(s)\}} \qquad (6.7\text{-}121)$$

The z transforms associated with $D(s)$, $G(s)$, $\epsilon^{Ts/2}D(s)$, and $\epsilon^{-Ts/2}G(s)$ are found to be

$$D(z) = \frac{0.632}{z - 0.368} \tag{6.7-122}$$

$$G(z) = \frac{0.5K}{z - 1} \tag{6.7-123}$$

$$\mathfrak{z}\{\epsilon^{Ts/2}D(s)\} = \frac{0.393z + 0.239}{z - 0.368} \tag{6.7-124}$$

$$\mathfrak{z}\{\epsilon^{-Ts/2}G(s)\} = \frac{0.5K}{z - 1} \tag{6.7-125}$$

Substituting the above z transforms into Eq. (6.7-121) and simplifying yield

$$E(z) = \frac{(z^2 - 1.368z + 0.368)R(z)}{z^2 - (1.368 - 0.196K)z + (0.368 + 0.436K)} \tag{6.7-126}$$

The characteristic equation of this system is

$$z^2 - (1.368 - 0.196K)z + (0.368 + 0.436K) = 0 \tag{6.7-127}$$

Applying the simplified stability criterion given in Eq. (6.2-56), it is found that the maximum allowable gain for stability is

$$K_m = 1.46 \tag{6.7-128}$$

It can readily be shown that the maximum allowable gain for the corresponding single-rate system is 1. The above analysis thus points out that the high-speed sampler tends to make the system more stable.

When the gain constant is set at 0.5 and the input to this system is a unit step function, Eq. (6.7-126) reduces to

$$\begin{aligned} E(z) &= \frac{z^3 - 1.368z^2 + 0.368z}{z^3 - 2.27z^2 + 1.856z - 0.586} \\ &= 1 + 0.902z^{-1} + 0.560z^{-2} + 0.183z^{-3} - 0.095z^{-4} - 0.228z^{-5} \\ &\quad - 0.235z^{-6} - 0.166z^{-7} - 0.075z^{-8} - 0.001z^{-9} \\ &\quad + 0.042z^{-10} + \cdots \end{aligned} \tag{6.7-129}$$

which describes the system error at the sampling instants. Since

$$C(z) = R(z) - E(z) \tag{6.7-130}$$

and

$$R(z) = \frac{z}{z - 1} = 1 + z^{-1} + z^{-2} + z^{-3} + z^{-4} + \cdots \tag{6.7-131}$$

the z transform of the system output is then given by

$$\begin{aligned} C(z) &= 0.098z^{-1} + 0.440z^{-2} + 0.817z^{-3} + 1.095z^{-4} + 1.228z^{-5} + 1.235z^{-6} \\ &\quad + 1.166z^{-7} + 1.075z^{-8} + 1.001z^{-9} + 0.958z^{-10} + \cdots \end{aligned} \tag{6.7-132}$$

The coefficients of Eq. (6.7-132) form the output sequence of the given system in response to a unit step-function input. Plotted in Fig. 6.7-16 are the output sequences of this multirate system and its corresponding single-rate system. A comparison between these two plottings reveals the effects of the high-speed sampler upon the transient behavior of the system. It is placed in evidence that with multirate compensation great improvement in the system performance results.

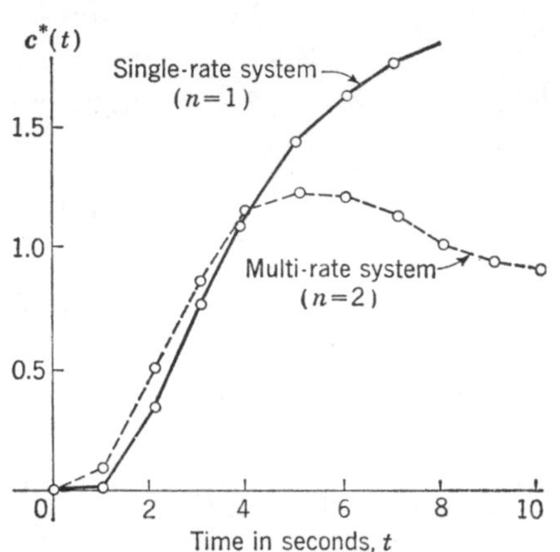

Fig. 6.7-16. The output sequences of the multirate system of Example 6.7-3 and the corresponding single-rate system.

6.8. Sampled-data Systems with Nonsynchronized Samplers. The preceding sections present the z-transform analysis of the single-rate and the multirate sampled-data systems, the samplers of which operate at a constant rate and are synchronized. There exists a type of sampled-data system, the samplers of which operate with the same rate but are not synchronized in phase. Such systems may be referred to as sampled-data systems with nonsynchronized samplers, or simply nonsynchronized sampled-data systems. Nonsynchronized sampling either occurs inherently in the control system, or is introduced deliberately into the system for improving the system stability.

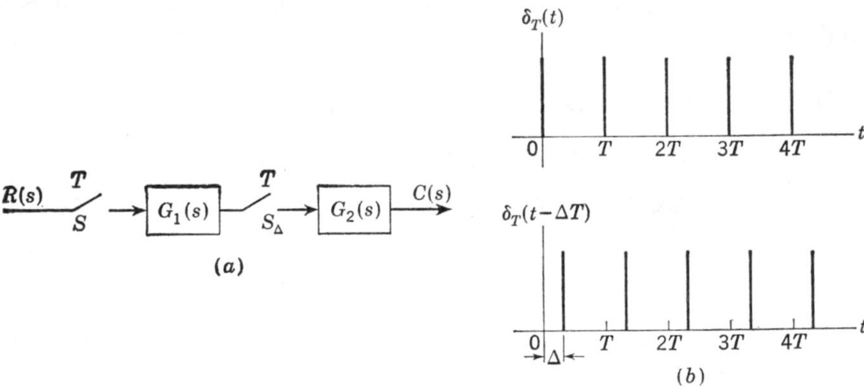

Fig. 6.8-1. (a) Block diagram of an open-loop nonsynchronized sampled-data system; (b) the sampling functions of the basic and the delayed samplers.

Nonsynchronized sampled-data systems may be analyzed by means of the z-transform techniques. Shown in Fig. 6.8-1a is the block diagram of an open-loop sampled-data system with nonsynchronized samplers. The sampling instants of the second sampler, S_Δ, occur a fraction of the sampling period T later than the corresponding sampling instants of the first sampler, as demonstrated in Fig. 6.8-1*b*. In other words, the second sampler "slips" behind the first one by ΔT sec, where Δ is a fraction and may be referred to as the *slip factor*. In order to apply the commonly used z-transform techniques, it is essential that the delayed sampler S_Δ be represented by an equivalent sampler which operates in synchronism with the first (basic) sampler. In Sec. 6.7 it has been shown that a delayed sampler may be represented by a basic sampler preceded by an advance element and followed by a delay element. Thus, the block diagram of the nonsynchronized system may be redrawn as shown in Fig. 6.8-2*a*. Since the input to the

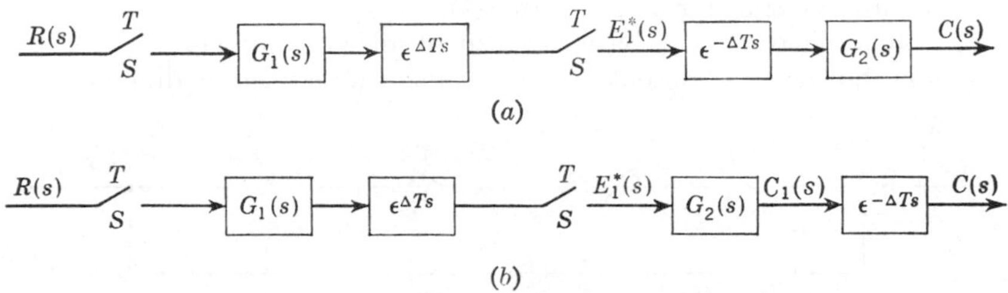

FIG. 6.8-2. (*a*) The equivalent block diagram of the system of Fig. 6.8-1(*a*); (*b*) the equivalent block diagram with $G_2(s)$ and the delay element transposed.

elements $G_2(s)$ remains the same in both configurations, the block diagram of Fig. 6.8-2*a* is equivalent to the block diagram of Fig. 6.8-1*a*. Clearly, with the nonsynchronized system represented by an equivalent synchronized system, the application of the z-transform techniques becomes fairly straightforward.

With reference to Fig. 6.8-2*a*, it is seen that the z transform and the modified z transform of the system output are

$$C(z) = \mathfrak{z}\{\epsilon^{\Delta Ts}G_1(s)\}\mathfrak{z}\{\epsilon^{-\Delta Ts}G_2(s)\}R(z) \tag{6.8-1}$$

$$C(z,m) = \mathfrak{z}\{\epsilon^{\Delta Ts}G_1(s)\}\mathfrak{z}_m\{\epsilon^{-\Delta Ts}G_2(s)\}R(z) \tag{6.8-2}$$

As discussed in the preceding section, the z transforms associated with $\epsilon^{\Delta Ts}G_1(s)$ and $\epsilon^{-\Delta Ts}G_2(s)$ can be put into compact forms by making use of the modified z transforms associated with $G_1(s)$ and $G_2(s)$. When $G_1(s)$ and $G_2(s)$ are rational polynomials in s, it follows from Eq. (6.7-9) and the definition of the modified z transform that

$$\mathfrak{z}\{\epsilon^{\Delta Ts}G_1(s)\} = zG_1(z,m)|_{m=\Delta} = zG_1(z,\Delta) \tag{6.8-3}$$

$$\mathfrak{z}\{\epsilon^{-\Delta Ts}G_2(s)\} = G_2(z,m)|_{m=1-\Delta} = G_2(z, 1 - \Delta) \tag{6.8-4}$$

To calculate the system output in response to an arbitrary input $r(t)$ generally requires the determination of the inverse transform of Eq. (6.8-2). Before the inverse can be taken, the modified z transform associated with $\epsilon^{-\Delta Ts}G_2(s)$ must be first determined. However, the evaluation of the system response can be simplified, if the block diagram of Fig. 6.8-2*a* is rearranged as shown in Fig. 6.8-2*b*, with the delay element $\epsilon^{-\Delta Ts}$ and the transfer function $G_2(s)$ transposed. From Fig. 6.8-2*b* it is seen that

$$C_1(z,m) = \mathfrak{z}\{\epsilon^{-\Delta Ts}G_1(s)\}G_2(z,m)R(z) \tag{6.8-5}$$

$$C(s) = \epsilon^{-\Delta Ts}C_1(s) \tag{6.8-6}$$

The inverse transform of Eq. (6.8-5) describes the time function $c_1^*(t,m)$, which is related to the system output $c^*(t,m)$ by

$$c^*(t,m) = c_1^*(t - \Delta T, m) \tag{6.8-7}$$

Consequently, the transient response of the system can readily be derived from the inverse transform of Eq. (6.8-5).

The block diagram of a basic nonsynchronized sampled-data feedback system is shown in Fig. 6.8-3*a*. The *z* transform and the modified *z* trans-

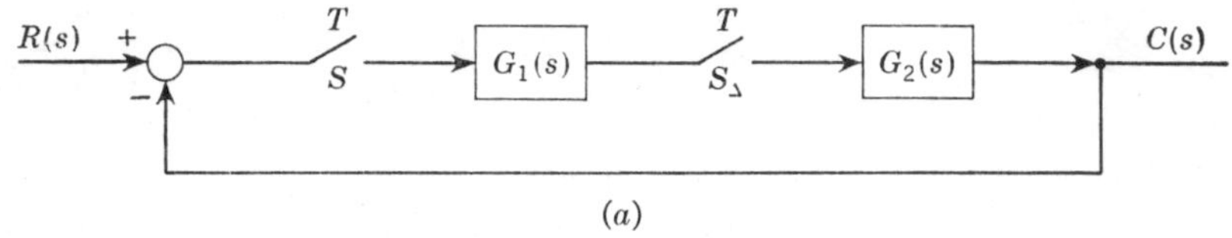

(*a*)

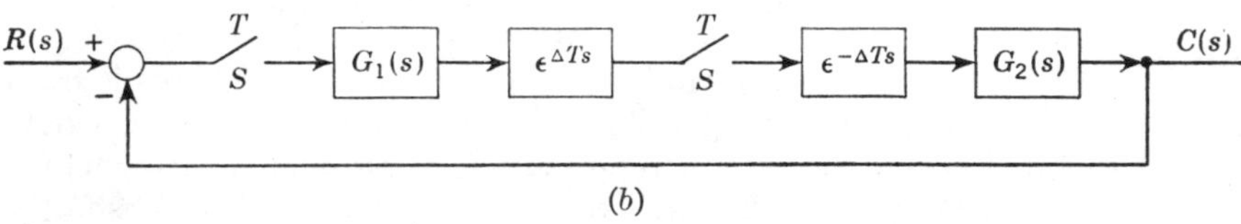

(*b*)

FIG. 6.8-3. (*a*) The block diagram of a basic unity-feedback nonsynchronized sampled-data system; (*b*) the equivalent block diagram of the system of (*a*).

form of the system output can readily be derived from the equivalent block diagram shown in Fig. 6.8-3*b*. They are

$$C(z) = \frac{\mathfrak{z}\{\epsilon^{\Delta Ts}G_1(s)\}\mathfrak{z}\{\epsilon^{-\Delta Ts}G_2(s)\}R(z)}{1 + \mathfrak{z}\{\epsilon^{\Delta Ts}G_1(s)\}\mathfrak{z}\{\epsilon^{-\Delta Ts}G_2(s)\}} \tag{6.8-8}$$

$$C(z,m) = \frac{\mathfrak{z}\{\epsilon^{\Delta Ts}G_1(s)\}\mathfrak{z}_m\{\epsilon^{-\Delta Ts}G_2(s)\}R(z)}{1 + \mathfrak{z}\{\epsilon^{\Delta Ts}G_1(s)\}\mathfrak{z}\{\epsilon^{-\Delta Ts}G_2(s)\}} \tag{6.8-9}$$

The stability of the system is determined by the location of the roots of the characteristic equation

$$1 + \mathfrak{z}\{\epsilon^{\Delta Ts}G_1(s)\}\mathfrak{z}\{\epsilon^{-\Delta Ts}G_2(s)\} = 0 \tag{6.8-10}$$

To test for system stability, use can be made of the methods described in Sec. 6.2. The transient response of the system to an arbitrary input $r(t)$ is obtained by taking the inverse transform of Eq. (6.8-9) in the same manner as discussed above.

Shown in Fig. 6.8-4a is the block diagram of a nonunity feedback nonsynchronized sampled-data system. It follows immediately from the equiv-

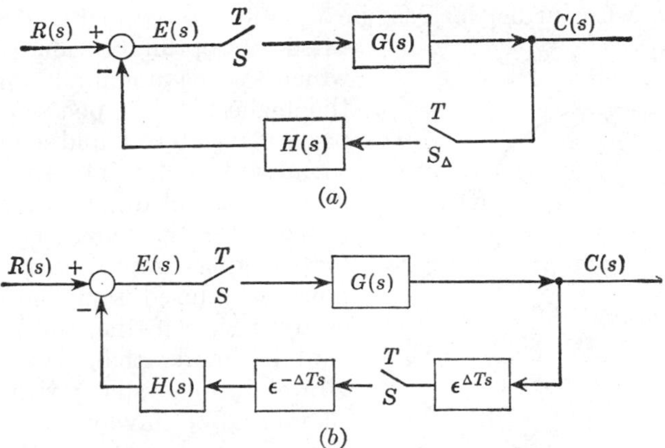

FIG. 6.8-4. (a) The block diagram of a nonunity feedback nonsynchronized sampled-data system; (b) the equivalent block diagram of the system of (a).

alent block diagram depicted in Fig. 6.8-4b that the output transforms of the system are given by

$$C(z) = \frac{G(z)R(z)}{1 + \mathfrak{Z}\{\epsilon^{\Delta Ts}G(s)\}\mathfrak{Z}\{\epsilon^{-\Delta Ts}H(s)\}} \tag{6.8-11}$$

and

$$C(z,m) = \frac{G(z,m)R(z)}{1 + \mathfrak{Z}\{\epsilon^{\Delta Ts}G(s)\}\mathfrak{Z}\{\epsilon^{-\Delta Ts}H(s)\}} \tag{6.8-12}$$

The characteristic equation of this system is

$$1 + \mathfrak{Z}\{\epsilon^{\Delta Ts}G(s)\}\mathfrak{Z}\{\epsilon^{-\Delta Ts}H(s)\} = 0 \tag{6.8-13}$$

which determines the stability and various modes of transient behavior of the system. The output transforms of more complicated nonsynchronized sampled-data systems can be derived in the same manner as the conventional sampled-data systems, provided that the nonsynchronized systems are represented by equivalent block diagrams with synchronized samplers. The slip factor Δ may vary between 0 and 1. When Δ is equal to 0 or 1, Eq. (6.8-13) reduces to

$$1 + G(z)H(z) = 0 \tag{6.8-14}$$

which is obviously the characteristic equation of the corresponding synchronized sampled-data system.

As can readily be seen from Eqs. (6.8-10) and (6.8-13), the slip factor Δ has much influence over the nature of the characteristic roots and the stability of the system. Application of the stability conditions to the characteristic equation generally leads to one or several expressions relating the maximum allowable gain for stability to the slip factor Δ. It is interesting to note that, in most cases, when Δ is increased from 0 to 1, the maximum allowable gain first increases with Δ and, after reaching a peak, it decreases with further increase in Δ, as illustrated in Fig. 6.8-5. There exists an optimum value of Δ with which the maximum allowable gain is the highest. This phenomenon is of particular interest and may be used to advantage for improving the stability of sampled-data systems. It is conceivable that greater possibilities for making improvements through nonsynchronized sampling may generally result if the control systems contain more than two samplers. However, for systems with more nonsynchronized samplers, the necessary computations involved in determining the optimum values of the slip factors become extremely lengthy and unwieldy, and thus resort is usually made to a digital computer in order to find an accurate solution in a short time.

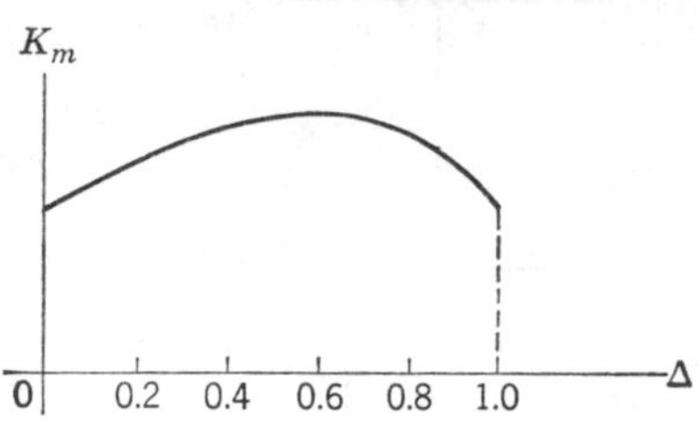

FIG. 6.8-5. Illustration of the maximum allowable gain for stability vs. the slip factor.

6.9. Cyclic Variable-rate Sampled-data Systems. The preceding sections consider the analysis of sampled-data and digital control systems which are characterized by constant rate of sampling. Whether the sampled-data control system is of the single-rate type, the multirate type,

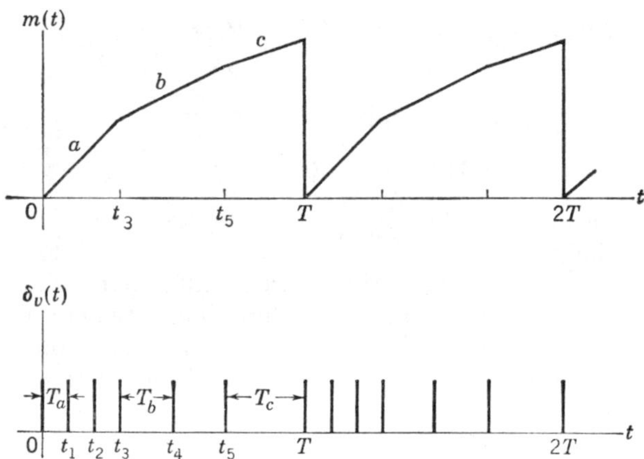

FIG. 6.9-1. The waveforms of a cyclic-variable sampling function and the modulating signal.

or the nonsynchronized type, the sampling periods of the samplers are maintained constant. Such sampled-data control systems fall into the category of constant-rate sampled-data systems, which form the majority of sampled-data and digital control systems. In contrast to the constant-rate type, there is a distinct class of sampled-data systems in which the duration between consecutive sampling pulses is not constant, but varies cyclically or is controlled by a certain function of the input of the sampler. Such control systems are commonly known as the *variable-rate sampled-data systems.* The simplest kind of variable-rate sampled-data control system is the cyclic variable-rate type. A cyclic variable-rate sampled-data or digital control system is characterized by the sampling of the data at a rate

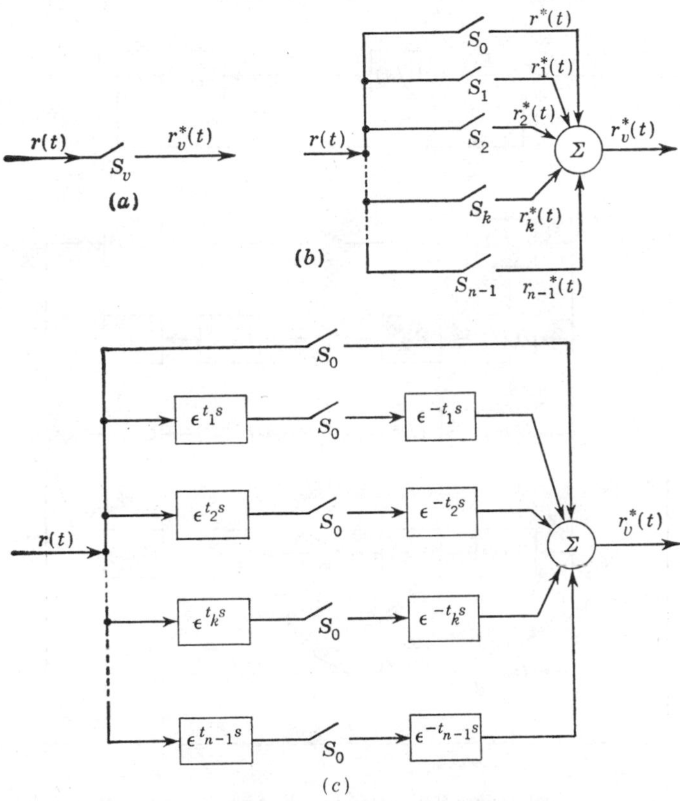

FIG. 6.9-2. (*a*) A cyclic variable-rate sampler; (*b*) a cyclic variable-rate sampler is represented by a bank of nonsynchronized samplers; (*c*) a cyclic variable-rate sampler is represented by a bank of basic samplers with appropriate advance and delay.

which varies periodically. The sampling function may be considered a *frequency-modulated* function. The sampling frequency of the sampler is varied in accordance with a specified periodic modulating signal. This section is concerned with the analysis of cyclic variable-rate sampled-data control systems.

In Fig. 6.9-1 are depicted the waveforms of a periodic modulating signal with period T and the modulated sampling function. The sampling frequency is proportional to the slope of the modulating signal $m(t)$. Between the instants 0 and t_3, the sampling frequency is $1/T_a$; during the interval from t_3 to t_5, the sampling frequency is $1/T_b$; and during the interval from t_5 to T, the sampling frequency is $1/T_c$. The sampling function repeats itself during the following periods of the modulating signal. Examination of the waveform of the sampling function reveals that the duration between the corresponding sampling pulses in two consecutive periods of the modulating signal is constant and is equal to the period T. Thus, the periodically modulated sampling function may be thought of as the sum of many a

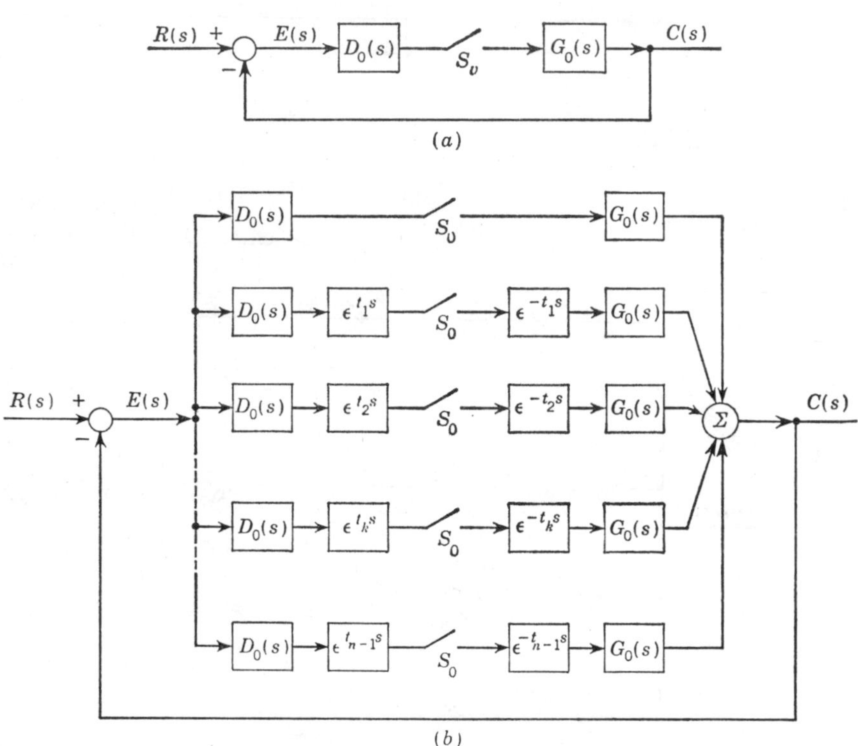

FIG. 6.9-3. (a) The block diagram of a basic cyclic variable-rate sampled-data feedback control system; (b) the equivalent block diagram of the system of (a).

simple sampling function with a constant sampling period T, and a sampler operating at a cyclic variable rate may be represented by a number of samplers operating at a constant rate, each being successively delayed by the time interval between two consecutive samples, as shown in Fig. 6.9-2. In other words, a cyclic variable-rate sampler of period T is identical to a bank of n nonsynchronized constant-rate samplers with sampling period T. The slip factor of the kth sampler is equal to t_k/T. Following the argument discussed in the preceding section, each delayed sampler may be represented by a basic sampler preceded by an appropriate fictitious advance element and followed by an appropriate fictitious delay element, and Fig. 6.9-2b may be redrawn as shown in Fig. 6.9-2c.

The block diagram of a basic cyclic variable-rate sampled-data feedback control system is shown in Fig. 6.9-3a. This variable-rate system may be reduced to an equivalent constant-rate system if the cyclic variable-rate sampler S_v is replaced by the equivalent representation of Fig. 6.9-2c. Assume that during the period from 0 to T sec the variable-rate sampler samples at the instants $t = 0, t_1, t_2, \ldots, t_{n-1}$. Then this cyclic variable-rate system may be converted into a system with n constant-rate samplers, as shown in Fig. 6.9-3b, each sampler being preceded by an appropriate advance element and followed by an appropriate delay element. Consequently, with the equivalent representation of Fig. 6.9-3b, the problem is reduced to the analysis of a constant-rate sampled-data feedback system containing n parallel branches in the forward path.[180,200]

In the following analysis, the transfer functions of the system components including the fictitious advance or delay element are denoted by $D_k(s)$ and $G_k(s)$, which are separated from each other by a sampler. Then

$$D_k(s) = \epsilon^{t_k s} D_0(s) \tag{6.9-1}$$

$$G_k(s) = \epsilon^{-t_k s} G_0(s) \tag{6.9-2}$$

Inspection of the block diagram of Fig. 6.9-3b reveals that

$$\begin{aligned} C(s) &= G_0(s)ED_0^*(s) + G_1(s)ED_1^*(s) + \cdots + G_k(s)ED_k^*(s) \\ &\qquad + \cdots + G_{n-1}(s)ED_{n-1}^*(s) \\ &= \sum_{k=0}^{n-1} G_k(s)ED_k^*(s) \end{aligned} \tag{6.9-3}$$

and

$$\begin{aligned} E(s) &= R(s) - C(s) \\ &= R(s) - [G_0(s)ED_0^*(s) + G_1(s)ED_1^*(s) + \cdots + G_k(s)ED_k^*(s) \\ &\qquad + \cdots + G_{n-1}(s)ED_{n-1}^*(s)] \end{aligned} \tag{6.9-4}$$

Taking the z transform of both sides of Eq. (6.9-3) gives

$$C(z) = \sum_{k=0}^{n-1} G_k(z)ED_k(z) \tag{6.9-5}$$

Multiplying both sides of Eq. (6.9-4) by $D_k(s)$, taking the z transform and rearranging yields

$$\begin{aligned} G_0D_k(z)ED_0(z) + G_1D_k(z)ED_1(z) + \cdots + [1 + G_kD_k(z)]ED_k(z) \\ + \cdots + G_{n-1}D_k(z)ED_{n-1}(z) = RD_k(z) \end{aligned} \tag{6.9-6}$$

Thus, it can readily be shown that the functions $ED_k(z)$ and $RD_k(z)$

are related by the single matrix equation

$$[GD]\{ED\} = \{RD\} \tag{6.9-7}$$

where $\{ED\}$ and $\{RD\}$ are column matrices, the elements of which are the functions $ED_k(z)$ and $RD_k(z)$, namely,

$$\{ED\} = \begin{Bmatrix} ED_0(z) \\ ED_1(z) \\ \cdots\cdots \\ ED_k(z) \\ \cdots\cdots \\ ED_{n-1}(z) \end{Bmatrix} \tag{6.9-8}$$

$$\{RD\} = \begin{Bmatrix} RD_0(z) \\ RD_1(z) \\ \cdots\cdots \\ RD_k(z) \\ \cdots\cdots \\ RD_{n-1}(z) \end{Bmatrix} \tag{6.9-9}$$

and $[GD]$ is a square matrix of order n:

$$[GD] = \begin{bmatrix} 1 + G_0D_0(z) & G_1D_0(z) & \cdots & G_kD_0(z) & \cdots & G_{n-1}D_0(z) \\ G_0D_1(z) & 1 + G_1D_1(z) & \cdots & G_kD_1(z) & \cdots & G_{n-1}D_1(z) \\ \cdots\cdots & \cdots\cdots & & \cdots\cdots & & \cdots\cdots \\ G_0D_k(z) & G_1D_k(z) & \cdots & 1 + G_kD_k(z) & \cdots & G_{n-1}D_k(z) \\ \cdots\cdots & \cdots\cdots & & \cdots\cdots & & \cdots\cdots \\ G_0D_{n-1}(z) & G_1D_{n-1}(z) & \cdots & G_kD_{n-1}(z) & \cdots & 1 + G_{n-1}D_{n-1}(z) \end{bmatrix} \tag{6.9-10}$$

The solution of Eq. (6.9-7) is then given by

$$\{ED\} = [GD]^{-1}\{RD\} \tag{6.9-11}$$

The functions $ED_k(z)$ are obtained by carrying out the necessary matrix manipulations. Likewise, the solution of Eq. (6.9-7) may be conveniently derived by applying Cramer's rule. The determinant of the system is

$$B(z) = \begin{vmatrix} 1 + G_0D_0(z) & G_1D_0(z) & \cdots & G_kD_0(z) & \cdots & G_{n-1}D_0(z) \\ G_0D_1(z) & 1 + G_1D_1(z) & \cdots & G_kD_1(z) & \cdots & G_{n-1}D_1(z) \\ \cdots\cdots & \cdots\cdots & & \cdots\cdots & & \cdots\cdots \\ G_0D_k(z) & G_1D_k(z) & \cdots & 1 + G_kD_k(z) & \cdots & G_{n-1}D_k(z) \\ \cdots\cdots & \cdots\cdots & & \cdots\cdots & & \cdots\cdots \\ G_0D_{n-1}(z) & G_1D_{n-1}(z) & \cdots & G_kD_{n-1}(z) & \cdots & 1 + G_{n-1}D_{n-1}(z) \end{vmatrix} \tag{6.9-12}$$

and Eq. (6.9-7) is found to have a unique solution given by

$$ED_k(z) = \frac{Q_k(z)}{B(z)} \tag{6.9-13}$$

where $Q_k(z)$ is the determinant formed by replacing the elements of the kth column of the system determinant by $RD_0(z)$, $RD_1(z)$, . . . , $RD_k(z)$, . . . , $RD_{n-1}(z)$, respectively. Consequently, substituting Eq. (6.9-13) into Eq. (6.9-5) yields the z transform of the system output as

$$C(z) = \frac{\sum_{k=0}^{n-1} G_k(z)Q_k(z)}{B(z)} \tag{6.9-14}$$

In like manner, the modified z transform of the system output is found to be

$$C(z,m) = \frac{\sum_{k=0}^{n-1} G_k(z,m)Q_k(z)}{B(z)} \tag{6.9-15}$$

For example, in the case of a system with two parallel forward branches (that is, $n = 2$), the z transform and the modified z transform of the output are given by

$$C(z) = \frac{\begin{gathered}[RD_0(z) + RD_0(z)G_1D_1(z) - RD_1(z)G_1D_0(z)]G_0(z) \\ + [RD_1(z) + RD_1(z)G_0D_0(z) - RD_0(z)G_0D_1(z)]G_1(z)\end{gathered}}{[1 + G_0D_0(z)][1 + G_1D_1(z)] - G_0D_1(z)G_1D_0(z)} \tag{6.9-16a}$$

$$C(z,m) = \frac{\begin{gathered}[RD_0(z) + RD_0(z)G_1D_1(z) - RD_1(z)G_1D_0(z)]G_0(z,m) \\ + [RD_1(z) + RD_1(z)G_0D_0(z) - RD_0(z)G_0D_1(z)]G_1(z,m)\end{gathered}}{[1 + G_0D_0(z)][1 + G_1D_1(z)] - G_0D_1(z)G_1D_0(z)} \tag{6.9-16b}$$

By the substitution of Eqs. (6.9-1) and (6.9-2) into Eq. (6.9-14) or Eq. (6.9-15), the stability of the cyclic variable-rate sampled-data system can be determined in the usual manner, and the transient response of the system to an arbitrary input $r(t)$ can be obtained by taking the inverse transform of Eq. (6.9-15). As can readily be seen, the introduction of a cyclic variable-rate sampler into a sampled-data system does not present any startling problem. The concept of equivalent samplers enables the analysis of cyclic variable-rate sampled-data control systems and related problems to be performed by the widely used z-transform and the modified z-transform methods in a systematic manner. To illustrate the analysis of cyclic variable-rate sampled-data feedback control systems by means of the techniques described in the preceding paragraphs, a simple numerical example is presented below.

EXAMPLE 6.9-1. Consider the cyclic variable-rate error-sampled feedback system shown in Fig. 6.9-4. The sampler operates at the instants

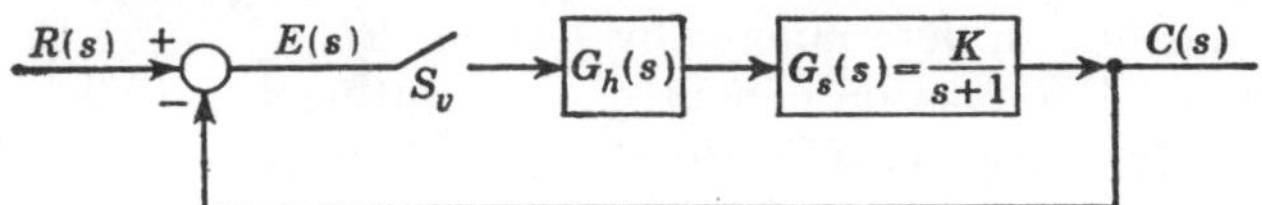

FIG. 6.9-4. Block diagram of the system of Example 6.9-1.

$t = 0, T/4; T, 5T/4; \ldots ; kT, (k + 1/4)T; \ldots$. T is assumed to be 1 sec. A zero-order hold is used as the smoothing device. The transfer function of the controlled system is

$$G_s(s) = \frac{K}{s+1} \tag{6.9-17}$$

Investigate the system stability and determine the transient response of the system to a unit step-function input for $K = 4$.

The given cyclic variable-rate sampled-data system is equivalent to the constant-rate sampled-data system shown in Fig. 6.9-5, in which equivalent

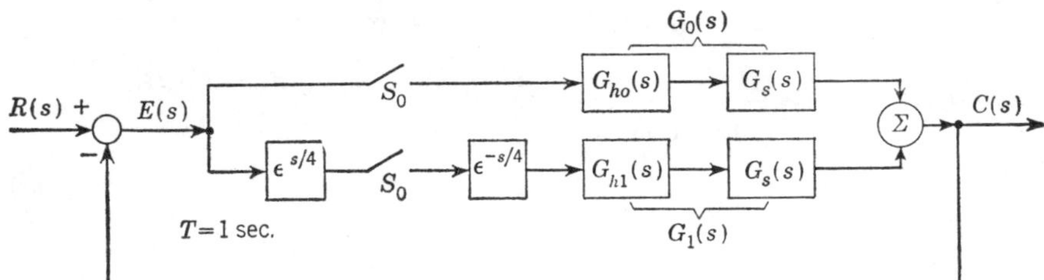

FIG. 6.9-5. The equivalent block diagram of the system of Example 6.9-1.

constant-rate samplers take the place of the cyclic variable-rate sampler S_v. In view of the fact that the sampling period of S_v is not constant, the transfer function of the zero-order hold $G_h(s)$ is different from the conventional transfer function derived in Sec. 4.6. The waveform of the signal from the zero-order hold $G_h(s)$ is depicted in Fig. 6.9-6a. When the block diagram of Fig. 6.9-4 is reduced to that of Fig. 6.9-5, the zero-order hold is split into two parts, one for each branch. The zero-order hold for the first branch $G_{h0}(s)$ clamps the signal samples occurring at the instants $t = 0, T, 2T, 3T, \ldots,$ for a period of $T/4$ sec. The zero-order hold for the second branch $G_{h1}(s)$ clamps the signal samples occurring at the instants $t = T/4, T + T/4, 2T + T/4, \ldots,$ for a period of $3T/4$ sec. From the waveforms of the signals from $G_{h0}(s)$ and $G_{h1}(s)$ shown in Fig. 6.9-6b and c, it can readily be shown that the transfer functions of the zero-order holds are

$$G_{h0}(s) = \frac{1 - \epsilon^{-s/4}}{s} \tag{6.9-18}$$

$$G_{h1}(s) = \frac{1 - \epsilon^{-3s/4}}{s} \tag{6.9-19}$$

Now, define the following transfer functions:

$$D_0(s) = 1 \tag{6.9-20}$$

$$D_1(s) = \epsilon^{s/4} \tag{6.9-21}$$

$$G_0(s) = \frac{1 - \epsilon^{-s/4}}{s} \frac{K}{s+1} \tag{6.9-22}$$

$$G_1(s) = \frac{\epsilon^{-s/4}(1 - \epsilon^{-3s/4})}{s} \frac{K}{s+1} \tag{6.9-23}$$

Equation (6.9-16) may be used to determine the unit step-function response of the system. In order to apply Eq. (6.9-16), the z transforms associated with the following transfer functions must be derived first:

$$G_0D_0(s) = \frac{K(1 - \epsilon^{-s/4})}{s(s+1)} \tag{6.9-24}$$

$$G_1D_0(s) = \frac{K(\epsilon^{-s/4} - \epsilon^{-s})}{s(s+1)} \tag{6.9-25}$$

$$G_0D_1(s) = \frac{K(\epsilon^{s/4} - 1)}{s(s+1)} \tag{6.9-26}$$

$$G_1D_1(s) = \frac{K(1 - \epsilon^{-3s/4})}{s(s+1)} \tag{6.9-27}$$

$$RD_0(s) = \frac{1}{s} \tag{6.9-28}$$

$$RD_1(s) = \frac{\epsilon^{s/4}}{s} \tag{6.9-29}$$

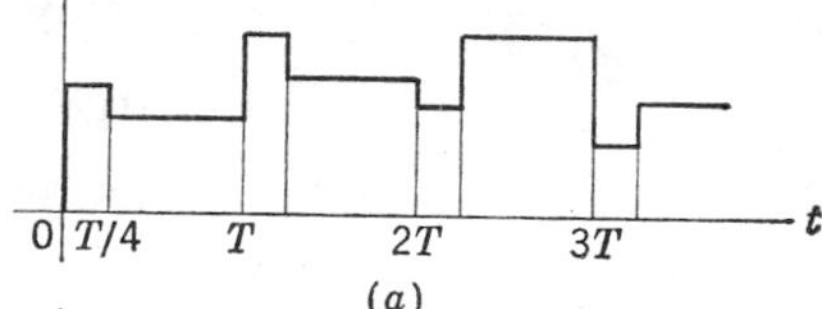

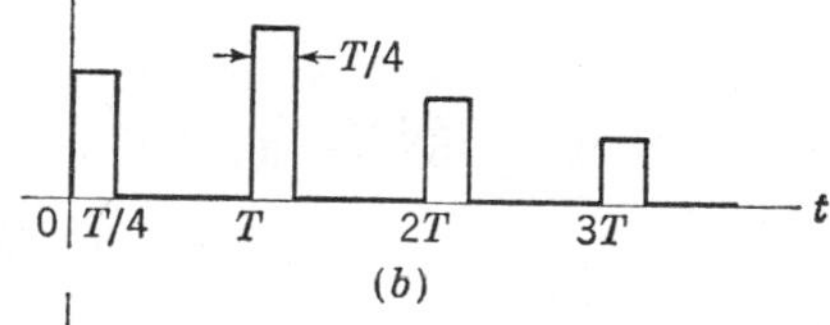

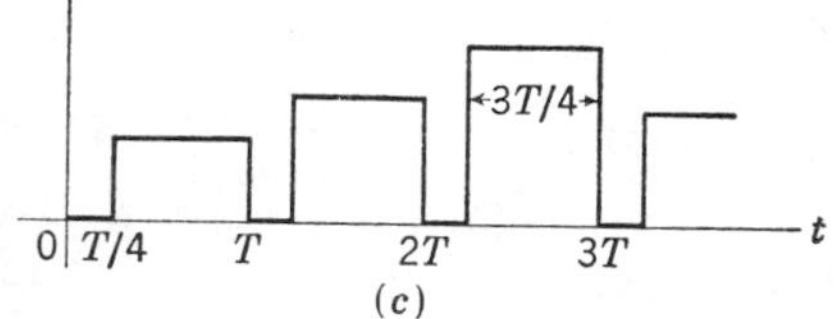

FIG. 6.9-6. Waveforms of the signals from the zero-order holds.

Making use of Eq. (6.7-9) and the properties of the modified z transform, the corresponding z transforms are found to be

$$G_0D_0(z) = \mathfrak{z}\left\{\frac{K}{s(s+1)}\right\} - \mathfrak{z}_m\left\{\frac{K}{s(s+1)}\right\}\bigg|_{m=3/4} = \frac{0.104K}{z - 0.368} \tag{6.9-30}$$

$$G_1D_0(z) = \mathfrak{z}_m\left\{\frac{K}{s(s+1)}\right\}\bigg|_{m=3/4} - z^{-1}\mathfrak{z}\left\{\frac{K}{s(s+1)}\right\} = \frac{0.528K}{z - 0.368} \tag{6.9-31}$$

$$G_0D_1(z) = z\mathfrak{z}_m\left\{\frac{K}{s(s+1)}\right\}\Big|_{m=\frac{1}{4}} - \mathfrak{z}\left\{\frac{K}{s(s+1)}\right\} = \frac{0.221Kz}{z-0.368} \tag{6.9-32}$$

$$G_1D_1(z) = \mathfrak{z}\left\{\frac{K}{s(s+1)}\right\} - \mathfrak{z}_m\left\{\frac{K}{s(s+1)}\right\}\Big|_{m=\frac{1}{4}} = \frac{0.411K}{z-0.368} \tag{6.9-33}$$

$$RD_0(z) = \mathfrak{z}\left\{\frac{1}{s}\right\} = \frac{z}{z-1} \tag{6.9-34}$$

$$RD_1(z) = z\mathfrak{z}_m\left\{\frac{1}{s}\right\}\Big|_{m=\frac{1}{4}} = \frac{z}{z-1} \tag{6.9-35}$$

It is also to be noted that

$$G_0(z) = G_0D_0(z) \tag{6.9-36}$$

$$G_1(z) = G_1D_0(z) \tag{6.9-37}$$

Substituting Eqs. (6.9-30) through (6.9-33) into the denominator of Eq. (6.9-16a) and equating the result to zero yields the characteristic equation of the cyclic variable-rate sampled-data system as

$$F(z) = z^2 - (0.117K^2 - 0.515K + 0.736)z + (0.0428K^2 - 0.1895K + 0.1355) = 0 \tag{6.9-38}$$

The system is stable if both the zeros of $F(z)$ lie inside the unit circle of the z plane. In terms of the coefficients of the polynomial, these conditions are given by Eq. (6.2-56) and are repeated below:

$$|F(0)| < 1 \qquad F(1) > 0 \qquad F(-1) > 0 \tag{6.9-39}$$

Application of these conditions to Eq. (6.9-38) yields the following inequalities:

$$K^2 - 4.42K - 20.15 < 0 \tag{6.9-40}$$

$$-K^2 + 4.39K + 5.39 > 0 \tag{6.9-41}$$

$$K^2 - 4.41K + 11.69 > 0 \tag{6.9-42}$$

The third inequality (6.9-42) is satisfied as long as K is real. From the first and the second inequality (6.9-40) and (6.9-41), one obtains

$$K < 7.21 \qquad K < 5.39 \tag{6.9-43}$$

Consequently, the maximum allowable gain for stability is

$$K_m = 5.39 \tag{6.9-44}$$

Now, when the gain constant K is set at 4, by proper substitution Eq. (6.9-16a) reduces to

$$C(z) = \frac{0.662z^2 - 0.245z}{z^3 - 1.545z^2 + 0.607z - 0.0613} = 0.662z^{-1} + 0.777z^{-2} + 0.798z^{-3} + 0.798z^{-4} + \cdots \tag{6.9-45}$$

The coefficients of Eq. (6.9-45) represent the values of the system response at the sampling instants $t = 0, T, 2T, 3T, \ldots$. The system response between these instants may be determined from Eq. (6.9-16*b*) in the usual manner. For instance, to evaluate the response at the instants $t = kT + T/4$, it is necessary to find the modified z transforms $G_0(z,m)$ and $G_1(z,m)$ for $m = \frac{1}{4}$. Thus,

$$G_0(z,\tfrac{1}{4}) = \mathfrak{Z}_m \left\{ \frac{4(1 - \epsilon^{-s/4})}{s(s+1)} \right\} \Bigg|_{m=\frac{1}{4}} = \mathfrak{Z} \left\{ \frac{4(1 - \epsilon^{-s/4})\epsilon^{s/4}}{s(s+1)} \right\}$$

$$= \frac{0.884z}{z - 0.368} \tag{6.9-46}$$

$$G_1(z,\tfrac{1}{4}) = \mathfrak{Z}_m \left\{ \frac{4(1 - \epsilon^{-3s/4})\epsilon^{-s/4}}{s(s+1)} \right\} \Bigg|_{m=\frac{1}{4}} = \mathfrak{Z} \left\{ \frac{4(1 - \epsilon^{-3s/4})}{s(s+1)} \right\}$$

$$= \frac{1.644}{z - 0.368} \tag{6.9-47}$$

It follows immediately from Eq. (6.9-16*b*) after proper substitution and simplification that

$$C(z,\tfrac{1}{4}) = \frac{0.884z^3 - 0.549z^2 + 0.079z}{z^3 - 1.545z^2 + 0.607z - 0.0613}$$

$$= 0.884 + 0.812z^{-1} + 0.794z^{-2} + 0.794z^{-3} + \cdots \tag{6.9-48}$$

In like manner, it is found that

$$G_0(z,\tfrac{1}{2}) = \frac{0.692z}{z - 0.368} \tag{6.9-49}$$

$$G_1(z,\tfrac{1}{2}) = \frac{0.884z + 0.952}{z - 0.368} \tag{6.9-50}$$

$$G_0(z,\tfrac{3}{4}) = \frac{0.536z}{z - 0.368} \tag{6.9-51}$$

$$G_1(z,\tfrac{3}{4}) = \frac{1.575z + 0.416}{z - 0.368} \tag{6.9-52}$$

The modified z transforms of the output for $m = \frac{1}{2}$ and $m = \frac{3}{4}$ are then given by

$$C(z,\tfrac{1}{2}) = \frac{0.795z^3 - 0.426z^2 + 0.046z}{z^3 - 1.545z^2 + 0.607z - 0.0613}$$

$$= 0.794 + 0.802z^{-1} + 0.800z^{-2} + 0.803z^{-3} + \cdots \tag{6.9-53}$$

$$C(z,\tfrac{3}{4}) = \frac{0.719z^3 - 0.325z^2 + 0.02z}{z^3 - 1.545z^2 + 0.607z - 0.0613}$$

$$= 0.719 + 0.786z^{-1} + 0.799z^{-2} + 0.801z^{-3} + \cdots \quad (6.9\text{-}54)$$

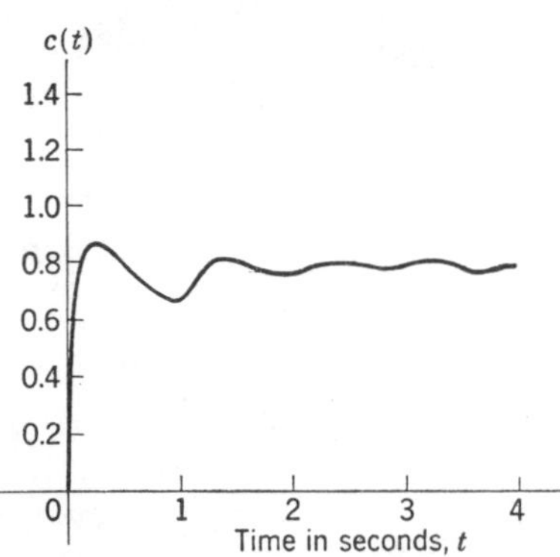

FIG. 6.9-7. The unit step-function response of the system of Example 6.9-1.

The unit step-function response of this system is plotted in Fig. 6.9-7.

6.10. Sampled-data Feedback Control Systems with Transport Lags.[84] Transport lag or distance-velocity lag occurs in many control systems. For instance, in feedback control systems including a human operator within the loop, the reaction time of the human operator forms a distance-velocity lag; in process control systems, the plant can generally be described by a system with several time constants and a transport lag; in digital control systems, the computation time and the analog-digital conversion time reflect as a transport lag in the system. The presence of a transport lag in a continuous-data control system generally complicates the analysis of the system. The usefulness of the root-locus method is severely limited, and the commonly used Bode-diagram techniques become more difficult to apply. On the other hand, the presence of a transport lag in a sampled-data control system brings about no complication of the analysis procedures. The various methods discussed in the previous sections can be applied in much the same manner as they are used in analyzing sampled-data systems without transport lags.

Indeed, the introduction of a transport lag into a sampled-data system does not create any new problem; nevertheless in the presence of a transport lag some interesting phenomena generally occur. It has been pointed out in Chap. 4 that a transport lag could yield a stabilizing effect. In sampled-data feedback control systems, a transport lag has practically the same influence upon the system stability as a phase-lag network. Consequently, a sampled-data control system, which would require phase-lag compensation, may generally be stabilized by means of a transport-lag element. On the contrary, in continuous-data systems the presence of a transport lag always makes the stabilization of the system more difficult to effect. A transport lag in the forward path increases the phase lag through the system and hence tends to decrease the stability margin.

The block diagram of a basic sampled-data feedback control system with a transport lag is shown in Fig. 6.10-1. As discussed in Sec. 2.1, the transfer function of transport-lag element is $\epsilon^{-T_d s}$, where T_d is the dead-time delay introduced by this element. From Fig. 6.10-1, it is seen that the open-loop transfer function in s is

$$G(s) = G_h(s)G_1(s)\epsilon^{-T_d s} \tag{6.10-1}$$

and the open-loop pulse-transfer function in z is given by the z transform

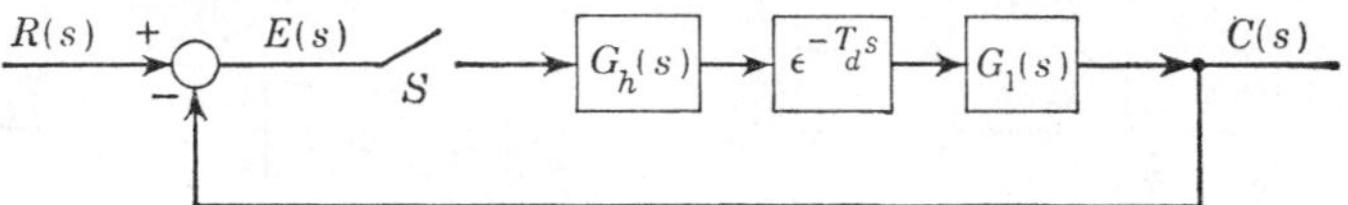

Fig. 6.10-1. The block diagram of a sampled-data feedback control system with a transport lag.

associated with Eq. (6.10-1). If a zero-order hold is used, the z transform is

$$G(z) = \mathfrak{z}\left\{(1 - \epsilon^{-Ts})\epsilon^{-T_d s}\frac{G_1(s)}{s}\right\} \tag{6.10-2}$$

which may be written as

$$G(z) = (1 - z^{-1})\mathfrak{z}\left\{\epsilon^{-T_d s}\frac{G_1(s)}{s}\right\} \tag{6.10-3}$$

By letting $G_0(s) = G_1(s)/s$ and making use of the modified z transformation, the open-loop pulse-transfer function may be put into the form

$$G(z) = (1 - z^{-1})G_0(z,m)|_{m=1-T_d/T} = (1 - z^{-1})G_0(z, 1 - T_d/T) \tag{6.10-4}$$

in which $G_0(z,m)$ is the modified z transform associated with $G_0(s)$ and T_d is assumed to be less than T. In case T_d exceeds T such that $T_d = nT + \lambda T$, where n is an integer and λ is a fraction, $\epsilon^{-T_d s} = \epsilon^{-nTs}\epsilon^{-\lambda Ts}$. Then, in taking the z transform, ϵ^{-nTs} may be separated from the other part, and it is transformed to z^{-n} by direct substitution.

Clearly, the characteristic equation of the system is $1 + G(z) = 0$, that is,

$$z + (z - 1)G_0(z, 1 - T_d/T) = 0 \tag{6.10-5}$$

As usual, the stability is determined by the roots of the characteristic equation. The Routh and Hurwitz criteria can be used to test for stability, if Eq. (6.10-5) is transformed into the w plane through a bilinear transformation, as discussed in Sec. 6.2. However, when the characteristic equation is of the second order, the simplified criterion stated in Eq. (6.2-56) is probably the most convenient method of testing the stability and determining the maximum allowable gain. The output sequence of the system in response to an arbitrary input $r(t)$ can readily be evaluated from the output transform

$$C(z) = \frac{G(z)}{1 + G(z)}R(z)$$

$$= \frac{(z - 1)G_0(z, 1 - T_d/T)}{z + (z - 1)G_0(z, 1 - T_d/T)}R(z) \tag{6.10-6}$$

A numerical example is presented below to illustrate the analysis of sampled-data control systems with transport lags and to afford discussion of the effect of the transport lag upon the stability of the system.

EXAMPLE 6.10-1. The block diagram of the system to be considered is shown in Fig. 6.10-2. Assume that the transport lag T_d is smaller than the

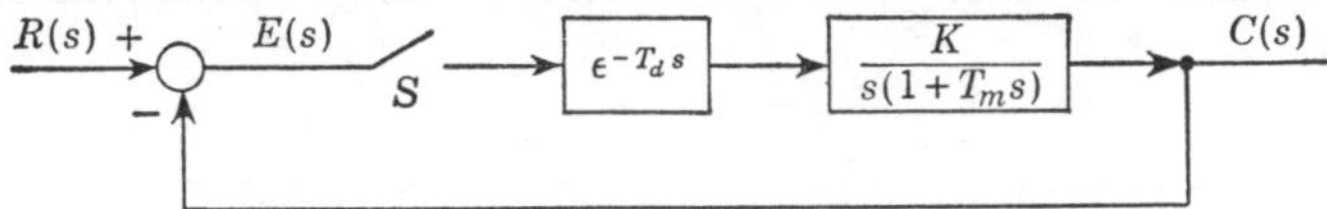

FIG. 6.10-2. The block diagram of the system of Example 6.10-1.

sampling period T, and the transfer function of the continuous part of the system is

$$G(s) = \frac{K}{s(1+T_m s)} \epsilon^{-T_d s} \tag{6.10-7}$$

Study the effect of the transport lag upon the system stability.

The open-loop pulse-transfer function is found to be

$$\begin{aligned} G(z) &= \mathfrak{z}\left\{\frac{K}{s(1+T_m s)} \epsilon^{-T_d s}\right\} \\ &= \mathfrak{z}_m \left\{\frac{K}{s(1+T_m s)}\right\}\bigg|_{m=1-T_d/T} \\ &= \frac{K}{z-1} - \frac{K\epsilon^{-(T-T_d)/T_m}}{z-\epsilon^{-T/T_m}} \end{aligned} \tag{6.10-8}$$

The characteristic equation is given by

$$1 + G(z) = 0 \tag{6.10-9}$$

Substituting Eq. (6.10-8) into Eq. (6.10-9) and simplifying yields

$$\begin{aligned} F(z) = z^2 - [1 + \epsilon^{-T/T_m} + K\epsilon^{-(T-T_d)/T_m} - K]z \\ + (1-K)\epsilon^{-T/T_m} + K\epsilon^{-(T-T_d)/T_m} = 0 \end{aligned} \tag{6.10-10}$$

Applying the simplified criterion given by Eq. (6.2-56) leads to the following inequalities:

$$K\epsilon^{-(T-T_d)/T_m} - K\epsilon^{-T/T_m} + \epsilon^{-T/T_m} < 1 \tag{6.10-11}$$

$$K - K\epsilon^{-T/T_m} > 0 \tag{6.10-12}$$

$$2(1+\epsilon^{-T/T_m}) - K(1+\epsilon^{-T/T_m}) + 2K\epsilon^{-(T-T_d)/T_m} > 0 \tag{6.10-13}$$

Since K, T, and T_m are always positive, the second inequality, (6.10-12), is fulfilled. Transposing and simplifying reduces inequality (6.10-11) to

$$K < \frac{\epsilon^{T/T_m} - 1}{\epsilon^{T_d/T_m} - 1} \tag{6.10-14}$$

In like manner, inequality (6.10-13) can be reduced to

$$K < \frac{2}{1 - 2\epsilon^{T_d/T_m}/(1 + \epsilon^{T/T_m})} \qquad (6.10\text{-}15)$$

Clearly, these two inequalities, (6.10-14) and (6.10-15), determine the stability boundary of the system. For specified values of T and T_m, the stability boundaries are the curves relating the maximum allowable value of the gain constant K to the transport lag T_d, as shown in Fig. 6.10-3. Inequality (6.10-15) imposes a limit upon the maximum allowable gain for small values of the transport lag T_d, and the inequality (6.10-14) controls the maximum allowable gain for values of T_d greater than a certain fraction of the sampling period T, which is determined by the intersecting point of these two boundary lines, as demonstrated in Fig. 6.10-3.

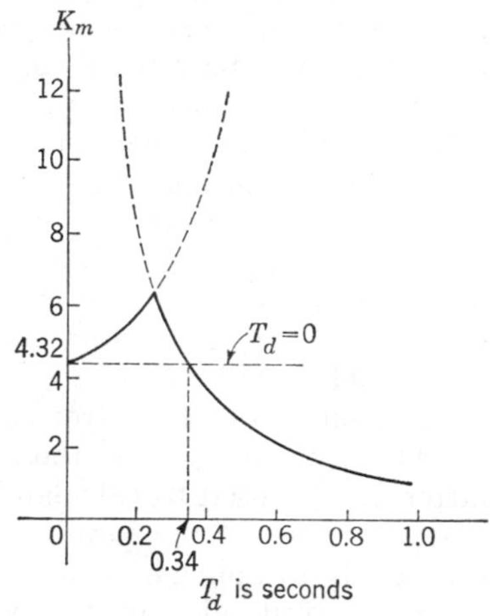

Fig. 6.10-3. The stability boundary of a sampled-data system with a transport lag ($T = 1$ sec and $T_m = 1$ sec).

It has been shown in Sec. 6.2 that, in the absence of the transport lag T_d, the maximum allowable gain of this system is given by Eq. (6.2-67), and is repeated below:

$$K < \frac{2(1 + \epsilon^{-T/T_m})}{1 - \epsilon^{-T/T_m}} \qquad (6.10\text{-}16)$$

For $T = 1$ sec and $T_m = 1$ sec, the maximum allowable gain is found to be

$$K_m = 4.32 \qquad (6.10\text{-}17)$$

From the stability boundary plotted in Fig. 6.10-3 for the case of $T = 1$ sec and $T_m = 1$ sec, it is seen that when the transport lag T_d is less than 0.34 sec, the system with the transport lag has a value of the maximum allowable gain higher than that of the corresponding system without a transport lag. However, when the transport lag is increased beyond this value, the maximum allowable gain decreases rapidly. For instance, when the transport lag is equal to the sampling period, the maximum allowable gain of the system is only 1, against a K_m of 4.32 for $T_d = 0$. This example makes evident that when the values of T_d fall within a certain range, the transport lag provides a stabilizing effect.

6.11. Conclusion. In this chapter, an attempt has been made to present the analysis of digital and sampled-data control systems by means of the z-transform techniques. To secure the stability of a pulsed-data feedback control system it is necessary that all the closed-loop poles of the system lie inside the unit circle in the z plane, with the exception of a possible pole at $z = 1$. Three methods of determining the stability of digital and sampled-data control systems are discussed. The Schur-Cohn criterion provides an analytical tool for testing the system stability. The Nyquist criterion provides a graphical means of determining the stability. The bilinear transformation technique allows the use of the Routh and Hurwitz criteria and facilitates the application of the Bode-diagram method for stability analysis. The transient response of a sampled-data control system to a test input may be readily evaluated by taking the inverse of the z transform or the modified z transform of the system output.

The digital and sampled-data control systems may be classified according to the number of poles at $z = 1$ contained in the open-loop pulse-transfer function $G(z)$. For instance, a system with $G(z)$ possessing no pole at $z = 1$ may be termed a type 0 system, whereas a system with $G(z)$ containing one pole at $z = 1$ may be classified as a type 1 system. In pulsed-data control systems, the performance of a given system to a certain input may be characterized by system parameters which are commonly known as the error coefficients. The error coefficients for a pulsed-data control system have the same meaning as those for a continuous-data control system. The latter can be used to calculate the steady-state error of continuous-data systems, whereas the former can be used to determine the steady-state error at the sampling instants of pulsed-data systems. The error coefficients for a sampled-data control system can be readily evaluated from the system-error pulse-transfer function in starred transform.

The concept of equivalent samplers enables the analysis and synthesis of multirate sampled-data control systems, cyclic variable-rate control systems, pulsed-data systems with nonsynchronized samplers and other related problems to be performed by the widely used z transform and modified z-transform methods in a systematic manner. The multirate sampling technique is a means to reduce the ripple content in the system output and to increase the response speed of the system. Furthermore, it can be used to analyze nonlinear sampled-data control systems.† The nonsynchronized sampling technique provides a means of improving the stability of pulsed-data feedback control systems. The introduction of a transport lag into sampled-data control systems does not present any new problems. The z-transform method is directly applicable. The stability of control systems with distributed constants and transport lags may be improved by making use of the sampling operation.

† E. Kinnen, "An Analysis of Nonlinear Sampled-data Control Systems," doctoral dissertation, Purdue University, Lafayette, Indiana, 1958.

CHAPTER 7

TRANSIENT RESPONSE AND SYSTEM-ERROR ANALYSIS

7.1. Effect of the Pole-zero Configurations in the z Plane upon the System Transient Behavior. In the preceding chapter the analysis of sampled-data and digital control systems by means of the z transform and the modified z-transform methods has been discussed. The system stability and the system performance can be determined from a plot of the z-transform locus of the open-loop pulse-transfer function of the system, or from a study of the roots of the characteristic equation in z. As discussed in Sec. 6.2, for stable operation the characteristic roots of a sampled-data control system must be located inside the unit circle of the z plane. The relative stability and the general transient behavior of sampled-data control systems are intimately related to the locations of the characteristic roots inside the unit circle. Consequently, a knowledge of the correlation between the locations of the poles and zeros of the system function in z and transient behavior generally enables the designer to control the transient response and facilitates the synthesis of sampled-data control systems to meet time-domain specifications. This section and the following one are concerned with the effect of the pole-zero distribution of sampled-data control systems upon the transient behavior.[106, 161]

It has been shown in Sec. 6.1b that the input and output transforms of the several basic configurations of sampled-data feedback control systems (Fig. 6.1-5 to Fig. 6.1-8) are related by either

$$\frac{C(z)}{R(z)} = \frac{G(z)}{1 + GH(z)} \tag{7.1-1}$$

or

$$\frac{C(z)}{R(z)} = \frac{G(z)}{1 + G(z)H(z)} \tag{7.1-2}$$

where $R(z)$ and $C(z)$ are the z transforms of the input $r(t)$ and the output $c(t)$; and $G(z)$, $H(z)$, and $GH(z)$ denote the z transforms (or pulse-transfer functions) associated with $G(s)$, $H(s)$, and $G(s)H(s)$ respectively, $G(s)$ and $H(s)$ being the transfer functions of the elements in the forward and feedback paths and $G(s)H(s)$ being the open-loop transfer function. The equations obtained by putting the denominators of Eqs. (7.1-1) and (7.1-2) equal to zero are the characteristic equations of the sampled-data control systems:

$$1 + GH(z) = 0 \tag{7.1-3}$$

$$1 + G(z)H(z) = 0 \tag{7.1-4}$$

the roots of which determine the general nature of the transient behavior of the corresponding system subjected to a specified input.

The pulse-transfer functions $G(z)$, $H(z)$, and $GH(z)$ are rational functions of z and are usually expressed in the form of the ratio of two rational polynomials in z. Then Eqs. (7.1-1) and (7.1-2) may be written as

$$\frac{C(z)}{R(z)} = G_o(z) = \frac{KP(z)}{Q(z)} \tag{7.1-5}$$

where K is a constant, $P(z)$ and $Q(z)$ are the rational polynomials in z, and $G_o(z)$ is the closed-loop sampled-data system function (closed-loop pulse-transfer function). The zeros of $P(z)$ are often referred to as the closed-loop zeros, and the zeros of $Q(z)$ are the closed-loop poles. If $G(z)$ contains no factor common to $1 + GH(z)$ or $1 + G(z)H(z)$, the closed-loop poles are the roots of the characteristic equation, Eq. (7.1-3) or Eq. (7.1-4). Thus, the different modes of the transient behavior are characterized by the location of the closed-loop poles inside the unit circle of the z plane. A positive real pole of Eq. (7.1-5) would give rise to a response, the values of which at sampling instants form an exponentially decaying sequence; a negative real pole indicates an oscillatory output sequence which converges to zero; and a pair of conjugate complex poles corresponds to the case of a damped oscillatory output sequence.

Now, assuming that the system function $G_o(s)$ contains $(M + 1)$ zeros and $(N + 1)$ poles, then

$$P(z) = (z - z_0)(z - z_1) \cdots (z - z_k) \cdots (z - z_m) = \prod_{k=0}^{M} (z - z_k) \tag{7.1-6}$$

and

$$Q(z) = (z - p_0)(z - p_1) \cdots (z - p_k) \cdots (z - p_n) = \prod_{k=0}^{N} (z - p_k) \tag{7.1-7}$$

where the z_k's and p_k's represent the closed-loop zeros and poles which may be either real or complex. It is assumed that the order of $Q(z)$ is equal to or higher than that of $P(z)$, and that $G_o(z)$ contains no multiple pole. The magnitude of pole p_k is less than 1,

$$|p_k| < 1 \tag{7.1-8}$$

since the sampled-data control system is assumed to be stable. From Eqs. (7.1-5), (7.1-6), and (7.1-7), the output transform $C(z)$ is given by

$$C(z) = \frac{KP(z)R(z)}{Q(z)} = \frac{K \prod_{k=0}^{M} (z - z_k)}{\prod_{k=0}^{N} (z - p_k)} R(z) \tag{7.1-9}$$

When the system is subjected to a unit step-function input, the output transform becomes

$$C(z) = \frac{z}{z-1}\frac{KP(z)}{Q(z)} = \frac{z}{z-1}\frac{K\prod_{k=0}^{M}(z-z_k)}{\prod_{k=0}^{N}(z-p_k)} \tag{7.1-10}$$

since for a unit step function the z transform is $z/(z-1)$. Taking the inverse z transform of Eq. (7.1-10) yields the output sequence of the system in response to a unit step-function input. In view of Eq. (5.6-4) the output sequence $c(nT)$ is given by

$$c(nT) = \frac{1}{2\pi j}\oint_{\Gamma}\frac{KP(z)}{Q(z)}\frac{z^n}{z-1}\,dz$$

$$= \frac{1}{2\pi j}\oint_{\Gamma}\frac{K\prod_{k=0}^{M}(z-z_k)}{\prod_{k=0}^{N}(z-p_k)}\frac{z^n}{z-1}\,dz \tag{7.1-11}$$

where Γ is a contour of integration which encloses all the singularities of the integrand. By applying Cauchy's residue theorem, the output sequence is evaluated as

$$c(nT) = \frac{KP(1)}{Q(1)} + \sum_{p_r\ \text{real}}\frac{KP(p_r)}{(p_r-1)Q'(p_r)}(p_r)^n$$

$$+ \sum_{p_i=\alpha_i+j\beta_i} 2\left|\frac{KP(p_i)}{(p_i-1)Q'(p_i)}\right| |p_i|^n \cos(n\theta_i + \phi_i) \tag{7.1-12}$$

where $Q'(p_i)$ is the derivative of $Q(z)$ with respect to z evaluated at $z = p_i$; θ_i is the phase angle of the complex pole $p_i = \alpha_i + j\beta_i$; and ϕ_i is the phase angle of $P(p_i)/[(p_i-1)Q'(p_i)]$

Thus,

$$Q'(p_r) = \left.\frac{dQ(z)}{dz}\right|_{z=p_r} \tag{7.1-13}$$

$$Q'(p_i) = \left.\frac{dQ(z)}{dz}\right|_{z=p_i} \tag{7.1-14}$$

$$\theta_i = \tan^{-1}(\beta_i/\alpha_i) \tag{7.1-15}$$

and

$$\phi_i = \underline{/\ P(p_i)} - \underline{/\ p_i - 1} - \underline{/\ Q'(p_i)} \tag{7.1-16}$$

Equation (7.1-12) is the general solution of the transient response at the sampling instants of the system which is subjected to a unit step-function input. The first term of the right-hand side of Eq. (7.1-12) is a constant which represents the steady-state value of the sequence response. The second term contains the factor $(p_r)^n$ the absolute value of which is less than one for all values of n greater than zero, since $|p_r| < 1$. Consequently, the second term may give rise to two possible modes of transient behavior, depending upon the location of this real pole inside the unit circle. When p_r is positive (i.e., the real pole is located in the right half of the unit circle), $(p_r)^n$ is always positive and decreases steadily as n increases. Thus, for positive real poles the second term of Eq. (7.1-12) describes a steadily decaying sequence. When p_r is negative (i.e., the real pole is located in the left half of the unit circle), the absolute value of $(p_r)^n$ decreases with increase in n, but $(p_r)^n$ is positive for n being even and negative for n being odd. $(p_r)^n$ would form an alternating sequence which converges to zero. Hence a negative real pole gives rise to an oscillatory output sequence of diminishing amplitudes. The third term of Eq. (7.1-12), which is due to the complex poles of the system function with magnitude less than 1, indicates damped oscillations. Consequently, a pair of conjugate complex poles would yield a damped oscillatory output sequence. The results of the above discussion are summarized in Table 7.1-1 and Fig. 7.1-1.

TABLE 7.1-1

Location of closed-loop poles	*Mode of transient behavior*
Outside the unit circle	Unstable operation
Inside the unit circle	Stable operation
a. Real pole in the right half of the unit circle	*a.* Decaying output sequence
b. Real pole in the left half of the unit circle	*b.* Alternating output sequence of diminishing amplitudes
c. Conjugate complex poles in the unit circle	*c.* Damped oscillatory output sequence

The above conclusions may also be derived from a different way of reasoning. As discussed in Chap. 5, the z transformation is a mapping process. The primary and complementary strips of the left half of the s plane are mapped into the interior of the unit circle of the z plane; the negative real axis and the center lines of the complementary strips are mapped into that section of the positive real axis of the z plane inside the unit circle and the boundaries of the primary and complementary strips are mapped into the negative real axis inside the unit circle. Consequently, a real pole in the left half of the s plane corresponds to a real pole on the positive real axis inside the unit circle of the z plane; and a pair of conjugate complex poles in the left half of the s plane corresponds to a pair of conjugate complex poles in the unit circle or two real poles on the negative real axis inside the unit circle. For instance, an s-plane pole at $s = 0$ is mapped into a z-plane pole at

$$z = 1 \tag{7.1-17}$$

an s-plane pole at $s = -a$ is mapped into a z-plane pole at

$$z = \epsilon^{-aT} \tag{7.1-18}$$

and a pole pair at $s = -\alpha_1 \pm j\omega_1$ is mapped into the pole pair at

$$z = \epsilon^{-\alpha_1 T}\epsilon^{\pm j\omega_1 T} \tag{7.1-19}$$

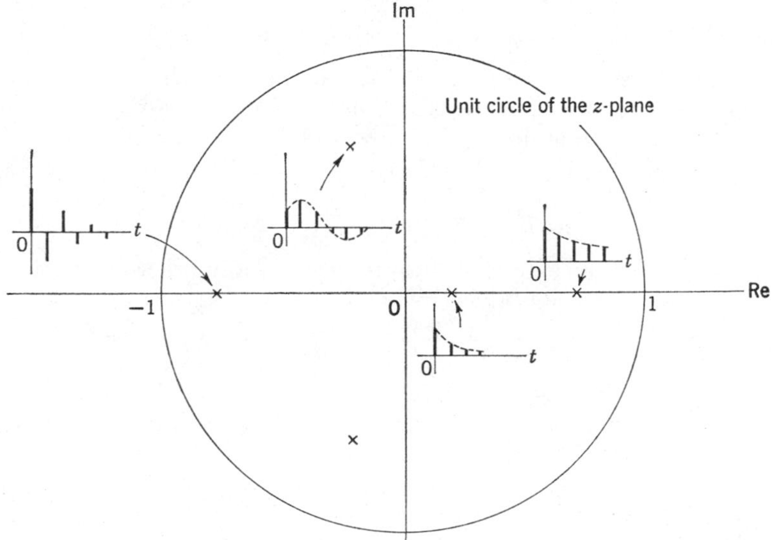

FIG. 7.1-1. Various forms of the response sequence corresponding to various pole locations inside the unit circle of the z plane.

which are conjugate complex poles inside the unit circle of the z plane. It is noted that when $\omega_1 T$ equals π or its odd multiples,

$$\epsilon^{-j\omega_1 T} = -1 \tag{7.1-20}$$

and these two conjugate complex poles of Eq. (7.1-19) degenerate into two negative real poles of equal magnitude. Thus, a positive real pole inside the unit circle of the z plane would give rise to an output sequence which decays exponentially, whereas two negative real poles and a pair of conjugate complex poles inside the unit circle correspond to a response sequence which has a damped oscillatory form, as shown in Fig. 7.1-1.

7.2. Maximum Transient Overshoot and Peak Time of the Output Sequence. The maximum and minimum values of a continuous function are determined from the first derivative of the function. By analogy, the maximum and minimum values of the sequence of a pulsed-data function may be determined from the first difference of the pulsed-data function. Let

$$c(0), c(T), c(2T), \ldots, c(nT), \ldots \tag{7.2-1}$$

be the sequence of a pulsed-data function. Then the sequence of the first difference is defined as follows:

$$\Delta c(0) = c(T) - c(0)$$
$$\Delta c(T) = c(2T) - c(T)$$
$$\Delta c(2T) = c(3T) - c(2T)$$
$$\cdots\cdots\cdots\cdots\cdots\cdots$$

In general, $$\Delta c(nT) = c[(n+1)T] - c(nT) \tag{7.2-2}$$

The symbol Δ can be considered as an operator which converts the sequence $c(nT)$ into the sequence of the first difference $\Delta c(nT)$. The differences of the sequence of first differences just defined are called the second differences of the original sequence (7.2-1). Thus, the second difference is defined as

$$\Delta^2 c(nT) = \Delta c[(n+1)T] - \Delta c(nT) \tag{7.2-3}$$

This definition can be extended to differences of any order. For instance, the $(k+1)$th difference is given by

$$\Delta^{k+1} c(nT) = \Delta^k c[(n+1)T] - \Delta^k c(nT) \tag{7.2-4}$$

For the sequence of a pulsed-data function the maximum value may occur either at two consecutive instants or at a single instant as shown in Fig. 7.2-1*a* and Fig. 7.2-1*b*. The maximum of the sequence (7.2-1) occurs

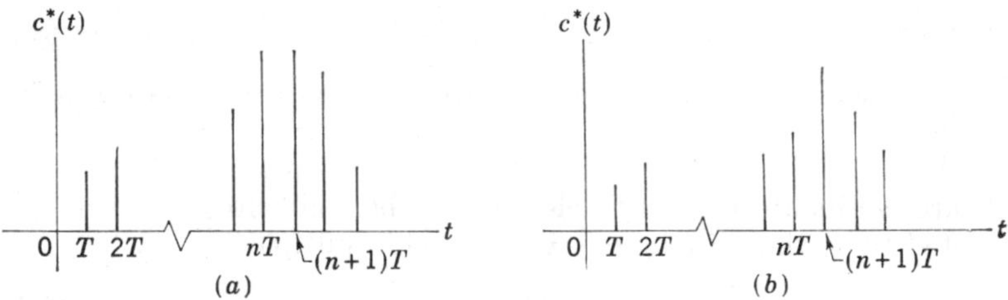

FIG. 7.2-1. (*a*) Maximum of the pulsed-data function occurs at sampling instants nT and $(n+1)T$; (*b*) maximum of the pulsed-data function occurs at sampling instant $(n+1)T$.

at both nT and $(n+1)T$ (Fig. 7.2-1*a*) provided that the first difference $\Delta c(nT)$ equals zero,

$$\Delta c(nT) = c[(n+1)T] - c(nT) = 0 \tag{7.2-5}$$

and the second difference $\Delta^2 c(nT)$ is negative,

$$\Delta^2 c(nT) < 0$$

(or the first difference $\Delta c[(n-1)T]$ is positive). The maximum value is then equal to $c(nT)$ or $c[(n+1)T]$. On the other hand, when the maximum of the sequence occurs at the instant $(n + 1)T$, the first difference $\Delta c(nT)$ no longer equals zero. In this case the values of n obtained from the difference equation $\Delta c(nT) = 0$ will not be integers. Then the instants corresponding to the maxima of the sequence are given by the upper integer of the values of n determined from $\Delta c(nT) = 0$. For instance, when the value of n is found to be 3.6, the maximum of the sequence will occur at the instant $4T$ and its value is equal to $c(4T)$, provided that the second difference is less than zero.

The maximum transient overshoot and the peak time of the output sequence of a sampled-data control system, Eq. (7.1-12), may be evaluated from the first difference of the sequence

$$\Delta c(nT) = 0$$

The peak time is defined as the instant at which the first maximum overshoot of the output sequence occurs. On account of the complexity of Eq. (7.1-12), it seems that a simple and compact working formula expressing the maximum overshoot and the peak time in terms of the closed-loop poles and zeros of the system function in z can hardly be derived. However, approximate expressions of the maximum overshoot and the peak time may be obtained provided that the sampled-data control system is assumed to have a pair of conjugate complex poles which predominate all other poles of the system function in z. A predominating pole is defined as one which is much closer to the unit circle of the z plane than all other poles. In other words, all other poles lie in the vicinity of the origin of the z plane whereas the pair of the predominating conjugate complex poles are located far away from the origin. Shown in Fig. 7.2-2 is the distribution diagram of the poles and zeros of the system function $G_o(z)$, in which the pair of conjugate complex poles p_0 and p_1 are the predominating poles. Since all other poles fall in the vicinity of the origin, their magnitudes are much less than one. Consequently, the transient response due to these poles dies out rather quickly and their contribution to the over-all transient behavior of the system becomes insignificant. In view of these properties it can be assumed that all the modes of the transient behavior of Eq. (7.1-12) may be neglected except the steady-state term and the term due to the pair of predominating poles p_0 and p_1. It should be pointed out that this assumption does not neglect any pole but it ignores only the portion of the over-all transient response contributed by all other less important poles.

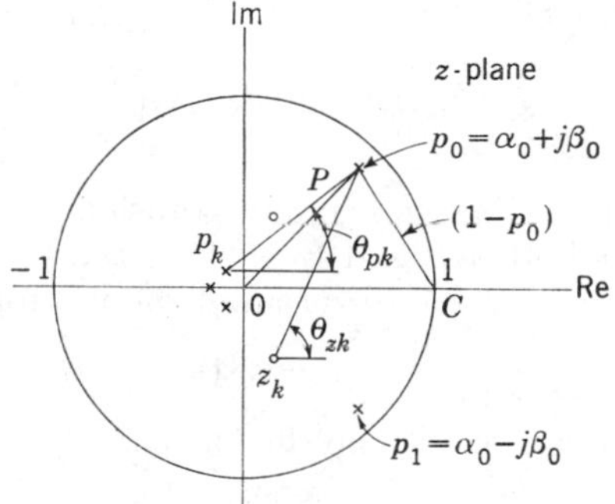

FIG. 7.2-2. Pole-zero distribution diagram.

Under the above assumption Eq. (7.1-12) may be approximated as

$$c(nT) = \frac{KP(1)}{Q(1)} + 2\left|\frac{KP(p_0)}{(p_0 - 1)Q'(p_0)}\right| |p_0|^n \cos(n\theta_0 + \phi_0) \qquad (7.2\text{-}6)$$

where

$$p_0 = \alpha_0 + j\beta_0 \qquad (7.2\text{-}7)$$

$$|p_0| = \sqrt{\alpha_0^2 + \beta_0^2} \qquad (7.2\text{-}8)$$

$$Q'(p_0) = \left.\frac{dQ(z)}{dz}\right|_{z=p_0}$$

$$\theta_0 = \tan^{-1}(\beta_0/\alpha_0) \qquad (7.2\text{-}9)$$

and

$$\phi_0 = \underline{/P(p_0)} - \underline{/p_0 - 1} - \underline{/Q'(p_0)} \qquad (7.2\text{-}10)$$

The value of the output sequence next to $c(nT)$ in line is obtained from Eq. (7.2-6) by substituting $(n + 1)$ for n, thus,

$$c[(n+1)T] = \frac{KP(1)}{Q(1)} + 2\left|\frac{KP(p_0)}{(p_0 - 1)Q'(p_0)}\right| |p_0|^{n+1} \cos[(n+1)\theta_0 + \phi_0] \qquad (7.2\text{-}11)$$

Then the first difference of the output sequence is given by

$$\Delta c(nT) = c[(n+1)T] - c(nT)$$
$$= 2\left|\frac{KP(p_0)}{(p_0 - 1)Q'(p_0)}\right| |p_0|^n \{|p_0| \cos[(n+1)\theta_0 + \phi_0 - \cos(n\theta_0 + \phi_0)\} \qquad (7.2\text{-}12)$$

If the first maximum transient overshoot of the output sequence occurs at both nT and $(n + 1)T$, the peak time may be evaluated by equating Eq. (7.2-12) to zero and solving for n, thus,

$$|p_0| \cos[(n+1)\theta_0 + \phi_0] - \cos(n\theta_0 + \phi_0) = 0 \qquad (7.2\text{-}13)$$

It can readily be shown that

$$n = n_p = \frac{1}{\theta_0}\left(\frac{\pi}{2} - \sum_{k=0}^{M} \theta_{zk} + \sum_{k=1}^{N} \theta_{pk}\right) \qquad (7.2\text{-}14)$$

The peak time and the maximum overshoot are then given by

$$T_p = \frac{T}{\theta_0}\left(\frac{\pi}{2} - \sum_{k=0}^{M} \theta_{zk} + \sum_{k=1}^{N} \theta_{pk}\right) \qquad (7.2\text{-}15)$$

$$M_m = \left(\prod_{k=2}^{N} \frac{|1 - p_k|}{a_k}\right)\left(\prod_{k=0}^{M} \frac{b_k}{|1 - z_k|}\right) |p_0|^{T_p/T} \qquad (7.2\text{-}16)$$

in which

$$\sum_{k=0}^{M} \theta_{zk} = \underline{/P(p_0)} \qquad \sum_{k=1}^{N} \theta_{pk} = \underline{/Q'(p_0)} \qquad (7.2\text{-}17)$$

$$a_k \underline{/\theta_{pk}} = p_0 - p_k \qquad b_k \underline{/\theta_{zk}} = p_0 - z_k \tag{7.2-18}$$

$|1 - p_k|$ is the distance from the point (1,0) of the z plane to the pole p_k; and $|1 - z_k|$ is the distance from the point (1,0) of the z plane to the zero z_k.

If the first maximum transient overshoot of the output sequence, Eq. (7.2-6), occurs at the instant $(n + 1)T$, the first difference of Eq. (7.2-12) is no longer zero and the value of n obtained by solving Eq. (7.2-13) would not be an integer. In this case, the instant corresponding to the first maximum of the output sequence is given by the upper integer of the value of n determined from Eq. (7.2-13). Then

$$n_p = n + q = \frac{1}{\theta_0}\left(\frac{\pi}{2} - \sum_{k=0}^{M} \theta_{zk} + \sum_{k=1}^{N} \theta_{pk}\right) + q \tag{7.2-19}$$

where q is a positive number less than 1, which makes the sum $(n + q)$ an integer. The peak time and the first maximum overshoot are then given by

$$T_p = \frac{T}{\theta_0}\left(\frac{\pi}{2} - \sum_{k=0}^{M} \theta_{zk} + \sum_{k=1}^{N} \theta_{pk}\right) + qT \tag{7.2-20}$$

$$M_m = k_c \prod_{k=2}^{N} \left(\frac{|1 - p_k|}{a_k}\right) \prod_{k=0}^{M} \left(\frac{b_k}{|1 - z_k|}\right) |p_0|^{T_p/T} \tag{7.2-21}$$

where k_c is a correction factor given by

$$k_c = \cos q\theta_0 + \frac{1 - \alpha_0}{\beta_0} \sin q\theta_0 \tag{7.2-22}$$

In deriving Eqs. (7.2-16) and (7.2-21), it is assumed that the sampled-data system is of zero-position error.

Examination of Eqs. (7.2-15) and (7.2-20) reveals that the zeros of the sampled-data system function cause a decrease in the peak time, whereas the introduction of poles would increase the peak time. Furthermore, the peak time could be decreased by shifting the zeros to the right and the poles to the left. Equations (7.2-15) and (7.2-20) further indicate that the peak time is decreased by shifting the predominating poles toward the negative real axis (i.e., the value of θ_0 is increased), and it is increased by moving the predominating poles toward the positive real axis. This can also be visualized from the fact that poles close to the positive real axis of the z plane correspond to poles near the negative real axis of the s plane.

In the case of a second-order sampled-data feedback control system having no closed-loop zero,

$$\sum_k \theta_{zk} = 0 \qquad \sum_k \theta_{pk} = \pi/2 \tag{7.2-23}$$

The peak time of a second-order sampled-data system is then given by

$$T_p = \frac{\pi T}{\theta_0} \tag{7.2-24}$$

or

$$T_p = \frac{\pi T}{\theta_0} + qT \tag{7.2-25}$$

where θ_0 is the phase angle of the pole $p_0 = \alpha_0 + j\beta_0$ of the second-order system, as shown in Fig. 7.2-3. It is noted that the peak time is decreased with the increase in θ_0. Thus, a pair of conjugate complex poles near the positive real axis would give rise to a longer peak time.

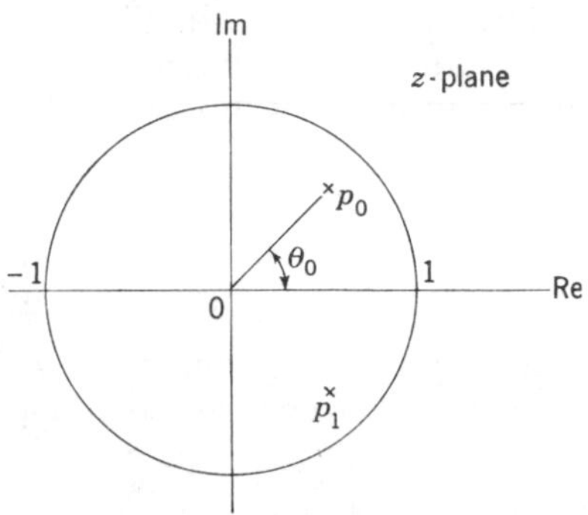

FIG. 7.2-3. Closed-loop poles of a second-order sampled-data control system.

By making use of Eqs. (7.2-16) and (7.2-21) the maximum overshoot can be determined approximately from the peak time T_p and the closed-loop poles and zeros of the sampled-data control system. The approximation is good provided that the predominating conjugate complex poles are far from the origin of the z plane and all the other poles and the zeros are close to the origin. In case the contribution of a certain simple mode

$$\frac{KP(p_r)}{(p_r - 1)Q'(p_r)} (p_r)^n \tag{7.2-26}$$

to the over-all transient behavior of the system must be accounted for, the magnitude of this mode at the peak time T_p may be evaluated and added to the approximate expressions for the maximum overshoot as a correction factor for second approximation.

Although Eqs. (7.2-20) and (7.2-21) provide only approximate formulas for the evaluation of the peak time and the maximum overshoot of the output sequence of a sampled-data control system in response to a unit step-function input, these equations shed much light upon the correlation between the transient behavior of the system and the locations of the closed-loop poles and zeros. These relationships are often of help in time-domain synthesis of sampled-data control systems which contain a pair of predominating conjugate complex poles. It is seen from Eq. (7.2-21) that the larger the peak time the smaller the maximum overshoot. Equation (7.2-21) further points out that the maximum overshoot can generally be diminished by decreasing the ratios $|1 - p_k|/a_k$ and $b_k/|1 - z_k|$. The effect of poles and zeros of the closed-loop transfer function upon the maximum overshoot and the peak time becomes more obvious when reference is made to Fig. 7.2-4. It is observed that a real pole (or a complex pole near the real axis) in the right half of the unit circle of the z plane would make the ratio $|1 - p_k|/a_k$ smaller than that due to a pole in the left half of the unit circle; and that a real zero (or a complex zero near the real axis) in the left half of the unit circle would make the ratio $b_k/|1 - z_k|$ smaller than that due to a zero in the right half of the unit circle. Consequently, in order to design a sampled-data control system with a small or moderate overshoot in the step-function response it is desirable to keep the poles in the right half and the zeros in the left half of the unit circle. Figure 7.2-4

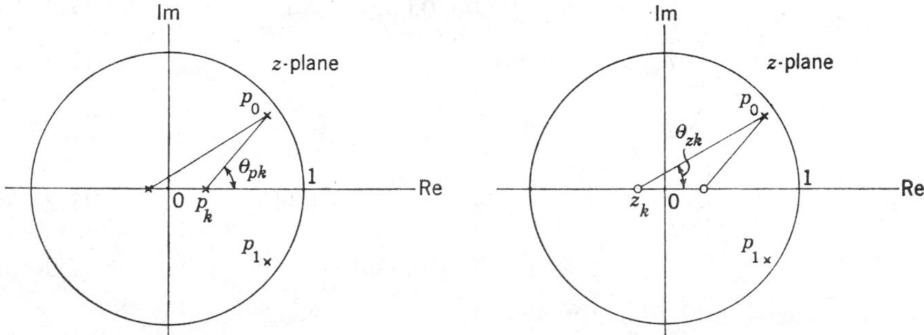

FIG. 7.2-4. Illustrations of the effect of pole-zero locations upon maximum overshoot and peak time.

further indicates that the phase angle θ_{pk} becomes larger if a pole p_k is moved to the right half of the unit circle, and that the phase angle θ_{zk} becomes smaller if a zero z_k is pushed to left half of the unit circle. This implies that the pole-zero distribution which is favorable for a small overshoot would cause an undesirably longer peak time. Thus, a compromise is required in the choice of peak time and maximum overshoot.

As an illustration of the application of the above method to determine the peak time and the maximum overshoot of the output sequence of sampled-data feedback control systems, a simple numerical example is presented below.

EXAMPLE 7.2-1. Consider the sampled-data feedback control system of Fig. 6.3-3. The sampling period is 0.1 sec, and the transfer function of the controlled system is

$$G(s) = \frac{2}{s(1 + 0.1s)} \tag{7.2-27}$$

Determine the peak time and the maximum overshoot of the output sequence of the system in response to a unit step-function input.

It has been found in Sec. 6.3 that the over-all pulse-transfer function of the system is given by Eq. (6.3-19), and is repeated below:

$$\frac{C(z)}{R(z)} = G_o(z) = \frac{1.264z}{z^2 - 0.104z + 0.368} \tag{7.2-28}$$

Factoring the denominator reduces Eq. (7.2-28) to

$$G_o(z) = \frac{1.264z}{[z - (0.052 + j0.605)][z - (0.052 - j0.605)]} \tag{7.2-29}$$

The system has a pair of conjugate complex poles,

$$p_0 = 0.052 + j0.605 \qquad p_1 = 0.052 - j0.605 \tag{7.2-30}$$

and a zero,

$$z_0 = 0 \tag{7.2-31}$$

The distribution diagram of the closed-loop poles and zero is shown in Fig. 7.2-5, from which it is found that

$$\theta_0 = \tan^{-1}(0.605/0.052) = 85.1° \tag{7.2-32}$$

$$\sum \theta_{pk} = \theta_{p1} = 90° \tag{7.2-33}$$

$$\sum \theta_{zk} = \theta_0 = 85.1° \tag{7.2-34}$$

Then

$$n = \frac{90° - 85.1° + 90°}{85.1°} = 1.115 \tag{7.2-35}$$

and

$$q = 2 - 1.115 = 0.885 \tag{7.2-36}$$

Hence, from Eq. (7.2-20) the peak time is obtained:

$$T_p = 2T \tag{7.2-37}$$

To evaluate the maximum overshoot, the value of the correction factor k_c is first computed from Eq. (7.2-22). Thus,

$$k_c = \cos(0.885 \times 85.1°) + \frac{1 - 0.052}{0.605} \sin(0.885 \times 85.1°) = 1.774 \tag{7.2-38}$$

Since there is only one zero at $z = 0$, the ratio

$$\prod_{k=0}^{M} \frac{b_k}{|1 - z_k|} = |p_0| = 0.606 \tag{7.2-39}$$

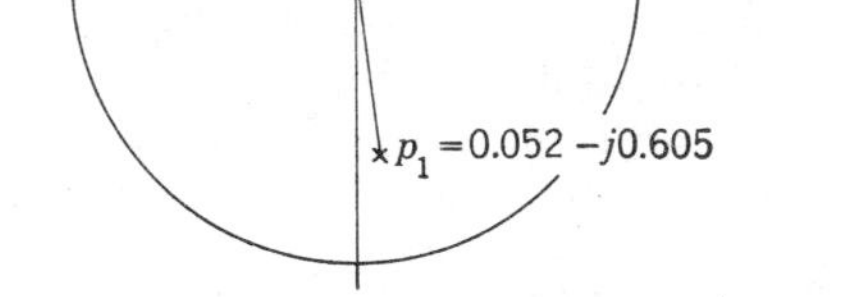

FIG. 7.2-5. Pole-zero diagram of Example 7.2-1.

Since the system has only two closed-loop conjugate complex poles p_0 and p_1, the ratio $\prod_{k=2}^{N} (|1 - p_k|/a_k)$ of Eq. (7.2-21) is equal to unity. Thus, by substituting these values into Eq. (7.2-21) the maximum overshoot is found as

$$M_m = k_c|p_0|^3 = 1.774 \times (0.606)^3 = 0.396 \tag{7.2-40}$$

The values of the peak time and the maximum overshoot of the output sequence thus determined check with the values obtained from Eq. (6.3-30) of Sec. 6.3. By making use of Eqs. (7.2-20) and (7.2-21), it can readily be computed that the maximum overshoot of the output sequence is reduced to 34.5 per cent if a zero at $z_c = -0.104$ and a pole at $p_c = 0.104$ are introduced. However, it should be pointed out that the maximum overshoot of the output sequence is generally less than the actual maximum overshoot of the transient response, as indicated in Fig. 6.3-4, although for well-behaved systems the difference is small. The actual maximum overshoot usually occurs in the vicinity of the peak time found from Eq. (7.2-20).

In case all the zeros and the poles except the predominating pole pair p_0 and p_1 are very close to the origin of the z plane, the following approximation may be made:

$$\frac{|1 - p_k|}{a_k} \approx \frac{1}{|p_0|} \qquad \frac{b_k}{|1 - z_k|} \approx |p_0| \tag{7.2-41}$$

and the system can be approximated by a second-order system. Equation (7.2-21) is then reduced to

$$M_m \approx k_c |p_0|^{M-N+2} |p_0|^{T_p/T} \tag{7.2-42}$$

For the poles and zeros very near the origin of the z plane,

$$\sum_{k=0}^{M} \theta_{zk} \approx (M + 1)\theta_0 \qquad \sum_{k=1}^{N} \theta_{pk} \approx N\theta_0 \tag{7.2-43}$$

By substituting these values into Eq. (7.2-20) an approximate expression for the peak time is obtained,

$$\frac{T_p}{T} \approx \frac{\pi}{2\theta_0} - (M + 1) + N + q \tag{7.2-44}$$

Then the maximum overshoot can be simplified to

$$M_m \approx k_c |p_0|^{(1+q+\pi/2\theta_0)} \tag{7.2-45}$$

The above equation reveals that if the predominating pole pair p_0 and p_1 fall in the left half of the unit circle the maximum overshoot would be given by

$$M_m \approx k_c |p_0|^2 \tag{7.2-46}$$

which occurs at the second sampling instant. When the poles p_0 and p_1 lie in the right half of the unit circle, however, the maximum overshoot would be smaller and the peak time would become longer.

The correction factor k_c given by Eq. (7.2-22) may be written as

$$k_c = \cos q\theta_0 + \left(\frac{1}{|p_0|} \csc \theta_0 - \cot \theta_0 \right) \sin q\theta_0 \tag{7.2-47}$$

By making use of Eqs. (7.2-45) and (7.2-47), contours of constant maximum overshoot for second-order sampled-data feedback control systems and systems having closed-loop zeros and poles very near the origin of the z plane except the predominating pole pair can readily be constructed.

The contour of constant maximum overshoot is a polar plot of $|p_0|$ versus θ_0 with M_m as a parameter. The contours for M_m varying from 5 to 45 per cent are plotted in Fig. 7.2-6. When the maximum overshoot is specified, with the aid of these charts the desirable locations of the predomi-

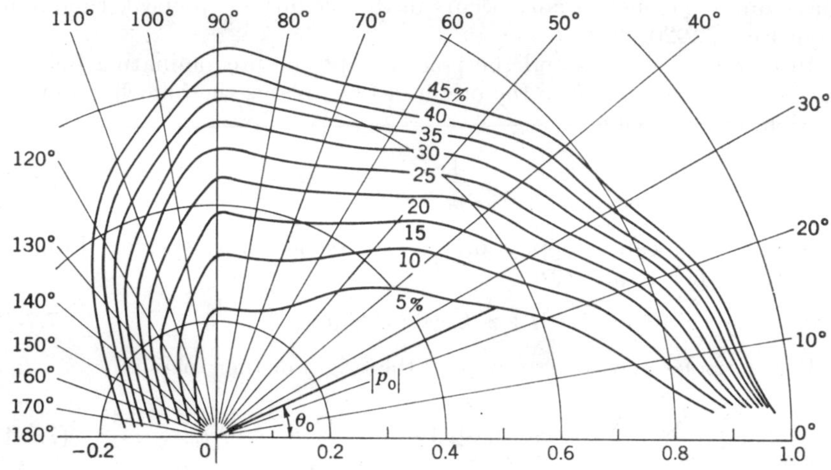

FIG. 7.2-6. Contours of constant maximum overshoot.

nating pole pair may be quickly determined. These charts will find applications in the synthesis of sampled-data feedback control systems.

7.3. Analysis of System Error and Intersampling Ripples. As discussed in the preceding chapters, sampled-data and digital control offers several advantages. For instance, sampling makes possible the control of tremendous power by sensitive control elements without excessive power amplification; the use of sampling in control systems allows time sharing of important equipments of the system; digital control permits system compensation by programming and data-processing techniques; sampling facilitates the design of adaptive control systems; etc. On the other hand, sampled-data and digital control is by no means free from shortcomings. For example, sampling gives rise to unwanted ripples in the output. These ripples which result in system error are often difficult to eradicate.

It is shown in Chap. 4 that the output of a sampling device contains both the primary component as well as the complementary components of the signal. In a sampled-data feedback control system (e.g., error-sampled system), the actuating signal from the sampler of the system contains both primary and complementary components of which only the primary component is able to reduce the effect of external disturbance. The complementary components form intersampling ripples in the output and produce no beneficial effect upon the system performance. Intersampling ripples are always objectionable, because the ripples not only form the system error, but also cause a loss of power in the actuator, increase wear of the mechanical couplings, and impair the system performance.

In most sampled-data control systems, the complementary components caused by sampling must be removed before the signal reaches the output. Although a large portion of the high-frequency components of the signal is rejected by the system components between the sampler and the output, more effective smoothing of the ripples is often accomplished by the introduction of a holding device into the system. However, a holding or smoothing device introduces a delay which is detrimental to system stability. The selection of a holding or smoothing device thus requires a compromise between the tolerable ripple content and the specified system stability and dynamic performance. The design of sampled-data control systems often calls for a balance between the ripple rejection and the resulting delay. In view of the importance of the effect of the ripple content upon the performance of sampled-data control systems, this section is devoted to the analysis of intersampling ripples and system error.

Shown in Fig. 7.3-1 is the block diagram of a basic sampled-data feedback control system in which the actuating-error signal appears in sampled

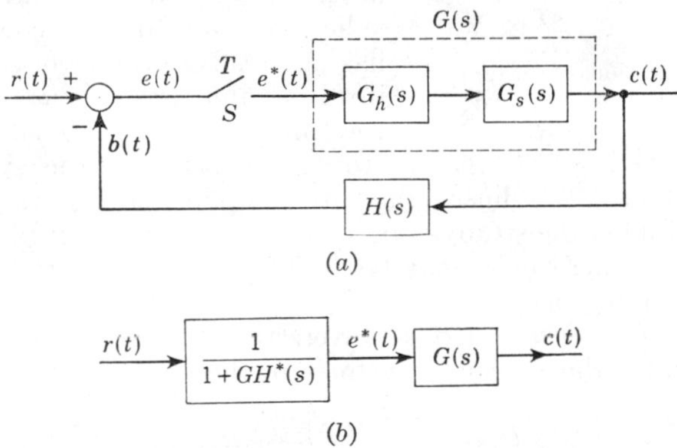

FIG. 7.3-1. (a) Block diagram of a basic sampled-data feedback control system; (b) equivalent open-loop representation of the system of (a).

form. This type of control system is often referred to as an error-sampled system. The input to this system is $r(t)$ and the output is $c(t)$. In Fig. 7.3-1, $G_s(s)$ is the transfer function of the controlled system; $G_h(s)$ is the transfer function of the holding or smoothing device; $H(s)$ is the transfer function of the feedback path; and S is a sampler which operates with a sampling period equal to T sec. The transfer function of the forward path is $G(s)$, which is given by

$$G(s) = G_h(s)G_s(s) \tag{7.3-1}$$

The most commonly used smoothing device is a linear low-pass filter or a standard clamping circuit, often referred to as a zero-order holding device. As in the case of continuous-data control systems, the system error resulting from the application of a test input function is an important design parameter in a sampled-data feedback control system. The system error is defined as the difference between the desired output $c_d(t)$ and the actual output $c(t)$ of the system, that is,

$$\varepsilon(t) = c_d(t) - c(t) \tag{7.3-2}$$

In continuous-data systems, the system error is brought about by the energy-storage elements of the system. But in sampled-data systems, the system error is brought about not only by the energy-storage elements but also by the sampling process. As a result of the sampling process, intersampling ripples occur in pulsed-data systems. During transient disturbances the intersampling ripples are small and insignificant, whereas under steady-state conditions the ripples may be the primary component of the system error which must be considered in the design of sampled-data control systems.[88] When a sampled-data control system has a steady-state error at sampling instants, this error is attributable to the finite forward gain and the energy-storage elements of the system. But, as shown in Fig. 7.3-2, during the intersampling periods the ripples are superimposed upon the steady-state error.

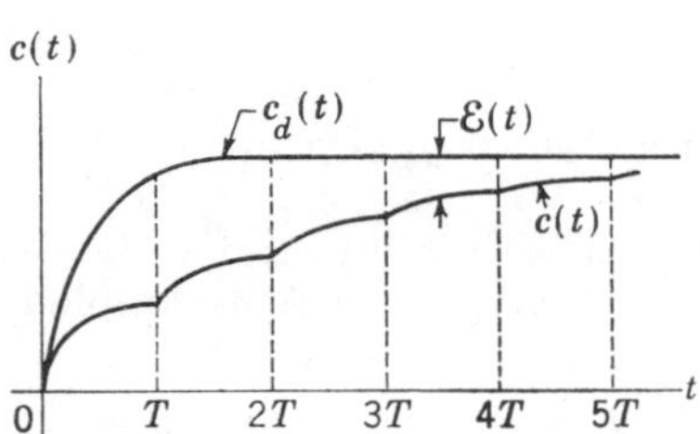

FIG. 7.3-2. Illustrations of the desired output, the actual output, and the system error.

The intersampling ripples may be analyzed by various methods, two of which are described below.

a. Pulse-train Response Method. Referring to Fig. 7.3-1, as has been shown in Sec. 6.1 the Laplace transform of the system output is given by

$$C(s) = \frac{G(s)}{1 + GH^*(s)} R^*(s) \tag{7.3-3}$$

where $R^*(s)$ is the Laplace transform of the sampled input $r^*(t)$ and $GH^*(s)$ is the starred transform associated with $G(s)H(s)$. The determination of the intersampling ripples in the output of the system would require the evaluation of the inverse transform of Eq. (7.3-3). However, because the terms $R^*(s)$ and $GH^*(s)$ of the right-hand side of Eq. (7.3-3) are multivalued functions in s,

$$R^*(s) = \frac{1}{T} \sum_{n=-\infty}^{\infty} R(s + jn\omega_s) \tag{7.3-4}$$

and

$$GH^*(s) = \frac{1}{T} \sum_{n=-\infty}^{\infty} GH(s + jn\omega_s) \tag{7.3-5}$$

to perform the inverse transformation of Eq. (7.3-3) is a rather difficult task. As a result, it seems necessary to have recourse to other means by which the system response $c(t)$ may be computed readily.

In terms of the z transforms, Eq. (7.3-3) becomes

$$C(z) = \frac{G(z)}{1 + GH(z)} R(z) \tag{7.3-6}$$

Reference to Fig. 7.3-1 indicates that the z transforms of the actuating error signal $e(t)$ and the feedback signal $b(t)$ are related by

$$E(z) = R(z) - B(z) \tag{7.3-7}$$

and

$$B(z) = GH(z)E(z) \tag{7.3-8}$$

Eliminating $B(z)$ between Eqs. (7.3-7) and (7.3-8) yields the z transform of the actuating signal as

$$E(z) = \frac{R(z)}{1 + GH(z)} \tag{7.3-9}$$

Then the output sequence $c(nT)$ and the actuating-error sequence $e(nT)$ of the sampled-data system can be obtained by taking the inverse z transforms of Eqs. (7.3-6) and (7.3-9):

$$c(nT) = \mathfrak{z}^{-1}\left\{\frac{G(z)R(z)}{1 + GH(z)}\right\} \tag{7.3-10}$$

and

$$e(nT) = \mathfrak{z}^{-1}\left\{\frac{R(z)}{1 + GH(z)}\right\} \tag{7.3-11}$$

Between two consecutive sampling instants, the control loop of the feedback system is open, and the open-loop analysis may be applied. It can readily be seen from Fig. 7.3-1b that during the intersampling periods the output $c(t)$ of the system is essentially the response of the forward-path transfer function $G(s)$ to an input function $e^*(t)$ which is a train of very narrow pulses occurring at the sampling instants of the system. The magnitude of $e^*(t)$ at sampling instant nT is given by Eq. (7.3-11). As discussed in Sec. 4.1, for the convenience of system analysis a very narrow pulse is represented by an equivalent impulse with strength equal to the magnitude of the pulse. Consequently, the system output between the sampling instants nT and $(n + 1)T$ can be considered as the response of $G(s)$ to an input of n impulses of various strength, which are delayed successively by the sampling period T, as shown in Fig. 7.3-3. Thus, if the impulse response of $G(s)$ is $g(t)$, the system output is given by

$$c(t) = \sum_{k=0}^{n} g[t - (n - k)T]e[(n - k)T] \qquad \text{for } nT \leq t \leq (n + 1)T \tag{7.3-12}$$

This idea sounds fairly simple and straightforward; unfortunately, the evaluation of the sum of the impulse responses of $G(s)$ is quite involved.

However, the difficulty can be overcome if $G(s)$ is expanded in partial fractions, the pulse-train responses of which are readily computed. As-

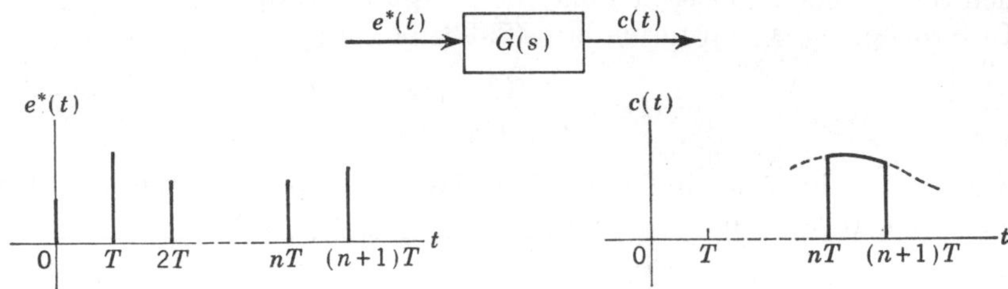

FIG. 7.3-3. Response between sampling instants nT and $(n + 1)T$.

suming

$$G_1(s), G_2(s), \ldots, G_k(s), \ldots, G_N(s) \tag{7.3-13}$$

to be the partial fractions of $G(s)$, and

$$c_1(t), c_2(t), \ldots, c_k(t), \ldots, c_N(t) \tag{7.3-14}$$

to be the corresponding output during the intersampling periods in response to the pulse-train input $e^*(t)$, the forward-path transfer function may be written as

$$G(s) = G_1(s) + G_2(s) + \cdots + G_k(s) + \cdots + G_N(s) \tag{7.3-15a}$$

$$= \sum_{k=1}^{N} G_k(s) \tag{7.3-15b}$$

and during intersampling periods the output of the sampled-data system in response to the input $r(t)$ is given by

$$c(t) = c_1(t) + c_2(t) + \cdots + c_k(t) + \cdots + c_N(t) \tag{7.3-16a}$$

$$= \sum_{k=1}^{N} c_k(t) \tag{7.3-16b}$$

For physical systems, the forward-path transfer function $G(s)$ possesses more poles than zeros; and frequently the poles are simple, although a double pole may occur occasionally. Thus, all the $G_k(s)$'s are simple fractions of the form

$$\frac{1}{s}, \frac{1}{s^2}, \frac{K_a}{s + a}, \frac{K_b}{(s + b)^2} \tag{7.3-17}$$

where a and b can be real, imaginary, or complex. In view of Eq. (7.3-15), the block diagram of Fig. 7.3-1b can be redrawn in the form shown in Fig. 7.3-4. The forward path is resolved into a number of simple parallel channels corresponding to each term of Eq. (7.3-15a).

The system error between sampling instants is then given by

$$\varepsilon(t) = c_d(t) - \sum_{k=1}^{N} c_k(t) \tag{7.3-18}$$

which describes both the error brought about by the energy storage elements of the control system and the error resulting from sampling. To

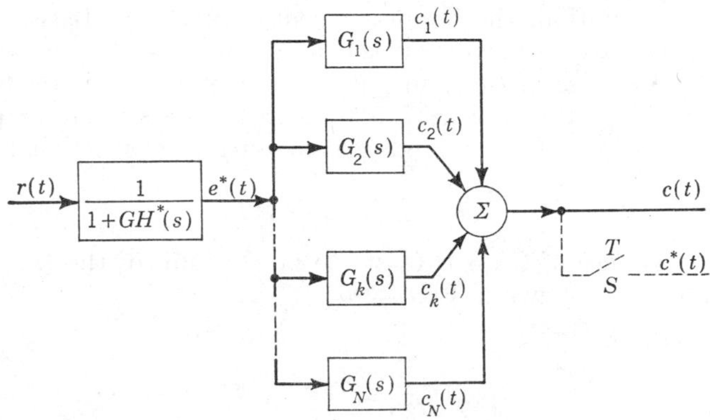

FIG. 7.3-4. Equivalent block diagram of the system of Fig. 7.3-1(a).

compute the system error it is necessary to specify the desired output function. For example, in a unity-feedback control system the desired output is generally taken equal to the input. For sampled-data control systems having no steady-state error at the sampling instants, Eq. (7.3-18) would represent in the steady state the intersampling ripples.

It follows from the above discussions that the determination of the system error and the intersampling ripples from Eq. (7.3-18) requires the pulse-train responses of the parallel channels of the forward path (Fig. 7.3-4). As an illustration, the evaluation of the pulse-train response of a simple linear network is presented below.

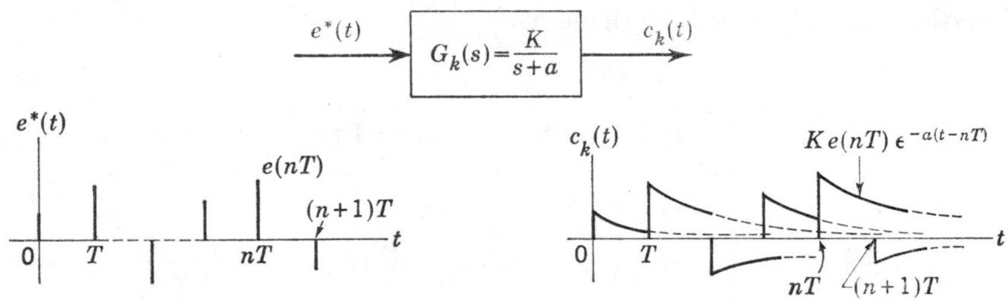

FIG. 7.3-5. Components of the response of $G_k(s)$ to pulse train $e^*(t)$.

Consider the kth channel $G_k(s)$ of the forward path shown in Fig. 7.3-5. Assuming the transfer function of this channel to be

$$G_k(s) = \frac{K}{s + a} \tag{7.3-19}$$

the output function $c_k(t)$ of $G_k(s)$ in response to the pulse-train input $e^*(t)$ is derived as follows:

The inverse Laplace transform of Eq. (7.3-19) is given by

$$\mathcal{L}^{-1}\{G_k(s)\} = g_k(t) = K\epsilon^{-at} \tag{7.3-20}$$

which is, by definition, the impulse response of $G_k(s)$. Based upon the assumption that a very narrow pulse can be represented by an equivalent impulse, the response of $G_k(s)$ to pulse-train input $e^*(t)$ is readily determined by making use of Eq. (7.3-20) and the superposition principle. Each of the pulses of $e^*(t)$ produces an output proportional to $g_k(t)$. During the interval

$$nT \leq t \leq (n + 1)T \tag{7.3-21}$$

the output response of $G_k(s)$ is found to be the sum of the $(n + 1)$ individual responses as shown in Fig. 7.3-5:

$$\begin{aligned} c_k(t) &= Ke(nT)\epsilon^{-a(t-nT)} + Ke[(n-1)T]\epsilon^{-a[t-(n-1)T]} \\ &\qquad + Ke[(n-2)T]\epsilon^{-a[t-(n-2)T]} + \cdots \\ &\qquad + Ke(T)\epsilon^{-a(t-T)} + Ke(0)\epsilon^{-at} \\ &= K\epsilon^{-a(t-nT)}\{e(nT) + e[(n-1)T]\epsilon^{-aT} + e[(n-2)T]\epsilon^{-2aT} \\ &\qquad + \cdots + e(T)\epsilon^{-a(n-1)T} + e(0)\epsilon^{-anT}\} \\ &= K\epsilon^{-a(t-nT)} \sum_{k=0}^{n} e[(n-k)T]\epsilon^{-kaT} \end{aligned} \tag{7.3-22}$$

Since the value of $c_k(t)$ at $t = nT$ is

$$c_k(nT) = K \sum_{k=0}^{n} e[(n-k)T]\epsilon^{-kaT} \tag{7.3-23}$$

Equation (7.3-22) may be written as

$$c_k(t) = c_k(nT)\epsilon^{-a(t-nT)} \tag{7.3-24}$$

in which the values of $c_k(nT)$ can be determined from the inverse z transformation:

$$c_k(nT) = \mathfrak{Z}^{-1}\{G_k(z)E(z)\} \tag{7.3-25}$$

where $G_k(z)$ is the z transform associated with $G_k(s)$ and $E(z)$ is given by Eq. (7.3-9).

In like manner, the pulse-train response of other branches of the forward path of Fig. 7.3-4, which have transfer functions of the form other than Eq. (7.3-19), can also be derived. Table 7.3-1 lists the pulse-train responses of several basic forms of $G_k(s)$.

TABLE 7.3-1

$G_k(s)$	$c_k(t)$ for $nT \leq t \leq (n+1)T$
$\dfrac{1}{s}$	$c_k(nT)u(t - nT)$
$\dfrac{1}{s^2}$	$c_k(nT) + (t - nT)[c_k(\overline{n+1}T) - c_k(nT)]/T$
$\dfrac{1}{s+a}$	$c_k(nT)\epsilon^{-a(t-nT)}$
$\dfrac{1}{(s+a)^2 + b^2}$	$\dfrac{c_k(nT)\epsilon^{anT} \sin bt - c_k(0) \sin b(t - nT)}{\sin bnT} \epsilon^{-at}$

In the case of conjugate complex poles, the analysis becomes less simple. The pulse-train response of a linear network having a pair of conjugate complex poles is evaluated as follows:

Assume that the transfer function of the ith channel is

$$G_i(s) = \frac{K}{(s+a)^2 + b^2} \tag{7.3-26}$$

The impulse response of $G_i(s)$ is given by the inverse Laplace transform of Eq. (7.3-26). Thus,

$$g_i(t) = \mathcal{L}^{-1}\{G_i(s)\} = \frac{K\epsilon^{-at}}{b} \sin bt \tag{7.3-27}$$

Based upon the same assumption made above, during the interval $nT \leq t \leq (n+1)T$, the output response of $G_i(s)$ is found to be the sum of $(n+1)$ impulse-response functions, that is,

$$\begin{aligned} c_i(t) &= e(nT)g_i(t - nT) + e[(n-1)T]g_i[t - (n-1)T] + \cdots \\ &\quad + e[(n-k)T]g_i[t - (n-k)T] + \cdots + e(T)g_i(t - T) \\ &\quad + e(0)g_i(t) \\ &= \frac{K}{b} \sum_{k=0}^{n} e[(n-k)T]\epsilon^{-a[t-(n-k)T]} \sin b[t - (n-k)T] \end{aligned} \tag{7.3-28}$$

Trigonometric manipulation reduces Eq. (7.3-28) to

$$\begin{aligned} c_i(t) &= \frac{K}{b} \epsilon^{-a(t-nT)} \sin b(t - nT) \sum_{k=0}^{n} e[(n-k)T]\epsilon^{-akT} \cos bkT \\ &\quad + \frac{K}{b} \epsilon^{-a(t-nT)} \cos b(t - nT) \sum_{k=0}^{n} e[(n-k)T]\epsilon^{-akT} \sin bkT \end{aligned} \tag{7.3-29}$$

When $t = nT$, Eq. (7.3-29) yields the value of the output at this instant as

$$c_i(nT) = \frac{K}{b} \sum_{k=0}^{n} e[(n-k)T]\epsilon^{-akT} \sin bkT \tag{7.3-30}$$

Thus, Eq. (7.3-29) may be written as

$$c_i(t) = \frac{K}{b} \epsilon^{-a(t-nT)} \sin b(t-nT) \sum_{k=0}^{n} e[(n-k)T]\epsilon^{-akT} \cos bkT + c_i(nT)\epsilon^{-a(t-nT)} \cos b(t-nT) \tag{7.3-31}$$

When $t = 0$, Eq. (7.3-31) gives the initial value of the output as

$$c_i(0) = -\frac{K}{b} \epsilon^{anT} \sin bnT \sum_{k=0}^{n} e[(n-k)T]\epsilon^{-akT} \cos bkT + c_i(nT)\epsilon^{anT} \cos bnT \tag{7.3-32}$$

Transposing,

$$\frac{K}{b} \sum_{k=0}^{n} e[(n-k)T]\epsilon^{-akT} \cos bkT = \frac{c_i(nT) \cos bnT - c_i(0)\epsilon^{-anT}}{\sin bnT} \tag{7.3-33}$$

Combining Eqs. (7.3-31) and (7.3-33) yields

$$c_i(t) = \frac{\sin b(t-nT)}{\sin bnT} \epsilon^{-a(t-nT)}[c_i(nT) \cos bnT - c_i(0)\epsilon^{-anT}] + c_i(nT)\epsilon^{-a(t-nT)} \cos b(t-nT) \tag{7.3-34}$$

After simplification, Eq. (7.3-34) may be put into the form

$$c_i(t) = \frac{c_i(nT)\epsilon^{anT} \sin bt - c_i(0) \sin b(t-nT)}{\sin bnT} \epsilon^{-at} \tag{7.3-35}$$

in which the values of $c_i(nT)$ can be obtained from Eq. (7.3-36):

$$c_i(nT) = \mathfrak{z}^{-1}\{G_i(z)E(z)\} \tag{7.3-36}$$

where $G_i(z)$ is the z transform associated with $G_i(s)$ and $E(z)$ is given by Eq. (7.3-9).

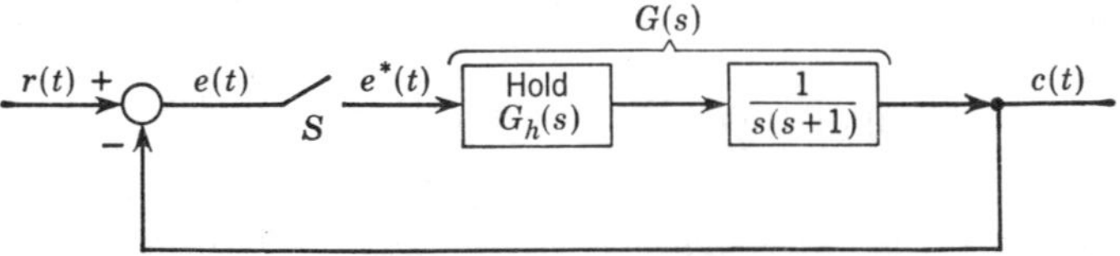

FIG. 7.3-6. Block diagram of the system of Example 7.3-1.

EXAMPLE 7.3-1. Consider the sampled-data feedback control system shown in Fig. 7.3-6. The sampling period is 0.5 sec. A zero-order hold is used as a smoothing device. The transfer function of the controlled system is

$$G_s(s) = \frac{1}{s(s+1)} \tag{7.3-37}$$

Determine the system error resulting from the application of a unit step-function input.

The transfer function of the forward path is given by

$$G(s) = G_h(s)G_s(s) = \frac{1 - \epsilon^{-Ts}}{s^2(s+1)} \tag{7.3-38}$$

The z transform associated with $G(s)$ is

$$G(z) = \frac{(1 - z^{-1})(0.106z + 0.091)z}{(z-1)^2(z-0.606)}$$

$$= \frac{0.106z + 0.091}{(z-1)(z-0.606)} \tag{7.3-39}$$

The z transform of the system error is then given by

$$E(z) = \frac{R(z)}{1 + G(z)}$$

$$= \frac{(z-1)(z-0.606)}{(z-1)(z-0.606) + 0.106z + 0.091} \frac{z}{z-1}$$

$$= \frac{z^2 - 0.606z}{z^2 - 1.5z + 0.697}$$

$$= 1 + 0.894z^{-1} + 0.643z^{-2} + 0.342z^{-3} + 0.065z^{-4} + \cdots \tag{7.3-40}$$

The coefficients of the above series describe the error sequence of the system.

The given system may be represented by the equivalent open-loop block diagram shown in Fig. 7.3-7*a*, in which

$$G_a(s) = \frac{1}{s^2(s+1)} \tag{7.3-41}$$

Reference to Fig. 7.3-7*a* indicates that the z transform of the input $e_1^*(t)$ to $G_a(s)$ is

$$E_1(z) = (1 - z^{-1})E(z) \tag{7.3-42a}$$

$$= 1 - 0.106z^{-1} - 0.251z^{-2} - 0.301z^{-3} - 0.277z^{-4} - \cdots \tag{7.3-42b}$$

Thus, the input signal applied to $G_a(s)$ is

$$e_1^*(t) = \delta(t) - 0.106\delta(t-T) - 0.251\delta(t-2T)$$

$$- 0.301\delta(t-3T) - 0.277\delta(t-4T) - \cdots \tag{7.3-43}$$

The partial fractions of $G_a(s)$ are

$$G_1(s) = \frac{1}{s^2} \qquad G_2(s) = -\frac{1}{s} \qquad G_3(s) = \frac{1}{s+1} \tag{7.3-44}$$

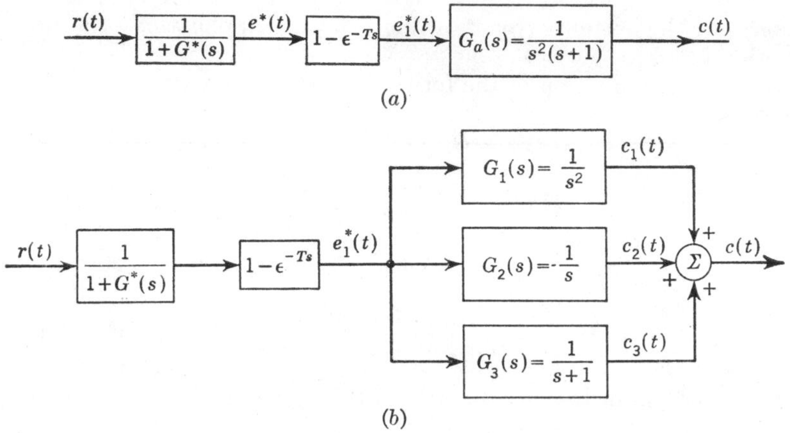

FIG. 7.3-7. (a) Equivalent open-loop representation of the system of Example 7.3-1; (b) equivalent block diagram with $G(s)$ represented by partial fractions.

and the corresponding z transforms are

$$G_1(z) = \frac{0.5z}{(z-1)^2} \quad G_2(z) = \frac{-z}{z-1} \quad G_3(z) = \frac{z}{z-0.606} \tag{7.3-45}$$

Referring to Fig. 7.3-7b, it is found that

$$C_1(z) = \frac{1-z^{-1}}{1+G(z)} G_1(z)R(z) \tag{7.3-46}$$

$$C_2(z) = \frac{1-z^{-1}}{1+G(z)} G_2(z)R(z) \tag{7.3-47}$$

$$C_3(z) = \frac{1-z^{-1}}{1+G(z)} G_3(z)R(z) \tag{7.3-48}$$

Proper substitution yields

$$C_1(z) = \frac{0.5z^2 - 0.303z}{z^3 - 2.5z^2 + 2.197z - 0.697} \tag{7.3-49a}$$

$$= 0.5z^{-1} + 0.947z^{-2} + 1.27z^{-3} + 1.44z^{-4} + 1.47z^{-5} + \cdots \tag{7.3-49b}$$

$$C_2(z) = -\frac{z^2 - 0.606z}{z^2 - 1.5z + 0.697} \tag{7.3-50a}$$

$$= -[1 + 0.894z^{-1} + 0.643z^{-2} + 0.342z^{-3} + 0.065z^{-4} - \cdots] \tag{7.3-50b}$$

$$C_3(z) = \frac{z^2 - z}{z^2 - 1.5z + 0.697} \tag{7.3-51a}$$

$$= 1 + 0.5z^{-1} + 0.053z^{-2} - 0.27z^{-3} - 0.424z^{-4} - \cdots \tag{7.3-51b}$$

Thus, the output sequences are

$$c_1^*(t) = 0.5\delta(t - T) + 0.947\delta(t - 2T) + 1.27\delta(t - 3T) + 1.44\delta(t - 4T) + \cdots \tag{7.3-52}$$

$$c_2^*(t) = -[\delta(t) + 0.894\delta(t - T) + 0.643\delta(t - 2T) + 0.342\delta(t - 3T) + 0.065\delta(t - 4T) - \cdots] \tag{7.3-53}$$

$$c_3^*(t) = \delta(t) + 0.5\delta(t - T) + 0.053\delta(t - 2T) - 0.27\delta(t - 3T) - 0.424\delta(t - 4T) - \cdots \tag{7.3-54}$$

Since the output response of the system is given by

$$c(t) = c_1(t) + c_2(t) + c_3(t) \tag{7.3-55}$$

making use of Table 7.3-1, it is found that, during the interval $nT \leq t \leq (n + 1)T$,

$$c(t) = \left\{c_1(nT) + \frac{(t - nT)}{T}\,[c_1(\overline{n + 1}T) + c_1(nT)]\right\} - c_2(nT)u(t - nT) + c_3(nT)\epsilon^{-(t-nT)} \tag{7.3-56}$$

in which $e_1(nT)$, $c_1(nT)$, $c_2(nT)$, and $c_3(nT)$ are given by Eqs. (7.3-43), (7.3-52), (7.3-53), and (7.3-54), respectively. Consequently, for the interval $0 \leq t \leq T$, the output response is

$$c(t) = (0 + t) - 1 + \epsilon^{-t} = t + \epsilon^{-t} - 1 \tag{7.3-57}$$

and the system error is

$$\epsilon(t) = 1 - c(t) = 2 - t - \epsilon^{-t} \tag{7.3-58}$$

For the interval $T \leq t \leq 2T$,

$$c(t) = [0.5 + 2(t - 0.5)(0.947 - 0.5)] - 0.894 + 0.5\epsilon^{-(t-0.5)}$$
$$= -0.394 + 0.894(t - 0.5) + 0.5\epsilon^{-(t-0.5)} \tag{7.3-59}$$
$$\epsilon(t) = 1.394 - 0.894(t - 0.5) - 0.5\epsilon^{-(t-0.5)} \tag{7.3-60}$$

For the interval $2T \leq t \leq 3T$,

$$c(t) = [0.947 + 2(t - 1)(1.27 - 0.947)] - 0.643 + 0.053\epsilon^{-(t-1)}$$
$$= 0.304 + 0.636(t - 1) + 0.053\epsilon^{-(t-1)} \tag{7.3-61}$$
$$\epsilon(t) = 0.696 - 0.636(t - 1) - 0.053\epsilon^{-(t-1)} \tag{7.3-62}$$

Clearly, if $e_1(nT)$, $c_1(nT)$, $c_2(nT)$, and $c_3(nT)$ are derived by the use of the inversion formula given by Eq. (5.6-4), the general expression of $c(t)$ can be obtained.

b. The Modified z-transform Method. The system error of a feedback control system subjected to an input is equal to the difference between the desired output and the actual output, with the former being specified and the latter to be computed. Thus, the determination of the system error necessitates the evaluation of the actual output of the system. In the preceding paragraphs there has been described a fairly straightforward method of finding the actual output from which the system error and the intersampling ripples can be determined. It has also been discussed in Chap. 6 that the actual output of a sampled-data system may be readily obtained from the modified z-transform analysis.[25] In consequence, the application of the modified z-transform method to the determination of system error and intersampling ripples is a natural outcome. When the modified z-transform method is employed, the evaluation of the actual output is simply reduced to determination of the inverse modified z transformation of the output transform of the system, thus enabling the system error to be determined in a systematic manner.

Making use of the procedures outlined in Sec. 6.1 the modified z transform of the output of the sampled-data system shown in Fig. 7.3-1 is found to be

$$C(z,m) = \frac{G(z,m)}{1 + GH(z)} R(z) \tag{7.3-63}$$

where $G(z,m)$ is the modified z transform associated with $G(s)$. The actual output of the system in response to the input $r(t)$ is then given by the inverse transform of Eq. (7.3-63), that is,

$$c(nT,m) = \frac{1}{2\pi j} \oint_\Gamma \frac{G(z,m)}{1 + GH(z)} R(z) z^{n-1}\, dz \tag{7.3-64}$$

where the contour Γ encloses all the singularities of the integrand. By applying Cauchy's residue theorem the integral of Eq. (7.3-64) can readily be evaluated.

Thus, during the period $(n-1)T \le t \le nT$, the system error is given by

$$\varepsilon(t) = c_d(t) - c(nT,m) \qquad 0 \le m \le 1 \tag{7.3-65}$$

where $c_d(t)$ is the desired output of the system, which in the analysis of output ripples may be taken as the ripple-free output. Since $(n-1)T \le t \le nT$ and $0 \le m \le 1$, the variable t of Eq. (7.3-65) may be replaced by $(n + m - 1)T$. With this substitution, Eq. (7.3-65) becomes

$$\varepsilon[(n + m - 1)T] = c_d[(n + m - 1)T] - c(nT,m) \qquad 0 \le m \le 1 \tag{7.3-66}$$

By varying the parameter m from 0 to 1, the above equation describes the system error between any two consecutive sampling instants $(n-1)T \le t \le nT$. Furthermore, letting n of Eq. (7.3-66) approach infinity, the limit thus obtained would yield the steady-state ripples of the output. The steady-state ripples can also be determined in a quick manner from the modified z transform of the system output by applying the final value theorem discussed in Sec. 5.7.

This section presents two analytical methods of determining the intersampling ripples of sampled-data and digital control systems. The first method requires the partial fraction expansion of the forward-transfer function $G(s)$, and the computation of the pulse-train responses. If all the poles of the forward transfer function $G(s)$ are distinct, the evaluation of the intersampling ripples is an easy task since the pulse-train responses of the basic forms of the partial fractions of $G(s)$ are tabulated in Table 7.3-1. However, the presence of multiple poles in the transfer function $G(s)$ complicates considerably the evaluation of the ripples by this method. The second method is fairly straightforward. With the aid of an extensive table of the z transforms and the modified z transforms, much computational labor can be saved. This method is particularly useful in finding the steady-state intersampling ripples in the system output. In the case of very complicated systems, both the above methods would involve considerable computational labor, and probably analog simulation is the most convenient way to find a quick solution.

7.4. Determination of Sampling Frequency; Ripple Factor. In the preceding section the methods of evaluating the system error and the intersampling ripples of sampled-data and digital control systems have been discussed, and an equation formulating the system error and the ripples as function of time t and sampling period T has been derived. For a specified value of the sampling period T the results of the above section, Eqs. (7.3-18) and (7.3-66), may be used to ascertain whether the error and the ripple content exceed some maximum allowable tolerance. It is conceivable that the system error due to intersampling ripples depends upon the sampling rate of the system. Generally speaking, higher sampling rate would give rise to less ripple content in the system output. Consequently, there is a minimum sampling rate which would be required to meet certain ripple-content (error) specification. In view of the fact that at any instant the system error equation of a sampled-data or digital control system, Eq. (7.3-18) or (7.3-66), provides a relationship between the error and the sampling period, the desired sampling rate may be determined from either equation when the maximum allowable error is specified. However, in many control-system design problems the rms error of the system, rather than the maximum error, is specified; especially when the input signals are not sudden disturbances but are continuous time functions which can be described either by a Fourier series or by a spectral density. In such cases the sampling rate should be so determined that the rms error specification is fulfilled. The following paragraphs are concerned with the analysis of rms system error and the determination of the sampling frequency from the rms error.[88]

Shown in Fig. 7.4-1 is the block diagram of a basic sampled-feedback control system, the output transform of which has been found to be

$$C(s) = \frac{G(s)}{1 + GH^*(s)} R^*(s) \tag{7.4-1}$$

Now, assume that the input to the control system has only one frequency component. Such an input may be described by Eq. (7.4-2),

$$r(t) = A\epsilon^{j\omega t} \tag{7.4-2}$$

As a matter of fact, a general result could be obtained if the input function is taken as an exponential or sum of exponentials of the form given by

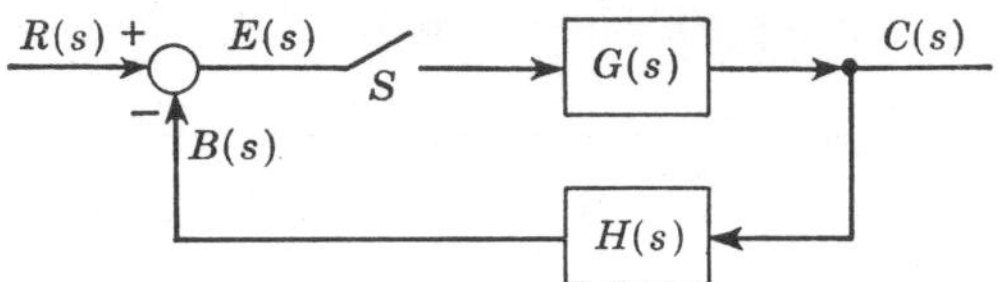

FIG. 7.4-1. The block diagram of a basic sampled-data feedback control system.

Eq. (7.4-2). The Laplace transformation of Eq. (7.4-2) yields

$$R(s) = \frac{A}{s - j\omega} \tag{7.4-3}$$

The starred transform associated with $R(s)$ is

$$R^*(s) = \frac{1}{T} \sum_{n=-\infty}^{\infty} R(s + jn\omega_s)$$

$$= \frac{A}{T} \sum_{n=-\infty}^{\infty} \frac{1}{s - j(\omega - n\omega_s)} \tag{7.4-4}$$

Substituting Eq. (7.4-4) into Eq. (7.4-1), the output transform of the system becomes

$$C(s) = \frac{AG(s)}{T[1 + GH^*(s)]} \sum_{n=-\infty}^{\infty} \frac{1}{s - j(\omega - n\omega_s)} \tag{7.4-5}$$

The inverse transform of Eq. (7.4-5) yields the output function $c(t)$ of the system in response to the test input $A\epsilon^{j\omega t}$. The output function contains both the transient output function $c_t(t)$ and the steady-state output function $c_s(t)$. In view of the fact that in the analysis of the rms error due to output ripples only the steady-state operation is significant in deriving an expression for the rms error, only the steady-state component of the output function $c(t)$ needs to be considered. It can readily be shown that the steady-state output function is given by the sum of the residues of $C(s)\epsilon^{ts}$ evaluated at the poles of the input transform, $R^*(s)$. Since the poles of the input transform, Eq. (7.4-4), occur at

$$s = j(\omega - n\omega_s) \tag{7.4-6}$$

the steady-state output function is then given by

$$c_s(t) = \frac{A}{T} \sum_{n=-\infty}^{\infty} \frac{G[j(\omega - n\omega_s)]}{1 + GH^*[j(\omega - n\omega_s)]} \epsilon^{j(\omega - n\omega_s)t} \tag{7.4-7}$$

where $c_s(t)$ is a rational function of t. Making use of the periodicity property of starred transforms,

$$GH^*[j(\omega - n\omega_s)] = GH^*(j\omega) \tag{7.4-8}$$

Eq. (7.4-7) reduces to

$$c_s(t) = \frac{A}{T} \sum_{n=-\infty}^{\infty} \frac{G[j(\omega - n\omega_s)]}{1 + GH^*(j\omega)} \epsilon^{j(\omega - n\omega_s)t} \tag{7.4-9}$$

The steady-state output function $c_s(t)$ may be considered as consisting of two parts: the primary component and the complementary components. The former represents the signal component of the system output whereas the latter form the unwanted error or noise in the output which is often referred to as the output ripples. Thus, in the study of the ripple effect the primary component which is obtained from Eq. (7.4-9) by putting n equal to zero can be taken the desired output function $c_d(t)$:

$$c_d(t) = \frac{AG(j\omega)}{T[1 + GH^*(j\omega)]} \epsilon^{j\omega t} \tag{7.4-10}$$

The components of Eq. (7.4-9) for $n \neq 0$ (i.e., the complementary components) yield the system error or output ripples which is given by

$$\epsilon(t) = \frac{A \sum_{n=1}^{\infty} \{G[j(\omega + n\omega_s)]\epsilon^{j(\omega + n\omega_s)t} + G[j(\omega - n\omega_s)]\epsilon^{j(\omega - n\omega_s)t}\}}{T[1 + GH^*(j\omega)]} \tag{7.4-11}$$

The system error or ripple content is then given by the difference between the steady-state output $c_s(t)$ and the desired output $c_d(t)$, that is,

$$\varepsilon(t) = c_s(t) - c_d(t) \tag{7.4-12}$$

Squaring both sides of Eq. (7.4-12) and taking the average yields the mean-square error as

$$\overline{[\varepsilon(t)]^2} = \overline{[c_s(t) - c_d(t)]^2} \tag{7.4-13}$$

where the bar over a time function stands for the average value of the function. Expanding the right-hand side of Eq. (7.4-13), the mean-square error becomes

$$\overline{[\varepsilon(t)]^2} = \overline{[c_s(t)]^2} - \overline{2[c_s(t)c_d(t)]} + \overline{[c_d(t)]^2} \tag{7.4-14}$$

Due to the fact that when $n \neq 0$, $c_s(t)$ and $c_d(t)$ are orthogonal and the average value of their product is zero, and that when $n = 0$, $c_s(t)$ becomes $c_d(t)$,

$$\overline{[c_s(t)c_d(t)]} = \overline{[c_d(t)]^2} \tag{7.4-15}$$

Consequently, the mean-square error may be written as

$$\overline{[\varepsilon(t)]^2} = \overline{[c_s(t)]^2} - \overline{[c_d(t)]^2} \tag{7.4-16}$$

The system error can also be expressed as a percentage of the desired output. If both sides of Eq. (7.4-16) are divided by $\overline{[c_d(t)]^2}$, there results

$$\frac{\overline{[\varepsilon(t)]^2}}{\overline{[c_d(t)]^2}} = \frac{\overline{[c_s(t)]^2}}{\overline{[c_d(t)]^2}} - 1 \tag{7.4-17}$$

The square root of Eq. (7.4-17) may be defined as the *ripple factor*, and denoted by k_r. Thus,

$$k_r = \sqrt{\frac{\overline{[c_s(t)]^2}}{\overline{[c_d(t)]^2}} - 1} \tag{7.4-18}$$

Equations (7.4-16) and (7.4-17) point out that to find an expression for the mean-square error requires the evaluation of the mean-square values of the steady-state output and the desired output of the system. The mean-square value of the desired output can readily be obtained from Eq. (7.4-10):

$$\overline{[c_d(t)]^2} = \frac{A^2|G(j\omega)|^2}{T^2|1 + GH^*(j\omega)|^2} \tag{7.4-19}$$

In like manner, the mean-square value of the steady-state output can be derived from Eq. (7.4-9). It follows from Eq. (7.4-9) that the steady-state output $c_s(t)$ may be written as:

$$c_s(t) = \frac{A \sum_{n=-\infty}^{\infty} G[j(\omega - n\omega_s)]\epsilon^{-jn\omega_s t}}{T[1 + GH^*(j\omega)]} \epsilon^{j\omega t} \tag{7.4-20}$$

and the absolute value of the output function is

$$|c_s(t)| = \frac{A\left|\sum_{n=-\infty}^{\infty} G[j(\omega - n\omega_s)]\epsilon^{-jn\omega_s t}\right|}{T|1 + GH^*(j\omega)|} \tag{7.4-21}$$

The square of the steady-state output is then given by

$$[c_s(t)]^2 = \frac{A^2\left|\sum_{n=-\infty}^{\infty} G[j(\omega - n\omega_s)]\epsilon^{-jn\omega_s t}\right|^2}{T^2|1 + GH^*(j\omega)|^2} \tag{7.4-22}$$

It has been shown by Sklansky[88] and Ragazzini that the mean of the numerator of Eq. (7.4-22) is equal to

$$A^2 \sum_{n=-\infty}^{\infty} |G[j(\omega - n\omega_s)]|^2$$

Thus, the mean-square value of $c_s(t)$ is

$$\overline{[c_s(t)]^2} = \frac{A^2 \sum_{n=-\infty}^{\infty} |G[j(\omega - n\omega_s)]|^2}{T^2|1 + GH^*(j\omega)|^2} \tag{7.4-23}$$

Substituting Eqs. (7.4-19) and (7.4-23) into Eq. (7.4-17) yields the per unit mean-square error:

$$\frac{\overline{[\varepsilon(t)]^2}}{\overline{[c_d(t)]^2}} = \frac{\sum_{n=-\infty}^{\infty} |G[j(\omega - n\omega_s)]|^2}{|G(j\omega)|^2} - 1 \tag{7.4-24}$$

Equation (7.4-24) indicates that the per unit ripple content of the system depends only upon the forward transfer function $G(s)$ and is independent of the feedback transfer function $H(s)$ of the system. This is an important property which can be utilized in the design of sampled-data and digital control systems when the system error is a stringent factor.

Both Eqs. (7.4-23) and (7.4-24) can be further simplified. Let

$$Y(s) = G(s)G(-s) \tag{7.4-25}$$

The starred transform of Eq. (7.4-25) is

$$Y^*(s) = \frac{1}{T} \sum_{n=-\infty}^{\infty} G(s - jn\omega_s)G(-s + jn\omega_s) \tag{7.4-26}$$

For $s = j\omega$, Eq. (7.4-26) becomes

$$Y^*(j\omega) = \frac{1}{T} \sum_{n=-\infty}^{\infty} G[j(\omega - n\omega_s)]G[-j(\omega - n\omega_s)]$$

$$= \frac{1}{T} \sum_{n=-\infty}^{\infty} |G[j(\omega - n\omega_s)]|^2 \tag{7.4-27}$$

which leads to

$$\sum_{n=-\infty}^{\infty} |G[j(\omega - n\omega_s)]|^2 = TY^*(j\omega) \tag{7.4-28}$$

By substituting Eq. (7.4-28) into Eq. (7.4-24) the expression for the per unit mean-square error becomes

$$\frac{\overline{[\varepsilon(t)]^2}}{\overline{[c_d(t)]^2}} = \frac{TY^*(j\omega)}{|G(j\omega)|^2} - 1 \tag{7.4-29}$$

The ripple factor is then given by

$$k_r = \sqrt{\frac{TY^*(j\omega)}{|G(j\omega)|^2} - 1} \tag{7.4-30†}$$

It is noted that $Y^*(j\omega)$ may be derived from the z transform of Eq. (7.4-25) with z replaced by $\epsilon^{j\omega T}$, where T is the sampling period, that is,

$$Y^*(j\omega) = Y(z)|_{z=\epsilon^{j\omega T}=\epsilon^{j2\pi\omega/\omega_s}} \tag{7.4-31}$$

Since $Y^*(j\omega)$ is a function of the signal frequency ω and the sampling frequency ω_s, Eq. (7.4-29) relates the mean-square error to the input frequency and the sampling frequency. In consequence, when the tolerable rms error and the frequency range of the input signal are specified the desired sampling rate can be determined from the above error equation. The techniques of system error analysis, as described above for the case of a simple exponential input, can also be applied to the study of periodic and random inputs.

To illustrate the application of Eq. (7.4-30), a numerical example is presented. Consider the sampled-data feedback system of Fig. 7.4-2. The

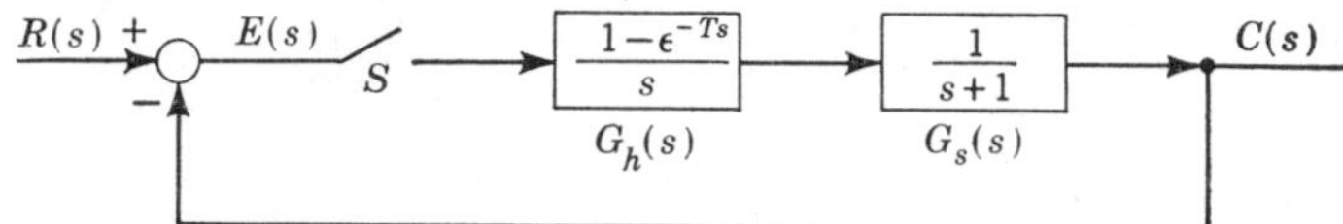

FIG. 7.4-2. The block diagram of the system of the illustrative example.

transfer function of the controlled system is

$$G_s(s) = \frac{1}{s+1} \tag{7.4-32}$$

The analysis is initiated with a determination of $Y^*(j\omega)$ and $|G(j\omega)|^2$. Without the zero-order hold,

$$G(s) = G_s(s) = \frac{1}{s+1} \tag{7.4-33}$$

$$Y(s) = G(s)G(-s) = \frac{1}{1-s^2} \tag{7.4-34}$$

The z transform associated with $Y(s)$ is found to be

$$Y(z) = \frac{\sinh T}{2\cosh T - (z + z^{-1})} \tag{7.4-35}$$

Thus,

$$Y^*(j\omega) = Y(z)|_{z=\epsilon^{j\omega T}}$$

$$= \frac{\sinh T}{2(\cosh T - \cos \omega T)} \tag{7.4-36}$$

† When a zero-order hold is used, Eq. (7.4-30) is still applicable. It can readily be shown that the factor $(1 - \epsilon^{-Ts})$ of the zero-order hold may be dropped in performing the computations. In other words, the transfer function $G(s)$ remains a rational polynomial in s.

It follows from Eq. (7.4-33) that

$$|G(j\omega)|^2 = \frac{1}{1 + \omega^2} \tag{7.4-37}$$

Combining Eqs. (7.4-36), (7.4-37), and (7.4-30) yields

$$k_r^2 = \frac{T(1 + \omega^2)\sinh T}{2(\cosh T - \cos \omega T)} - 1 \tag{7.4-38}$$

For a given value of T, the above equation provides the relationship between the ripple factor k_r and the input frequency ω. A curve relating k_r to ω/ω_s for $T = 0.693$ sec is sketched in Fig. 7.4-3. Similar ripple factor curves (k_r versus ω/ω_s) can be plotted from Eq. (7.4-38) for various values of T. When the ripple factor is specified, these curves may be used to determine the desirable sampling frequency.

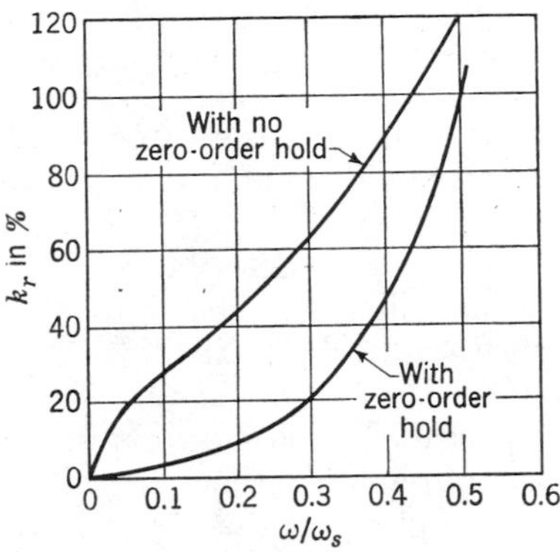

FIG. 7.4-3. The ripple factor curves for $T = 0.693$ sec with and without the zero-order hold.

By use of a zero-order hold, the ripple content can be reduced, as demonstrated in the following analysis. With a zero-order hold, the transfer function of the forward path becomes

$$G_h(s)G_s(s) = \frac{1 - \epsilon^{-Ts}}{s}\frac{1}{s + 1} \tag{7.4-39}$$

Then

$$G(s) = \frac{1}{s(s + 1)} \tag{7.4-40}$$

$$Y(s) = G(s)G(-s) = \frac{1}{s^2(s^2 - 1)} \tag{7.4-41}$$

It can readily be shown that the z transform associated with $Y(s)$ is

$$Y(z) = \frac{-Tz}{(z - 1)^2} - \frac{\sinh T}{2\cosh T - (z + z^{-1})} \tag{7.4-42}$$

Thus,

$$Y^*(j\omega) = Y(z)|_{z=\epsilon^{j\omega T}}$$

$$= \frac{T}{4\sin^2(\omega T/2)} - \frac{\sinh T}{2(\cosh T - \cos \omega T)} \tag{7.4-43}$$

From Eq. (7.4-40),

$$|G(j\omega)|^2 = \frac{1}{\omega^2(1 + \omega^2)} \tag{7.4-44}$$

Combining Eqs. (7.4-43), (7.4-44), and (7.4-30) gives

$$k_r^2 = \frac{T\omega^2(1 + \omega^2)}{2} \left[\frac{T}{\sin^2 (\omega T/2)} - \frac{\sinh T}{(\cosh T - \cos \omega T)} \right] - 1 \qquad (7.4\text{-}45)$$

For various values of the sampling period T, the ripple factor curves can be plotted from the above equation. Sketched in Fig. 7.4-3 is the ripple factor curve for $T = 0.693$ sec. These ripple factor curves make evident the effect of the zero-order hold upon the ripple content in the system output. It is observed from Fig. 7.4-3 that to keep the ripple factor below 15 per cent, it is necessary to set the sampling frequency at about four times the maximum input frequency for the given system using a zero-order hold. On the other hand, at this sampling frequency the ripple factor would be about 55 per cent for the same system without using a zero-order hold.

This section describes a method of determining the ripple factor and the sampling frequency to meet the allowable rms error specification. Since relatively small differences of large numbers are involved in computing the ripple factors, the use of a desk calculator is generally indispensable. It is shown in this section that the ripple factor depends upon the sampling frequency and the elements $G(s)$ in the forward path between the sampler and the output, and is independent of the other elements of the system. Thus, in determining the sampling frequencies of sampled-data and digital control systems to meet the rms error specifications, $G(s)$ is the only transfer function which needs to be considered. The analysis described in this section may be extended to more complicated systems.

7.5. High-frequency Oscillations between Sampling Instants. In any feedback control system it is desired to have the controlled variable or output of the system bear a definite and known relationship to the reference input. To this end it is essential that the system be so designed that the transient disturbances will decay quickly enough to permit rapid recovery by the controlled variable. The ability of a control system to damp its transient response to a change of state or any temporary disturbance is measured by the stability of the system. A system which would exhibit undamped oscillations in the system output is considered as unstable. It is a well-known fact that oscillation of the output of a control system is not only undesirable but also dangerous, because it would cause undue wear of the system components and would put the system out of control. Consequently, above all, satisfactory system stability is imperative regardless of other considerations of system performance.

The stability of sampled-data and digital feedback control systems has been discussed in Chap. 6. A sampled-data control system is said to be stable if all the roots of the system characteristic equation in terms of z lie inside the unit circle of the z plane. The stability criteria described in Sec. 6.2 are nothing but the methods of detecting the presence of any characteristic root falling outside or on the unit circle. However, it should be pointed out that these criteria are formulated on the basis of the z-transform theory, which fails to yield correct information during the intersampling periods. The test for system stability based upon the methods of Sec. 6.2 would indicate whether the output sequence of the system in response to any temporary disturbance, rather than the complete output response, will quickly die out.

As a matter of fact, there exist sampled-data control systems in which, when subjected to a temporary disturbance, the system transient response at the sampling instants is well damped; but, on the other hand, the output time function of the system might be quite oscillatory, because oscillations could exist between sampling instants. It is obvious that for such systems the condition of stability indicated by the test procedures based upon the z-transform method could be misleading, since these test procedures fail to reveal any oscillations between sampling instants. These high-frequency oscillations are sometimes referred to as *hidden oscillations*, and the system instability as a result of oscillations between sampling instants is sometimes called *hidden instability*.[25,147] The high-frequency oscillations between sampling instants are named hidden oscillations simply because they are, so to speak, hiding behind the output sequence of the system and the z-transform method fails to indicate their presence. No doubt, hidden oscillations are detrimental to the performance of sampled-data control systems. Thus, in control system analysis the possibility of high-frequency oscillations taking place between sampling instants should not be overlooked.

As can be seen from Fig. 7.5-1, the main factors essential for the occurrence of high-frequency oscillations between the sampling instants in

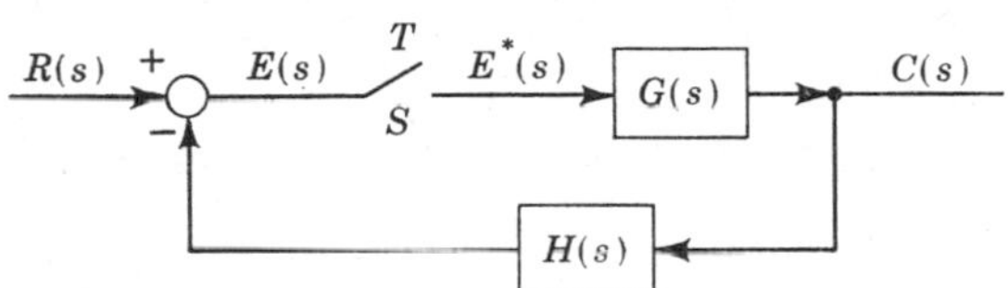

FIG. 7.5-1. A basic sampled-data feedback control system.

sampled-data feedback systems are (1) that the impulse response of the transfer function $G(s)$ between the sampler and the output of the system be oscillatory, and (2) that the sampling period of the system be large. In most sampled-data feedback control systems, the impulse response of the transfer function $G(s)$ of the system generally takes one of several basic forms. They are either oscillatory or nonoscillatory, as shown in Fig. 7.5-2. The impulse response decays monotonically if the transfer function $G(s)$ contains one or more poles than zeros and all the poles are real and negative. The impulse response rises monotonically provided that the transfer function $G(s)$ contains two or more poles than zeros and all the poles are real and negative with one pole at the origin. It is quite obvious that if the impulse response of the transfer function $G(s)$ falls into these categories, no high-frequency oscillations could exist between sampling instants. On the other hand, if the transfer function $G(s)$ contains conjugate complex poles the impulse response would be oscillatory, as demonstrated in (*c*), (*d*), and (*e*) of Fig. 7.5-2. In these three cases, high-frequency oscillations could take place between sampling instants, provided that the sampling period of the system is greater than half the period of

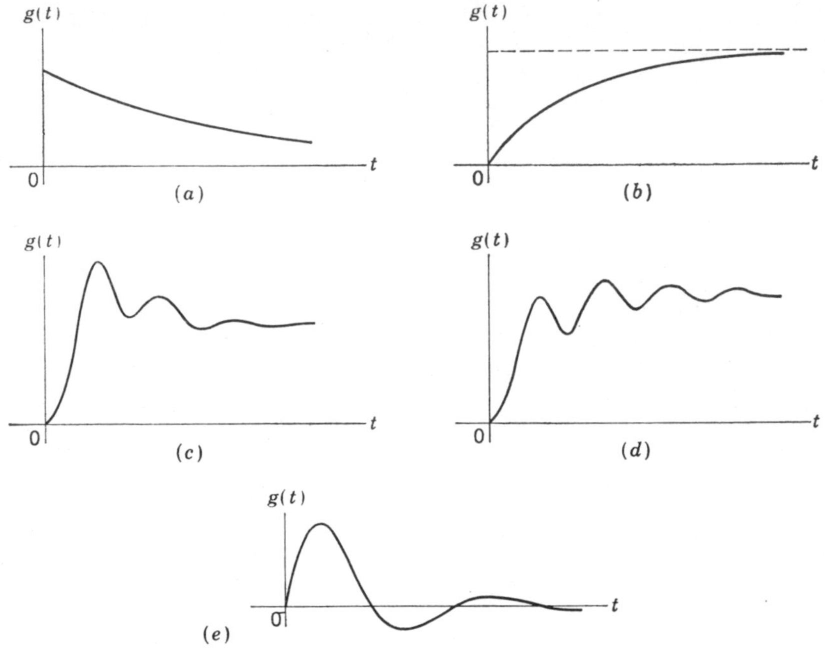

FIG. 7.5-2. Basic forms of the impulse response.

oscillation of the impulse response. Consequently, the occurrence of *hidden oscillations* in sampled-data control systems depends primarily upon the impulse-response characteristics of the forward-transfer function of the system and the value of the sampling period.

It has been discussed and illustrated in Secs. 6.3 and 6.4 that if the response of a sampled-data control system is well behaved (i.e., nonoscillatory between sampling instants), approximate values of the system response between sampling instants could be obtained from the z-transform method of analysis. However, if the system response is oscillatory with frequency of oscillation being high in comparison with the sampling frequency, then the information between the sampling instants derived from the z-transform analysis could be completely incorrect and misleading. In such cases, it seems imperative that one would have recourse to other methods of analysis than the z-transform technique. One of the most popular and powerful methods for the evaluation of the system response between the sampling instants is the modified z-transform method. As demonstrated in the preceding chapters, the modified z-transform analysis is a direct extension of the basic z-transformation theory. Just like the z-transform technique, the modified z-transform method permits the analysis of sampled-data systems to be carried out in a straightforward and systematic manner. Once the existence of hidden oscillations in a sampled-data control system is detected from the impulse-response characteristic of the forward transfer function of the system, the modified z-transform method is probably the most convenient one for the determination of the magnitude of these high-frequency oscillations.

The *hidden oscillations* and *hidden instability* of sampled-data control systems are unveiled when the modified z-transform method of analysis is applied. Consider the open-loop sampled-data system of Fig. 7.5-3. The transfer function of the system is $G(s)$. Let the z transform and the modified z transform associated with $G(s)$ be expressed as the ratio of two polynomials in z:

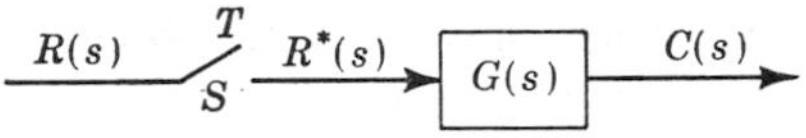

R(s) T S R*(s) G(s) C(s)

FIG. 7.5-3. Open-loop sampled-data system.

$$G(z) = \frac{P(z)}{Q(z)} \tag{7.5-1}$$

and

$$G(z,m) = \frac{P_1(z,m)}{Q_1(z)} \tag{7.5-2}$$

where $P_1(z,m)$ is a polynomial in z with m as a parameter varying between 0 and 1. The system is said to be stable if all the poles of $G(s)$ lie in the left half of the s plane (except possibly a single pole at the origin). In other words, for stable operation the poles of $G(z)$ and $G(z,m)$ must fall inside the unit circle of the z plane. The locations of these poles inside the unit circle would determine the different modes of transient behavior at sampling instants, as has been studied in Sec. 7.1. The poles of $G(z)$ are usually identical to those of $G(z,m)$ except that the modified z transform $G(z,m)$ may contain more poles than the corresponding z transform $G(z)$, depending upon the impulse-response characteristic of the transfer function $G(s)$ and the sampling frequency of the system. To illustrate this point, assume that the transfer function $G(s)$ of Fig. 7.5-3 takes the form

$$G(s) = \frac{s^2 + (2a + \omega_0)s + (a^2 + \omega_0^2)}{s[(s + a)^2 + \omega_0^2]} \tag{7.5-3}$$

which has an oscillatory impulse response with frequency of oscillation equal to ω_0. Upon expanding into partial fractions, Eq. (7.5-3) becomes

$$G(s) = \frac{1}{s} + \frac{\omega_0}{(s + a)^2 + \omega_0^2} \tag{7.5-4}$$

Making use of the z-transform table in Appendix 1, the z transform associated with $G(s)$ is found to be

$$G(z) = \frac{z}{z - 1} + \frac{z\epsilon^{-aT} \sin \omega_0 T}{z^2 - 2z\epsilon^{-aT} \cos \omega_0 T + \epsilon^{-2aT}} \tag{7.5-5}$$

In like manner, the modified z transforms associated with the terms of the right-hand side of Eq. (7.5-4) are readily obtained from the modified z-transform table in Appendix 1 (or they can be derived by following the procedures outlined in Chap. 5). The modified z transform associated with $G(s)$ is found to be

$$G(z,m) = \frac{1}{z-1} + \frac{z \sin m\omega_0 T + \epsilon^{-aT} \sin (1-m)\omega_0 T}{z^2 - 2z\epsilon^{-aT} \cos \omega_0 T + \epsilon^{-2aT}} \epsilon^{-amT} \tag{7.5-6}$$

From Eqs. (7.5-5) and (7.5-6), it is noted that both $G(z)$ and $G(z,m)$ have the same poles. However, if the sampling frequency of the system is made equal to the frequency of oscillation of the impulse response of $G(s)$, that is, $\omega_s = \omega_0$, then $\omega_0 T = 2\pi$ and Eq. (7.5-5) is reduced to

$$G(z) = \frac{z}{z-1} \tag{7.5-7}$$

which has a single pole $z = 1$ corresponding to the pole $s = 0$ of $G(s)$ in the s plane. Apparently, two other poles of $G(z)$ corresponding to the poles $s = -a \pm j\omega_0$ of $G(s)$ have disappeared, or are hidden, so to speak. The substitution of 2π for $\omega_0 T$ converts Eq. (7.5-6) into

$$\begin{aligned} G(z,m) &= \frac{1}{z-1} + \frac{z \sin 2m\pi + \epsilon^{-aT} \sin 2(1-m)\pi}{(z-\epsilon^{-aT})^2} \epsilon^{-amT} \\ &= \frac{1}{z-1} + \frac{\epsilon^{-amT} \sin 2m\pi}{z - \epsilon^{-aT}} \end{aligned} \tag{7.5-8}$$

which may be written as

$$G(z,m) = \frac{(1 + \epsilon^{-amT} \sin 2m\pi)z - (\epsilon^{-aT} + \epsilon^{-amT} \sin 2m\pi)}{(z-1)(z-\epsilon^{-aT})} \tag{7.5-9}$$

The above discussion points out that under such conditions $G(z,m)$ would contain one more pole than $G(z)$, that is, the pole at $z = \epsilon^{-aT}$ which is missing in $G(z)$. As a result, system analysis by the z-transform method fails to reveal the mode of transient behavior due to this pole and the results of the z-transform analysis would be incomplete. On the other hand, the modified z-transform analysis yields not only all the possible modes of transient behavior at the sampling instants but also the high-frequency oscillations between sampling instants.

Now, let us investigate the possibility of hidden instability in sampled-data feedback systems. Referring to the block diagram of a basic sampled-data feedback control system shown in Fig. 7.5-1, the output and the input of the system are related by

$$C(s) = \frac{G(s)}{1 + GH^*(s)} R^*(s) \tag{7.5-10}$$

It has been shown in the previous chapter that the z transform and the modified z transform associated with $C(s)$ of Eq. (7.5-10) are

$$C(z) = \frac{G(z)}{1 + GH(z)} R(z) \tag{7.5-11}$$

and

$$C(z,m) = \frac{G(z,m)}{1 + GH(z)} R(z) \tag{7.5-12}$$

respectively.

Let the transforms $GH(z)$, $G(z)$, and $G(z,m)$ be expressed as ratios of two polynomials in z:

$$GH(z) = \frac{P(z)}{Q(z)} \tag{7.5-13}$$

$$G(z) = \frac{P_a(z)}{Q_a(z)} \tag{7.5-14}$$

$$G(z,m) = \frac{P_b(z,m)}{Q_b(z)} \tag{7.5-15}$$

Then it follows from Eqs. (7.5-11), (7.5-13), and (7.5-14) that the closed-loop pulse-transfer function of the system is given by

$$\frac{C(z)}{R(z)} = \frac{P_a(z)}{P(z) + Q(z)} \frac{Q(z)}{Q_a(z)} = \frac{P_a(z)D(z)}{P(z) + Q(z)} \tag{7.5-16}$$

where

$$D(z) = Q(z)/Q_a(z) \tag{7.5-17}$$

is a polynomial in z. Substituting Eqs. (7.5-14) and (7.5-15) into Eq. (7.5-12) yields the closed-loop transfer function in terms of the modified z transforms,

$$\frac{C(z,m)}{R(z)} = \frac{P_b(z,m)}{P(z) + Q(z)} \frac{Q(z)}{Q_b(z)} \tag{7.5-18}$$

where $Q_b(z)$ may contain factors which $Q(z)$ does not have.

Equation (7.5-18) shows that the different modes of transient behavior of the system are determined by the roots of $P(z) + Q(z) = 0$ as well as the zeros of $Q_b(z)$, which are not contained in $Q(z)$ [i.e., the extra poles of $G(z,m)$ which are different from the poles of $GH(z)$]. It is clear from Eq. (7.5-16) that the z-transform analysis fails to yield the modes of transient behavior due to the extra poles of $G(z,m)$.

If some of the roots of $P(z) + Q(z) = 0$ (i.e., the characteristic roots) lie outside the unit circle of the z plane, the output sequence of the system would increase in magnitude indefinitely. Both the z transform and the modified z-transform analysis, Eqs. (7.5-16) and (7.5-18), would show that the system is unstable. On the other hand, if all the roots of $P(z) + Q(z) = 0$ lie inside the unit circle, based upon the z-transform analysis [Eq. (7.5-16)], the system would be considered stable. However, this does not provide a sufficient indication of system stability. In fact, this condition merely points out that the output sequence of the system is bounded. While the system may prove stable at sampling instants, it could show undamped oscillations between sampling instants provided that the extra poles of $G(z,m)$ fall outside the unit circle. Because of the fact that the z-transform analysis fails to reveal this sort of instability, it is sometimes referred to as *hidden instability* in the literature.[25] Hidden instability would arise when the forward transfer function $G(s)$ is unstable and $G(z,m)$ has more poles than $G(z)$. Apparently, if $G(s)$ is the transfer function of the components between the sampler and the output of the system, it is unlikely that $G(s)$ would contain poles in the right half of the s plane, thus eliminating the possibility of hidden instability. However, if the system has a minor loop in the forward path, hidden instability could take place, provided that the minor loop is unstable. Although the chance of getting into hidden instability is slim, the investigation of its occurrence in sampled-data systems should not be overlooked. In order to eliminate the possible existence of hidden instability the minor loop of the sampled-data feedback control system is often made stable.

An example is presented in the following paragraphs to illustrate the evaluation of high-frequency oscillations between sampling instants in sampled-data control systems. Consider the unity-feedback sampled-data control system containing a minor loop as shown in Fig. 7.5-4a. The

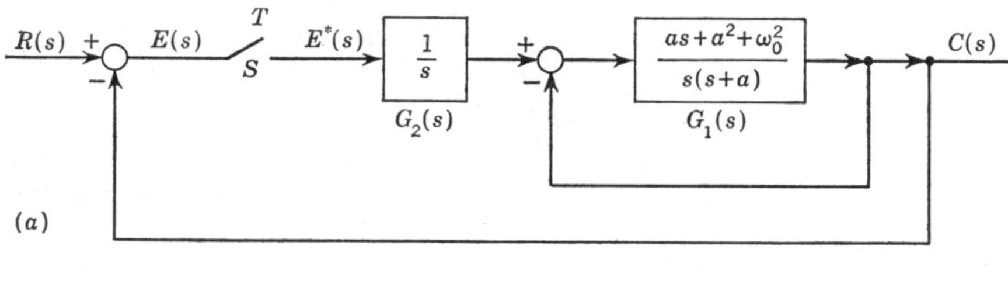

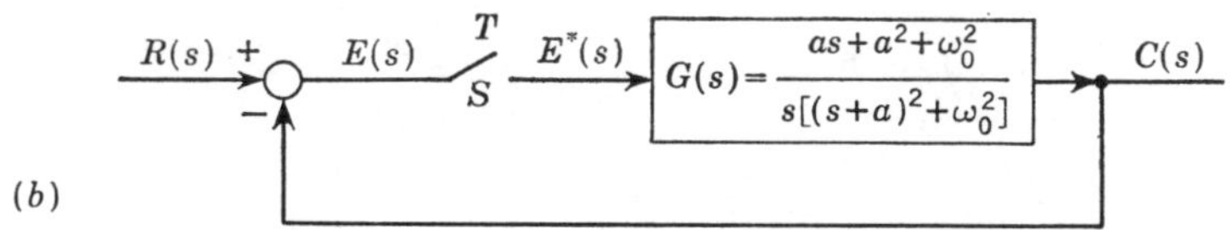

FIG. 7.5-4. (a) Sampled-data system of the example illustrating the evaluation of hidden oscillations; (b) simplified block diagram of the illustrative example.

transfer functions describing the components of this error-sampled system are

$$G_1(s) = \frac{as + a^2 + \omega_0^2}{s(s + a)} \tag{7.5-19}$$

and

$$G_2(s) = \frac{1}{s} \tag{7.5-20}$$

It is assumed that the sampling frequency ω_s of the system is 2π radians/sec, sampling period T is 1 sec, $\omega_0 = 2\omega_s$, and $a = 2$. Determine the hidden oscillations in the output when the system is subjected to a unit step-function input.

It can readily be shown that the transfer function of the forward path of the system is given by

$$G(s) = \frac{G_1(s)G_2(s)}{1 + G_1(s)}$$

$$= \frac{as + a^2 + \omega_0^2}{s[(s + a)^2 + \omega_0^2]} \tag{7.5-21}$$

The block diagram of the system can then be simplified into the form shown in Fig. 7.5-4*b*.

By partial-fraction expansion, Eq. (7.5-21) becomes

$$G(s) = \frac{1}{s} - \frac{s + a}{(s + a)^2 + \omega_0^2} \tag{7.5-22}$$

The z transform associated with $G(s)$ is found to be

$$G(z) = \frac{z}{z - 1} - \frac{z(z - \epsilon^{-aT} \cos \omega_0 T)}{z^2 - 2z\epsilon^{-aT} \cos \omega_0 T + \epsilon^{-2aT}} \tag{7.5-23}$$

Since

$$\omega_0 T = 2\omega_s T = 4\pi \qquad aT = 2 \tag{7.5-24}$$

Eq. (7.5-23) is reduced to

$$G(z) = \frac{(1 - \epsilon^{-aT})z}{(z - 1)(z - \epsilon^{-aT})}$$

$$= \frac{0.865z}{(z - 0.135)(z - 1)} \tag{7.5-25}$$

The z transforms of the system output and input are related by

$$C(z) = \frac{G(z)}{1 + G(z)} R(z) \tag{7.5-26}$$

where $G(z)$ is given by Eq. (7.5-25) and

$$R(z) = \frac{z}{z - 1} \tag{7.5-27}$$

Substituting Eqs. (7.5-25) and (7.5-27) into Eq. (7.5-26) and simplifying yields the output transform as

$$C(z) = \frac{(1 - \epsilon^{-aT})z^2}{(z - 1)(z^2 - 2\epsilon^{-aT}z + \epsilon^{-aT})}$$

$$= \frac{0.865z^2}{(z - 1)(z^2 - 0.270z + 0.135)} \tag{7.5-28}$$

By long division, $C(z)$ is expanded into an infinite series of z^{-1}:

$$C(z) = 0.865z^{-1} + 1.10z^{-2} + 1.006z^{-3} + 0.901z^{-4} + 0.841z^{-5} + 0.798z^{-6} + \cdots \quad (7.5\text{-}29)$$

The coefficients of the above series form the output sequence of the system in response to a unit step-function input:

$$c(0) = 0, \quad c(T) = 0.865, \quad c(2T) = 1.10, \quad c(3T) = 1.006, \quad \cdots \quad (7.5\text{-}30)$$

In view of the fact that the impulse response of $G(s)$ is oscillatory and its frequency of oscillation is higher than the sampling frequency of the system, high-frequency oscillations may be expected to take place between the sampling instants. These hidden oscillations are readily determined by applying the modified z-transform analysis. The modified z transform associated with $G(s)$ of Eq. (7.5-22) is found to be

$$G(z,m) = \frac{1}{z-1} - \frac{z \cos m\omega_0 T - \epsilon^{-aT} \cos (1-m)\omega_0 T}{z^2 - 2z\epsilon^{-aT} \cos \omega_0 T + \epsilon^{-2aT}} \epsilon^{-amT} \quad (7.5\text{-}31)$$

By substitution of the known constants, Eq. (7.5-31) becomes

$$G(z,m) = \frac{(z - \epsilon^{-aT}) - (z-1)\epsilon^{-amT} \cos 4m\pi}{(z-1)(z-\epsilon^{-aT})}$$

$$= \frac{(z - 0.135) - (z-1)\epsilon^{-2m} \cos 4m\pi}{(z-0.135)(z-1)} \quad (7.5\text{-}32)$$

In the case of the single-loop unity-feedback configuration of Fig. 7.5-4*b* the modified z transform of the output $C(z,m)$ is given by the relation

$$C(z,m) = \frac{G(z,m)}{1 + G(z)} R(z) \quad (7.5\text{-}33)$$

Substituting Eqs. (7.5-25) and (7.5-32) into Eq. (7.5-33), the modified z transform of the system output in response to a unit step-function input takes the form

$$C(z,m) = \frac{z[(z - \epsilon^{-aT}) - (z-1)\epsilon^{-amT} \cos 4m\pi]}{(z-1)(z^2 - 2\epsilon^{-aT}z + \epsilon^{-aT})}$$

$$= \frac{z[(z - 0.135) - (z-1)\epsilon^{-2m} \cos 4m\pi]}{(z-1)(z^2 - 0.270z + 0.135)} \quad (7.5\text{-}34)$$

The initial and the steady-state values of the system response can readily be obtained from Eq. (7.5-34) if the initial and the final value theorems of Sec. 5.7 are applied. The initial value of the system response is given by

$$c(0) = \lim_{\substack{m=0 \\ z \to \infty}} zC(z,m)$$

$$= \lim_{z\to\infty} \frac{0.865z^2}{(z-1)(z^2 - 0.270z + 0.135)} = 0 \quad (7.5\text{-}35)$$

Thus, the system output at $t = 0$ is zero. In like manner, the steady-state response of the system is given by

$$\lim_{n\to\infty} c(nT,m) = \lim_{z\to 1} \frac{z-1}{z} C(z,m)$$

$$= \lim_{z\to 1} \frac{(z - 0.135) - (z-1)\epsilon^{-2m}\cos 4m\pi}{z^2 - 0.270z + 0.135}$$

$$= 1 \qquad (7.5\text{-}36)$$

This implies that in the steady state the output is equal to the input of the system.

It has been shown in Sec. 5.7 that the system response during the first sampling period can be derived from the modified z transform of the system output without taking the inverse transformation. During the interval $0 \le t \le T$

$$c(t) = c(mT) = \lim_{\substack{z\to\infty \\ 0\le m\le 1}} zC(z,m) \qquad (7.5\text{-}37)$$

The above equation follows from Eq. (5.7-81) of Sec. 5.7. Substituting Eq. (7.5-34) into Eq. (7.5-37) and evaluating the limit yield the system response during the first sampling period

$$c(mT) = 1 - \epsilon^{-amT}\cos 4m\pi = 1 - \epsilon^{-2m}\cos 4m\pi \qquad (7.5\text{-}38)$$

In fact, Eq. (7.5-38) is the impulse response of $G(s)$, with t replaced by mT.

It is clear from Eq. (7.5-38) that high-frequency oscillation takes place between sampling instants. The maximum and minimum values of the oscillation can readily be determined by applying the conventional rules. The overshoots and undershoots of $c(mT)$ occur at such values of m that satisfy the following equation:

$$\frac{dc(mT)}{dm} = 0 \qquad (7.5\text{-}39)$$

Differentiating Eq. (7.5-38) with respect to m and equating the derivative with zero yields

$$4\pi \sin 4m\pi + 2\cos 4m\pi = 0 \qquad (7.5\text{-}40)$$

or

$$\tan 4m\pi = -\frac{1}{2\pi} \qquad (7.5\text{-}41)$$

The solutions of the above equation for $0 \le m \le 1$ are

$$m = 0.2375, \quad 0.4875, \quad 0.7375, \quad 0.9875 \qquad (7.5\text{-}42)$$

Since the system response would reach a peak first, the values of m corresponding to the maxima of $c(mT)$ are

$$m = \begin{cases} 0.2375 \\ 0.7375 \end{cases} \qquad (7.5\text{-}43)$$

and the values of m corresponding to the minima of $c(mT)$ are

$$m = \begin{cases} 0.4875 \\ 0.9875 \end{cases} \tag{7.5-44}$$

The maximum and minimum values of $c(mT)$ are computed from Eq. (7.5-38) and are tabulated below:

m	$c(mT)$	*Overshoot, %*
0.2375	1.614	61.4
0.4875	0.629	−37.1
0.7375	1.226	22.6
0.9875	0.863	−13.7

It should be pointed out that in the presence of hidden oscillations the formula, given by Eq. (7.2-21), for estimating the maximum overshoot does not apply.

The system output during the nth sampling period (i.e., during the interval $(n - 1)T \leq t \leq nT$) is given by the inverse transform of $C(z,m)$. Making use of the inversion formula given by Eq. (5.7-65) yields the system response as

$$c(nT,m) = \frac{1}{2\pi j} \oint_{\Gamma} \frac{(z - 0.135) - (z - 1)\epsilon^{-2m} \cos 4m\pi}{(z - 1)(z^2 - 0.270z + 0.135)} z^n \, dz \tag{7.5-45}$$

The contour integration of the above equation can readily be evaluated by means of the residue theorem.

The output sequence and the output time function of the system in response to a unit step-function input are plotted in Fig. 7.5-5. It is clear from the above analysis that in the presence of hidden oscillations between the sampling instants system analysis by the z-transform method provides inadequate information, whereas the use of modified z-transform technique, which is the direct extension of the basic z-transform method, provides all pertinent information.

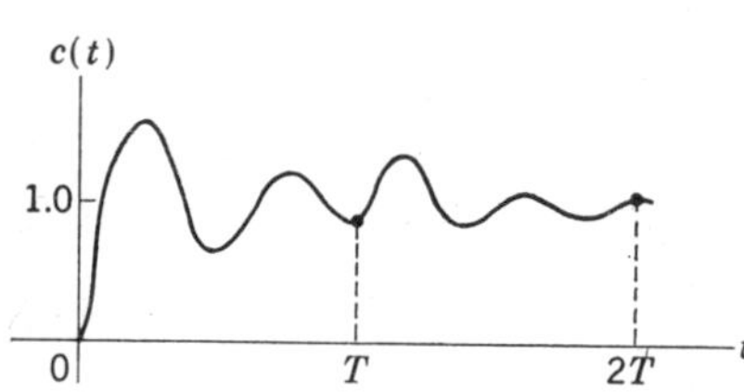

FIG. 7.5-5. The unit step-function response of the system of Fig. 7.5-4.

From the above analysis, it may be concluded that no hidden oscillation will occur if the complex poles of the controlled system lie within the primary strip, and that hidden oscillations will arise when the complex poles fall outside the primary strip of the s plane. In the control systems for aircraft and missiles, the possibility of hidden oscillations should not be overlooked, since high-frequency mechanical or other resonances in aircraft and missile structures may be well above the cutoff frequency of the control system.

7.6. Conclusion. The transient behavior of digital and sampled-data control systems may be determined from the location of the closed-loop poles and zeros of the system in the z plane. Systems with closed-loop poles lying outside the unit circle are unstable. A positive real pole inside the unit circle of the z plane would give rise to an output sequence which decays exponentially, whereas two negative real poles or a pair of conjugate complex poles inside the unit circle correspond to a response sequence which exhibits a damped oscillation. In this chapter, two analytical methods of determining the intersampling ripples and system error are described. The first method is based upon the partial-fraction expansion of the forward transfer function and the computation of the pulse-train responses. The second method makes use of the modified z transforms. The evaluation of the ripple factor and the rms error has also been discussed. When the allowable rms error is specified, the desired sampling frequency of a sampled-data control system may be determined from the ripple-factor equation. The phenomenon of hidden oscillation and hidden instability is discussed in the last section. The occurrence of hidden oscillations in the system output depends primarily upon the impulse-response characteristics of the forward transfer function of the system and the sampling period. Hidden oscillations may arise when the complex poles of the controlled system fall outside the primary strip in the left half of the s plane.

CHAPTER 8

ANALOG-DIGITAL CONVERSION PRINCIPLES

8.1. Introduction. The previous chapters present a fairly extensive analysis of the stability, the accuracy, the ripple content, and the steady-state and transient behavior of sampled-data and digital control systems. Before discussing the design and synthesis techniques for such control systems, another important problem which arises when digital computers and digital techniques are utilized in control systems will first be studied. This is the problem of analog-digital conversion.

Digital control systems are control systems which make use of digital information-processing equipments. Such control systems can generally be divided into two major categories: (1) *digital open-loop control systems*, and (2) *digital feedback control systems*. Shown in Fig. 8.1-1 is the simplified

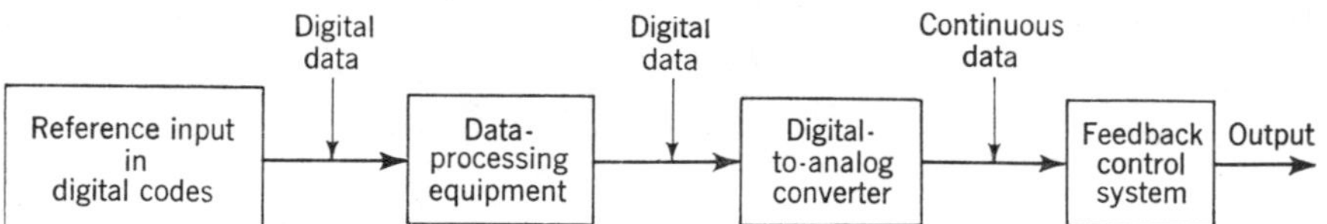

FIG. 8.1-1. The simplified block diagram of a digital open-loop control system.

block diagram of a digital *open-loop* control system, which utilizes a digital data processor to operate and monitor a feedback control system. The input data to this digital control system are stored or punched on tapes, cards, or other media in the form of a digital program. The programmed information is first sent to the digital equipment for data processing, before it is applied to the feedback control system. In view of the fact that signals in the form of numerical codes are incapable of actuating control devices of the system, the digital equipment cannot operate and monitor the control system unless the digital data are converted into signals of analog form. Thus, in a digital open-loop control system, the digital-to-analog conversion device is indispensable.

A digital *feedback* control system, as discussed in Chap. 1, contains a digital computer or data processor in the control loop, which performs the necessary numerical computation and system compensation as well as error detection. Since the digital equipment and the control system adopt different languages, they cannot communicate with each other. Clearly, the interconnection of the digital equipment and the control system requires certain conversion devices which serve as interpreters to translate analog information into digital codes and vice versa. A device which converts signals in analog form into digital form is termed an analog-to-digital converter or *encoder* and the device which performs the reverse process is referred to as a digital-to-analog converter. This chapter is concerned with the analog-to-digital and digital-to-analog conversion principles.

8.2. Number Systems for Digital Control. Numbers are symbols which represent quantities and serve as the basic medium in performing computations. The commonly used number systems include the decimal system, the octal system, the binary system, the binary-coded decimal system, and the cyclic binary system. The first three are often referred to as the conventional number systems, and the other two may be termed the modified number systems. The decimal system has long been the most common numbering system in everyday use, probably because the human being is equipped with 10 fingers which have helped him in first learning arithmetic. Although the decimal system is reasonably convenient for human beings to perform calculations, it is quite awkward for use in high-speed digital data-processing equipments.

The generating equation for a conventional number system or digital code is

$$N = \sum_{k=0}^{n} a_k r^k \tag{8.2-1}$$

In Eq. (8.2-1), N is the integer number represented by the digital code; r is the base of a number system and is commonly known as the radix; and the coefficients a_k stand for the digit symbols. The smallest digit symbol is 0 and the largest one is $(r - 1)$. The only radices of practical importance are 2 for the binary system, 8 for the octal system, and 10 for the decimal system. For a number system with radix r, there must be actually r different digit symbols, each of which is associated with one of the values from 0 to $(r - 1)$. These digits are ordered from right to left, the least significant being the zero and the most significant being the nth. Thus, the positional notation of an integer number N is

$$N = a_n a_{n-1} a_{n-2} \cdots a_k \cdots a_1 a_0 \tag{8.2-2}$$

In the decimal system,

$$r = 10 \qquad a_k = 0, 1, 2, \ldots, 9 \tag{8.2-3}$$

Then

$$N = a_n \times 10^n + a_{n-1} \times 10^{n-1} + \cdots + a_k \times 10^k + \cdots + a_1 \times 10^1 + a_0 \times 10^0 \tag{8.2-4}$$

For instance, the number 100 is represented by

$$100 = 1 \times 10^2 + 0 \times 10^1 + 0 \times 10^0 \tag{8.2-5}$$

In the binary system,

$$r = 2 \qquad a_k = 0 \text{ or } 1 \tag{8.2-6}$$

Then

$$N = a_n \times 2^n + a_{n-1} \times 2^{n-1} + \cdots + a_k \times 2^k + \cdots + a_1 \times 2^1 + a_0 \times 2^0 \tag{8.2-7}$$

For instance, the decimal number 100 is represented by

$$100 = 1 \times 2^6 + 1 \times 2^5 + 0 \times 2^4 + 0 \times 2^3 + 1 \times 2^2 + 0 \times 2^1 + 0 \times 2^0 \tag{8.2-8}$$

Thus, in the binary system the positional notation for the number 100 is 1100100, and

$$\text{Decimal } 100 = \text{binary } 1100100 \tag{8.2-9}$$

Equation (8.2-1) is valid for integer numbers only. In the case of improper fractions, the number can be represented by

$$N = \sum_{k=-i}^{n} a_k r^k \tag{8.2-10}$$

The positional notation of a noninteger number N is

$$N = a_n a_{n-1} \cdots a_k \cdots a_1 a_0 \cdot a_{-1} a_{-2} \cdots a_{-i} \tag{8.2-11}$$

The position of a_0 is indicated by a dot to its right, which is referred to as the radix point. It is the decimal point in decimal system and the binary point in binary system. For instance, the improper fraction 85/8 or the digit symbol 10.625 in the decimal system is represented by

$$10.625 = 1 \times 10^1 + 0 \times 10^0 + 6 \times 10^{-1} + 2 \times 10^{-2} + 5 \times 10^{-3} \tag{8.2-12}$$

In the binary system, it is represented by

$$10.625 = 1 \times 2^3 + 0 \times 2^2 + 1 \times 2^1 + 0 \times 2^0 + 1 \times 2^{-1} + 0 \times 2^{-2} + 1 \times 2^{-3} \tag{8.2-13}$$

Thus,

$$\text{Decimal } 10.625 = \text{binary } 1010.101 \tag{8.2-14}$$

The rules of arithmetic in the binary number system are particularly simple, and can be stated in three extremely simple tables:

1. The binary addition table,

$$\begin{array}{r} 1 \\ +1 \\ \hline 0^1 \end{array} \qquad \begin{array}{r} 1 \\ +0 \\ \hline 1 \end{array} \qquad \begin{array}{r} 0 \\ +1 \\ \hline 1 \end{array} \qquad \begin{array}{r} 0 \\ +0 \\ \hline 0 \end{array}$$

where the superscript at the upper right corner denotes a carry.

2. The binary subtraction table,

$$\begin{array}{r} 1 \\ -1 \\ \hline 0 \end{array} \qquad \begin{array}{r} 1 \\ -0 \\ \hline 1 \end{array} \qquad \begin{array}{r} 0 \\ -1 \\ \hline {}^{1}1 \end{array} \qquad \begin{array}{r} 0 \\ -0 \\ \hline 0 \end{array}$$

where the superscript at the upper left corner denotes a borrow.

3. The binary multiplication table,

$$\begin{array}{r} 1 \\ \times 1 \\ \hline 1 \end{array} \qquad \begin{array}{r} 1 \\ \times 0 \\ \hline 0 \end{array} \qquad \begin{array}{r} 0 \\ \times 1 \\ \hline 0 \end{array} \qquad \begin{array}{r} 0 \\ \times 0 \\ \hline 0 \end{array}$$

Just like the division for decimal numbers, the binary division is performed by successive subtraction.

A decimal number can readily be converted to a binary number, and vice versa. Let $N_D = N$ be a number in decimal system and N_B be the binary equivalent of N_D. Then the digit symbols of N_B can be derived by subtraction as follows:

$$\begin{array}{cccccccccc} & N & N - 2^n & N - 2^n - 2^{n-1} & \cdots & & & & & \\ - & 2^n & 2^{n-1} & 2^{n-2} & 2^{n-3} & \cdots & 2^k & \cdots & 2^1 & 2^0 \\ \hline & a_n & a_{n-1} & a_{n-2} & \cdots & \cdots & a_k & \cdots & a_1 & a_0 \end{array}$$

where n is so chosen that 2^n is the integer nearest to but smaller than the given number N. If the difference is positive, enter the difference in the next column. If the difference is negative, shift the minuend to the next column. The digits of N_B are readily determined from the coefficients a_k. The kth digit of N_B is 1 if $a_k \geq 0$; and it is zero if $a_k < 0$. As an illustration, consider a number $N_D = N = 106$. Following the above procedure,

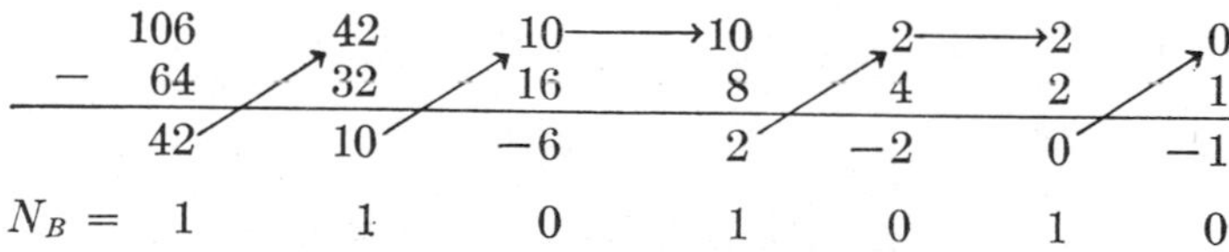

$N_B =$ 1 1 0 1 0 1 0

The conversion of a binary number to the decimal equivalent is fairly simple, involving successive addition. For example, consider the binary number $N_B = 1101010$. The decimal equivalent follows immediately from Eq. (8.2-7). That is

$$\begin{aligned} N &= 1 \times 2^6 + 1 \times 2^5 + 0 \times 2^4 + 1 \times 2^3 + 0 \times 2^2 + 1 \times 2^1 + 0 \times 2^0 \\ &= 64 + 32 + 8 + 2 = 106 \qquad (8.2\text{-}15) \end{aligned}$$

While the decimal system is the most familiar to human beings, it is rather awkward and inconvenient for use in high-speed digital computing machinery. On the other hand, the use of the binary system in digital data-processing devices offers greater convenience and more advantages than the decimal system. The arithmetic in the binary system is extremely simple; to represent a number by the binary code requires less equipment than by the decimal code; and many reliable electronic devices with two stable states representing 0 and 1 are available. Consequently, from the engineering design point of view, the number system used in digital data-processing devices is restricted to the binary system. However, the decimal system can still be used to advantage, if each decimal digit is represented by a group of four binary digits constituting the binary-coded decimal system. Four binary digits can form 16 different combinations, but only 10 of the 16 available number representations are assigned to the 10 different decimal digits. This number system gathers some features of the binary and the decimal system; nevertheless it is wasteful and inefficient. One possible binary-coded decimal system is formed by using the ten binary representations of the number 0 through 9. For instance, the decimal number 106 is 0001 0000 0110 in the binary-coded decimal system. The corresponding representation in binary system is 1101010. As can readily be seen, to represent a number between 000 and 999 would require 10 bits for the binary system and 12 bits for the binary-coded decimal system. In general, any decimal code is always less efficient than a conventional binary code. Decimal codes are used in digital data-processing equipment only for communication between man and machine.

TABLE 8.2-1. THE FIRST 16 DECIMAL NUMBERS AND THEIR REPRESENTATIONS IN BINARY, BINARY-CODED DECIMAL, AND CYCLIC BINARY CODES

Decimal	Binary	Binary-coded decimal	Cyclic binary
00	0000	000000	0000
01	0001	000001	0001
02	0010	000010	0011
03	0011	000011	0010
04	0100	000100	0110
05	0101	000101	0111
06	0110	000110	0101
07	0111	000111	0100
08	1000	001000	1100
09	1001	001001	1101
10	1010	010000	1111
11	1011	010001	1110
12	1100	010010	1010
13	1101	010011	1011
14	1110	010100	1001
15	1111	010101	1000

Listed in Table 8.2-1 are the first 16 decimal numbers (0 through 15) and their equivalent representations in the binary, the binary-coded decimal, and the cyclic binary system. Inspection of the second column of Table 8.2-1 reveals that, in the conventional binary number system, in passing from one number to the next in either direction, sudden changes from the "0" state to the "1" state, or vice versa, may occur in several code elements. As a result, a slight position error or misalignment in the reading device may cause a serious numerical error. Indeed, this presents a major problem in the reading type of the analog-to-digital converters. The numerical error resulting from the misalignment of the reading device of an analog-to-digital converter can be easily visualized, if reference is made to Fig. 8.2-1*a*, which depicts the binary mask or code pattern of the converter. Assume that the reading device is located over the pattern corresponding to 0100. If the reading line moves in the direction of decreasing numbers, the next number read should be 0011, which is 3 in decimal system. However, due to a slight misalignment of the reading line, as illustrated in Fig. 8.2-1*a*, the number 0100 will be followed by 0111, which is 7,

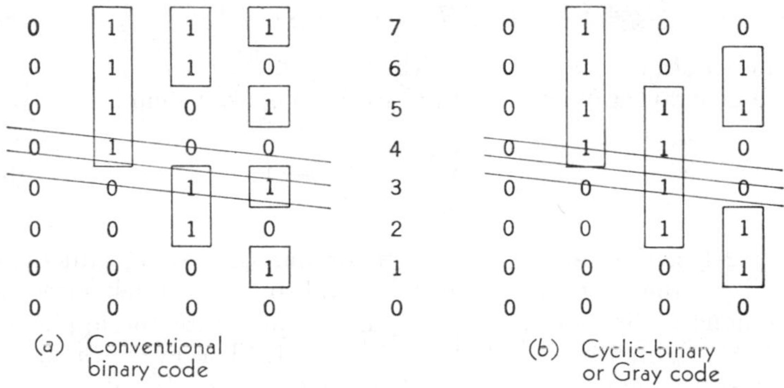

FIG. 8.2-1. The code pattern on the binary mask.

and then by 0011. Evidently, the intermediate reading is wrong and, should it be used, would lead to a serious numerical error in the output of the converter.

As can readily be seen, the error thus introduced is caused by the very nature of the conventional binary number system in which more than one digit can undergo a change at the transition between two consecutive numbers. Consequently, in order to eliminate this error, it is necessary to choose a number system for the code pattern of the analog-to-digital converter in which, in proceeding from one number to the next in either direction, one and only one code element shall change its state, either from a 1 to a 0 or from a 0 to a 1. Such a number system is referred to as a unit-distance number system or code, which finds wide application in analog-to-digital conversion.

A commonly used unit-distance binary code is the cyclic or reflected binary code, which is also referred to as the Gray code, named after the inventor. The cyclic binary codes for the first 16 decimal numbers are tabulated in the last column of Table 8.2-1. It is observed that between two consecutive numbers one and only one code element can change from the 0 state to the 1 state or vice versa. Since only one code element is changed at a transition, a slight position error can shift the result by one digit from the correct value, whereas in conventional binary system a slight position error can cause a big difference between the correct and the recorded values. In the case of a binary mask coded in the cyclic binary number system, either the old number or the next one is read at a transition in spite of a slight misalignment of the reading line, as demonstrated in Fig. 8.2-1*b*.

The cyclic binary representation of a number has the following properties: Assume that the conventional binary representation of a decimal number N is

$$N_B = a_n a_{n-1} a_{n-2} \cdots a_k \cdots a_1 a_0 \tag{8.2-16}$$

and the cyclic binary representation of the number N is

$$N_C = b_n b_{n-1} b_{n-2} \cdots b_k \cdots b_1 b_0 \tag{8.2-17}$$

where the values of a_k and b_k are either 1 or 0.

1. The generating function for the cyclic binary system is

$$N = \sum_{k=0}^{n} \pm b_k (2^{k-1} - 1) \tag{8.2-18}$$

In Eq. (8.2-18), the plus sign is taken for the most significant digit, the minus sign for the next one to the right, and so forth. Each succeeding b_k which is nonzero has an alternate sign. To illustrate the application of Eq. (8.2-18), reference is made to Table 8.2-1. The cyclic binary representation for the number 9 is 1101. Applying Eq. (8.2-18), it is found that

$$\begin{aligned} N &= 1 \times (2^4 - 1) - 1 \times (2^3 - 1) + 1 \times (2^1 - 1) \\ &= 15 - 7 + 1 = 9 \end{aligned} \tag{8.2-19}$$

2. The parity of N_C is even or odd according to whether

$$a_0 = 0 \quad \text{or} \quad a_0 = 1 \tag{8.2-20}$$

The parity of N_C is defined as the sum of the digits b_k of the cyclic binary representation N_C, to modulus 2. That is,

$$\begin{aligned} \text{Parity of } N_C &= b_n + b_{n-1} + b_{n-2} + \cdots + b_k + \cdots + b_1 + b_0 \\ &= a_0 \end{aligned} \tag{8.2-21}$$

3. The digits of N_B and N_C are related by

$$b_n = a_n \qquad b_k = a_k + a_{k+1} \qquad \text{without carry} \tag{8.2-22}$$

$$a_{k+1} = a_k + b_k \qquad \text{without carry} \tag{8.2-23}$$

where

$$b_k = \begin{cases} 0 & \text{if } a_k = a_{k+1} \\ 1 & \text{if } a_k \neq a_{k+1} \end{cases} \tag{8.2-24}$$

$$a_{k+1} = \begin{cases} 0 & \text{if } a_k = b_k \\ 1 & \text{if } a_k \neq b_k \end{cases} \tag{8.2-25}$$

For instance, the conventional binary and the cyclic binary representations of the number 9 are $N_B = 01001$ and $N_C = 01101$. Then it is seen that $b_3 = 1 + 0 = 1$, $b_1 = 0 + 0 = 0$, $a_3 = 0 + 1 = 1$, and $a_1 = 1 + 1 = 0$.

4. The cyclic binary representations of any pair of successive numbers, N and $N + 1$, differ in only one column. This is an important property, which makes the cyclic binary system very useful in analog-to-digital conversion devices. Mechanization of binary-to-cyclic and cyclic-to-binary conversions is discussed in the sections to follow.

Making use of the above properties, the cyclic binary code can be derived from the conventional binary notation by a single column shift followed by a logical addition (i.e., addition without carry). Thus,

$$\begin{array}{llllllllll} N_B = & a_n & a_{n-1} & a_{n-2} & \cdots & a_k & \cdots & a_1 & a_0 & \\ & \searrow & \searrow & \searrow & & \searrow & \searrow & \searrow & \searrow & \\ \oplus & & a_n & a_{n-1} & \cdots & a_{k+1} & \cdots & a_2 & a_1 & (a_0) \\ \hline N_C = & b_n & b_{n-1} & b_{n-2} & \cdots & b_k & \cdots & b_1 & b_0 & \end{array}$$

The symbol $\oplus$ means "add without carry." As an illustration, consider the decimal number 106 which has the binary representation 1101010. Then

$$\begin{array}{lcccccccc} N_B = & 1 & 1 & 0 & 1 & 0 & 1 & 0 & \\ \oplus & & 1 & 1 & 0 & 1 & 0 & 1 & (0) \\ \hline N_C = & 1 & 0 & 1 & 1 & 1 & 1 & 1 & \end{array}$$

which is the cyclic binary representation of the given number.

In like manner, the conversion from the cyclic binary code to the conventional binary notation can be effected as follows:

$$\begin{array}{lccccccccc} N_C = & b_n & b_{n-1} & b_{n-2} & \cdots & b_k & \cdots & b_1 & b_0 \\ \oplus & & a_n & a_{n-1} & \cdots & a_{k+1} & \cdots & a_2 & a_1 \\ \hline N_B = & a_n & a_{n-1} & a_{n-2} & \cdots & a_k & \cdots & a_1 & a_0 \end{array}$$

To illustrate this procedure, consider the decimal number 106 which has the cyclic binary representation 1011111. Then

$$\begin{array}{lccccccc} N_C = & 1 & 0 & 1 & 1 & 1 & 1 & 1 \\ \oplus & & 1 & 1 & 0 & 1 & 0 & 1 \\ \hline N_B = & 1 & 1 & 0 & 1 & 0 & 1 & 0 \end{array}$$

which is the conventional binary notation of the given number.

8.3. Basic Conversion Requirements. In designing analog-digital conversion devices, several basic requirements must be taken into consideration:

Sampling Rate. This is the rate at which the readings of the signal value are taken. Clearly, by increasing the sampling rate, one can obtain a better approximation to the waveform of the original signal which is being digitized. The sampling rate is thus a conversion characteristic of primary importance. The sampling process is discussed at length in Chap. 3 and part of Chap. 4.

Resolution. Resolution determines the precision of conversion at each interval. The precision of conversion is, in turn, determined by the accuracy or *fineness* of quantization in the analog-digital conversion process. If a signal value is quantized by 7 bits (binary digits) the precision of conversion would be 1/128; and if a signal value is quantized by 10 bits, the precision of conversion would be 1/1024. Thus, resolution is a function of the number of bits in the binary code which is used in the conversion device. For instance, a resolution of one part in 1000 would require 10 bits in the binary code.

As discussed in Sec. 3.6, quantizing inherently introduces a distortion in the measured value. This distortion resulting from the quantization process is referred to as the quantization error. In terms of numerical analysis, quantization error is equivalent to a round-off error. This round-off error results because of the limited number capacity of the digital part of the conversion device. In this respect it is similar to noise, since any variation of the input signal within a single quantization step does not change the output signal. With the quantization error likened to noise the maximum amplitude of which is equal to one quantizing step, the necessity of keeping the quantizing step small for high precision and fine resolution of the conversion devices is obvious.

Conversion Time. The conversion time is defined as the time interval between the instant at which an input signal to be converted is applied to the conversion device and the instant at which the output signal has been established within desired accuracy. In other words, it is the time required to complete one encoding or decoding process. The conversion time is related to the sampling rate and must be much smaller than the sampling period. The frequency of conversion, defined as the reciprocal of conversion time, may be likened to the bandwidth of an analog system. This is readily seen by noting that as the frequency of the input signal to the conversion device increases, the accuracy of the output decreases, if the conversion frequency is kept constant. The conversion frequency of an encoder or decoder is related to the time constants of the conversion device in much the same manner as the bandwidth of an analog system is related to the various time constants of the system.

As can be seen, if the accuracy of the output signal from the conversion device is to be maintained within one quantization step at all times, it is necessary to establish a new value of the output each time the input signal changes from one quantization level to another. The rate at which the input signal changes levels depends upon the slope of the input waveform and the size of the quantization steps of the conversion device. With small quantization steps, the time required for the input signal to change from one quantization level to another is approximately equal to the ratio of the size of the quantization steps to the slope of the input waveform. This relationship may be used to estimate the upper limit of the conversion time.

Furthermore, the conversion time adds to the total loop delay of the digital feedback control system. Since too long a delay is not desirable, the conversion time should be maintained very short. Values of conversion time vary with different types of conversion devices, and may fall anywhere in the range from several microseconds to tens of milliseconds. When the conversion device is time shared by several information channels, lower values of the conversion time are more preferable.

Antiambiguity. As discussed in the preceding section, in a certain type of analog-to-digital converter which adopts the conventional binary system, an ambiguity problem exists at the transition between two consecutive numbers. Numerical error generally results when a value is exactly halfway between two possible conditions 0 and 1. A commonly used method of solving the problem of ambiguity at the transition between successive numbers is to adopt a unit-distance binary code. The cyclic or reflected binary code, which is of unit-distance nature, is usually used. Among other means of avoiding errors due to ambiguity at the transition are the double-brush method, the V-scan method and the use of antiambiguity circuits.[142]

Temporary Storage Requirement. In converting analog quantities to digital form, it is often necessary to insure that the analog input quantity being measured (or sampled) remain constant throughout the conversion period. Clearly, this would require a temporary storage or clamping device to maintain the value of the input until the conversion process can be completed. Temporary storage device also finds other applications in digital control systems. For instance, in control systems where data samples appear at random instants at the input of a device, such as a digital computer, the samples must be temporarily stored until they can be used. Temporary storage is also required when the output of the computer of a control system must remain constant between successive solutions.

8.4. Encoding Techniques. The process of converting analog quantities to digital form is often referred to as the encoding process. The conversion from analog to digital form generally involves three basic steps:

1. Break the time scale into a number of equal intervals. This is, in fact, a sampling process.
2. Measure the amplitude of the curve of the input signal at each interval. This is a reading process.
3. Indicate the measured amplitude in some numerical code form, such as the binary code. This step involves the process of quantization.

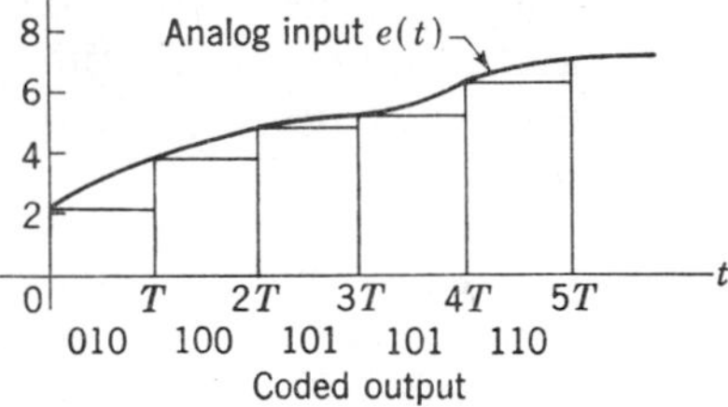

FIG. 8.4-1. Illustration of the three steps of analog-to-digital conversion.

The operation of these three basic steps is illustrated in Fig. 8.4-1. A signal in analog form $e(t)$ is to be converted to a digital representation. The signal is first sampled at the instants 0, T, $2T$, ... Each of the signal samples is then measured, quantized, and represented by a binary code. For instance, the sample at $t = 0$ is represented by 010; the sample at $t = T$, by 100; the sample at $t = 2T$, by 101; and so forth.

Although the process of converting data from analog to digital form can be accomplished by a number of different schemes, practically all the encoders are designed on the basis of one of the four fundamental principles, i.e., time encoding, spatial encoding, encoding by comparison or weighing, and feedback encoding.[37,45,129] The time-encoding techniques involve intermediate conversion into a time interval. Analog-to-digital converters following the time-encoding principles are often referred to as encoders of the counting type, because they are the encoders which count. The spatial-encoding techniques make use of a spatial geometric configuration for direct reading in coded form. Thus, analog-to-digital converters characterized by spatial encoding are commonly known as encoders of the reading type. In the method of encoding by comparison or weighing, trial voltages in powers of 2 are successively weighed against the input-analog voltage. Analog-to-digital converters working on this principle are often termed encoders of the weighing type. The feedback encoding is based upon comparison of the input voltage sample with a feedback voltage which is varied by a control circuit until the two voltages become equal. Analog-to-digital converters utilizing feedback principles are sometimes referred to as encoders of the feedback type. In this section these four encoding techniques are discussed and illustrated.

Time Encoding and Encoders of the Counting Type. The counting-type encoder[45,129] is the most fundamental and highly developed analog-to-digital converter, which utilizes a train of discrete marks or pulses expressing the size of the input analog in a unitary code. In this encoder, an electronic switch is held open during the interval of time to be measured, gating an oscillator to generate a pulse train, which is collected in a binary or decimal counter to convert the analog quantity into a binary or decimal code. Examples of the counting-type encoders are the time-base encoders (e.g., the Anodige†), which are voltage encoders, and the angle encoders, which are shaft or electromechanical encoders. As an illustration of the time encoding principles, an all-electronic time-base encoder and an electromechanical angle encoder are discussed in the following paragraphs.

TIME-BASE ENCODER. A time-base encoder[42,129] comprises four basic circuits: a linear sweep circuit, a counting circuit, a comparison circuit, and a control circuit, which are simultaneously operated to provide analog-to-digital conversion. The block diagram of a typical time-base encoder is shown in Fig. 8.4-2.

This device is referred to as a time-base encoder because the amplitude of the analog voltage input to be coded is transformed into a time signal which is proportional to the analog voltage. As demonstrated in Fig. 8.4-3,

† M. L. Kuder, Anodige, an Electronic Analogue-to-digital Converter, *Nat. Bur. Standards, Rep.* 1117, August, 1951.

the conversion of the voltage signal to a time signal makes use of a linear sweep voltage which sweeps upward at each conversion interval to an amplitude higher than that of the analog voltage input. Reference to Fig. 8.4-3 indicates that the time for the sweep voltage to change from a fixed reference voltage to the amplitude of the analog voltage signal to be coded

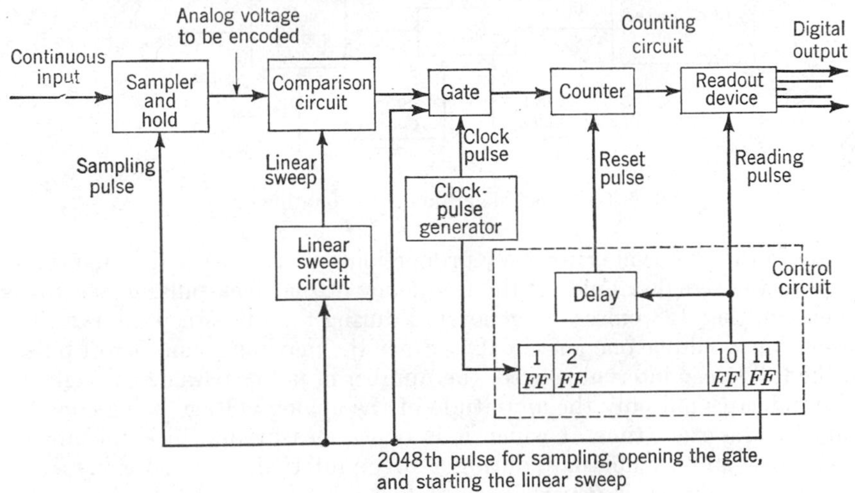

FIG. 8.4-2. Block diagram of a typical time-base encoder.

is directly proportional to the analog voltage at that instant. The time intervals t_1, t_2, t_3, . . . are measured by a counting circuit which is illustrated in Fig. 8.4-4. At the instant corresponding to point A_1, the gate is opened to allow a set of pulses to flow into the binary counter. At the instant corresponding to point B_1, the gate is closed. Thus, the counter

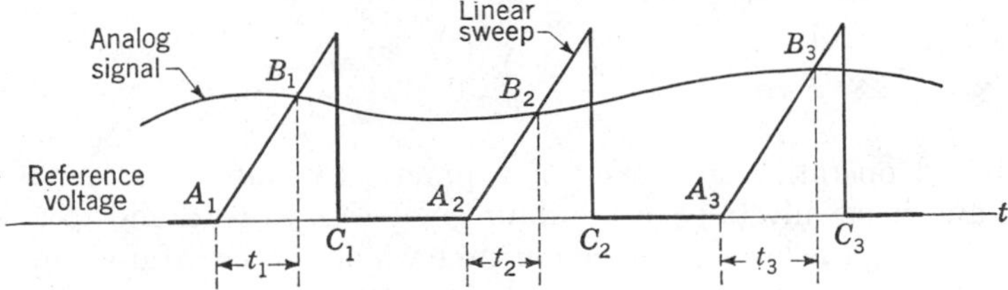

FIG. 8.4-3. Conversion of an analog voltage into a time signal through linear sweep.

starts the counting at the instant corresponding to point A_1, and stops the counting at the instant corresponding to point B_1, where the sweep voltage is equal to the analog voltage being encoded. The number of pulses from the clock-pulse generator passing through the gate during the time interval t_1 is then counted on the binary counter. Some time after that (e.g., at the instant corresponding to point C_1), a pulse is generated to reset the counter to zero. Shortly thereafter, at the instant corresponding to point A_2, the gate is opened again and the conversion cycle repeats.

The resolution of such conversion device depends upon the number of clock pulses contained in the full sweep interval. The number of clock

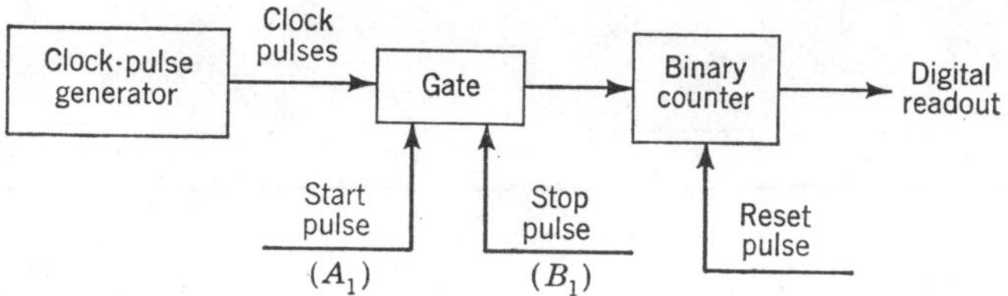

FIG. 8.4-4. Block diagram of the counting circuit.

pulses in that interval is inversely proportional to the size of the quantizing steps of the signal sample. If the frequency of the clock-pulse generator is so chosen that 128 pulses are generated during the full sweep interval, the resolution would be one part in 128. Since the maximum number of pulses in the full sweep interval is fixed, the number of pulses passing through the gate indicates not only the amplitude of the analog voltage being encoded but also the exact time at which it is being measured. Since the analog voltage signal may fluctuate during a sweep interval, a temporary storage or clamping device is generally employed in order to sample the analog signal at precise intervals and to hold the voltage constant throughout the sweep period. Through temporary storage the readings can thus be obtained at constant intervals. The accuracy of the time-base encoder is determined by the linearity of the sweep-signal waveform, and the accuracy of the comparison circuit. The conversion time of the time-base encoders depends upon the counting speed of the counter v_c and the maximum number N to be coded. If the time required for reading and clearing the counter is t_r, the conversion time t_c is given by

$$t_c = \frac{N}{v_c} + t_r \tag{8.4-1}$$

The highest operating frequency of a practical counter is about 5 megacycles; and it usually takes a minimum of 1 μsec to read and to reset the counter. Thus, the lowest conversion time which can be attained in a time-base encoder is

$$t_c = \frac{N + 5}{5} \qquad \mu\text{sec} \tag{8.4-2}$$

For instance, if the maximum number to be coded is of two decimal digits, then 7 bits are required in the binary code and the lowest conversion time would be 26.6 μsec; if the maximum number to be coded is of three decimal digits, 10 bits are required in the binary notation and the conversion time would not be smaller than 205.8 μsec.

Referring to the typical time-base encoder of Fig. 8.4-2, assume that the clock-pulse generator emits 2^{10} or 1024 pulses during the full sweep interval. A resolution of one part in 1024 can then be obtained. The 10 flip-flops of the control unit are used to make a maximum of 2^{10} counts. If the sweep circuit is triggered on every 2048th pulse by the output of the eleven binary counters, the encoding circuit can have a rest period of 1024 pulses during each conversion cycle. The analog voltage to be encoded and the sweep voltage are continuously compared in the amplitude-comparison circuit. When these two voltages are equal, the comparison circuit generates a stop pulse to close the gate and to read the counter. Some time after that, the control unit sends out a reset pulse to clear the counter for the next opening of the gate to repeat the conversion cycle. The clock-pulse generator is either a multivibrator or a crystal-controlled oscillator. The commonly used linear sweep circuit is a phantastron circuit, as shown in Fig. 8.4-5.

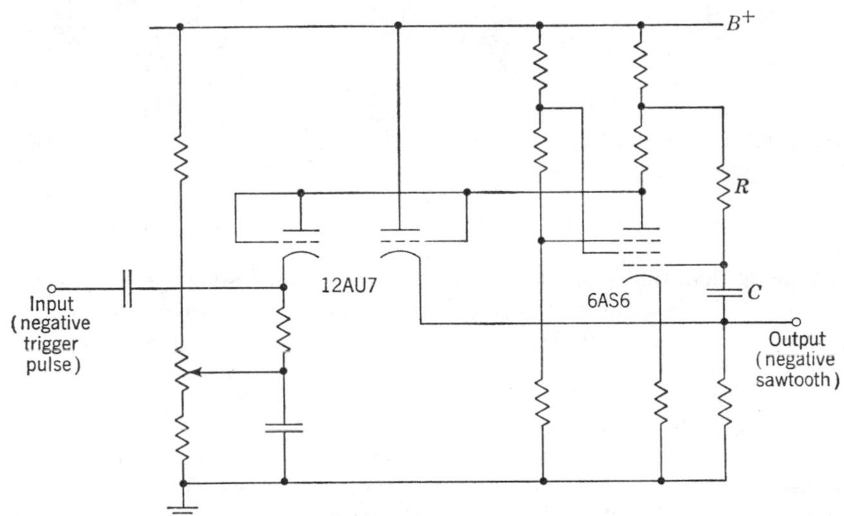

FIG. 8.4-5. Cathode-coupled phantastron circuit.

There are a number of different comparison circuits. Among the voltage comparators in common use are the Schmitt trigger circuit as shown in Fig. 8.4-6 and the multiar,† which is a diode-controlled regenerative amplifier. The block diagram of an elementary binary counter which makes use of flip-flops is illustrated in Fig. 8.4-7.

The time-base encoder offers the advantages of the simplicity of circuitry and the ease of construction. This conversion device uses only a few basic circuits and involves no complex logical circuitry. In view of the fact that the minimization of drift in the discriminating element poses a big problem

† B. Chance, V. Hughes, and others, "Waveforms," p. 343, McGraw-Hill Book Company, Inc., New York, 1949.

in the design of high-quality amplitude-comparison circuit, the conversion accuracy which can be achieved in the time-base encoder is limited by the comparison circuit. The conversion accuracy is also restricted by the linear sweep circuit. The frequency of the flip-flops of the counter imposes a

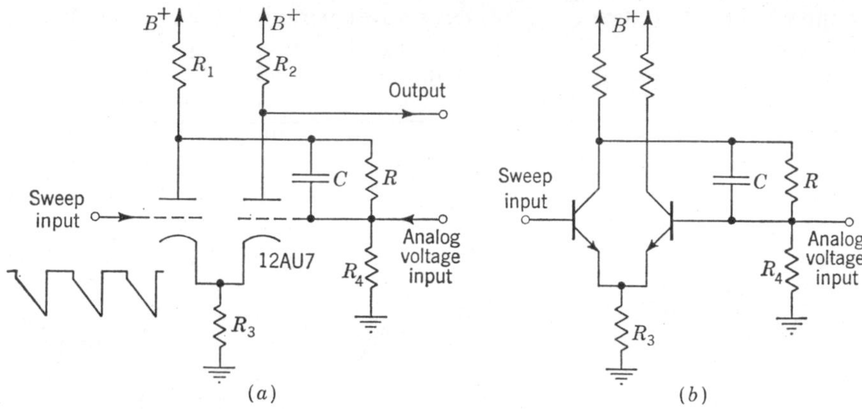

FIG. 8.4-6. (a) Schmitt trigger circuit used as the comparison circuit; (b) transistorized comparison circuit.

limitation upon the speed of the time-base encoder, as demonstrated in Eq. (8.4-1). Probably the principal problem involved in designing a time-base encoder is that the readings of the input signal are taken at irregular intervals. This problem can be solved by using a hold or temporary storage device to keep the input signal constant throughout the conversion period.

ANGLE ENCODER. Shown in Fig. 8.4-8 is a simplified schematic diagram of a counting-type angle encoder.[45] This is one of the simplest methods of converting a shaft displacement into a digital representation. This conversion device consists of two basic components, a drum and a counting circuit. The drum is made of magnetic material, on which *quantum marks* are engraved with uniform spacing all the way around one cylindrical track. When the drum rotates continuously, these quantum marks induce clock pulses in the reading head A. The reference marks on the drum are used

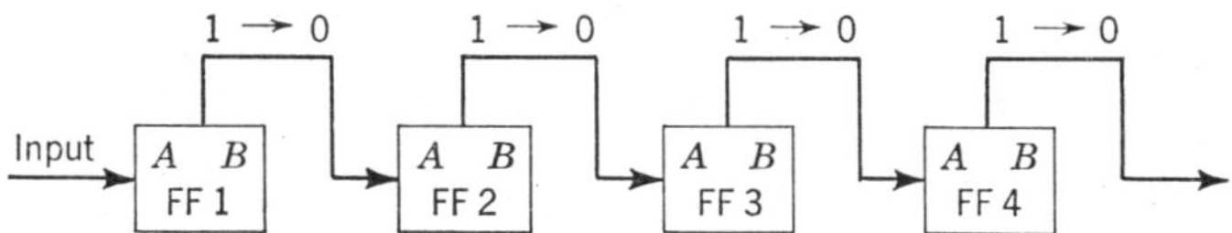

FIG. 8.4-7. Block diagram of an elementary binary counter.

to indicate the start and the stop positions. One of these marks induces a *start pulse* in the stationary reading head B in each revolution of the drum. The other reference mark induces a *stop pulse* in the movable reading head C. The gate is opened by the start pulse and is closed by the stop pulse. The number of clock pulses induced between the start and the stop will be proportional to the angular displacement of the input shaft, which is equal to the angle between the fixed and the movable reading heads. The quantum and the reference marks on the drum can be formed magnetically instead of mechanically. The resolution of this conversion device is determined by the number of quantum marks engraved upon the circumference of the drum, and the conversion accuracy depends upon the accuracy of the reading heads.

Spatial Encoding and Encoders of the Reading Type. The spatial encoding is the most direct encoding method, which utilizes a spatial geometric configuration for direct reading in coded form. This type of encoder compares the analog signal with a spatial coded pattern. To illustrate the principles of spatial encoding a few reading-type encoders are described in the following paragraphs.

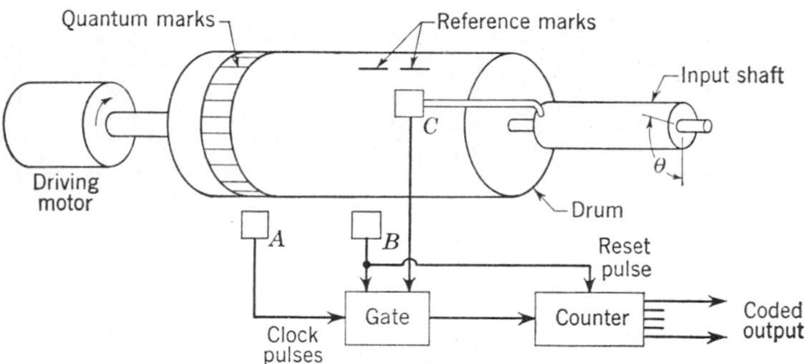

FIG. 8.4-8. Schematic diagram of an angle encoder.

BINARY READING ENCODER. Shown in Fig. 8.4-9*a* is the schematic diagram of a simplified binary reading encoder, which comprises a diode matrix connecting to commutator segments. This encoder converts a linear or angular displacement into a binary code. The input to this encoder is expressed as the position of the brush. The digital output is taken from the terminals *A*, *B*, and *C*. The terminal charged with a negative voltage represents a 1, and the terminal with zero voltage represents a 0. A table of binary numbers is stored in the diode matrix. For example, when the brush contacts segment 5, terminals *A* and *C* are negatively charged and terminal *B* has no voltage. The output reading is 101; that is, position 5 is coded in the binary notation 101. As the position of the brush is moved from one commutator segment to another, different binary combinations are formed at the output terminals. The number of different binary combinations which this device can generate is equal to the number of the commutator segments. If it is required to represent the output signal by 7 binary digits, a total of 2^7 or 128 commutator segments are needed. The resolution of this encoder is determined by the number of the commutator segments.

Inspection of Fig. 8.4-9*a* reveals that if the width of the brush is smaller than the spacing between successive segments, there will be brush positions corresponding to 000 between every pair of segments. On the other hand, if the width of the brush is larger than the spacing between consecutive segments, two adjacent segments can be shorted to result in a false code. For instance, if segments 3 and 4 are shorted by the brush, the output reading will be 111, which corresponds to 7 in the decimal system. Apparently, a large error is created at this instant. This ambiguity problem, which occurs in all reading-type encoders, is often solved by resorting to a unit-distance code discussed in Sec. 8.2. The schematic diagram of a simplified cyclic binary reading encoder is depicted in Fig. 8.4-9*b*. The diode matrix is so arranged that the segment positions are represented by cyclic

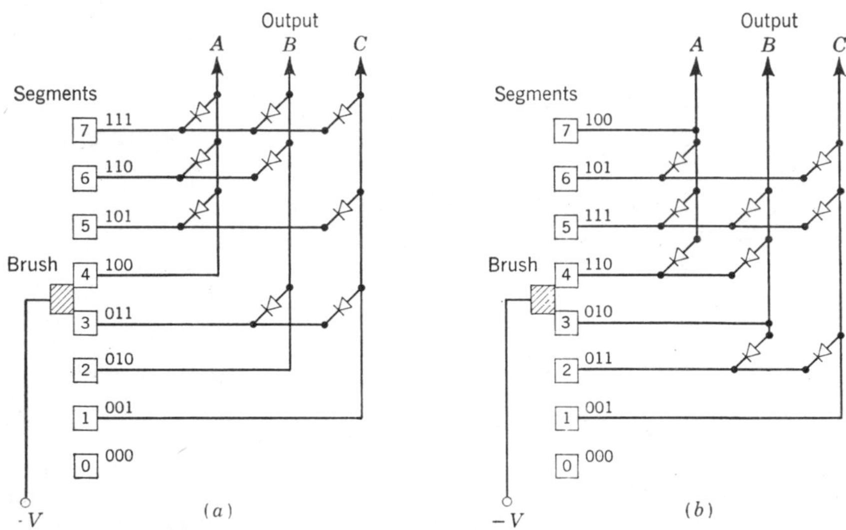

FIG. 8.4-9. (*a*) A simplified binary reading encoder; (*b*) a simplified cyclic binary reading encoder.

binary codes. Now, if segments 3 and 4 are shorted by the brush, the output would read 110, which corresponds to 4 in the decimal system.

SHAFT DIGITIZER. This conversion device translates the shaft position into digital notation by making use of a mechanically rotating shaft and coding disk.[77] The coding disk is carefully centered on the shaft, the angular displacement of which is to be read out in binary codes. Figure 8.4-10 illustrates a coding disk for a shaft digitizer made by Librascope, Inc., and is typical of this type of encoder. The brushes contact the disk along the reading line at the points shown. A signal on the brush marked "common" appears on parallel output brushes in a unique code for each position of the encoder shaft. It is seen that on the coding disk there are concentric rings representing 2^0, 2^1, 2^2, . . . , 2^n, and that each ring is divided into conducting and nonconducting sectors. For instance, in an n-channel coding disk the smallest ring is divided into two conducting and two nonconducting sectors; and the largest ring is divided into n conducting and n nonconducting sectors. The resolution of this encoder is determined by the exponent n. For a 10-channel coding disk (that is, $n = 10$), a resolution of one part in 1024 is achieved. Since the exponent n can be any number, depending upon the diameter of the coding disk, the potentialities of this type of encoder are impressive. Besides, the resolution of a shaft digitizer may be improved by making use of two coding disks instead of enlarging the diameter and increasing the number of channels on one disk. The principle involved is simply to count the revolutions of one coding disk which is geared at the desired ratio to another coding disk. Through a geared arrangement, a resolution of one part in a million may be attained.

To avoid ambiguity, the cyclic binary code is often used in shaft digitizers. However, when the conventional binary code is retained, resort is

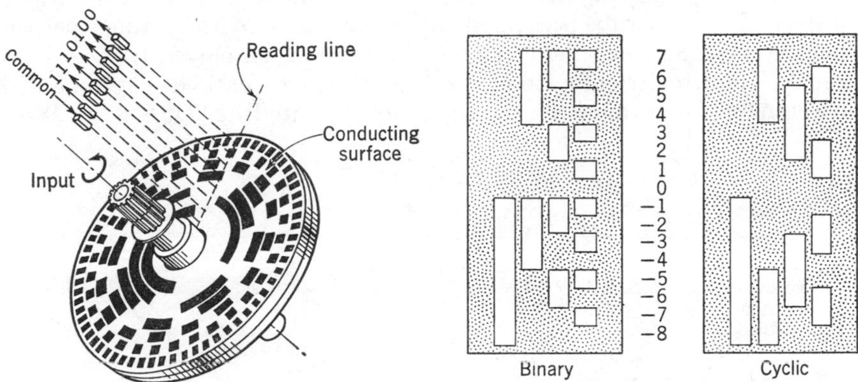

Fig. 8.4-10. Code disk for typical shaft position-to-digital converter.

Fig. 8.4-11. Cathode-ray tube masks.

usually made to the "double-brush" method [142] of preventing errors at the sector boundaries. In this method, a single brush is used to sense the commutator segments on the largest ring corresponding to the 2^0 digit (the least significant digit), but there are two brushes for each of the other rings. One brush on each ring is advanced with respect to the angular position being encoded, and the other brush is retarded by an equal angular displacement with respect to this position. The spacing between two brushes on each ring is made equal to the "angular" width of a commutator segment on the largest ring. With this arrangement of the brushes, the possible error which may be created is limited to one least significant digit in the corresponding decimal notation.

Another form of the commonly used shaft digitizer employs a glass coding disk which carries a special pattern of alternate transparent and opaque areas arranged in concentric rings representing $2^0, 2^1, 2^2, \ldots, 2^n$. Photocells view the pattern through a radial slit to read the angular position in a digital code. This device can achieve very high precision.

BINARY-MASK VOLTAGE ENCODER. This conversion device makes use of a binary mask for direct reading in coded form. A typical encoder of this category is the cathode-ray voltage encoder, which utilizes a cathode-ray tube. The binary mask is placed inside the cathode-ray tube between the electron gun and a collector anode, with the vertical windows of the mask perpendicular to the horizontal sweep. A typical binary mask is shown in Fig. 8.4-11, in which the blank areas represent the windows of the mask. In the absence of a signal on the Y-deflection plates, a sawtooth signal on the X-deflection plates sweeps the electron beam over the row marked zero. No current reaches the collector because this row is devoid of openings. When a voltage is applied on the Y-deflection plates, a binary number which measures the vertical deflection is generated serially as the electron beam sweeps horizontally over the binary mask. The digital output can also be read in parallel mode if a sheet-beam tube is used instead.

An ordinary cathode-ray tube can be used for encoding, if the screen of the cathode-ray tube is covered by a binary mask with openings perpendicular to the horizontal sweep, and a photocell is employed to receive the signal. The circuitry of a simple encoder utilizing a cathode-ray tube with a rectangular code mask on the screen is presented in Fig. 8.4-12. When

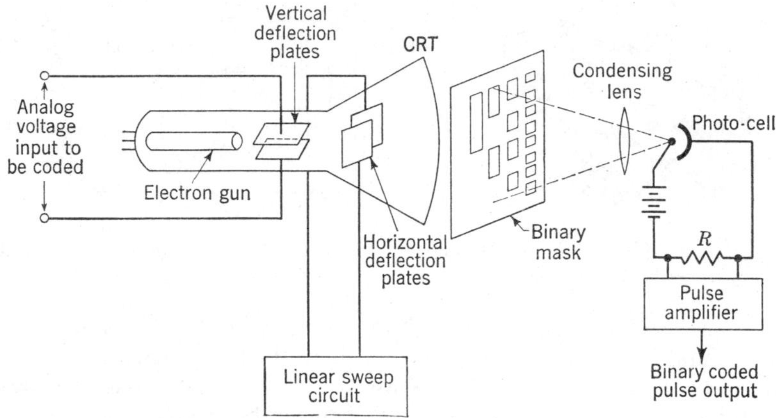

FIG. 8.4-12. Schematic diagram of a voltage encoder utilizing a cathode-ray tube.

the horizontal sweep is applied at the desired sampling interval, the output from the photocell gives a binary representation of the analog voltage applied to the vertical-deflection plates. The resolution of binary-mask voltage encoders is determined by the number of bits contained in the code pattern of the mask. For instance, a 10-bit mask will provide a resolution of 1 part in 1024. Like the other schemes of the reading-type encoders, the cyclic binary code is usually used in binary-mask voltage encoders. This type of encoder has the highest conversion speed.

When the output of a reading-type encoder employing the cyclic binary code is to be connected to a digital data-processing equipment which is organized to deal with the conventional binary code, a cyclic to binary translator is required. Shown in Fig. 8.4-13 is the block diagram of a cyclic to binary translator[38] which transforms a cyclic code with the least significant digit first into its conventional binary representation, also with

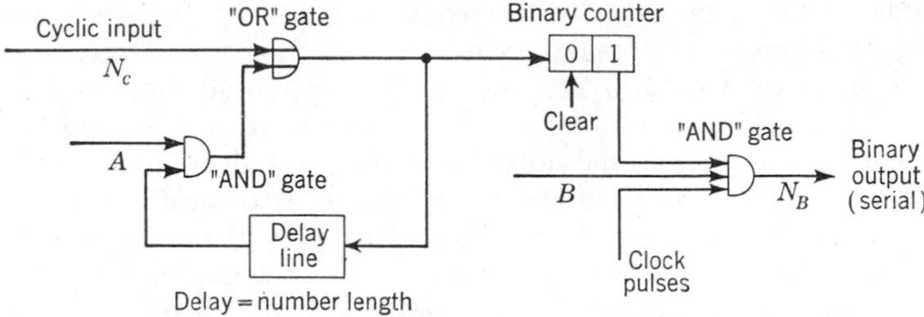

Fig. 8.4-13. Block diagram of a cyclic-to-binary converter (with the least significant digit first).

the least significant digit first. The fundamental principles involved in this translator are based upon the properties of the cyclic binary code outlined in Sec. 8.2. Let the cyclic binary and the conventional binary notations of a number be denoted respectively by

$$N_C = b_n b_{n-1} \cdots b_k \cdots b_1 b_0 \tag{8.4-3}$$

and

$$N_B = a_n a_{n-1} \cdots a_k \cdots a_1 a_0 \tag{8.4-4}$$

where the digits a_k and b_k are either 0 or 1. It is stated in Sec. 8.2 as property 2 that

$$a_0 = b_0 + b_1 + b_2 + \cdots + b_n \tag{8.4-5}$$

Then the first digit a_0 of the binary representation N_B can be determined by counting the number of 1's in N_C in a binary counter which is initially reset to 0. The state of the counter after the counting is done represents the digit a_0. In view of property 3 stated in Sec. 8.2, the digit a_1 can be obtained by adding b_0 to a_0 in the binary counter, and all other digits a_{k+1} of the binary output can be found by adding b_k to a_k in the binary counter. Thus, the binary representation N_B may be obtained by counting the cyclic number in the binary counter twice, with the second counting delayed from the first one by an appropriate amount of time. The first counting results in the least significant digit a_0 of the binary output. The second counting will yield successively the sums of b_0 and a_0, b_1 and a_1, b_2 and a_2, . . . , which determine the digits a_1, a_2, a_3, . . . of the binary output in sequence, if the cyclic number is delayed by an interval equal to the number length and is fed back to the input of the binary counter serially, as shown in Fig. 8.4-13. In the block diagram the control pulse A is used to prevent the cyclic number from circulating more than once, and the control pulse B is used for opening and closing the gate in order to make a correct reading of the output.

Encoding by Comparison or Weighing. The encoding of a voltage by weighing is based upon the principle that the weight of an object is accurately measured by means of a balance. For instance, to measure the weight of an object to the nearest milligram on a balance, one usually tries the heavy weights first, then the medium weights in succession, and finally adds one or two 1-mg weights to secure a balance. In like manner, to encode a voltage into a binary code to the nearest quantizing step, trial voltages in powers of two are successively weighted against the input voltage. A weighing procedure is possible whenever the digital output is to be expressed in a positional notation, such as the decimal and the binary codes. In the process of encoding by weighing, if the trial voltage exceeds the net voltage to be "weighed," it is rejected and no pulse is emitted. However, if the trial voltage is less than the net voltage, it is subtracted from the net voltage and one pulse is emitted. No pulse signifies a 0 and one pulse signifies a 1.

Referring to Fig. 8.4-14, the input voltage to a binary weighing encoder is assumed to be 74 volts during the conversion period. If the first trial

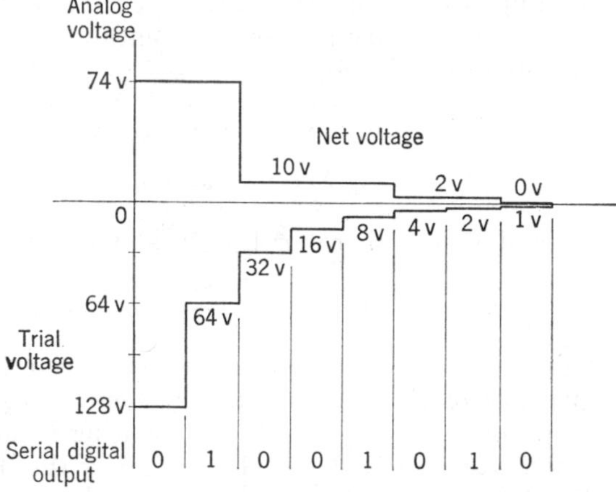

Fig. 8.4-14. Voltage curves illustrating the operation of a binary-weighing encoder.

voltage applied to the encoder is 2^7 or 128 volts, it is rejected and no pulse is emitted, resulting in a 0 in the output at this instant. If a second trial voltage of 2^6 or 64 volts is now applied to the encoder, a pulse is emitted and a net voltage of 10 volts is left behind. The third and the fourth trial voltages are 32 volts and 16 volts, which exceed the net voltage of 10 volts. Thus, no pulse is emitted at these two positions. The fifth trial voltage is 8, which is less than 10, so it generates a pulse and leaves out a net voltage of 2 volts. Following this process, it is seen that the sixth trial voltage gives no pulse, the seventh trial voltage emits one pulse, and the last trial voltage again generates no pulse. Consequently, the output of the encoder will read 1001010, which is the binary representation for the decimal number 74.

The trial voltages are all in powers of two which represent a binary coding of the analog voltage. The technique to accomplish this encoding device makes use of logical switching circuitry, ring counter, voltage-comparison circuit, and summing circuit. The simplified block diagram of an encoder of the weighing type is illustrated in Fig. 8.4-15. The sampler and the hold

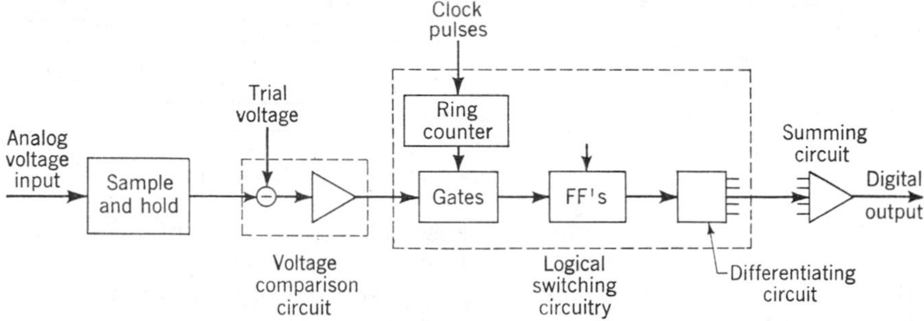

Fig. 8.4-15. Simplified block diagram of a binary-weighing encoder.

are used to clamp the input-analog voltage during the conversion period in which successive trials are being made. The comparison circuit and the logical switching circuit execute the rejection or acceptance of the trial voltages. The comparison circuit comprises voltage dividers to generate the trial voltages. The flip-flops are biased by the trial voltages, and are triggered only when the unknown voltage (or the successive difference) exceeds the trial voltage. The ring counter is used to trigger the coincidence gates. The summing circuit feeds the pulse-coded output of the flip-flops to a single output line and also provides isolation between them.

Encoders of the weighing type are limited in conversion accuracy by the accuracy of the trial voltage and the voltage comparison circuit. When the trial voltages are obtained from the voltage dividers, the conversion accuracy also depends upon the stability and accuracy of the reference voltage and the resistors of the voltage dividers used. The conversion speed of this type of encoding is faster than that of the time encoding. By using a beam-switch tube of the magnetron type, a conversion time of as low as 10 μsec can be achieved. The primary disadvantage of this encoder is the need for a logical switching circuitry to subtract or to reject the trial voltages. The conventional switching circuitry is very complicated, but it can be simplified by using a beam-switching tube.

Feedback Encoding. Encoders of the feedback type make use of a decoder which converts the generated digital output into analog form for comparison with the analog-input signal. A decoder can code if it is inverted by means of feedback.[40] The block diagram of a feedback encoder is shown in Fig. 8.4-16. The decoder generates a feedback voltage which is then subtracted from (or added to) the analog-input voltage. The polarity of the voltage difference is sensed by the polarity circuit. When the voltage difference is other than zero, the control circuit turns on the reversible counter so that the clock pulses are injected into the counter. The reversible counter can count the clock pulses in either the forward or the backward direction. It counts in the forward direction when the polarity circuit shows a positive sign; and it counts in the reverse direction

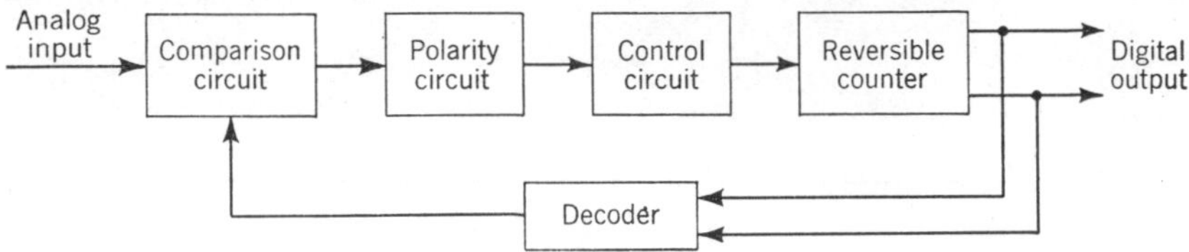

FIG. 8.4-16. Block diagram of a feedback encoder.

when the polarity circuit indicates a negative sign. The counter comes to a stop whenever the polarity circuit observes zero voltage difference. Thus, the feedback encoding system will reach a state of equilibrium only when the digital output measures the analog voltage being coded. The conversion time of this type of encoder depends upon the mode of operation of the control circuit. The conversion accuracy of this encoder is limited only by the accuracies of the decoder and the voltage comparison circuit. An accuracy of one part in several thousands can be achieved.

8.5. A High-speed Encoder Utilizing Operational Amplifiers. In the preceding section, the four basic encoding techniques are discussed and several encoding devices are studied. Indeed, practically all encoders are just variations of the four basic types. There is a very interesting encoder, developed by Smith,[125] which makes use of operational amplifiers. This device, which may be considered as a variation of the weighing-type encoders, finds much use in digital control systems and simulation. The design principles and the operating characteristics of this encoder are presented here.

This analog-to-digital conversion device is designed by cascading a number of single-digit binary encoding stages which are made up of high-gain d-c operational amplifiers serving as the 1-bit coder-decoder circuit and the

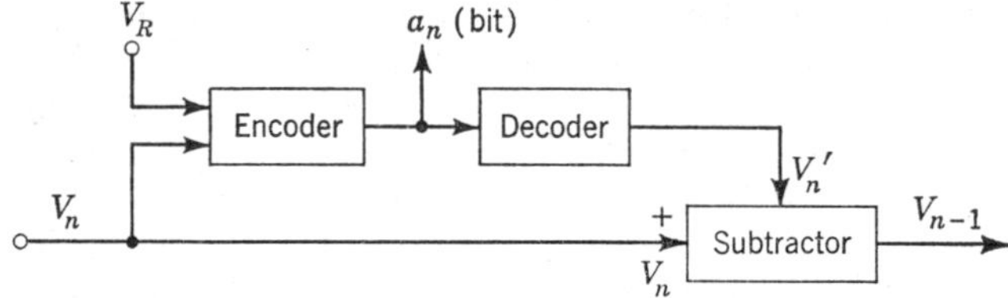

FIG. 8.5-1. Block diagram of a single-bit encoding stage.

subtracting circuit of each stage. An n-digit binary number can be derived by connecting n single-bit encoding stages in cascade. Shown in Fig. 8.5-1 is the block diagram of a single-bit encoding stage, in which V_n is the analog voltage input to the encoder; V_R, the reference voltage; a_n, the digit of the coded output which is either 0 or 1; V'_n, the voltage output of the decoder; and V_{n-1}, the error voltage from the subtractor, which is equal to $V_n - V'_n$. When the analog voltage V_n exceeds the reference voltage V_R, $a_n = 1$ and $V'_n = V_R$; but when V_n is less than V_R, $a_n = 0$ and $V'_n = 0$. As can readily be seen, if the error voltage V_{n-1} is fed into another single-bit encoding stage, a second binary digit can be obtained at the same time. Now, if the error voltage V_{n-2} of the second encoding stage is applied to another single-bit encoding stage, a third binary digit can be derived in addition to the digits obtainable with two encoding stages. Consequently, an n-digit binary representation of the input voltage V_n can be derived, if n single-bit encoding stages are connected in cascade, as shown in Fig. 8.5-2. The first single-bit encoding stage of this analog-to-digital conversion

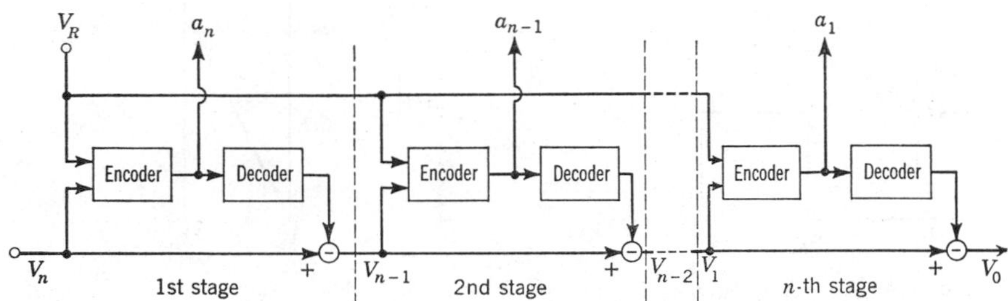

FIG. 8.5-2. Block diagram of an encoder with n single-bit encoding stages in cascade.

system accepts the input voltage V_n, determines the most significant binary digit a_n, generates a dual-level first approximation to the input signal, and supplies a voltage, which is equal to the difference between the input voltage V_n and the first approximation V'_n, into the second single-bit encoding stage. This process is repeated through as many encoding stages as desired. Each stage generates a binary digit and provides a voltage signal for the next encoding stage. In principle, an n-digit binary-encoding system can be built by connecting n simple single-bit encoding circuits in cascade. A one-bit coder-decoder circuit can be made of an amplitude comparison circuit, such as the Schmitt circuit described in Sec. 8.4, or a high-gain d-c operational amplifier the output of which is limited between two fixed voltages.

Design of the Binary Encoding Stage. From the above discussion, it is seen that the transfer characteristics of a stage to perform one-bit encoding can be described by two expressions relating the input to the outputs. When an input voltage V_k is applied to the kth encoding stage, two outputs are generated: the binary digit output a_k and the error voltage output V_{k-1}. The digital output a_k is related to the input voltage V_k by

$$a_n = \begin{cases} 0 & \text{for } V_k < V_R \\ 1 & \text{for } V_k \geq V_R \end{cases} \tag{8.5-1}$$

Equation (8.5-1) is described graphically in Fig. 8.5-3, indicating a step-function transfer characteristic of the encoding stage. The reference voltage V_R is chosen as one-half the full conversion range specified for the encoding system. The output voltage V_{k-1} is related to the input voltage V_k by

$$V_{k-1} = \begin{cases} 2V_k & \text{for } V_k < V_R \\ 2(V_k - a_k V_R) & \text{for } V_k \geq V_R \end{cases} \tag{8.5-2}$$

It is to be noted that a gain factor of 2 is introduced in order to eliminate the need for a separate reference voltage for each stage. Equation (8.5-2) is described graphically in Fig. 8.5-4. The voltage transfer characteristic

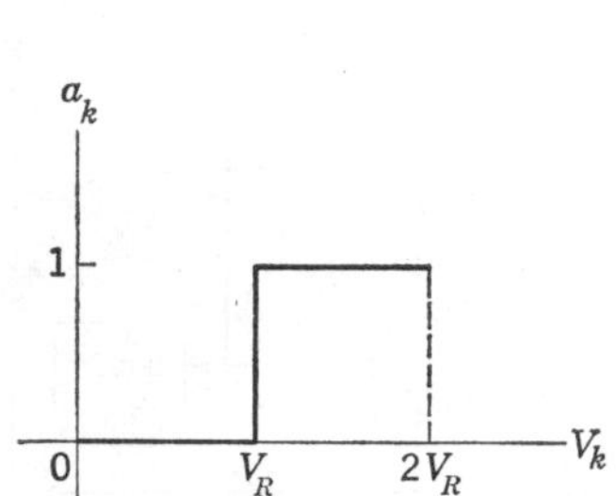

FIG. 8.5-3. The step-function transfer characteristic of a single-bit encoding stage for the digital output.

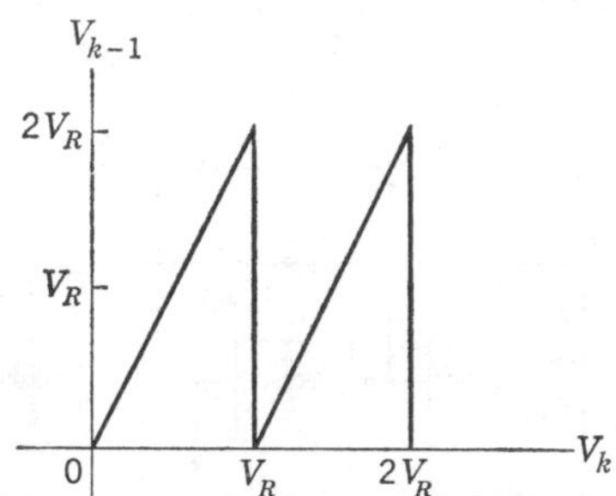

FIG. 8.5-4. The saw-tooth transfer characteristic of a single-bit encoding stage for the voltage output.

required for each stage of a binary encoder of the cascading type is of the saw-tooth form. Consequently, by cascading a number of the single-bit encoding stages which possess the transfer characteristics given by Eqs. (8.5-1) and (8.5-2), one can design a binary encoder which converts any given input voltage into parallel digital output. As an illustration, consider a six-stage cascaded encoder designed for a full conversion range from 0 to 64. Then the reference voltage V_R must be 64/2 or 32 volts. If an input signal of 50 volts is applied to this encoder, the voltages and the digits in each stage are computed from Eqs. (8.5-1) and (8.5-2) in the following manner:

$$\begin{aligned} V_5 &= 50 & a_5 &= 1 \\ V_4 &= 2(50 - 32) = 36 & a_4 &= 1 \\ V_3 &= 2(36 - 32) = 8 & a_3 &= 0 \\ V_2 &= 2(8 - 0) = 16 & a_2 &= 0 \\ V_1 &= 2(16 - 0) = 32 & a_1 &= 1 \\ V_0 &= 2(32 - 32) = 0 & a_0 &= 0 \end{aligned}$$

Thus, the signal of 50 volts is coded into the binary notation as 110010.

The above discussion points out that a single-bit encoding stage must possess a step-function transfer characteristic for the digital output (Fig.

8.5-3), and a saw-tooth transfer characteristic for the voltage output (Fig. 8.5-4). The realization of the required transfer characteristics of each encoding stage can be accomplished by using two operational amplifiers which are high-gain d-c amplifiers with balanced inputs. The circuit diagram of a single-bit encoding stage is shown in Fig. 8.5-5. The first am-

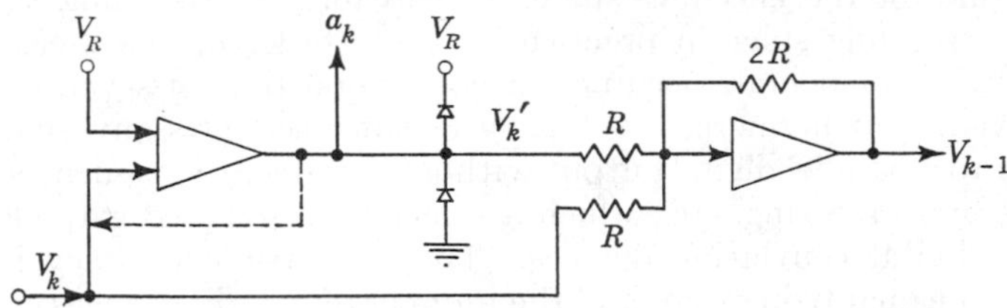

Fig. 8.5-5. Schematic diagram of a single-bit encoding stage utilizing operational amplifiers.

plifier performs the function of a one-bit coder-encoder circuit. When V_k is less than V_R, a_k is zero, and the amplifier yields zero output. When V_k exceeds V_R, a_k is 1 and the voltage output V_k' of the amplifier is V_R. The diodes are used to limit the voltage output to the desired values which are either 0 or V_R, provided that this limiting is not already available in the output stage of the amplifier. In order to improve the step-function transfer characteristic of the encoding stage, use can be made of positive feedback, as shown in dotted lines in Fig. 8.5-5. This positive feedback makes the amplifier unstable for any value of the amplifier output other than 0 or V_R so as to flip the output rapidly from one state to the other. This could eliminate encoding errors caused by ambiguous digital output when the input is at or very near the reference voltage V_R. The second amplifier serves as the subtractor which combines the input signal V_k being encoded and the voltage output V_k' of the first amplifier to generate the desired voltage V_{k-1} for the following stage. This amplifier is so connected that when V_k is less than V_R, $V_{k-1} = 2V_k$, and when V_k exceeds V_R, $V_{k-1} = 2(V_k - a_kV_R)$. Thus, the conditions of Eq. (8.5-2) are fulfilled.

An alternate method of realizing the step-function transfer characteristic of the encoding stage is to employ an amplitude-comparison circuit, as demonstrated in Fig. 8.5-6. The amplitude-comparison circuit performs

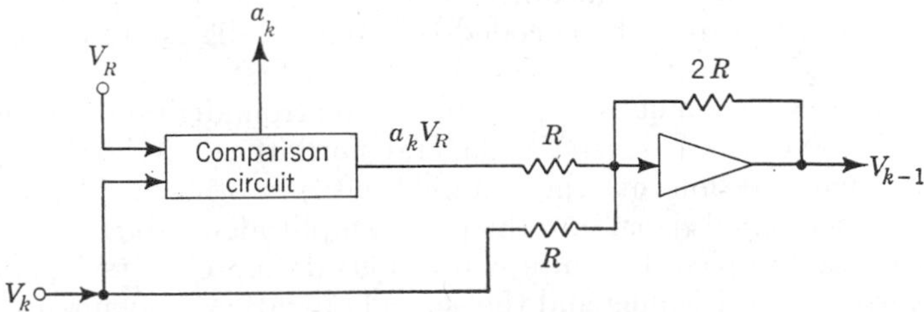

Fig. 8.5-6. Schematic diagram of a single-bit encoding stage utilizing a comparison circuit and an operational amplifier.

the function of the coder-decoder circuit of a single-bit encoding stage.

This type of binary encoder features high speed of conversion. The conversion rate is faster than that of any of the encoding schemes described in the preceding section except the cathode-ray voltage encoder. The conversion time required by an encoder of this type depends upon the total settling time of the encoding stages in cascade. The settling time of a single-bit encoding stage in practice is of the order of one μsec. Consequently, within moderate accuracy, a conversion time of several μsec can be achieved. Furthermore, this binary encoder converts any given input voltage into a parallel digital output without any operations such as timing, counting, synchronizing, etc., which are usually associated with electronic analog-to-digital conversion devices. The conversion accuracy is determined by the quantizing steps and the number of encoding stages employed in the conversion system.

If serial digital output is desired, the encoding circuit of the conversion system may be greatly simplified. This requires only one single-bit encoding stage and a delay line which are connected to form a loop as shown in Fig. 8.5-7. The single-bit encoding stage is used repeatedly to generate all

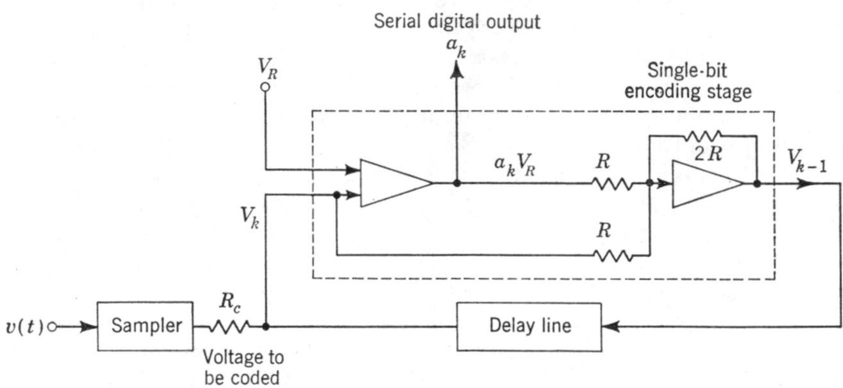

FIG. 8.5-7. Block diagram of a serial encoder using a delay line.

the digits in succession. In Fig. 8.5-7, V_k is the voltage (sample) to be encoded. The voltage output V_{k-1} at one instant becomes the input to the encoding stage at the next instant. Thus, following the application of a voltage input which is to be encoded, the output digits are developed in regular sequence with the most significant digit first.

8.6. Decoding Techniques. The conversion from digital to analog form generally involves two basic steps: (1) Transform the digital data expressed in a positional notation into the sampled data; in other words, convert a pulse-code-modulated signal into the pulse-amplitude-modulated form. (2) Transform the sampled data into continuous data. The first operation is often referred to as decoding and the second operation is commonly known as holding. The process of digital-to-analog conversion is explained by the block diagram of Fig. 8.6-1. The decoder is a device which converts signals in digital codes into sampled-data form. The hold is a device which converts sampled-data signals into continuous-data or analog form. The device which performs the operations of decoding and holding is referred to as a digital-to-analog converter. The properties of the holds (or holding devices)

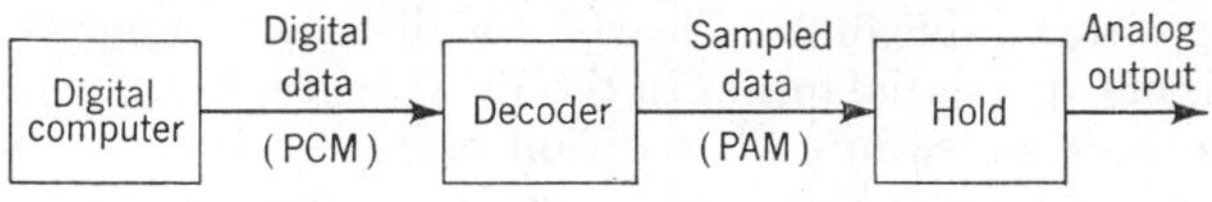

FIG. 8.6-1. Block diagram illustrating the digital-to-analog conversion process.

are studied in Sec. 4.6. The present section is concerned with the decoding techniques and the characteristics of the decoders.

In binary notations, a number N is represented by

$$N_B = a_n a_{n-1} a_{n-2} \cdots a_k \cdots a_1 a_0 \tag{8.6-1}$$

where N_B is a positional notation and the digits a_k are either 0 or 1. If the position of a digit of 1 is replaced by a positive pulse and that of a digit of 0 is replaced by a zero pulse, a binary number is then represented by a train of positive and zero code pulses, forming a PCM signal. For example, the binary number 1100100 can be represented by a train of two positive pulses followed by two zero pulses, one positive pulse and then two zero pulses in succession, as illustrated in Fig. 8.6-2. The decoding process is,

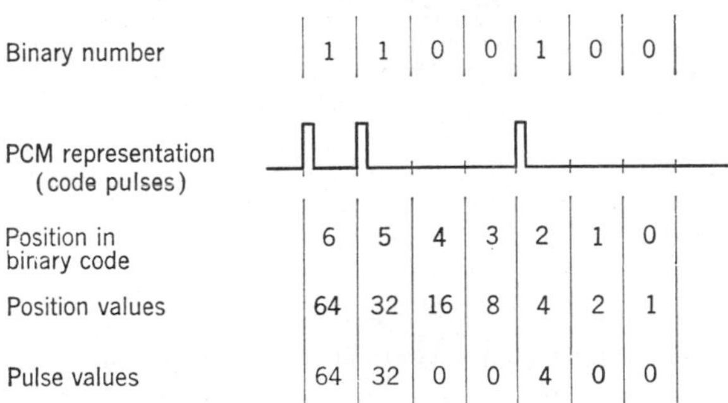

FIG. 8.6-2. A binary number and its PCM representation.

in effect, the process of converting the code pulses of a binary number into a single pulse, the amplitude of which represents the value of the number.

The actual value represented by the binary notation of Eq. (8.6-1) is given by

$$N = a_n \times 2^n + a_{n-1} \times 2^{n-1} + \cdots + a_k \times 2^k + \cdots + a_1 \times 2^1 + a_0 \times 2^0 \tag{8.6-2}$$

The above equation implies that each position in the binary notation has a position value. In passing from the right to the left, the position values are increased successively by a factor of 2. The first from the right (i.e., the least significant position) has a position value of 1, the second position from the right has a position value of 2, and the $(k + 1)$th position from the right has a position value of 2^k. Clearly, the distribution curve of the position values is of exponential form. In the PCM representation of the binary number, the code pulse in each position carries a value, which may be referred to as the pulse value. A pulse value is equal to the product of the position value and the corresponding digit. For instance, the pulse value represented by the first pulse from the right is $a_0 \times 2^0$, which is zero when $a_0 = 0$ and 1 when $a_0 = 1$. The pulse value of the $(k + 1)$th pulse is $a_k \times 2^k$. As a numerical example, the position values and the pulse values of the binary number 1100100 are listed in Fig. 8.6-2. Consequently, it follows from Eq. (8.6-2) that the value represented by a binary-coded pulse group is equal to the sum of the pulse values in each position. Since the decoding is essentially the process of finding the value represented by a binary-coded pulse group, the decoder is, in effect, a device which performs the arithmetic operations involved in Eq. (8.6-2). In view of the exponential shape of the position-value distribution curve, the decoding process can be carried out by taking advantage of the fact that the discharge of a capacitor through a resistor follows an exponential curve.

Serial Decoding Circuits. Shown in Fig. 8.6-3 is a simple RC circuit with a switching relay, which may be used to perform the serial decoding opera-

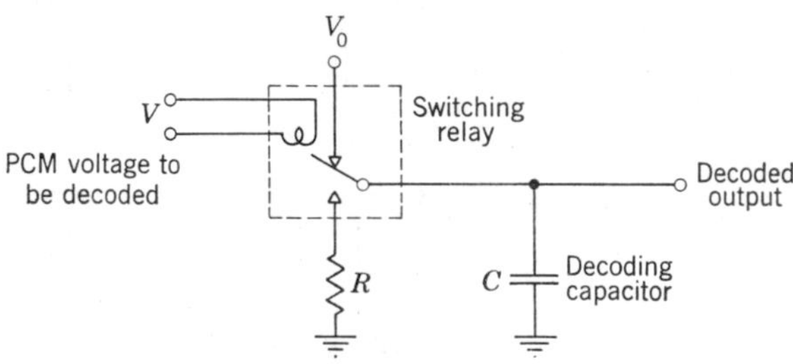

FIG. 8.6-3. A very simple decoding circuit.

tion[8] if an appropriate value of the discharge time constant is chosen. When a code pulse is applied to the relay coil, the relay makes the upper contact, and the capacitor is charged instantly to a voltage of V_0 volts. When the code pulse is removed, the relay makes the lower contact and the capacitor is discharged through the resistor R. Following the application of a code pulse to the relay coil, the voltage across the capacitor will reach a value given by

$$V_k = V_0 \epsilon^{-kp/RC} \tag{8.6-3}$$

after a duration of k code pulses, i.e., at the instant $t = kp$, where p is the time interval between two consecutive code pulses. At this instant the charge on the capacitor will be

$$Q_k = Q_0 \epsilon^{-kp/RC} \tag{8.6-4}$$

where $Q_0 = CV_0$. Substituting 2^r for ϵ in Eq. (8.6-4) yields

$$Q_k = Q_0 2^{-(rp/RC)k} \tag{8.6-5}$$

Now, if the values of the capacitance and resistance of the RC circuit are so chosen that

$$RC = rp = \frac{p}{\ln 2} \tag{8.6-6}$$

Equation (8.6-5) is reduced to

$$Q_k = Q_0 2^{-k} = \frac{Q_0}{2^k} \tag{8.6-7}$$

By making $Q_0 = 2^n$, Eq. (8.6-7) becomes

$$Q_k = 2^{n-k} \tag{8.6-8}$$

which yields

$$Q_1 = 2^{n-1} \qquad Q_2 = 2^{n-2} \qquad \cdots \qquad Q_{n-1} = 2^1 \qquad Q_n = 2^0 \tag{8.6-9}$$

That is, the values of the charge on the capacitor at the instants $t = 0, p, 2p, 3p, \ldots, np$, can be expressed in powers of 2. This property suggests that a simple RC circuit can be used to perform decoding.

If n nonzero code pulses are applied to the relay coil in sequence, the capacitor C will be charged at the instants $t = 0, p, 2p, 3p, \ldots, (n-1)p$, and it will discharge through resistor R during the interpulse periods. Then at the instant $t = np$, the first code pulse will cause an accumulation of charge of 2^0 coulomb on the capacitor, the second code pulse will cause an accumulation of charge of 2^1 coulombs on the capacitor, the third code pulse will cause a charge of 2^2 coulombs to be accumulated on the capacitor, . . . , and the nth code pulse will cause a charge of 2^{n-1} to be accumulated on the capacitor. Consequently, the values of the charges left on the capacitor at the instant $t = np$, as a result of the application of n nonzero code pulses in succession, represent the position values of an n-digit binary notation. The pulse value is equal to the position value when the corresponding code pulse is positive; and the pulse value is equal to zero when the corresponding code pulse is zero. Thus, the values of the charges left on the capacitor at the instant $t = np$ resulting from the application of n serial code pulses of a binary number, with the least significant code pulse first, represent the pulse values in each position. If the relay of the R-C circuit of Fig. 8.6-3 is actuated by the n code pulses of a binary number, with the least significant code pulse first, the total charge accumulated on the capacitor C at the instant $t = np$ is equal to the value represented by the given binary number. The RC circuit of Fig. 8.3-3 thus performs the decoding operation.

As an illustration, consider the decoding of the binary number 1100100 by the RC circuit. In this case, $n = 7$. The code pulses of the binary number are applied to the relay coil in sequence, beginning with the least significant code pulse which is a zero in this number. The train of the code pulses is shown in Fig. 8.6-4. It is seen that during the interval $0 \leq t \leq 2p$

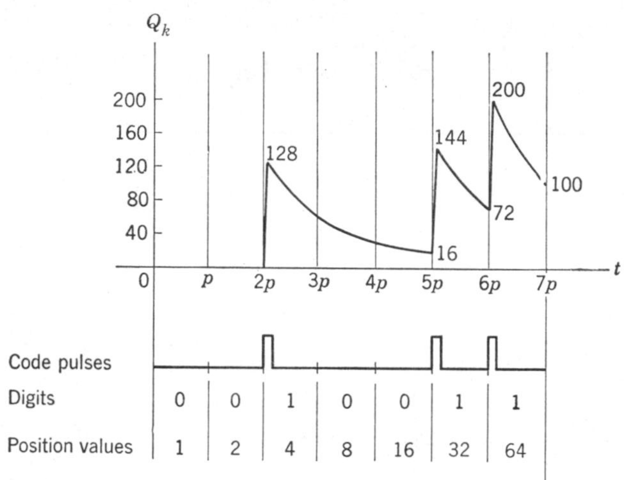

FIG. 8.6-4. Illustration of the decoding of the binary number 1100100 by the circuit of Fig. 8.6-3.

the relay is not energized and the capacitor carries no charge. At the instant $t = 2p$, when a positive code pulse is applied to the relay coil, the relay makes the upper contact and the capacitor is instantly charged to a voltage of $2^7/C$ (or $128/C$) volts. At this instant the capacitor carries a charge of 128 coulombs. During the interval $2p < t \leq 5p$, the relay remains nonenergized and the capacitor discharges through resistor R according to Eq. (8.6-4) to a value of 128/8 or 16 coulombs, as shown in Fig. 8.6-4. At the instant $t = 5p$, another positive code pulse is applied to energize the relay, and the capacitor is again instantly charged with an additional 128 coulombs. The total charge accumulated on the capacitor at this instant is (16 + 128) or 144 coulombs, in which the 16 coulombs are the charge deposited on the capacitor when it is charged the second time. During the interval $5p < t \leq 6p$, the capacitor discharges to a value of 72 coulombs. At the instant $t = 6p$, another positive code pulse arrives and the capacitor is again charged with an additional 128 coulombs. The total charge accumulated on the capacitor at this instant is (72 + 128) or 200 coulombs. During the interval $6p < t < 7p$, the capacitor discharges through resistor R; and at the instant $t = 7p$, the charge accumulated on the capacitor is 200/2 or 100 coulombs. Clearly, 100 is the value represented in the binary notation 1100100. The RC circuit thus completes a decoding operation. It should be pointed out that, if the RC circuit of Fig. 8.6-3 is used to decode digital data in binary codes, the capacitor C

must be completely discharged after each decoding operation (i.e., the conversion of a group of coded pulses to the equivalent sampled pulse).

A practical decoding circuit for serial binary representation is shown in Fig. 8.6-5, which is commonly known as the Shannon-Rack decoder.[8] This

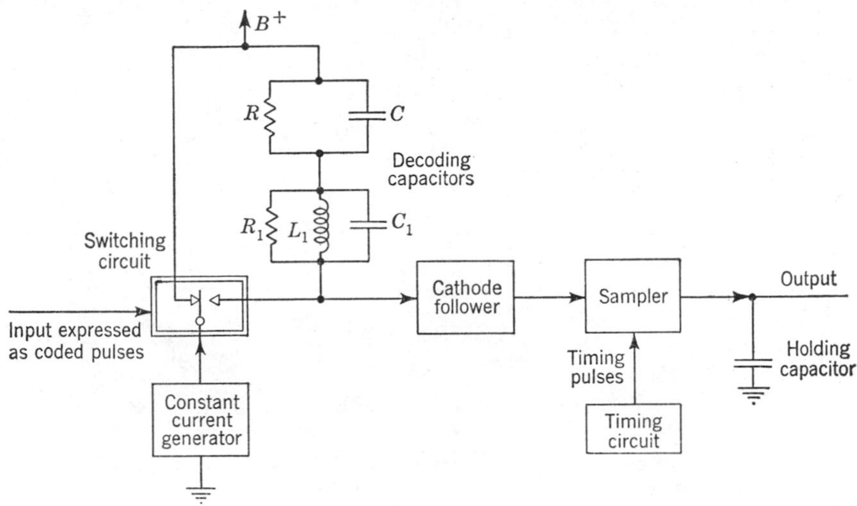

FIG. 8.6-5. The Shannon-Rack decoding circuit.

decoder employs two capacitor-discharging circuits in series. In the upper circuit, the capacitor C, which is shunted by a resistor R, discharges exponentially. In the lower circuit, the capacitor C_1, which is shunted by a resistor R_1 and an inductor L_1, discharges as an exponentially decaying sinusoid. The insertion of the underdamped RLC circuit in series with the RC decoding circuit makes the waveform of the voltage across the decoding capacitors flat at $t = np$, thus eliminating the need for a very precise timing circuit for the sampler.

The preceding paragraphs describe a method of decoding binary numbers by means of an RC decoding circuit. This method is applicable only to the decoding of binary numbers expressed in serial form with the least significant digit first. In the paragraphs to follow, several techniques of decoding binary numbers given in parallel form are discussed.

Parallel Decoding Circuits. In practice most of the decoding circuits for binary numbers given in parallel form make use of the switching of binary-weighted resistors. Shown in Fig. 8.6-6 is a resistance-switching circuit† which can perform the parallel decoding operation, if the value of any of the parallel resistors is

$$R_k = \frac{R}{2^k} \tag{8.6-10}$$

† R. L. Walquist, Analysis and Design of Digital-to-analog Decoder, Report R-220, Digital Computer Laboratory, Massachusetts Institute of Technology, 1953.

that is, the parallel resistors are binary weighted. The switches of this decoding circuit represent the binary digits a_k in each position of a binary number. Counting from the left, the first switch represents the most significant digit a_n and the last switch represents the least significant digit a_0.

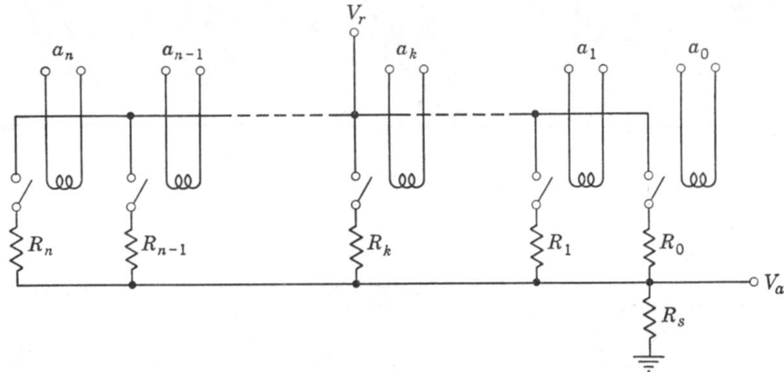

FIG. 8.6-6. A basic resistor-switching decoder.

When the switch is open, the digit which it represents is a 0; when the switch is closed, the digit which it represents is a 1. These switches are normally open and are to be actuated by the code pulses of a binary number being decoded. A positive code pulse (i.e., a digit of 1) will close a switch and connect the corresponding resistor into the circuit. A zero code pulse (i.e., a digit of 0) will leave the switch open and the resistor disconnected. With the sizes of the parallel resistors determined by Eq. (8.6-10) the values of the conductance of these resistors represent the position values in each position of a binary number. Furthermore, the pulse value is proportional to the conductance value if the corresponding switch is closed, and the pulse value is zero if the corresponding switch is open. Thus, the value N represented by a binary number is proportional to the total conductance of the parallel combination of the weighted resistors R_0, R_1, R_2, . . . , R_n, following the application of the code pulses of the binary number to the corresponding switches of the circuit.

Let R_e be the equivalent resistance of a parallel combination of the binary-weighted resistors corresponding to the binary notation N_B of a number N. Then the total conductance is

$$\frac{1}{R_e} = \sum_{k=0}^{n} \frac{a_k}{R_k} = \frac{1}{R} \sum_{k=0}^{n} a_k \times 2^k \tag{8.6-11}$$

where a_k is either 0 or 1, depending upon whether this particular bit is present in N_B or not. Since the value represented by the binary number is

$$N = \sum_{k=0}^{n} a_k \times 2^k \tag{8.6-12}$$

Eq. (8.6-11) yields

$$N = \frac{R}{R_e} \tag{8.6-13}$$

and

$$R_e = \frac{R}{N} \tag{8.6-14}$$

When the code pulses of this binary number N_B are applied to the switches, the voltage output of this resistance-switching network is given by

$$V_a = \frac{R/a}{R/a + R_e} V_r \tag{8.6-15}$$

where R/a is the resistance of the summing resistor R_s. Substituting Eq. (8.6-14) into Eq. (8.6-15) and simplifying yields

$$V_a = \frac{NV_r}{N + a} \tag{8.6-16}$$

which may be expanded into

$$V_a = \frac{NV_r}{a}\left[1 - \frac{N}{a} + \left(\frac{N}{a}\right)^2 - \left(\frac{N}{a}\right)^3 + \cdots\right] \tag{8.6-17}$$

When a is made much greater than N, Eq. (8.6-17) reduces to the following approximation:

$$V_a \approx \frac{V_r}{a} N \tag{8.6-18}$$

The above equation implies that if a is much larger than N, the output voltage V_a is proportional to the value represented by the binary number applied, and the decoding operation is accomplished.

From the above discussions it can readily be seen that the conversion accuracy of this decoder is determined by the ratio N/a. High conversion accuracy requires N to be much smaller than a. When the value of N is increased, the linear relationship between V_a and N no longer holds, and the conversion accuracy becomes poorer. The resolution of this decoder depends upon the number of bits used to represent a number. Since the parallel resistors are binary weighted, the values of the resistance used in a high-precision decoder of this type extend over a very wide range. The need for large resistance values presents considerable difficulty when a short rise time of the output is desired. Furthermore, because the value of a must be very large and the resistance of R_s small in comparison with the other resistances of the circuit, the full-scale value of the output voltage is generally limited to less than 1 volt.

The basic resistance-switching decoder may be improved if the denominator of Eq. (8.6-16) is made constant so that a linear-decoding circuit would result. Equation (8.6-16) may be written as

$$V_a = \frac{N/R}{N/R + a/R} V_r \tag{8.6-19}$$

where $R/N = R_e$ and R/a is the load resistance. Since N/R increases as N is increased, the value of $(N/R + a/R)$ can be maintained constant provided that the load resistance is made to vary with N in direct proportion. This can be accomplished if single-throw double-pole switches are used to connect the weighted resistors corresponding to the digits of 0 in parallel with the summing resistor R_s. The circuit diagram of an improved resistance-switching decoder is shown in Fig. 8.6-7. The improved circuit

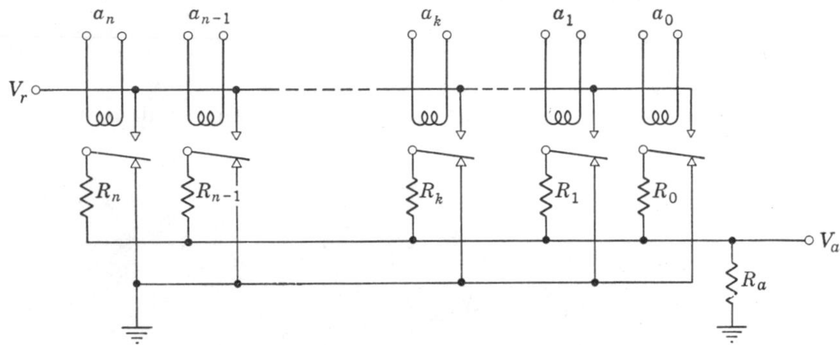

FIG. 8.6-7. Circuit diagram of an improved resistor-switching decoder.

functions in the same manner as the basic circuit described above, except that when a certain binary digit a_k of the input binary number is a 0, the binary-weighted resistor R_k corresponding to this digit or code pulse is connected in parallel with the summing resistor.

Let R_l be the total resistance of all R_k's in parallel. Then R_l represents the minimum value of the equivalent resistance R_e, corresponding to the maximum binary number (i.e., all digits are 1) which can be decoded by this decoding circuit. It follows from Eq. (8.6-14) that

$$R_l = \frac{R}{N_m} \tag{8.6-20}$$

where N_m is the maximum value of N, which the decoding circuit can convert. Now, let the total resistance of the parallel combination of the binary-weighted resistors which correspond to the digits of 0 of the binary number be R_0. In other words, R_0 is the resistance of the binary-weighted resistors which are to be connected in parallel with the summing resistor R_s. Then, the following relationships are obtained:

$$\frac{1}{R_l} = \frac{1}{R_e} + \frac{1}{R_0} \tag{8.6-21}$$

and

$$\frac{1}{R_0} = \frac{1}{R_l} - \frac{1}{R_e} \tag{8.6-22}$$

Substituting Eqs. (8.6-14) and (8.6-20) into Eq. (8.6-22) yields

$$\frac{1}{R_0} = \frac{N_m - N}{R} \tag{8.6-23}$$

which may be written as

$$R_0 = \frac{R}{N_m - N} \tag{8.6-24}$$

Clearly, the load resistance R_L across which the output voltage V_a is obtained is given by the parallel combination of R_0 and R_s. That is,

$$\frac{1}{R_L} = \frac{a}{R} + \frac{N_m - N}{R} = \frac{N_m - N + a}{R} \tag{8.6-25}$$

or

$$R_L = \frac{R}{N_m - N + a} \tag{8.6-26}$$

Consequently, the output voltage V_a is given by

$$V_a = \frac{R_L}{R_e + R_L} V_r = \frac{V_r}{N_m + a} N \tag{8.6-27}$$

The above equation indicates that the output voltage is directly proportional to the value represented by the input digital number. Unlike the basic resistance-switching decoder of Fig. 8.6-6, the improved decoding circuit imposes no restriction upon the ratio N/a. The full-scale value of the output voltage of the improved resistance-switching decoder may approach the reference voltage V_r.

The switching of the binary-weighted resistors can be performed by single-throw double-pole relays, as illustrated in Fig. 8.6-7. The relays, which normally make the lower contacts, are actuated by the code pulses of a binary number to be decoded. When the code pulse of a digit 0 is applied to the relay coil of the kth switch, the lower contact remains closed and the resistor R_k is connected in parallel with the summing resistor R_s. When the relay coil of the kth switch is energized by the code pulse of a digit 1, the relay makes the upper contact and the resistor R_k is connected in series with the summing resistor R_s. However, the relay-operated switches are slow acting in nature. To secure high speed, switching transistors are usually employed to take the place of the double-throw single-pole relays.

Another scheme of the resistor-switching decoder is shown in Fig. 8.6-8. This decoding device makes use of an operational amplifier. The feedback circuit is made up of $(n + 1)$ binary-weighted resistors, each being shunted by a normally closed relay. The relays are operated by code pulses of a binary number to be decoded. If the kth digit a_k of the binary number is a 0, the kth relay contact remains closed and the kth resistor remains shorted. If the kth digit is a 1, the relay is energized, thus opening the relay contact and connecting the kth resistor into the feedback circuit.

Consequently, following the application of the code pulses of a binary number N_B to this decoding circuit, the output voltage will be

$$V_a = \frac{\sum_{k=0}^{n} a_k \times 2^k R}{R_0} V_r = \frac{RV_r}{R_0} N \tag{8.6-28}$$

where $a_k = 1$ when the switch is opened by a digit 1; $a_k = 0$ when the

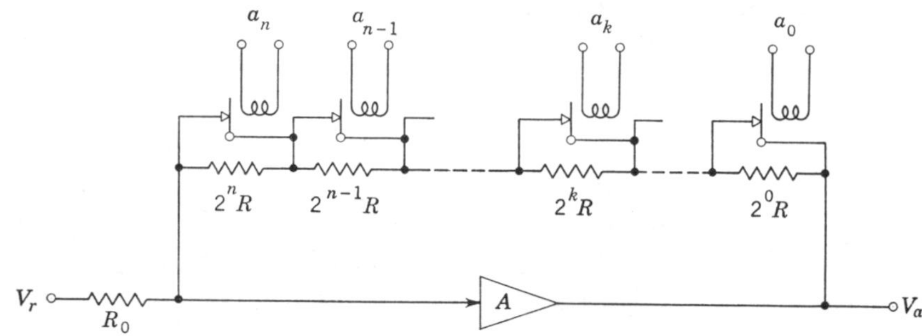

FIG. 8.6-8. A resistor-switching decoder utilizing an operational amplifier.

switch is closed by a digit 0; and

$$N = \sum_{k=0}^{n} a_k \times 2^k \tag{8.6-29}$$

is the value represented by the binary number N_B.

8.7. Conclusion. Analog-digital converters play an important role in digital control systems. Since the digital equipment and the control system adopt different languages, they cannot communicate with each other without the aid of an interpreter. The analog-digital converters serve as interpreters to translate analog information into digital codes and vice versa. To design such conversion devices, the following points should be taken into consideration, namely, sampling rate, resolution, conversion time, anti-ambiguity, and temporary storage. In this chapter, the number systems for digital control have been briefly reviewed, and several basic encoding and decoding techniques have been discussed and illustrated by practical circuits. The counting-type encoder is the most fundamental and highly developed analog-to-digital converter. The shaft digitizer translates the shaft position into digital notation. The cathode-ray voltage encoder features very high conversion speed. In practice most of the decoding circuits for binary numbers given in parallel form make use of the switching of binary-weighted resistors. The operational amplifier encoders and decoders are particularly useful in the simulation of digital control systems on a commercial analog computer.

CHAPTER 9

GENERAL DESIGN PRINCIPLES

9.1. Introduction. Up to this point the basic theory and principles of the analysis of sampled-data and digital control systems have been discussed. It seems logical at this moment to apply these principles to the actual design of pulsed-data systems. Chapter 4 presents the analysis of sampled-data systems by extending the conventional frequency-response approach for continuous-data systems. The stability and general behavior of a sampled-data system are analyzed and interpreted in terms of the polar plot of the open-loop frequency characteristic of the system in much the same manner as continuous-data systems are treated. It is conceivable that the conventional frequency-response design procedure may be extended to the design of sampled-data control systems to meet certain performance specifications.

In Chaps. 6 and 7, the z transform and the modified z transform methods of analysis are discussed. The performance of a sampled-data feedback control system is characterized by the closed-loop poles and zeros of the system in the z plane, and can be determined from the z-transform locus of the open-loop pulse-transfer function of the system, from the z-plane root loci of the system, or from the output transform of the system. It is essential in this connection to point out that the z-transform technique is not only a powerful method for system analysis but also a useful tool for the synthesis of sampled-data systems.

Because of the simplicity and ease with which the Bode diagrams of a control system can be reshaped to meet performance specifications, the Bode-diagram approach has gained great popularity as a means of analyzing and synthesizing continuous-data control systems. It would be a natural consequence to extend the Bode-diagram technique to the synthesis of sampled-data feedback control systems. As discussed in Sec. 6.2, the open-loop transfer function (starred) of sampled-data feedback control system is a transcendental function of s, which is multivalued. The multivalued nature of the transfer function in s makes the application of the Bode-diagram techniques to sampled-data control systems extremely difficult. However, through appropriate transformation the widely used Bode-diagram method may easily and directly be applied.

Among the many methods for the design of continuous-data control systems, the root-locus approach offers the advantages of simultaneous control over both transient and frequency responses of the system, as briefly discussed in Sec. 2.6. The root-locus plot of a control system places in evidence the effects of the variation of the characteristic roots upon the transient behavior of the system. In view of the simplicity of this method, the extension of the root-locus approach to the design of sampled-data control systems is warranted. Just as the Nyquist-diagram and Bode-diagram techniques of analysis are carried over to the design of pulsed-data control systems, it is reasonable to apply the ideas of the root-locus method to sampled-data control system synthesis.

The present chapter is concerned with the design and synthesis of sampled-data and digital control systems. Before taking into consideration the general design principles, it seems desirable to have a brief discussion of some of the most useful properties of the open-loop frequency characteristic of sampled-data feedback control systems. Shown in Fig. 9.1-1 is

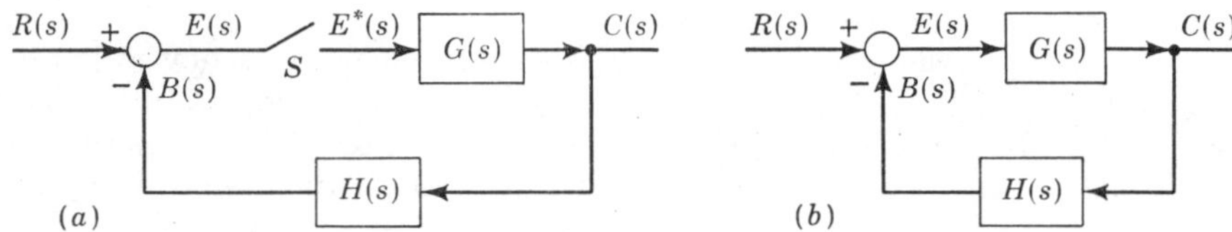

FIG. 9.1-1. (a) A basic sampled-data feedback control system; (b) the corresponding continuous-data system.

the block diagram of a basic sampled-data feedback control system. The input and output of the system are related by

$$\frac{C(s)}{R^*(s)} = \frac{G(s)}{1 + A_0^*(s)} \tag{9.1-1}$$

or, in terms of z transforms,

$$\frac{C(z)}{R(z)} = \frac{G(z)}{1 + A_0(z)} \tag{9.1-2}$$

where
$$A_0^*(s) = GH^*(s) \tag{9.1-3}$$

and
$$A_0(z) = GH(z) \tag{9.1-4}$$

denote the open-loop transfer function of the sampled-data system. The former gives the representation in s (or, more precisely, in ϵ^{Ts}) and is sometimes referred to as the starred transfer function, whereas the latter expresses the function in z and is usually termed the pulse-transfer function. By the substitution

$$z = \epsilon^{Ts} \tag{9.1-5}$$

$A_0^*(s)$, which may be expressed as a function in ϵ^{Ts}, is readily converted to $A_0(z)$. The open-loop transfer function $A_0^*(s)$ is a periodic function in s with period $j\omega_s$, where ω_s is the sampling frequency in radians/sec. The degree of the denominator of the starred transfer function $A_0^*(s)$ in ϵ^{-Ts} [or the pulse-transfer function $A_0(z)$ in z^{-1}] is equal to the degree of the corresponding open-loop transfer function $A_0(s)$ of the system if the sampler were absent. When the corresponding $A_0(s)$ contains no pole at the origin of the s plane, the open-loop frequency-response function $A_0^*(j\omega)$ is always real for $\omega = 0$ and $\omega = n\omega_s/2$, where n is an integer.

The z-transform locus of $A_0(z)$ [that is, the polar plot of $A_0(z)$ for z traversing in the counterclockwise direction once around the unit circle] usually takes the shape as shown in Fig. 9.1-2, depending upon the number of poles of $A_0(z)$ at $z = 1$. Figure 9.1-2*a* depicts the polar plot of $A_0(z)$ which contains no pole on the unit circle (i.e., the system having no integration). In this case, the pulse-transfer function is finite for all values of z and it is real at both $z = 1$ and $z = -1$. When $A_0(z)$ contains no pole on the unit circle except a single pole at $z = 1$, the polar plot extends to infinity at $z = 1$ and closes at infinity via an infinite semicircle in the right half of the A_0 plane, as illustrated in Fig. 9.1-2*b*. It is noted that the z-transform locus of $A_0(z)$ with one pole at $z = -1$ may intersect the real axis of the $A_0(z)$ plane at more than one finite point besides the point corresponding to $z = -1$, as shown in Fig. 9.1-2*b*. When $A_0(z)$ contains no pole on the unit circle except a double pole at $z = 1$, the polar plot is closed at infinity via two infinite semicircles in the upper half and the lower half of the A_0 plane, as demonstrated in Fig. 9.1-2*c*. The pole at $z = 1$ in the z plane is mapped into the point at infinity of the A_0 plane. When $A_0(z)$ contains no pole on the unit circle except a triple pole at $z = 1$, the polar plot is closed at infinity via two infinite three-quarter circles, as shown in Fig. 9.1-2*d*. Examination of these polar plots reveals that stabilization of control systems with higher-order integration through the use of linear networks is quite difficult.

When the preliminary analysis of a sampled-data control system in its primitive form reveals that the over-all performance of the system is inadequate, compensation techniques for improving the system performance must be employed. Compensation means to improve the system performance by reshaping the open-loop pulse-transfer-function loci of the system. The simplest and most direct way of changing the performance is through the adjustment of the system gain. However, for the majority of pulsed-data control systems the design specifications cannot be fulfilled by gain adjustment alone. It appears necessary that compensating devices or networks, sometimes referred to as equalizers, be introduced into the control loops. Just as in the design of continuous-data control systems, the compensation of a sampled-data control system can generally be accomplished either by inserting an element in series with other components of the system or by introducing an element in parallel with one or more components and forming a minor loop. The former arrangement is referred to as cascade compensation or series equalization, and the latter is usually termed feedback compensation or parallel equalization. However, the sampling operation in the pulsed-data control system makes the design of feedback compensation more difficult. Unlike continuous-data systems, cascade compensation of sampled-data feedback control systems may be effected by

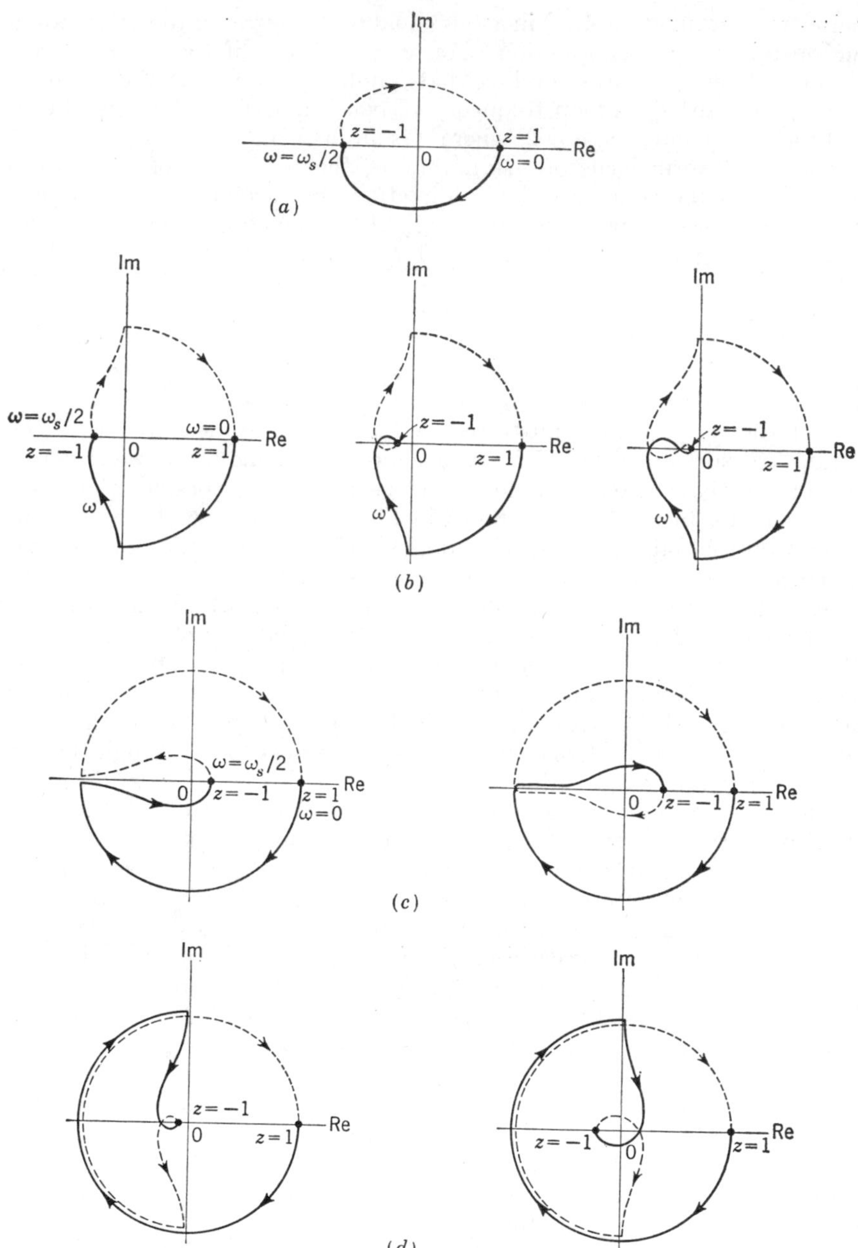

Fig. 9.1-2. Various shapes of the z-transform loci of $A_0(z)$: (*a*) $A_0(z)$ has no pole at $z = 1$; (*b*) $A_0(z)$ has a single pole at $z = 1$; (*c*) $A_0(z)$ has a double pole at $z = 1$; (*d*) $A_0(z)$ has a triple pole at $z = 1$.

two general methods, as illustrated in Fig. 9.1-3. They are (1) cascade compensation by continuous-data devices or networks; (2) cascade compensation by pulsed-data devices or networks or its equivalent. The former makes use of continuous-data compensating networks connected in series

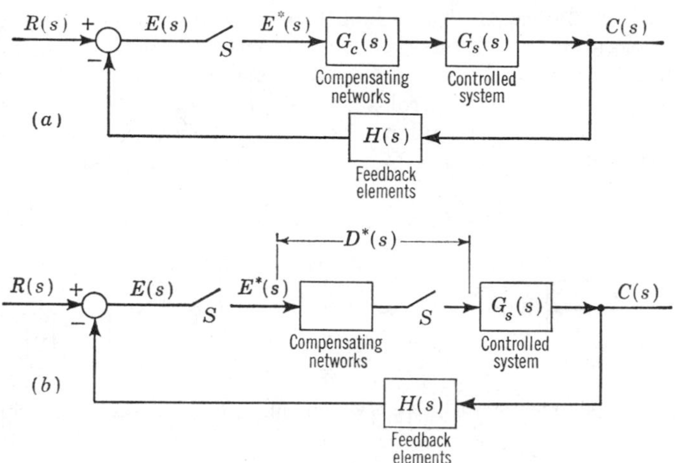

FIG. 9.1-3. Two methods of cascade compensation: (*a*) compensation by continuous-data networks; (*b*) compensation by pulsed-data networks.

with other components, much the same as the cascade compensation of continuous-data control systems, whereas the latter employs pulsed-data compensating networks in place of the continuous-data compensating networks. A pulsed-data network is a network of which the output is sampled in synchronism with its input, at a constant rate. The pulsed-data processing unit represents one of the most commonly used pulsed-data devices for system compensation. The equivalent of the pulsed-data network refers to the compensating program of a digital computer in the case of digital control systems. A pulsed-data network performs the same function as its equivalent digital program or data-processing unit.

The techniques for treating sampled-data feedback control systems are no more complicated in principle than those for treating continuous-data systems. The purposes of system compensation are to provide satisfactory response characteristics of the system, to make the system insensitive to output disturbances and gain variations, and to reduce output ripples. The evaluation of the ripple contents of the system output is described in Chap. 7. The sensitivity to gain change of the system is measured from the changes of the system performance as a result of the gain variations. The insensitivity to output disturbances is usually obtainable in the steady state by high loop gain or low error coefficients. The response characteristics of the system can readily be judged from the system analysis described in the preceding chapters.

9.2. Sinusoidal Sequences. The frequency-response approach to the design of continuous-data feedback control systems has been used extensively for a number of years by control engineers. By the frequency-response method of system design, use is made of the response of the output of the system to sinusoidally varying input signals. In view of the fact that the frequency-response approach has proved extremely effective and successful in designing continuous-data control systems, it would be a natural consequence to apply the frequency-response method to the design of sampled-data and digital control systems. The methods of conventional frequency-response analysis and synthesis have their analogs in pulsed-data systems. Shown in Fig. 9.2-1a is a simple sampled-data system which is

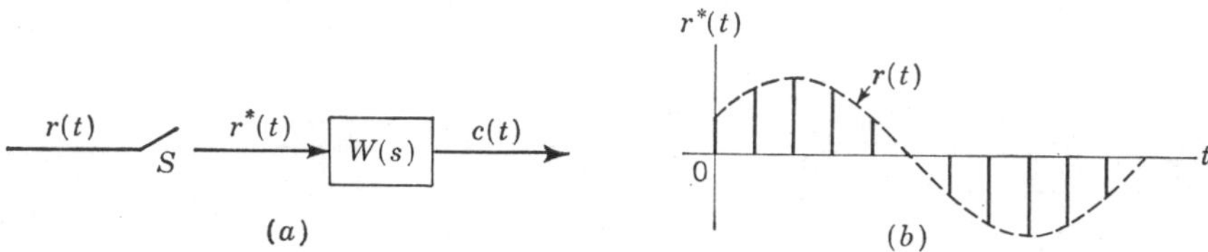

FIG. 9.2-1. (a) A simple sampled-data system subjected to a sinusoidal input; (b) a sinusoidal sequence.

subjected to a sinusoidal input. As can readily be seen, sampling a sinusoidal function yields a *sinusoidal sequence,* as illustrated in Fig. 9.2-1b. If the sinusoidal input to the system is

$$r(t) = a \sin (\omega t + \theta) \tag{9.2-1}$$

the corresponding sinusoidal sequence is given by

$$r(nT) = a \sin (\omega nT + \theta) \tag{9.2-2}$$

where a and θ denote, respectively, the amplitude and phase of the input sinusoid, ω is the frequency of the input signal in radians/sec, and T is the sampling period in seconds. Unlike the continuous function, the sequence of Eq. (9.2-2) is not periodic unless the signal frequency ω and the sampling frequency $\omega_s = 2\pi/T$ are commensurable.[2]

If the weighting sequence of the system $W(s)$ of Fig. 9.2-1a is w_n, the output sequence is given by

$$\begin{aligned} c(nT) &= w_0 a \sin (\omega nT + \theta) + w_1 a \sin [\omega(n-1)T + \theta] \\ &\qquad + w_2 a \sin [\omega(n-2)T + \theta] + \cdots \\ &\qquad + w_k a \sin [\omega(n-k)T + \theta] + \cdots \\ &= a \sum_{k=0}^{n} w_k \sin [\omega(n-k)T + \theta] \end{aligned} \tag{9.2-3}$$

Since
$$\sin [\omega(n-k)T + \theta] = \operatorname{Im}\{\epsilon^{j[\omega(n-k)T+\theta]}\} \tag{9.2-4}$$

Eq. (9.2-3) may be written as

$$c(nT) = \text{Im}\left\{a \sum_{k=0}^{n} w_k \epsilon^{j[\omega(n-k)T+\theta]}\right\}$$

$$= \text{Im}\left\{a\epsilon^{j(\omega nT+\theta)} \sum_{k=0}^{n} w_k \epsilon^{-jk\omega T}\right\} \tag{9.2-5}$$

where Im means "the imaginary part of." In Sec. 5.1 is defined

$$W^*(s) = \sum_{k=0}^{n} w_k \epsilon^{-kTs} \tag{9.2-6}$$

which is the starred transform of the impulse response $w(t)$ of the system [or the Laplace transform of the sampled-data function $w^*(t)$]. Substituting $j\omega$ for s in Eq. (9.2-6) yields

$$W^*(j\omega) = \sum_{k=0}^{n} w_k \epsilon^{-jk\omega T} \tag{9.2-7}$$

Making use of the above relationship reduces Eq. (9.2-5) to

$$c(nT) = \text{Im}\{a\epsilon^{j(\omega nT+\theta)} W^*(j\omega)\} \tag{9.2-8}$$

Furthermore, Eq. (9.2-8) may be put in the form

$$c(nT) = \text{Im}\{a|W^*(j\omega)|\epsilon^{j(\omega nT+\theta+\alpha)}\} \tag{9.2-9}$$

where $|W^*(j\omega)|$ and α are the magnitude and phase angle of $W^*(j\omega)$ respectively. Therefore, the output sequence of the system is given by

$$c(nT) = |W^*(j\omega)|a \sin(\omega nT + \theta + \alpha) \tag{9.2-10}$$

The above equation implies that, in response to a sinusoidal input of frequency ω, the output sequence of the sampled-data system (Fig. 9.2-1a) has an envelope which is also a sinusoidal function of the same frequency, but with the magnitude attenuated by $|W^*(j\omega)|$ and the phase angle increased by α.

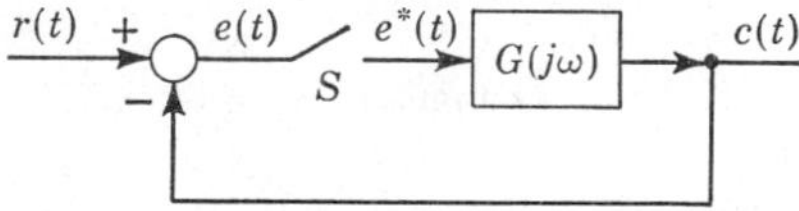

FIG. 9.2-2. A basic sampled-data feedback control system subjected to a sinusoidal input.

Following the above argument, one can readily show that in the case of the error-sampled feedback control system, as shown in Fig. 9.2-2, the output sequence in response to a sinusoidal input given by Eq. (9.2-1) is

$$c(nT) = \frac{|G^*(j\omega)|}{|1 + G^*(j\omega)|} a \sin(\omega nT + \theta + \alpha) \tag{9.2-11}$$

where α is the phase angle of the over-all pulse-transfer function

$$\frac{G^*(j\omega)}{1 + G^*(j\omega)} \tag{9.2-12}$$

In other words, α is the angle between the phasors of $G^*(j\omega)$ and $1 + G^*(j\omega)$ in the $G^*(j\omega)$ plane, as illustrated in Fig. 9.2-3. Thus, in this type of sampled-data feedback control system, the envelope of the output sequence in response to a sinusoidal input is also sinusoidal and of the same frequency as the input signal. Examination of the system of Fig. 9.2-2 reveals that the over-all pulse-transfer function is

$$\frac{C(z)}{R(z)} = G_0(z) = \frac{G(z)}{1 + G(z)} \tag{9.2-13}$$

Alternatively, the over-all pulse-transfer function may be written as

$$\frac{C^*(s)}{R^*(s)} = G_0^*(s) = \frac{G^*(s)}{1 + G^*(s)} \tag{9.2-14}$$

which, by substituting $j\omega$ for s, leads to

$$G_0^*(j\omega) = \frac{G^*(j\omega)}{1 + G^*(j\omega)} \tag{9.2-15}$$

When z traverses the unit circle of the z plane (i.e., the frequencies vary through a range of ω_s radians/sec once), the z-transform locus of the over-all pulse-transfer function $G_0(z)$ describes the relationship between the envelopes of the input and output sinusoidal sequence. The z-transform locus of $G_0(z)$ is often referred to as the over-all frequency response of the sampled-data system; and the expression of Eq. (9.2-15) is the over-all frequency-response function. Figure 9.2-3 and Eq. (9.2-15) indicate that the over-all frequency response can be directly obtained from the polar plot of $G^*(j\omega)$, which is usually plotted for effecting a stability analysis. However, with the aid of auxiliary curves, which are described in the following paragraph, the determination of the over-all frequency response can be simplified.

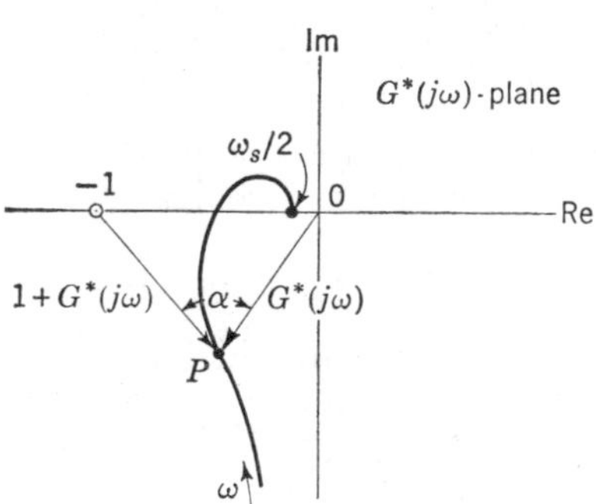

FIG. 9.2-3. The polar plot of $G^*(j\omega)$.

As discussed in most standard textbooks on linear servo theory, the ratio of the output amplitude to the input amplitude of a continuous-data feedback control system is a direct measure of the response of the system. The maximum magnitude-ratio M_p is often used as a design parameter, and the design procedure is facilitated by plotting auxiliary curves for constant magnitude ratio in the $G(j\omega)$ plane. With the aid of the constant magnitude-ratio contours, the reshaping of the Nyquist diagram to meet certain performance specifications can be carried out with ease. This concept may readily be carried over to the design of sampled-data feedback control systems, if the Nyquist-diagram approach is followed. Referring to Fig. 9.2-2, the system is subjected to a sinusoidal input. The magnitude and phase angle of the output-to-input ratio are assumed to be M and α, respectively. Then

$$\frac{C^*(j\omega)}{R^*(j\omega)} = \frac{G^*(j\omega)}{1 + G^*(j\omega)} = M\epsilon^{j\alpha} \tag{9.2-16}$$

where both M and α are functions of the frequency ω of the sinusoidal input. It should be pointed out that, unlike continuous-data systems, the magnitude ratio for sampled-data systems refers to the ratio of the amplitude of the envelope of the sinusoidal sequence of the output to that of the input. The equations describing the contours of constant M and constant α are readily derived. The constant-M loci in the complex plane comprise a family of circles of radii

$$\left|\frac{M}{M^2 - 1}\right| \tag{9.2-17}$$

with their centers located on the real axis at the point

$$\left(-\frac{M^2}{M^2 - 1}, 0\right) \tag{9.2-18}$$

The constant-α loci in the complex plane comprise a family of circles of radii

$$\tfrac{1}{2}[1 + (\cot\alpha)^2]^{\frac{1}{2}} \tag{9.2-19}$$

with their centers located at

$$(-\tfrac{1}{2}, \tfrac{1}{2}\cot\alpha) \tag{9.2-20}$$

In fact, these circles are exactly the same as the constant-M and constant-α circles for continuous-data systems. Consequently, the maximum magnitude-ratio criterion and the associated design rules for continuous-data systems may be satisfactorily applied to the design of sampled-data feedback control systems.

9.3. Reshaping of the Open-loop Frequency-characteristic Locus. In system design by means of the Nyquist-diagram technique, it is customary to effect system compensation by reshaping the open-loop frequency-characteristic locus of the system. The discussions of Sec. 6.1 indicate that in the case of an error-sampled feedback control system there exists the over-all pulse-transfer function which is independent of the input. For instance, the over-all pulse-transfer function of the sampled-data system of Fig. 9.1-1a is given by

$$G_0(z) = \frac{C(z)}{R(z)} = \frac{G(z)}{1 + GH(z)} \tag{9.3-1}$$

where $GH(z)$ is the z transform associated with the open-loop transfer function $G(s)H(s)$. Equation (9.3-1) may also be put into the equivalent expression

$$G_0^*(s) = \frac{C^*(s)}{R^*(s)} = \frac{G^*(s)}{1 + GH^*(s)} \tag{9.3-2}$$

From Fig. 9.1-1*b*, it is noted that the over-all transfer function of the corresponding continuous-data feedback control system is

$$\frac{C(s)}{R(s)} = \frac{G(s)}{1 + G(s)H(s)} \tag{9.3-3}$$

Because of the close resemblance in form of Eq. (9.3-2) to Eq. (9.3-3), many of the frequency-locus reshaping techniques of compensation for continuous-data feedback control systems may be applied to the design of pulsed-data feedback control systems, at least as far as the system performance at the sampling instants is concerned.

In Sec. 4.1, it is shown that the Laplace transform of a function and its starred transform are related by

$$GH^*(s) = \frac{1}{T} \sum_{n=-\infty}^{\infty} GH(s + jn\omega_s) \tag{9.3-4}$$

where T is the sampling period and ω_s is the sampling frequency. Thus, the Nyquist diagram of a sampled-data system may be directly obtained from the Nyquist diagram of the corresponding continuous-data system. The construction is described in Sec. 4.4. The polar plot of $GH^*(j\omega)$ differs from that of $GH(j\omega)$ primarily in that the former locus is periodic with a period of ω_s, while the latter is nonperiodic. A complete polar plot of $GH^*(j\omega)$ is derived when the frequency ω is varied over a finite range from zero to ω_s, whereas a polar plot of $GH(j\omega)$ is completed only when the frequency ω is varied from $-\infty$ to $+\infty$. On account of the periodic nature of $GH^*(j\omega)$, an infinite number of identical polar plots of $GH^*(j\omega)$ can be sketched within the frequency range $0 \leq \omega \leq \infty$. Furthermore, the polar plot of $GH^*(j\omega)$ corresponding to frequencies between $\omega_s/2$ and ω_s is the mirror image of the polar plot for the frequency range $0 \leq \omega \leq \omega_s/2$. Consequently, only the part of the Nyquist diagram corresponding to frequencies between zero and $\omega_s/2$ is of special interest.

Gain Adjustment. In the design of control systems, the parameters of the controlled systems are fixed; and in most cases, they cannot be adjusted for the purpose of obtaining a satisfactory performance. The problem of control-system design is essentially a problem of adjusting the gain constant of the system and introducing adequate compensation into the system so as to fulfill the specified performance requirements. In general, a change in loop gain of the system affects practically all of the system-design parameters. An increase in system gain would, in many cases, give rise to the following effects on the sampled-data control system:

1. A reduction of the system error and a decrease in the degree of stability.

2. An increase in the magnitude of the complex poles of the over-all pulse-transfer function of the system. This would cause a reduction in the damping factor and would make the system more oscillatory.

3. An increase in the phase angles of the complex poles of the over-all pulse-transfer function of the system. This would result in higher speed of response of the control system.

4. A decrease in the magnitude of the real poles of the over-all pulse-transfer function of the system. This would also result in higher response speed. These effects become more obvious when the root locus of the pulsed-data control system is plotted. The root-locus method for the synthesis ot sampled data systems is advanced in Sec. 9.8.

Analogous to the gain determination in continuous-data control systems, the desired loop gain of a sampled-data feedback control system can be readily determined from the Nyquist diagram of the system and the constant-M circles. The procedure for determining the gain constant required in a given continuous-data feedback control system for the purpose of satisfying the magnitude-ratio (M_p) specification can be applied to the selection of the gain constant of sampled-data system. Reference is now made to the unity-feedback error-sampled system of Fig. 9.3-1. The trans-

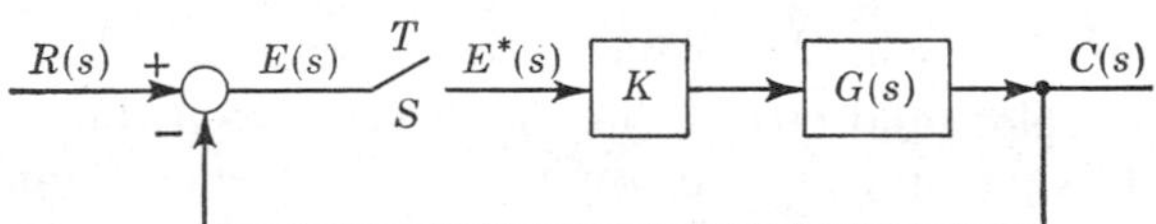

FIG. 9.3-1. A unity-feedback error-sampled system.

fer function of the controlled system is $G(s)$; and the gain constant of the amplifier is K. The open-loop pulse-transfer function of the system is then given by

$$A(z) = KG(z) \tag{9.3-5}$$

where $G(z)$ is the z transform associated with $G(s)$. The equivalent expression of Eq. (9.3-5) is the starred transform

$$A^*(s) = KG^*(s) \tag{9.3-6}$$

The value of K required for a given value of maximum magnitude ratio M_p is to be determined. The suggested procedure is as follows:

1. Plot the Nyquist diagram of $G^*(j\omega)$ for the frequency range $0 \leq \omega \leq \omega_s/2$ [or the z-transform locus of $G(z)$] in the complex plane.

2. Draw a line through the origin 0 at an angle $\phi = \sin^{-1}(1/M_p)$ with the negative real axis, as shown in Fig. 9.3-2.

3. Construct a circle with center C on the negative real axis and tangent to both the $G^*(j\omega)$ plot and the ϕ-line.

4. The required gain constant K is then given by

$$K = \frac{M_p^2/(M_p^2 - 1)}{\overline{OC}} \tag{9.3-7a}$$

or

$$K = \frac{1}{\overline{OD}} \tag{9.3-7b}$$

where $\overline{OC}$ is the distance from the origin of the complex plane to the center of the M_p circle tangent to the $G^*(j\omega)$ plot, $M_p^2/(M_p^2 - 1)$ is the distance

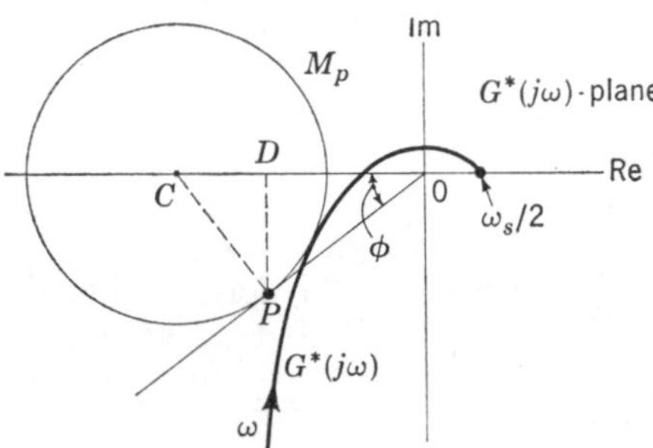

FIG. 9.3-2. Illustrations of the determination of the gain constant for a specified M_p.

from the origin of the complex plane to the center of the M_p circle tangent to the $KG^*(j\omega)$ plot, and $\overline{OD}$ is the distance between the origin and the point D which is the projection of the point of tangency P on the negative real axis.

With reference to Fig. 9.3-2, it is seen that

$$\overline{OD} = \overline{OP} \cos \phi = \overline{OC} \cos^2 \phi \tag{9.3-8}$$

Since

$$\sin \phi = \frac{1}{M_p} \tag{9.3-9}$$

and

$$\cos \phi = \left(1 - \frac{1}{M_p^2}\right)^{1/2} \tag{9.3-10}$$

Eq. (9.3-8) reduces to

$$\overline{OD} = \frac{\overline{OC}(M_p^2 - 1)}{M_p^2} \tag{9.3-11}$$

or

$$\frac{1}{\overline{OD}} = \frac{M_p^2/(M_p^2 - 1)}{\overline{OC}} \tag{9.3-12}$$

which is equal to the gain constant K.

The design of series equalizers by means of the Nyquist-diagram techniques is discussed in the following sections.

9.4. Cascade Compensation by Continuous-data Networks. One of the standard techniques of compensating a continuous-data feedback control system is to insert an equalizing network in cascade with the components of the controlled system. Apparently, this technique of compensation can also be applied to pulsed-data feedback control systems. In the continuous-data unity-feedback control system of Fig. 9.4-1a, the insertion of a com-

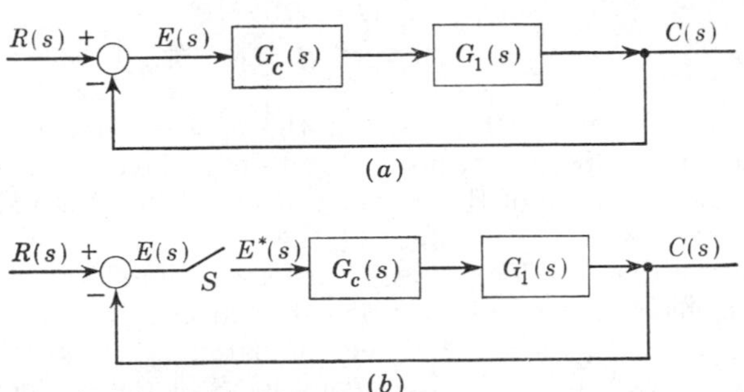

FIG. 9.4-1. (a) Cascade compensation of a continuous-data feedback system; (b) cascade compensation of a sampled-data feedback system.

pensating network $G_c(s)$ in series with the other components of the system $G_1(s)$ results in a change of the open-loop transfer function from

$$A_0(s) = G_1(s) \tag{9.4-1}$$

to

$$A_c(s) = G_c(s)G_1(s) \tag{9.4-2}$$

The open-loop transfer-function locus of the compensated system may be easily estimated from the open-loop transfer-function locus of the original system and the transfer-function locus of the compensating network, since the computation involves simply the multiplication of two vector quantities $G_1(j\omega)$ and $G_c(j\omega)$. The effect of the compensating network upon the shape of the open-loop transfer-function locus, resulting from the adjustment and variation of the parameters or time constants of the network, is conspicuous and controllable. Thus, the determination of the desired compensating network is fairly straightforward. Moreover, when $G_1(s)$ is expressed in factored form or can readily be factorized in linear and quadratic factors, the Bode-diagram technique makes the design of the compensating networks even simpler. On the other hand, in the case of cascade compensation of sampled-data feedback control systems (Fig. 9.4-1b), the frequency locus of the open-loop pulse-transfer function of the compensated system cannot be directly obtained from the locus of the open-loop pulse-transfer function of the original uncompensated system and the locus of the pulse-transfer function of the compensating network. The open-loop pulse-transfer function of the original system is found to be

$$A_0(z) = G_1(z) \tag{9.4-3}$$

or

$$A_0^*(s) = G_1^*(s) \tag{9.4-4}$$

With the introduction of a series equalizer $G_c(s)$, the open-loop pulse-transfer function of the system reduces to

$$A_c(z) = G_cG_1(z) \tag{9.4-5}$$

or

$$A_c^*(s) = G_cG_1^*(s) \tag{9.4-6}$$

Since

$$G_cG_1^*(s) \neq G_c^*(s)G_1^*(s) \tag{9.4-7}$$

and

$$G_cG_1(z) \neq G_c(z)G_1(z) \tag{9.4-8}$$

the open-loop pulse-transfer function of the compensated system is not related to the open-loop pulse-transfer function of the original system and the pulse-transfer function of the compensating network in a simple manner. As a matter of fact, the effect of the compensating network $G_c(s)$ upon the shape of the open-loop pulse-transfer-function locus of a sampled-data system is generally dependent upon the parameters of the controlled system, thus obscuring the direct effect of parameter adjustment of the compensating network upon the frequency locus of the compensated system. The interaction between the controlled system and the compensating network in reshaping the open-loop pulse-transfer-function locus, resulting from the sampling process, makes the conventional locus-reshaping technique very difficult to apply. Nevertheless, this difficulty can be overcome, if use is made of certain appropriate approximations.[21,84]

a. Finite Sum Approximation. By making use of the results of Sec. 4.1, one obtains the following identity:

$$G_cG_1^*(s) = \frac{1}{T}\sum_{n=-\infty}^{\infty} G_cG_1(s + jn\omega_s) \tag{9.4-9}$$

$$= \frac{1}{T}[G_cG_1(s) + G_cG_1(s - j\omega_s) + G_cG_1(s + j\omega_s) + G_cG_1(s - j2\omega_s) + \cdots] \tag{9.4-10}$$

In view of the fact that in the majority of feedback control systems the controlled system behaves as a low-pass filter and the function $G_cG_1(j\omega)$ attenuates rapidly at high frequencies, the terms representing the higher frequencies in the above summation are of secondary importance. In addition, the hold circuit, often used in the system as a smoothing device, is a kind of low-pass filter which cuts off at the sampling frequency, as demonstrated in Sec. 4.6. Consequently, as a first approximation the right-hand side of Eq. (9.4-10) may be represented by the first two terms, thus,

$$G_cG_1^*(s) \approx \frac{1}{T}[G_c(s)G_1(s) + G_c(s - j\omega_s)G_1(s - j\omega_s)] \tag{9.4-11}$$

Clearly, the above approximation is valid under the condition that $s = j\omega$, that frequency ω be kept within the limits $0 \leq \omega \leq \omega_s/2$, and that the transfer function $G_cG_1(j\omega)$ introduce high attenuation for frequencies larger than half the sampling frequency. In fact, all other terms obtainable from $G_c(s)G_1(s)$ are evaluated at frequencies higher than the sampling frequency, and thus may be ignored. Only in the exceptional cases in which the cutoff frequency exceeds the sampling frequency can these other terms contribute appreciably to the summation.

On the basis of the approximation of Eq. (9.4-11), the conventional locus-reshaping techniques can be applied to the evaluation of $G_c(s)$ of the desired compensating network. However, the presence of the second term of the right-hand member of Eq. (9.4-11) slightly complicates the study of the effects of added compensation. This requires the determination of the sum of the products of transfer functions rather than simply the product of transfer functions. The first term is, in effect, the predominant term, indicating the general area in which the transfer-function locus of the compensated system would possibly locate. The second term may be thought of as the correction term which, when added vectorially to the plot of

$$\frac{1}{T} G_c(s)G_1(s)\Big|_{s=j\omega} \tag{9.4-12}$$

yields the approximate locus of $G_cG_1^*(s)$. In consequence, the reshaping of the frequency locus of $G_1^*(j\omega)$ is reduced to the reshaping of $T^{-1}G_1(j\omega)$ locus, including a safety factor intended to counteract the effect of the correction term of Eq. (9.4-11). This correction term usually tends to push the compensated frequency locus to the left, as discussed in Sec. 4.4. Thus, to determine the desired $G_c(s)$ from the polar plot of $T^{-1}G_1(j\omega)$, a value of the maximum input-output magnitude ratio M_p' smaller than the specified value M_p should be selected so that the $G_cG_1^*(j\omega)$ locus of the compensated system may meet the maximum magnitude ratio specification. The selection of M_p' is made on the basis of an estimate of the geometrical relationship between the loci of $T^{-1}G_cG_1(j\omega)$ and $G_cG_1^*(j\omega)$ which may, in turn, be estimated from the geometrical relationship between the polar plots of $T^{-1}G_1(j\omega)$ and $G_1^*(j\omega)$. The latter may be obtained from the z transform $G_1(z)$ by letting z traverse once around the unit circle. As can readily be seen, designing the series equalizer is a trial-and-error process, and thus it depends somewhat upon the designer's experience. The graphical determination of the frequency locus of the desired equalizer is illustrated in Fig. 9.4-2.

In summary, to derive the transfer function $G_c(s)$ of the compensating network required for a specified M_p, the procedure outlined below may be followed.

1. Plot the Nyquist diagrams of $T^{-1}G_1(j\omega)$ and $G_1^*(j\omega)$ for the uncompensated system either from transfer functions or from experimental data.
2. Construct the M circles for $M = M_p$ and $M = M_p'$ respectively, where M_p' is smaller than the specified M_p and can be estimated from the plots of $T^{-1}G_1(j\omega)$ and $G_1^*(j\omega)$.
3. By applying the general procedure for the design of compensating networks for continuous-data control systems,† determine the transfer

† The reader is referred to any standard textbook on elementary linear servo theory.

function $G_c(s)$ of the desired compensator so as to bring the $T^{-1}G_cG_1(j\omega)$ locus tangent to the M'_p circle at the desired frequency. This may be carried out either from the polar plot directly, as demonstrated in Fig. 9.4-2, or with the aid of the Bode-diagram technique, as briefly reviewed in Chap. 2.

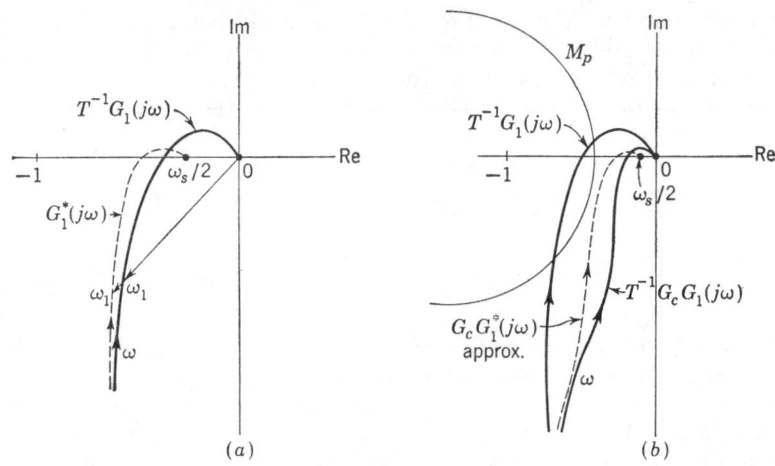

FIG. 9.4-2. (a) Relationship between $T^{-1}G_1(j\omega)$ locus and $G_1^*(j\omega)$ locus; (b) graphical determination of the compensation.

4. By making use of the method described in Sec. 4.4, construct the approximate locus of $G_cG_1^*(j\omega)$ from the $T^{-1}G_cG_1(j\omega)$ locus.

5. If the approximate locus of $G_cG_1^*(j\omega)$ is close to the M_p circle, $G_c(s)$ thus obtained may be satisfactory. To justify this, a final check is made on the above approximation by plotting the exact open-loop frequency characteristic of the compensated system. Since $G_c(s)$ is determined, the z transform $G_cG_1(z)$ associated with $G_c(s)G_1(s)$ can readily be computed by means of the methods described in Sec. 5.2. Then, plot the z-transform locus of $G_cG_1(z)$, which describes the exact open-loop frequency characteristic of the compensated system.

6. If the z-transform locus of $G_cG_1(z)$ is tangent to (or sufficiently close to) the specified M_p circle at the desired frequency, $G_c(s)$ determined in step 3 is considered satisfactory. The z transform $G_cG_1(z)$ is then used to calculate the time-domain performance of the system. However, if the z-transform locus of $G_cG_1(z)$ derived above is not sufficiently close to the desired result and the time-domain performance is not satisfactory, the design of the compensating network must be repeated. A few trials will usually lead to a satisfactory result. It should be pointed out in passing that the M_p criterion is a useful design criterion, only when no hidden oscillation exists in the system output.

EXAMPLE 9.4-1. Consider the unity-feedback error-sampled system of Fig. 9.4-3, which employs a zero-order hold as the smoothing device. The controlled system (or plant) is described by the transfer function

$$G_s(s) = \frac{1.2}{s(1 + 0.5s)} \tag{9.4-13}$$

The sampling period is 1 sec. It is required to design a continuous-data compensator so that the resonant peak of the system is 1.35 and occurs at a frequency around 2.5 radians/sec.

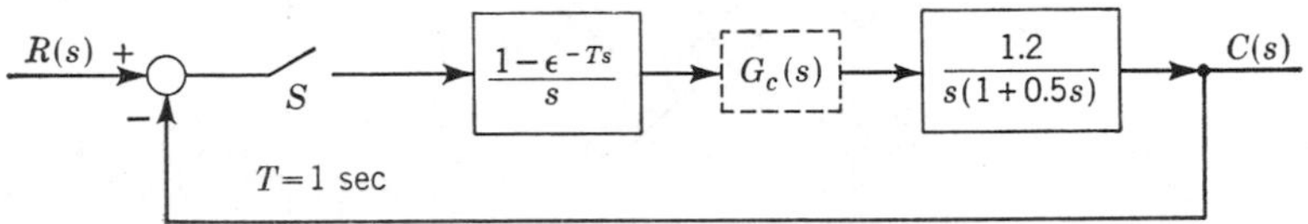

FIG. 9.4-3. The block diagram of the system of Example 9.4-1.

Referring to Fig. 9.4-3, the transfer function of the forward elements of the original system is

$$G_1(s) = G_h(s)G_s(s) = \frac{1.2(1 - \epsilon^{-Ts})}{s^2(1 + 0.5s)} \tag{9.4-14}$$

The Nyquist diagram of $T^{-1}G_1(j\omega)$ is first plotted in curve *a* of Fig. 9.4-4, from which the approximate polar plot of $G_1^*(j\omega)$, curve *b*, is constructed by following the procedures described in Sec. 4.4. As evidenced from these plottings, the original system exhibits a large resonant peak. The $T^{-1}G_1(j\omega)$ plot is then reshaped by a series equalizer with the transfer function given by

$$G_c(s) = \frac{1 + s}{1 + s/15} \tag{9.4-15}$$

The polar plot of $T^{-1}G_1(j\omega)$ is brought to a new location, curve *c* of Fig. 9.4-4, where it is almost tangent to the M circle for an estimated value of $M_p = 1.1$. The determination of the equalizer $G_c(s)$ follows the general procedures for the design of compensating networks for continuous-data control systems. From the polar plot of $T^{-1}G_1G_c(j\omega)$, the approximate polar plot of $G_1G_c^*(j\omega)$ is constructed, as shown in curve *d* of Fig. 9.4-4. It is observed that the approximate polar plot for the compensated system stays outside of the specified M circle, but is close to it. Thus, $G_c(s)$ given by Eq. (9.4-15) is satisfactory. This is substantiated by the *z*-transform locus of $G_1G_c(z)$, which is tangent to the M circle for $M_p = 1.35$ at the desirable frequency, as shown in curve *e*.

b. Dual-rate Sampling Approximation. The previous discussions reveal that the design of a continuous-data compensating network for a sampled-data feedback control system is greatly facilitated, if the starred transfer function is represented by an adequate approximate expression. In the preceding paragraphs, an approximation for $G_cG_1^*(s)$ is derived from the summation expression of Eq. (9.4-9). This approximation is obvious and straightforward provided that the function $G_cG_1(s)$ attenuates rapidly at frequencies higher than half the sampling frequency. Furthermore, based upon the fundamental theorem of sampling described in Sec. 3.5, the starred transfer function may be approximated by another convenient expression which can simplify the procedure of designing the compensating networks for sampled-data control systems. The derivation of this approximation is presented in the following paragraphs.

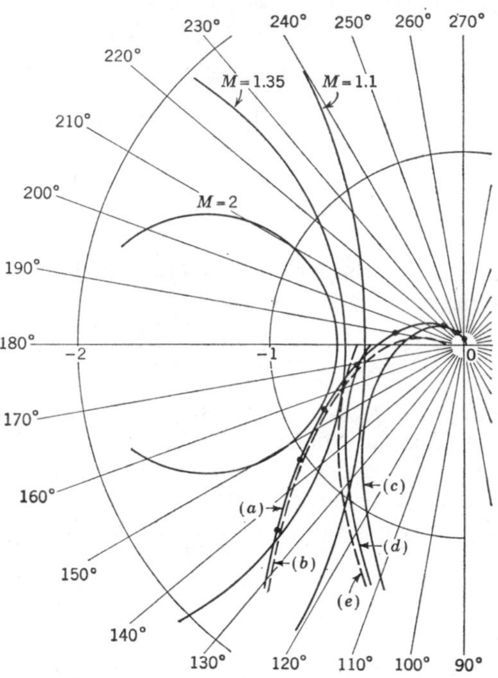

FIG. 9.4-4. Polar plots for Example 9.4-1.

In Sec. 3.5, it is shown that a signal $f(t)$ with bandwidth $\omega_0 = 2\pi f_0$ radians/sec can be reconstructed from its samples taken at a constant rate equal to twice the highest signal frequency f_0, and that the signal $f(t)$ and its samples $f(kT_n)$ are related by Eq. (3.5-15) which, repeated below, is

$$f(t) = \sum_{k=-\infty}^{\infty} f(kT_n) \frac{\sin \omega_0(t - kT_n)}{\omega_0(t - kT_n)} \tag{9.4-16}$$

where the sampling period T_n is equal to π/ω_0. By placing

$$w_s(t) = \frac{\sin \omega_0 t}{\omega_0 t} \tag{9.4-17}$$

one may write Eq. (9.4-16) as

$$f(t) = \sum_{k=-\infty}^{\infty} w_s(t - kT_n) f(kT_n) \tag{9.4-18}$$

Equation (9.4-18) describes a convolution summation which yields the relationship between the continuous output and the sampled input of a network with an impulse response or weighting function $w_s(t)$ given by Eq. (9.4-17). Since the sampled input $f(kT_n)$ is identical to the samples taken from the continuous output, Eq. (9.4-18) implies that the signal $f(t)$ is recovered if it is sampled at a constant rate

$$\frac{1}{T_n} = 2f_0 = \frac{\omega_0}{\pi} \tag{9.4-19}$$

and is then fed into a network with an impulse response $w_s(t)$. This operation is illustrated in Fig. 9.4-5, where the sampling period of the sampler

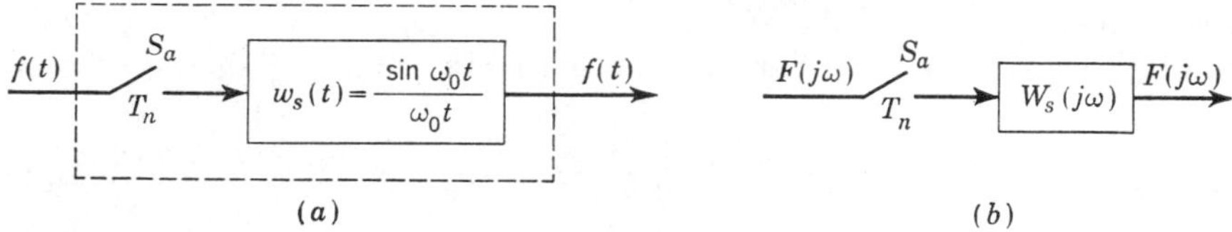

FIG. 9.4-5. Sampled-data representation of a continuous-data function.

is T_n, the input to the system is $f(t)$, and the output is also $f(t)$. It can be shown that the Fourier transform of $w_s(t)$ is

$$W_s(j\omega) = \begin{cases} \pi/\omega_0 & \text{for } -\omega_0 \le \omega \le \omega_0 \\ 0 & \text{otherwise} \end{cases} \tag{9.4-20}$$

The waveforms of $w_s(t)$ and $W_s(j\omega)$ are plotted in Fig. 9.4-6. Clearly, this

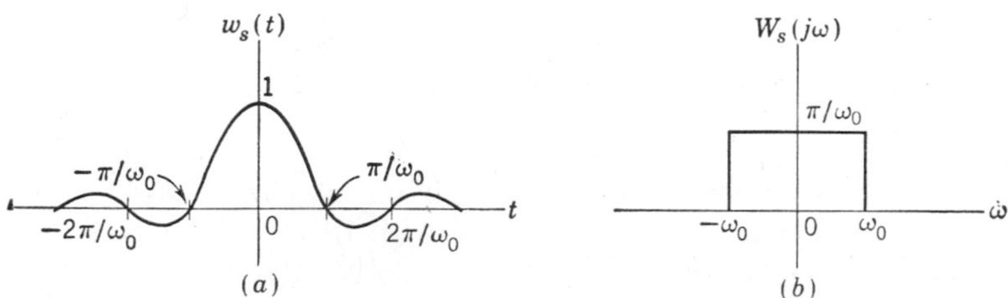

FIG. 9.4-6. The function $(\sin \omega_0 t)/\omega_0 t$ and its Fourier transform.

network offers constant transmission for frequencies less than ω_0 and it cuts off sharply at ω_0.

The above discussion leads to the conclusion that the circuit of Fig. 9.4-5 may be inserted in a control system without causing any disturbance as long as the sampling frequency of the auxiliary sampler S_a is equal to twice the highest frequency of the signal at the point of insertion. Thus, the sampled-data system of Fig. 9.4-7 may be represented by the block diagram of Fig. 9.4-8 in which the transfer functions $G_c(s)$ and $G_s(s)$ are transposed and the circuit of Fig. 9.4-5 is inserted between them. In other words, a single-rate sampled-data feedback control system is converted into an equivalent multirate sampled-data feedback control system. In Fig. 9.4-7, $G_h(s)$, $G_c(s)$, and $G_s(s)$ stand for the transfer functions of the holding device,

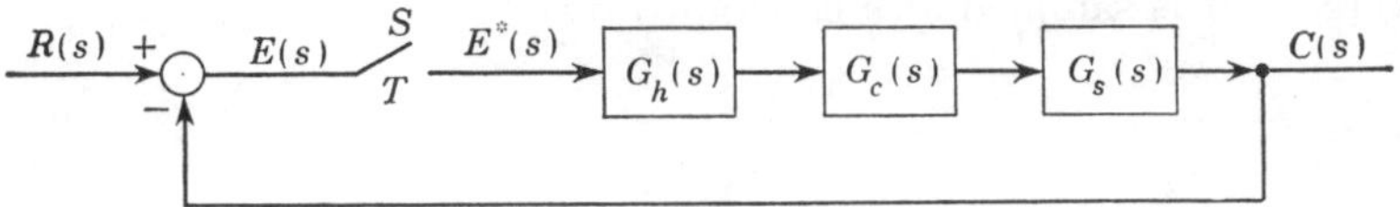

FIG. 9.4-7. A sampled-data feedback control system with cascade compensation.

if any, the compensating network to be designed, and the controlled system, respectively. For the sake of simplicity, it is assumed that T_n be a submultiple of the sampling period T of the main sampler S of the system, that is,

$$T_n = \frac{T}{n} \tag{9.4-21}$$

where n is a positive integer. When the highest frequency component of the signal at the point of insertion of the auxiliary sampler is

$$\omega_0 = \tfrac{1}{2}n\omega_s \tag{9.4-22}$$

the permissible maximum sampling period of the auxiliary sampler is given by Eq. (9.4-21).

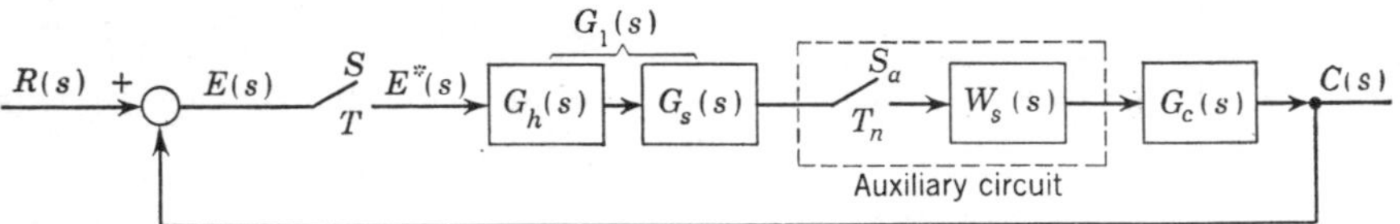

FIG. 9.4-8. The multirate sampled-data feedback control system equivalent to the system of Fig. 9.4-7.

In view of the properties of the hold circuit, as illustrated in Fig. 4.6-6, the components of the actuating signal with frequencies larger than the sampling frequency ω_s of the system are highly attenuated, and thus can be ignored without causing a loss of much accuracy. This allows approximating the bandwidth of the signal at the point of insertion of the multirate sampling circuit by the sampling frequency ω_s. Under this assumption, the frequency ω_0 of Eq. (9.4-17) is given by

$$\omega_0 = \omega_s = \frac{2\pi}{T} \tag{9.4-23}$$

Substitution of Eq. (9.4-23) into Eq. (9.4-19) yields the sampling period of the auxiliary sampler,

$$T_n = \frac{T}{2} \tag{9.4-24}$$

That is, the auxiliary sampler S_a must operate at least twice as fast as the main sampler S of the pulsed-data control system. Thus, the sampled-data feedback system of Fig. 9.4-7 may be approximated by the dual-rate sampled-data feedback system shown in Fig. 9.4-9. The auxiliary sampler

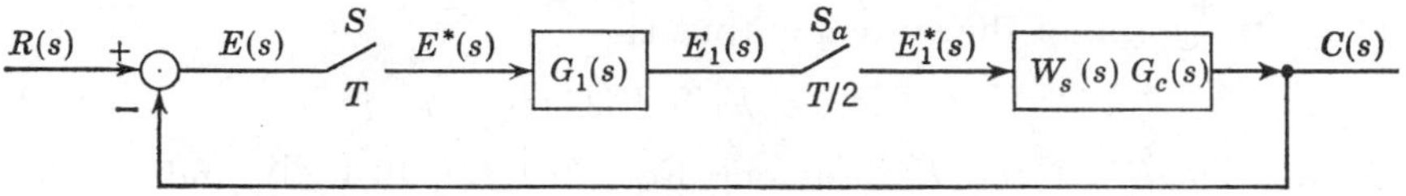

FIG. 9.4-9. The dual-rate-sampling approximation of the system of Fig. 9.4-7.

S_a operates twice as fast as the main sampler S. In fact, the validity of this approximation depends upon the low-pass characteristic of $G_1(j\omega)$. Even though the holding device is not used, this approximation is still valid, provided that $G_s(j\omega)$ of the system cuts off at frequencies below the sampling frequency of the main sampler.

It is shown in the following paragraphs that, on the basis of the dual-rate sampling approximation, one can derive the useful expression of Eq. (9.4-25):

$$G_1G_c^*(s) \approx \tfrac{1}{2}G_c(s)G_1^*(\epsilon^{\frac{1}{2}Ts}) + \tfrac{1}{2}G_c(s - j\omega_s)G_1^*(\epsilon^{\frac{1}{2}T(s-j\omega_s)}) \qquad (9.4\text{-}25a)$$

or the equivalent expression

$$G_1G_c(z) \approx \tfrac{1}{2}G_c(s)G_1(z_2) + \tfrac{1}{2}G_c(s - j\omega_s)G_1(-z_2) \qquad (9.4\text{-}25b)$$

where $z_2^2 = z$, and $G_1^*(\epsilon^{\frac{1}{2}Ts})$ and $G_1(z_2)$ refer to sampling period $T/2$. As a result of this approximation, $G_c(s)$ is freed from the bond of $G_1G_c^*(s)$ and the effect of the series equalizer $G_c(s)$ upon the shape of the open-loop pulse-transfer-function locus becomes almost independent of the parameters of the controlled system, thus making the effect of parameter adjustment of the equalizer easier to visualize and to control.

Reference to the equivalent dual-rate sampled-data system of Fig. 9.4-9 indicates that the actuating error signal is given by

$$E(s) = R(s) - C(s) \qquad (9.4\text{-}26)$$

In terms of the z transforms, Eq. (9.4-26) reduces to

$$E(z) = R(z) - C(z) \qquad (9.4\text{-}27)$$

From Fig. 9.4-9, it is also obtained that

$$E_1(s) = E^*(s)G_1(s) \qquad (9.4\text{-}28)$$

If the z_2 transforms associated with $E_1(s)$ and $G_1(s)$ are $E_1(z_2)$ and $G_1(z_2)$, respectively, then

$$E_1(z_2) = E(z)G_1(z_2) \qquad (9.4\text{-}29)$$

where, by definition,

$$z = \epsilon^{Ts} \qquad (9.4\text{-}30)$$

and

$$z_2 = \epsilon^{Ts/2} \qquad (9.4\text{-}31)$$

Here the z transform of a function refers to a sampling period of T sec; whereas the z_2 transform is the z transform with respect to a sampling period of $T/2$ sec; and z is related to z_2 by

$$z = z_2^2 \tag{9.4-32}$$

The z_2 transform of the system output is

$$C(z_2) = E_1(z_2)W_sG_c(z_2) \tag{9.4-33}$$

Eliminating $E_1(z_2)$ and $E(z_2)$ among Eqs. (9.4-27), (9.4-29), and (9.4-33) yields

$$C(z_2) = [R(z) - C(z)]G_1(z_2)W_sG_c(z_2) \tag{9.4-34}$$

Rearranging Eq. (9.4-34) results in

$$C(z_2) + G_1(z_2)W_sG_c(z_2)C(z) = G_1(z_2)W_sG_c(z_2)R(z) \tag{9.4-35}$$

In view of Eq. (6.7-3), the z_2 transform $C(z_2)$ is given by

$$C(z_2) = \sum_{k=0}^{\infty} c\left(\frac{kT}{2}\right) z_2^{-k} \tag{9.4-36}$$

which expands into

$$C(z_2) = c(0) + c\left(\frac{T}{2}\right) z_2^{-1} + c(T)z_2^{-2} + c\left(\frac{3T}{2}\right) z_2^{-3} + c(2T)z_2^{-4} + \cdots + c\left(\frac{kT}{2}\right) z_2^{-k} + \cdots \tag{9.4-37}$$

Now, with z_2 replaced by $-z_2$, Eq. (9.4-37) reduces to

$$C(-z_2) = c(0) - c\left(\frac{T}{2}\right) z_2^{-1} + c(T)z_2^{-2} - c\left(\frac{3T}{2}\right) z_2^{-3} + c(2T)z_2^{-4} + \cdots + (-1)^k c\left(\frac{kT}{2}\right) z_2^{-k} + \cdots \tag{9.4-38}$$

Summation of Eqs. (9.4-37) and (9.4-38) yields

$$C(z_2) + C(-z_2) = 2[c(0) + c(T)z_2^{-2} + c(2T)z_2^{-4} + \cdots + c(kT)z_2^{-2k} + \cdots] \tag{9.4-39}$$

Substituting Eq. (9.4-32) into Eq. (9.4-39) gives

$$C(z_2) + C(-z_2) = 2[c(0) + c(T)z^{-1} + c(2T)z^{-2} + \cdots + c(kT)z^{-k} + \cdots] = 2\sum_{k=0}^{\infty} c(kT)z^{-k} \tag{9.4-40}$$

Hence, it follows from Eq. (9.4-40) and the definition of the z transform that

$$C(z_2) + C(-z_2) = 2C(z) \tag{9.4-41}$$

This relationship plays an important role in the simplification of Eq. (9.4-35).

Substitution of $-z_2$ for z_2 in Eq. (9.4-35) leads to

$$C(-z_2) + G_1(-z_2)W_sG_c(-z_2)C(z) = G_1(-z_2)W_sG_c(-z_2)R(z) \quad (9.4\text{-}42)$$

It is noted that since $z = z_2^2$, $C(z)$ and $R(z)$ remain unchanged after the above substitution is made. As can be seen, $C(z_2)$ and $C(-z_2)$ are eliminated from Eqs. (9.4-35) and (9.4-42), if their sum is taken and use is made of Eq. (9.4-41). The result is

$$[2 + G_1(z_2)W_sG_c(z_2) + G_1(-z_2)W_sG_c(-z_2)]C(z) = [G_1(z_2)W_sG_c(z_2) + G_1(-z_2)W_sG_c(-z_2)]R(z) \quad (9.4\text{-}43)$$

Thus, the z transforms of the output and the input of the dual-rate sampling representation of the original system are related by

$$C(z) = \frac{\frac{1}{2}[G_1(z_2)W_sG_c(z_2) + G_1(-z_2)W_sG_c(-z_2)]}{1 + \frac{1}{2}[G_1(z_2)W_sG_c(z_2) + G_1(-z_2)W_sG_c(-z_2)]} R(z) \quad (9.4\text{-}44)$$

But, the input-output relationship of the original system with series equalizer $G_c(s)$ shown in Fig. 9.4-7 is found to be

$$C(z) = \frac{G_1G_c(z)}{1 + G_1G_c(z)} R(z) \quad (9.4\text{-}45)$$

where $G_1G_c(z)$ is the z transform associated with $G_1(s)G_c(s)$, and $G_1(s) = G_h(s)G_s(s)$. Equation (9.4-44) gives an approximate representation of the output transform, whereas Eq. (9.4-45) is the exact expression.

Comparing Eq. (9.4-44) with Eq. (9.4-45) results in

$$G_1G_c(z) \approx \tfrac{1}{2}[G_1(z_2)W_sG_c(z_2) + G_1(-z_2)W_sG_c(-z_2)] \quad (9.4\text{-}46)$$

Equation (9.4-46) provides a useful approximation of the z transform associated with $G_1(s)G_c(s)$ of the system of Fig. 9.4-7. Clearly, in evaluating the z transforms, this approximation breaks the tie between G_c of the equalizer, which is to be determined, and G_1 of the hold and the controlled system, which is known. It is this tie which complicates the design of continuous-data compensating networks for sampled-data systems. As a result of the above approximation, the z-transform locus of the pulse-transfer function $G_1G_c(z)$ of the compensated system can then be directly obtained from the z_2-transform locus of the pulse-transfer function $G_1(z_2)$ of the uncompensated system and that of the series equalizer. Apparently, this approximation will lead to simplification in the design of the desired series equalizer. However, the approximation of Eq. (9.4-46) may be further reduced to a simpler expression.

Making use of the definition of the z transform and the Poisson summation rule, one obtains the following identity:

$$W_sG_c(z_2)\big|_{z_2=\epsilon^{Ts/2}} = \frac{1}{T/2} \sum_{k=-\infty}^{\infty} W_s(s + j2k\omega_s)G_c(s + j2k\omega_s) \quad (9.4\text{-}47)$$

The above expression expands into

$$W_sG_c(z_2)|_{z_2=\epsilon^{Ts/2}} = \frac{2}{T}[W_s(s)G_c(s) + W_s(s - j2\omega_s)G_c(s - j2\omega_s) + W_s(s + j2\omega_s)G_c(s + j2\omega_s) + \cdots + W_s(s - j2k\omega_s)G_c(s - j2k\omega_s) + \cdots] \quad (9.4\text{-}48)$$

In the case of the dual-rate sampling approximation, the frequency characteristic of $W_s(j\omega)$, as shown in Fig. 9.4-6b, is described analytically by

$$W_s(j\omega) = \begin{cases} T/2 & \text{for } |\omega| \leq \omega_s \\ 0 & \text{otherwise} \end{cases} \quad (9.4\text{-}49)$$

Equation (9.4-49) leads to the following relationship

$$W_s(s + j2k\omega_s)|_{s=j\omega} = 0 \quad (9.4\text{-}50)$$

for $|\omega| < \omega_s$ and $k \neq 0$. Thus, within the frequency range of interest

$$0 \leq \omega \leq \omega_s/2 \quad (9.4\text{-}51)$$

Eq. (9.4-48) reduces to

$$W_sG_c(z_2)|_{z_2=\epsilon^{Ts/2}} = G_c(s) \quad (9.4\text{-}52)$$

In like manner, one can readily simplify the function $W_sG_c(-z_2)$ of Eq. (9.4-46). By definition,

$$W_sG_c(-z_2)|_{z_2=\epsilon^{Ts/2}} = W_sG_c^*(-\epsilon^{Ts/2}) = W_sG_c^*(\epsilon^{Ts/2}\epsilon^{-j\pi}) \quad (9.4\text{-}53)$$

Since $2\pi/T = \omega_s$, Eq. (9.4-53) may be written as

$$W_sG_c(-z_2)|_{z_2=\epsilon^{Ts/2}} = W_sG_c^*(\epsilon^{\frac{1}{2}T(s-j\omega_s)}) \quad (9.4\text{-}54)$$

Application of the Poisson summation rule yields

$$W_sG_c(-z_2)|_{z_2=\epsilon^{Ts/2}} = \frac{2}{T}\sum_{k=-\infty}^{\infty} W_s(s - j\omega_s + j2k\omega_s)G_c(s - j\omega_s + j2k\omega_s) \quad (9.4\text{-}55)$$

which expands into

$$W_sG_c(-z_2)|_{z_2=\epsilon^{Ts/2}} = \frac{2}{T}[W_s(s - j\omega_s)G_c(s - j\omega_s) + W_s(s + j\omega_s)G_c(s + j\omega_s) + W_s(s - j3\omega_s)G_c(s - j3\omega_s) + W_s(s + j3\omega_s)G_c(s + j3\omega_s) + \cdots + W_s(s + jk\omega_s)G_c(s + jk\omega_s) + \cdots] \quad (9.4\text{-}56)$$

In view of Eq. (9.4-49), within the frequency range $0 \leq \omega \leq \omega_s/2$, it is found that

$$W_s(s + jk\omega_s)|_{s=j\omega} = \begin{cases} \dfrac{T}{2} & \text{for } k = -1 \\ 0 & \text{otherwise} \end{cases} \qquad (9.4\text{-}57)$$

and Eq. (9.4-56) can then be simplified to

$$W_sG_c(-z_2)|_{z_2=\epsilon^{Ts/2}} = G_c(s - j\omega_s) \qquad (9.4\text{-}58)$$

Substituting Eqs. (9.4-52) and (9.4-58) into (9.4-46), therefore, yields the simplified expression of Eq. (9.4-25) which, repeated below, is

$$G_1G_c(z) \approx \tfrac{1}{2}G_1(z_2)G_c(s) + \tfrac{1}{2}G_1(-z_2)G_c(s - j\omega_s) \qquad (9.4\text{-}59)$$

Clearly, this approximation frees $G_c(s)$ from the bond of $G_1G_c(z)$ [or $G_1G_c^*(s)$] so that the design of the desired series equalizer may be carried out in a simpler manner. The first term of the right-hand member of Eq. (9.4-59) is the predominating term which determines the approximate location of the z-transform locus of $G_1G_c(z)$; whereas the second term provides the necessary correction.

A SPECIAL CASE. When the sampling frequency ω_s is greater than twice the bandwidth of $G_1(j\omega)$ at the point of insertion of the auxiliary circuit, as shown in Fig. 9.4-8, the frequency components of the signal higher than half the sampling frequency are of little importance. The highest frequency ω_0 of the significant component of the signal can be assumed to be half the sampling frequency, thus

$$\omega_0 = \frac{\omega_s}{2} \qquad (9.4\text{-}60)$$

From Eqs. (9.4-19) and (9.4-60), the sampling period of the auxiliary sampler S_a is found to be

$$T_n = \frac{2\pi}{\omega_s} = T \qquad (9.4\text{-}61)$$

Consequently, the output transform is related to the input transform by

$$C(z) = \frac{G_1(z)W_sG_c(z)}{1 + G_1(z)W_sG_c(z)} R(z) \qquad (9.4\text{-}62)$$

Comparing Eq. (9.4-62) with Eq. (9.4-45) reveals that if Eq. (9.4-60) is valid one may obtain the approximation

$$G_1G_c(z) \approx G_1(z)W_sG_c(z) \qquad (9.4\text{-}63)$$

Now, by definition,

$$\begin{aligned} W_sG_c(z)|_{z=\epsilon^{Ts}} &= W_sG_c^*(s) \\ &= \frac{1}{T}\sum_{k=-\infty}^{\infty} W_s(s + jk\omega_s)G_c(s + jk\omega_s) \end{aligned} \qquad (9.4\text{-}64)$$

In view of the frequency characteristic of $W_s(j\omega)$,

$$W_s(s)|_{s=j\omega} = \begin{cases} T & \text{for } |\omega| \leq \omega_s/2 \\ 0 & \text{otherwise} \end{cases} \tag{9.4-65}$$

for $|\omega| < \omega_s/2$ and $k \neq 0$

$$W_s(s + jk\omega_s)|_{s=j\omega} = 0 \tag{9.4-66}$$

Consequently, within the frequency range of interest

$$0 \leq \omega \leq \omega_s/2 \tag{9.4-67}$$

Eq. (9.4-64) becomes

$$W_sG_c(z)|_{z=\epsilon^{Ts}} = G_c(s) \tag{9.4-68}$$

and Eq. (9.4-63) is then simplified to

$$G_1G_c(z) \approx G_1(z)G_c(s) \tag{9.4-69}$$

Indeed, by the approximation of Eq. (9.4-69), $G_c(s)$ is freed from the bond of $G_1G_c(z)$, thus facilitating greatly the design of the desired compensating network.

In summary, the above discussions lead to the following conclusions:

1. When the highest frequency of the significant components of the output signal of $G_1(s)$ is equal to (or less than) half the sampling frequency of the main sampler, the sampling frequency of the auxiliary sampler is the same as that of the main sampler, and for the frequency range $0 \leq \omega \leq \omega_s/2$, $G_1G_c(z)$ is approximated by

$$G_1G_c(z) \approx G_1(z)G_c(s) \tag{9.4-70}$$

2. When the highest frequency of the significant components of the output signal of $G_1(s)$ is equal to (or slightly less than) the sampling frequency of the main sampler, the sampling frequency of the auxiliary sampler must be at least twice as large as that of the main sampler—dual-rate sampling approximation (Fig. 9.4-9)—and for the frequency range $0 \leq \omega \leq \omega_s/2$, $G_1G_c(z)$ may be approximated by

$$G_1G_c(z) \approx \tfrac{1}{2}G_c(s)G_1(z_2) + \tfrac{1}{2}G_c(s - j\omega_s)G_1(-z_2) \tag{9.4-71}$$

3. When the highest frequency of the significant components of the output signal of $G_1(s)$ is equal to $n\omega_s/2$, the sampling frequency of the auxiliary sampler must be at least n times that of the main sampler, as shown in Fig. 9.4-8.

9.5. Cascade Compensation by Pulsed-data Networks. In the preceding section, equalization of sampled-data feedback systems by continuous-data networks is discussed. Although equalization by continuous-data networks is a convenient and economical way of improving the performance of sampled-data control systems, direct determination of the transfer function of the desired equalizer is by no means simple. In order to simplify the design procedure, approximation methods are introduced. These approximations overcome the difficulties encountered in the system design, and thus enable the conventional locus-reshaping techniques to be readily applied. On the other hand, as mentioned in Sec. 9.1, compensation of sampled-data control systems can also be accomplished by the use of pulsed-data networks. If pulsed-data networks or devices are employed for system compensation, the conventional locus-reshaping technique may readily be used to determine the pulse-transfer function of the equalizer directly from the z-transform locus of the open-loop pulse-transfer function of the original uncompensated system in much the same manner as continuous-data systems are designed.

With reference to the sampled-data feedback control system of Fig 9.5-1, it is seen that the insertion of a pulsed-data compensating network

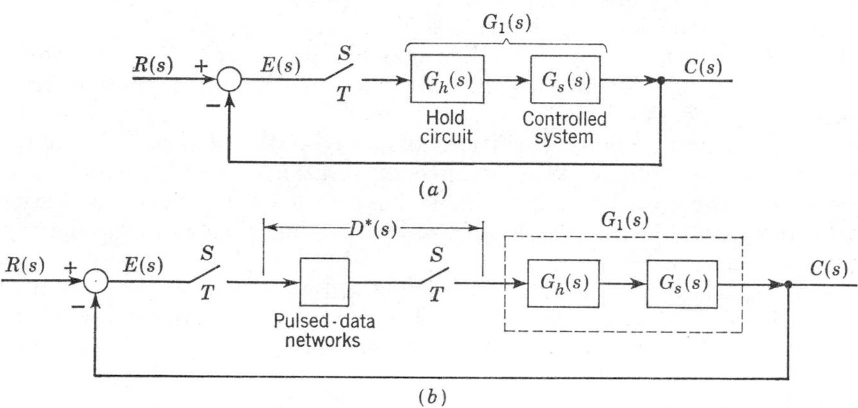

FIG. 9.5-1. (*a*) An error-sampled feedback system; (*b*) a sampled-data system with pulsed-data network compensation.

$D(z)$ or $D^*(s)$ in series with the other components $G_1(s)$ of the system results in a change of the open-loop pulse-transfer function from

$$A_0(z) = G_1(z) \tag{9.5-1}$$

to

$$A_c(z) = D(z)G_1(z) \tag{9.5-2}$$

where $A_0(z)$ and $A_c(z)$ denote the open-loop pulse-transfer functions of the original and the compensated systems respectively, and $G_1(z)$ is the z transform associated with $G_1(s)$. Equation (9.5-2) places in evidence that the z-transform locus of $A_c(z)$ of the compensated system may readily be plotted from the z-transform loci of $G_1(z)$ of the original system and $D(z)$ of the pulsed-data network, and that the effect of the compensating network upon the shape of the z-transform locus of $G_1(z)$, resulting from the adjustment and variation of the poles and zeros of the pulsed-data network, is quite obvious and controllable. Thus, the reshaping of the z-transform locus of $G_1(z)$ is entirely at the command of the designer, and the determination of the desired pulsed-data compensating network is fairly straightforward, although the selection of the desired compensation is still a trial-and-error process. Clearly, the problem of system compensation for sampled-data feedback control systems is quite analogous to that for continuous-data systems. To design the sampled-data feedback control system through locus reshaping by the use of a pulsed-data compensating network, the designer has almost the same freedom to select a realizable pulse-transfer function $D(z)$ of the equalizer, which will lead to a satisfactory system performance, as he does with the design of a continuous-data feedback system through locus reshaping.

The simplicity and ease with which the desired pulsed-data compensating network can be determined make system compensation by pulsed-data networks a desirable alternative to system compensation by continuous-data networks. The determination of the transfer function of the pulsed-data compensating network may be effected by the use of the Nyquist-diagram technique or the method of synthesis through pole-zero configurations. Without modification, however, the Bode-diagram technique is rather difficult to apply. Before entering into the determination of pulsed-data compensating networks, it seems desirable to have a brief discussion of the realizability and stability conditions of pulsed-data networks.[59,149] If the synthesis of a suitable pulsed-data compensating network is to be approached logically, the designer must have at least a surface familiarity with the general characteristics of the transfer functions of most common pulsed-data networks.

A pulsed-data network or device is defined as a system, the output of which is sampled in synchronism with its input at a constant rate. The input and output of a linear pulsed-data network at the sampling instants are related by a transfer function in ϵ^{-Ts} or z^{-1}, which is often referred to

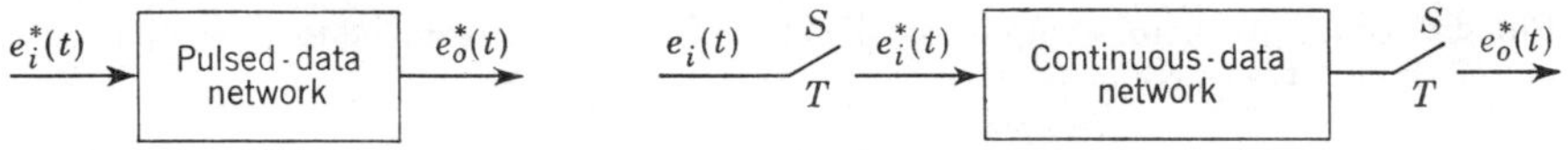

FIG. 9.5-2. Block diagram representation of a pulsed-data network.

as a pulse-transfer function. Shown in Fig. 9.5-2 is the block diagram of a pulsed-data network, the transfer function of which is defined as

$$D^*(s) = \frac{\mathcal{L}\{e_o^*(t)\}}{\mathcal{L}\{e_i^*(t)\}} = \frac{E_o^*(s)}{E_i^*(s)} \tag{9.5-3}$$

or

$$D(z) = \frac{E_o(z)}{E_i(z)} \tag{9.5-4}$$

In view of the fact that the z transforms $E_i(z)$ and $E_o(z)$ are rational functions of z, $D(z)$ may be expressed as the ratio of two polynomials in z^{-1}. Thus, if $D(z)$ contains an equal number of zeros and poles,

$$D(z) = \frac{\sum_{k=0}^{n} a_k z^{-k}}{b_0 + \sum_{k=1}^{n} b_k z^{-k}} \tag{9.5-5a}$$

and if $D(z)$ contains m zeros and n poles,

$$D(z) = \frac{z^{-r} \sum_{k=0}^{m} a_{r+k} z^{-k}}{b_0 + \sum_{k=1}^{n} b_k z^{-k}} \tag{9.5-5b}$$

where $\quad m + r = n$

In fact, Eq. (9.5-5a) is reduced to Eq. (9.5-5b) when $a_k = 0$ for $0 \leq k \leq r$.

A pulsed-data network is said to be physically realizable, if the output signal of the network does not depend upon the future information of the input signal. Cross multiplying Eq. (9.5-5a) yields

$$\left(b_0 + \sum_{k=1}^{n} b_k z^{-k}\right) E_0(z) = \sum_{k=0}^{n} a_k z^{-k} E_i(z) \tag{9.5-6}$$

Taking the inverse z transform of Eq. (9.5-6) term by term gives the difference equation as

$$b_0 e_0^*(t) + \sum_{k=1}^{n} b_k e_0^*(t - kT) = \sum_{k=0}^{n} a_k e_i^*(t - kT) \tag{9.5-7}$$

The output signal of the pulsed-data network is then given by

$$e_0^*(t) = \frac{a_0 e_i^*(t) + \sum_{k=1}^{n} a_k e_i^*(t - kT) - \sum_{k=1}^{n} b_k e_0^*(t - kT)}{b_0} \tag{9.5-8}$$

Equation (9.5-8) implies that if

$$b_0 \neq 0 \tag{9.5-9}$$

the output signal $e_0^*(t)$ is dependent upon the present information of the input $a_0 e_i^*(t)$, and the past (or stored) information of the input $\sum_{k=1}^{n} a_k e_i^*(t - kT)$ and the output $\sum_{k=1}^{n} b_k e_0^*(t - kT)$. Thus, under the condition of Eq. (9.5-9), the output of the pulsed-data network can be computed. Accordingly, this network is physically realizable. On the other hand, if $b_0 = 0$, Eq. (9.5-7) becomes

$$b_1 e_0^*(t - T) + \sum_{k=2}^{n} b_k e_0^*(t - kT) = \sum_{k=0}^{n} a_k e_i^*(t - kT) \tag{9.5-10}$$

which leads to

$$e_0^*(t - T) = \frac{a_0 e_i^*(t) + \sum_{k=1}^{n} a_k e_i^*(t - kT) - \sum_{k=2}^{n} b_k e_0^*(t - kT)}{b_1} \tag{9.5-11}$$

Equation (9.5-11) implies that the output signal $e_0^*(t - T)$ depends not only upon the present information of the input signal and the past information of the input and the output signal but also upon the future information of the input signal $a_0e_i^*(t)$ which is, unfortunately, unknown at the time of computing the output signal. $e_0^*(t - T)$ of Eq. (9.5-11) is indeterminate; and the corresponding pulsed-data network is thus not realizable.

Consequently, the necessary and sufficient condition for the pulse-transfer function of Eq. (9.5-5) to be physically realizable is that *the coefficient b_0 must not be zero,* as given in Eq. (9.5-9). Furthermore, the pulse-transfer function $D(z)$ may be expressed as the ratio of two polynomials in z. In case $D(z)$ is so described, the realizability condition reads: The pulse-transfer function $D(z)$ is physically realizable provided that $D(z)$ *contains no more zeros than poles.* However, in either expressions of $D(z)$, the above statements of the realizability condition of a pulse-transfer function may also be restated as follows: *The Laurent series expansion of $D(z)$ about the origin must contain no positive powers of z.*

The stability of a pulsed-data network may be studied in terms of either the variable s or z. In terms of the variable s, stability is indicated by the absence of poles of $D^*(s)$ in the right half of the s plane and on the imaginary axis, with the exception of a single pole at the origin, as discussed in Sec. 6.2. This can be determined graphically from the polar plot of $D^*(j\omega)$ [or the z-transform locus of $D(z)$]. The stability condition requires that the polar plot (or Nyquist diagram) of $D^*(j\omega)$ makes no encirclement of the origin. Moreover, the distance by which the polar plot avoids the origin is an indication of the relative stability. In terms of the variable z, stability is determined by the absence of poles of $D(z)$ outside and on the unit circle of the z plane. These poles can be detected by making use of the Schur-Cohn criterion described in Sec. 6.2. A pulsed-data network is said to be stable if the magnitudes of the poles of $D(z)$ are less than unity, with the exception of a single pole at $z = 1$. The radial distances from the poles to the unit circle provide an indication of relative stability. The zeros of $D(z)$ may reside outside the unit circle, but they usually give rise to an unsatisfactory result.

Furthermore, the stability of a pulsed-data network may be interpreted in the time domain. As an illustration, consider the sampled-data network with transfer function given by

$$D(z) = \frac{E_0(z)}{E_i(z)} = \frac{1}{b_0 - b_1z^{-1}} \tag{9.5-12}$$

which has a pole at b_1/b_0. Cross multiplying and taking the inverse transform yield

$$e_0^*(t) = \frac{1}{b_0}\,e_i^*(t) + \frac{b_1}{b_0}\,e_0^*(t - T) \tag{9.5-13}$$

Now, if the input $e_i^*(t)$ is a single equivalent impulse of unit strength at one sampling instant, the output $e_0^*(t)$ will be $1/b_0$ at this instant. But at the next sampling instant, the output sample will be b_1/b_0^2, and at the following sampling instants, the output samples will be $(b_1/b_0)^2/b_0$, $(b_1/b_0)^3/b_0$, $(b_1/b_0)^4/b_0$, . . . , successively. In fact, these values of the output samples form the weighting sequence of the pulsed-data network, which may be obtained from Eq. (9.5-12) if $D(z)$ is expanded in an infinite series in z^{-1}. Thus, by long division, Eq. (9.5-12) reduces to

$$E_0(z) = \frac{1}{b_0}\left[1 + \frac{b_1}{b_0}z^{-1} + \left(\frac{b_1}{b_0}\right)^2 z^{-2} + \cdots + \left(\frac{b_1}{b_0}\right)^k z^{-k} + \cdots\right] E_i(z) \tag{9.5-14}$$

Taking the inverse transform of Eq. (9.5-14) term by term yields

$$e_0^*(t) = \frac{1}{b_0}\left[e_i^*(t) + \frac{b_1}{b_0} e_i^*(t - T) + \left(\frac{b_1}{b_0}\right)^2 e_i^*(t - 2T) + \cdots + \left(\frac{b_1}{b_0}\right)^k e_i^*(t - kT) + \cdots\right] \tag{9.5-15}$$

For a unit impulse input $e_i^*(t) = \delta(t)$, and the output is then given by

$$e_0^*(t) = \frac{1}{b_0}\left[\delta(t) + \frac{b_1}{b_0}\delta(t - T) + \left(\frac{b_1}{b_0}\right)^2 \delta(t - 2T) + \cdots + \left(\frac{b_1}{b_0}\right)^k \delta(t - kT) + \cdots\right] \tag{9.5-16}$$

It is clear that the output sample at the kth sampling instant is

$$e_0(kT) = \frac{1}{b_0}\left(\frac{b_1}{b_0}\right)^k \tag{9.5-17}$$

Consequently, if

$$\left|\frac{b_1}{b_0}\right| > 1 \tag{9.5-18}$$

the output samples increase in magnitude indefinitely, and the pulsed-data network is unstable. It is readily seen that if

$$\frac{b_1}{b_0} = -1 \tag{9.5-19}$$

the output samples will be $1/b_0$ and $-1/b_0$ alternatively. This corresponds to a sustained oscillation, and the pulsed-data network is considered unstable. On the other hand, if

$$\left|\frac{b_1}{b_0}\right| < 1 \tag{9.5-20}$$

the output samples will diminish to zero, and if

$$\frac{b_1}{b_0} = 1 \tag{9.5-21}$$

the output samples will reach a constant value $1/b_0$ in the steady state. Thus, if Eq. (9.5-20) or Eq. (9.5-21) holds, this pulsed-data network is stable.

The design of sampled-data feedback control system is fundamentally concerned with the selection of a suitable compensating network $D(z)$, which will lead to a satisfactory system performance. Shown in Fig. 9.5-3 is the z-transform locus of $G_1(z)$ of a unity-feedback error-sampled system (Fig. 9.5-1a). It is assumed that all the poles of $G_1(z)$ lie inside the unit circle of the z plane, except possibly a simple pole at $z = 1$. An examination

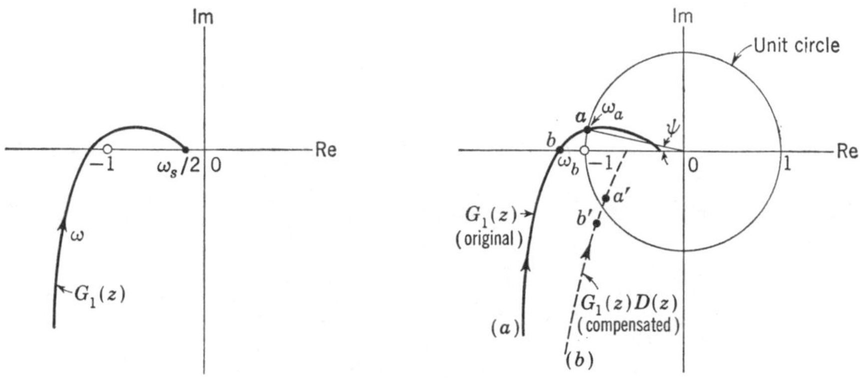

FIG. 9.5-3. The z-transform locus of $G_1(z)$.

FIG. 9.5-4. Reshaping of the z-transform locus.

of the frequency plot of Fig. 9.5-3 reveals that the system is unstable because of the encirclement of the critical point $(-1 + j0)$. To secure system stability it is necessary that the z-transform locus be reshaped so as to avoid the encirclement of the critical point. Clearly, a phase-lead network can accomplish this objective. The reshaping of the locus is illustrated in Fig. 9.5-4. Curve a describes the original system, and curve b, the z-transform locus of $G_1(z)D(z)$, represents the compensated system. The original locus is reshaped by the insertion of a pulsed-data network

$$D(z) = \frac{z - \alpha_1}{z + \beta_1} \tag{9.5-22}$$

The compensating network $D(z)$ shifts point a to a', point b to b', and curve a of the original system to curve b of the compensated system. Point a is the intersection between the original locus and the unit circle, and point b is the first crossover point of the original locus on the real axis of the complex plane. In order to make this system stable, it is necessary that the phase angle of vector $0a$ be advanced through an angle greater than ψ, which is the angle between vector $0a$ and the negative real axis. This increase in phase shift is derived from the pulsed-data network $D(z)$. Let the phase shift of $D(z)$ at frequency ω be ϕ. Then ϕ is given by the angle subtended by the zero α_1 and the pole β_1 at a point on the unit circle corresponding to frequency ω or position angle θ, as shown in Fig. 9.5-5. The frequency and the position angle are related by

$$\theta = \omega T \tag{9.5-23}$$

where T is the sampling period of the system. It is pointed out in passing that convenience generally results if, instead of the frequency ω, the position angle θ of the z plane is considered as the parameter in plotting the z-transform locus, and various values of θ are labeled on the plot. As evidenced in Fig. 9.5-4, if at the frequency ω_a or the position angle $\theta_a = \omega_a T$ the pulsed-data network $D(z)$ has a phase shift ϕ_a larger than the angle ψ of the vector $0a$ and a gain (or amplitude ratio) g_a less than unity, the z-transform locus of the compensated system will not encircle the critical point and the system becomes stable. Furthermore, the degree of stability can be increased with an increase in the phase angle ϕ_a of $D(z)$ at the position angle θ_a. The value of ϕ_a is closely related to the locations of the zero α_1 and the pole β_1, and can be increased by increasing the distance between the zero and the pole. Thus, when ψ and ω_a are obtained from the z-transform locus of the original system and a value of the desired ϕ_a is selected, the values of α_1 and β_1 are readily determined.

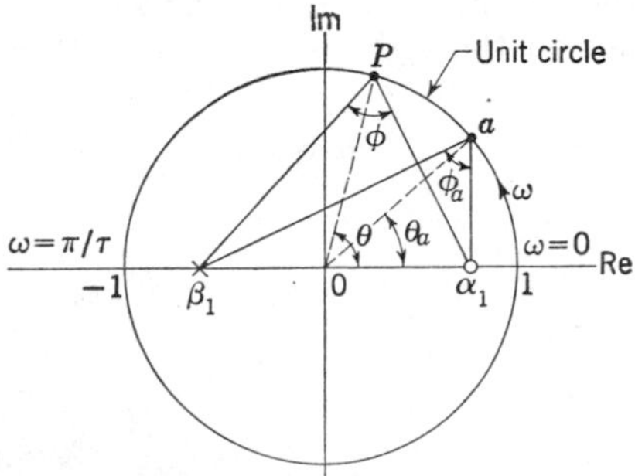

FIG. 9.5-5. The pole-zero distribution and the phase shift of $D(z) = (z - \alpha_1)/(z + \beta_1)$.

The locus-reshaping process in sampled-data feedback control systems is no more complicated than that in continuous-data systems. Both of them involve the selection of the desired equalizer by a trial-and-error process. Nevertheless, the design of a sampled-data compensation may be simplified if use is made of the close relationship between the gain and phase of the pulsed-data network and the location of its poles and zeros. The transfer function of a pulsed-data compensating network normally comprises several poles and zeros inside the unit circle of the z plane. Although complex poles and zeros may be assigned to the pulsed-data network, it generally complicates the computation. A pulsed-data compensating network with real poles and real zeros can be described by the transfer function

$$D_c(z) = \frac{K(z - \alpha_1)(z - \alpha_2) \cdots (z - \alpha_m)}{(z + \beta_1)(z + \beta_2) \cdots (z + \beta_n)} \qquad m \leq n \tag{9.5-24}$$

of which
$$D(z) = \frac{z - \alpha_1}{z + \beta_1} \tag{9.5-25}$$

is a basic form. The pole-zero configuration of Eq. (9.5-25) is given in Fig

9.5-5. A basic pulsed-data network with the zero in the right half and the pole in the left half of the unit circle provides a phase lead within the frequency range $0 < \omega < \omega_s/2$, as evidenced in Fig. 9.5-5. On the other hand, a basic network with the zero in the left half and the pole in the right half of the unit circle provides a phase lag for the frequency range $0 < \omega < \omega_s/2$. In general, a basic pulsed-data network having a zero and a pole in its transfer function is of the phase-lead type, if the pole lies to the left of the zero; on the other hand, it is of the phase-lag type, if the pole lies to the right of the zero. Shown in Fig. 9.5-6 are the pulse-transfer

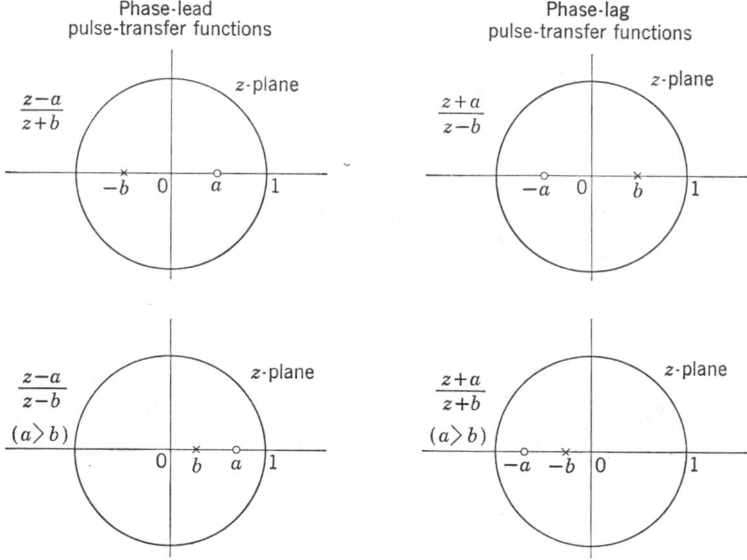

Fig. 9.5-6. Pole-zero configurations of several simple phase-lead and phase-lag pulse-transfer functions.

functions and the corresponding pole-zero configurations of several basic pulsed-data networks. From Fig. 9.5-6, it is apparent that more phase lead is obtainable from a simple pulsed-data network provided that its zero is placed in the right half and its pole in the left half of the unit circle. Thus, if phase lead is required for system compensation, as the case shown in Fig. 9.5-4, a pulsed-data compensating network with zeros in the right half and poles in the left half of the unit circle and with equal number of zeros and poles seems preferable.

The transfer function of Eq. (9.5-25) may be split into two parts as

$$D(z) = D_1(z)D_2(z) \tag{9.5-26}$$

where

$$D_1(z) = \frac{z - \alpha_1}{z} = 1 - \alpha_1 z^{-1} \tag{9.5-27}$$

and
$$D_2(z) = \frac{z}{z + \beta_1} = \frac{1}{1 + \beta_1 z^{-1}} \tag{9.5-28}$$

The pole-zero configurations of $D_1(z)$ and $D_2(z)$ are illustrated in Fig. 9.5-7. At point P on the unit circle corresponding to frequency ω and position angle θ, the phase shift of $D_1(z)$ is measured by the angle ϕ_1 subtended by the zero at α_1 and the pole at the origin, and the phase shift of $D_2(z)$ is measured by the angle ϕ_2 subtended by the pole at $-\beta_1$ and the zero at the origin. Evidently, the phase shift of $D(z)$ at this frequency is given by

$$\phi = \phi_1 + \phi_2 \tag{9.5-29}$$

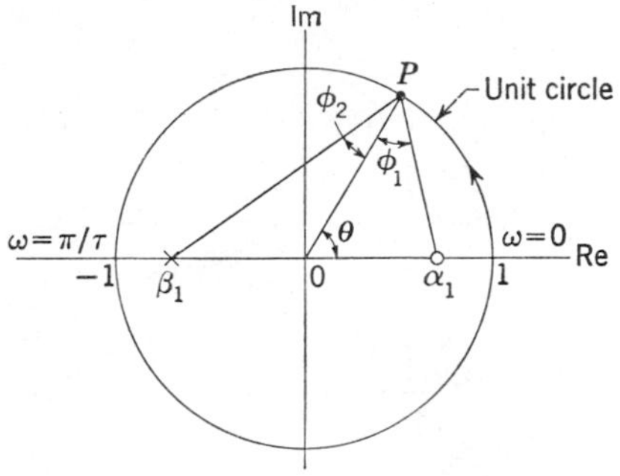

FIG. 9.5-7. Phase shifts of $D_1(z) = (z - \alpha_1)/z$ and $D_2(z) = z/(z + \beta_1)$.

From Fig. 9.5-7, it is seen that the amplitude ratios (or gain) of $D_1(z)$ and $D_2(z)$ corresponding to this frequency are

$$g_1 = \frac{P\alpha_1}{P0} \tag{9.5-30}$$

and
$$g_2 = \frac{P0}{P\beta_1} \tag{9.5-31}$$

respectively. The gain of $D(z)$ at this frequency is then given by

$$g = \frac{P\alpha_1}{P\beta_1} = \frac{g_1}{g_2} \tag{9.5-32}$$

Consequently, once the gain and phase of $D_1(z)$ and $D_2(z)$ are known, the gain and phase of $D(z)$ can easily be computed from Eqs. (9.5-29) and (9.5-32). Because of the simplicity in form of $D_1(z)$ and $D_2(z)$, the relationship between the gain and phase of $D_1(z)$ and its zero α_1 can be geometrically determined in a simple manner. So can the relationship between the gain and phase of $D_2(z)$ and its pole β_1. In view of Eqs. (9.5-29) and (9.5-32), the determination of the desired pulsed-data compensating network $D(z)$ is facilitated, if the charts relating the phase and gain of $D_1(z)$ and $D_2(z)$ to their zeros and poles are made available.[112] These phase and gain charts are plotted in Fig. 9.5-8 and Fig. 9.5-9 respectively. The phase chart is the plot of phase ϕ_1 (or ϕ_2) versus the position angle θ with the zero α_1 (or the pole β_1) as a parameter. By making use of these charts, the designer will find that the determination of the zero α_1 and pole-β_1 of the desired pulsed-data network $D(z)$ from estimated values of ϕ at various frequencies (or position angles) is a simple matter. While the design of an equalizer is a "cut-and-try" process, with the aid of these design charts a considerable

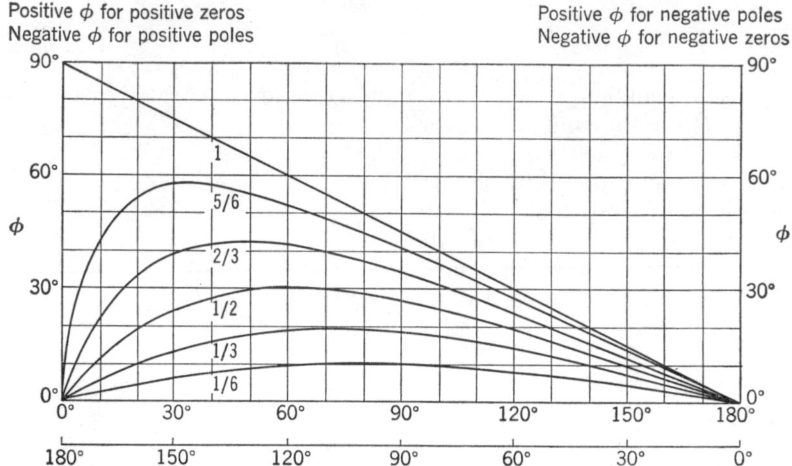

FIG. 9.5-8. The phase-shift charts for real zeros and poles.

amount of labor can be saved in performing the necessary computations. In fact, the charts narrow down the scope of trials and thus enable the designer to obtain a satisfactory solution in a quick manner.

From Fig. 9.5-8, it is evident that zeros located in the right half of the unit circle give rise to phase-lead characteristics, whereas zeros located in the left half give rise to phase-lag characteristics. The converse is true

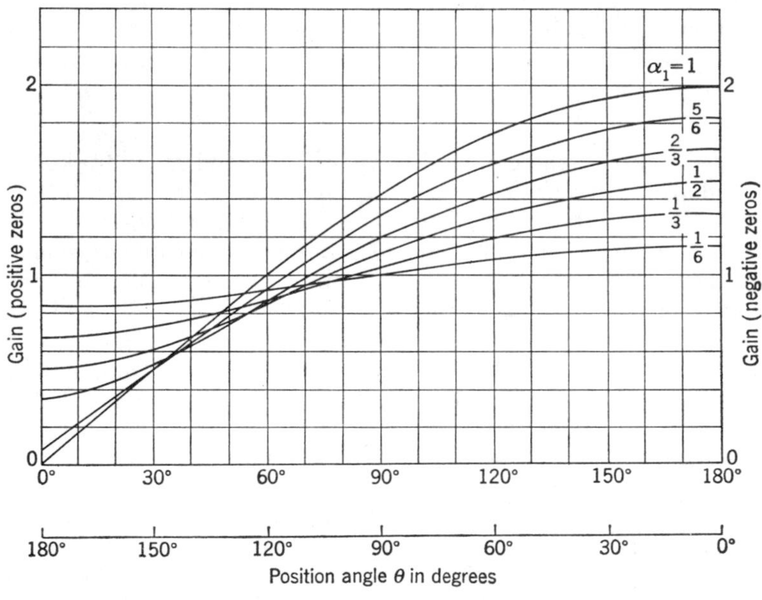

FIG. 9.5-9a.

when poles are being considered. Moreover, within the frequency range $0 < \omega < \omega_s/4$, positive zeros can provide large phase lead, and negative poles, small phase lead. But, within the frequency range $\omega_s/4 < \omega < \omega_s/2$, positive zeros can provide only small phase lead and negative poles, large phase lead. The gain characteristics plotted in Fig. 9.5-9 indicate that for

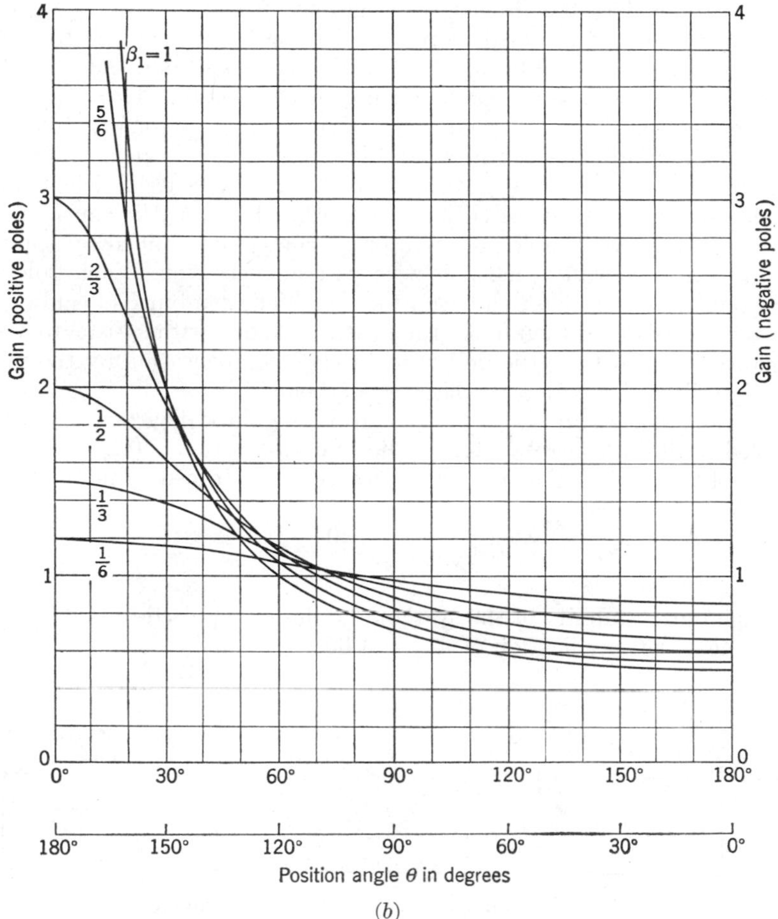

(b)

Fig. 9.5-9. (a) The gain charts for positive and negative zeros; (b) the gain charts for positive and negative poles.

positive zeros and negative poles the gain is less than unity within the frequency range $0 < \omega < \omega_s/4$, and it is larger than unity within the frequency range $\omega_s/4 < \omega < \omega_s/2$, whereas for negative zeros and positive poles the gain exceeds unity within the frequency range $0 < \omega < \omega_s/4$, and it is less than unity within the frequency range $\omega_s/4 < \omega < \omega_s/2$. Thus, the selection of the zeros and poles of the desired pulsed-data network depends upon the frequency range within which the original locus should be adequately reshaped. The application of these charts is quite simple. For instance, at a given position angle θ_a (or frequency $\omega_a = \theta_a/T$), the values of the zero and pole of a simple pulsed-data network, required for introducing an additional phase advance of ϕ_a, can be read off from the phase and gain charts. In the process of determining α_1 and β_1, special attention is paid to the frequency range within which the original locus is in the vicinity of the critical point $(-1 + j0)$, such as the frequency range from ω_b to ω_a of Fig. 9.5-4. The simple pulsed-data network thus determined will shift the locus to an improved location. However, if the performance specifications, such as relative stability, resonant frequency, etc., cannot be fulfilled by the introduction of a simple pulsed-data network, more elaborate compensating networks have to be used. The transfer function of an elaborate pulsed-data network, which may be considered as consisting of several simple pole-zero pairs, can be determined by applying the above procedure to each pole-zero pair in succession. Each pole-zero pair would shift the locus to a better location. The combined effect of these pole-zero pairs would then make the system respond with satisfactory performance. To illustrate the design of cascade compensation by the procedure described above an example is given below.

EXAMPLE 9.5-1. Shown in Fig. 9.5-10 is the block diagram of an error-sampled feedback control system. The sampling period is 0.1 sec. A zero-order hold is used as the smoothing device. The transfer function of the controlled system is

$$G_s(s) = \frac{30}{s(1 + 0.1s)} \tag{9.5-33}$$

Investigate the stability of the system and design a pulsed-data compensator to meet the specification of $M_p = 1.35$.

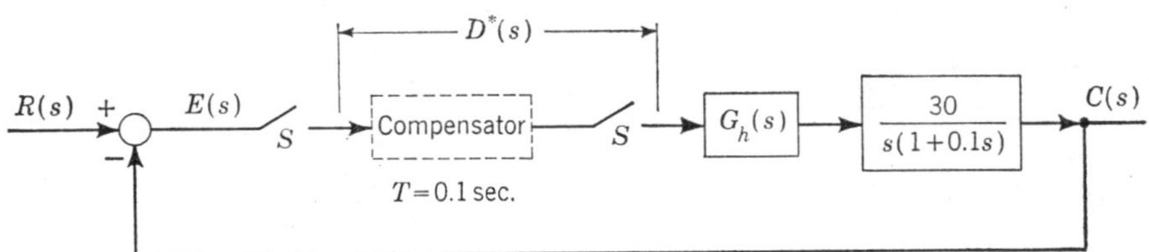

FIG. 9.5-10. Block diagram of the system of Example 9.5-1.

Referring to Fig. 9.5-10, it is seen that the original forward transfer function is

$$G(s) = \frac{30(1 - \epsilon^{-Ts})}{s^2(1 + 0.1s)} \tag{9.5-34}$$

The z transform associated with $G(s)$ is found to be

$$G(z) = \frac{1.104(z + 0.718)}{(z - 1)(z - 0.368)} \tag{9.5-35}$$

Since the given system is of unity feedback, Eq. (9.5-35) also describes the open-loop pulse-transfer function of the system. To investigate the system stability, the z-transform locus of $G(z)$ is plotted in Fig. 9.5-11 (curve I). From this plot it is noted that the locus crosses the unit circle at a frequency of 15 radians/sec and the phase margin is about $-7.5°$. Evidently, this system is unstable.

In order to fulfill the specification, the locus must be reshaped by a compensator. Examination of the z-transform locus reveals that a phase shift ϕ of about 50° is needed to satisfy the M_p specification. By looking at the phase and gain charts shown in Figs. 9.5-8 and 9, it is found that a pulsed-data compensator with a zero at 0.5 and a pole at -0.5 may provide the required phase shift. From the charts it is obtained that at the frequency $\omega = 15$ radians/sec or the position angle $\theta = \omega T = 1.5$ radians or 86°, this compensator has a phase shift of 54° and a gain of 0.93. As a first trial, choose the pulse-transfer function of the compensator as

$$D_1(z) = \frac{z - 0.5}{z + 0.5} \tag{9.5-36}$$

The gain and phase of $D_1(z)$ at various position angles can readily be read from the design charts. By adding the phase shifts of $D_1(z)$ and multiplying the gains of $D_1(z)$ to the corresponding points of the z-transform locus of

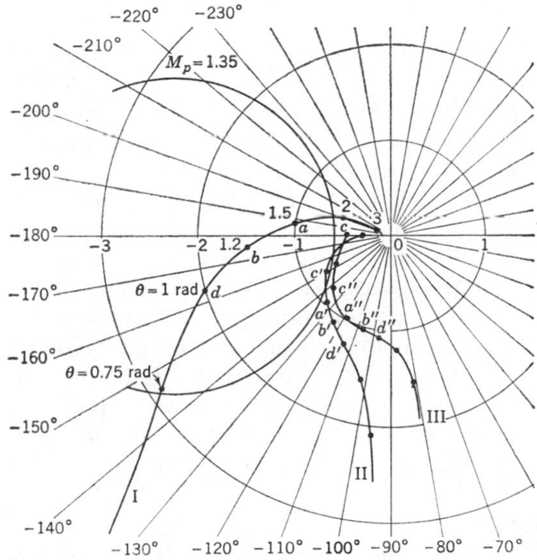

FIG. 9.5-11. Polar plots of the original and the compensated system of Example 9.5-1.

$G(z)$ (curve I), the z-transform locus of $G(z)D_1(z)$ is obtained, which is plotted as curve II of Fig. 9.5-11. It is seen that the given system is stabilized by the introduction of the compensator $D_1(z)$. However, the M_p

specification is not quite satisfied yet. Clearly, either a different pulse-transfer function other than that given by Eq. (9.5-36) must be chosen, which will provide sufficient compensation, or another pulsed-data compensator must be inserted in tandem with $D_1(z)$ in order to meet the requirement.

Examination of the design charts reveals that a pulsed-data compensator having the transfer function given by

$$D_2(z) = \frac{z - 0.333}{z} \tag{9.5-37}$$

may be able to shift curve II to a desirable location, when it is connected in cascade with the compensator $D_1(z)$. In choosing the desirable pulse-transfer function from the gain and phase charts, past experience and familiarity with the charts are always of great help. The gain and phase of $D_2(z)$ at various position angles can easily be read from the design charts. By adding the phase shifts of $D_2(z)$ and multiplying the gain of $D_2(z)$ to the corresponding points of the z-transform locus of $G(z)D_1(z)$ (curve II), the z-transform locus of $G(z)D_1(z)D_2(z)$ is derived, which is plotted as curve III of Fig. 9.5-11. It is observed that the new locus meets the requirement of $M_p = 1.35$. Consequently, the pulse-transfer function of the compensator recommended is

$$D(z) = D_1(z)D_2(z) = \frac{(z - 0.5)(z - 0.333)}{z(z + 0.5)} \tag{9.5-38}$$

The realization of pulse-transfer functions is discussed in detail in the following section.

9.6. Realization of Pulse-transfer Functions. The realization of a pulse-transfer function is primarily concerned with the determination of a pulsed-data network or device which will yield the specified pulse-transfer function relating the output to the input. There are three fundamental approaches by which pulse-transfer functions can be synthesized.

1. Digital programming. The pulse-transfer function can be realized by a digital program, when the control system comprises a digital computer. By designing an appropriate program for the computer, the function of a specified pulse-transfer function is then performed by the computer.

2. Delay-line networks. The pulse-transfer function can be realized by a delay-line network, sometimes referred to as a pulsed-data processing unit, through the use of delay elements, potentiometers, and summing amplifiers, if a digital computer is not available or not economically feasible.

3. Pulsed-data RC networks. The pulse-transfer function can also be realized by a pulsed-data network consisting of resistors and capacitors. Inductors are avoided, because in the usual frequency range of digital and sampled-data control systems, the sizes and weights of the required inductors would be prohibitive and the losses would be excessive. Pulsed-data RC networks have the advantages of simplicity in structure and economy in implementation.

Of these three schemes, the first one is often used when the control system involves a digital computer. Realization by digital programming is relatively simple. The second scheme has the advantage of flexibility in parameter adjustment and is used when the coefficients of the pulse-transfer function require independent control. The third one is quite simple and economical though less flexible. These techniques for synthesizing pulse-transfer functions are discussed in this section.

Digital Programming. Digital programming implies the preparation of a problem for a digital computer by putting it in a form which the computer can understand and then entering this program into the computer storage unit. A problem to be solved by a digital computer must be expressed in mathematical terms that the computer can work with. In control systems utilizing a digital computer, the method of realizing a pulse-transfer function by a digital program offers the advantage of simplicity, convenience, and flexibility. The program realization can generally be carried out by means of three different methods:[59] (1) *direct programming,* (2) *iterative programming,* and (3) *parallel programming.*

A physically realizable pulse-transfer function $D(z)$ containing m zeros and n poles can be expressed in the general form

$$D(z) = \frac{E_0(z)}{E_i(z)} = \frac{z^{-r}(a_r + a_{r+1}z^{-1} + \cdots + a_{r+m}z^{-m})}{1 + b_1z^{-1} + b_2z^{-2} + \cdots + b_nz^{-n}} \tag{9.6-1a}$$

where $m + r = n$. In case $r = 0$ and $m = n$, Eq. (9.6-1a) reduces to

$$D(z) = \frac{E_0(z)}{E_i(z)} = \frac{a_0 + a_1z^{-1} + a_2z^{-2} + \cdots + a_nz^{-n}}{1 + b_1z^{-1} + b_2z^{-2} + \cdots + b_nz^{-n}} \tag{9.6-1b}$$

The processed signal $e_0^*(t) = \mathfrak{z}^{-1}\{E_0(z)\}$ is to be evaluated by the digital computer. Cross multiplying Eq. (9.6-1a) and taking the inverse-transform yields

$$e_0^*(t) = \sum_{k=r}^{m+r} a_ke_i^*(t - kT) - \sum_{k=1}^{n} b_ke_0^*(t - kT) \tag{9.6-2a}$$

Applying similar operations to Eq. (9.6-1b) leads to

$$e_0^*(t) = \sum_{k=0}^{n} a_ke_i^*(t - kT) - \sum_{k=1}^{n} b_ke_0^*(t - kT) \tag{9.6-2b}$$

The above two difference equations describing the processed output signal are referred to as the programming functions. Equation (9.6-2) is essentially a form of numerical quadrature formula, which is often used in numerical analysis. The computations involved in Eq. (9.6-2a) and Eq. (9.6-2b) can readily be performed by a conventional digital computer. Clearly, the program that solves Eq. (9.6-2a) involves the arithmetical operations of addition, subtraction, multiplication, and storage transfer. Since the right-hand member of Eq. (9.6-2a) contains $(m + n + 1)$ terms, $(m + n)$ additions and subtractions and $(m + n + 1)$ multiplications are required. The operations of addition, subtraction, and multiplication are repeated in every sampling period, but not with the same data. The storage transfer operations of the program bring the data up to date. The sample $e_i^*(t)$ of the present computation becomes $e_i^*(t - T)$ in the next computation. Thus, the present sample $e_i^*(t)$ must be entered into the storage location associated with $e_i^*(t - T)$. Similar manipulations take account of the aging of other input and output data, and these manipulations are accomplished by means of the storage transfer operations. Examination of Eq. (9.6-2*a*) also indicates that $(m + n)$ transfers are required in the program. In fact, most conventional digital computers are capable of performing these operations. The realization of a digital program based upon Eq. (9.6-2) is referred to as *direct programming.*

A physically realizable pulse-transfer function $D(z)$ containing m real and simple zeros and n real and simple poles can be written in factored form as

$$D(z) = \frac{E_0(z)}{E_i(z)} = \frac{K(z + z_1)(z + z_2)(z + z_3) \cdots (z + z_m)}{(z + p_1)(z + p_2)(z + p_3) \cdots (z + p_n)} \tag{9.6-3}$$

For $m < n$, Eq. (9.6-3) may be factorized as

$$D(z) = \frac{z + z_1}{z + p_1}\frac{z + z_2}{z + p_2}\frac{z + z_3}{z + p_3} \cdots \frac{z + z_m}{z + p_m}\frac{1}{z + p_{m+1}} \cdots \frac{K}{z + p_n} \tag{9.6-4}$$

$$= D_1(z)D_2(z)D_3(z) \cdots D_m(z)D_{m+1}(z) \cdots D_n(z) \tag{9.6-5}$$

where

$$D_1(z) = \frac{E_1(z)}{E_i(z)} = \frac{z + z_1}{z + p_1}$$

$$D_2(z) = \frac{E_2(z)}{E_1(z)} = \frac{z + z_2}{z + p_2}$$

$$\cdots\cdots\cdots\cdots\cdots\cdots$$

$$D_m(z) = \frac{E_m(z)}{E_{m-1}(z)} = \frac{z + z_m}{z + p_m} \tag{9.6-6}$$

$$D_{m+1}(z) = \frac{E_{m+1}(z)}{E_m(z)} = \frac{1}{z + p_{m+1}}$$

$$\cdots\cdots\cdots\cdots\cdots\cdots$$

$$D_n(z) = \frac{E_0(z)}{E_{n-1}(z)} = \frac{K}{z + p_n}$$

Eqs. (9.6-4) and (9.6-5) suggest that the pulse-transfer function $D(z)$ may be replaced by n simpler pulse-transfer functions connected in cascade (Fig. 9.6-1). Each of the n pulse-transfer functions, as defined in Eq. (9.6-6), can be realized by a simple digital program. The first pulse-transfer function $D_1(z)$ may be written as

$$D_1(z) = \frac{E_1(z)}{E_i(z)} = \frac{1 + z_1 z^{-1}}{1 + p_1 z^{-1}} \tag{9.6-7}$$

Cross multiplying and taking the inverse transform yield the first processed signal $e_1^*(t)$ as

$$e_1^*(t) = e_i^*(t) + z_1 e_i^*(t - T) - p_1 e_1^*(t - T) \tag{9.6-8}$$

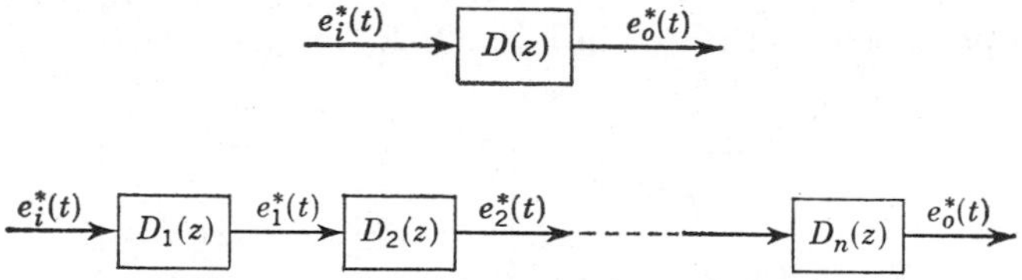

$e_i^*(t)$ → $D(z)$ → $e_o^*(t)$

$e_i^*(t)$ → $D_1(z)$ → $e_1^*(t)$ → $D_2(z)$ → $e_2^*(t)$ → ----- → $D_n(z)$ → $e_o^*(t)$

FIG. 9.6-1. Iterative programming.

In like manner, from the nth pulse-transfer function $D_n(z)$,

$$D_n(z) = \frac{E_0(z)}{E_{n-1}(z)} = \frac{Kz^{-1}}{1 + p_n z^{-1}} \tag{9.6-9}$$

the corresponding difference equation or programming function is obtained:

$$e_0^*(t) = Ke_{n-1}^*(t - T) - p_n e_0^*(t - T) \tag{9.6-10}$$

The n programming functions for the n pulse-transfer functions of Eq. (9.6-6) are given below.

$$\begin{aligned}
e_1^*(t) &= e_i^*(t) + z_1 e_i^*(t - T) - p_1 e_1^*(t - T) \\
e_2^*(t) &= e_1^*(t) + z_2 e_1^*(t - T) - p_2 e_2^*(t - T) \\
&\cdots\cdots\cdots\cdots\cdots\cdots\cdots\cdots \\
e_m^*(t) &= e_{m-1}^*(t) + z_m e_{m-1}^*(t - T) - p_m e_m^*(t - T) \\
e_{m+1}^*(t) &= e_m^*(t - T) - p_{m+1} e_{m+1}^*(t - T) \\
&\cdots\cdots\cdots\cdots\cdots\cdots\cdots\cdots \\
e_0^*(t) &= Ke_{n-1}^*(t - T) - p_n e_0^*(t - T)
\end{aligned} \tag{9.6-11}$$

Clearly, the computations involved in Eq. (9.6-11) can readily be performed by a conventional digital computer. Equation (9.6-11) indicates that to solve this set of equations the program is required to perform $(m + n)$ additions and subtractions, $(m + n + 1)$ multiplications, and n transfers. This method of program realization is referred to as *iterative programming*.

The third method of program realization of a pulse-transfer function is based upon the partial fraction expansion of $D(z)$. Let the partial fractions of pulse-transfer function $D(z)$ be

$$\begin{aligned}
D_a(z) &= \frac{E_a(z)}{E_i(z)} = \frac{k_1}{z + p_1} = \frac{k_1 z^{-1}}{1 + p_1 z^{-1}} \\
D_b(z) &= \frac{E_b(z)}{E_i(z)} = \frac{k_2}{z + p_2} = \frac{k_2 z^{-1}}{1 + p_2 z^{-1}} \\
&\cdots\cdots\cdots\cdots\cdots\cdots\cdots\cdots \\
D_n(z) &= \frac{E_n(z)}{E_i(z)} = \frac{k_n}{z + p_n} = \frac{k_n z^{-1}}{1 + p_n z^{-1}}
\end{aligned} \tag{9.6-12}$$

Then $$D(z) = D_a(z) + D_b(z) + \cdots + D_n(z) \tag{9.6-13}$$

Evidently, each of the pulse-transfer functions given in Eq. (9.6-12) can be realized by a simple digital program. In view of Eq. (9.6-13), the pulse-transfer function $D(z)$ may be realized by n simple digital programs operating in parallel as illustrated in Fig. 9.6-2. This is referred to as *parallel*

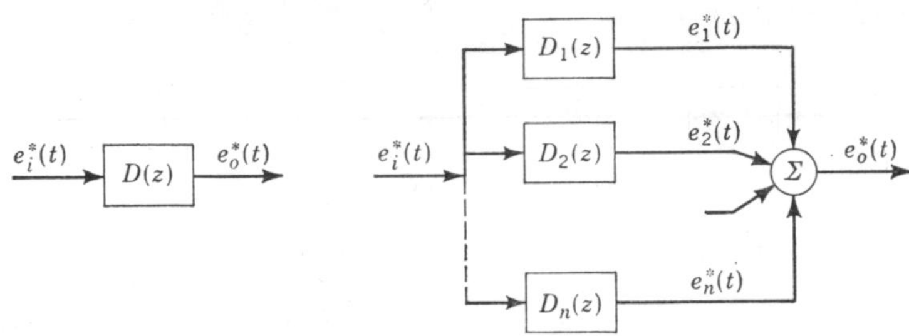

FIG. 9.6-2. Parallel programming.

programming. Cross multiplication and inverse transformation of Eq. (9.6-12) lead to the corresponding set of programming function:

$$\begin{aligned} e_a^*(t) &= k_1 e_i^*(t - T) - p_1 e_a^*(t - T) \\ e_b^*(t) &= k_2 e_i^*(t - T) - p_2 e_b^*(t - T) \\ &\cdots\cdots\cdots\cdots\cdots\cdots \\ e_n^*(t) &= k_n e_i^*(t - T) - p_n e_n^*(t - T) \end{aligned} \tag{9.6-14}$$

Then the processed signal $e_0^*(t)$ is given by

$$\begin{aligned} e_0^*(t) &= e_a^*(t) + e_b^*(t) + \cdots + e_n^*(t) \\ &= \sum_{j=1}^{n} k_j e_i^*(t - T) - \sum_{k=1}^{n} p_k e_k^*(t - T) \end{aligned} \tag{9.6-15}$$

From Eq. (9.6-15) it is evident that to solve the above equations the digital program is required to perform $(2n - 1)$ additions and subtractions, $2n$ multiplications, and $(n + 1)$ transfers.

So far as the computing efficiency is concerned, iterative programming seems to be the most favorable. Indeed, the iterative method is often used in numerical analysis. Although the computing time and the number of storage registers may be used to judge the programming method, the particular computer in use and the instruction code of the computer bear a strong influence upon the selection of the programming technique. For instance, inclusion into the code of the Whirlwind computer of an instruction which exchanges the contents of the arithmetic unit and the selected storage register makes the direct programming technique more efficient than the iterative method. The direct programming method can minimize the delay due to computation, because all terms of Eq. (9.6-2*b*), except $a_0 e_i^*(t)$, can be calculated before the input $e_i^*(t)$ is taken. The delay due to computation results in a transport lag in a digital control system, which would generally impair the system performance. Thus, minimization of the delay due to computation is quite desirable. When several terms in $D(z)$ of Eq. (9.6-1b) are nil (or when there are more poles than zeros), the direct programming method may be more favorable than the iterative method, because in this case the computing time and the total operations are reduced due to the missing terms of $D(z)$; on the other hand, no gain is obtainable with iterative programming. Nevertheless, iterative programming has the advantage of yielding intermediate results, which are sometimes very useful. When a pulse-transfer function and the corresponding digital program are to be designed by experimental methods, iterative programming offers the advantage of flexibility. Moreover, if the design is based upon the pole-zero configurations, considerable convenience generally results in iterative programming, since the poles and zeros of the pulse-transfer function $D(z)$ form the coefficients of the programming functions of Eq. (9.6-11). The effects due to the variation in a pole or a zero of the pulse-transfer function can readily be investigated by changing the corresponding coefficient of Eq. (9.6-11). Although the parallel programming method offers similar advantages, it is not generally used, for parallel programming could affect the basic design of a computer.

Delay-line Networks and Pulsed-data Processing Units. A pulse-transfer function can be realized by a device through the use of one or more delay elements, summing devices, potentiometers, and amplifiers. Such a device is sometimes referred to as a delay-line network or a pulsed-data processing unit.[61] In essence, a pulse-transfer function is synthesized by combining the properly weighted data taken from the delay elements as demonstrated in the following. Before discussing the realization of a pulse-transfer function in the general form of Eq. (9.6-1), the synthesis of a few simple pulse-transfer functions is first illustrated. Consider a pulse-transfer function given by

$$D(z) = \frac{E_0(z)}{E_i(z)} = a_0 + a_1 z^{-1} \tag{9.6-16}$$

Cross multiplication yields

$$E_0(z) = a_0 E_i(z) + a_1 z^{-1} E_i(z) \tag{9.6-17}$$

Equation (9.6-17) implies that the output of the pulsed-data network is given by the sum of the input and the delayed input, which are properly weighted with a_0 and a_1, respectively. It is quite obvious that the delay-line network realizing Eq. (9.6-16) will comprise a delay element with time delay equal to the sampling period T, a summing amplifier, and two potentiometers. This delay-line network is illustrated in Fig. 9.6-3. The summing amplifier provides the necessary gain if the weighting factors are greater than unity.

The pulse-transfer function to be considered next is given by Eq. (9.6-18).

$$D(z) = \frac{E_0(z)}{E_i(z)} = \frac{a_0}{1 + b_1 z^{-1}} \tag{9.6-18}$$

This transfer function contains a zero at $z = 0$ and a pole at $z = -b_1$. Cross multiplying Eq. (9.6-18) leads to

$$E_0(z) = a_0 E_i(z) - b_1 z^{-1} E_0(z) \qquad (9.6\text{-}19)$$

The delay-line network realizing Eq. (9.6-18) can readily be derived from Eq. (9.6-19), which indicates that the output of the network is equal to the

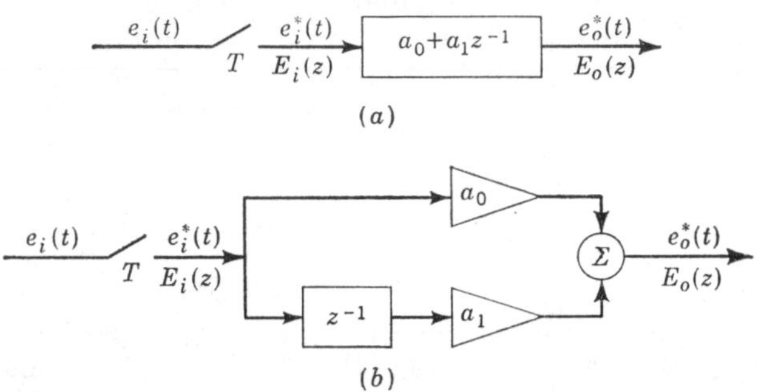

FIG. 9.6-3. Delay-line network for $D(z) = a_0 + a_1 z^{-1}$.

difference between the input weighted with a_0 and the delay output weighted with b_1. Thus, to realize the given pulse-transfer function requires a delay element with time delay T, a summing amplifier and two potentiometers. The block diagram of this delay-line network is shown in Fig. 9.6-4, which is self-explanatory.

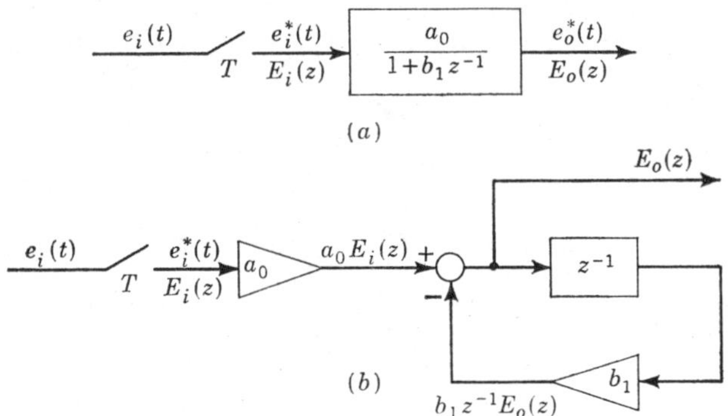

FIG. 9.6-4. Delay-line network for $D(z) = a_0/(1 + b_1 z^{-1})$.

Now, consider a pulse-transfer function having a zero at $z = -a_1/a_0$ and a pole at $z = -b_1$, as described by Eq. (9.6-20).

$$D(z) = \frac{E_0(z)}{E_i(z)} = \frac{a_0 + a_1 z^{-1}}{1 + b_1 z^{-1}} \qquad (9.6\text{-}20)$$

Equation (9.6-20) may be written as

$$D(z) = D_1(z) + D_2(z) \tag{9.6-21}$$

where

$$D_1(z) = \frac{E_{01}(z)}{E_i(z)} = \frac{a_0}{1 + b_1 z^{-1}} \tag{9.6-22}$$

$$D_2(z) = \frac{E_{02}(z)}{E_i(z)} = \frac{a_1 z^{-1}}{1 + b_1 z^{-1}} \tag{9.6-23}$$

and

$$E_{01}(z) + E_{02}(z) = [D_1(z) + D_2(z)]E_i(z) = E_0(z) \tag{9.6-24}$$

Since the pulse-transfer function of Eq. (9.6-22) is the same as that of Eq. (9.6-18), the delay-line network realizing Eq. (9.6-22) is identical to that shown in Fig. 9.6-4*b*. From Eqs. (9.6-22) and (9.6-23), it is seen that

$$E_{02}(z) = \frac{a_1}{a_0} z^{-1} E_{01}(z) \tag{9.6-25}$$

Consequently, this delay-line network also realizes the pulse-transfer function of Eq. (9.6-23), provided that the signal from the delay element multiplied by a factor a_1/a_0, is taken as the output of the network, as shown in Fig. 9.6-5*b*. It is noted that the input signal to the delay element is

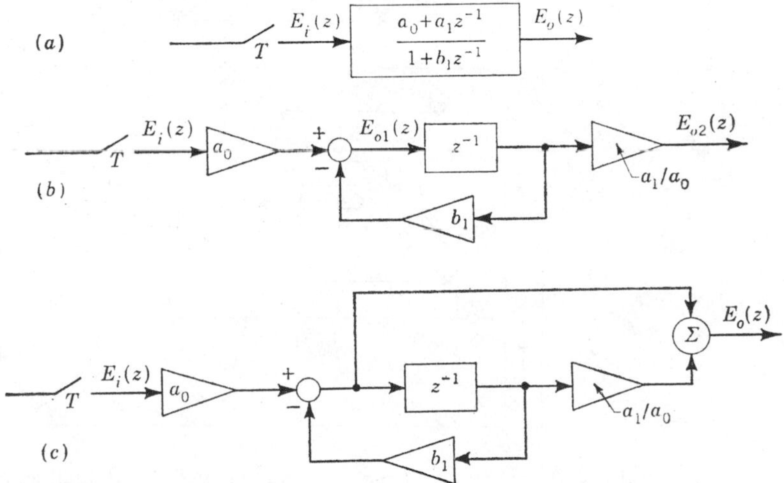

FIG. 9.6-5. Realization of a pulsed-data network by a delay-line network. (*a*) A pulsed-data network; (*b*) delay-line network for $a_1 z^{-1}/(1 + b_1 z^{-1})$; (*c*) delay-line network for $(a_0 + a_1 z^{-1})/(1 + b_1 z^{-1})$.

$e_{01}^*(t)$. In view of Eq. (9.6-24), the output of the delay-line network for the specified pulse-transfer function of Eq. (9.6-20) is given by the sum of the input $e_{01}^*(t)$ to the delay element and the properly weighted output $e_{02}^*(t)$ from the delay element. Thus, if these two signals are fed into a summing amplifier the desired delay-line network results. The implementation of this network is illustrated in Fig. 9.6-5*c*.

Following the reasoning and the techniques discussed above, one should have no difficulty in deriving the delay-line network for realizing the pulse-transfer function:

$$D(z) = \frac{E_0(z)}{E_i(z)} = \frac{a_0}{1 + \sum_{k=1}^{n} b_k z^{-k}} \tag{9.6-26}$$

Cross multiplying and rearranging yield

$$E_0(z) = a_0 E_i(z) - \sum_{k=1}^{n} b_k z^{-k} E_0(z) \tag{9.6-27}$$

In view of the similarity between Eq. (9.6-27) and Eq. (9.6-19), it is to be expected that the delay-line network realizing the pulse-transfer function of Eq. (9.6-26) resembles the network shown in Fig. 9.6-4*b*. As can readily be determined from Eq. (9.6-27), this network consists of n delay elements with a time delay of T sec each, $(n + 1)$ potentiometers, and a summing amplifier with $(n + 1)$ input terminals. The block diagram of this network is depicted in Fig. 9.6-6. These delay elements are connected in series form-

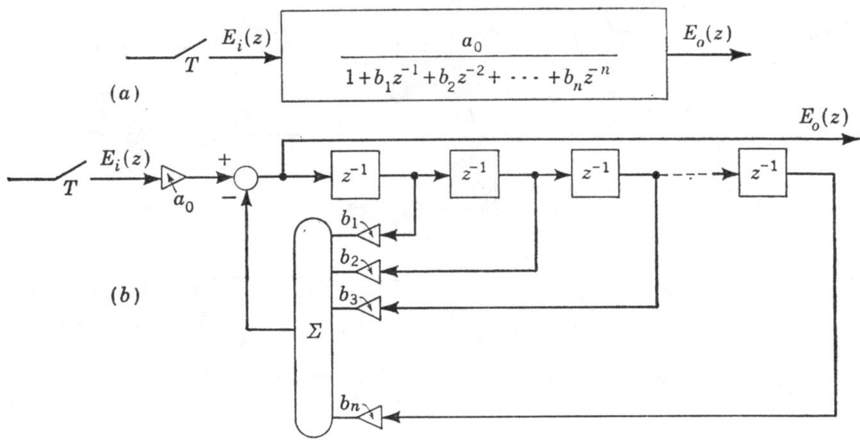

FIG. 9.6-6. (*a*) A pulsed-data network; (*b*) the delay-line network for the pulsed-data network of (*a*).

ing an n section delay line with a total time delay of nT sec. Feedback signals are picked up from each delay element in succession and are properly weighted before feeding into the summing amplifier. The output of this delay-line network is taken from the output terminal of the subtracting device, which may be considered as a part of the multi-input summing amplifier.

Now, by making use of the circuits and the techniques discussed in the preceding paragraphs, the synthesis of a pulse-transfer function of the general form

$$D(z) = \frac{E_0(z)}{E_i(z)} = \frac{\sum_{k=0}^{n} a_k z^{-k}}{1 + \sum_{k=1}^{n} b_k z^{-k}} \tag{9.6-28}$$

can be carried out with ease. Apparently, $D(z)$ of Eq. (9.6-28) may be written as

$$D(z) = \frac{a_0}{1 + \sum_{k=1}^{n} b_k z^{-k}} + \frac{a_1 z^{-1}}{1 + \sum_{k=1}^{n} b_k z^{-k}} + \cdots + \frac{a_j z^{-j}}{1 + \sum_{k=1}^{n} b_k z^{-k}} + \cdots + \frac{a_n z^{-n}}{1 + \sum_{k=1}^{n} b_k z^{-k}} \tag{9.6-29}$$

$$= D_1(z) + D_2(z) + \cdots + D_j(z) + \cdots + D_n(z) \tag{9.6-30}$$

where

$$D_j(z) = \frac{a_j z^{-j}}{1 + \sum_{k=1}^{n} b_k z^{-k}} \tag{9.6-31}$$

Since $D_1(z)$ is identical to the pulse-transfer function given in Eq. (9.6-26), the delay-line network to realize $D_1(z)$ is the same as that shown in Fig. 9.6-6*b*. It is observed that the signals from the first, the second, . . . and the nth delay element represent the output signals delayed by T, $2T$, . . . , nT sec, respectively. They are $e_0^*(t - T)$, $e_0^*(t - 2T)$, . . . $e_0^*(t - nT)$. Indeed, the circuit of Fig. 9.6-6*b* can also realize the pulse-transfer function $D_j(z)$, provided that the signal from the jth delay element, multiplied by a factor of a_j/a_0, is considered as the output of the delay-line network. Consequently, according to Eq. (9.6-29), by summing the properly weighted signals from the delay elements of Fig. 9.6-6*b*, the pulse-transfer function of Eq. (9.6-28) is synthesized. As illustrated in Fig. 9.6-7*b*, this network consists of n delay elements, $(2n + 1)$ potentiometers, and 2 summing amplifiers.

From the above discussions, the following conclusions may be drawn. To realize a pulse-transfer function with n poles by a delay-line network generally requires n delay elements, each having a time delay equal to the sampling period. The number of potentiometers needed in the network is determined by the number of the coefficients of the given pulse-transfer function, and the input circuits of the summing amplifier. To realize a pulse-transfer function having one or more zeros which are not located at the origin of the z plane, 2 summing amplifiers are required in the delay-line network.

Pulsed-data RC Networks. A pulse-transfer function can be realized by a pulsed-data RC network. The basic structures of a pulsed-data network

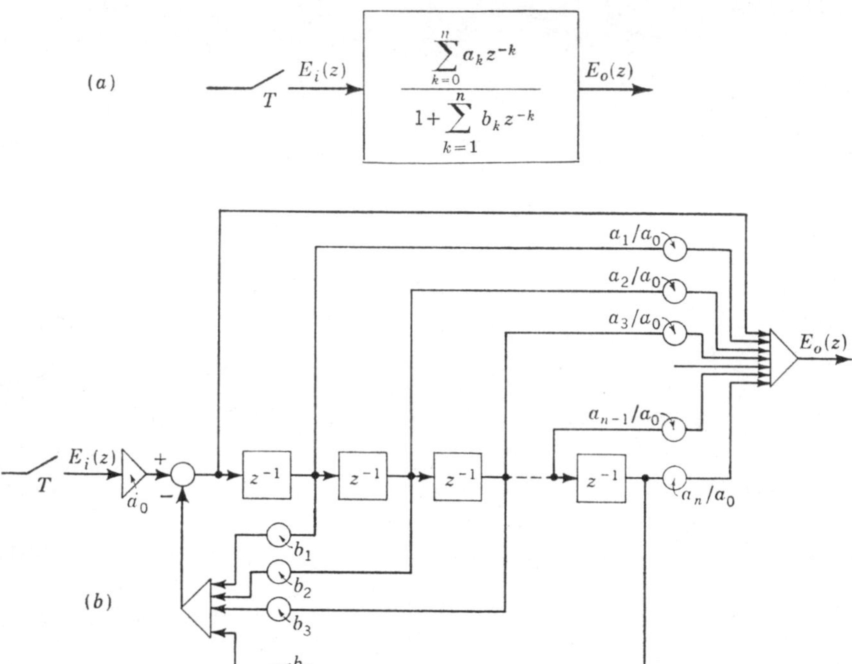

FIG. 9.6-7. (a) A pulsed-data network; (b) the delay-line network for the pulsed-data network of (a).

are the basic series structure and the basic feedback structure.[114] Each of these basic pulsed-data RC networks consists of a single conventional passive RC network and a zero-order hold, which are connected in a simple series or feedback arrangement as illustrated in Fig. 9.6-8 and Fig. 9.6-9,

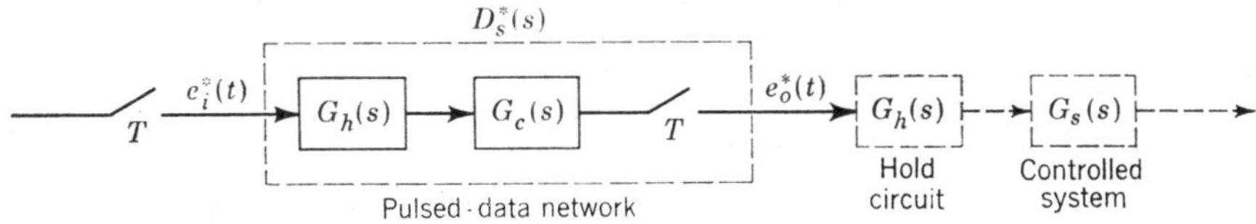

FIG. 9.6-8. Basic series structure of pulsed-data network.

respectively. The basic series structure is characterized by the pulse-transfer function

$$D_s(z) = \frac{E_0(z)}{E_i(z)} = G_hG_c(z) \qquad (9.6\text{-}32)$$

$G_hG_c(z)$ is the z transform associated with $G_h(s)G_c(s)$. Here, $G_h(s)$ is the transfer function of the zero-order hold and $G_c(s)$ is the transfer function of the RC network of the basic series structure. The pulse-transfer function characterizing the basic feedback structure, as derived from the block diagram of Fig. 9.6-9a, is given by

$$D_f(z) = \frac{E_0(z)}{E_i(z)} = \frac{1}{1 + G_hH_c(z)} \tag{9.6-33}$$

in which $G_hH_c(z)$ is the z transform associated with $G_h(s)H_c(s)$. $G_h(s)$ and

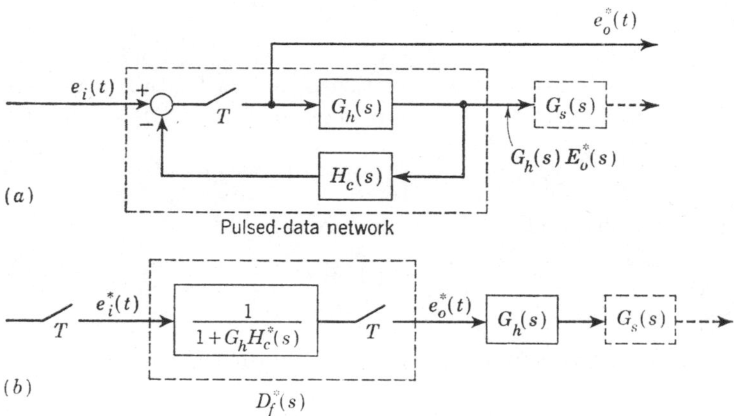

FIG. 9.6-9. (a) Basic parallel structure of pulsed-data network; (b) the equivalent representation.

$H_c(s)$ denote, respectively, the transfer functions of the zero-order hold and the RC network of the basic feedback structure.

As can be seen from Fig. 9.6-8, when a pulse-transfer function is synthesized by a basic series structure, an additional hold circuit is often required to smooth the processed signal $e_0^*(t)$ from the pulsed-data network, before feeding it into the controlled system $G_s(s)$. In the case of the basic feedback structure, however, the processed signal $e_0^*(t)$ is smoothed by the hold circuit of the pulsed-data network, thus enabling the basic feedback pulsed-data network to be connected directly to $G_s(s)$ of the controlled system. In other words, the pulsed-data network and the controlled system share the same hold circuit. But, it is noted that in the basic feedback structure a hold circuit is saved at the expense of a subtracting device.

In addition to the basic structures mentioned above a number of the variations may be derived through combinations of these two basic structures.[114] Among the most useful ones are the cascaded series-feedback structure, the parallel series-feedback structure, and the more general feedback structure. As shown in the following, both the basic series structure and the basic feedback structure have limited applications. However, combination of these two basic structures can synthesize any rational and physically realizable pulse-transfer functions in pulsed-data RC networks.

BASIC SERIES STRUCTURE. The realization of a pulse-transfer function by the basic series structure is primarily concerned with the determination of the transfer function $G_c(s)$ and the corresponding RC network such that the z transform associated with $G_h(s)G_c(s)$ [or simply $G_c(s)$ if the hold device is not used] is equal to the specified pulse-transfer function $D_s(z)$.

Let the given pulse-transfer function $D_s(z)$ having m zeros and n poles be expressed in the form

$$D_s(z) = \frac{z^{-r}(a_r + a_{r+1}z^{-1} + a_{r+2}z^{-2} + \cdots + a_{r+m}z^{-m})}{(1 - p_1z^{-1})(1 - p_2z^{-1})(1 - p_3z^{-1}) \cdots (1 - p_nz^{-1})} \tag{9.6-34}$$

where $m + r = n$, a's are constants, p's are the poles of $D_s(z)$ which fall inside the unit circle, and $D_s(z)$ satisfies the realizability and stability conditions described in the preceding section. Then it is required to find $G_c(s)$ such that

$$G_hG_c(z) = \mathfrak{z}\{G_h(s)G_c(s)\} = D_s(z) \tag{9.6-35}$$

Since the transfer function of the zero-order hold is found to be

$$G_h(s) = \frac{1 - \epsilon^{-Ts}}{s} \tag{9.6-36}$$

The z transform associated with $G_h(s)G_c(s)$ is then given by

$$G_hG_c(z) = (1 - z^{-1})\mathfrak{z}\left\{\frac{G_c(s)}{s}\right\} \tag{9.6-37}$$

Substituting Eq. (9.6-35) into Eq. (9.6-37) yields the z transform associated with $G_c(s)/s$ as

$$\mathfrak{z}\left\{\frac{G_c(s)}{s}\right\} = \frac{D_s(z)}{1 - z^{-1}} \tag{9.6-38}$$

Equation (9.6-38) implies that $G_c(s)/s$ is the $\mathcal{L}$ transform corresponding to the pulse-transfer function $D_s(z)/(1 - z^{-1})$. Consequently, the transfer function $G_c(s)$ can be determined, if the $\mathcal{L}$ transform corresponding to $D_s(z)/(1 - z^{-1})$ can be evaluated. A convenient method of finding the $\mathcal{L}$ transform corresponding to a z transform is by using the partial-fraction expansion technique. The $\mathcal{L}$ transforms corresponding to the partial fractions are then identified with the aid of the z-transform table. Now, if the specified pulse-transfer function $D_s(z)$ contains no multiple poles, $D_s(z)/(1 - z^{-1})$ can be expanded into the form

$$\frac{D_s(z)}{1 - z^{-1}} = \frac{K_0}{1 - z^{-1}} + \sum_{r=1}^{n} \frac{K_r}{1 - p_rz^{-1}} \tag{9.6-39}$$

provided that $D_s(z)$ has no pole at $z = 1$. In case $D_s(z)$ contains a simple pole at $z = 1$, it is easy to show that $D_s(z)/(1 - z^{-1})$ can be written as

$$\frac{D_s(z)}{1 - z^{-1}} = \frac{K_0}{1 - z^{-1}} + \frac{K_0'Tz^{-1}}{(1 - z^{-1})^2} + \sum_{r=2}^{n} \frac{K_r}{1 - p_r z^{-1}} \tag{9.6-40}$$

where T is the sampling period. The $\mathcal{L}$ transform corresponding to each term of the right-hand member of Eq. (9.6-39) and Eq. (9.6-40) can be recognized from the z-transform table. An examination of the short table of z transforms in Sec. 5.2 reveals that the $\mathcal{L}$ transforms corresponding to the first and the second term of Eq. (9.6-40) are K_0/s and K_0'/s^2 respectively, and that the $\mathcal{L}$ transform corresponding to $K_r/(1 - p_r z^{-1})$ is

$$\frac{K_r}{s + a_r} \tag{9.6-41a}$$

where p_r and a_r are related by

$$p_r = \epsilon^{-a_r T} \qquad \text{or} \qquad -a_r = \frac{1}{T} \ln p_r \tag{9.6-41b}$$

with T denoting the sampling period. Substituting Eq. (9.6-38) into Eq. (9.6-39) and taking the corresponding $\mathcal{L}$ transform for each term yield

$$\frac{G_c(s)}{s} = \frac{K_0}{s} + \sum_{r=1}^{n} \frac{K_r}{s + a_r} \tag{9.6-42}$$

However, it should be pointed out that the $\mathcal{L}$ transforms of Eq. (9.6-42) are the principal $\mathcal{L}$ transforms. As discussed in Sec. 5.6, the transformation from the z domain to the s domain is not unique. An infinite number of the $\mathcal{L}$ transforms can be derived from the corresponding z transform. But, usually only the principal $\mathcal{L}$ transform is used. Clearly, Eq. (9.6-42) yields the desired transfer function $G_c(s)$ as

$$G_c(s) = K_0 + \sum_{r=1}^{n} \frac{K_r s}{s + a_r} \tag{9.6-43}$$

Then the RC network to realize the transfer function of Eq. (9.6-43) is designed by applying the standard techniques for network synthesis. Now, if the specified $D_s(z)$ contains a pole at $z = 1$, the desired transfer function $G_c(s)$ can be obtained, in like manner, from Eq. (9.6-38) and Eq. (9.6-40). Thus,

$$G_c(s) = K_0 + \frac{K_0'}{s} + \sum_{r=2}^{n} \frac{K_r s}{s + a_r} \tag{9.6-44}$$

Since the given pulse-transfer function $D_s(z)$ is stable and is assumed to contain only real and simple poles, the poles of $D_s(z)$ must lie in the interval between 0 and 1. From Eq. (9.6-41b) it is seen that under these conditions a_r is real, simple, finite, and positive. This implies that the poles of $G_c(s)$ are real, simple, finite, and negative [possibly with a pole at $s = 0$ corresponding to the pole at $z = 1$ of $D_s(z)$]. In fact, these restrictions are necessary for conventional transfer functions to be realized in RC networks. Consequently, in order to realize a pulse-transfer function by a basic series structure of pulsed-data RC network, it is required that *the poles of the given pulse-transfer function must be real, simple, and positive and lie inside the unit circle.* In addition to the general realizability conditions stated in Sec. 9.5, these are the realizability restrictions upon the basic series structure.

As an illustration, a simple example is presented below.

EXAMPLE 9.6-1. Given a pulse-transfer function

$$D(z) = \frac{z - a}{z - b} \tag{9.6-45}$$

where $0 < b < 1$ and $0 < a \leq 1$. It is required to realize this pulse-transfer function by a basic series pulsed-data RC network. The sampling period is T sec.

The given pulse-transfer function is realizable in a basic series structure, since the pole of $D(z)$ meets the realizability restrictions. The z transform associated with $G_c(s)/s$ is

$$\mathfrak{z}\left\{\frac{G_c(s)}{s}\right\} = \frac{D_s(z)}{1 - z^{-1}} = \frac{1 - az^{-1}}{(1 - z^{-1})(1 - bz^{-1})} \tag{9.6-46}$$

Expanding Eq. (9.6-46) into partial fractions yields

$$\mathfrak{z}\left\{\frac{G_c(s)}{s}\right\} = \frac{1 - a}{1 - b}\frac{1}{1 - z^{-1}} + \frac{a - b}{1 - b}\frac{1}{1 - bz^{-1}} \tag{9.6-47}$$

Thus,

$$G_c(s) = \frac{1 - a}{1 - b} + \frac{a - b}{1 - b}\frac{s}{s + \alpha} \tag{9.6-48}$$

where α is given by

$$-\alpha = \frac{1}{T}\ln b \tag{9.6-49}$$

Equation (9.6-48) reduces to

$$G_c(s) = \frac{s + \dfrac{(1 - a)\alpha}{(1 - b)}}{s + \alpha} \tag{9.6-50}$$

Evidently, $G_c(s)$ can readily be synthesized by a simple RC network if $a \leq 1$. However, when a exceeds unity, $G_c(s)$ becomes a nonminimum-phase transfer function. It is noted that $G_c(s)$ describes a lead network if $a > b$, and a lag network if $a < b$. The block diagram of the basic series pulsed-data RC network realizing $D(z)$ of Eq. (9.6-45) is illustrated in Fig. 9.6-10.

BASIC FEEDBACK STRUCTURE. The realization of a pulse-transfer function by the basic feedback structure of pulsed-data RC networks, as shown in Fig. 9.6-9a, involves the determination of the transfer function $H_c(s)$ and the corresponding RC network such that the z transform for this configuration is equal to the specified pulse-transfer function $D_f(z)$.

Since the transfer function of the zero-order hold is

$$G_h(s) = \frac{1 - \epsilon^{-Ts}}{s} \tag{9.6-51}$$

the z transform associated with $G_h(s)H_c(s)$ is given by

$$G_hH_c(z) = (1 - z^{-1})\mathfrak{z}\left\{\frac{H_c(s)}{s}\right\} \tag{9.6-52}$$

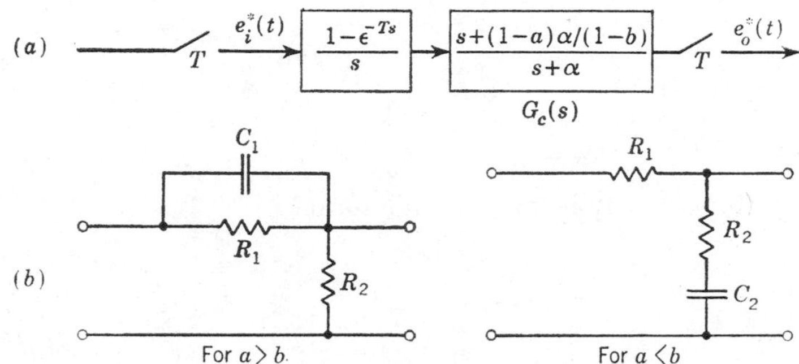

FIG. 9.6-10. (a) Realization of $D(z) = (z - a)/(z - b)$ by a basic series structure; (b) RC networks realizing $G_c(s)$.

In view of Eq. (9.6-33), the pulse-transfer function of Fig. 9.6-9a relating the signal $e_0^*(t)$ to the input signal $e_i^*(t)$ is

$$D_f(z) = \frac{E_0(z)}{E_i(z)} = \frac{1}{1 + (1 - z^{-1})\mathfrak{z}\left\{\frac{H_c(s)}{s}\right\}} \tag{9.6-53}$$

which leads to

$$\mathfrak{z}\left\{\frac{H_c(s)}{s}\right\} = \frac{1 - D_f(z)}{(1 - z^{-1})D_f(z)} \tag{9.6-54}$$

According to the realizability conditions stated in Sec. 9.5, the pulse-transfer function of the right-hand member of Eq. (9.6-54) is physically realizable only if its denominator does not contain z^{-1} as a factor. Thus, the specified pulse-transfer function $D_f(z)$ must not contain z^{-1} as a factor. In other words, $D_f(z)$ must have equal number of poles and zeros. Then the given pulse-transfer function $D_f(z)$ may be written as

$$D_f(z) = \frac{1 + \sum_{k=1}^{n} a_k z^{-k}}{\sum_{k=0}^{n} b_k z^{-k}} \tag{9.6-55}$$

By the substitution of Eq. (9.6-55),

$$\frac{1 - D_f(z)}{D_f(z)} = \frac{\sum_{k=0}^{n} b_k z^{-k} - \sum_{k=1}^{n} a_k z^{-k} - 1}{1 + \sum_{k=1}^{n} a_k z^{-k}} \tag{9.6-56}$$

$$= \frac{\sum_{k=0}^{n} c_k z^{-k}}{1 + \sum_{k=1}^{n} a_k z^{-k}} \tag{9.6-57}$$

where $\qquad c_0 = b_0 - 1 \qquad c_k = b_k - a_k$

Thus, Eq. (9.6-54) may be put into the form

$$\mathfrak{z}\left\{\frac{H_c(s)}{s}\right\} = \frac{\sum_{k=0}^{n} c_k z^{-k}}{(1 - z^{-1})(1 - z_1 z^{-1})(1 - z_2 z^{-1}) \cdots (1 - z_n z^{-1})} \tag{9.6-58}$$

where $z_1, z_2, \ldots, z_n$ are the zeros of $D_f(z)$.

By comparing Eqs. (9.6-57) and (9.6-55), it is seen that the denominator of Eq. (9.6-57) is the numerator of the specified pulse-transfer function. As a result, if the specified pulse-transfer function $D_f(z)$ contains no multiple zeros, the right-hand member of Eq. (9.6-58) may be expanded into simple partial fractions as

$$\mathfrak{z}\left\{\frac{H_c(s)}{s}\right\} = \frac{N_0}{1 - z^{-1}} + \sum_{r=1}^{n} \frac{N_r}{1 - z_r z^{-1}} \tag{9.6-59}$$

or

$$\mathfrak{z}\left\{\frac{H_c(s)}{s}\right\} = \frac{N_0}{1 - z^{-1}} + \frac{N_0' T z^{-1}}{(1 - z^{-1})^2} + \sum_{r=2}^{n} \frac{N_r}{1 - z_r z^{-1}} \tag{9.6-60}$$

depending upon whether the specified $D_f(z)$ contains a zero at $z = 1$ or not. Evidently, the $\mathfrak{L}$ transform corresponding to each term of the right-hand member of Eq. (9.6-60) is recognizable from the z-transform table. Thus, Eq. (9.6-59) leads to

$$H_c(s) = N_0 - \sum_{r=1}^{n} \frac{N_r s}{s + b_r} \tag{9.6-61}$$

where b_r is related to z_r by

$$-b_r = \frac{1}{T} \ln z_r \tag{9.6-62}$$

with T as the sampling period. Similarly, Eq. (9.6-60) leads to

$$H_c(s) = N_0 + \frac{N_0'}{s} + \sum_{r=2}^{n} \frac{N_r s}{s + b_r} \tag{9.6-63}$$

In view of the fact that to realize transfer function $H_c(s)$ by an RC network it is required that the poles of $H_c(s)$ must be real, simple, finite, and nonpositive, z_r of Eq. (9.6-59) and Eq. (9.6-60) must be real and simple and lie in the interval $0 < z_r \leq 1$. Consequently, a pulse-transfer function is realizable in a basic feedback structure of pulsed-data RC networks, if the given pulse-transfer function contains *equal number of zeros and poles, and the zeros are real, simple, and positive and lie inside the unit circle.* These are the *realizability restrictions* upon the basic feedback structure. It is interesting to note that pulse-transfer functions having poles outside the unit circle may be realized by a basic feedback structure of pulsed-data RC networks as long as the above restrictions are complied with.

To illustrate the realization of a pulse-transfer function by a basic feedback structure, an example is described in the following paragraphs.

EXAMPLE 9.6-2. Given a pulse-transfer function

$$D(z) = \frac{z - a}{z - b} \tag{9.6-64}$$

where $0 < a < 1$ and $b > 1$. It is required to realize this pulse-transfer function by a pulsed-data RC network.

Since the given pulse-transfer function is unstable, it is not realizable as a basic series pulsed-data RC network. However, since the zero of $D(z)$ is real, positive, and inside the unit circle, the given $D(z)$ may be realized by a basic feedback structure, as shown in Fig. 9.6-9a. From Eq. (9.6-54), the z transform associated with $H_c(s)/s$ is found to be

$$\mathfrak{z}\left\{\frac{H_c(s)}{s}\right\} = \frac{(a - b)z^{-1}}{(1 - z^{-1})(1 - az^{-1})} \tag{9.6-65}$$

$$\mathfrak{z}\left\{\frac{H_c(s)}{s}\right\} = \frac{a - b}{1 - a}\left(\frac{1}{1 - z^{-1}} - \frac{1}{1 - az^{-1}}\right) \tag{9.6-66}$$

Thus,

$$H_c(s) = \frac{a - b}{1 - a}\left(1 - \frac{s}{s + \alpha}\right) \tag{9.6-67}$$

where α is given by

$$-\alpha = \frac{1}{T} \ln a \tag{9.6-68}$$

T being the sampling period. Eq. (9.6-67) reduces to

$$H_c(s) = \frac{a - b}{1 - a} \frac{\alpha}{s + \alpha} \tag{9.6-69}$$

Clearly, $H_c(s)$ given above can readily be realized by a simple RC lag network. The block diagram of the basic feedback pulsed-data RC network realizing the specified $D(z)$ is illustrated in Fig. 9.6-11. However, it is pointed out that, since $a < b$, $H_c(s)$ of Eq. (9.6-69) is negative, and thus positive feedback should be used.

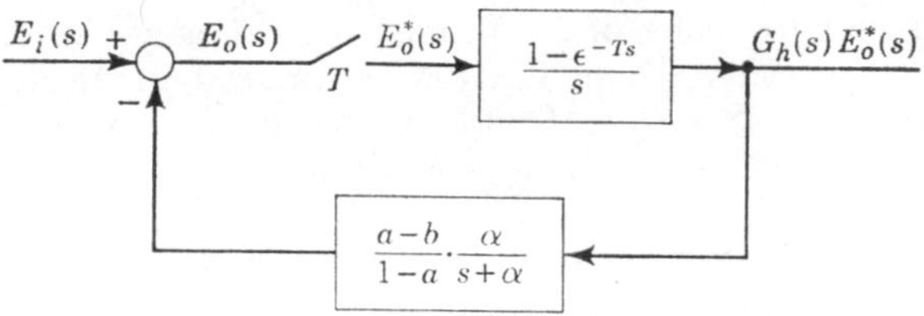

FIG. 9.6-11. Realization of $D(z) = (z - a)/(z - b)$ by a basic feedback structure.

COMBINATION OF THE BASIC SERIES AND THE BASIC FEEDBACK STRUCTURE. The above discussions have made clear that both the basic series structure and the basic feedback structure suffer from some restrictions in the realization of pulse-transfer functions. The basic series structure can realize only those pulse-transfer functions which contain *positive, real, and simple poles inside the unit circle.* These poles will be referred to as realizable poles. Yet no restriction is imposed upon the zeros except that the number of zeros cannot exceed the number of poles. The basic feedback structure can realize only those pulse-transfer functions which contain *positive, real, and simple zeros inside the unit circle.* These zeros will be referred to as realizable zeros. Besides the requirement that the number of poles must equal the number of zeros, no restriction is imposed upon the poles. Even pulse-transfer functions with poles outside the unit circle can be realized by the basic feedback structure, provided that the zeros meet the realizability restrictions. Consequently, on the basis of the realization characteristics described above, it is conceivable that, through appropriate combination, these two basic structures of pulsed-data *RC* networks may be used to advantage to realize any pulse-transfer function which is rational in z and physically realizable.

As can be seen, one solution to the realization problem is to make use of the series combination of a basic series and a basic feedback structure forming a cascaded series-feedback structure as shown in Fig. 9.6-12. It

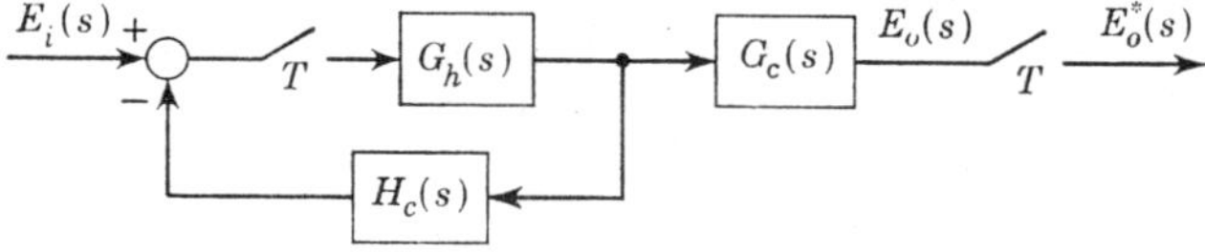

FIG. 9.6-12. Cascade series-feedback structure.

is evident that the pulse-transfer function describing this cascade combination is given by

$$D(z) = D_s(z)D_f(z) \tag{9.6-70}$$

where $$D_s(z) = G_hG_c(z) \tag{9.6-71}$$

and $$D_f(z) = \frac{1}{1 + G_hH_c(z)} \tag{9.6-72}$$

Thus, to realize a pulse-transfer function by a cascaded series-feedback structure, the first step is to write the given pulse-transfer function $D(z)$ as

$$D(z) = D_a(z)D_b(z) \tag{9.6-73}$$

Only the poles of $D(z)$, which are positive, real, and simple and lie inside the unit circle, are assigned to $D_a(z)$. Only the zeros of $D(z)$, which are positive, real, and simple and lie inside the unit circle, are assigned to $D_b(z)$. Moreover, $D_b(z)$ must be assigned with equal number of zeros and poles. In other words, $D_a(z)$ and $D_b(z)$ are made to comply with the realizability restrictions upon the basic series structure and the basic feedback structure, respectively. As an illustration, consider the pulse-transfer function defined in Eq. (9.6-74):

$$D(z) = \frac{z^{-1}(1 - 0.5z^{-1})(1 - 0.8z^{-1})(1 - z^{-1} + 0.55z^{-2})}{(1 - z^{-1})(1 - 0.9z^{-1})(1 - 0.2z^{-1})(1 - 2z^{-1})(1 - 1.5z^{-1})} \tag{9.6-74}$$

Evidently, this pulse-transfer function is rational in z and is physically realizable, although it is considered unstable. Nevertheless $D(z)$ can neither be realized by a basic series pulsed-data RC network because two poles of $D(z)$ reside outside the unit circle, nor can it be realized by a basic feedback structure on account of the presence of the complex zeros and the zero at infinity. Yet, $D(z)$ of Eq. (9.6-74) can be realized by a cascaded series-feedback structure. Equation (9.6-74) can be written as

$$D(z) = \frac{z^{-1}(1 - z^{-1} + 0.55z^{-2})}{(1 - z^{-1})(1 - 0.9z^{-1})(1 - 0.2z^{-1})} \cdot \frac{(1 - 0.5z^{-1})(1 - 0.8z^{-1})}{(1 - 2z^{-1})(1 - 1.5z^{-1})} \tag{9.6-75}$$

The first fraction is identified as $D_a(z)$ and the second fraction as $D_b(z)$. Thus, the realizable poles are confined in $D_a(z)$, and the realizable zeros are confined in $D_b(z)$ which also contains equal number of zeros and poles. It is clear that $D_a(z)$ can be realized by a basic series structure and $D_b(z)$ can be realized by a basic feedback structure. As a result, cascading of these two basic structures realizes the given pulse-transfer function.

The techniques described above are based upon the factorization of $D(z)$ to meet the realizability restrictions. However, it is not always possible to factor $D(z)$ in such a way that $D_a(z)$ and $D_b(z)$ may be realized by the basic series and the basic feedback structure, respectively. For instance, the simple pulse-transfer function

$$D(z) = 1 - 2z^{-1} \tag{9.6-76}$$

cannot be factored as required for the realization by a cascaded series-feedback structure. Under such circumstances, additional zeros and poles must be introduced to $D(z)$ so as to make factorization possible and satisfactory. Equation (9.6-76) may be written as

$$D(z) = \frac{1 - 2z^{-1}}{1 - az^{-1}} (1 - az^{-1}) \qquad (9.6\text{-}77)$$

where $0 < a \leq 1$. The added zero and pole must be of the realizable type. The first factor of the right-hand side of Eq. (9.6-77) can be realized by a basic series structure, whereas the second factor can be realized by a

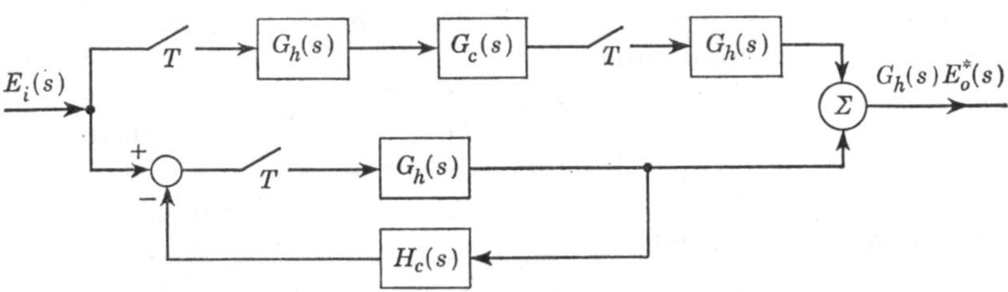

FIG. 9.6-13. Parallel series-feedback structure, $D(z) = G_hG_c(z) + 1/[1 + G_hH_c(z)]$.

basic feedback structure. In general, if $D_b(z)$ of Eq. (9.6-73) falls short of realizable zeros, arbitrary zeros, which are different from the zeros of $D_b(z)$ and are simple, positive, real, and residing inside the unit circle, are introduced to $D_b(z)$ so as to make the number of realizable zeros of $D_b(z)$ equal its number of poles. Meanwhile, poles of the same value as the added zeros are introduced in $D_a(z)$ so that the specified pulse-transfer function $D(z)$ remains unchanged.

In addition to the cascaded series-feedback structure described above, several other combinations are possible. The basic structures may be con-

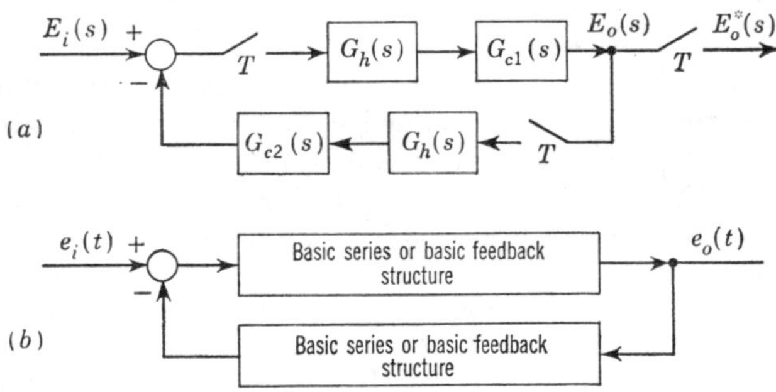

FIG. 9.6-14. General feedback structure of pulsed-data network.

nected in parallel, as illustrated in Fig. 9.6-13, or connected in feedback combination, as illustrated in Fig. 9.6-14. By following the arguments discussed above, the realization of a pulse-transfer function by these structures can be carried out without difficulty.

9.7. Synthesis in the w Plane by the Bode-diagram Technique. Up to this point, discussions have been centered upon the extension of the conventional Nyquist-diagram techniques to the design of sampled-data and digital feedback control systems. Both the continuous-data network and the pulsed-data network can be used for system compensation, although the design of pulsed-data network compensation is easier to carry out. Once the pulse-transfer function of the desired compensation is determined, the realization techniques described in Sec. 9.6 may be applied to synthesize the pulse-transfer function by a digital program, a pulsed-data processing unit or a pulsed-data RC network, whichever is applicable and preferable.

In view of the fact that the Bode-diagram technique has been the most convenient and widely used method of designing continuous-data control systems, the extension of the conventional Bode-diagram method to the synthesis of sampled-data and digital control systems is warranted. As a matter of fact, in the design of continuous-data control systems, the Nyquist-diagram technique is used primarily for systems which have exceedingly complicated transfer functions or in cases where the data are available experimentally only. When the transfer functions are in factored form, the control engineers always work with the Bode diagrams because of the simplicity and ease with which the asymptotic Bode diagrams of a transfer function can be plotted and reshaped. It can be expected that, in the design of sampled-data control systems, considerable convenience generally results if use is made of the Bode-diagram technique. This section is concerned with the extension of the Bode method to the design and synthesis of sampled-data and digital feedback control systems.[6,87]

The value of the Bode-diagram method as a tool of designing continuous-data control systems cannot be overemphasized. However, the Bode-diagram approach generally loses its usefulness as a convenient method if the transfer functions of the control system to be worked with are not rational functions in s and cannot be readily factored into linear and quadratic factors. It is shown in Chaps. 4 and 6 that the characteristic equation in s of a pulsed-data feedback control system is a transcendental equation and the open-loop transfer function of the system is a transcendental function in s. The difficulties encountered in plotting Bode diagrams of a transcendental function discourage the application of the Bode-diagram technique to the design of sampled-data control systems. As discussed in Chap. 5, the z transformation converts the transcendental function in s [for example, $GH^*(s)$] into a rational function in z; however, this process maps the primary and the complementary strips of the left half of the s plane into the unit circle of the z plane, which fails to conform with the requirements of the Bode method. The complex variable z and the frequency ω are related by

$$z = \epsilon^{sT} = \epsilon^{j\omega T} \tag{9.7-1}$$

As the frequency varies, the complex variable z moves along the circumference of the unit circle about the origin of the z plane. Clearly, the conventional Bode-diagram technique is not directly applicable to transfer functions in z. The Bode method requires that as the frequency varies, the complex variable moves along the imaginary axis of the complex plane. However, as can be conceived, if through an appropriate transformation the unit circle of the z plane is mapped into the imaginary axis of another complex plane, say w plane, and the interior of the unit circle into the entire left half of the w plane, the applicability of the Bode-diagram technique to transfer functions in w becomes apparent. With the new complex variable w replaced by jv, where v is a fictitious frequency, conventional rules may be used to plot the gain and phase diagrams of the transfer functions in w. This process of mapping the interior of the unit circle of the z plane into the entire left half of the w plane can be effected by means of the bilinear transformation[6,84,87]

$$z = \frac{1 + w}{1 - w} \tag{9.7-2}$$

The actual frequency ω and the fictitious frequency v are closely related. Inverting Eq. (9.7-2) yields

$$w = \frac{1 - z^{-1}}{1 + z^{-1}} \tag{9.7-3}$$

On the unit circle of the z plane, $z = \epsilon^{j\omega T}$. Since the unit circle is mapped into the imaginary axis of the w plane by the mapping function defined in Eq. (9.7-2), on the imaginary axis of the w plane the new variable w is given by Eq. (9.7-3) with z replaced by $\epsilon^{j\omega T}$. Thus,

$$w = \frac{1 - \epsilon^{-j\omega T}}{1 + \epsilon^{-j\omega T}} = j \tan \frac{\omega T}{2} \tag{9.7-4}$$

which is imaginary as expected. Equation (9.7-4) implies that the fictitious frequency v is given by

$$v = \tan \frac{\omega T}{2} \tag{9.7-5}$$

The above equation describes the relationship between the fictitious frequency v and the actual frequency ω. From Eq. (9.7-5), it is seen that the fictitious frequency v is a periodic function of ω, with period equal to ω_s, the sampling frequency of the system. When the actual frequency ω increases from 0 to $\omega_s/2$, the fictitious frequency v increases from zero to infinity. When ω increases from $\omega_s/2$ to ω_s, v increases from negative infinity to zero. This process repeats itself when ω is increased by ω_s. The relationship between the fictitious frequency v and the actual frequency ω for the frequency range between 0 and $\omega_s/2$ is illustrated in Fig. 9.7-1. Consequently, through the two mapping processes described above (the z transformation and the bilinear transformation), any of the strips of the left half of the s plane is first mapped into the interior of the unit circle of the z plane, and then mapped into the entire left half of the w plane, as illustrated in Fig. 6.2-12. The positive real axis of the z plane inside the unit circle is mapped into the section of the negative real axis of the w plane within the range from 0 to -1. The negative real axis of the z plane inside the unit circle is mapped into the section of the negative real axis of the w plane from -1 to $-\infty$. The origin of the z plane is mapped into the point $w = -1$ of the w plane. When s varies from 0 to $j\omega_s/2$ along the imaginary axis, z varies from 1 to -1 along the unit circle, and w varies from zero to infinity along the imaginary axis. In the w plane, the Bode-diagram technique can be used to advantage.

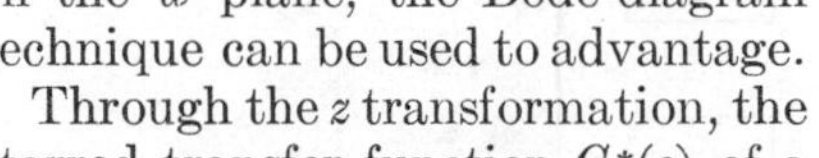

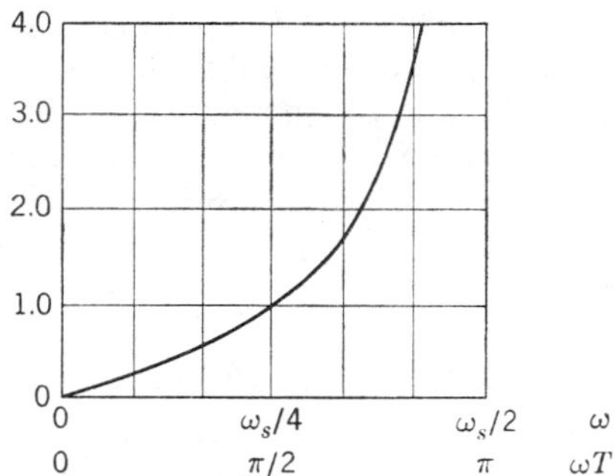

FIG. 9.7-1. Relationship between the fictitious frequency and the actual frequency.

Through the z transformation, the starred transfer function $G^*(s)$ of a pulsed-data system is converted to $G(z)$; and by the substitution of Eq. (9.7-2), the pulse-transfer function $G(z)$ is transformed to the w transform $G(w)$, which may be treated as a conventional transfer function in w. As can readily be seen, when s is increased from 0 to $j\omega_s/2$ along the imaginary axis, the transfer functions $G^*(s)$, $G(z)$, and $G(w)$ will trace out three loci which are identical in shape. In other words, the frequency locus of $G(jv)$ for the fictitious frequency range from zero to infinity is identical to the z-transform locus of $G(z)$, which is in turn the same as the frequency locus of $G^*(j\omega)$ for the frequency range from 0 to $\omega_s/2$. Here, the actual frequency ω and the fictitious frequency v are related by

$$\omega = \frac{2}{T} \tan^{-1} v \tag{9.7-6}$$

The value of $G(jv)$ at $v = v_1$ is identical to the value of $G^*(j\omega)$ at $\omega = \omega_1 = (2/T) \tan^{-1} v_1$. Once the gain and phase diagrams of $G(jv)$ are plotted by applying the standard asymptotic techniques, the frequency characteristics of the pulse-transfer function $G(z)$ [or $G^*(s)$] can readily be determined. In fact, it is much easier to work with the fictitious frequency v than with the actual frequency ω. Considerable convenience therefore results if the design of sampled-data and digital control systems is carried out in the w plane by means of the Bode-diagram technique. Design in the w plane offers several advantages. The well-known Routh-Hurwitz criterion may be used, instead of the fairly complicated Schur-Cohn criterion, to determine the absolute stability of pulsed-data control systems. The asymptotic plotting techniques can be applied for obtaining the gain and phase diagrams from which the gain margin and the phase margin may be quickly evaluated. With the aid of Nichols charts, the maximum magnitude ratio M_p and the resonant frequency ω_r of the pulsed-data system may be estimated. The general procedure for designing the desired compensator is simplified.

To design a sampled-data system by the Bode-diagram techniques it is essential that the pulse-transfer functions in z of the system are transformed to transfer functions in w by the bilinear transformation defined in Eq. (9.7-2). Referring to Fig. 9.7-3, the pulsed-data control system is compensated by the pulsed-data network $D^*(s)$. Without compensation, the z transform of the output is given by

$$C(z) = \frac{G(z)}{1 + GH(z)} R(z) \tag{9.7-7}$$

where $GH(z)$ is the z transform associated with $G(s)H(s)$, and is defined

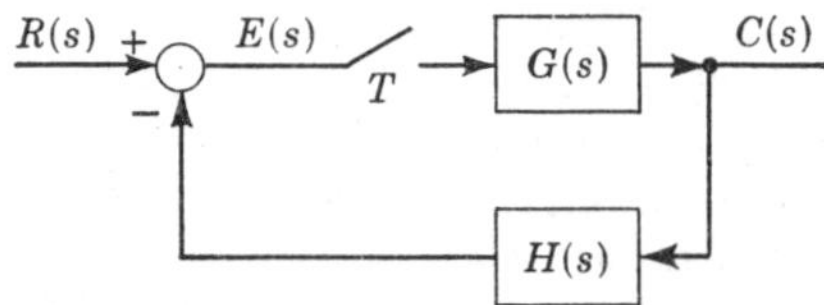

FIG. 9.7-2. Block diagram of the original system.

as the open-loop pulse-transfer function of the original system (Fig. 9.7-2). With compensation, the z transform of the output is

$$C(z) = \frac{D(z)G(z)}{1 + D(z)GH(z)} R(z) \tag{9.7-8}$$

where $D(z)GH(z)$ is the open-loop pulse-transfer function of the compen-

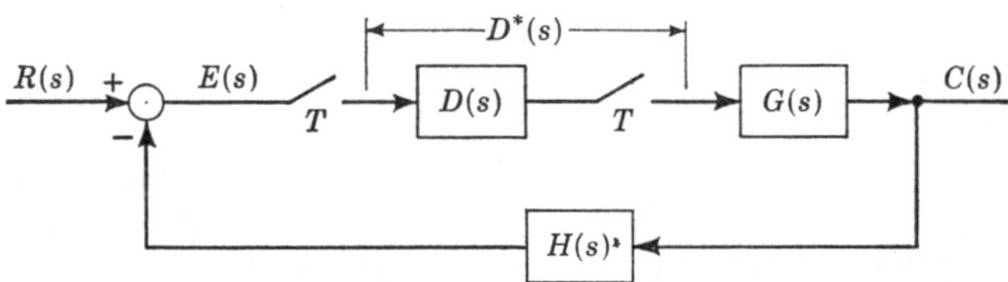

FIG. 9.7-3. Block diagram of the compensated system.

sated system (Fig. 9.7-3). The w transform of the output of the original system is obtained from Eq. (9.7-7) by the substitution

$$z = \frac{1 + w}{1 - w} \tag{9.7-9}$$

Thus,

$$C(w) = \frac{G(w)}{1 + GH(w)} R(w) \tag{9.7-10}$$

where $R(w)$ and $C(w)$ are the w transforms of the input $R(z)$ and the output $C(z)$ respectively, and $GH(w)$ is the w transform of $GH(z)$. In like manner, the w transform of the output of the compensated system as derived from Eq. (9.7-8) is

$$C(w) = \frac{D(w)G(w)}{1 + D(w)GH(w)} R(w) \tag{9.7-11}$$

Thus, the insertion of a pulsed-data network in series with the fixed components of the pulsed-data system results in a change of the open-loop transfer function from $GH(w)$ to $D(w)GH(w)$. The stability and performance of the original system, which are determined by the location of the poles and zeros of Eq. (9.7-10) in the w plane, can be evaluated from the Bode diagrams (gain and phase plots) of $GH(w)$. The compensator $D(w)$ required for meeting the specifications may be determined by the use of the conventional design techniques for continuous-data systems.

In view of Eq. (9.7-5), the specifications in terms of the actual frequency ω can readily be translated into the specifications in terms of the fictitious frequency v. For instance, if the specified resonant frequency is ω_r, the corresponding resonant frequency in the w domain is $\tan(\omega_r T/2)$. The correlation between the Nyquist diagram for $G^*(s)$ [or the z-transform locus of $G(z)$] and the gain and phase plots for the corresponding w transform $G(w)$ is illustrated in Fig. 9.7-4. If the Bode plot crosses the unity gain level at a fictitious frequency $v = v_c$, the Nyquist diagram will cross the unit circle at a frequency $\omega_c = (2/T)\tan^{-1} v_c$, which is the actual frequency at gain crossover. In view of the fact that $w = j\infty$ in the w domain corresponds to $s = j\omega_s/2$ in the s domain at which $G^*(s)$ is real and finite,

$$G(w)\Big|_{w=j\infty} = G^*(s)\Big|_{s=j\frac{\omega_s}{2}} \tag{9.7-12}$$

is always real and finite. This value is a measure of the gain margin, when the Nyquist diagram crosses the real axis only once, as shown in Fig. 9.7-4a. As can readily be seen, the system is unstable, if the gain plot does not cross the unity-gain level and stays above it. This corresponds to a gain margin less than unity. Furthermore, since $G(w)$ is always finite at $w = j\infty$, the w transform always contains equal number of poles and zeros. One or more zeros of $G(w)$ may reside in the right half of the w plane, making $G(w)$ a nonminimum-phase type transfer function. Thus, care should be taken in applying the Bode-diagram techniques to transfer functions in the w plane. After the transfer function $D(w)$ has been selected from the Bode diagrams the pulse-transfer function $D(z)$ of the desired pulsed-data compensator is then derived by the substitution

$$w = \frac{1 - z^{-1}}{1 + z^{-1}} \tag{9.7-13}$$

Based upon the above discussions, the synthesis procedure may be summarized as follows:

1. Derive the open-loop pulse-transfer function of the original system $A_0(z)$.
2. Transform the original open-loop pulse-transfer function $A_0(z)$ to a

transfer function $A_0(w)$ through the bilinear transformation defined in Eq. (9.7-9).

3. Plot the Bode diagrams for $A_0(w)$ with $w = jv$, where v is a fictitious frequency.

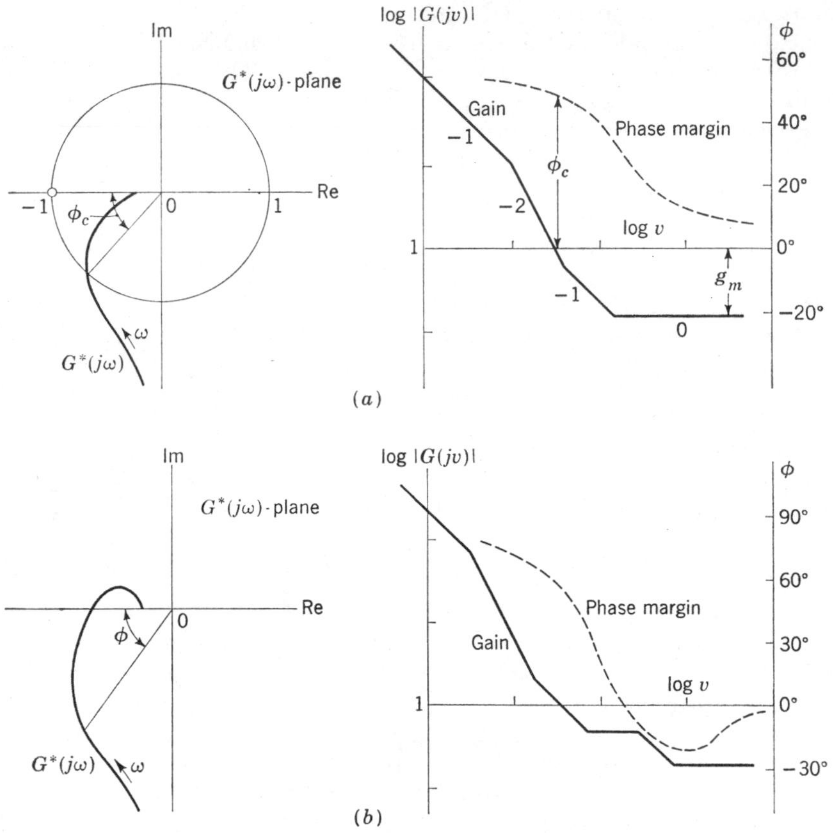

Fig. 9.7-4. Typical forms of the Nyquist diagram of $G^*(j\omega)$ and the gain and phase plots of the corresponding w transform $G(w)$ (not drawn to scale).

4. Compute the phase margin and gain margin of $A_0(jv)$ and other design parameters from the Bode diagrams, and with the aid of Nichols charts estimate the resonant peak M_p and the resonant frequency ω_r.

5. By means of the conventional techniques for continuous-data control systems determine the transfer function $D(w)$ of the desired equalizer. The open-loop transfer function of the compensated system is then given by

$$A_c(w) = D(w)A_0(w) \tag{9.7-14}$$

in which $D(w)$ is expressed as the ratio of two polynomials in w.

6. Transform the transfer function $D(w)$ derived in step 5 to $D(z)$

through the bilinear transformation defined in Eq. (9.7-13). $D(z)$ is the pulse-transfer function of the desired pulsed-data compensating network.

7. By making use of the techniques described in Sec. 9.6, realize the pulse-transfer function $D(z)$ by a digital program, a pulsed-data processing unit or a pulsed-data RC network, whichever is most suitable.

Continuous-data Network Compensation. In case continuous-data network compensation is preferred to pulsed-data network compensation, the transfer function of the desired continuous-data equalizer may be determined from the pulsed-transfer function $D(z)$ obtained above. Referring to the unity-feedback sampled-data system of Fig. 9.7-5, it is seen that,

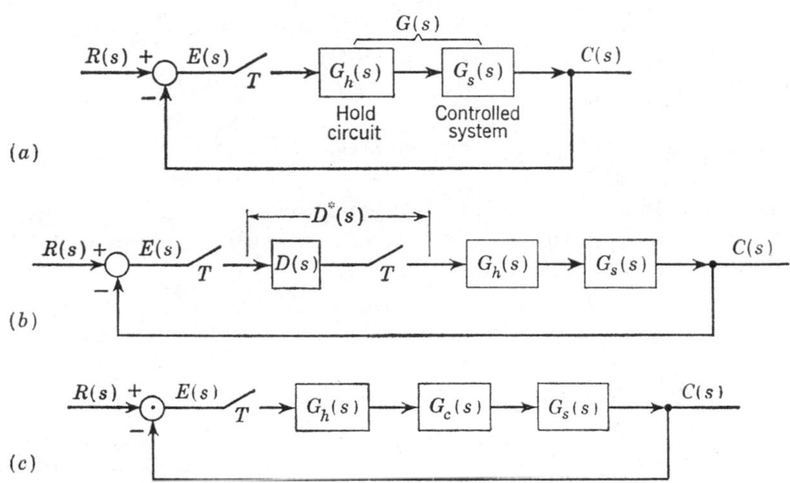

FIG. 9.7-5. System with cascade compensation. (*a*) The original system; (*b*) with pulsed-data network compensation; (*c*) with continuous-data network compensation.

when the pulsed-data network $D(z)$ is used for system compensation, the output transform is found to be

$$C(z) = \frac{D(z)G_hG_s(z)}{1 + D(z)G_hG_s(z)} R(z) \tag{9.7-15}$$

On the other hand, if a continuous-data network $G_c(s)$ is used for compensation, as shown in Fig. 9.7-5*c*, the output transform is then given by

$$C(z) = \frac{G_cG_hG_s(z)}{1 + G_cG_hG_s(z)} R(z) \tag{9.7-16}$$

where $G_cG_hG_s(z)$ is the z transform associated with $G_c(s)G_h(s)G_s(s)$. In order that both the pulsed-data network $D(z)$ and the continuous-data network $G_c(s)$ will provide the same compensation effect upon the system performance at the sampling instants, Eq. (9.7-16) must be identical to Eq. (9.7-15) and

$$G_cG_hG_s(z) = D(z)G_hG_s(z) \tag{9.7-17}$$

That is, the z transform associated with $G_c(s)G_h(s)G_s(s)$ must equal $D(z)G_hG_s(z)$. In symbols,

$$\mathfrak{Z}\{G_c(s)G_h(s)G_s(s)\} = D(z)G_hG_s(z) \tag{9.7-18}$$

Since $G_hG_s(z)$ is the z transform associated with $G_h(s)G_s(s)$, which is known, and $D(z)$ is readily determined from the synthesis procedure outlined in the preceding paragraph (or from the procedure described in Sec. 9.5), the required transfer function $G_c(s)$ may be derived from Eq. (9.7-18). Clearly, $G_c(s)$ can be obtained by dividing the $\mathfrak{L}$ transform associated with the right-hand member of Eq. (9.7-18) by $G_h(s)G_s(s)$. If $D(z)G_hG_s(z)$ contains no multiple poles, it can be expanded into the sum of simple fractions of the standard form $Kz/(z - a)$ of which the principal $\mathfrak{L}$ transform may be recognized from the table of the z transforms.

When a zero-order hold is used, Eq. (9.7-18) may be reduced to

$$\mathfrak{Z}\left\{\frac{G_c(s)G_s(s)}{s}\right\} = D(z)\,\mathfrak{Z}\left\{\frac{G_s(s)}{s}\right\} \tag{9.7-19}$$

The right-hand member of Eq. (9.7-19) may be expanded into the expression of Eq. (9.7-20), provided that it contains no multiple pole and that $G_s(s)$ does not have a pole at $s = 0$.

$$D(z)\mathfrak{Z}\left\{\frac{G_s(s)}{s}\right\} = \frac{K_0z}{z-1} + \sum_r \frac{K_rz}{z-p_r} \tag{9.7-20}$$

Equation (9.7-20) is obtained by expanding

$$\frac{D(z)}{z}\,\mathfrak{Z}\left\{\frac{G_s(s)}{s}\right\} \tag{9.7-21}$$

into partial fractions which are then multiplied by z. Substituting Eq. (9.7-20) into Eq. (9.7-19) yields

$$\mathfrak{Z}\left\{\frac{G_c(s)G_s(s)}{s}\right\} = \frac{K_0z}{z-1} + \sum_r \frac{K_rz}{z-p_r} \tag{9.7-22}$$

With the aid of the z-transform table, it is evident that for p_r being real, positive, and less than unity the required transfer function $G_c(s)$ is then given by

$$G_c(s) = \frac{1}{G_s(s)}\left\{K_0 + \sum_r \frac{K_rs}{s+a_r}\right\} \tag{9.7-23}$$

where

$$a_r = -\frac{1}{T}\ln p_r \tag{9.7-24}$$

In like manner, it can readily be shown that, if $G_s(s)$ has a pole at $s = 0$,

$$\mathfrak{Z}\left\{\frac{G_c(s)G_s(s)}{s}\right\} = \frac{K_0z}{z-1} + \frac{K_0'Tz}{(z-1)^2} + \sum_r \frac{K_rz}{z-p_r} \tag{9.7-25}$$

Thus, for p_r being real, positive, and less than unity,

$$G_c(s) = \frac{1}{G_s(s)}\left(K_0 + \frac{K_0'}{s} + \sum_r \frac{K_r s}{s + a_r}\right) \tag{9.7-26}$$

The above discussions indicate a method for arriving at a continuous-data compensation function. In view of the fact that $G_s(s)$ always contains more poles than zeros, the transfer functions given by Eq. (9.7-23) and Eq. (9.7-26) are not physically realizable as *RC* networks. However, the realization could be made possible if $G_c(s)$ is approximated by $G_c'(s)$ which contains equal number of poles and zeros. This approximation can generally be accomplished by introducing negative, real poles remote from the origin of the *s* plane to $G_c(s)$. The required continuous-data compensating network may then be synthesized from the approximate transfer function $G_c'(s)$ within reasonable accuracy.

VELOCITY-ERROR CONSTANT K_v. In the *w* domain, the velocity-error constant K_v of a sampled-data control system (Fig. 9.7-5*a*) is equal to twice the gain constant of the *w* transform of the open-loop transfer function of the system. Referring to Fig. 9.7-5*a*, the *z* transform of the system error is

$$E(z) = \frac{R(z)}{1 + G(z)} \tag{9.7-27}$$

where

$$G(z) = G_hG_s(z) \tag{9.7-28}$$

is the *z* transform associated with $G_h(s)G_s(s)$. In Sec. 6.5 it is shown that the steady-state error of the system subjected to a unit ramp input is given by

$$\varepsilon_{ss} = \frac{T}{\lim\limits_{z\to 1}\{(z-1)G(z)\}} \tag{9.7-29}$$

Since the velocity-error constant K_v is defined as the reciprocal of the steady-state velocity error multiplied by the sampling period T,

$$K_v = \frac{T}{\varepsilon_{ss}} = \lim_{z\to 1}\{(z-1)G(z)\} \tag{9.7-30}$$

In terms of *w* transforms, K_v is given by

$$K_v = \lim_{w\to 0}\left\{\frac{2w}{1-w}G(w)\right\} \tag{9.7-31}$$

Equation (9.7-31) is obtained from Eq. (9.7-30) by the substitution

$$z = \frac{1+w}{1-w} \tag{9.7-32}$$

and $G(w)$ is the *w* transform associated with $G(z)$. If the system shown in Fig. 9.7-5*a* is a type 1 system and $G_h(s)$ is a zero-order hold, $G_s(s)$ contains a pole at $s = 0$ and $G(s)$ can be assumed to take the form

$$\begin{aligned} G(s) &= G_h(s)G_s(s) \\ &= K(1 - \epsilon^{-Ts}) \frac{(1 + b_1s)(1 + b_2s) \cdots (1 + b_ms)}{s^2(1 + a_1s)(1 + a_2s) \cdots (1 + a_ns)} \end{aligned} \tag{9.7-33}$$

in which $-1/b_1, -1/b_2, \ldots, -1/b_m$ are the zeros and $-1/a_1, -1/a_2, \ldots, -1/a_n$ are the poles of $G(s)$. Equation (9.7-33) may be expanded into

$$G(s) = K(1 - \epsilon^{-Ts}) \left[\frac{1}{s^2} + \frac{k_0}{s} + \sum_r \frac{k_r}{s + (1/a_r)} \right] \tag{9.7-34}$$

where the k_0 and k_r's are constants determined by the values of a's and b's. The z transform associated with $G(s)$ is

$$G(z) = K \left[\frac{T}{z - 1} + k_0 + (z - 1) \sum_r \frac{k_r}{z - p_r} \right] \tag{9.7-35}$$

where p_r's are the corresponding poles in the z plane. The w transform associated with $G(z)$ is then given by

$$G(w) = K \left[\frac{T(1 - w)}{2w} + k_0 + \text{terms containing } w \text{ as a factor} \right] \tag{9.7-36}$$

which reduces to

$$G(w) = \frac{KT}{2w} \left[1 - \left(1 - \frac{2k_0}{T} \right) w + \text{terms containing } w^2 \text{ as a factor} \right] \tag{9.7-37}$$

Clearly, the gain constant of the w transform of the open-loop transfer function $G(w)$ is $KT/2$. Substituting Eq. (9.7-37) into Eq. (9.7-31) and passing through the limit yields

$$K_v = KT \tag{9.7-38}$$

which is twice the gain constant of $G(w)$.

In order to demonstrate the procedures discussed in this section an illustrative example is presented in the following paragraphs.

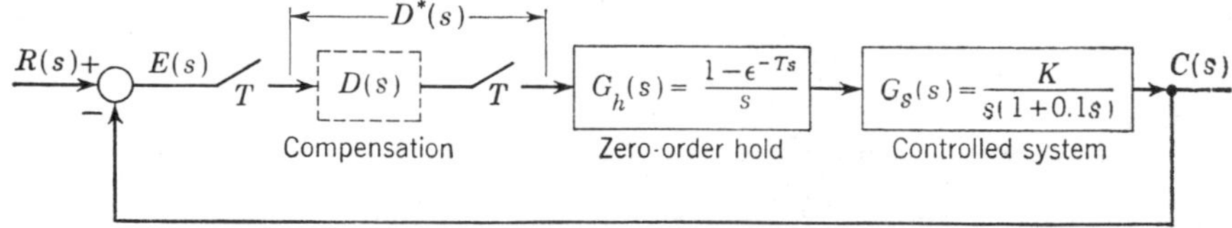

FIG. 9.7-6. The block diagram of the system of Example 9.7-1.

EXAMPLE 9.7-1. Shown in Fig. 9.7-6 is a sampled-data feedback control system which uses a zero-order hold as the smoothing device. The fixed part of the system is described by the transfer function

$$G_s(s) = \frac{K}{s(1 + 0.1s)} \tag{9.7-39}$$

The sampling period is 0.1 sec. It is required to design a pulsed-data compensator to meet the following specifications:

1. The velocity-error constant K_v must be equal to or larger than 3.
2. The gain margin must exceed 6.
3. The phase margin must be greater than 50°.
4. The resonant peak must be around 1.3.

The first step in the design involves a determination of the open-loop pulse-transfer function of the original system $A_0(z)$ which is, in this case, simply the z transform associated with $G_h(s)G_s(s)$. Referring to Fig. 9.7-6, it is seen that the transfer function for the continuous-data part of the system is

$$A_0(s) = G_h(s)G_s(s) = \frac{K(1 - \epsilon^{-Ts})}{s^2(1 + 0.1s)} \tag{9.7-40}$$

The z transform associated with $A_0(s)$ is found to be

$$A_0(z) = K\left[\frac{T}{z - 1} - 0.1 + \frac{0.1(z - 1)}{z - \epsilon^{-10T}}\right] \tag{9.7-41}$$

or

$$A_0(z) = \frac{K[(0.1\epsilon^{-10T} + T - 0.1)z - (0.1 + T)\epsilon^{-10T} + 0.1]}{(z - 1)(z - \epsilon^{-10T})} \tag{9.7-42}$$

For $T = 0.1$ sec, Eq. (9.7-42) reduces to

$$A_0(z) = \frac{0.1K(0.368z + 0.264)}{(z - 1)(z - 0.368)} \tag{9.7-43}$$

Transforming to the w domain by the substitution $z = (1 + w)/(1 - w)$ yields

$$\begin{aligned} A_0(w) &= \frac{0.1K(1 - w)(0.632 + 0.104w)}{2w(0.632 + 1.368w)} \\ &= \frac{K}{20}\,\frac{(1 - w)[1 + (w/6.07)]}{w[1 + (w/0.462)]} \end{aligned} \tag{9.7-44}$$

Clearly, the gain constant of $A_0(w)$ is $K/20$. Since the velocity-error constant is equal to twice this gain constant,

$$K_v = \frac{K}{10} \tag{9.7-45}$$

From the first specification, $K_v \geq 3$, the gain constant K of the system is found to be

$$K \geq 30 \tag{9.7-46}$$

If the gain constant K is set at 30, Eq. (9.7-44) becomes

$$A_0(w) = \frac{1.5(1 - w)[1 + (w/6.07)]}{w[1 + (w/0.462)]} \tag{9.7-47}$$

The asymptotic Bode diagram for $A_0(jv)$ is plotted in Fig. 9.7-7. At this gain setting, the system without compensation is unstable, since the Bode plot stays above the unity-gain level. From the Bode plot it is seen that in this case phase-lead compensation fails to be an effective means and

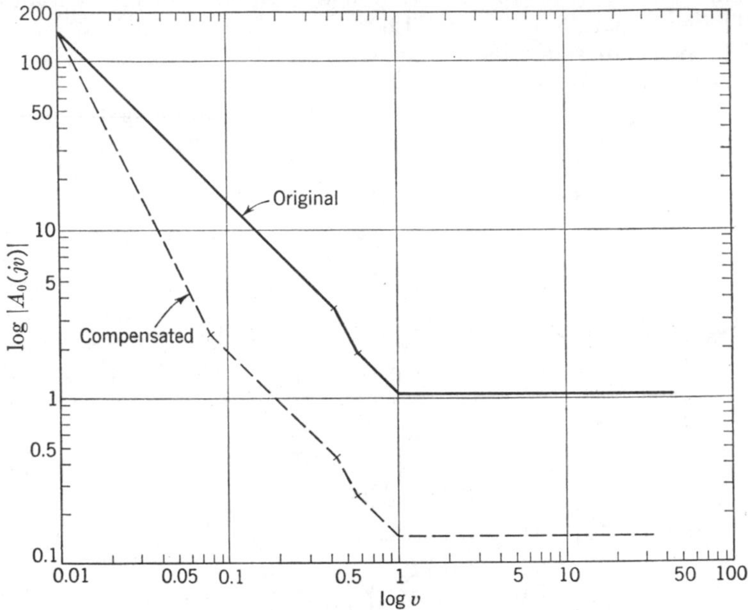

FIG. 9.7-7. Bode plots of Example 9.7-1.

system stabilization must be accomplished by phase-lag compensation.

Following the conventional design rules, it is found that a phase-lag network described by the transfer function

$$D(w) = \frac{1 + (w/0.08)}{1 + (w/0.01)} \tag{9.7-48}$$

when connected in cascade, will raise the gain margin and the phase margin of the system to the specified values. Thus, the w transform of the open-loop transfer function of the compensated system is given by

$$\begin{aligned} A_c(w) &= A_0(w)D(w) \\ &= \frac{1.5(1 - w)[1 + (w/6.07)][1 + (w/0.08)]}{w[1 + (w/0.462)][1 + (w/0.01)]} \end{aligned} \tag{9.7-49}$$

The asymptotic Bode diagram of the compensated system is also plotted in Fig. 9.7-7. The gain plot crosses the unity-gain level at a frequency (fictitious)

$$v_c = 0.2 \tag{9.7-50}$$

From Eq. (9.7-49), the phase margin at gain crossover is found to be 54.6°, which meets the specification. Also, the Bode plot indicates a gain margin of 6.67, which is sufficient. With the aid of Nichols charts, the resonant peak and the resonant frequency (fictitious) are determined. They are

$$M_p = 1.3 \qquad v_r = 0.10$$

The log gain versus phase diagram is plotted with Nichols charts in Fig. 9.7-8. The actual resonant frequency is, then, given by

$$\omega_r = \frac{2}{T} \tan^{-1} v_r = 2 \text{ radians/sec}$$

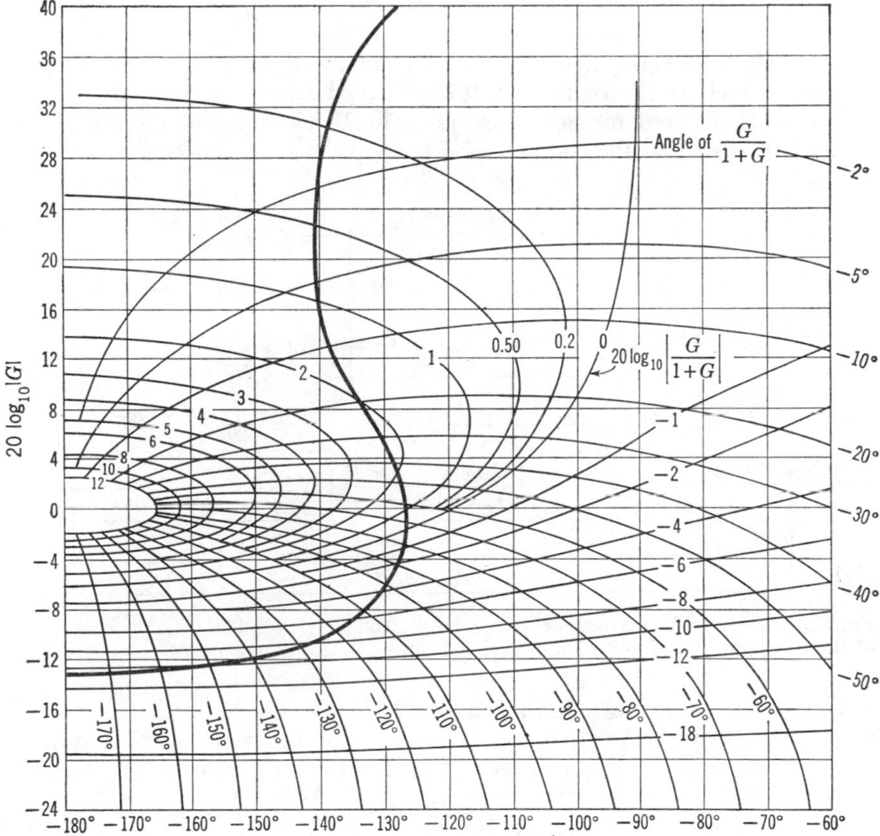

FIG. 9.7-8. Log gain vs. phase plot of Example 9.7-1 (with compensation).

Thus, the phase-lag network described by Eq. (9.7-48) is considered satisfactory, and the next step is to transform $D(w)$ to $D(z)$ and to realize $D(z)$ by a pulsed-data network.

By the substitution $w = (1 - z^{-1})/(1 + z^{-1})$, Eq. (9.7-48) leads to

$$D(z) = \frac{0.134(z - 0.852)}{(z - 0.98)} \tag{9.7-51}$$

By applying the techniques described in Sec. 9.6, the realization of the pulse-transfer function defined in Eq. (9.7-51) can readily be carried out. As an illustration, $D(z)$ of Eq. (9.7-51) is to be realized as a pulsed-data *RC* network. $D(z)$ may be realized by a basic series pulsed-data *RC* network, as described in Sec. 9.6, since it satisfies the realizability restrictions. Making use of the results of Example 9.6-1, one obtains the transfer function $G_c(s)$ of the required *RC* network as

$$G_c(s) = \frac{0.134(s + 1.465)}{(s + 0.198)} = \frac{(1 + 0.683s)}{(1 + 5.05s)} \tag{9.7-52}$$

Clearly, $G_c(s)$ of Eq. (9.7-52) can readily be synthesized by a simple *RC* network which is shown in Fig. 9.7-9*a*. If the basic series pulsed-data *RC* network is used for compensation, the block diagram illustrated in Fig. 9.7-9*b* describes the compensated system.

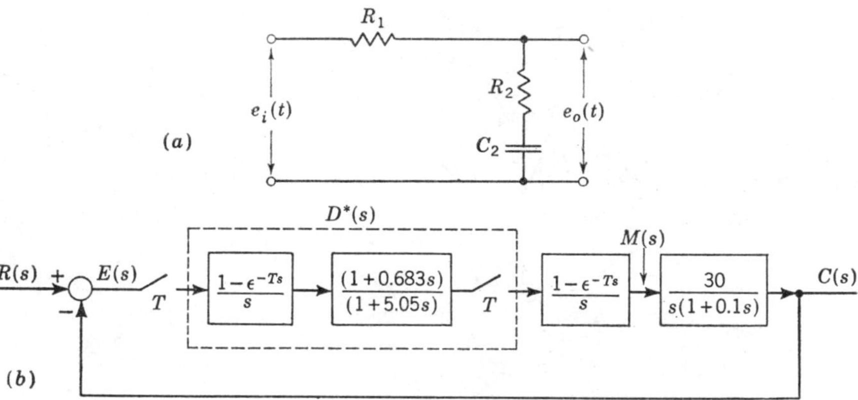

FIG. 9.7-9. (*a*) An *RC* network for $G_c(s) = (1 + 0.683s)/(1 + 5.05s)$; (*b*) block diagram of the system compensated with a cascaded pulsed-data *RC* network.

Furthermore, $D(z)$ of Eq. (9.7-51) may also be realized by a basic feedback pulsed-data *RC* network. If the transfer function of the required *RC* network is $H_c(s)$, application of the results of Example 9.6-2 leads to

$$H_c(s) = \frac{-0.116}{1 + (s/1.6)} \tag{9.7-53}$$

which can easily be realized by a simple *RC* network as shown in Fig. 9.7-10*a*. If system compensation is effected by the basic feedback pulsed-data *RC* network, the compensated system may be described by the block diagram illustrated in Fig. 9.7-10*c*. Comparison between the block diagrams of Fig. 9.7-9*b* and Fig. 9.7-10*c* indicates that system compensation with a basic feedback pulsed-data *RC* network appears simpler and more economical. In fact, pulsed-data network compensation by a basic feedback structure is essentially a form of minor-loop compensation by a continuous-data network.

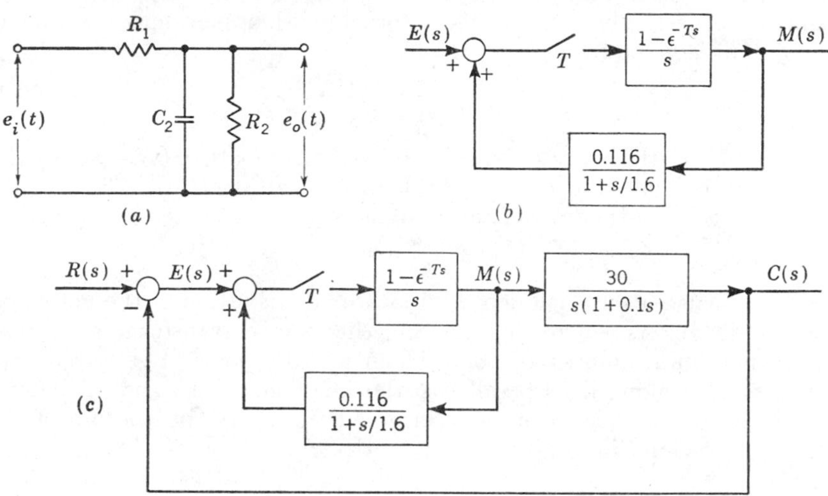

FIG. 9.7-10. (*a*) An *RC* network for $H_c(s) = 0.116/(1 + s/1.6)$; (*b*) a pulsed-data network of the basic parallel structure; (*c*) block diagram of the system compensated with a pulsed-data network of the basic parallel structure.

9.8. Root-locus Method in the *z* Plane. Just as the Nyquist-diagram and Bode-diagram techniques of analysis are carried over to the design of sampled-data and digital control systems, it is quite reasonable to consider the possibility of extending the much used root-locus techniques to the analysis and synthesis of pulsed-data systems.[84,106,161] In Secs. 7.1 and 7.2 it is shown that transient behavior of a pulsed-data control system is determined completely by the nature of the zeros and poles of its closed-loop system function. These poles are the characteristic roots of the system. Once the closed-loop poles of the pulsed-data system are determined, the different modes of the transient response become known. As a result, the control system engineer will find the design of the pulsed-data system relatively easy to carry out, if he possesses a general knowledge of how the variation of the closed-loop poles or characteristic roots will influence the transient behavior of the system. Indeed, such knowledge can be readily gathered from a plot of the locus of the characteristic roots of the pulsed-data system with the system loop gain as a parameter. A plot of this sort is referred to as the root locus. A knowledge of the properties of the loci along which the characteristic roots migrate provides penetrating insight into system behavior. With the aid of the root-locus plot, the design of pulsed-data control systems can be accomplished by simply adjusting the loop gain and the closed-loop poles and zeros of the system so as to end up with an improved closed-loop system function with new pole-zero distributions which will give rise to the desired transient response.

Shown in Fig. 9.8-1 is the block diagram of a basic sampled-data feedback control system, in which $G_h(s)$, $G_s(s)$, and $H(s)$ stand for the transfer functions of the holding device, the controlled system, and the feedback element, respectively. The over-all (or closed-loop) system function of this system is given by

$$G_0^*(s) = \frac{C^*(s)}{R^*(s)} = \frac{G^*(s)}{1 + A^*(s)} \tag{9.8-1}$$

where $G^*(s)$ is the starred transform associated with $G(s) = G_h(s)G_s(s)$ and $A^*(s)$ is that associated with $A(s) = G_h(s)G_s(s)H(s)$. Clearly, the characteristic equation in s of this system is

$$1 + A^*(s) = 0 \tag{9.8-2}$$

The root-locus pattern will depend upon the distribution of the poles and zeros of $A^*(s)$. As can readily be seen, the starred transform $A^*(s)$ possesses an infinite number of poles which are the poles of $A(s)$ repeated every $j\omega_s$ unit along lines parallel to the imaginary axis, and an infinite number of zeros, which can be determined from $A(s)$ by the use of the following relationship:

$$A^*(s) = \sum_k \text{residues of } \frac{A(\chi)}{1 - \epsilon^{-T(s-\chi)}} \qquad \text{at } \chi = s_k \tag{9.8-3}$$

where $A(\chi)$ is equal to $A(s)$ with s replaced by χ. Since the poles of $A^*(s)$ are infinite in number, the root locus for Eq. (9.8-2) would comprise an infinite number of branches. Consequently, unlike the root-locus plot for continuous-data systems, the construction of the root-locus plot for a pulsed-data system from the starred transfer function is by no means a simple matter. Besides, the complicated nature of the root-locus plot in the s plane makes it rather difficult to study the effects of added compensation. The complexity and difficulties involved in the root-locus method in the s plane discourage its application to the design of pulsed-data control systems.

However, the aforesaid difficulties can be alleviated if use is made of the z transform techniques. In terms of the z transforms, the over-all system function of the system shown in Fig. 9.8-1 is given by

$$G_0(z) = \frac{C(z)}{R(z)} = \frac{G(z)}{1 + A(z)} \tag{9.8-4}$$

where $A(z) = GH(z)$, the z transform associated with $G(s)H(s)$, is referred to as the open-loop pulse-transfer function. $G_0(z)$ is also referred to as the over-all (or closed-loop) pulsed-transfer function of the system. The characteristic equation, then, becomes

$$1 + A(z) = 0 \tag{9.8-5}$$

In view of the fact that $A(z)$ is a rational function in z and contains a finite number of poles and zeros, the rules for constructing the root-locus plots of continuous-data systems outlined in most standard textbooks on feedback control systems[84] can be used to advantage to construct the

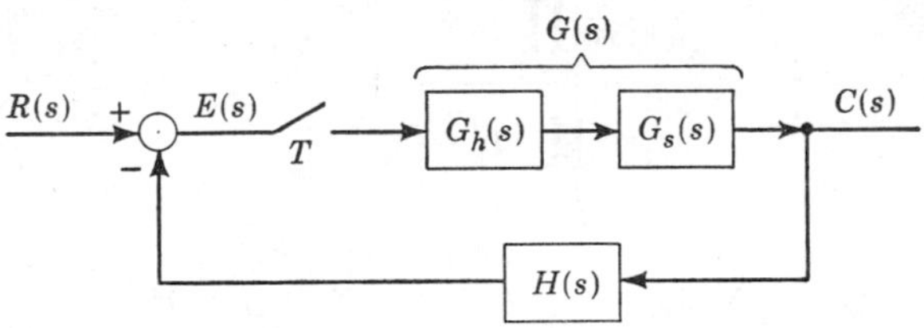

FIG. 9.8-1. A basic sampled-data feedback control system.

z-plane root-locus plots of sampled-data control systems. Equation (9.8-5) may be written as

$$A(z) = -1 = \epsilon^{j(180^\circ \pm n360^\circ)} \tag{9.8-6}$$

where n is an integer or zero. Since $A(z)$ is a function of complex variable z, Eq. (9.8-6) may be split into two equations by equating, respectively, the magnitude and the phase angle of both sides. They are the magnitude equation

$$|A(z)| = 1 \tag{9.8-7}$$

and the phase-angle equation

$$\underline{/A(z)} = 180^\circ \pm n360^\circ \tag{9.8-8}$$

The plot of the phase-angle equation with the gain factor as a parameter is referred to as the z-plane root locus of the pulsed-data system. The magnitude equation determines the value of the gain of each point of the locus.

Assume that the open-loop pulse-transfer function be given by

$$A(z) = \frac{K \prod_{k=1}^{m} (z - z_k)}{\prod_{k=1}^{n} (z - p_k)} \qquad n \geq m \tag{9.8-9}$$

By the substitution

$$z - p_k = a_k \underline{/\theta_{pk}} \qquad z - z_k = b_k \underline{/\theta_{zk}} \tag{9.8-10}$$

Eq. (9.8-9) may be written as

$$A(z) = \frac{K \prod_{k=1}^{m} b_k}{\prod_{k=1}^{n} a_k} \underline{\Big/ \sum_{k=1}^{m} \theta_{zk} - \sum_{k=1}^{n} \theta_{pk}} \tag{9.8-11}$$

where $a_k(b_k)$ is the distance from pole p_k (zero z_k) to point z on the root locus, and $\theta_{pk}(\theta_{zk})$ is the corresponding phase angle, as illustrated in Fig. 9.8-2. Then the magnitude and the phase-angle equations are given by

$$\frac{K \prod_{k=1}^{m} b_k}{\prod_{k=1}^{n} a_k} = 1 \tag{9.8-12}$$

and

$$\sum_{k=1}^{m} \theta_{zk} - \sum_{k=1}^{n} \theta_{pk} = 180° \pm n360° \tag{9.8-13}$$

respectively.

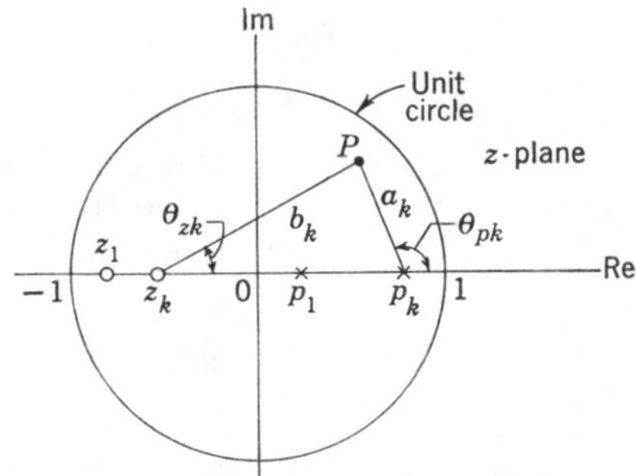

FIG. 9.8-2. Open-loop pole-zero distribution.

Design in Terms of the z-plane Root Loci. As an illustration, consider the basic sampled-data control system shown in Fig. 9.8-1, with the transfer functions given by

$$G_h(s) = \frac{1 - \epsilon^{-Ts}}{s} \tag{9.8-14}$$

$$G_s(s) = \frac{K}{s(1 + T_m s)} \tag{9.8-15}$$

$$H(s) = 1 \tag{9.8-16}$$

where $T_m = T/k$ is the time constant of the system; T, the sampling period; k, the ratio between the sampling period and the system time constant; and K, the gain constant of the system. Then, the open-loop transfer function $A(s)$ is given by

$$A(s) = G_h(s)G_s(s)H(s) = \frac{K(1 - \epsilon^{-Ts})}{s^2(1 + T_m s)} \tag{9.8-17}$$

The corresponding z transform is

$$A(z) = \frac{aTK(z - z_1)}{(z - 1)(z - p_1)} = \frac{K_0(z - z_1)}{(z - 1)(z - p_1)} \tag{9.8-18}$$

in which

$$z_1 = -\frac{1 - (1 + k)\epsilon^{-k}}{k - 1 + \epsilon^{-k}} \tag{9.8-19}$$

$$p_1 = \epsilon^{-k} \tag{9.8-20}$$

$$a = \frac{k - 1 + \epsilon^{-k}}{k} \tag{9.8-21}$$

$$K_0 = aTK \tag{9.8-22}$$

The pole-zero configuration for $A(z)$ is shown in Fig. 9.8-3a. Following the procedures described in Ref. 84, one can easily construct the root locus in the z plane for the characteristic equation

$$1 + \frac{K_0(z - z_1)}{(z - 1)(z - p_1)} = 0 \qquad (9.8\text{-}23)$$

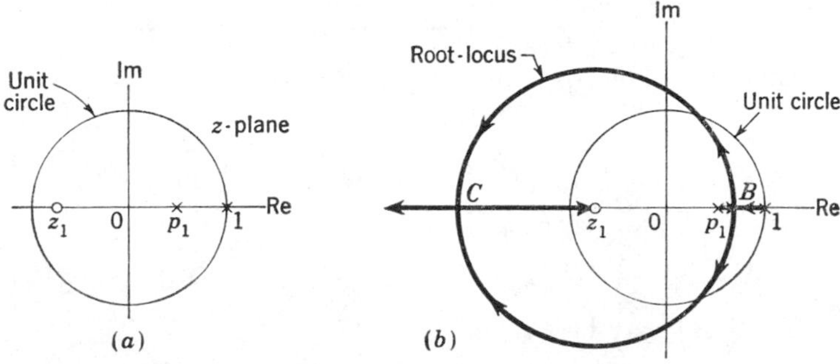

FIG. 9.8-3. (a) Pole-zero configuration for $A(z) = aKT(z - z_1)/(z - 1)(z - p_1)$; ($b$) the z-plane root-locus plot for $1 + A(z) = 0$.

The root locus, plotted in Fig. 9.8-3b, starts from the open-loop poles at $z = 1$ and $z = p_1$, where K_0 is zero. As K_0 is increased, the two branches of the root locus move along the real axis until they meet at point B, the breakaway point. At this point, the two characteristic roots of the system are identical. Simplifying Eq. (9.8-23) yields

$$z^2 - (1 + p_1 - K_0)z + p_1 - K_0z_1 = 0 \qquad (9.8\text{-}24)$$

At the breakaway point B, the characteristic roots are thus equal to $(1 + p_1 - K_{0e})/2$, where K_{0e} is the lower value of K_0 determined from

$$(1 + p_1 - K_0)^2 - 4(p_1 - K_0z_1) = 0 \qquad (9.8\text{-}25)$$

Then with the further increase in K_0 one branch of the root locus moves along the upper semicircle and the other branch moves along the lower semicircle. These two branches meet again on the negative real axis. At this intersection point C, the characteristic roots are equal to $(1 + p_1 - K_{0h})/2$, where K_{0h} is the higher value of K_0 obtained from Eq. (9.8-25). From here on, as K_0 is increased further, one branch continues its motion along the negative real axis toward the open-loop zero $z = z_1$, and the other branch moves in the opposite direction until it terminates at infinity. At the open-loop zero $z = z_1$ and at infinity, K_0 is infinite. Since there are two open-loop poles and one open-loop zero, the root locus of this system consists of two branches, one of which is finite.

The circular part of the root-locus diagram may be analytically determined from the phase-angle equation. It follows from Eq. (9.8-23) that

$$\frac{K_0(z - z_1)}{(z - 1)(z - p_1)} = -1 \qquad (9.8\text{-}26)$$

Let
$$z = x + jy \tag{9.8-27}$$
then
$$\frac{K_0(x - z_1 + jy)}{(x - 1 + jy)(x - p_1 + jy)} = -1 \tag{9.8-28}$$
from which the phase-angle equation is found to be
$$\tan^{-1}\frac{y}{x - z_1} - \tan^{-1}\frac{y(2x - p_1 - 1)}{x^2 - y^2 - x(1 + p_1) + p_1} = \pi \tag{9.8-29}$$
Transposing and taking the tangents of both sides yield
$$\frac{1}{x - z_1} = \frac{2x - p_1 - 1}{x^2 - y^2 - x(1 + p_1) + p_1} \tag{9.8-30}$$
Cross multiplying and rearranging lead to
$$x^2 - 2z_1x + y^2 + z_1(p_1 + 1) - p_1 = 0 \tag{9.8-31}$$
Equation (9.8-31) may be written as
$$(x - z_1)^2 + y^2 = (z_1 - p_1)(z_1 - 1) \tag{9.8-32}$$
This is an equation of a circle with the center at $(z_1,0)$ and the radius equal to $[(z_1 - p_1)(z_1 - 1)]^{1/2}$. Thus, the circular part of the root locus is the circle with its center located at the open-loop zero $z = z_1$, and its radius equal to $[(z_1 - p_1)(z_1 - 1)]^{1/2}$. The intercepts of the circle with the real axis, as computed from Eq. (9.8-32), are
$$x = z_1 + [(z_1 - p_1)(z_1 - 1)]^{1/2} \tag{9.8-33}$$
$$x = z_1 - [(z_1 - p_1)(z_1 - 1)]^{1/2} \tag{9.8-34}$$

In view of the fact that the z transformation maps the left half of the s plane into the interior of the unit circle of the z plane, absolute stability requires that all poles of the over-all pulse-transfer function (or more generally, all poles of the output z transform) lie inside the unit circle. In other words, for stable operation the root locus of a sampled-data system must be confined in the unit circle. The gain at which instability occurs is the system gain at which the root locus intersects the unit circle, and will be referred to as the maximum allowable gain. The point of intersection may be determined from Eq. (9.8-32) and the equation describing the unit circle,
$$x^2 + y^2 = 1 \tag{9.8-35}$$
Subtracting Eq. (9.8-35) from Eq. (9.8-31) yields the abscissa of the point of intersection as
$$x = \frac{(1 - p_1) + z_1(1 + p_1)}{2z_1} \tag{9.8-36}$$

The ordinates of the points of intersection are then obtained from Eq. (9.8-35) as

$$y = \frac{\pm[(1 - p_1)(z_1 - 1)(1 - p_1 + 3z_1 + z_1p_1)]^{1/2}}{2z_1} \tag{9.8-37}$$

The gain at which the system starts sustained oscillation may be derived from Eq. (9.8-35), Eq. (9.8-36), and the magnitude equation

$$\frac{K_0|z - z_1|}{|z - 1|\,|z - p_1|} = 1 \tag{9.8-38}$$

By the substitution of Eq. (9.8-27), the magnitude equation becomes

$$\frac{K_0^2[(x - z_1)^2 + y^2]}{[(x - 1)^2 + y^2][(x - p_1)^2 + y^2]} = 1 \tag{9.8-39}$$

In view of Eq. (9.8-35), the above equation reduces to

$$K_0^2 = \frac{2(1 - x)(1 + p_1^2 - 2p_1x)}{(1 + z_1^2 - 2z_1x)} \tag{9.8-40}$$

Substituting Eq. (9.8-36) into Eq. (9.8-40) and simplifying yield the maximum allowable value of K_0

$$K_0 = \frac{1 - p_1}{|z_1|} \tag{9.8-41}$$

Since $K_0 = aTK$, the maximum allowable system gain is

$$K_m = \frac{1 - p_1}{aT|z_1|} \tag{9.8-42}$$

As can readily be seen from Eq. (9.8-36), the above expression is valid for

$$z_1 \leq -\frac{1 - p_1}{3 + p_1} \tag{9.8-43}$$

When z_1 exceeds this valuc, the root-locus circle no longer intersects the unit circle.

In fact, z_1 given by Eq. (9.8-19) satisfies the condition of Eq. (9.8-43) for all values of k. Substituting Eqs. (9.8-19), (9.8-20), and (9.8-21) into Eq. (9.8-42) yields

$$K_m = \frac{k}{T[1 - (k\epsilon^{-k}/1 - \epsilon^{-k})]} \tag{9.8-44}$$

$$= \frac{1}{T_m[1 - (k\epsilon^{-k}/1 - \epsilon^{-k})]} \tag{9.8-45}$$

Equations (9.8-42) and (9.8-44) place in evidence that the relative stability of the system can be improved by reducing the sampling period. The effect of k upon the system stability can be seen from Eq. (9.8-45). The relationship between K_m and k becomes more conspicuous, if K_m is plotted against the system time constant T_m with k as a parameter. Such plottings are referred to as the maximum allowable gain charts. Equation (9.8-45) may be written as

$$K_m T_m = \frac{1}{1 - (k\epsilon^{-k}/1 - \epsilon^{-k})} \tag{9.8-46}$$

For a given value of k, Eq. (9.8-46) describes a rectangular hyperbola. The maximum allowable gain charts for a second-order system, as plotted in Fig. 9.8-4, consist of a family of rectangular hyperbolas.

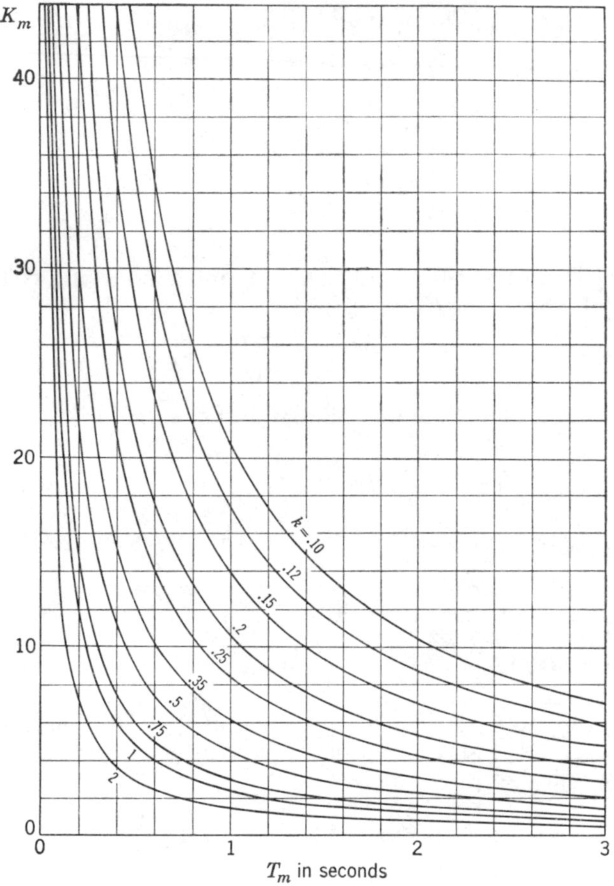

Fig. 9.8-4. Maximum allowable gain charts for a second-order sampled-data feedback control system with a zero-order hold.

The expressions for maximum gain described by Eqs. (9.8-41) and (9.8-42) are valid only when the zero z_1 satisfies the condition of Eq. (9.8-43). Under this circumstance, instability occurs when the root-locus circle crosses the unit circle, as demonstrated in Fig. 9.8-3*b*. However, if z_1 exceeds the value given by Eq. (9.8-43), the circular part of the root locus will not cross the unit circle, and instability occurs when the root-locus plot crosses the unit circle at the -1 point. Clearly, in this case one characteristic root is

$$z = -1 \tag{9.8-47}$$

The other root follows immediately from Eq. (9.8-24), if use is made of the relationships between the roots and the coefficients of a rational algebraic equation. The sum of these two roots equals $(1 + p_1 - K_0)$, and the product of these two roots equals $(p_1 - K_0z_1)$. The first relationship yields the second characteristic root as

$$z = 2 + p_1 - K_0 \tag{9.8-48}$$

From the second relationship, it is found that instability occurs for a value of K_0 given by the equation

$$-(2 + p_1 - K_0) = p_1 - K_0z_1 \tag{9.8-49}$$

Thus, the maximum value of K_0 without causing instability is

$$K_0 = \frac{2(1 + p_1)}{(1 + z_1)} \tag{9.8-50}$$

Effects of Shifting an Open-loop Zero or an Open-loop Pole. The effects of shifting an open-loop zero or an open-loop pole can generally be examined from the expressions for the maximum allowable gain constant in terms of the zeros and poles. Consider the system described above. The effects of shifting the zero z_1 and the pole p_1 can readily be seen from the maximum allowable gain-constant expressions given in Eqs. (9.8-41) and (9.8-50). Equation (9.8-50) indicates that the system stability could be improved by shifting the pole p_1 away from the origin and shifting the zero z_1 toward the -1 point. However, the values of p_1 and z_1 must satisfy the relationship

$$z_1 \geq -\frac{1 - p_1}{3 + p_1} \tag{9.8-51a}$$

or

$$p_1 \leq \frac{1 + 3z_1}{1 - z_1} \tag{9.8-51b}$$

For instance, when $p_1 = \frac{1}{9}$, $z_1 \geq -\frac{2}{7}$. On the other hand, when the values of p_1 and z_1 fail to satisfy Eq. (9.8-51a) or Eq. (9.8-51b), the expression for maximum gain given in Eq. (9.8-50) no longer holds and Eq. (9.8-41) should be used instead. As evidenced from Eq. (9.8-41), the system could be made more stable by shifting both the pole p_1 and the zero z_1 toward the origin; but the values of p_1 and z_1 must fulfill the relationship

$$p_1 \geq \frac{1 + 3z_1}{1 - z_1} \tag{9.8-52}$$

From the above discussions, it is seen that for a specified value of p_1 between 0 and 1 the optimum location of the zero z_1 is given by

$$z_1 = -\frac{1 - p_1}{3 + p_1} \tag{9.8-53}$$

On the other hand, for a specified value of z_1, the optimum location of the pole p_1 is given by

$$p_1 = \frac{1 + 3z_1}{1 - z_1} \tag{9.8-54}$$

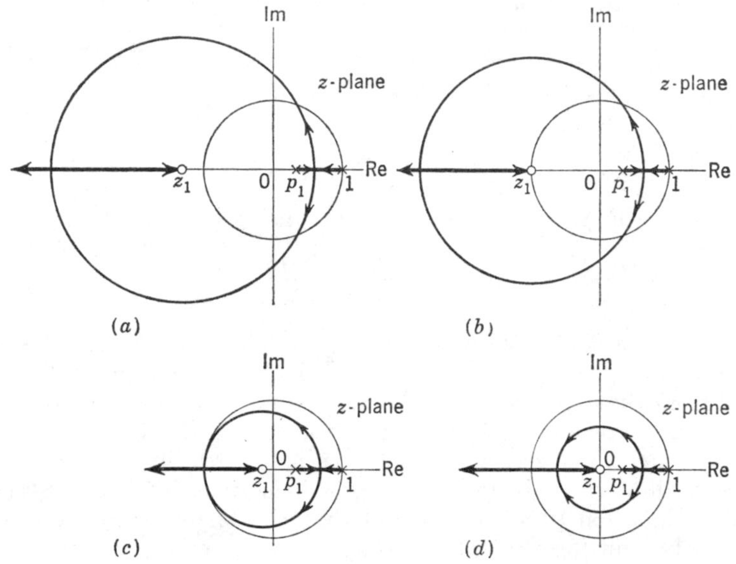

FIG. 9.8-5. The root-locus diagrams for various values of z_1.

The root-locus plots for several values of z_1 are sketched in Fig. 9.8-5. The shifting of the zero may be accomplished by introducing a pole to cancel the unwanted zero and placing a new zero at a desirable location, if use is made of the pulsed-data network compensation. The effects of

TABLE 9.8-1

z_1	p_1	K_0
$-\frac{1}{4}$	$\frac{3}{4}$	1
$-\frac{1}{4}$	$\frac{1}{2}$	2
$-\frac{1}{4}$	$\frac{1}{5}$	$3\frac{1}{5}$
$-\frac{1}{4}$	0	$2\frac{2}{3}$
$-\frac{1}{4}$	$-\frac{1}{8}$	$2\frac{1}{3}$

shifting the pole p_1 are illustrated in Fig. 9.8-6. For $z_1 = -\frac{1}{4}$, several values of p_1 and the corresponding maximum allowable values for K_0 are tabulated in Table 9.8-1, and the root-locus plots are sketched in Fig.

9.8-6. The maximum allowable value of K_0 is highest when the zero z_1 and the pole p_1 satisfy Eq. (9.8-54). This substantiates the conclusions made above. The shifting of the pole may be effected by introducing a zero to cancel the unwanted pole and reinserting a new pole at a desirable location.

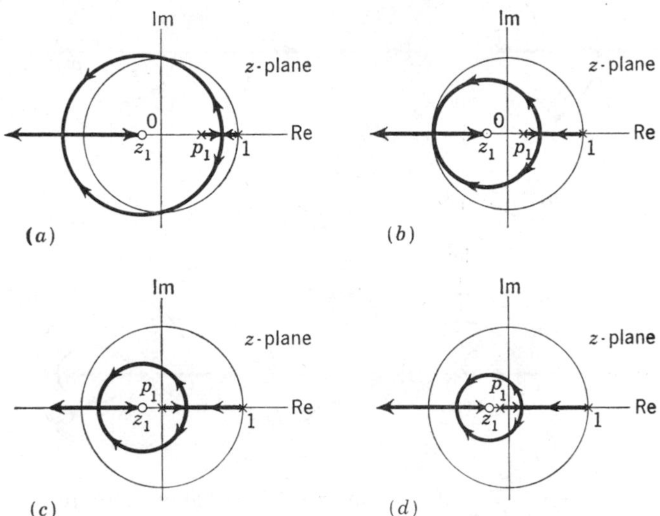

FIG. 9.8-6. The root-locus diagrams for various values of p_1.

The effects of imperfect cancellation of a zero are demonstrated in Fig. 9.8-7. The original root loci are plotted in dotted line, and the compensated root loci are shown in solid line. In Fig. 9.8-7*a*, the zero z_1 falls outside the unit circle. Simple cancellation compensation requires an unstable pulsed-data compensator. If the cancellation is imperfect, as shown in Fig. 9.8-7*a*, for certain desirable values of the gain constant the third characteristic root, which is real and negative, may be too close to the unit circle, if not falling outside of it. This is certainly undesirable. However, if the zero z_1 lies inside the unit circle, no such problems arise, provided that the compensating pole p_c sits to the right of the zero z_1, as illustrated in Fig. 9.8-7*b*. Thus, it is preferable to have the open-loop zeros of the pulsed-data control system inside the unit circle. Figures 9.8-7*c* and 9.8-7*d* illustrate other effects resulting from imperfect cancellation. It is seen that when the compensating pole p_c lies to the left of the zero z_1, even at a moderate gain the third real and negative characteristic root will fall outside the unit circle, thus causing instability of the system, whereas without compensation it might be stable at this gain level. Consequently, if imperfect cancellation cannot be avoided, the compensating pole should be kept to the right of the zero which is to be partially cancelled.

The effects of imperfect cancellation of a pole are illustrated in Fig. 9.8-8, where the compensated root loci are shown in heavy solid line. It is seen that imperfect cancellation produces no serious effect, although it may

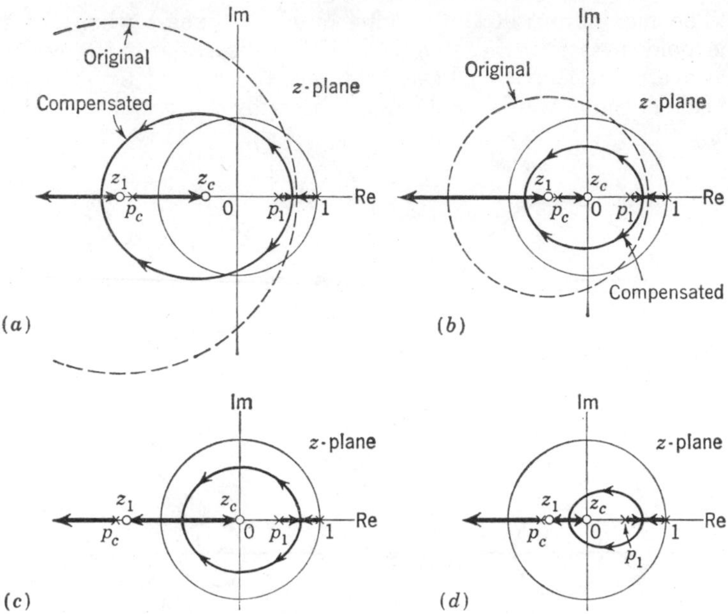

Fig. 9.8-7. The effect of imperfect cancellation of a zero.

cause considerable change in the root-locus plot. Sometimes it is preferable to have the compensating zero sit to the left of the pole which is to be partially cancelled.

In addition to the cancellation (or the pole-zero shifting) compensation,

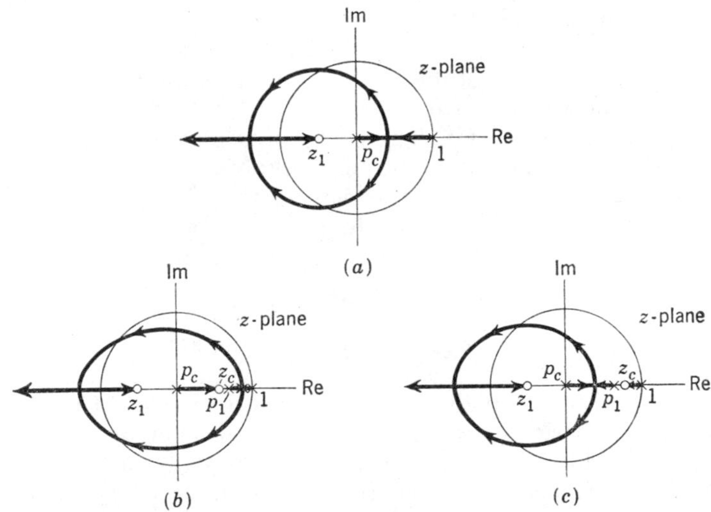

Fig. 9.8-8. The effect of imperfect cancellation of a pole. (*a*) Perfect cancellation; (*b*) and (*c*), imperfect cancellation.

the performance of pulsed-data control system may be improved by the phase-lag (or integral) and the phase-lead (or derivative) compensation. The phase-lag compensation may be used to increase the velocity constant without adversely affecting the relative stability; and the phase-lead compensation provides a means of increasing the phase shift in the vicinity of crossover. In general, by the introduction of appropriate pole-zero combinations, the root locus of a sampled-data system is so modified that the characteristic roots may be shifted to the desired locations which would result in improved transient response as well as frequency response. From the z-plane root locus of the sampled-data control system, the pulse-transfer function of a desired cascade pulsed-data compensating network can generally be determined in the usual manner.

Decrement Factor and Settling-time Specifications. The performance of a continuous-data feedback control system is often dominated by a pair of conjugate complex poles. The quadratic factor associated with these complex poles is

$$\frac{1}{s^2 + 2\zeta\omega_n s + \omega_n^2} = \frac{1}{(s + \alpha_0 - j\omega_0)(s + \alpha_0 + j\omega_0)} \tag{9.8-55}$$

where ζ is the damping ratio; ω_n, the undamped natural frequency; $\alpha_0 = \zeta\omega_n$, the decrement factor; and $\omega_0 = \omega_n\sqrt{1 - \zeta^2}$, the frequency of the transient oscillation. The transient term associated with these poles is

$$A\epsilon^{-\alpha_0 t} \sin (\omega_0 t + \theta) \tag{9.8-56}$$

It is shown in Sec. 2.6 that, for a system with a transfer function characterized to the desired accuracy by this pair of predominating conjugate complex poles, the settling time is given approximately by

$$T_s \approx \frac{4}{\alpha_0} \tag{9.8-57}$$

Thus, the decrement factor α_0 is a measure of how rapidly the oscillation decays. Control systems with small settling time generally require large decrement factors. In the s plane the locus of constant decrement factor α_0 is a straight line parallel to the imaginary axis, as shown in Fig. 9.8-9a. The equation describing the decrement-factor locus is simply

$$s = -\alpha_0 \tag{9.8-58}$$

To meet the specification of a decrement factor α_0 (or of settling time T_s), the pair of predominating conjugate complex poles must lie to the left of the decrement-factor line.

The decrement factor and the settling time concept can be carried over to the study of the relative stability of sampled-data control systems.[84] The z transformation maps the decrement-factor line $s = -\alpha_0$ into a circle with center at the origin and the radius equal to $\epsilon^{-\alpha_0 T}$, as illustrated in Fig. 9.8-9b. Consequently, design of a sampled-data system with a specified decrement factor or settling time for the output sequence requires that all the poles of the over-all pulse-transfer function of the system (or the poles of the output z transform) lie inside the specified decrement-factor circle. The highest system gain to give a step-function response with an adequate settling time is, then, the gain constant cor-

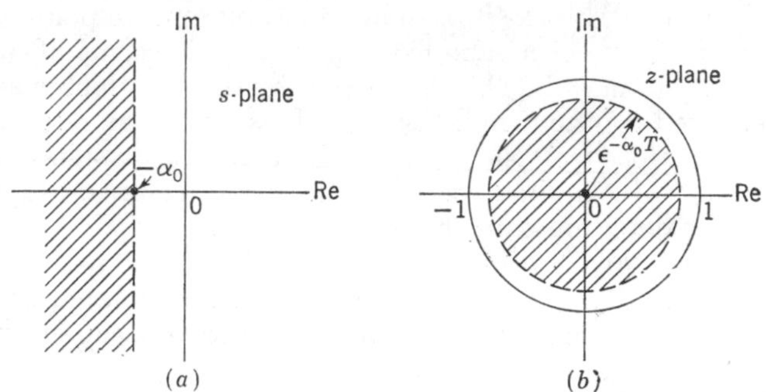

FIG. 9.8-9. (a) Decrement-factor locus in the s plane; (b) decrement-factor locus in the z plane.

responding to the intersection point between the root locus of the sampled-data system and the decrement-factor circle.

As an illustration, consider the second-order system discussed above. The equation describing the circular part of the root locus, as given in Eq. (9.8-32), is repeated below:

$$(x - z_1)^2 + y^2 = (z_1 - p_1)(z_1 - 1) \tag{9.8-59}$$

The decrement-factor circle is described by the equation

$$x^2 + y^2 = r_0^2 \tag{9.8-60}$$

where

$$r_0 = \epsilon^{-\alpha_0 T} \tag{9.8-61}$$

The points of intersection between the root-locus plot and the decrement-factor circle are defined by the solution of Eqs. (9.8-59) and (9.8-60). They are found to be

$$x = \frac{(r_0^2 - p_1) + z_1(1 + p_1)}{2z_1} \tag{9.8-62}$$

$$y = \frac{\{[z_1(2r_0 - p_1 - 1) - (r_0^2 - p_1)][z_1(2r_0 + p_1 + 1) + (r_0^2 - p_1)]\}^{1/2}}{2z_1} \tag{9.8-63}$$

The corresponding gain constant, computed from the magnitude equation (9.8-38), is

$$K_0 = \left|\frac{\epsilon^{-2\alpha_0 T} - p_1}{z_1}\right| \tag{9.8-64}$$

Equation (9.8-64) is valid only for the values of p_1 and z_1 related by

$$z_1 \leq -\frac{\epsilon^{-2\alpha_0 T} - p_1}{2\epsilon^{-2\alpha_0 T} + p_1 + 1} \tag{9.8-65}$$

But, when the above relationship is not satisfied (i.e., when the values of p_1 and z_1 are such that the circular part of the root locus does not intersect the decrement-factor circle), the highest gain to yield a response with the specified settling time is given by

$$K_0 = \left| \frac{1 + 2p_1 + \epsilon^{-\alpha_0 T}}{1 + z_1} \right| \tag{9.8-66}$$

Equation (9.8-66) may be derived in the same manner as Eq. (9.8-50).

Inspection of Eq. (9.8-64) reveals that K_0 is increased by shifting both the pole p_1 and the zero z_1 toward the origin. On the other hand Eq. (9.8-66) places in evidence that K_0 is increased by moving the pole p_1 toward the $+1$ point and the zero z_1 toward the -1 point. Consequently, for a specified value of p_1 between 0 and 1 the optimum location of the zero z_1 is given by

$$z_1 = -\frac{\epsilon^{-2\alpha_0 T} - p_1}{2\epsilon^{-2\alpha_0 T} + p_1 + 1} \tag{9.8-67}$$

Constant-damping Locus in the z Plane. In the time domain the relative stability of a continuous-data system is often specified in terms of a damping ratio associated with the pair of predominating conjugate complex poles. The quadratic factor describing these complex poles takes the general form

$$\frac{1}{s^2 + 2\zeta\omega_n s + \omega_n^2} = \frac{1}{[s + (\zeta - j\sqrt{1 - \zeta^2})\omega_n][s + (\zeta + j\sqrt{1 - \zeta^2})\omega_n]} \tag{9.8-68}$$

where ζ is the damping ratio and ω_n is the undamped natural frequency of the mode of transient oscillation associated with the predominating pole pair. In the s plane the locus of constant ζ is a semi-infinite straight line from the origin making an angle ψ with the negative real axis, and is described by the equation

$$\psi = \cos^{-1} \zeta \tag{9.8-69}$$

The smaller the angle ψ is, the higher the damping ratio. The concept of constant damping line can be carried over to the study of sampled-data control systems. In sampled-data systems the damping criterion refers to the output sequences. The z transformation maps the constant damping line in the s plane into a logarithmic spiral in the z plane,[84] as illustrated in Fig. 9.8-10. Let $s = \alpha + j\omega$; then the damping line in the s plane may be described by

$$\omega = -\alpha \tan \psi = -\frac{\alpha\sqrt{1 - \zeta^2}}{\zeta} \tag{9.8-70}$$

or
$$\alpha = -\frac{\zeta}{\sqrt{1-\zeta^2}}\,\omega \tag{9.8-71}$$

Since
$$z = \epsilon^{Ts} = \epsilon^{\alpha T}\epsilon^{j\omega T} \tag{9.8-72}$$

the constant damping locus in the z plane is given by

$$z = \epsilon^{-\zeta\omega T/\sqrt{1-\zeta^2}}\,\epsilon^{j\omega T} \tag{9.8-73}$$

For specified values of ζ and T, Eq. (9.8-73) describes a logarithmic spiral, as ω is increased. From Eq. (9.8-73), it is seen that when $\omega = 0$,

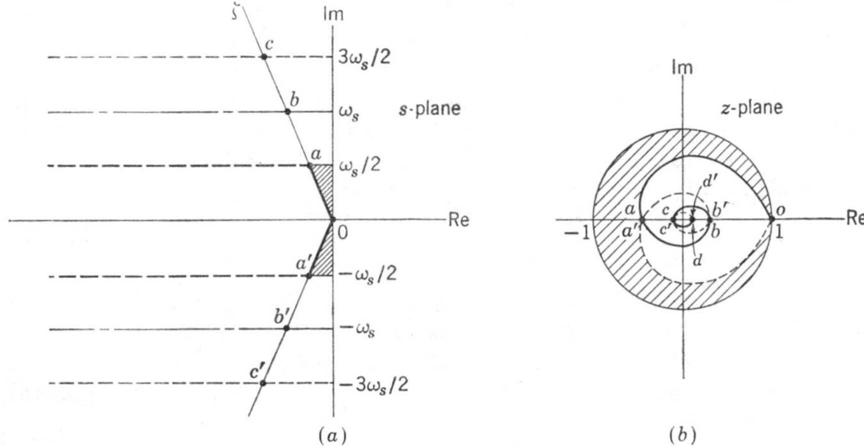

Fig. 9.8-10. (a) Constant damping line in the s plane; (b) constant damping spiral in the z plane.

$z = 1$. The spiral starts from the point (1,0). As ω is increased, the magnitude of Eq. (9.8-73) decreases logarithmically and the phase angle increases linearly. The spiral crosses the real axis at frequencies $\omega = n\omega_s/2$, where n is an integer. In Fig. 9.8-10b, the spiral in dotted line corresponds to the negative frequencies. The damping line in the s plane may be considered as being made up of an infinite number of segments. Referring to Fig. 9.8-10, the damping line segment oa lying inside the primary strip is mapped into the portion of the spiral from o to a in the z plane. The line segments from a to b and from b to c correspond to the parts of the spiral from a to b and from b to c, respectively. For negative frequencies, the line segments oa', $a'b'$, $b'c'$, . . . are mapped into the corresponding parts of the spiral as illustrated in Fig. 9.8-10b. The area of the primary strip to the left of the damping line is mapped into the interior of the heart-shaped constant-ζ curve $oaa'o$ in the z plane, as shown in Fig. 9.8-11. The semi-infinite lines (the boundaries between the primary and the complementary strips) from a and a' to infinity are mapped into the segment of the negative real axis of the z plane from a (and a') to the origin.

To meet the damping ratio specification, it is required that all the characteristic roots (or closed-loop poles) in the s plane lie to the left of the damping line of a specified ζ. Thus, the characteristic roots in the z plane must lie inside the innermost area bounded by the damping spirals of

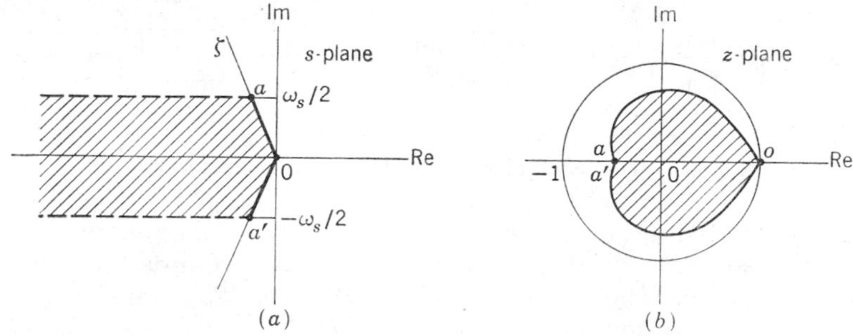

FIG. 9.8-11. (a) The primary strip of the s plane; (b) the primary constant-damping locus in the z plane.

positive and negative frequencies. In view of the fact that the innermost area approaches zero as a limit, it appears that the damping ratio specification for pulsed-data systems could never be fulfilled. However, in practice some of the elements in the forward branch of a feedback control system are of low-pass nature and introduce attenuation at high frequencies, thus making the high-frequency poles of little importance. As a result, the significant innermost area bounded by the spirals will never be zero. When the transfer function of the forward elements attenuates rapidly at frequencies higher than $3\omega_s/2$, only the poles in the primary and the two adjacent complementary strips of the s plane are significant and the poles in other complementary strips may be ignored. In such cases, to meet the damping ratio specification, the characteristic roots must lie inside the heart-shaped constant-ζ curve $bcc'b'$ corresponding to the damping line segments from b to c and from b' to c', as shown in Fig. 9.8-10. If the forward-transfer function of the pulsed-data system attenuates rapidly at frequencies higher than the sampling frequency ω_s, the significant innermost area would be the one bounded by the constant-ζ curve $abb'a'$ corresponding to the damping line segments from a to b and from a' to b'. Furthermore, if the forward-transfer function of the system attenuates rapidly at frequencies higher than $\omega_s/2$, the design of a pulsed-data system with a certain damping ratio then requires that the characteristic roots lie inside the heart-shaped constant-ζ curve $oaa'o$ corresponding to the damping line segments oa and oa' inside the primary strip, as shown in Fig. 9.8-11. This heart-shaped constant-ζ curve may be referred to as the primary constant-damping locus. With a specified damping ratio, the allowable gain constant of a pulsed-data system can then be determined from the intersection point of the z-plane root locus of the system and the significant innermost constant-damping locus.

As an illustration of the application of the root-locus method to the synthesis of sampled-data and digital control systems, a numerical example is presented below.

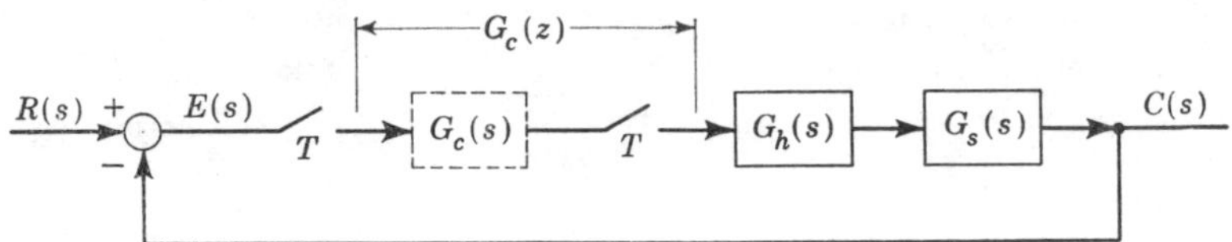

FIG. 9.8-12. The block diagram of the system of Example 9.8-1.

EXAMPLE 9.8-1. Shown in Fig. 9.8-12 is the block diagram of an error-sampled feedback control system which uses a zero-order hold as the smoothing device. The sampling period is 0.1 sec. The transfer function of the controlled system is

$$G_s(s) = \frac{K}{s(1 + 0.1s)(1 + 0.05s)} \tag{9.8-74}$$

Plot the root loci of the system in the z plane; determine the maximum allowable gain for stability; and design a pulsed-data compensator to meet the specifications of $\zeta = 0.7$ and $K_v > 1.5$.

The design is initiated with a determination of the open-loop pulse-transfer function from which a plot of the root-locus diagram is to be constructed. The open-loop transfer function in the s domain is

$$A_0(s) = G_h(s)G_s(s) = \frac{K(1 - \epsilon^{-Ts})}{s^2(1 + 0.1s)(1 + 0.05s)} \tag{9.8-75}$$

The z transform associated with $A_0(s)$ is found to be

$$\begin{aligned} A_0(z) &= \frac{0.0164K(z^2 + 2.05z + 0.232)}{(z - 1)(z - 0.368)(z - 0.135)} \\ &= \frac{0.0164K(z + 0.12)(z + 1.93)}{(z - 1)(z - 0.368)(z - 0.135)} \end{aligned} \tag{9.8-76}$$

According to the conventional rules of construction, the root-locus diagram of the original system is plotted in Fig. 9.8-13, from which it is found that the maximum allowable gain for stability is about 13.2.

In order to determine the required gain constant for meeting the damping specification, the damping locus for $\zeta = 0.7$ is also plotted in Fig. 9.8-13. It is observed that the allowable gain for a damping factor of 0.7 is about 2.6. When the gain of the original system is set at this value, the velocity constant is found to be

$$K_v = KT = 0.26 \tag{9.8-77}$$

which is apparently much lower than the specified value. As can readily be seen, if the gain is increased to meet the K_v specification, the system will not be able to fulfill the damping requirement. Clearly, gain adjustment alone is not enough; and a compensator appears indispensable.

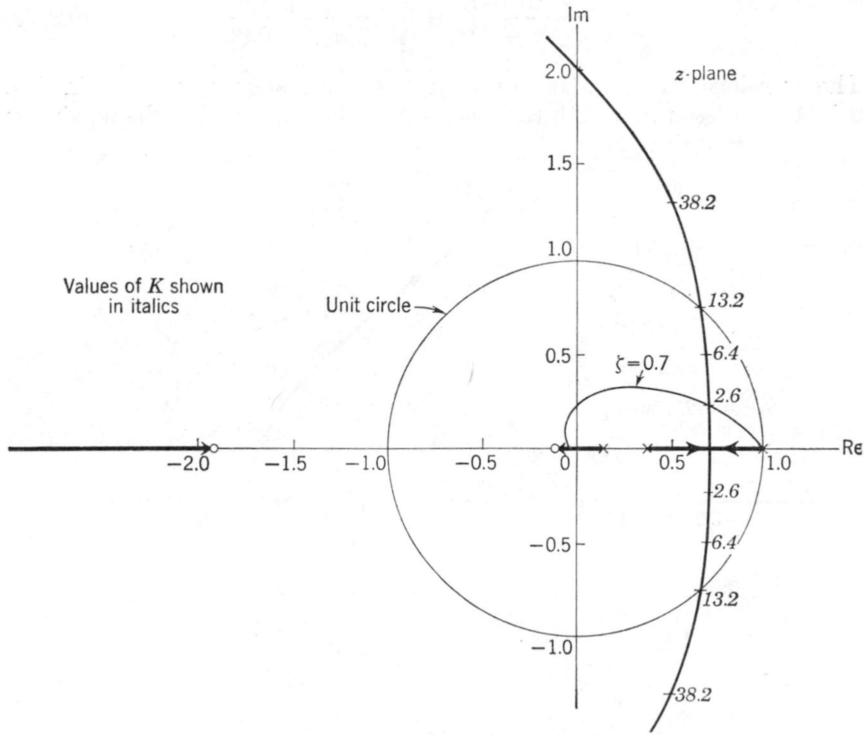

FIG. 9.8-13. The root-locus diagram for the original system.

Examination of the root-locus diagram of the original system reveals that in order to fulfill both the damping and the velocity-constant requirements the root locus must be displaced to the left so that it may intersect the specified damping locus at a gain higher that 15. To this end, a pulsed-data compensator with a positive zero and a negative pole is introduced. The positive zero is used to cancel the pole at $z = 0.368$, and the negative pole is used to "pull" the root locus to the left. Following the conventional rules of the root-locus method, a compensator with a zero at 0.368 and a pole at -0.95 is found to be satisfactory.

The pulse-transfer function of the recommended phase-lead compensator is

$$G_c(z) = \frac{z - 0.368}{z + 0.950} \tag{9.8-78}$$

Thus, the open-loop pulse-transfer function of the compensated system is given by

$$A_c(z) = A_0(z)G_c(z)$$

$$= \frac{0.0164K(z + 0.12)(z + 1.93)}{(z - 1)(z - 0.135)(z + 0.95)} \tag{9.8-79}$$

The root-locus diagram of the compensated system is plotted in Fig. 9.8-14. It is seen that with the recommended compensation the maximum

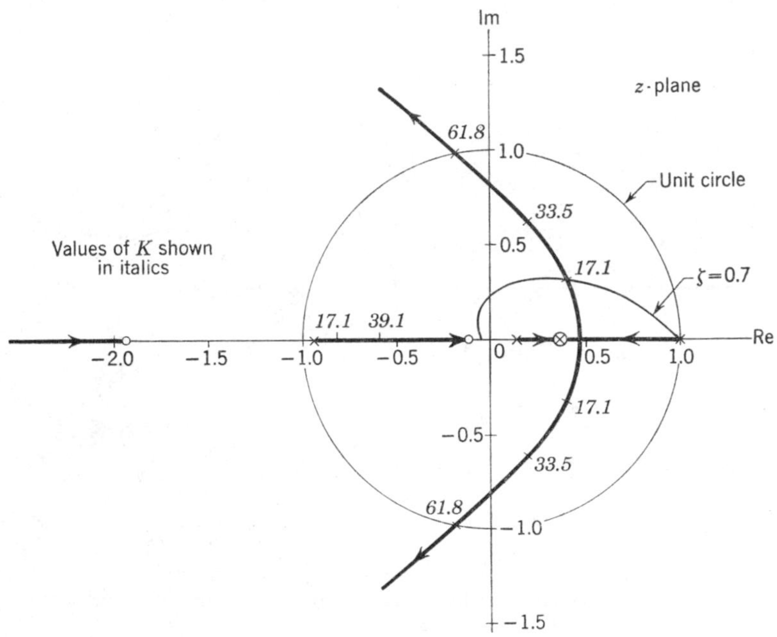

FIG. 9.8-14. The root-locus diagram for the compensated system with pulsed-data compensator $G_c(z) = (z - 0.368)/(z + 0.950)$.

allowable gain for stability is increased to 61.8, and that the allowable gain for a damping factor of 0.7 is raised to 17.1. When the gain is set at this value, the compensated system will have a velocity constant of 1.71 which, evidently, meets the specification. Therefore, the compensator having the pulse-transfer function $G_c(z)$ given by Eq. (9.8-78) is considered satisfactory.

After a suitable pulse-transfer function is determined, the next step is the realization of the compensator. As an illustration, the pulse-transfer function $G_c(z)$ is to be realized as an *RC* pulsed-data network. Since $G_c(z)$ has a real negative pole, it cannot be realized by a basic series structure. However, it may be realized by a basic feedback structure. Making use of Eq. (9.6-54) yields

$$\mathfrak{z}\left\{\frac{H_c(s)}{s}\right\} = \frac{1 - G_c(z)}{(1 - z^{-1})G_c(z)} = \frac{1.318z}{(z-1)(z-0.368)}$$

$$= \frac{2.08z}{z-1} - \frac{2.08z}{z-0.368} \tag{9.8-80}$$

It follows from Eq. (9.8-80) that

$$\frac{H_c(s)}{s} = \frac{2.08}{s} - \frac{2.08}{s+10} \tag{9.8-81}$$

Therefore,

$$H_c(s) = \frac{20.8}{s+10} \tag{9.8-82}$$

Clearly, Eq. (9.8-82) gives the transfer function of a simple *RC* lag network which can readily be synthesized.

The block diagram of the compensated system is depicted in Fig. 9.8-15. It is interesting to note that in the present form this system is essentially

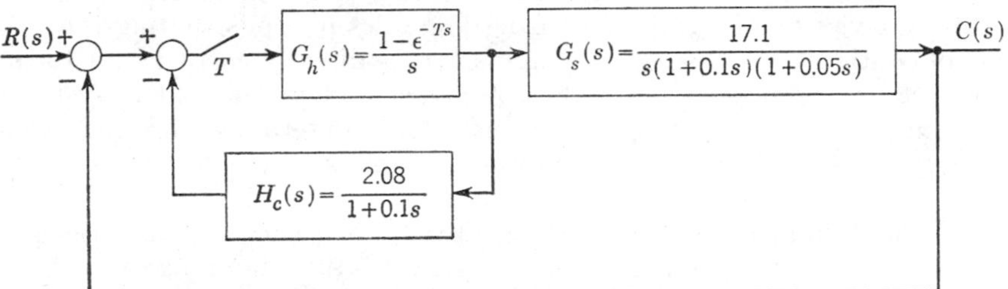

FIG. 9.8-15. The block diagram of the compensated system.

compensated by an *RC* lag network forming a minor loop around the zero-order hold. The above example thus illustrates the procedure of designing minor-loop compensation for sampled-data feedback control systems.

9.9. Conclusion. In this chapter, an attempt has been made to present a few of the more important basic techniques for the design of sampled-data and digital control systems. Compensation of a sampled-data feedback control system may be accomplished either by means of continuous-data networks or by use of pulsed-data networks. Two methods are introduced for the design of continuous-data compensation. They are the method of finite sum approximation and the method of dual-rate-sampling approximation. These approximation methods allow the application of the commonly used Nyquist-diagram techniques and the M_p criterion to the determination of the desired continuous-data compensation.

The design of pulsed-data compensation may be carried out in a number of ways. This chapter introduces three basic methods: the *z*-transform locus technique, the *w*-plane approach, and the root-locus method. To facilitate the application of the *z*-transform locus technique, design charts are provided, which are the gain and phase charts of the basic pulsed-data compensators. These charts may relieve the designer of much computational labor. The z-transform locus (or Nyquist-diagram) technique is primarily useful when the data are available experimentally only.

The w-plane approach simplifies the application of the extensively used Bode-diagram technique to the design of pulsed-data control systems. Since the numerator of the open-loop pulse-transfer function in z does not appear in factored form, the corresponding w transform is not expressed as a product of simple factors. This presents some difficulty when the Bode-diagram technique is applied. In constructing the asymptotic Bode plots, it is essential that the numerator of the open-loop pulse-transfer function must be factored. Although polynomial factoring can be carried out by various methods, such as those of Oldenburger[177] and of Lin, in the case of high-order systems it is generally a laborious task. To save computational labor, it is advisable that the numerator of the open-loop pulse-transfer function in z be first put in factored form before the pulse-transfer function is transformed into the w domain.

The extension of Evan's root-locus method, originally developed for continuous-data systems, to the synthesis of pulsed-data control systems is quite obvious and straightforward. The rules for constructing the root loci of continuous-data control systems can be directly carried over to the construction of the root loci in the z plane of pulsed-data control systems. The maximum allowable gain for stability is determined by the intersection points of the root loci and the unit circle. Needless to say, the graphical construction of the root loci and the determination of the gain of a pulsed-data control system are greatly simplified by the use of a spirule. When the realization of specified relative damping is of basic interest, the maximum allowable gain of the pulsed-data system is given by the gain of the point where the root loci meet the specified constant damping spirals. The techniques involved in the reshaping of the root-locus diagrams of pulsed-data control systems to meet the design specifications are, in fact, no more complicated in principle than those for the reshaping of the root-locus diagrams of continuous-data control systems.

CHAPTER 10

OPTIMUM CONTROL THROUGH DIGITAL COMPENSATION

10.1. Introduction. In the preceding chapter, the techniques of designing the compensation for continuous-data control systems are extended to the design of pulsed-data control systems. In essence, compensation of a feedback control system may be viewed as primarily the job of obtaining satisfactory stability from the system which is satisfactory from a performance basis. Practically speaking, all the conventional methods may be carried over to the treatment of sampled-data and digital control problems. Thus far in the feedback control field, principal efforts have been directed toward the optimization and self-optimization of control systems. Common practice attempts to design control systems having optimum performance. The term optimum control signifies the problem of setting the adjustable parameters of a control loop or the problem of designing an appropriate compensation for the system so that the control action resulting from a disturbance may take place in the best possible manner. The design of an optimum system is based upon the criterion defining the optimum performance. However, the choice of such a criterion is rather subjective and generally depends upon the particular requirements of each application. For instance, a control system may be designed on the basis of transient behavior in response to a step-function input, or it may be optimized on the basis of minimum rms error. Consequently, no optimum control will be universally applicable. A control system which is optimized on the basis of one criterion may fail to give an optimum performance when measured by another standard of merits. This chapter is concerned with the optimum control of pulsed-data systems through digital compensation.

In the optimum design of feedback control systems several important factors need be considered. They are (1) the purpose of the system, (2) the nature of the inputs, (3) the performance criterion upon which the design is based, (4) the freedom of choice to be allowed in the design, and (5) the cost of the system. The performance criteria for the design of optimum control vary with the particular requirements of each application. In common practice, for certain types of sampled-data control problems, minimum settling time and zero steady-state error of the system output in response to a test input, which is a step, a ramp, or a parabolic (constant acceleration) function, are often considered as the requirements for an optimum system. For certain other types of control problems, optimization of the system is sometimes sought by adjustment of the system parameters so as to minimize the sum of the squares of the error samples. In the case of sampled-data control systems subjected to stochastic inputs, minimum mean-square error is frequently used as the criterion for optimum design. Based upon these criteria the optimum control of sampled-data systems by means of digital compensation is discussed in the sections to follow.

10.2. Systems Having Fastest Response and Zero Steady-state Error at the Sampling Instants. In view of the flexibility associated with digital techniques, digital compensation greatly facilitates the design of sampled-data control systems which can respond to a test input of a step function, a ramp function, or a parabolic function with minimum settling time.[61] Figure 10.2-1 illustrates the block diagram of a unity-feedback control

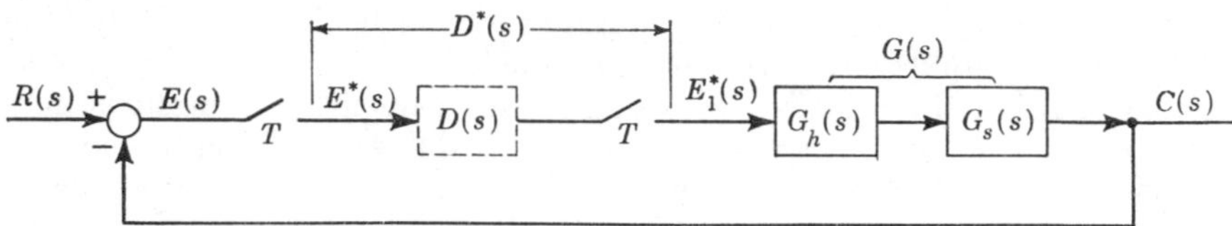

FIG. 10.2-1. The block diagram of a basic sampled-data feedback control system with digital compensation.

system which is to be compensated by a digital controller $D(z)$ for obtaining fastest response and zero steady-state error at the sampling instants. The z transforms of the system error $e(t)$ and the system input $r(t)$ have the following relationship:

$$\frac{E(z)}{R(z)} = W_e(z) = \frac{1}{1 + D(z)G(z)} \tag{10.2-1}$$

where $W_e(z)$ is referred to as the system-error pulse-transfer function. The over-all pulse-transfer function of the system is given by

$$\frac{C(z)}{R(z)} = G_0(z) = \frac{D(z)G(z)}{1 + D(z)G(z)} \tag{10.2-2}$$

It is shown in Sec. 6.6 that the sampled system-error $e(nT)$ may be expanded into a series as

$$e(nT) = \frac{1}{K_p} r(nT) + \frac{T}{K_v} r'(nT) + \frac{T^2}{K_a} r''(nT) + \frac{T^3}{K_j} r'''(nT) + \cdots \tag{10.2-3}$$

in which T is the sampling period, $r(nT)$ is the sampled input,

$$r'(nT) = \frac{r(nT) - r(\overline{n-1}T)}{T} \tag{10.2-4}$$

$$r''(nT) = \frac{r'(nT) - r'(\overline{n-1}T)}{T}$$

$$= \frac{r(nT) - 2r(\overline{n-1}T) + r(\overline{n-2}T)}{T^2}, \text{ etc.} \tag{10.2-5}$$

and K_p, K_v, K_a, K_j, . . . denote the position-error constant, the velocity-error constant, the acceleration-error constant, the "jerk"-error constant, . . . , respectively. In terms of the z transforms, Eq. (10.2-3) reduces to

$$E(z) = \left[\frac{1}{K_p} + \frac{1 - z^{-1}}{K_v} + \frac{(1 - z^{-1})^2}{K_a} + \frac{(1 - z^{-1})^3}{K_j} + \cdots\right] R(z) \tag{10.2-6}$$

Combining Eqs. (10.2-1) and (10.2-6) yields the series expansion for $W_e(z)$ as

$$W_e(z) = \frac{1}{K_p} + \frac{1 - z^{-1}}{K_v} + \frac{(1 - z^{-1})^2}{K_a} + \frac{(1 - z^{-1})^3}{K_j} + \cdots \tag{10.2-7}$$

It follows from Eq. (10.2-3) that the conditions for zero steady-state error at the sampling instants are:

1. $K_p = \infty$ for a step-function input
2. $K_p = K_v = \infty$ for a ramp-function input
3. $K_p = K_v = K_a = \infty$ for a parabolic-function input

As can be seen from Eq. (10.2-7), in order for the step-function response, the ramp-function response, or the parabolic-function response, . . . to have a finite settling time the system-error pulse-transfer function $W_e(z)$ must be a finite polynomial in z^{-1}. For instance, if the input is a step function, the z transform of the system error is given by

$$E(z) = R(z)W_e(z) = \frac{W_e(z)}{1 - z^{-1}} \tag{10.2-8}$$

Since $W_e(z)$ contains $(1 - z^{-1})$ as a factor, $E(z)$ can be either an infinite series or a polynomial in z^{-1} depending upon the nature of $W_e(z)$. Clearly, the system error at the sampling instants will settle to zero in a finite number of sampling periods, provided that $W_e(z)$ is a polynomial in z^{-1}. The same situation applies to a ramp function and a parabolic-function input. Consequently, a sampled-data control system will respond to a test input with zero steady-state error and finite settling time for the output sequence, if the following conditions are satisfied:

1. For a step-function input,

$$W_e(z) = (1 - z^{-1})F(z) \tag{10.2-9}$$

2. For a ramp-function input,

$$W_e(z) = (1 - z^{-1})^2F(z) \tag{10.2-10}$$

3. For a parabolic-function input,

$$W_e(z) = (1 - z^{-1})^3F(z) \tag{10.2-11}$$

4. For an input having the z transform given by

$$R(z) = \frac{N_k(z)}{(1 - z^{-1})^k} \tag{10.2-12}$$

where $N_k(z)$ is a polynomial in z^{-1},

$$W_e(z) = (1 - z^{-1})^kF(z) \tag{10.2-13}$$

In the above equations, $F(z)$ is a rational polynomial in z^{-1}, which is yet to be chosen.

The settling time depends upon the order of $W_e(z)$. Clearly, the minimum order of $W_e(z)$ is obtained by setting $F(z)$ equal to unity or a constant. Thus, under such conditions, the system output in response to a step-function input, a ramp-function input, and a parabolic-function input will settle in one sampling period, two sampling periods, and three sampling periods, respectively. In fact, these are the minimum values of the settling time which a unity-feedback error-sampled control system can have. The rational polynomial of $F(z)$ cannot be chosen arbitrarily. It should be selected in such a way that the resulting pulse-transfer function $D(z)$ is physically realizable. As derived from Eqs. (10.2-1) and (10.2-2), the pulse-transfer function $D(z)$ of the required compensator is given by

$$D(z) = \frac{1 - W_e(z)}{G(z)W_e(z)} = \frac{G_0(z)}{G(z)W_e(z)} \tag{10.2-14}$$

In view of the fact that, with the exception of very simple and extreme cases, $G(z)$ always contains z^{-1} as a factor, to make $D(z)$ of Eq. (10.2-14) physically realizable the over-all pulse-transfer function

$$G_0(z) = 1 - W_e(z) \tag{10.2-15}$$

must contain z^{-1} as a factor. Consequently, $F(z)$ should be so chosen that $W_e(z)$ is a polynomial in z^{-1} containing the constant term 1.

Tabulated in Table 10.2-1 are the expressions of $W_e(z)$ for a sampled-data control system responding to a test input with a minimum settling time. However, as will be discussed later in this section, these expressions are applicable only if $G(z)$ is a stable pulse-transfer function with no transport lag and contains no zero on or outside the unit circle. In other words, minimum settling time is obtainable only if these conditions are fulfilled. It should be pointed out that, in case the controlled system involves a transport lag, the lowest power of z^{-1} in $G_0(z)$ must be the same as that of the pulse-transfer function of the controlled system. Under this circumstance, $F(z)$ should be so chosen as to meet this requirement.

TABLE 10.2-1

Test input $r(t)$	$R(z)$	System-error pulse-transfer function $W_e(z)$	Settling time T_s
$u(t)$	$\dfrac{1}{1 - z^{-1}}$	$1 - z^{-1}$	T
t	$\dfrac{Tz^{-1}}{(1 - z^{-1})^2}$	$(1 - z^{-1})^2$	$2T$
$\dfrac{t^2}{2}$	$\dfrac{T^2z^{-1}(1 + z^{-1})}{2(1 - z^{-1})^3}$	$(1 - z^{-1})^3$	$3T$

To illustrate the design of a digital compensation for providing minimum settling time and zero steady-state error at the sampling instants, a numerical example is presented below.

EXAMPLE 10.2-1. Consider the system shown in Fig. 10.2-1. The transfer functions of the holding device and the controlled system are

$$G_h(s) = \frac{1 - \epsilon^{-Ts}}{s} \tag{10.2-16}$$

$$G_s(s) = \frac{10}{s(1 + s)} \tag{10.2-17}$$

The sampling period is assumed to be 1 sec. Design a digital compensation so that the system may respond to a unit ramp-function input with a minimum settling time and zero steady-state error at the sampling instants.

The design is initiated with a determination of the forward pulse-transfer function $G(z)$ of the original system and the selection of an appropriate system-error pulse-transfer function $W_e(z)$. Since the forward transfer function in the s domain is

$$G(s) = G_h(s)G_s(s) = \frac{10(1 - \epsilon^{-Ts})}{s^2(1 + s)} \tag{10.2-18}$$

the forward pulse-transfer function is given by the corresponding z transform:

$$G(z) = \frac{3.68z^{-1}(1 + 0.718z^{-1})}{(1 - z^{-1})(1 - 0.368z^{-1})} \tag{10.2-19}$$

With reference to Table 10.2-1, for a ramp-function input the system-error pulse-transfer function leading to a minimum settling time is given by

$$W_e(z) = (1 - z^{-1})^2 \tag{10.2-20}$$

Substituting Eq. (10.2-20) into Eq. (10.2-14) yields the pulse-transfer function $D(z)$ of the required digital compensator as

$$D(z) = \frac{0.543(1 - 0.5z^{-1})(1 - 0.368z^{-1})}{(1 - z^{-1})(1 + 0.718z^{-1})} \tag{10.2-21}$$

This pulse-transfer function can be physically realized by the techniques discussed in Sec. 9.6.

The over-all pulse-transfer function $G_0(z)$ of the compensated system is readily derived by the substitution of Eq. (10.2-20) into Eq. (10.2-15):

$$G_0(z) = 2z^{-1} - z^{-2} \tag{10.2-22}$$

Thus, the z transform of the output of the compensated system in response to a ramp-function input is given by

$$C(z) = \frac{z^{-1}(2z^{-1} - z^{-2})}{(1 - z^{-1})^2} \tag{10.2-23}$$

which, upon expansion into an infinite series in z^{-1}, yields

$$C(z) = 2z^{-2} + 3z^{-3} + 4z^{-4} + 5z^{-5} + \cdots \tag{10.2-24}$$

The coefficients of the above series describe the output sequences in response to a ramp-function input. Clearly, the output sequence settles in two sampling periods.

In order to compare the performance of the compensated system following the application of other test inputs than a ramp function, the responses of the system to a step-function input and a parabolic-function input are investigated. The z transforms of the system output in response to these two test inputs are found to be

For a step-function input:

$$\begin{aligned} C(z) &= \frac{2z^{-1} - z^{-2}}{1 - z^{-1}} \\ &= 2z^{-1} + z^{-2} + z^{-3} + z^{-4} + \cdots \end{aligned} \tag{10.2-25}$$

For a parabolic-function input:

$$\begin{aligned} C(z) &= \frac{z^{-1}(1 + z^{-1})(2z^{-1} - z^{-2})}{2(1 - z^{-1})^3} \\ &= z^{-2} + 3.5z^{-3} + 7z^{-4} + 11.5z^{-5} + \cdots \end{aligned} \tag{10.2-26}$$

The output sequences of the compensated system in response to these three basic inputs are plotted in Fig. 10.2-2. It is observed from Fig. 10.2-2*a* that while the output sequence in response to a step-function input settles in two sampling periods, it exhibits a 100 per cent overshoot at the sampling instant $t = T$. This is certainly an undesirable phenomenon. Figure 10.2-2*c* indicates that a steady-state error of unity (that is, T^2) occurs in the output sequence resulting from the application of a parabolic-function input. Clearly, this compensated system does not have an optimum performance when it is subjected to an input other than a ramp function for which the system is specifically designed. The above discussion makes evident that a control which is optimized on the basis of a certain performance criterion (or criteria) may fail to behave in an optimum (or even acceptable) manner when its performance is measured by other criteria.

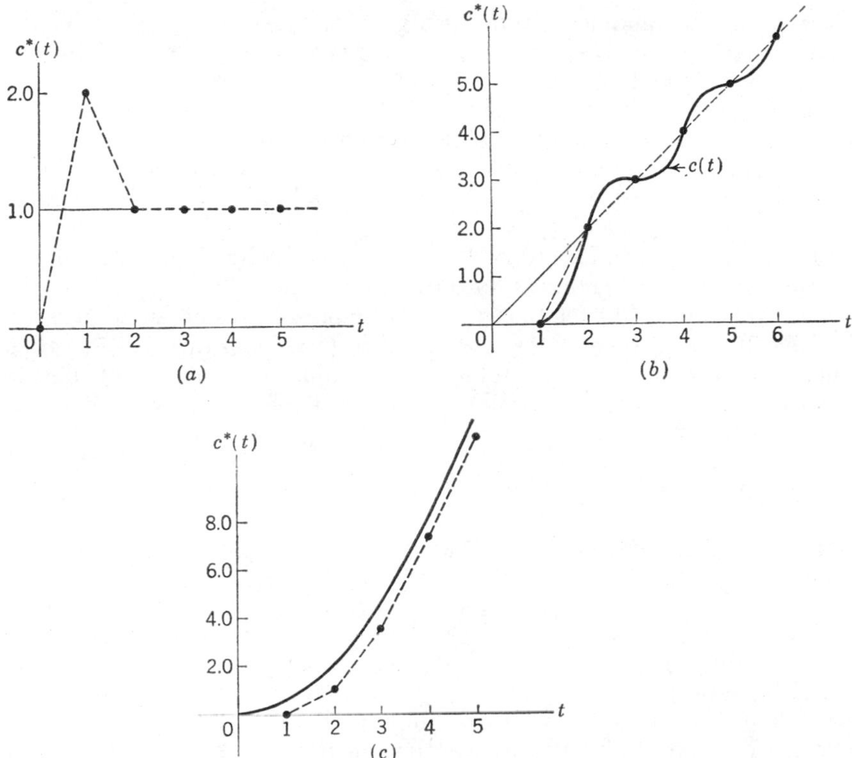

FIG. 10.2-2. Output sequences of the compensated system in response to a unit step function, a ramp function, and a parabolic-function input.

The complete transient response of the compensated system can be readily evaluated by applying the modified z-transform analysis, as demonstrated in Sec. 6.4. Referring to the block diagram of the system shown in Fig. 10.2-1, the modified z transform of the system output is given by the following:

$$C(z,m) = \frac{D(z)G(z,m)}{1 + D(z)G(z)} R(z) \tag{10.2-27}$$

where $G(z,m)$ is the modified z transform associated with the forward transfer function $G(s)$ given by Eq. (10.2-18). The modified z transform of the output of the compensated system is obtained from Eq. (10.2-27) by proper substitution. Thus, for a ramp-function input,

$$C(z,m) = \frac{5.43z^{-2}(1 - 0.5z^{-1})\{(m - 1 + \epsilon^{-m}) + (2.368 - 1.368m - 2\epsilon^{-m})z^{-1} + [0.368(m - 2) + \epsilon^{-m}]z^{-2}\}}{1 - 1.282z^{-1} - 0.436z^{-2} + 0.718z^{-3}} \tag{10.2-28}$$

Inversion of this modified z transform gives the transient response of the compensated system to a ramp-function input, which is plotted in Fig. 10.2-2*b*. It is noted that an appreciable amount of ripples exists in the system output. This is not an unexpected phenomenon. In fact, sampled-data control systems designed to respond with minimum settling time generally contain ripples in the output. As a result, this design will be considered satisfactory, only if the ripple content does not exceed a tolerable amount.

An examination of Eq. (10.2-14) reveals that if $G(z)$ is a stable pulse-transfer function and contains no zero on or outside the unit circle in the z plane, the expressions of the system-error pulse-transfer function listed in Table 10.2-1 may be chosen for $W_e(z)$ to produce a minimum settling time. However, if $G(z)$ is unstable and contains zeros on or outside the unit circle, the expressions of $W_e(z)$ listed in Table 10.2-1 are not applicable. If they were used, $D(z)$ given by Eq. (10.2-14) would describe a pulse-transfer function which is physically unrealizable.[109] Consequently, in determining $W_e(z)$, it is essential that $D(z)$ of Eq. (10.2-14) should be made to describe a physically realizable pulse-transfer function.

It follows from Eq. (10.2-14) that the over-all pulse-transfer function is given by

$$G_0(z) = D(z)G(z)W_e(z) \tag{10.2-29}$$

To secure the stability of the system, the over-all pulse-transfer function should have no poles on or outside the unit circle in the z plane. Thus, any pole of $G(z)$ lying on or outside the unit circle must be properly cancelled. Equation (10.2-29) suggests that an unwanted pole of $G(z)$ may be either cancelled by a zero of the digital compensator $D(z)$ or absorbed by the system-error pulse-transfer function $W_e(z)$. To insure system stability requires the perfect cancellation of the unstable poles. Pole cancellation by the zeros of the digital compensator $D(z)$ is not allowable, however, since imperfect cancellation resulting from a slight drift of the zeros of the compensator can hardly be avoided. Slightly imperfect cancellation may cause system instability. As a practical matter, a system must not become unstable in the face of small parameter variations. Consequently, in order to avoid imperfect cancellation, all the unstable poles of $G(z)$ should form the zeros of $W_e(z)$. In view of the fact that $D(z)$ is not allowed to have poles lying on or outside the unit circle in the z plane and that $W_e(z)$ has been chosen as a polynomial in z^{-1}, the zeros of $G(z)$ lying on or outside the unit circle can neither be cancelled by the poles of $D(z)$ nor be absorbed in $W_e(z)$. As a result, these zeros of $G(z)$ would reflect as the zeros of the over-all pulse-transfer function $G_0(z)$.

The above discussions lead to the following restrictions which are imposed upon the selection of $W_e(z)$ for producing a minimum allowable settling time. The restrictions are:

1. $W_e(z)$ should contain as its zeros all the poles of $G(z)$, which lie on or outside the unit circle of the z plane.

2. $G_0(z)$ or $1 - W_e(z)$ should contain as its zeros all the zeros of $G(z)$, which lie on or outside the unit circle of the z plane.

3. $G_0(z)$ or $1 - W_e(z)$ should contain z^{-1} as a factor.

Referring to Eq. (10.2-13), it is noted that the unspecified polynomial $F(z)$ can be put equal to unity, only if $G(z)$ is a stable pulse-transfer function and contains no zero on or outside the unit circle in the z plane. On the other hand, if $G(z)$ is an unstable pulse-transfer function, $F(z)$ must contain as its zeros all the poles of $G(z)$ lying on or outside the unit circle (except the pole at $z = 1$). If $G(z)$ contains zeros on or outside the unit circle, such zeros must remain as zeros of $G_0(z) = 1 - (1 - z^{-1})^k F(z)$. Clearly, the shortest settling time obtainable in the last two cases is longer than the minimum settling time obtainable with systems having a stable pulse-transfer function $G(z)$ which contains no zeros on or outside the unit circle of the z plane. To clarify the above discussions, a numerical example is presented in the following paragraph.

Example 10.2-2. Consider the sampled-data control system shown in block-diagram form in Fig. 10.2-1, which employs a zero-order hold. The transfer function of the controlled system is

$$G_s(s) = \frac{10}{s(1 + 0.1s)(1 + 0.05s)} \tag{10.2-30}$$

The sampling period is assumed to be 0.2 sec. Design a digital compensation so that the system output sequence in response to a step-function input has a shortest settling time.

The forward transfer function in the s domain of the original system is

$$G(s) = \frac{10(1 - \epsilon^{-0.2s})}{s^2(1 + 0.1s)(1 + 0.05s)} \tag{10.2-31}$$

The z transform associated with $G(s)$ is given in Eq. (6.2-78) and is repeated below:

$$G(z) = \frac{0.76z^{-1}(1 + 0.05z^{-1})(1 + 1.065z^{-1})}{(1 - z^{-1})(1 - 0.135z^{-1})(1 - 0.0185z^{-1})} \tag{10.2-32}$$

Clearly, $G(z)$ has a zero outside the unit circle. To fulfill restrictions 2 and 3 stated above, $1 - W_e(z)$ must contain z^{-1} as a factor and a zero at $z = -1.065$. Thus, the order of $W_e(z)$ in z^{-1} cannot be lower than 2, and the shortest settling time is two sampling periods. The optimum $W_e(z)$ can be determined from the following equations which are formulated in accordance with Eq. (10.2-9) and the restrictions 2 and 3:

$$W_e(z) = (1 - z^{-1})(1 + a_1 z^{-1}) \tag{10.2-33}$$

$$1 - W_e(z) = b_1 z^{-1}(1 + 1.065z^{-1}) \tag{10.2-34}$$

Combining Eqs. (10.2-33) and (10.2-34) leads to the following identity:

$$(1 - a_1)z^{-1} + a_1z^{-2} = b_1z^{-1} + 1.065b_1z^{-2} \tag{10.2-35}$$

Equating the coefficients of the corresponding terms of both sides yields

$$b_1 = 1 - a_1 \tag{10.2-36}$$

$$a_1 = 1.065b_1 \tag{10.2-37}$$

The solutions of the above two equations are

$$a_1 = 0.516 \qquad b_1 = 0.484 \tag{10.2-38}$$

Hence, the desired $W_e(z)$ is

$$W_e(z) = (1 - z^{-1})(1 + 0.516z^{-1}) \tag{10.2-39}$$

and the desired over-all pulse-transfer function is

$$G_0(z) = 1 - W_e(z) = 0.484z^{-1}(1 + 1.065z^{-1}) \tag{10.2-40}$$

Substituting Eqs. (10.2-32), (10.2-39), and (10.2-40) into Eq. (10.2-14) and simplifying yield the pulse-transfer function of the required digital compensator as

$$D(z) = \frac{0.636(1 - 0.0185z^{-1})(1 - 0.135z^{-1})}{(1 + 0.05z^{-1})(1 + 0.516z^{-1})} \tag{10.2-41}$$

which can be realized by the techniques presented in Sec. 9.6.

The z transform of the output of the compensated system in response to a unit step-function input is then given by

$$\begin{aligned} C(z) &= \frac{0.484z^{-1} + 0.516z^{-2}}{1 - z^{-1}} \\ &= 0.484z^{-1} + z^{-2} + z^{-3} + z^{-4} + \cdots \end{aligned} \tag{10.2-42}$$

The output sequence is plotted in Fig. 10.2-3. It has been shown in Sec. 6.2 that without compensation this system is unstable.

On the other hand, if the system is designed for its ramp-function response sequence to have the shortest possible settling time and zero steady-state error, the output sequence will exhibit a large overshoot when subjected to a step-function input. This point has been demonstrated in the preceding example, and further discussion is presented in Sec. 10.4.

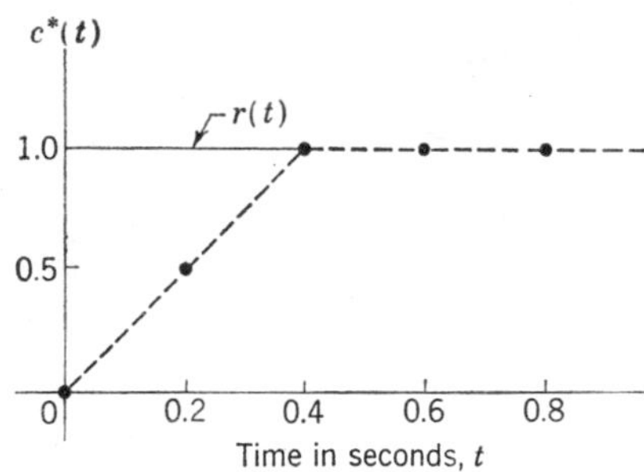

FIG. 10.2-3. Step-function response sequence of the compensated system of Example 10.2-2.

From Table 10.2-1 it is seen that the minimum settling time of a step-function response is one sampling period. On the other hand, the shortest settling time of a step-function response obtainable with this system is $2T$ sec. The increase in settling time by one sampling period is due to the presence of a zero of $G(z)$ outside the unit circle of the z plane. In general, the increase in shortest possible settling time is proportional to the number of zeros of $G(z)$ on or outside the unit circle. Moreover, the presence of unstable poles in $G(z)$ also causes an increase in the shortest possible settling time proportionately. However, the minimum settling time listed in Table 10.2-1 may be attained if $G(s)$ can be compensated by a continuous-data network so as to free the pulse-transfer function $G(z)$ from zeros and poles on or outside the unit circle of the z plane.

As illustrated in Example 10.2-1, the sampled-data control system designed on the basis of a minimum settling-time criterion generally contains an appreciable amount of ripples in the output. Consequently, the system compensated for producing a minimum settling time can be considered to have optimum performance only if the ripple content in the output does not exceed the tolerable limit. The design of ripple-free sampled-data control systems is presented in the following section.

While the step-function response of this compensated system may be regarded as *optimum* in certain applications in which the ripples in the output are not objectionable, the system fails to behave satisfactorily when an external disturbance is exerted on the controlled system $G_s(s)$. This point is explained as follows: The block diagram of the given system with an external disturbance $U(s)$ exerted on $G_s(s)$ is shown in Fig. 10.2-4. The

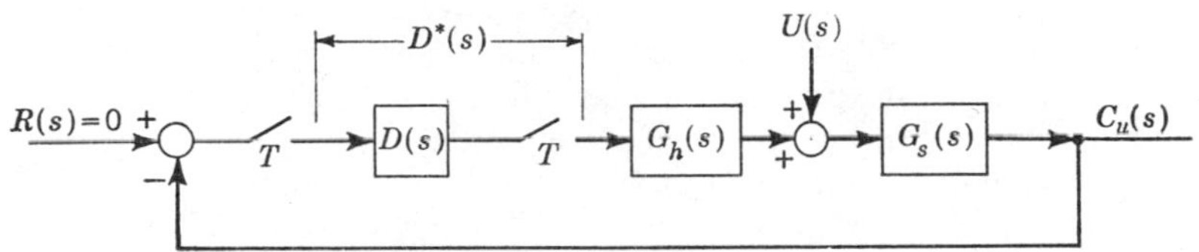

FIG. 10.2-4. A sampled-data control system with disturbance input.

z transform of the system output $C_u(s)$ in response to the disturbance $U(s)$ can readily be derived from the block diagram:

$$C_u(z) = \frac{UG_s(z)}{1 + D(z)G_sG_h(z)} = \frac{UG_s(z)}{1 + D(z)G(z)} \tag{10.2-43}$$

As an illustration, assume that the disturbance is a unit step function.

Then
$$UG_s(s) = \frac{10}{s^2(1 + 0.1s)(1 + 0.05s)} \tag{10.2-44}$$

and the corresponding z transform is

$$UG_s(z) = \frac{0.76z^{-1}(1 + 0.05z^{-1})(1 + 1.065z^{-1})}{(1 - z^{-1})^2(1 - 0.135z^{-1})(1 - 0.0185z^{-1})} \tag{10.2-45}$$

The denominator of Eq. (10.2-43) is given by

$$1 + D(z)G(z) = \frac{1}{W_e(z)} = \frac{1}{(1 - z^{-1})(1 + 0.516z^{-1})} \tag{10.2-46}$$

Substituting Eqs. (10.2-45) and (10.2-46) into Eq. (10.2-43) yields the z transform of the system output as

$$C_u(z) = \frac{0.76z^{-1} + 1.24z^{-2} + 0.478z^{-3} + 0.0209z^{-4}}{1 - 1.1535z^{-1} + 0.156z^{-2} - 0.0025z^{-3}} \tag{10.2-47}$$

Inversion of this z transform gives the output sequence in response to the disturbance, which is plotted in Fig. 10.2-5. Application of the final-value theorem indicates a steady-state output (error) equal to 2.16, which is certainly unacceptable. The above analysis makes evident that this system fails to respond satisfactorily when it is subjected to an external disturbance. The design of sampled-data control systems with multiple inputs is discussed in Sec. 10.5.

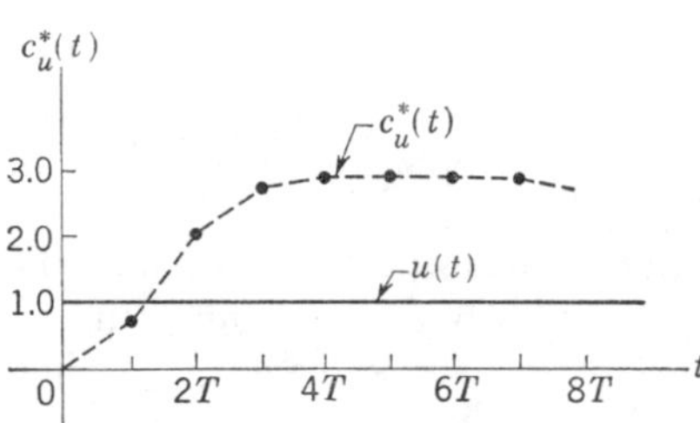

FIG. 10.2-5. Output sequence of the compensated system in response to a disturbance input.

10.3. Suppression of Intersampling Ripples. In the preceding section it is pointed out that sampled-data control systems optimized on the basis of a minimum settling-time criterion suffer from several shortcomings, one of which is the presence of intersampling ripples in the system output. Indeed, ripples in the output are quite objectionable in certain control applications such as control systems involving mechanical components. The intersampling ripples not only form the system error, but also cause a loss of power in the actuator and increase the wear of the mechanical couplings. When the control system can tolerate no ripple contents, the effort of optimum design should be directed toward the elimination of intersampling ripples. A desirable performance criterion for such a design is that the system response to a basic input contains no ripples after the shortest possible transient period has passed. This section introduces a method of designing ripple-free systems.

In view of the fact that the z-transform method fails to provide adequate information between sampling instants, probably the design of ripple-free systems is best effected by resorting to the modified z-transform technique,[25,146] which is discussed in Chaps. 6 and 7. Referring to the basic sampled-data control system of Fig. 10.2-1, it is seen that the modified z transform of the output of the compensated system is given by the following relationship:

$$C(z,m) = E_1(z)G(z,m) = G_c(z)G(z,m)R(z) \tag{10.3-1}$$

where $E_1(z)$ is the z transform of the processed error, $G(z,m)$ is the modified

z transform associated with $G(s)$, and $G_e(z)$ is an error-pulse-transfer function given by

$$G_e(z) = \frac{E_1(z)}{R(z)} = \frac{D(z)}{1 + D(z)G(z)} \tag{10.3-2}$$

The inversion of the modified z transform given by Eq. (10.3-1) yields the transient response of the system. It can be shown that the pulse-transfer function $G_e(z)G(z,m)$ as a polynomial in z^{-1} is the necessary condition for the system response to a basic input to be free from ripples after a reasonably short transient period has elapsed. In other words, the error-pulse-transfer function $G_e(z)$ must be a polynomial in z^{-1} and contain as its zeros all the poles of $G(z,m)$ or $G(z)$. It is noted that the poles of $G(z,m)$ are generally identical to those of $G(z)$. In view of the relationship

$$G_e(z) = \frac{1 - W_e(z)}{G(z)} = \frac{G_0(z)}{G(z)} \tag{10.3-3}$$

to design a ripple-free system it is necessary that the over-all pulse-transfer function $G_0(z) = 1 - W_e(z)$ be a polynomial in z^{-1} and contain as its zeros all the zeros of $G(z)$. The other restrictions imposed upon $W_e(z)$ are that $W_e(z)$ must be a polynomial in z^{-1} and contain as its zeros all the poles of $G(z,m)$, which lie outside the unit circle of the z plane, and that $W_e(z)$ must fulfill the conditions for zero steady-state error, which are stated in Sec. 10.2. Once $W_e(z)$ is determined, the pulse-transfer function $D(z)$ of the required digital compensator follows immediately from Eq. (10.2-14). As can readily be seen from the above discussion, a sampled-data system designed to meet the ripple-free requirement generally responds more slowly than the system designed on the basis of minimum settling time. Indeed, ripple-free systems are obtained at the expense of longer settling time. The numerical examples given in the following paragraphs illustrate the design of ripple-free sampled-data control systems based upon the above principles.

Example 10.3-1. Consider the sampled-data system of Example 10.2-1. The performance specifications are (1) the system can have no ripple and no error in the steady state of the step-function response, and (2) the transient must die out in the shortest possible time. Design a digital compensator to meet these requirements.

The forward transfer function in the s domain of the original system is

$$G(s) = \frac{10(1 - \epsilon^{-Ts})}{s^2(1 + s)} \tag{10.3-4}$$

The z transform and the modified z transform associated with $G(s)$ are found to be

$$G(z) = \frac{3.68z^{-1}(1 + 0.718z^{-1})}{(1 - z^{-1})(1 - 0.368z^{-1})} \tag{10.3-5}$$

$$G(z,m) = 10z^{-1}\left[\frac{z^{-1}}{1 - z^{-1}} + \frac{\epsilon^{-m}(1 - z^{-1})}{1 - 0.368z^{-1}} + (m - 1)\right] \tag{10.3-6}$$

To determine the desired $W_e(z)$ and $D(z)$ according to the principles stated above, assume that

$$1 - W_e(z) = b_0 z^{-1}(1 + 0.718z^{-1}) \tag{10.3-7}$$

$$W_e(z) = (1 - z^{-1})(1 + a_1 z^{-1}) \tag{10.3-8}$$

Combining Eqs. (10.3-7) and (10.3-8) leads to the following identity:

$$b_0(z^{-1} + 0.718z^{-2}) = (1 - a_1)z^{-1} + a_1 z^{-2} \tag{10.3-9}$$

Equating the coefficients of the corresponding terms of both sides yields

$$1 - a_1 = b_0 \tag{10.3-10}$$

$$a_1 = 0.718b_0 \tag{10.3-11}$$

which have the solution

$$a_1 = 0.418 \qquad b_0 = 0.582 \tag{10.3-12}$$

Hence

$$W_e(z) = (1 - z^{-1})(1 + 0.418z^{-1}) \tag{10.3-13}$$

$$1 - W_e(z) = 0.582z^{-1}(1 + 0.718z^{-1}) \tag{10.3-14}$$

The pulse-transfer function $D(z)$ of the required digital compensator follows immediately from Eq. (10.2-14) by proper substitution. Thus,

$$D(z) = \frac{0.1582(1 - 0.368z^{-1})}{(1 + 0.418z^{-1})} \tag{10.3-15}$$

which can readily be realized by the techniques discussed in Sec. 9.6.

To evaluate the step-function response, the error-pulse-transfer function $G_e(z)$ is first computed. Substituting Eqs. (10.3-5) and (10.3-14) into Eq. (10.3-3) yields

$$G_e(z) = 0.1582(1 - z^{-1})(1 - 0.368z^{-1}) \tag{10.3-16}$$

By proper substitution into Eq. (10.3-1), the modified z transform of the output of the compensated system in response to a unit step-function input is found to be

$$C(z,m) = \frac{1.582z^{-1}(1 - z^{-1})(1 - 0.368z^{-1})}{1 - z^{-1}}\left[\frac{z^{-1}}{1 - z^{-1}} + \frac{(1 - z^{-1})\epsilon^{-m}}{1 - 0.368z^{-1}} + (m - 1)\right] \tag{10.3-17}$$

Upon expanding into a power series in z^{-1} by long division, Eq. (10.3-17) becomes

$$C(z,m) = 1.582(m - 1 + \epsilon^{-m})z^{-1} + (2.164 - 0.582m - 1.582\epsilon^{-m})z^{-2} + z^{-3} + z^{-4} + z^{-5} + \cdots \tag{10.3-18}$$

By varying m from 0 to 1 the coefficients of the above series describe the behavior of the compensated system during the corresponding intersampling period. It is noted that during the first sampling period, the output is given by

$$c(T,m) = 1.582(m - 1 + \epsilon^{-m}) \tag{10.3-19}$$

During the period $T \leq t \leq 2T$, the output is defined by

$$c(2T,m) = 2.164 - 0.582m - 1.582\epsilon^{-m} \tag{10.3-20}$$

and during the other intersampling periods, the output remains constant at unity as m is increased from 0 to 1. Consequently, the step-function response of the compensated system settles in two sampling periods with no ripple. The step-function response is plotted in Fig. 10.3-1.

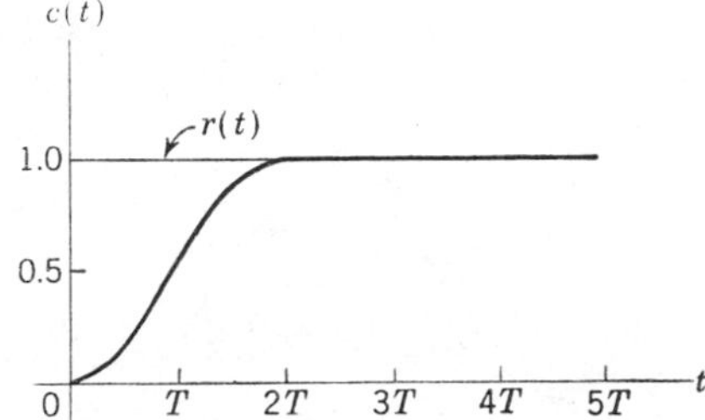

Fig. 10.3-1. The step-function response of the compensated system of Example 10.3-1.

To investigate the performance of this compensated system in response to another basic test input, the ramp-function response is computed as follows: The modified z transform of the system output in response to a unit ramp-function input as obtained from Eq. (10.3-1) by proper substitution is

$$C(z,m) = \frac{1.582z^{-2}(1 - z^{-1})(1 - 0.368z^{-1})}{(1 - z^{-1})^2} \left[\frac{z^{-1}}{1 - z^{-1}} + \frac{(1 - z^{-1})\epsilon^{-m}}{1 - 0.368z^{-1}} + (m - 1)\right] \tag{10.3-21}$$

which expands into the following series in z^{-1} by long division

$$C(z,m) = 1.582(m - 1 + \epsilon^{-m})z^{-2} + (m + 0.582)z^{-3} + (m + 1.582)z^{-4} + (m + 2.582)z^{-5} + \cdots \tag{10.3-22}$$

The coefficients of the above series describe the ramp-function response during the corresponding intersampling period, which is plotted in Fig. 10.3-2. Although the system output is free from ripples, a steady-state error of 1.418 units exists in the output. This can be expected, since the forward pulse-transfer function $D(z)G(z)$ of the compensated system contains only one pole at $z = 1$. The above discussion demonstrates that the sampled-data systems which are designed for the shortest possible settling time with no ripple and zero error in the steady state generally fail to give satisfactory performance when subjected to a test input other than that for which they are designed. This point is further demonstrated in the following illustrative example.

Example 10.3-2. Consider the sampled-data system of the above example. It is required to design a digital compensator to meet the following performance specifications: (1) The system can have no ripple and no error in the steady state of the ramp-function response, and (2) the settling time for the transient response must be as short as possible.

The design is again initiated with the determination of the system-error pulse-transfer function $W_e(z)$. In accordance with the design principles described above, assume that

$$W_e(z) = (1 - z^{-1})^2(1 + a_1 z^{-1}) \tag{10.3-23}$$

$$1 - W_e(z) = z^{-1}(1 + 0.718z^{-1})(b_0 + b_1 z^{-1}) \tag{10.3-24}$$

As demonstrated in the previous example, the coefficients a_1, b_0, and b_1 are determined from the identity resulting from the elimination of $W_e(z)$

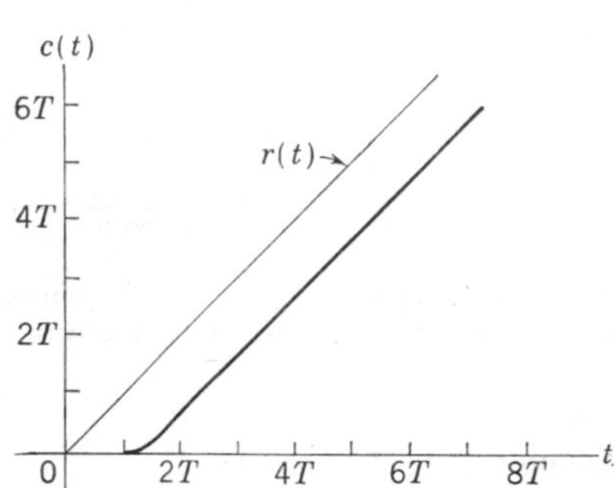

FIG. 10.3-2. The ramp-function response of the compensated system of Example 10.3-1.

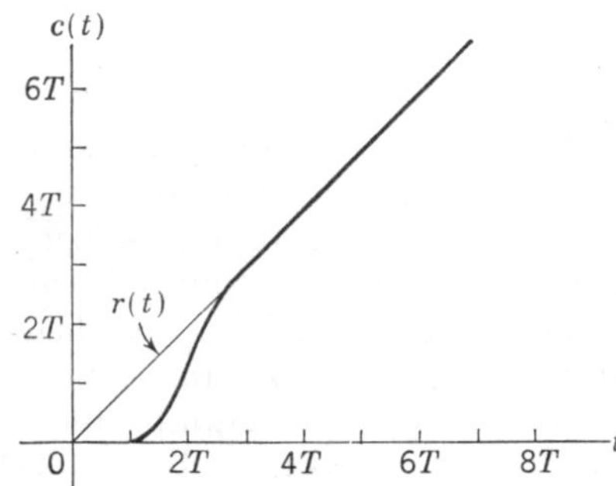

FIG. 10.3-3. The ramp-function response of the compensated system of Example 10.3-2.

between Eqs. (10.3-23) and (10.3-24). The values of the coefficients are found to be

$$a_1 = 0.593 \qquad b_0 = 1.407 \qquad b_1 = -0.825 \tag{10.3-25}$$

Consequently,

$$W_e(z) = (1 - z^{-1})^2(1 + 0.593z^{-1}) \tag{10.3-26}$$

$$1 - W_e(z) = 1.407z^{-1}(1 - 0.586z^{-1})(1 + 0.718z^{-1}) \tag{10.3-27}$$

Equation (10.3-27) indicates that the transient response will settle in three sampling periods. The pulse-transfer function $D(z)$ of the required digital compensator is given by

$$D(z) = \frac{0.383(1 - 0.368z^{-1})(1 - 0.586z^{-1})}{(1 - z^{-1})(1 + 0.593z^{-1})} \tag{10.3-28}$$

The ramp-function response of the compensated system is determined as follows: The error-pulse-transfer function $G_e(z)$ is first computed by the substitution of Eqs. (10.3-5) and (10.3-24) into Eq. (10.3-3). Thus,

$$G_e(z) = 0.383(1 - 0.368z^{-1})(1 - 0.586z^{-1})(1 - z^{-1}) \tag{10.3-29}$$

The modified z transform of the output of the compensated system in response to a unit ramp-function input can then be found from Eq. (10.3-1) by proper substitution:

$$C(z,m) = \frac{3.83z^{-2}(1 - 0.368z^{-1})(1 - 0.586z^{-1})}{1 - z^{-1}} \left[\frac{z^{-1}}{1 - z^{-1}} + \frac{(1 - z^{-1})\epsilon^{-m}}{1 - 0.368z^{-1}} + (m - 1) \right] \qquad (10.3\text{-}30)$$

Series expansion converts Eq. (10.3-30) into

$$C(z,m) = 3.83(m - 1 + \epsilon^{-m})z^{-2} + (3.65 + 0.175m - 2.24\epsilon^{-m})z^{-3} + (m + 3)z^{-4} + (m + 4)z^{-5} + \cdots + (m + k - 1)z^{-k} + \cdots \qquad (10.3\text{-}31)$$

The coefficients of the above power series determine the ramp-function response, which settles in three sampling periods with no ripple. The response is plotted in Fig. 10.3-3.

Apparently, the performance specifications are met by using the digital compensation described in Eq. (10.3-28). However, the above design is not perfect. A shortcoming of the optimum design based upon the ripple-free criterion is disclosed when an attempt is made to investigate the behavior of the optimized system subjected to a step-function input. The modified z transform of the system output in response to a unit step-function input is obtained from Eq. (10.3-1) by proper substitution. Thus,

$$C(z,m) = 3.83z^{-1}(1 - 0.368z^{-1})(1 - 0.586z^{-1}) \left[\frac{z^{-1}}{1 - z^{-1}} + \frac{(1 - z^{-1})\epsilon^{-m}}{1 - 0.368z^{-1}} + (m - 1) \right]$$

$$= 3.83(m - 1 + \epsilon^{-m})z^{-1} + (7.48 - 3.65m - 6.07\epsilon^{-m})z^{-2} + (0.825m - 0.65 + 2.24\epsilon^{-m})z^{-3} + z^{-4} + z^{-5} + \cdots \qquad (10.3\text{-}32)$$

Although the step-function response settles down in three sampling periods with no ripple in the steady state, the system is considered unsatisfactory in responding to a step-function input. As shown in Fig. 10.3-4, this compensated system exhibits a 100 per cent overshoot in the step-function response. This is certainly unacceptable in most applications. Indeed, excessive overshoot in the step-function response is a serious shortcoming of the above design for ripple-free systems. Consequently, unless a large overshoot can be tolerated, the sampled-data control

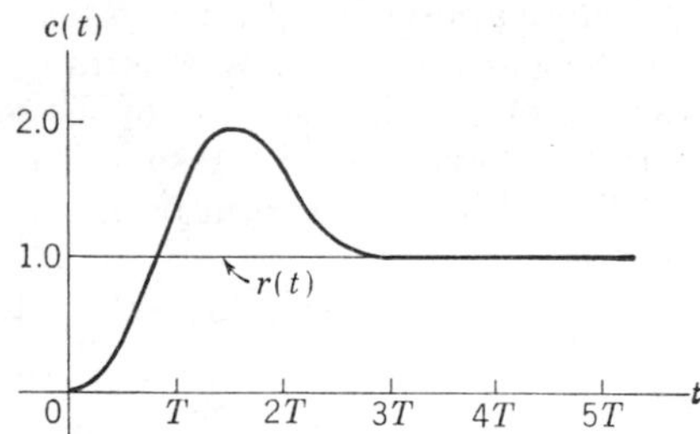

FIG. 10.3-4. The step-function response of the compensated system of Example 10.3-2.

system should be designed on a compromise between the ripple content, the settling time, and the overshoot so as to attain the most satisfactory performance.

10.4. Minimization of System Error. The sampled-data control systems designed in the previous sections suffer from a serious shortcoming. When the system is designed for optimum ramp-function response, the overshoot of the step-function response gets so large as to make the system performance unacceptable. The excessive overshoot severely limits the usefulness of the systems which are optimized for the shortest possible settling time with zero steady-state error in the output sequence. An approach to the optimum design of the system to reach a compromise between the settling time, the ripple content, and the overshoot is to minimize the sum of the squares of the error sequence in response to a test input.[24b,109]

In many applications the performance of a sampled-data feedback control system can be considered satisfactory if the system error is below a certain tolerable limit, and it is regarded as unsatisfactory if the error exceeds the tolerable limit. Under this circumstance a suitable performance criterion would be the percentage of the period during which error exceeds the allowable tolerance. A small percentage of this period gives an indication of good performance of the control system. This performance criterion appears quite simple and easily conceivable. Unfortunately, it is impossible, in general, to solve mathematically the problem of minimizing the system error on the basis of this performance criterion. Under other situations optimum performance is attained by minimizing the peak error of a sampled-data control system which is subjected to a test input. It is unfortunate that the minimization of the peak error is also an analytically insolvable problem. However, the minimization of the sum of squared-error sequence can be done analytically for a fairly general class of signals. Furthermore, minimizing the sum of the squares of the error sequence tends to limit the peak error exhibited by a sampled-data control system provided that the peak error can be controlled.

Before applying the criterion of minimum sum of squared-error samples to the optimum design of sampled-data control systems, a very useful expression relating the sum of the squares of a pulse sequence to its z transform[25] is first derived. Assume that the pulse sequence of a signal $e(t)$ be $e(kT)$ and its z transform be $E(z)$. Then

$$\sum_{k=0}^{\infty} [e(kT)]^2 = \frac{1}{2\pi j} \oint_{\Gamma} E(z)E(z^{-1})z^{-1}\, dz \tag{10.4-1}$$

This equation is derived as follows:

Application of the inverse z transform integral given in Eq. (5.6-4) yields

$$e(kT) = \frac{1}{2\pi j} \oint_{\Gamma} E(z)z^{k-1}\, dz \tag{10.4-2}$$

where the contour Γ is the unit circle in the z plane which encloses all the singularities of the integrand. It follows from Eq. (10.4-2) that the sum of the squares of the pulse sequence is given by

$$\sum_{k=0}^{\infty} [e(kT)]^2 = \sum_{k=0}^{\infty} e(kT) \frac{1}{2\pi j} \oint_{\Gamma} E(z) z^{k-1}\, dz \tag{10.4-3}$$

Interchanging the order of the integration and the summation yields

$$\sum_{k=0}^{\infty} [e(kT)]^2 = \frac{1}{2\pi j} \oint_{\Gamma} E(z) z^{-1}\, dz \sum_{k=0}^{\infty} e(kT) z^k \tag{10.4-4}$$

By the definition of the z transform,

$$E(z) = \sum_{k=0}^{\infty} e(kT) z^{-k} \tag{10.4-5}$$

Replacing z by z^{-1} reduces Eq. (10.4-5) to

$$E(z^{-1}) = \sum_{k=0}^{\infty} e(kT) z^{k} \tag{10.4-6}$$

which is the summation in Eq. (10.4-4). Combining Eqs. (10.4-4) and (10.4-6), therefore, leads to the relationship given by Eq. (10.4-1).

Now, turn back to the design problem. The optimum design may be carried out by introducing a *staleness-weighting factor*[24b] into the denominator of the system-error pulse-transfer function $W_e(z)$. The undesirable overshoot is reduced at the expense of longer settling time. If the test input is a ramp function, the system-error pulse-transfer function of the compensated system then takes the general form

$$\begin{aligned} W_e(z) &= \frac{(1 - z^{-1})^2 F(z)}{1 - \alpha z^{-1}} \\ &= \frac{(1 - z^{-1})^2 (1 + a_1 z^{-1} + a_2 z^{-2} + \cdots + a_n z^{-n})}{1 - \alpha z^{-1}} \end{aligned} \tag{10.4-7}$$

where α is often referred to as the staleness-weighting factor, which can take on any value between -1 and $+1$. The staleness-weighting factor has a direct influence over the overshoot in the output sequence. It is readily seen from Eq. (10.4-7) that the characteristic equation of the compensated system has a root at $z = \alpha$ and all other roots at $z = 0$.

The coefficients a_n of $F(z)$ and the staleness-weighting factor α are so chosen that (1) the system-error pulse-transfer function $W_e(z)$ contains as its zero all the poles of $G(z)$ which lie outside the unit circle in the z plane, (2) the over-all pulse-transfer function $G_0(z)$ contains as its zeros all the zeros of $G(z)$ which lie outside the unit circle in the z plane, (3) the sum of the squares of the error sequence $e(kT)$ is a minimum or a compromise reached between the values of the sum of the squares of the error sequence resulting from the application of a step-function input and a ramp-function input. The application of this method of design is best understood by means of an illustrative example.

EXAMPLE 10.4-1. Consider the sampled-data control system of Example 10.2-2. It is required to design a digital compensator so as to reach a compromise between the settling time and the overshoot of the output sequence in response to basic test inputs of step function and ramp function. The compensated system should have zero steady-state error at the sampling instants when subjected to a ramp-function input.

The forward transfer function in the s domain of the original system is

$$G(s) = \frac{10(1 - \epsilon^{-0.2s})}{s^2(1 + 0.1s)(1 + 0.05s)} \tag{10.4-8}$$

and the corresponding z transform is

$$G(z) = \frac{0.76z^{-1}(1 + 0.05z^{-1})(1 + 1.065z^{-1})}{(1 - z^{-1})(1 - 0.135z^{-1})(1 - 0.0185z^{-1})} \tag{10.4-9}$$

which has a zero lying outside the unit circle in the z plane. In accordance with the restrictions stated above, assume that

$$W_e(z) = \frac{(1 - z^{-1})^2(1 + a_1z^{-1})}{(1 - \alpha z^{-1})} \tag{10.4-10}$$

$$1 - W_e(z) = \frac{z^{-1}(1 + 1.065z^{-1})(b_0 + b_1z^{-1})}{(1 - \alpha z^{-1})} \tag{10.4-11}$$

The arbitrary constants in the above two equations are to be determined in the usual manner. Combining Eqs. (10.4-10) and (10.4-11) and equating the coefficients of the like terms of both sides of the resulting identity yield the following three simultaneous equations:

$$b_0 = 2 - a_1 - \alpha \tag{10.4-12}$$

$$b_1 + 1.065b_0 = 2a_1 - 1 \tag{10.4-13}$$

$$1.065b_1 = -a_1 \tag{10.4-14}$$

Apparently, one more equation is required in order to solve for these unknowns. The additional equation may be derived from condition 3 stated above. This problem can be solved in a simpler manner, if the relationship between a_1 and α is first determined from the above three equations. Solving for a_1 yields

$$a_1 = 0.782 - 0.266\alpha \tag{10.4-15}$$

The z transform of the system error resulting from the application of a unit ramp-function input is given by

$$E(z) = W_e(z)R(z) = \frac{0.2z^{-1}(1 + a_1z^{-1})}{1 - \alpha z^{-1}} \tag{10.4-16}$$

Making use of Eq. (10.4-1) yields the sum of the squares of the error pulses as

$$\sum_{k=0}^{\infty} [e(kT)]^2 = \frac{0.04}{2\pi j} \oint_{\Gamma} \frac{(1 + a_1 z)(z + a_1)}{z(1 - \alpha z)(z - \alpha)} dz \tag{10.4-17}$$

This integral can readily be evaluated by taking the residues at the poles $z = 0$ and $z = \alpha$. Thus,

$$\sum_{k=0}^{\infty} [e(kT)]^2 = \frac{0.04(1 + 2a_1\alpha + a_1^2)}{1 - \alpha^2} \tag{10.4-18}$$

Eliminating a_1 between Eqs. (10.4-15) and (10.4-18) yields

$$\sum_{k=0}^{\infty} [e(kT)]^2 = \frac{0.0644(1 - 0.286\alpha)}{1 - \alpha} \tag{10.4-19}$$

The relationship between the sum of the squared-error sequence and the staleness-weighting factor is plotted in Fig. 10.4-1. It is noted that the sum of the squared-error sequence decreases when α is decreased from 1; it equals 0.0644 when $\alpha = 0$; and reaches the lowest value 0.041 at $\alpha = -1$.

Following the application of a unit step-function input, the system error has the z transform given by

$$E(z) = \frac{(1 - z^{-1})(1 + a_1 z^{-1})}{1 - \alpha z^{-1}} \tag{10.4-20}$$

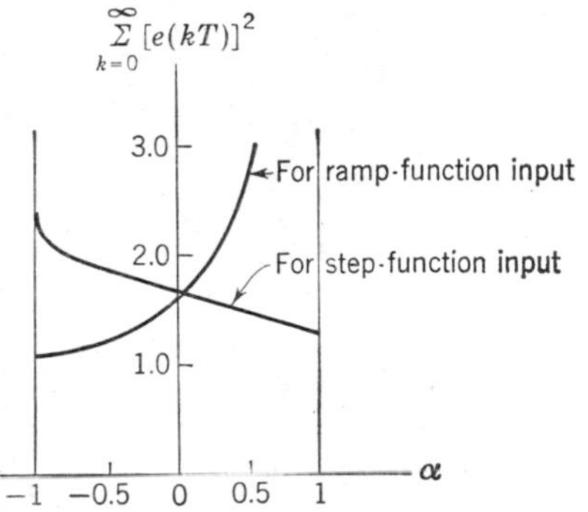

FIG. 10.4-1. The sum of the squared error as function of the staleness-weighting factor.

Making use of Eq. (10.4-1) yields the sum of the squares of the error sequence as

$$\sum_{k=0}^{\infty} [e(kT)]^2 = \frac{1}{2\pi j} \oint_{\Gamma} \frac{(1 - z^2)(z + a_1)(1 + a_1 z)}{z^2(z - \alpha)(\alpha z - 1)} dz$$

$$= \frac{2[(1 - a_1)^2 + a_1(1 + \alpha)]}{1 + \alpha} \tag{10.4-21}$$

The substitution of Eq. (10.4-15) reduces Eq. (10.4-21) to

$$\sum_{k=0}^{\infty} [e(kT)]^2 = \frac{1.659 + 1.264\alpha - 0.391\alpha^2}{1 + \alpha} \tag{10.4-22}$$

which is plotted in Fig. 10.4-1. It is seen that the sum of the squared-error sequence decreases when α is increased from -1; it equals 1.659 when $\alpha = 0$; and reaches the lowest possible value 1.266 at $\alpha = 1$.

However, in this particular example no minimum can be found which will result in optimum performance for both the step-function and the ramp-function inputs. Figure 10.4-1 indicates that the values of the sum

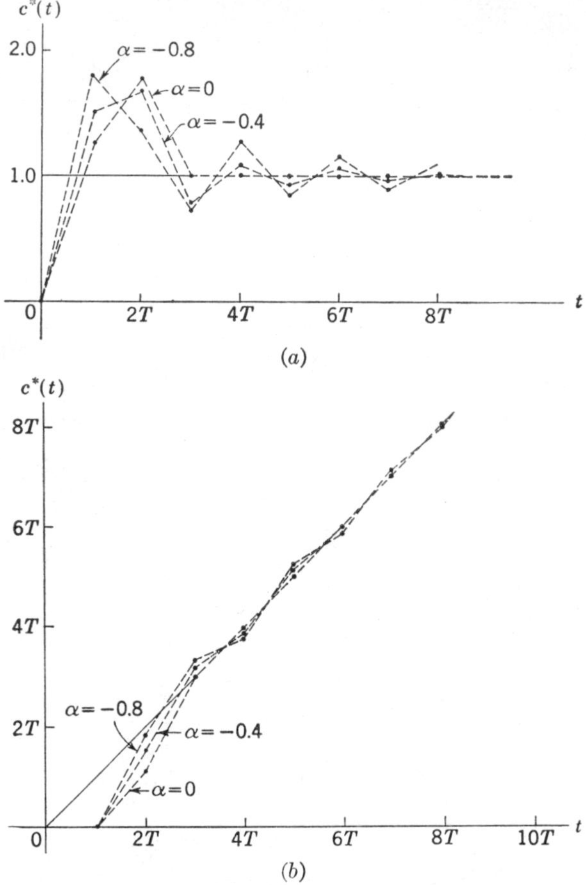

FIG. 10.4-2. (a) The step-function response of the system of Example 10.4-1 for several negative values of the staleness-weighting factor; (b) The ramp-function response of the system of Example 10.4-1 for several negative values of the staleness-weighting factor.

of the squared-error sequence for these two test inputs are the same when the staleness-weighting factor is set at 0.02, which corresponds to the intersecting point between these two curves. At this value of the staleness-weighting factor, however, the step-function response has a large overshoot which is usually objectionable. When α is set at zero corresponding to the case of no staleness weighting, the output sequences in response to a step-function and a ramp-function input settle down in three sampling periods with zero steady-state error. But the step-function response has an overshoot of 95 per cent, as illustrated in Fig. 10.4-2a. When the staleness-weighting factor is decreased to a negative value, the system becomes oscillatory. A negative staleness-weighting factor corresponds to a negative real characteristic root (or closed-loop pole). As discussed in Secs. 7.1 and 7.2, a negative real characteristic root results in an oscillatory response.

The output sequences of the compensated system in response to step-function and ramp-function inputs are plotted in Fig. 10.4-2a and Fig. 10.4-2b, respectively, for several negative values of α. It is observed that while the step-function response has a large overshoot (about 80 to 100 per cent) and becomes more oscillatory as α is decreased, the ramp-function response is slightly improved. Thus, a negative staleness-weighting factor favors the ramp-function response. On the other hand, a positive staleness-weighting factor produces just the opposite effect. When α is increased to a positive value, the system will exhibit a smaller overshoot in the step-function response but a longer settling time in both the step-function and the ramp-function responses, as demonstrated in Figs. 10.4-3a and 10.4-3b, in which are plotted the output sequences in response to these two test inputs for several positive values of α. The step-function response indicates an overshoot of 50 per cent for $\alpha = 0.6$, 25 per cent for $\alpha = 0.8$ against an overshoot of 80 per cent for $\alpha = 0$, and an approximate settling time of $9T$ sec for $\alpha = 0.6$ and $\alpha = 0.8$ against the shortest possible settling time of $3T$ sec for $\alpha = 0$. The ramp-function response shows a larger system error than the case of $\alpha = 0$, and the approximate settling time is $8T$ sec for $\alpha = 0.6$ but it is much longer for $\alpha = 0.8$. The plottings of Figs. 10.4-3a and 10.4-3b make evident that a positive staleness-weighting factor favors the step-function response. From the above discussions it may be concluded that a negative staleness-weighting factor cannot be chosen, since it will result in an unacceptable step-function response, whereas a staleness-weighting factor of 0.6 can provide a compromise between the overshoot and the settling time.

The output sequences of the compensated system in response to the unit step-function and the unit ramp-function inputs are evaluated as follows: Solving Eqs. (10.4-12), (10.4-13), and (10.4-14) for b_0 and b_1 in terms of α yields

$$b_0 = 1.218 - 0.734\alpha \tag{10.4-23}$$

$$b_1 = -0.735 + 0.25\alpha \tag{10.4-24}$$

When α is chosen as 0.6, the values of a_1, b_0, and b_1, as computed from Eqs. (10.4-15), (10.4-23), and (10.4-24), are

$$a_1 = 0.622, \qquad b_0 = 0.778, \qquad b_1 = -0.585 \tag{10.4-25}$$

The over-all pulse-transfer function of the compensated system is obtained from Eq. (10.4-11) by the substitution of $\alpha = 0.6$ and Eq. (10.4-25). Thus,

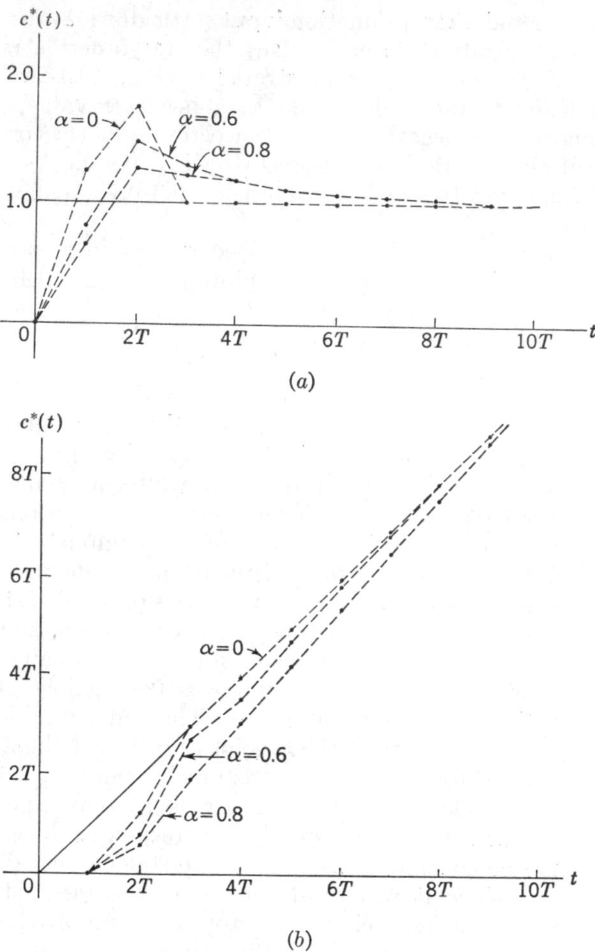

FIG. 10.4-3. (a) The step-function response of the system of Example 10.4-1 for several positive values of the staleness-weighting factor; (b) The ramp-function response of the system of Example 10.4-1 for several positive values of the staleness-weighting factor.

$$G_0(z) = 1 - W_e(z) = \frac{z^{-1}(1 + 1.065z^{-1})(0.778 - 0.585z^{-1})}{1 - 0.6z^{-1}} \tag{10.4-26}$$

The z transform of the system output in response to the unit step-function input is then given by

$$\begin{aligned} C(z) &= \frac{z^{-1}(1 + 1.065z^{-1})(0.778 - 0.585z^{-1})}{(1 - 0.6z^{-1})} \frac{1}{1 - z^{-1}} \\ &= \frac{0.778z^{-1} + 0.247z^{-2} - 0.625z^{-3}}{1 - 1.6z^{-1} + 0.6z^{-2}} \end{aligned} \tag{10.4-27}$$

Expanding the above expression into a power series in z^{-1} by long division yields

$$C(z) = 0.778z^{-1} + 1.493z^{-2} + 1.299z^{-3} + 1.180z^{-4} + 1.115z^{-5} + 1.067z^{-6} + \cdots \quad (10.4\text{-}28)$$

In like manner, the z transform of the system output in response to the unit ramp-function input is given by

$$C(z) = \frac{z^{-1}(1 + 1.065z^{-1})(0.778 - 0.585z^{-1})}{(1 - 0.6z^{-1})} \frac{Tz^{-1}}{(1 - z^{-1})^2} = \frac{T(0.778z^{-2} + 0.247z^{-3} - 0.625z^{-4})}{1 - 2.6z^{-1} + 2.2z^{-2} - 0.6z^{-3}} \quad (10.4\text{-}29)$$

which expands into

$$C(z) = 0.778Tz^{-2} + 2.271Tz^{-3} + 3.571Tz^{-4} + 4.751Tz^{-5} + 5.861Tz^{-6} + 6.928Tz^{-7} + 8.979Tz^{-8} + \cdots \quad (10.4\text{-}30)$$

The coefficients of the series given in Eqs. (10.4-28) and (10.4-30) describe the output sequence in response to a unit step-function input and a unit ramp-function input, respectively.

The pulse-transfer function $D(z)$ of the required digital compensator can be readily obtained from Eq. (10.2-14) by the substitution of Eqs. (10.4-9), (10.4-10), and (10.4-11). The staleness-weighting factor is set at 0.6 and the values of the coefficients a_1, b_0, and b_1 are given in Eq. (10.4-25). Thus,

$$D(z) = \frac{1.025(1 - 0.0185z^{-1})(1 - 0.135z^{-1})(1 - 0.752z^{-1})}{(1 + 0.05z^{-1})(1 - z^{-1})(1 + 0.632z^{-1})} \quad (10.4\text{-}31)$$

which can be realized by the techniques described in Sec. 9.6.

As can be seen from Eqs. (10.4-15), (10.4-23), and (10.4-24), the introduction of staleness weighting does not complicate the required digital program. For comparison, the pulse-transfer function of the required digital compensator for $\alpha = 0$ is also determined and is given below.

$$D(z) = \frac{1.602(1 - 0.0185z^{-1})(1 - 0.135z^{-1})(1 - 0.603z^{-1})}{(1 + 0.05z^{-1})(1 - z^{-1})(1 + 0.782z^{-1})} \quad (10.4\text{-}32)$$

An examination of Eqs. (10.4-31) and (10.4-32) reveals that both cases require the same number of storages in the digital program, and the only difference occurs in the gain constant and the locations of the zero and pole of $D(z)$ which are not contained in the open-loop pulse-transfer function $G(z)$ of the original system. This in no way causes any increase in complexity of the digital program design.

10.5. Systems with Multiple Inputs. In the preceding sections emphasis has been placed upon the design of sampled-data control systems having a single input to the system. However, in common practice the situation is not so simple. Frequently, there is more than one input or type of input to a control system operating at a given time. For instance, disturbances generally occur in the controlled system or plant. A well-designed control system should be able to minimize the objectionable effects of the disturbance upon the system performance. As illustrated in Example 10.2-2, a sampled-data control system designed in accordance with the procedure of Sec. 10.2 for shortest possible settling time may fail to cope with external disturbances. In this connection, the system design based upon a single input may be considered unsatisfactory. This section presents a brief discussion of the design of sampled-data control systems with multiple inputs.[149]

Figure 10.5-1 shows the block diagram of a sampled-data feedback control system subjected to an input signal $R(s)$ and an external dis-

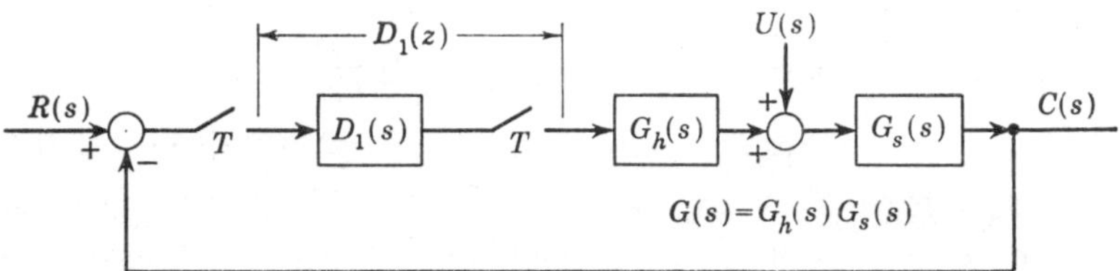

FIG. 10.5-1. A sampled-data feedback control system subjected to multiple inputs.

turbance $U(s)$ which is exerted on the controlled system $G_s(s)$. An approach to the design of linear sampled-data control systems subjected to external disturbances is to consider the effects of the input signal and the disturbance upon the system output separately. With the input signal acting alone, the optimum design of the system may be carried out on the basis of the performance criteria described in the preceding sections. With the disturbance acting alone, the desired output is normally zero, since any output following the disturbance results in an error of the system. Under this circumstance, a performance criterion may be specified in terms of the system output (or error). For optimum performance, the system output due to the external disturbance must be minimized. Consequently, in the design of the compensator, due attention should be paid to the adverse effect of the disturbance. The digital compensator $D_1(z)$ should be designed in such a way that the output in response to a disturbance will die out in the shortest possible time and leave no error in the steady state. When the external disturbance is of the nature of a simple definable function, such as a step function, the required digital compensator $D_1(z)$ may be determined in the same manner as described in Sec. 10.2.

An alternate method of compensation for sampled-data control systems subjected to external disturbances is to make use of feedforward control,[149] as illustrated in Fig. 10.5-2. In the block diagram of Fig. 10.5-2, $D_1(z)$ and $D_3(z)$ are the pulse-transfer functions of the digital compensators which are to be determined. With the reference input and the disturbance considered separately, the output can be expressed in terms of each input as

$$C(z) = \frac{G(z)[D_1(z) + D_3(z)]}{1 + G(z)D_1(z)} R(z) \tag{10.5-1}$$

and

$$C_u(z) = \frac{UG_s(z)}{1 + D_1(z)G(z)} \tag{10.5-2}$$

where $UG_s(z)$ is the z transform associated with $U(s)G_s(s)$, and $C_u(z)$ is the z transform of the system output when the disturbance is acting alone.

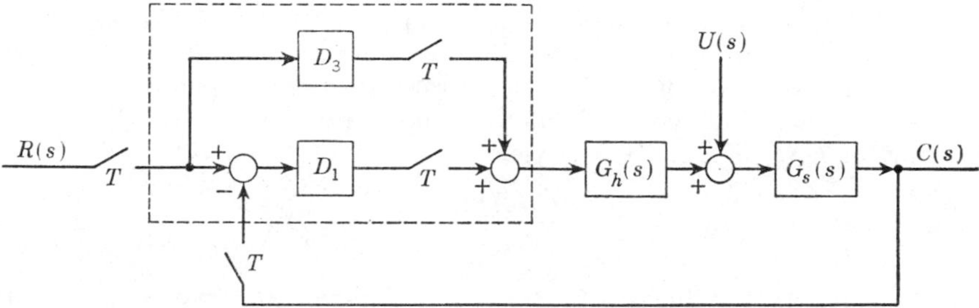

FIG. 10.5-2. A sampled-data feedback control system employing feedforward control.

It is noted that the system output due to the disturbance is independent of $D_3(z)$. Thus, so far as the external disturbance is concerned, the system design may be effected by selecting an appropriate $D_1(z)$ so that the output following the occurrence of the disturbance is reduced to a minimum or disappears in the shortest possible time.

The minimization of the effect of the external disturbance may be accomplished in a number of ways, depending upon the nature of the disturbance. In terms of frequencies, Eq. (10.5-2) reduces to

$$C_u^*(j\omega) = \frac{UG_s^*(j\omega)}{1 + D_1^*(j\omega)G^*(j\omega)} \tag{10.5-3}$$

The above equation points out that when the disturbance signal has a limited frequency band of ω_d radians/sec, the effect of the disturbance on the output may be reduced by making the value of $1 + D_1^*(j\omega)G^*(j\omega)$ large within this frequency range. Following the procedures described in Chap. 9, a desired digital compensator can be found to meet this requirement and the conditions for stability. When the disturbance is of the nature of a step function, a ramp function, or other simple definable function, the design of the digital compensator $D_1(z)$ may be based upon the reduction of the system error (output), due to the disturbance, to zero in the shortest possible time or the minimization of the sum of the squared error, as discussed in the preceding sections. On the other hand, when the disturbance is of stochastic or random nature, the system design may be carried out through the minimization of mean-square error.

Once the pulse-transfer function $D_1(z)$ of the required compensator has been determined, the next step is to design the necessary compensation for the system without disturbance. Referring to Eq. (10.5-1), the over-all pulse-transfer function $G_0(z)$ of the system with the reference input acting alone is given by

$$G_0(z) = \frac{C(z)}{R(z)} = \frac{G(z)[D_1(z) + D_3(z)]}{1 + G(z)D_1(z)} \tag{10.5-4}$$

The design of the required digital compensator $D_3(z)$ is essentially reduced to the specification of a suitable over-all pulse-transfer function $G_0(z)$, when Eq. (10.5-4) is used as the basic design equation. The procedures for designing a sampled-data control system with shortest possible settling time and zero ripples described in the preceding sections may be applied here for the selection of $G_0(z)$. The pulse-transfer function $D_3(z)$ of the desired digital compensator follows immediately from Eq. (10.5-4). Solving for $D_3(z)$ of Eq. (10.5-4) yields

$$D_3(z) = \frac{[1 + G(z)D_1(z)]G_0(z)}{G(z)} - D_1(z) \tag{10.5-5}$$

In order for the sampled-data system to have zero steady-state error at the sampling instants when it is subjected to a test input with the transform $R(s) = 1/s^k$, the system-error pulse-transfer function $W_e(z) = 1 - G_0(z)$ must contain $(1 - z^{-1})^k$ as a factor. As discussed in Sec. 10.2, the output sequence of the system will have a finite settling time, provided that the over-all pulse-transfer function is a polynomial in z^{-1}. Further restriction imposed upon the determination of the over-all pulse-transfer function $G_0(z)$ is that $G_0(z)$ must contain as its zeros all the zeros of $G(z)$ which lie outside the unit circle in the z plane. This restriction can readily be seen when reference is made to Eq. (10.5-5). If the zeros of $G(z)$ lying outside the unit circle were not cancelled by the zeros of $G_0(z)$, the pulse-transfer function $D_3(z)$ would become unstable. As long as the above restrictions are complied with, the desired over-all pulse-transfer function $G_0(z)$ may be determined in the same manner as illustrated in Sec. 10.2. The pulse-transfer function $D_3(z)$ is then obtained from Eq. (10.5-5) by proper substitution.

The design of the required compensation may be carried out in an alternate way. The over-all pulse-transfer function $G_0(z)$ can be made independent of $D_1(z)$ if an additional compensator $D_2(z)$ is introduced into the system, as demonstrated in Fig. 10.5-3. It is easy to show that without the external disturbance the system output is related to the input by[149]

$$C(z) = \frac{G(z)[D_1(z)D_2(z) + D_3(z)]}{1 + G(z)D_1(z)} R(z) \tag{10.5-6}$$

and the over-all pulse-transfer function is then given by

$$G_0(z) = \frac{G(z)[D_1(z)D_2(z) + D_3(z)]}{1 + G(z)D_1(z)} \tag{10.5-7}$$

However, if $D_2(z)$ is so chosen that

$$D_2(z) = D_3(z)G(z) \tag{10.5-8}$$

Eq. (10.5-7) reduces to the following very simple expression:

$$G_0(z) = D_2(z) = D_3(z)G(z) \tag{10.5-9}$$

which is independent of $D_1(z)$. In fact, when the relationship of Eq. (10.5-8) holds, the system is often referred to as a *conditional feedback* system.

In Fig. 10.5-3, all the samplers are assumed to be synchronized. It can readily be seen from the block diagram that in the absence of the dis-

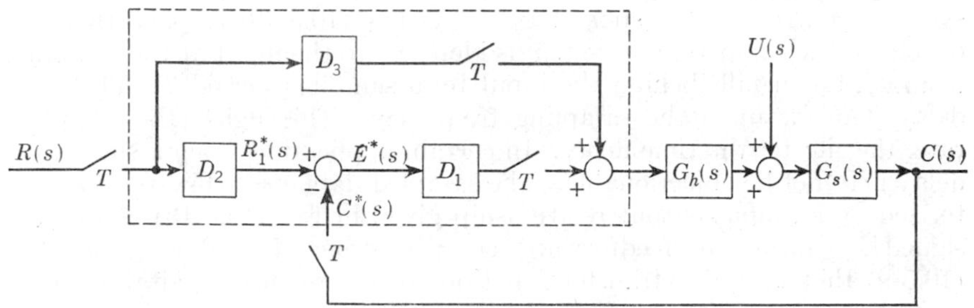

FIG. 10.5-3. Block diagram illustrating a conditional feedback control system.

turbance signal $U(s)$, if Eq. (10.5-8) is satisfied, $R_1^*(s)$ is equal to $C^*(s)$ and the actuating signal $E^*(s)$ is zero. This implies that without disturbance the feedback loop is inoperative and the input signal $R(s)$ is transmitted through the compensator $D_3(z)$ to the holding device $G_h(s)$ and the controlled system $G_s(s)$. Thus, the pulse-transfer function $D_1(z)$ does not appear in the over-all pulse-transfer function $C(z)/R(z)$. On the other hand, in the presence of the disturbance $U(s)$ the actuating signal no longer equals zero, but is given by

$$E^*(s) = -UG_s^*(s) \tag{10.5-10}$$

where $UG_s^*(s)$ is the starred transform associated with $U(s)G_s(s)$. This actuating signal tends to reduce the effect of the disturbance upon the system output to zero or a minimum through feedback operation. Thus, the feedback loop is in control only when a disturbance occurs in the system. The feedback operation of this system is primarily for the suppression of the external disturbances, and the digital compensator $D_1(z)$ is employed to achieve this objective.

Referring to Eq. (10.5-9), it is seen that if $G_0(z)$ is chosen as

$$G_0(z) = 1 \tag{10.5-11}$$

a sampled-data control system with zero settling time and no error at the sampling instants is obtained. So far as the behavior at the sampling instants is concerned, a system characterized by Eq. (10.5-11) may be considered optimum. This requires a digital compensator having the pulse-transfer function given by

$$D_3(z) = \frac{1}{G(z)} \tag{10.5-12}$$

Unfortunately, the pulse-transfer function defined in the above equation is not physically realizable, because the pulse-transfer functions of almost all controlled systems or plants contain z^{-1} as a factor. However, if $G_0(z)$ is chosen as

$$G_0(z) = z^{-1} \tag{10.5-13}$$

the required digital compensator can generally be realized if the controlled system involves no transport lag. Equation (10.5-13) implies that the output of the compensated system is identical to the input at the sampling instants, but it falls behind the input by a sampling period T. This time delay depends upon the sampling frequency. The higher the sampling rate, the shorter the time delay. In certain applications such a short time delay may not be objectionable. The sampled-data control system characterized by an input-output relationship given in Eq. (10.5-13) can be designed by means of feedforward compensation. It follows from Eq. (10.5-9) that the pulse-transfer functions of the required digital compensators are

$$D_2(z) = z^{-1} \tag{10.5-14}$$

$$D_3(z) = \frac{z^{-1}}{G(z)} \tag{10.5-15}$$

In the above discussion it is assumed that $G(z)$ is stable and contains no zero on or outside the unit circle in the z plane.

In many control applications a constant time delay in the output is not desirable. Under this circumstance, the system should be designed to eliminate the time delay. This can be done by choosing other over-all pulse-transfer functions than the one given by Eq. (10.5-13). In common practice, the system is usually designed to have the shortest possible settling time and zero error at the sampling instants in the steady state when it is subjected to a basic test input. In the system design based upon these performance criteria, the restrictions imposed upon the selection of $G_0(z)$, which are stated above, must be complied with. In addition, the controlled system or plant must have a stable pulse-transfer function. When a suitable over-all pulse-transfer function $G_0(z)$ is so selected, the pulse-transfer functions of the digital compensators $D_2(z)$ and $D_3(z)$ can be readily derived from Eq. (10.5-9). Although the above discussions are concerned with a basic sampled-data control system subjected to only one reference input and one external disturbance, the extension of the techniques described in this section to systems with a number of inputs is apparent, as long as the inputs may be treated separately and the principle of superposition applies.

10.6. Design of Multirate Compensators. In Sec. 6.7, the analysis of multirate sampled-data control systems is discussed. It is demonstrated that multirate sampling offers several advantages over single-rate sampling. At this point, it is logical to study the design of multirate compensators for improving the system performance.[160] The block diagram of a sampled-data feedback control system employing multirate compensation is shown in Fig. 10.6-1. The output of the digital compensator is

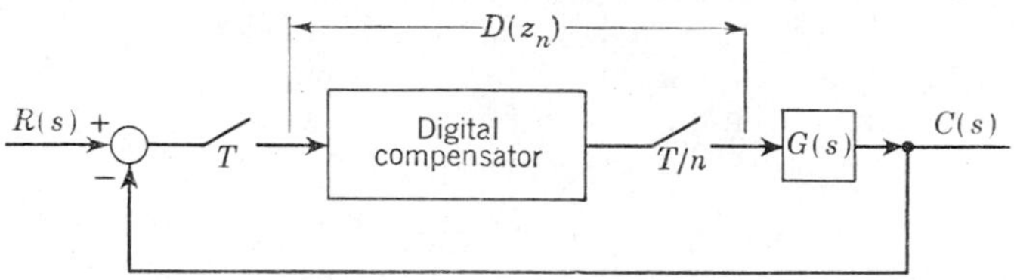

FIG. 10.6-1. The block diagram of a basic sampled-data feedback control system employing multirate compensation.

sampled n times as fast as the input. It is shown in Sec. 6.7 that the z transforms of the system error and the system output, when the system is subjected to an arbitrary input $r(t)$, are given by

$$E(z) = W_e(z)R(z) \tag{10.6-1}$$

$$C(z)_n = G_0(z)_nR(z) \tag{10.6-2}$$

where

$$W_e(z) = \frac{1}{1 + D(z)G(z) + \sum_{p=1}^{n-1} \mathfrak{Z}\{\epsilon^{sTp/n}D(s)\}\mathfrak{Z}\{\epsilon^{-sTp/n}G(s)\}} \tag{10.6-3}$$

is the system-error pulse-transfer function, and

$$G_0(z)_n = \frac{D(z)_nG(z)_n}{1 + D(z)G(z) + \sum_{p=1}^{n-1} \mathfrak{Z}\{\epsilon^{sTp/n}D(s)\}\mathfrak{Z}\{\epsilon^{-sTp/n}G(s)\}} \tag{10.6-4}$$

is the over-all pulse-transfer function of the system with multirate compensation.

In Eq. (10.6-4), $D(z)_n$ or $D(z_n)$, defined as the pulse-transfer function of the multirate compensator, is given by

$$D(z)_n = \frac{E_1(z)_n}{E(z)} \tag{10.6-5}$$

Combining Eqs. (10.6-3) and (10.6-4) yields

$$G_0(z)_n = D(z)_nG(z)_nW_e(z) \tag{10.6-6a}$$

or

$$G_0(z_n) = D(z_n)G(z_n)W_e(z_n{}^n) \tag{10.6-6b}$$

where $W_e(z_n{}^n)$ is obtained from $W_e(z)$ by the substitution $z = z_n{}^n$.

It is interesting to note that when $n = 1$, Eq. (10.6-6) reduces to Eq. (10.2-29) for the corresponding single-rate system. In view of the similarity between Eqs. (10.6-6) and (10.2-29), the optimum design techniques described in the previous sections for single-rate systems may be extended to the design of multirate compensators. The performance criteria specified in terms of settling time, overshoot, steady-state error, and ripple content also form the criteria for the synthesis of multirate systems. When Eq. (10.6-6) is used as the basic design equation, the design of a multirate compensator $D(z_n)$ is essentially reduced to the determination of $W_e(z)$ or $G_0(z_n)$ which will result in optimum performance of the system. Once $G_0(z_n)$ is determined, the pulse-transfer function of the multirate compensator $D(z_n)$ follows immediately from Eq. (10.6-6); that is,

$$D(z_n) = \frac{G_0(z_n)}{G(z_n)W_e(z_n{}^n)} \tag{10.6-7}$$

It is to be noted that $W_e(z_n{}^n) = 1 - G_0(z_n{}^n)$ and $G_0(z_n{}^n)$ may be obtained from $G_0(z_n)$ by selecting the $z_n{}^{-n}$ terms.

Following the discussions of Sec. 10.2, the pulse-transfer functions $W_e(z_n)$ and $G_0(z_n)$, desired for the system to have finite settling time and zero steady-state error at the sampling instants, are determined in this manner. With reference to Fig. 10.6-1, it is seen that

$$E(z_n) = R(z_n) - C(z_n) = W_e(z_n)R(z_n) \tag{10.6-8}$$

$$C(z_n) = G_0(z_n)R(z_n{}^n) \tag{10.6-9}$$

where $R(z_n{}^n)$ is derived from $R(z)$ by the substitution $z = z_n{}^n$. Combining Eqs. (10.6-8) and (10.6-9) yields the over-all pulse-transfer function as

$$G_0(z_n) = \frac{R(z_n)}{R(z_n{}^n)}[1 - W_e(z_n)] \tag{10.6-10}$$

Assume that the system is subjected to a test input, the Laplace transform of which is

$$R(s) = \frac{1}{s^k} \tag{10.6-11}$$

The corresponding z transform and the z_n transform are given by

$$R(z) = \frac{N(z)}{(1 - z^{-1})^k} \tag{10.6-12}$$

and

$$R(z_n) = \frac{N(z_n)}{(1 - z_n{}^{-1})^k} \tag{10.6-13}$$

where $N(z)$ and $N(z_n)$ are rational polynomials in z^{-1} and $z_n{}^{-1}$, respectively. Replacing z by $z_n{}^n$ in Eq. (10.6-12) yields

$$R(z_n{}^n) = \frac{N(z_n{}^n)}{(1 - z_n{}^{-n})^k} \tag{10.6-14}$$

By the substitution of Eqs. (10.6-13) and (10.6-14), Eq. (10.6-10) may be written as

$$G_0(z_n) = \frac{(1 - z_n^{-n})^k}{(1 - z_n^{-1})^k} \frac{N(z_n)}{N(z_n^n)} [1 - W_e(z_n)]$$

$$= [1 + z_n^{-1} + z_n^{-2} + \cdots + z_n^{-(n-1)}]^k P(z_n) \qquad (10.6\text{-}15)$$

where
$$P(z_n) = \frac{N(z_n)}{N(z_n^n)} [1 - W_e(z_n)] \qquad (10.6\text{-}16)$$

is yet to be determined. Since the necessary and sufficient condition for the output sequence of the system to have a finite settling time is that $G_0(z_n)$ and $W_e(z_n)$ be rational polynomials in z_n^{-1}, the z_n transform $P(z_n)$ given by Eq. (10.6-16) and the right-hand member of

$$W_e(z_n) = 1 - \frac{N(z_n^n)}{N(z_n)} P(z_n) \qquad (10.6\text{-}17)$$

must be rational polynomials in z_n^{-1}. Equation (10.6-17) is obtained from Eq. (10.6-16) by solving for $W_e(z_n)$.

It follows from Eqs. (10.6-8) and (10.6-13) that the z_n transform of the system error is

$$E(z_n) = \frac{N(z_n)}{(1 - z_n^{-1})^k} W_e(z_n) \qquad (10.6\text{-}18)$$

Consequently, in order for the system to have zero steady-state error at the sampling instants when it is subjected to a test input given by Eq. (10.6-13), the system-error pulse-transfer function $W_e(z_n)$ must contain $(1 - z_n^{-1})^k$ as a factor. Clearly, this implies that $W_e(z_n)$ and its first $(k - 1)$ derivatives evaluated at $z_n = 1$ are zero. Making use of this property leads to k equations from which the coefficients of the polynomial $P(z_n)$ can be readily determined. Once $P(z_n)$ is determined, the over-all pulse-transfer function $G_0(z_n)$ follows immediately from Eq. (10.6-15). By proper substitution into Eq. (10.6-7), the pulse-transfer function $D(z_n)$ is readily obtained. It should be pointed out that in the above procedure for the design of the multirate compensator the open-loop pulse-transfer function $G(z_n)$ of the original system contains no zero and no pole on or outside the unit circle in the z plane.

On the other hand, if $G(z_n)$ of the original system contains zeros and poles on or outside the unit circle in the z plane, additional restrictions are imposed upon the determination of $G_0(z_n)$ and $W_e(z_n^n)$. As discussed in Sec. 10.2, the cancellation of the zeros and poles of the original open-loop pulse-transfer function lying on or outside the unit circle in the z plane by the digital compensator is not allowed. Referring to Eq. (10.6-6*b*), for the same reason the zeros and poles of $G(z_n)$ lying on or outside the unit circle should not be cancelled by $D(z_n)$. Consequently, such zeros of $G(z_n)$ should be retained as the zeros of the over-all pulse-transfer function $G_0(z_n)$, and such poles of $G(z_n)$ must be cancelled by $W_e(z_n^n)$. This leads to these restrictions: (1) $G_0(z_n)$ must contain as its zeros all the zeros of

$G(z_n)$ which lie on or outside the unit circle in the z plane; (2) $W_e(z_n{}^n)$ must contain as its zeros all the poles of $G(z_n)$ which lie on or outside the unit circle in the z plane.

The first restriction is self-explanatory; but the second restriction needs further clarification, since $G(z_n)$ is a z_n transform and $W_e(z_n{}^n)$ is a z transform in which z is replaced by $z_n{}^n$. To cancel a pole of $G(z_n)$ requires a zero equal to this unwanted pole plus $(n - 1)$ complementary zeros in $W_e(z_n{}^n)$ because $W_e(z_n{}^n)$ is a function of $z_n{}^{-n}$. If $W_e(z_n{}^n)$ is to contain $(z_n - a)$ as a factor, it must have a zero at $z = z_n{}^n = a^n$. A zero (or pole) of the form $z_n = a$ does not occur by itself in $W_e(z_n{}^n)$, and it must coexist with the complementary zeros (or poles). Consequently, to cancel a pole of $G(z_n)$ at $z_n = a$, the system-error pulse-transfer function $W_e(z)$ must contain a zero at $z = a^n$; that is,

$$W_e(z) = W_e(z_n{}^n) = (1 - a^n z_n{}^{-n})F_1(z_n{}^n)$$

$$= (1 - az_n{}^{-1})[1 + az_n{}^{-1} + a^2 z_n{}^{-2} + \cdots + (az_n{}^{-1})^{n-1}]F_1(z_n{}^n) \qquad (10.6\text{-}19)$$

The zeros of the polynomial in the brackets are the complementary zeros to the zero $z_n = a$.

However, as can readily be seen from Eq. (10.6-7), all the complementary zeros in $W_e(z_n{}^n)$ will form the poles of $D(z_n)$, thus complicating the design of the digital program for the compensator. Apparently, this is undesirable. This problem may be solved by introducing the factor $(1 - a^n z_n{}^{-n})$ into $G_0(z_n)$ so that all the complementary zeros in $W_e(z_n{}^n)$ will not appear in $D(z_n)$ as poles because of cancellation. In so doing, the digital program is, in fact, made simpler at the expense of the settling time.

10.7. Statistical Design Principles. The design techniques described in the preceding sections and Chap. 9 involve a very basic assumption that the performance specifications of the system are expressed in terms of the characteristics of the sinusoidal, the step-function, or the ramp-function responses. The control system is designed to yield a satisfactory response to test-input signals which are chosen by the designer because he knows little about the characteristics of the actual input signal. The typical test inputs which are most commonly used include sinusoidal signals and simple aperiodic signals, such as the step function and the ramp function. Application of the design techniques already developed, guided by past experience and ingenuity, will in most cases lead to a satisfactory solution. However, the actual input to a sampled-data or digital control system, the load disturbance, the noise interference, and the actual system output are usually of stochastic nature and can, in general, be described only statistically. Any general characterization of the signals entering a control system must be statistical, based upon the characteristics of the signals averaged over all time. To broaden the design of sampled-data and digital control systems by including the consideration of general types of input signals, statistical design principles are presented in this section.

In view of the fact that sampled-data control systems resemble continuous-data control systems in many respects, the principles of statistical design for continuous-data control systems may be applied to the design of sampled-data and digital control systems.[95,120,135,138] Before discussing the statistical design of pulsed-data systems, the fundamental aspects involved in the statistical design of continuous-data systems are briefly reviewed. The following discussion is concerned with stationary random processes only. A stationary random process is characterized by probability-distribution functions which are independent of the origin of time. In other words, the random process does not change in time. In dealing with stationary random processes an important assumption can be made; namely, the time averages are equivalent to the ensemble averages. This is the so-called *ergodic hypothesis*, which implies that a large number of observations made on a single system of an ensemble at randomly chosen times will have the same statistical properties as the same number of observations made on randomly chosen systems at the same time.

The core of statistical design of control systems is the Wiener-Kolmogoroff theory. This very powerful theory deals with the problem of minimization of mean-square error between the actual output and the desired output of a filter or a system.[55,84] By applying this theory, the performance of a control system is evaluated on the basis of the mean-square-error criterion. In fact, this is not the only criterion upon which is based the statistical design of control systems. Other possible criteria for statistical design are, for instance, the minimum mean-absolute error, the minimum integral of weighted error, and the minimum probability that the error exceeds a certain amount. Indeed, the choice of minimization of mean-square error does not provide a better criterion for many applications than various other possible choices. However, the mean-square-error criterion has the advantage that it leads generally to a workable analysis.

The statistical design problem can be readily visualized by referring to Fig. 10.7-1, in which $G_0(s)$ is the over-all transfer function of a linear

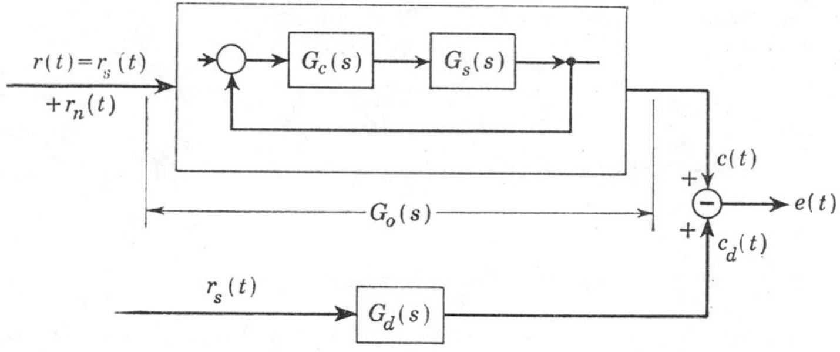

FIG. 10.7-1. Block diagram showing the relationship between the actual output and the desired output.

control system subjected to control signal $r_s(t)$ and noise $r_n(t)$; $G_d(s)$ is the desired transfer function; $c(t)$ is the actual output; and $c_d(t)$ is the desired output. The input to the system is

$$r(t) = r_s(t) + r_n(t) \tag{10.7-1}$$

and the system error is given by

$$e(t) = c(t) - c_d(t) = c_s(t) + c_n(t) - c_d(t) \tag{10.7-2}$$

where $c_s(t)$ is the system output in response to control signal $r_s(t)$ and $c_n(t)$ is the system output due to noise $r_n(t)$. The mean-square error of the system is defined as

$$\overline{e^2(t)} = \lim_{T_0 \to \infty} \frac{1}{2T_0} \int_{-T_0}^{T_0} e^2(t)\, dt \tag{10.7-3}$$

Substituting Eq. (10.7-2) into Eq. (10.7-3) and simplifying yield

$$\begin{aligned} \overline{e^2(t)} &= \lim_{T_0 \to \infty} \frac{1}{2T_0} \int_{-T_0}^{T_0} [c_s^2(t) + c_n^2(t) + c_d^2(t) + c_s(t)c_n(t) + c_n(t)c_s(t) \\ &\qquad - c_n(t)c_d(t) - c_d(t)c_n(t) - c_s(t)c_d(t) - c_d(t)c_s(t)]\, dt \\ &= \overline{c_s^2(t)} + \overline{c_n^2(t)} + \overline{c_d^2(t)} + \overline{c_s(t)c_n(t)} + \overline{c_n(t)c_s(t)} - \overline{c_n(t)c_d(t)} \\ &\qquad - \overline{c_d(t)c_n(t)} - \overline{c_s(t)c_d(t)} - \overline{c_d(t)c_s(t)} \end{aligned} \tag{10.7-4}$$

The design objective is to determine a desirable over-all transfer function $G_0(s)$ for the system so that the mean-square error given by Eq. (10.7-4) is reduced to a minimum.

Correlation Function and Spectral Density. When the minimization of the mean-square error is adopted as the performance criterion, the system design is usually initiated with the description of the signals by the correlation functions and spectral densities. The autocorrelation function of a signal $x(t)$ is defined as

$$\varphi_{xx}(\tau) = \lim_{T_0 \to \infty} \frac{1}{2T_0} \int_{-T_0}^{T_0} x(t)x(t+\tau)\, dt \tag{10.7-5}$$

The cross-correlation function between signals $x(t)$ and $y(t)$ is defined as

$$\varphi_{xy}(\tau) = \lim_{T_0 \to \infty} \frac{1}{2T_0} \int_{-T_0}^{T_0} x(t)y(t+\tau)\, dt \tag{10.7-6a}$$

and the cross-correlation function between signals $y(t)$ and $x(t)$ is given by

$$\varphi_{yx}(\tau) = \lim_{T_0 \to \infty} \frac{1}{2T_0} \int_{-T_0}^{T_0} y(t)x(t+\tau)\, dt \tag{10.7-6b}$$

The spectral density of a signal is given by the Fourier transform of its autocorrelation function and the cross-spectral density for two signals is given by the Fourier transform of their cross-correlation function. Thus, the spectral density and the autocorrelation function are related by

$$\phi_{xx}(\omega) = \int_{-\infty}^{\infty} \varphi_{xx}(\tau)\epsilon^{-j\omega\tau}\, d\tau \tag{10.7-7}$$

$$\varphi_{xx}(\tau) = \frac{1}{2\pi} \int_{-\infty}^{\infty} \phi_{xx}(\omega) \epsilon^{j\tau\omega} \, d\omega \tag{10.7-8}$$

and the cross-spectral density and the cross-correlation function are related by

$$\phi_{xy}(\omega) = \int_{-\infty}^{\infty} \varphi_{xy}(\tau) \epsilon^{-j\omega\tau} \, d\tau \tag{10.7-9}$$

$$\varphi_{xy}(\tau) = \frac{1}{2\pi} \int_{-\infty}^{\infty} \phi_{xy}(\omega) \epsilon^{j\tau\omega} \, d\omega \tag{10.7-10}$$

Inspection of Eq. (10.7-5) reveals that, when $\tau = 0$, the value of the autocorrelation function is given by

$$\varphi_{xx}(0) = \lim_{T_0 \to \infty} \frac{1}{2T_0} \int_{-T_0}^{T_0} x^2(t) \, dt = \overline{x^2(t)} \tag{10.7-11}$$

which is equal to the mean-square value of the signal $x(t)$. In like manner, when $\tau = 0$, Eq. (10.7-6) yields

$$\varphi_{xy}(0) = \lim_{T_0 \to \infty} \frac{1}{2T_0} \int_{-T_0}^{T_0} x(t)y(t) \, dt = \overline{x(t)y(t)} \tag{10.7-12}$$

which is equal to the mean value of the product of functions $x(t)$ and $y(t)$. Furthermore, it follows from Eqs. (10.7-8) and (10.7-10) that, when $\tau = 0$,

$$\varphi_{xx}(0) = \frac{1}{2\pi} \int_{-\infty}^{\infty} \phi_{xx}(\omega) \, d\omega \tag{10.7-13}$$

and

$$\varphi_{xy}(0) = \frac{1}{2\pi} \int_{-\infty}^{\infty} \phi_{xy}(\omega) \, d\omega \tag{10.7-14}$$

Combining Eqs. (10.7-11), (10.7-12), (10.7-13), and (10.7-14) yields

$$\overline{x^2(t)} = \varphi_{xx}(0) = \frac{1}{2\pi} \int_{-\infty}^{\infty} \phi_{xx}(\omega) \, d\omega \tag{10.7-15}$$

and

$$\overline{x(t)y(t)} = \varphi_{xy}(0) = \frac{1}{2\pi} \int_{-\infty}^{\infty} \phi_{xy}(\omega) \, d\omega \tag{10.7-16}$$

Thus, the mean-square value and the mean-product value can readily be evaluated from the correlation function or the spectral density. Consequently, the mean-square error of the system given in Eq. (10.7-4) may be expressed in terms of the correlation function or the spectral density:

$$\begin{aligned} \overline{e^2(t)} = {} & \varphi_{cscs}(0) + \varphi_{cncn}(0) + \varphi_{cdcd}(0) + \varphi_{cscn}(0) + \varphi_{cncs}(0) \\ & - \varphi_{cncd}(0) - \varphi_{cdcn}(0) - \varphi_{cscd}(0) - \varphi_{cdcs}(0) \end{aligned} \tag{10.7-17}$$

$$\begin{aligned} \overline{e^2(t)} = \frac{1}{2\pi} \int_{-\infty}^{\infty} & [\phi_{cscs}(\omega) + \phi_{cncn}(\omega) + \phi_{cdcd}(\omega) + \phi_{cscn}(\omega) + \phi_{cncs}(\omega) \\ & - \phi_{cncd}(\omega) - \phi_{cdcn}(\omega) - \phi_{cscd}(\omega) - \phi_{cdcs}(\omega)] \, d\omega \end{aligned} \tag{10.7-18}$$

These two expressions for the mean-square error appear quite complicated. In its present form, the minimization of the mean-square error cannot be carried out, since all the correlation functions and the spectral densities are unknown. However, the spectral densities contained in Eq. (10.7-18) may be expressed in terms of the spectral densities for the input signals and the transfer functions of the system, if use is made of certain properties of the correlation function and the spectral density which are outlined below.

1. $\varphi_{xx}(\tau)$ is an even function and $\varphi_{xx}(\tau) = \varphi_{xx}(-\tau)$.
2. $\varphi_{xy}(\tau) = \varphi_{yx}(-\tau)$.
3. $\phi_{xx}(-\omega) = \hat{\phi}_{xx}(\omega) = \phi_{xx}(\omega)$, where $\hat{\phi}_{xx}(\omega)$ is the conjugate of $\phi_{xx}(\omega)$.
4. $\phi_{xy}(\omega) = \phi_{yx}(-\omega) = \hat{\phi}_{yx}(\omega)$. These four properties are apparent when reference is made to the equations defining the correlation function and the spectral density. There are several other important relationships which are less obvious and are derived as follows:
5. Assuming that the output of the system $G(s)$ shown in Fig. 10.7-2a is $y(t)$ when it is subjected to an input $x(t)$, the output of the system $G(s)$

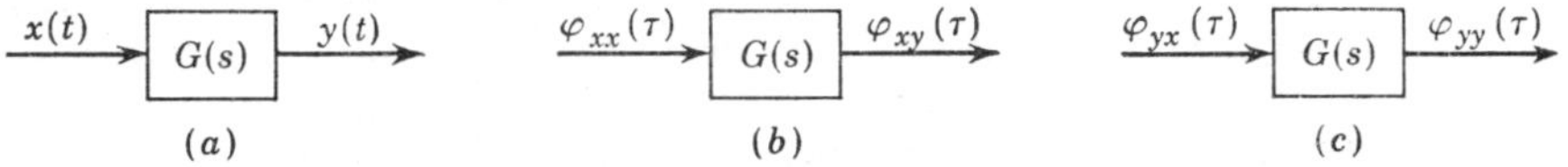

FIG. 10.7-2. Block diagrams showing the relationship between the correlation functions for the input and output of a linear system.

in response to input $\varphi_{xx}(\tau)$ is $\varphi_{xy}(\tau)$, and the output of the system in response to $\varphi_{yx}(\tau)$ is $\varphi_{yy}(\tau)$, as illustrated in Figs. 10.7-2b and c. Referring to Fig. 10.7-2b, the output of $G(s)$ in response to input $\varphi_{xx}(\tau)$ is given by

$$\int_{-\infty}^{\infty} g(\lambda)\varphi_{xx}(\tau - \lambda)\, d\lambda = \int_{-\infty}^{\infty} g(\lambda)\, d\lambda \lim_{T_0\to\infty} \frac{1}{2T_0}\int_{-T_0}^{T_0} x(t)x[t + (\tau - \lambda)]\, dt$$

$$= \lim_{T_0\to\infty} \frac{1}{2T_0}\int_{-T_0}^{T_0} x(t)\, dt \int_{-\infty}^{\infty} g(\lambda)x[(t+\tau) - \lambda]\, d\lambda$$

$$= \lim_{T_0\to\infty} \frac{1}{2T_0}\int_{-T_0}^{T_0} x(t)y(t+\tau)\, dt \tag{10.7-19}$$

which is equal to $\varphi_{xy}(\tau)$ by definition. In like manner, it is easy to show that the output of $G(s)$ in response to $\varphi_{yx}(\tau)$ is

$$\int_{-\infty}^{\infty} g(\lambda)\varphi_{yx}(\tau - \lambda)\, d\lambda = \varphi_{yy}(\tau) \tag{10.7-20}$$

6. The relationship between the spectral densities for the input and the output of a system $G(s)$ is given by

$$\phi_{yy}(\omega) = G(j\omega)G(-j\omega)\phi_{xx}(\omega) \tag{10.7-21}$$

From property 5 it is obtained that

$$\phi_{xy}(\omega) = G(j\omega)\phi_{xx}(\omega) \tag{10.7-22}$$

$$\phi_{yy}(\omega) = G(j\omega)\phi_{yx}(\omega) \tag{10.7-23}$$

Making use of properties 3 and 4 and combining Eqs. (10.7-22) and (10.7-23) yield Eq. (10.7-21).

7. The cross-correlation function and the cross-spectral density for the output signals of systems $G_1(s)$ and $G_2(s)$ possess characteristics as follows. Shown in Fig. 10.7-3 are two linear systems $G_1(s)$ and $G_2(s)$. The inputs which are correlated are $x_1(t)$ and $x_2(t)$, and the outputs are $y_1(t)$ and $y_2(t)$ as indicated in the block diagrams of Fig. 10.7-3 Now, if the system $G_1(s)$ is

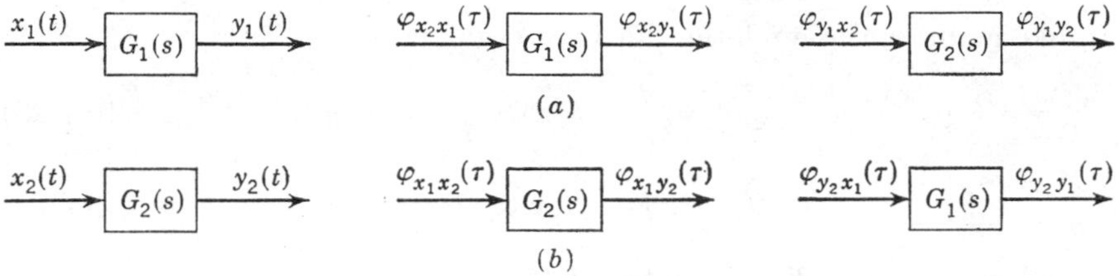

FIG. 10.7-3. Block diagrams showing the relationships between the correlation functions for the inputs and outputs of two linear systems.

subjected to an input $\varphi_{x_2x_1}(\tau)$, the response will be $\varphi_{x_2y_1}(\tau)$, and if the system $G_2(s)$ is subjected to an input $\varphi_{y_1x_2}(\tau)$, the response will be $\varphi_{y_1y_2}(\tau)$, as illustrated in Fig. 10.7-3*a*. The output of the system $G_1(s)$ in response to $\varphi_{x_2x_1}(\tau)$ is

$$\begin{aligned}\int_{-\infty}^{\infty} g_1(\lambda)\varphi_{x_2x_1}(\tau-\lambda)\,d\lambda &= \int_{-\infty}^{\infty} g_1(\lambda)\,d\lambda \lim_{T_0\to\infty}\frac{1}{2T_0}\int_{-T_0}^{T_0} x_2(t)x_1[t+(\tau-\lambda)]\,dt \\ &= \lim_{T_0\to\infty}\frac{1}{2T_0}\int_{-T_0}^{T_0} x_2(t)\,dt\int_{-\infty}^{\infty} g_1(\lambda)x_1[(t+\tau)-\lambda]\,d\lambda \\ &= \lim_{T_0\to\infty}\frac{1}{2T_0}\int_{-T_0}^{T_0} x_2(t)y_1(t+\tau)\,dt \end{aligned} \tag{10.7-24}$$

Then, by the definition of the cross-correlation function, Eq. (10.7-24) reduces to

$$\varphi_{x_2y_1}(\tau) = \int_{-\infty}^{\infty} g_1(\lambda)\varphi_{x_2x_1}(\tau-\lambda)\,d\lambda \tag{10.7-25}$$

The output of the system $G_2(s)$ in response to $\varphi_{y_1x_2}(\tau)$ is

$$\int_{-\infty}^{\infty} g_2(\lambda)\varphi_{y_1x_2}(\tau - \lambda)\,d\lambda$$

$$= \int_{-\infty}^{\infty} g_2(\lambda)\,d\lambda \lim_{T_0\to\infty} \frac{1}{2T_0}\int_{-T_0}^{T_0} y_1(t)x_2[t + (\tau - \lambda)]\,dt$$

$$= \lim_{T_0\to\infty} \frac{1}{2T_0}\int_{-T_0}^{T_0} y_1(t)\,dt \int_{-\infty}^{\infty} g_2(\lambda)x_2[(t+\tau) - \lambda]\,d\lambda$$

$$= \lim_{T_0\to\infty} \frac{1}{2T_0}\int_{-T_0}^{T_0} y_1(t)y_2(t+\tau)\,dt \qquad (10.7\text{-}26)$$

Hence,
$$\varphi_{y_1y_2}(\tau) = \int_{-\infty}^{\infty} g_2(\lambda)\varphi_{y_1x_2}(\tau - \lambda)\,d\lambda \qquad (10.7\text{-}27)$$

In like manner, these relationships are obtained:

$$\varphi_{x_1y_2}(\tau) = \int_{-\infty}^{\infty} g_2(\lambda)\varphi_{x_1x_2}(\tau - \lambda)\,d\lambda \qquad (10.7\text{-}28)$$

$$\varphi_{y_2y_1}(\tau) = \int_{-\infty}^{\infty} g_1(\lambda)\varphi_{y_2x_1}(\tau - \lambda)\,d\lambda \qquad (10.7\text{-}29)$$

According to the Fourier integral theorem and the definition of cross-spectral density, it is easily seen from Eqs. (10.7-25), (10.7-27), (10.7-28), and (10.7-29) that the cross-spectral densities for the input and output signals are related in the following manner:

$$\phi_{x_2y_1}(\omega) = G_1(j\omega)\phi_{x_2x_1}(\omega) \qquad (10.7\text{-}30)$$

$$\phi_{y_1y_2}(\omega) = G_2(j\omega)\phi_{y_1x_2}(\omega) \qquad (10.7\text{-}31)$$

$$\phi_{x_1y_2}(\omega) = G_2(j\omega)\phi_{x_1x_2}(\omega) \qquad (10.7\text{-}32)$$

$$\phi_{y_2y_1}(\omega) = G_1(j\omega)\phi_{y_2x_1}(\omega) \qquad (10.7\text{-}33)$$

Combining Eqs. (10.7-30) and (10.7-31) by making use of property 4 leads to

$$\phi_{y_1y_2}(\omega) = G_1(-j\omega)G_2(j\omega)\phi_{x_1x_2}(\omega) \qquad (10.7\text{-}34)$$

In like manner, combining Eqs. (10.7-32) and (10.7-33) yields

$$\phi_{y_2y_1}(\omega) = G_1(j\omega)G_2(-j\omega)\phi_{x_2x_1}(\omega) \qquad (10.7\text{-}35)$$

By applying Eqs. (10.7-23), (10.7-34), and (10.7-35) the mean-square error given in Eq. (10.7-18) can be readily converted into an expression in terms of the spectral densities of the input signals, which are known, the transfer function $G_d(j\omega)$, which is specified, and the transfer function $G_0(j\omega)$, which is to be determined. Thus,

$$\overline{e^2(t)} = \frac{1}{2\pi}\int_{-\infty}^{\infty} \{[G_0(j\omega) - G_d(j\omega)][G_0(-j\omega) - G_d(-j\omega)]\phi_{r_sr_s}(\omega) + G_0(j\omega)[G_0(-j\omega) - G_d(-j\omega)]\phi_{r_sr_n}(\omega) + G_0(-j\omega)[G_0(j\omega) - G_d(j\omega)]\phi_{r_nr_s}(\omega) + G_0(j\omega)G_0(-j\omega)\phi_{r_nr_n}(\omega)\}\,d\omega \quad (10.7\text{-}36)$$

This is the frequency-domain expression of the mean-square error. As discussed above, the design of the optimum system is the determination of a physically realizable $G_0(j\omega)$ which minimizes the mean-square error with the specified functions for $G_d(j\omega)$, $\phi_{r_sr_s}(\omega)$, $\phi_{r_nr_n}(\omega)$, and $\phi_{r_sr_n}(\omega)$. The minimization process can be carried out by applying the calculus of variations to the integral given in Eq. (10.7-36). This forms the basis of the Wiener-Kolmogoroff theory for the optimum design of filters and systems. It has been derived in the literature[55] that the solution of this optimization problem is given by

$$G_0(s) = \frac{1}{F(s)}\left\{\frac{G_d(s)[\phi_{r_sr_s}(s/j) + \phi_{r_nr_s}(s/j)]}{F(-s)}\right\}_+ \quad (10.7\text{-}37)$$

where

$$F(j\omega)F(-j\omega) = \phi_{r_sr_s}(\omega) + \phi_{r_nr_n}(\omega) + \phi_{r_sr_n}(\omega) + \phi_{r_nr_s}(\omega) \quad (10.7\text{-}38)$$

and the symbol $\{\ \}_+$ designates the operation of picking the part of a function of s with poles in the left half of the s plane. Equation (10.7-37) completely determines the characteristics of the optimum system, since the functions in the right-hand side of this equation are given.

The basic principles of statistical design of continuous-data control systems have been briefly reviewed in the preceding paragraphs. The statistical design procedures described above are now to be extended to the design of digital and sampled-data control systems. For the same reason as mentioned at the beginning of this section, the minimum mean-square error will be adopted as the design criterion for the digital and sampled-data control systems. Thus, the Wiener-Kolmogoroff theory of optimum filtering and prediction is applied in the development which follows. The concepts of correlation function and spectral density are carried over to the design of digital and sampled-data control systems. In order to make the analysis and synthesis easy to comprehend and apply, the following treatment of the statistical design problem is presented in close parallel with the above discussion for continuous-data control systems. As will be seen, a number of equations describing the statistical properties of continuous-data signals have their counterpart for sampled-data signals.

Mean-square Sampled Error. The statistical design problem can be readily visualized by referring to Fig. 10.7-4, which illustrates the evaluation of the error of a digital control system subjected to a sampled stochastic control signal $r_s(nT)$ and a sampled random noise $r_n(nT)$. The signal and the noise are assumed to be stationary random functions. In

Fig. 10.7-4, $G_0(z)$ is the over-all pulse-transfer function of the digital control system, $G_d(z)$ is the desired pulse-transfer function when there is no

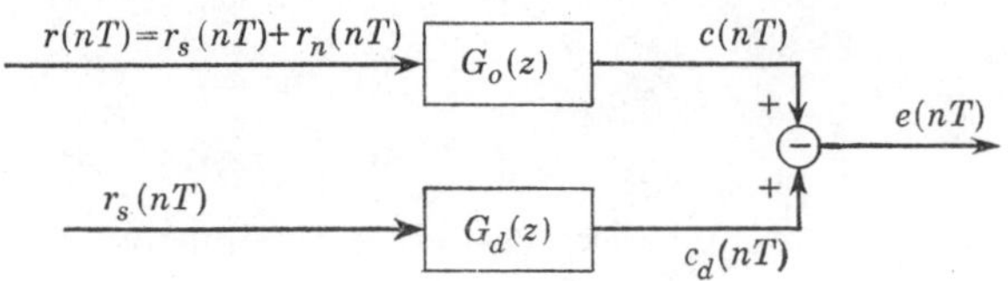

FIG. 10.7-4. Block diagram showing the relationship between the actual output sequence and the desired output sequence.

noise present, $c(nT)$ is the actual sampled output, and $c_d(nT)$ is the desired sampled output. Then the input to the control system is

$$r(nT) = r_s(nT) + r_n(nT) \tag{10.7-39}$$

and the error sequence of the system is given by

$$\begin{aligned} e(nT) &= c(nT) - c_d(nT) \\ &= c_s(nT) + c_n(nT) - c_d(nT) \end{aligned} \tag{10.7-40}$$

where $c_s(nT)$ is the system response to control signal $r_s(nT)$ and $c_n(nT)$ is the system response to noise $r_n(nT)$. The mean-square value of the error sequence of the system is defined as

$$\overline{e^2(nT)} = \lim_{N\to\infty} \frac{1}{2N+1} \sum_{n=-N}^{N} e^2(nT) \tag{10.7-41}$$

Substituting Eq. (10.7-40) into Eq. (10.7-41) and simplifying yield

$$\begin{aligned} \overline{e^2(nT)} = \lim_{N\to\infty} \frac{1}{2N+1} \sum_{n=-N}^{N} & [c_s^2(nT) + c_n^2(nT) + c_d^2(nT) + c_s(nT)c_n(nT) \\ & + c_n(nT)c_s(nT) - c_n(nT)c_d(nT) - c_d(nT)c_n(nT) \\ & - c_s(nT)c_d(nT) - c_d(nT)c_s(nT)] \\ = \overline{c_s^2(nT)} + \overline{c_n^2(nT)} &+ \overline{c_d^2(nT)} + \overline{c_s(nT)c_n(nT)} + \overline{c_n(nT)c_s(nT)} \\ - \overline{c_n(nT)c_d(nT)} - \overline{c_d(nT)c_n(nT)} &- \overline{c_s(nT)c_d(nT)} - \overline{c_d(nT)c_s(nT)} \end{aligned} \tag{10.7-42}$$

The design objective is the determination of the over-all pulse-transfer function $G_0(z)$ in such a way that the mean-square value of the error sequence is reduced to a minimum. The first step in the development of a synthesis procedure evidently involves a characterization of the input. In order to apply the Wiener-Kolmogoroff theory for optimum filter synthesis to the statistical design of sampled-data control systems, the concepts of correlation sequence and pulse-spectral density are introduced in the following manner.

Correlation Sequence and Pulse-spectral Density. The correlation sequence may be defined in a manner similar to the definition of the correlation function given in Eqs. (10.7-5) and (10.7-6). The autocorrelation sequence of a pulsed signal $x^*(t)$ or $x(nT)$ is defined as

$$\varphi_{xx}(kT) = \lim_{N\to\infty} \frac{1}{2N+1} \sum_{n=-N}^{N} x(nT)x(nT+kT) \qquad (10.7\text{-}43)$$

The cross-correlation sequence between pulsed-data signals $x^*(t)$ and $y^*(t)$ [or $x(nT)$ and $y(nT)$] is defined as

$$\varphi_{xy}(kT) = \lim_{N\to\infty} \frac{1}{2N+1} \sum_{n=-N}^{N} x(nT)y(nT+kT) \qquad (10.7\text{-}44a)$$

and the cross-correlation sequence between pulsed-data signals $y(nT)$ and $x(nT)$ is given by

$$\varphi_{yx}(kT) = \lim_{N\to\infty} \frac{1}{2N+1} \sum_{n=-N}^{N} y(nT)x(nT+kT) \qquad (10.7\text{-}44b)$$

The Fourier transform of the autocorrelation function of a continuous-data signal is defined as the spectral density of the signal, and the Fourier transform of the cross-correlation function between two continuous-data signals is defined as the cross-spectral density for these two signals. By analogy, the two-sided z transform of the autocorrelation sequence of a pulsed-data signal is defined in a similar fashion as the pulse-spectral density of the signal, and the two-sided z transform of the cross-correlation sequence between two pulsed-data signals is defined as the pulse-cross-spectral density for these two signals. Thus, the pulse-spectral density and the autocorrelation sequence are related by

$$\phi_{xx}(z) = \sum_{k=-\infty}^{\infty} \varphi_{xx}(kT)z^{-k} \qquad (10.7\text{-}45)$$

$$\varphi_{xx}(kT) = \frac{1}{2\pi j} \oint_{\Gamma} \phi_{xx}(z)z^{k-1}\,dz \qquad (10.7\text{-}46)$$

and the pulse-cross-spectral density and the cross-correlation sequence are related by

$$\phi_{xy}(z) = \sum_{k=-\infty}^{\infty} \varphi_{xy}(kT)z^{-k} \qquad (10.7\text{-}47)$$

$$\varphi_{xy}(kT) = \frac{1}{2\pi j} \oint_{\Gamma} \phi_{xy}(z)z^{k-1}\,dz \qquad (10.7\text{-}48)$$

where $z = \epsilon^{j\omega T}$ and the contour of integration Γ is the unit circle in the z plane. Equations (10.7-45) through (10.7-48) are the counterpart of Eqs. (10.7-7) through (10.7-10) which characterize continuous-data signals. In terms of frequency, the pulse-spectral density and the pulse-cross-spectral density are given by

$$\phi_{xx}(\epsilon^{j\omega T}) = \phi^*_{xx}(j\omega) = \sum_{k=-\infty}^{\infty} \varphi_{xx}(kT)\epsilon^{-jk\omega T} \tag{10.7-49}$$

and

$$\phi_{xy}(\epsilon^{j\omega T}) = \phi^*_{xy}(j\omega) = \sum_{k=-\infty}^{\infty} \varphi_{xy}(kT)\epsilon^{-jk\omega T} \tag{10.7-50}$$

The two-sided z transform is used in defining the pulse-spectral density, simply because the correlation sequence $\varphi_{xx}(kT)$ exists over all values of k, from $k = -\infty$ to $k = +\infty$. The conventional one-sided z transform is then an unsatisfactory analysis tool since this transform fails to place in evidence the nature of the sequence for negative time. Consequently, in order to characterize sequences for positive as well as negative time, the two-sided z transform is employed. Since k can take on both positive and negative integers, the contour integration given in Eq. (10.7-46) is evaluated in the following manner. For positive values of k, the integral is equal to the sum of the residues of $\phi_{xx}(z)z^{k-1}$ at the poles which lie inside the unit circle in the z plane; and for negative values of k, the integral is equal to the sum of the residues of $\phi_{xx}(z)z^{k-1}$ at the poles which lie outside the unit circle. Thus,

$$\varphi_{xx}(kT) = \sum_{\substack{\text{all poles}\\ \text{inside the}\\ \text{unit circle}}} \text{residues of } \phi_{xx}(z)z^{k-1} \quad \text{for } k \geq 0 \tag{10.7-51a}$$

$$\varphi_{xx}(kT) = \sum_{\substack{\text{all poles}\\ \text{outside the}\\ \text{unit circle}}} \text{residues of } \phi_{xx}(z)z^{k-1} \quad \text{for } k \leq 0 \tag{10.7-51b}$$

It is seen from Eq. (10.7-43) that, when $k = 0$, the value of the autocorrelation sequence is

$$\varphi_{xx}(0) = \lim_{N\to\infty} \frac{1}{2N+1} \sum_{n=-N}^{N} x^2(nT) = \overline{x^2(nT)} \tag{10.7-52}$$

which is equal to the mean-square value of the pulsed-data signal $x(nT)$ or $x^*(t)$. Setting k equal to zero reduces Eq. (10.7-44a) to

$$\varphi_{xy}(0) = \lim_{N\to\infty} \frac{1}{2N+1} \sum_{n=-N}^{N} x(nT)y(nT) = \overline{x(nT)y(nT)} \tag{10.7-53}$$

which is the mean value of the product of two sequences $x(nT)$ and $y(nT)$. Furthermore, it is obtained from Eqs. (10.7-46) and (10.7-48) that

$$\varphi_{xx}(0) = \frac{1}{2\pi j} \oint_{\Gamma} \phi_{xx}(z)z^{-1}\, dz \tag{10.7-54}$$

and
$$\varphi_{xy}(0) = \frac{1}{2\pi j} \oint_\Gamma \phi_{xy}(z) z^{-1}\, dz \tag{10.7-55}$$

Combining Eqs. (10.7-52) and (10.7-54) yields

$$\overline{x^2(nT)} = \varphi_{xx}(0) = \frac{1}{2\pi j} \oint_\Gamma \phi_{xx}(z) z^{-1}\, dz \tag{10.7-56}$$

From Eqs. (10.7-53) and (10.7-55) the following relationship is derived:

$$\overline{x(nT)y(nT)} = \varphi_{xy}(0) = \frac{1}{2\pi j} \oint_\Gamma \phi_{xy}(z) z^{-1}\, dz \tag{10.7-57}$$

Equations (10.7-56) and (10.7-57) may also be expressed in terms of frequency as

$$\overline{x^2(nT)} = \varphi_{xx}(0) = \frac{T}{2\pi} \int_{-\omega_s/2}^{\omega_s/2} \phi^*_{xx}(j\omega)\, d\omega \tag{10.7-58}$$

and
$$\overline{x(nT)y(nT)} = \varphi_{xy}(0) = \frac{T}{2\pi} \int_{-\omega_s/2}^{\omega_s/2} \phi^*_{xy}(j\omega)\, d\omega \tag{10.7-59}$$

respectively, where ω_s is the sampling frequency. Consequently, the mean-square value of a sequence and the mean value of the product of two sequences can readily be evaluated from the correlation sequence or the pulse-spectral density. It is interesting to note the resemblance between the expressions given in Eqs. (10.7-58) and (10.7-59) and the corresponding relationships for continuous-data signals given in Eqs. (10.7-15) and (10.7-16).

As demonstrated above, the minimization of the mean-square error for continuous-data control systems is carried out with ease by use of correlation function and spectral density. Now, the correlation sequence and the pulse-spectral density will be used to solve the minimization problem for a sampled-data control system. The mean-square value of the error sequence given in Eq. (10.7-42) may be expressed in terms of the correlation sequence or the pulse-spectral density by making use of the relationships derived above. Thus,

$$\overline{e^2(nT)} = \varphi_{c_sc_s}(0) + \varphi_{c_nc_n}(0) + \varphi_{c_dc_d}(0) + \varphi_{c_sc_n}(0) + \varphi_{c_nc_s}(0) - \varphi_{c_nc_d}(0) - \varphi_{c_de_n}(0) - \varphi_{c_sc_d}(0) - \varphi_{c_dc_s}(0) \tag{10.7-60}$$

$$\overline{e^2(nT)} = \frac{1}{2\pi j} \oint_\Gamma [\phi_{c_sc_s}(z) + \phi_{c_nc_n}(z) + \phi_{c_dc_d}(z) + \phi_{c_sc_n}(z) + \phi_{c_nc_s}(z) - \phi_{c_nc_d}(z) - \phi_{c_dc_n}(z) - \phi_{c_sc_d}(z) - \phi_{c_dc_s}(z)] z^{-1}\, dz \tag{10.7-61}$$

In order to carry out the minimization process it is necessary that the integrand of Eq. (10.7-61) be expressed in terms of the pulse-spectral densities for the input signal $r_s(nT)$ and the noise $r_n(nT)$. This step of reduction can be readily performed by making use of certain properties of the correlation sequence and the pulse-spectral density which are easily deduced from the preceding discussion and the definitions of correlation sequence and pulse-spectral density.

Properties of Correlation Sequence and Pulse-spectral Density.

1. The autocorrelation sequence is an even function and thus

$$\varphi_{xx}(kT) = \varphi_{xx}(-kT) \tag{10.7-62}$$

2. The cross-correlation sequences between two pulsed-data signals are related by

$$\varphi_{xy}(kT) = \varphi_{yx}(-kT) \tag{10.7-63}$$

3. The pulse-spectral density of a pulsed-data signal possesses the following property:

$$\phi_{xx}(z^{-1}) = \phi_{xx}(z) \tag{10.7-64}$$

4. The pulse-cross-spectral density between two pulsed-data signals is characterized by

$$\phi_{xy}(z^{-1}) = \phi_{yx}(z) \tag{10.7-65a}$$

$$\phi_{yx}(z^{-1}) = \phi_{xy}(z) \tag{10.7-65b}$$

The above four properties follow directly from the definitions of the correlation sequence and the pulse-spectral density and the proof is apparent. There are several other important relationships which are less obvious and are derived in the following paragraphs.

5. If the response of the pulsed-data system $G(z)$ to an input $x^*(t)$ is $y^*(t)$, then the response of this system to an input $\varphi_{xx}(kT)$ is $\varphi_{xy}(kT)$ and the response of this system to an input $\varphi_{yx}(kT)$ is $\varphi_{yy}(kT)$. These input-output relationships are illustrated in Fig. 10.7-5. With reference to Fig.

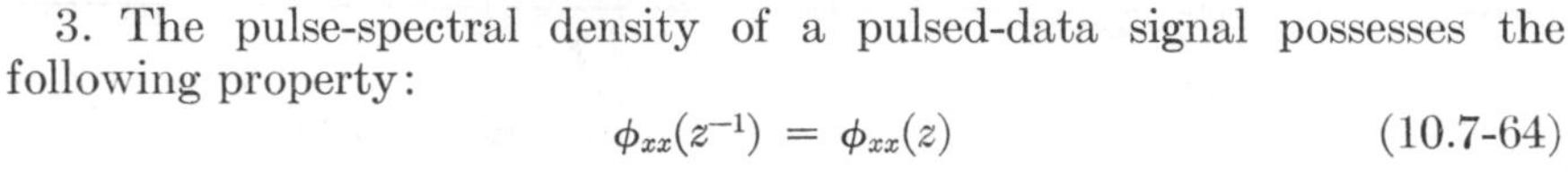

FIG. 10.7-5. Block diagrams showing the relationships between the correlation sequences for the input and output sequence of a linear pulsed-data system.

10.7-5*b*, the output of $G(z)$ in response to input $\varphi_{xx}(kT)$ is given by the convolution summation

$$\sum_{n=-\infty}^{\infty} g(nT)\varphi_{xx}(kT - nT)$$

$$= \sum_{n=-\infty}^{\infty} g(nT) \lim_{N\to\infty} \frac{1}{2N+1} \sum_{\xi=-N}^{N} x(\xi T)x[\xi T + (kT - nT)]$$

$$= \lim_{N\to\infty} \frac{1}{2N+1} \sum_{\xi=-N}^{N} x(\xi T) \sum_{n=-\infty}^{\infty} g(nT)x[(\xi T + kT) - nT]$$

$$= \lim_{N\to\infty} \frac{1}{2N+1} \sum_{\xi=-N}^{N} x(\xi T)y(\xi T - kT) \tag{10.7-66}$$

Hence, according to the definition of cross-correlation sequence,

$$\sum_{n=-\infty}^{\infty} g(nT)\varphi_{xx}(kT - nT) = \varphi_{xy}(kT) \tag{10.7-67}$$

In like manner, it can be easily shown that the output of $G(z)$ in response to $\varphi_{yx}(kT)$ is

$$\sum_{n=-\infty}^{\infty} g(nT)\varphi_{yx}(kT - nT) = \varphi_{yy}(kT) \tag{10.7-68}$$

6. The pulse-spectral densities for the input and the output sequences of a pulsed-data system $G(z)$ are related by

$$\phi_{yy}(z) = G(z)G(z^{-1})\phi_{xx}(z) \tag{10.7-69}$$

It follows from Eqs. (10.7-67) and (10.7-68) that

$$\phi_{xy}(z) = G(z)\phi_{xx}(z) \tag{10.7-70}$$

$$\phi_{yy}(z) = G(z)\phi_{yx}(z) \tag{10.7-71}$$

Combining Eqs. (10.7-70) and (10.7-71) by use of properties 3 and 4 leads to Eq. (10.7-69).

7. The cross-correlation sequence and the pulse-cross-spectral density for the output sequences of sampled-data systems $G_1(z)$ and $G_2(z)$ possess the following characteristics. Figure 10.7-6 depicts two linear sampled-

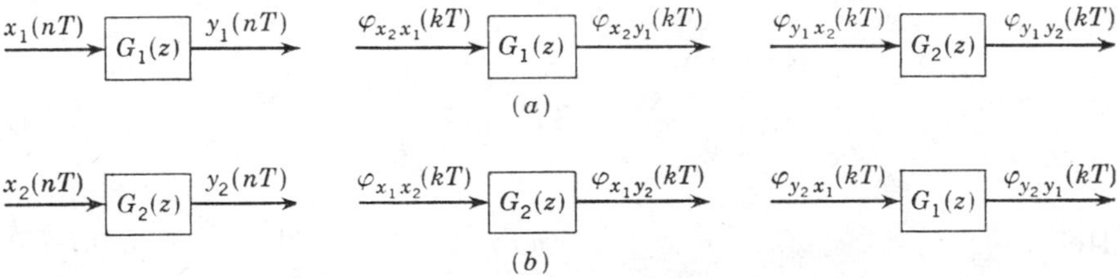

FIG. 10.7-6. Block diagrams showing the relationships between the correlation sequences for the input and output sequences of two linear pulsed-data systems.

data systems $G_1(z)$ and $G_2(z)$, which are subjected to input sequences $x_1(nT)$ and $x_2(nT)$, respectively. The output sequences in response to these inputs are $y_1(nT)$ and $y_2(nT)$, as indicated in the block diagrams of Fig. 10.7-6. It is assumed that these sequences are correlated. Then the output sequence of the system $G_1(z)$ is $\varphi_{x_2y_1}(kT)$ when it is subjected to an input sequence $\varphi_{x_2x_1}(kT)$; and the output sequence of the system $G_2(z)$ is $\varphi_{y_1y_2}(kT)$ when it is subjected to an input sequence $\varphi_{y_1x_2}(kT)$ as illustrated in Fig. 10.7-6a. The output sequence of the system $G_1(z)$ in response to $\varphi_{x_2x_1}(kT)$ is

$$\sum_{n=-\infty}^{\infty} g_1(nT)\varphi_{x_2x_1}(kT - nT)$$

$$= \sum_{n=-\infty}^{\infty} g_1(nT) \lim_{N\to\infty} \frac{1}{2N+1} \sum_{\xi=-N}^{N} x_2(\xi T)x_1[\xi T + (kT - nT)]$$

$$= \lim_{N\to\infty} \frac{1}{2N+1} \sum_{\xi=-N}^{N} x_2(\xi T) \sum_{n=-\infty}^{\infty} g_1(nT)x_1[(\xi T + kT) - nT]$$

$$= \lim_{N\to\infty} \frac{1}{2N+1} \sum_{\xi=-N}^{N} x_2(\xi T)y_1(\xi T + kT) \qquad (10.7\text{-}72)$$

By the definition of the cross-correlation sequence, Eq. (10.7-72) may be written as

$$\varphi_{x_2y_1}(kT) = \sum_{n=-\infty}^{\infty} g_1(nT)\varphi_{x_2x_1}(kT - nT) \qquad (10.7\text{-}73)$$

The output sequence of the system $G_2(z)$ in response to $\varphi_{y_1x_2}(kT)$ is

$$\sum_{n=-\infty}^{\infty} g_2(nT)\varphi_{y_1x_2}(kT - nT)$$

$$= \sum_{n=-\infty}^{\infty} g_2(nT) \lim_{N\to\infty} \frac{1}{2N+1} \sum_{\xi=-N}^{N} y_1(\xi T)x_2[\xi T + (kT - nT)]$$

$$= \lim_{N\to\infty} \frac{1}{2N+1} \sum_{\xi=-N}^{N} y_1(\xi T) \sum_{n=-\infty}^{\infty} g_2(nT)x_2[(\xi T + kT) - nT]$$

$$= \lim_{N\to\infty} \frac{1}{2N+1} \sum_{\xi=-N}^{N} y_1(\xi T)y_2(\xi T + kT) \qquad (10.7\text{-}74)$$

Hence,
$$\varphi_{y_1y_2}(kT) = \sum_{n=-\infty}^{\infty} g_2(nT)\varphi_{y_1x_2}(kT - nT) \qquad (10.7\text{-}75)$$

In like manner, the following relationships are derived:

$$\varphi_{x_1y_2}(kT) = \sum_{n=-\infty}^{\infty} g_2(nT)\varphi_{x_1x_2}(kT - nT) \qquad (10.7\text{-}76)$$

$$\varphi_{y_2y_1}(kT) = \sum_{n=-\infty}^{\infty} g_1(nT)\varphi_{y_2x_1}(kT - nT) \qquad (10.7\text{-}77)$$

As can readily be seen, the above equations relating the cross-correlation sequences are similar to Eqs. (10.7-25), (10.7-27), (10.7-28), and (10.7-29) describing the cross-correlation functions for continuous-data signals. By analogy, it follows from the above equations that the pulse-cross-spectral densities for the input and output sequences are related by the following equations:

$$\phi_{x_2y_1}(z) = G_1(z)\phi_{x_2x_1}(z) \tag{10.7-78}$$

$$\phi_{y_1y_2}(z) = G_2(z)\phi_{y_1x_2}(z) \tag{10.7-79}$$

$$\phi_{x_1y_2}(z) = G_2(z)\phi_{x_1x_2}(z) \tag{10.7-80}$$

$$\phi_{y_2y_1}(z) = G_1(z)\phi_{y_2x_1}(z) \tag{10.7-81}$$

In view of property 4, Eq. (10.7-79) may be written as

$$\phi_{y_1y_2}(z) = G_2(z)\phi_{x_2y_1}(z^{-1}) \tag{10.7-82}$$

Combining Eqs. (10.7-82) and (10.7-78) yields

$$\phi_{y_1y_2}(z) = G_1(z^{-1})G_2(z)\phi_{x_2x_1}(z^{-1}) \tag{10.7-83}$$

By using property 4, Eq. (10.7-83) reduces to

$$\phi_{y_1y_2}(z) = G_1(z^{-1})G_2(z)\phi_{x_1x_2}(z) \tag{10.7-84}$$

Similar manipulation of Eqs. (10.7-80) and (10.7-81) yields

$$\phi_{y_2y_1}(z) = G_1(z)G_2(z^{-1})\phi_{x_2x_1}(z) \tag{10.7-85}$$

Clearly, Eqs. (10.7-84) and (10.7-85) bear a close resemblance to Eqs. (10.7-34) and (10.7-35) for continuous-data signals.

Minimization of Mean-square Sampled Error. The properties of correlation sequence and pulse-spectral density described in the preceding paragraphs are now to be used in the minimization process. By making use of Eqs. (10.7-69), (10.7-84), and (10.7-85), the mean-square error given in Eq. (10.7-61) may be reduced to

$$\overline{e^2(nT)} = \frac{1}{2\pi j}\oint_\Gamma \phi_{ee}(z)z^{-1}\,dz \tag{10.7-86}$$

where
$$\begin{aligned}\phi_{ee}(z) = {} & [G_0(z) - G_d(z)][G_0(z^{-1}) - G_d(z^{-1})]\phi_{r_sr_s}(z) \\ & + G_0(z)[G_0(z^{-1}) - G_d(z^{-1})]\phi_{r_sr_n}(z) \\ & + G_0(z^{-1})[G_0(z) - G_d(z)]\phi_{r_nr_s}(z) \\ & + G_0(z)G_0(z^{-1})\phi_{r_nr_n}(z)\end{aligned} \tag{10.7-87}$$

In the above expression, all the functions of z are known except the over-all pulse-transfer function $G_0(z)$ of the given system. This minimization problem can then be solved by applying the calculus of variations to the integral of Eq. (10.7-86).

To determine the condition for the minimum of the mean-square sampled error, $G_0(z)$ of Eq. (10.7-86) is assumed to undergo a small variation $\eta(z)$. Then the first-order variation of the mean-square sampled error, $\delta\overline{e^2(nT)}$, is obtained from Eq. (10.7-86) by the substitution of $G_0(z) + \eta(z)$ for $G_0(z)$ and $G_0(z^{-1}) + \eta(z^{-1})$ for $G_0(z^{-1})$. Thus,

$$\delta\overline{e^2(nT)} = \frac{1}{2\pi j}\oint_\Gamma \eta(z)\{G_0(z^{-1})\phi(z) - G_d(z^{-1})[\phi_{r_sr_s}(z) + \phi_{r_sr_n}(z)]\}z^{-1}\,dz$$

$$+ \frac{1}{2\pi j}\oint_\Gamma \eta(z^{-1})\{G_0(z)\phi(z) - G_d(z)[\phi_{r_sr_s}(z) + \phi_{r_nr_s}(z)]\}z^{-1}\,dz \qquad (10.7\text{-}88)$$

in which

$$\phi(z) = \phi_{r_sr_s}(z) + \phi_{r_nr_n}(z) + \phi_{r_sr_n}(z) + \phi_{r_nr_s}(z) \qquad (10.7\text{-}89)$$

It is noted that for reasons of stability all the poles and zeros of $G_0(z)$ and $\eta(z)$ lie inside the unit circle in the z plane, and those of $G_0(z^{-1})$ and $\eta(z^{-1})$ lie outside the unit circle. In view of Eqs. (10.7-64) and (10.7-65), it is easy to show that

$$\phi(z) = \phi(z^{-1}) \qquad (10.7\text{-}90)$$

Consequently, $\phi(z)$ may be written as

$$\phi(z) = F(z)F(z^{-1}) \qquad (10.7\text{-}91)$$

where $F(z)$ is a function of z with poles and zeros lying inside the unit circle in the z plane, and $F(z^{-1})$ is a function of z with poles and zeros lying outside the unit circle.

Substituting Eq. (10.7-91) into Eq. (10.7-88) yields

$$\delta\overline{e^2(nT)} = \frac{1}{2\pi j}\oint_\Gamma \eta(z)\{G_0(z^{-1})F(z)F(z^{-1}) - G_d(z^{-1})[\phi_{r_sr_s}(z) + \phi_{r_sr_n}(z)]\}z^{-1}\,dz$$

$$+ \frac{1}{2\pi j}\oint_\Gamma \eta(z^{-1})\{G_0(z)F(z)F(z^{-1}) - G_d(z)[\phi_{r_sr_s}(z) + \phi_{r_nr_s}(z)]\}z^{-1}\,dz$$

$$= \frac{1}{2\pi j}\oint_\Gamma \eta(z)F(z)\left\{G_0(z^{-1})F(z^{-1}) - \frac{G_d(z^{-1})[\phi_{r_sr_s}(z) + \phi_{r_sr_n}(z)]}{F(z)}\right\}z^{-1}\,dz$$

$$+ \frac{1}{2\pi j}\oint_\Gamma \eta(z^{-1})F(z^{-1})\left\{G_0(z)F(z) - \frac{G_d(z)[\phi_{r_sr_s}(z) + \phi_{r_nr_s}(z)]}{F(z^{-1})}\right\}z^{-1}\,dz$$

$$(10.7\text{-}92)$$

Now if $G_0(z)$ is indeed the over-all pulse-transfer function of the optimum system which minimizes the mean-square sampled error, the variation $\delta\overline{e^2(nT)}$ should vanish for arbitrary $\eta(z)$. Consequently the quantities in the braces of Eq. (10.7-92) must be zero. This is the condition which leads to the optimum over-all pulse-transfer function for the system. However, before taking this step, the right-hand member of Eq. (10.7-92) should be further simplified. Since the second term in the braces of Eq. (10.7-92) contains poles inside the unit circle in the z plane as well as outside the unit circle, it may be written as

$$\frac{G_d(z)[\phi_{r_sr_s}(z) + \phi_{r_nr_n}(z)]}{F(z^{-1})} = \left\{\frac{G_d(z)[\phi_{r_sr_s}(z) + \phi_{r_nr_n}(z)]}{F(z^{-1})}\right\}_+ + \left\{\frac{G_d(z)[\phi_{r_sr_s}(z) + \phi_{r_nr_n}(z)]}{F(z^{-1})}\right\}_- \tag{10.7-93}$$

where the symbol $\{\ \}_+$ implies the operation of picking the part of a function of z with poles inside the unit circle in the z plane, and the symbol $\{\ \}_-$ denotes the operation of picking the part of a function of z with poles outside the unit circle in the z plane. It can be readily shown that the contour integral vanishes if the integrand has its poles either all inside the unit circle or all outside the unit circle. Thus,

$$\frac{1}{2\pi j}\oint_\Gamma \eta(z)F(z)\left\{\frac{G_d(z^{-1})[\phi_{r_sr_s}(z) + \phi_{r_sr_n}(z)]}{F(z)}\right\}_+ z^{-1}dz = 0 \tag{10.7-94}$$

$$\frac{1}{2\pi j}\oint_\Gamma \eta(z^{-1})F(z^{-1})\left\{\frac{G_d(z)[\phi_{r_sr_s}(z) + \phi_{r_nr_s}(z)]}{F(z^{-1})}\right\}_- z^{-1}dz = 0 \tag{10.7-95}$$

In view of this property, Eq. (10.7-92) may be reduced to

$$\begin{aligned}\delta\overline{e^2(nT)} &= \frac{1}{2\pi j}\oint_\Gamma \eta(z)F(z)\left[G_0(z^{-1})F(z^{-1}) - \left\{\frac{G_d(z^{-1})[\phi_{r_sr_s}(z) + \phi_{r_sr_n}(z)]}{F(z)}\right\}_-\right]z^{-1}\,dz \\ &\quad + \frac{1}{2\pi j}\oint_\Gamma \eta(z^{-1})F(z^{-1})\left[G_0(z)F(z) - \left\{\frac{G_d(z)[\phi_{r_sr_s}(z) + \phi_{r_nr_s}(z)]}{F(z^{-1})}\right\}_+\right]z^{-1}\,dz\end{aligned} \tag{10.7-96}$$

Then the condition which leads to the optimum over-all pulse-transfer function for the system is

$$G_0(z)F(z) = \left\{\frac{G_d(z)[\phi_{r_sr_s}(z) + \phi_{r_nr_s}(z)]}{F(z^{-1})}\right\}_+ \tag{10.7-97}$$

Therefore, the optimum pulse-transfer function is given by

$$G_0(z) = \frac{1}{F(z)}\left\{\frac{G_d(z)[\phi_{r_sr_s}(z) + \phi_{r_nr_s}(z)]}{F(z^{-1})}\right\}_+ \tag{10.7-98}$$

It is noted that in the absence of noise $\phi_{r_nr_n}(z) = \phi_{r_sr_n}(z) = \phi_{r_nr_s}(z) = 0$ and $F(z)F(z^{-1}) = \phi_{r_sr_s}(z)$; thus $G_0(z) = G_d(z)$ and $e(nT) = 0$. However, when the noise is present, the over-all pulse-transfer function is not identical to the desired pulse-transfer function, and it is in reality impossible to eliminate the mean-square sampled error even with an optimum system. Once an optimum over-all pulse-transfer function $G_0(z)$ is determined, the design of the required digital compensator $D(z)$ may be carried out by means of the conventional methods.

10.8. Adaptive Control. Throughout the treatment in the preceding sections and in Chap. 9, the design of digital and sampled-data control systems is based upon the assumption that the properties and characteristics of the system or process to be controlled are assumed to be known. The transfer function of the controlled system may be derived or the transfer characteristic may be measured. Thus, the system design is primarily the determination of the necessary compensation which is required for meeting certain performance specifications. The system so designed can cope only with problems foreseen and allowed for by the designer.

However, extreme accuracy of the characteristics of the controlled system cannot be expected. The manufacturing process always introduces some differences into supposedly identical parts. In most control systems the dynamic characteristics of the process generally vary under any operating conditions encountered during the lifetime of the control system. This may be caused by normal deterioration of the system due to wear and fatigue, drift of operating conditions, etc. Although slight variations can be counteracted by using feedback, the control system designed under the basic assumption of known transfer characteristic may fail to meet the performance requirements should the parameter variations become large. Examples where difficulties of this type are encountered exist in abundance. For instance, the change in the dynamics of an airframe with speed and altitude is appreciable, and dynamic characteristics of chemical processes usually undergo wide variations. In controlling a humidity process,† for example, generally there are four variables which specify the operating conditions that affect performance. These four variables are static dry-air pressure, dry-air stream velocity, dry-air temperature, and absolute humidity. In a typical process, the air pressure may vary with a range of 15 to 76 cm Hg abs, the air-stream velocity may vary with a range of 100 to 1600 ft/min, the air temperature may vary with a range of 350 to 700°K, and the absolute humidity may vary with a range of 0.0003 to 0.05 lb/lb. Such wide variations in system parameters would make the system difficult to control.

The problem of control becomes particularly acute when the controlled variable is not available for direct manipulation. The variation in the relationship between the available parameter and the controlled variable is entirely beyond the capacity of the control system to correct. For example, in annealing sheet steel, not the anneal but the temperature of annealing is directly controlled. The temperature of annealing effects the result. In this case, the assumed relationship between temperature and the anneal is beyond the control of the system. The control system is unable to cope with any drift in temperature-control parameters and any change in the steel composition.

In order to design control systems which are capable of solving the above-mentioned problems, there is the need for a new concept of control system design—*adaptive control.* The concept of adaptation in a complicated

† G. K. Tucker, An Adaptive Humidity Control System, *ASME paper* 58-IRD-1.

system came from the study of the behavior of living creatures, because there these characteristics are most common and conspicuous. Adaptation means the ability of self-modification or self-adjustment in accordance with varying conditions of environment. It is a basic attribute of living organisms. Certainly it is a desirable attribute for a control system. It is desired to design a control system which is capable of learning how to behave properly and has almost the *homeostatic mechanisms* of living organisms, which enable them to survive under changing conditions of environment or structure.

Adaptive control implies the ability of a control system to change its own parameters in response to a measured change in operating conditions. Adaptive control systems are distinguished by their ability to compensate automatically for either changes in the system input, such as a change in the signal-to-noise ratio, or changes in the system parameters, such as a change due to environmental variations. In recent years, interest in the problem of designing adaptive control systems has been growing steadily. A number of methods has been suggested. According to the way that adaptive behavior is achieved, adaptive control systems may be divided into *input-sensing adaptation*, *plant-sensing adaptation*, and *performance-criterion-sensing adaptation*;[189] alternately, they may be classified mainly as *passive adaptation*, *system-parameter adaptation*, and *system-characteristic adaptation*.[191] Control systems with passive adaptation achieve adaptive behavior without system parameter changes, but rather through design for operation over wide variations in environment. Examples of control systems of this nature are the conventional feedback systems and the conditional feedback systems. Control systems with system-parameter adaptation adjust their parameters in accordance with input-signal characteristics or measurements of the system variables. The *peak-holding* system[55] and the *homeostat*† are designed on the basis of system-parameter adaptation. Control systems with system-characteristic adaptation achieve adaptive behavior through measurement of transfer characteristics.

A useful approach to the design of adaptive control systems generally involves three basic principles: (1) Provision of a means for continuous measurement of system dynamic performance; (2) continuous evaluation of the dynamic performance on the basis of some predetermined criterion; and (3) continuous readjustment of system parameters for *optimum* operation by using the measured and evaluated results. These three operations can be performed by a control computer incorporated in the system. As can readily be seen, adaptive control systems are not necessarily digital or sampled-data systems. However, the use of digital techniques can generally facilitate the realization of adaptive systems operating on the above basic principles. Several adaptive systems are described in the following paragraphs:

In order to measure the system dynamic performance, the control sys-

† W. R. Ashby, "Design for a Brain," John Wiley & Sons, Inc., pp. 93–102, New York, 1954.

tem must be excited or perturbed. This can be done by introducing a test signal or perturbation into the system, or utilizing the system input as a means of excitation. The fact that the impulse response of a system is a convenient measure of its dynamic performance suggests the excitation of the system by a train of impulses. An impulse-excited adaptive system has been studied by Aseltine and others.[191] The block diagram of such an adaptive control system is shown in Fig. 10.8-1. The system is excited by

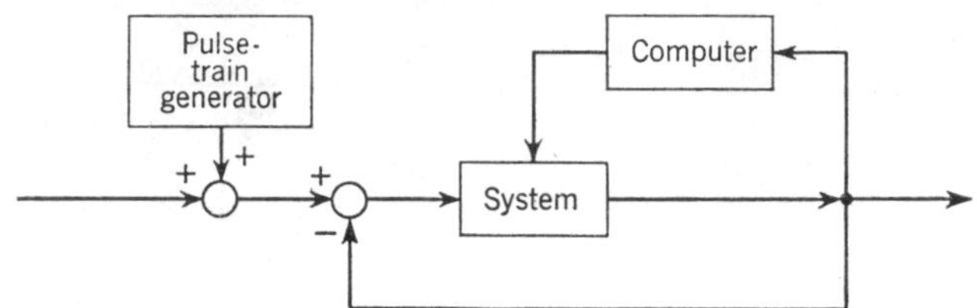

FIG. 10.8-1. An impulse-excited adaptive system.

an input disturbance in the form of a train of unit impulses with a repetition rate 5 to 10 times lower than the natural frequency of the system. A computer is used to evaluate the figure of merit from the impulse response. The figure of merit describes the relative stability of the system. The output of the computer measures the deviation from optimum due to variations of the system parameters, and forms the control signal to adjust the loop gain of the system and the parameters of the compensator so as to bring the response closer to the optimum.

The figure of merit describing the relative stability of a system can readily be computed from the system impulse responses. An examination of some typical impulse responses reveals that the ratio of positive area to negative area is a measure of system damping and stability. For undamped systems the area ratio is unity; for underdamped systems the area ratio is larger than one; and for critically damped systems the area ratio is infinite. Thus, the figure of merit can be expressed in terms of the area ratio, and is defined as

$$F_m = \frac{\int_0^\infty [w_+(t) + \gamma_0 w_-(t)]\, dt}{\int_0^\infty w(t)\, dt} = \frac{\gamma - \gamma_0}{\gamma - 1} \tag{10.8-1}$$

where $$w(t) = w_+(t) + w_-(t) \tag{10.8-2}$$

is the impulse response of the system with $w_+(t)$ and $w_-(t)$ denoting respectively the positive part and the negative part of the impulse response,

$$\gamma = -\frac{\int_0^\infty w_+(t)\, dt}{\int_0^\infty w_-(t)\, dt} \tag{10.8-3}$$

is the actual impulse-response area ratio, and γ_0 is the desired impulse-response area ratio. From Eq. (10.8-1) it is noted that the figure of merit is zero when the actual area ratio is equal to the desired area ratio. The figure of merit is positive when the actual area ratio is larger than the desired area ratio, i.e., when the system becomes more sluggish. The figure of merit is negative when the actual area ratio is less than the desired area ratio, i.e., when the system becomes less stable. Consequently, the figure of merit has zero value when the basic system is "optimally" adjusted and assumes positive or negative values depending upon the direction of deviation from the "optimum" condition.

For a second-order system having the over-all transfer function

$$G_0(s) = \frac{\omega_n^2}{s^2 + 2\zeta\omega_n s + \omega_n^2} \tag{10.8-4}$$

it can readily be shown that the impulse-response area ratio is given by

$$\gamma = \epsilon^{\pi\zeta/\sqrt{1-\zeta^2}} \tag{10.8-5}$$

Substituting Eq. (10.8-5) into Eq. (10.8-1) yields the figure of merit of the second-order system as

$$F_m = \frac{\epsilon^{\pi\zeta/\sqrt{1-\zeta^2}} - \epsilon^{\pi\zeta_0/\sqrt{1-\zeta_0^2}}}{\epsilon^{\pi\zeta/\sqrt{1-\zeta^2}} - 1} \tag{10.8-6}$$

where ζ_0 is the desired damping ratio. The relationship between the figure of merit and the damping ratio is illustrated in Fig. 10.8-2. The null point corresponds to the desired damping ratio.

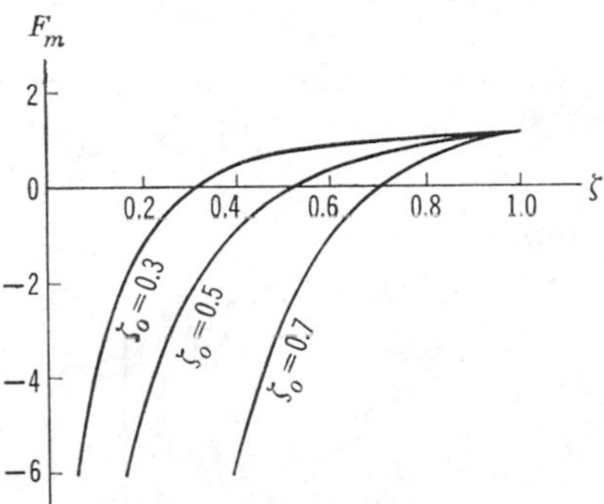

FIG. 10.8-2. Variation of the figure of merit with the damping ratio for a second-order system. (*From Anderson et al., A Selfadjusting System for Optimum Dynamic Performance, IRE Conv. Rec., pt. 4, p. 187, 1958.*)

Since the impulses may cause undesirable interference, adaptive control of this type can be applied only where such interference presents no problem. Anderson and others[18] suggest a noise-excited adaptive system, the block diagram of which is shown in Fig. 10.8-3. The system-impulse response is measured by the cross-correlation function of input and output when white noise is applied. The figure of merit and the required control signal are determined according to Eq. (10.8-1) from the measured impulse response by the computer. Assume that the impulse response of the control system is $w(t)$, which is excited by a noise input having autocorrelation function $\varphi_{ii}(\tau)$. It has been shown in Sec. 10.7 that the cross-correlation function of the system input and output is given by

$$\varphi_{io}(\tau) = \int_{-\infty}^{\infty} w(t)\varphi_{ii}(\tau - t)\, dt \tag{10.8-7}$$

However, if the noise input has a bandwidth 5 to 10 times larger than that of the system, $\varphi_{ii}(\tau)$ is effectively an impulse, and Eq. (10.8-7) reduces to

$$\varphi_{io}(\tau) = w(\tau) \tag{10.8-8}$$

Thus, each channel of cross-correlation provides a point on the impulse response of the system. In this adaptive system, the excitation noise level

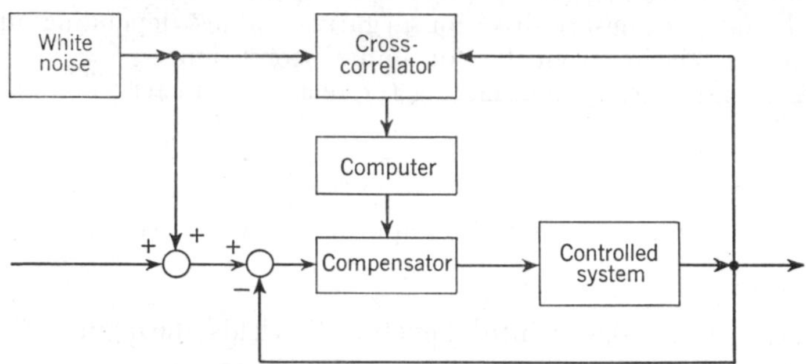

FIG. 10.8-3. A noise-excited adaptive system.

can be kept very low so that the undesirable interference caused by the excitation can be tolerated.

Adaptive control systems may be realized without introducing perturbation. Kalman describes a system[193] which employs a digital computer to estimate the pulse-transfer function of the controlled system or process. A simplified block diagram of this system is shown in Fig. 10.8-4. The

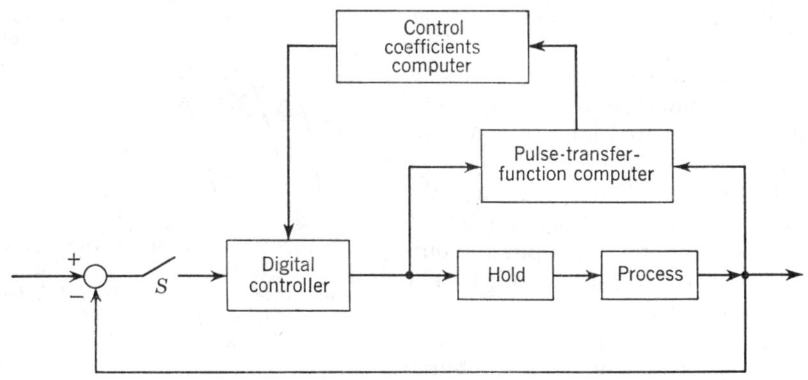

FIG. 10.8-4. Block diagram of an adaptive control system.

output of the pulse-transfer-function computer is fed to a computing device to determine the desired control coefficients. In general the design of an optimal controller depends upon two considerations: (1) the nature of the input and disturbance signals to the system; and (2) the performance criterion used. For instance, adjustments are sometimes made in the controller to achieve zero error in minimum time for a step-function input.

Self-optimizing systems may also be realized by making use of variable-rate sampling and switching technique. Figure 10.8-5 describes a possible scheme for such an adaptive control. The digital compensator is to adjust itself so that the response of the system is optimum in a defined sense. The

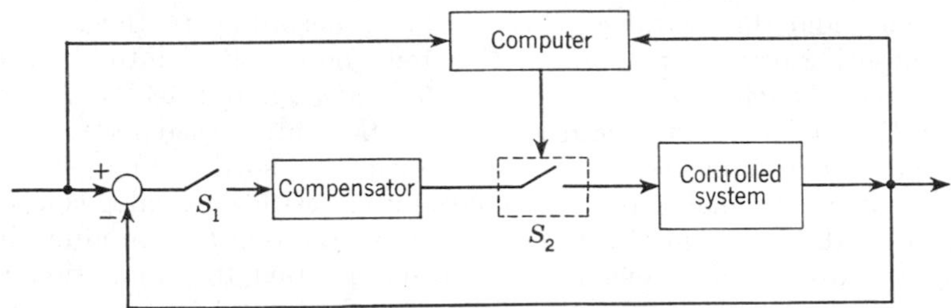

FIG. 10.8-5. Block diagram of a self-optimizing control system.

adjustment of the pulse-transfer function of the compensator is accomplished by varying the sampling function of sampler S_2. A control signal, which is determined on the basis of certain performance criteria by the computer, monitors the sampling and switching so as to yield a desired pulse-transfer function for the compensator.

10.9. Simulation. Up to this point discussion has been concerned primarily with the analytical approach of the design and synthesis of digital and sampled-data control systems. Although it is the most powerful means, the analytical approach is, in fact, just one of three techniques which are essential in system design. The other two important techniques are simulation study and experimental testing. Simulation is the imitation of the behavior of the actual system by the behavior of some other device which is easier and more economical to construct. Generally speaking, the analytical and simulation approaches are relatively inexpensive, and experimental testing usually tends to be more costly. Mathematical analysis is powerful and decisive in an environment where linearization is feasible. But with growing complication and with human beings in the control system, the analyst cannot but surrender. Under such circumstances mathematical analysis is usually aided or superseded by simulation study. Although the construction of an operational system allows test under actual conditions, even for control systems with moderate complexity the cost of construction is prohibitive of trial and the time consumed in constructing the system often limits the number of trials. In fact, no complicated system can, with economical reason, be built, tried, and discarded. However, simulation enables quick determination of system performance at a reasonable cost. In engineering applications, particularly for the study of complex systems, it is usually desirable to examine the dynamic behavior of the complete system by means of simulation which lends itself to ready evaluation of the effects of parameter variations upon the system performance. Any control system of reasonable complexity, such as a missile-guidance system, would never be designed without some simulation. With growing complication in control systems, simulation study plays a role of increasing importance in system design, while mathematical analysis is probably relegated to the role of preliminary design and operational construction to the final product.

The commonly used devices for performing the task of simulation are the analog and the digital computer. Thus, according to the nature of the computing devices used, simulation may be classified into three categories; namely, *analog simulation*, *digital simulation*, and *combined analog-digital simulation*. Digital and sampled-data control systems consist of both continuous-data and discrete-data elements; so they are sometimes simulated on both analog and digital computers, with the analog computer simulating the continuous-data elements and the digital computer simulating the discrete-data elements. Computers used for simulation purposes are sometimes referred to as simulators. According to the fashion in which the simulator is used, one may distinguish between two types of simulation: (1) *physical simulation* and (2) *mathematical simulation*. In physical simulation only part of the control system is described mathematically and set up on the simulator, and actual control system hardware is used. In mathematical simulation the control system is described completely by mathematical equations which are then set up on a computer and solved.

In the first type of simulation one attempts to duplicate in the laboratory the important characteristics of the environment to which the system components would ordinarily be subjected. The use of actual system hardware in a simulation permits the inclusion of many detailed hardware performance characteristics which might be overlooked or otherwise neglected in mathematical simulation. However, real-time solutions will be required to accommodate any actual components in the control loop being simulated. The real-time requirement imposes a greater burden upon the simulator. Real-time simulation necessitates the use of high-speed computing devices in order to simulate the performance of a control system at normal operating speed. On the other hand, the second type of simulation has the advantage that any convenient time scale may be used. Thus, it is not necessary to solve the problems in control system design on a real-time basis. However, this type of simulation has the disadvantage that the entire system must be represented by mathematical equations. Since in many digital and sampled-data control systems in practice it is too complicated or impracticable to describe mathematically the actual behavior of some of the system components used, it is imperative that mathematical expressions for such system hardware will be assumed. Clearly, this may overlook or ignore some operating features and characteristics of the actual system components, thus leading to inaccuracies in the simulated performance. In this respect, physical simulation excels mathematical simulation.

Digital and sampled-data control systems can be simulated on a commercial electronic analog computer. The simulation of the continuous-data components of a control system by established analog techniques using operational amplifiers and servo multipliers has received detailed discussion in standard textbooks on analog computers† and will not be pursued any further in the present discussion. However, this book is concerned with the simulation of pulsed-data and digital components of the control system by analog techniques. As discussed in Sec. 4.6, the sampling and holding operation may be simulated by a simple switching circuitry. The switching circuitry, which consists of a relay or a commutating device, operates in conjunction with an operational amplifier of the analog computer. A simple circuit diagram simulating a basic sampler-and-hold is illustrated in Fig. 4.6-3. The switching time constants are so arranged

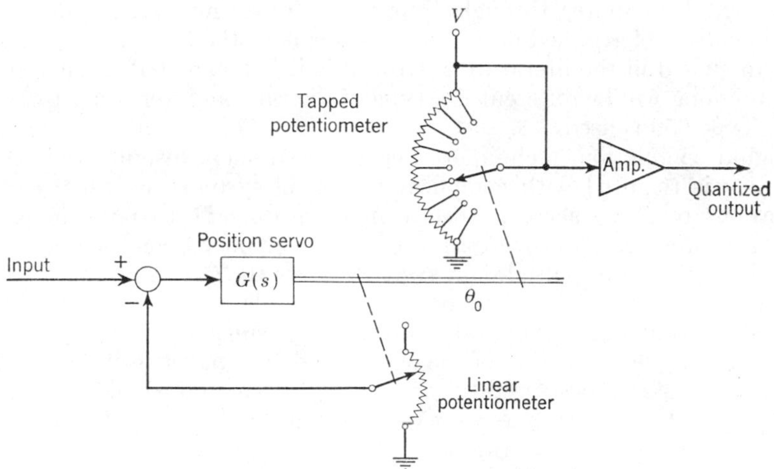

FIG. 10.9-1. A quantization simulator.

that continuous real-time operation of the computer is possible. The simulation of encoders and decoders of digital control systems by use of operational amplifiers is discussed in Secs. 8.5 and 8.6, respectively. Figure 8.5-7 depicts a simplified circuit diagram simulating an encoder by analog techniques. This simulation makes use of two operational amplifiers and a delay line. Shown in Fig. 8.6-8 is a circuit diagram illustrating the simulation of a decoder, which utilizes an operational amplifier and a switching circuitry. The principles of design and operation of these two simulators are discussed in detail in Secs. 8.5 and 8.6 and will not be repeated here.

It is discussed in Chaps. 3 and 8 that quantization is an important process in digital systems. To study the performance of digital control systems on an analog computer requires the simulation of a quantizer. Figure 10.9-1 illustrates a simplified schematic diagram which simulates

† See, for example, G. A. Korn and T. M. Korn, "Electronic Analog Computers," McGraw-Hill Book Company, Inc., New York, 1957.

a quantizer.[113] This simulator comprises mainly a positioning servo and a tapped precision potentiometer. The position servo turns the output shaft through an angular displacement proportional to the magnitude of the input signal. The precision potentiometer is provided with n taps, each tap representing one quantizing level or quantum. As the output shaft rotates, the output voltage of the quantizer will increase 1 quantizing level for each $360/n$ degrees of shaft rotation.

Mathematical simulation is sometimes employed to simulate digital and sampled-data control systems either on an analog computer or on a digital computer. In mathematical simulation of such control systems, the overall pulse-transfer function of the system must be first determined. Following the discussions of Sec. 9.6, the pulsed-data system can then be simulated by use of operational amplifiers and delay lines, or it can be simulated on a digital computer through appropriate programming. Examples of the simulation of sampled-data control systems on the IBM *Type 650* have been discussed in the literature.† However, it is noted that the computer programming will be different if a type of digital computer other than the IBM Type 650 is used.

Digital simulation techniques become extremely useful when high accuracy is required with complicated control systems, or when certain operations must be accomplished which are difficult to perform on an analog computer. However, as pointed out above, combined analog-digital simulation of pulsed-data systems offers the advantage that actual system hardware may be included in the simulated system. The interconnection of analog and digital computers in a single real-time simulation allows maximum utilization of the digital and the analog techniques. The digital computer is best used to carry out most computation. The analog computer not only serves as a connecting link between the digital equipment and the system hardware, but also performs operations involving high frequency effects and not requiring extreme accuracy, thus relieving the digital computer of some of its computing load and permitting the digital computer to operate at a lower sampling rate.‡ In combined analog-digital simulation, analog and digital computing equipments can supplement each other to a considerable extent. Consequently, combined analog-digital simulation appears preferable in the simulation of digital and sampled-data control systems.

10.10. Conclusion. In this chapter discussions are centered upon digital compensation of control systems. Through digital compensation, control systems may be optimized in a defined sense with relative ease. Pulsed-data control systems are designed either to respond to a test input with shortest settling time and zero steady-state error at the sampling instants, or to respond to a test input with no intersampling ripples. As demon-

† B. M. Tostanoski, The Analysis of Sampled-data Servomechanisms Performed on the IBM Type 650, *AIEE paper* 56-680.

‡ R. M. Leger and J. L. Greenstein, Simulate Digitally, or by Combining Analog and Digital Computing Facilities, *Control Eng.*, vol. 3, no. 9, pp. 145–153, September, 1956.

strated in the discussions of the preceding sections, a compensated system does not have an optimum performance when it is subjected to an input other than that for which the system is specifically designed. A pulsed-data control system which is designed for shortest settling time and zero steady-state error at the sampling instants in response to a ramp-function input would exhibit an excessive overshoot in its response to a step-function input. This problem may be solved by making use of the concept of staleness weighting. The undesirable overshoot is actually reduced at the expense of a longer settling time.

In common practice, control systems are usually subjected to multiple inputs. In designing linear sampled-data systems, the inputs can be treated separately since the principle of superposition applies. A well-designed control system is capable of minimizing the objectionable effects of disturbances upon the system performance.

Also discussed in this chapter are multirate compensation and the statistical design principles. The design of multirate compensators to meet certain performance criteria is no more difficult than the design of single-rate compensators. The optimum design techniques for single-rate pulsed-data systems may be extended to the design of multirate compensators. The core of statistical design of control systems is the Wiener-Kolmogoroff theory. By applying this theory the performance of a control system is evaluated on the basis of the mean-square-error criterion. Although the choice of minimization of mean-square error does not provide a better criterion for many applications than various other possible choices, the mean-square-error criterion has the advantage that it leads generally to a workable analysis. The problem of statistical design for digital and sampled-data systems can be studied in close parallel with the treatment of the statistical design for continuous-data systems.

This chapter concludes with a brief discussion of adaptive control and simulation techniques. The three techniques utilized in control-system design are analytical approach, simulation study, and experimental testing. With increasing complication in control systems, mathematical analysis often needs the aid of simulation in system design. Physical simulation allows the inclusion of actual system hardware in the simulated system, whereas mathematical simulation requires a complete description of the control system by mathematical equations. In simulating digital and sampled-data control systems with moderate complexity, combined analog-digital simulation appears preferable. Digital control can facilitate the realization of adaptive systems. It appears that perhaps adaptive control is by far the most important prospective application of the general concept of digital control systems.

CHAPTER 11

ANALYSIS OF SAMPLED-DATA CONTROL SYSTEMS WITH FINITE SAMPLING DURATION

11.1. Introduction. The analysis and synthesis of sampled-data control systems discussed in the preceding chapters are based upon the assumption that sampling occurs instantaneously and the sampling pulses are of infinitesimal width. Under this assumption, the sampled signal in the control system can be treated as a train of ideal pulses or equivalent impulses, the strengths of which are equal to the values of the corresponding continuous signal at the respective sampling instants. Indeed, this is a very important assumption which simplifies considerably the analysis as well as the synthesis of sampled-data control systems. As can be seen, this assumption is valid in the case of digital control systems and in sampled-data systems of which the sampling duration (or pulse width) is very short compared with the time constants of the control systems and where the sampling device is followed by a zero-order hold.

However, in many sampled-data control systems in practice sampling does not occur instantaneously and the pulse width cannot be ignored. The analysis of such systems by the methods already described will generally lead to an inadequate solution, because the concept of treating a sampler as an impulse modulator does not hold whenever the sampling duration becomes appreciable. Nevertheless, the concepts and the methods discussed in the preceding chapters can readily be extended so as to take into account the width and the shape of the pulses of the sampler output. This chapter introduces the techniques for analyzing sampled-data control systems with finite sampling duration. Two approaches are discussed in the sections to follow. One approach is based upon the delayed z transform (or starred transform) and the τ transform.[150] τ stands for the sampling duration and the τ transform is derived from the delayed z transform, which is closely related to the modified z transform discussed in Chap. 5. The other approach, which is to be presented, extends the widely used z-transform method to the analysis of sampled-data control systems with finite sampling duration.[180] In essence, both approaches are based upon the principle of superposition and the techniques of multirate sampling. The analysis is carried out on the basis that a pulse may be approximated by a succession of rectangular or trapezoidal pulses and that the envelope of the pulse may be approximately represented by a staircase waveform.

11.2. The Sampler and the Delayed z Transform. The basic component of a sampled-data control system is the sampler which converts continuous data into pulse-amplitude-modulated form. It is shown in Chaps. 4 and 5 that, based upon the concept of impulse modulation, the output transform of an ideal sampler is given by

$$X^*(s) = \sum_{n=0}^{\infty} x(nT)\epsilon^{-nTs} \tag{11.2-1}$$

or

$$X(z) = \sum_{n=0}^{\infty} x(nT)z^{-n} \tag{11.2-2}$$

where $x(nT)$ is equal to $x(t)$ at $t = nT$, and $x(t)$ is the input signal to the sampler. It should be pointed out that the above two expressions are valid only if the pulse has infinitesimal width and can thus be represented by equivalent impulse of strength equal to the height of the pulse.

However, in practice this ideal condition can hardly be realized and the representation of a pulse by an equivalent impulse may be considered inadequate. Under this circumstance, the sampling function is no longer a train of unit impulses occurring at the sampling instants, but it is a train of unit pulses of width h occurring at the sampling instants and it may be described by

$$u_T(t) = \sum_{n=-\infty}^{\infty} \{u(t - nT) - u[t - (nT + h)]\} \tag{11.2-3}$$

where $u(t)$ is a unit step function and h denotes the sampling duration or pulse width. Then the output of the sampler is given by

$$x_h^*(t) = \sum_{n=0}^{\infty} x(nT)\{u(t - nT) - u[t - (nT + h)]\} \tag{11.2-4}$$

The Laplace transform of the sampler output is

$$X_h^*(s) = \sum_{n=0}^{\infty} \frac{1 - \epsilon^{-hs}}{s} x(nT)\epsilon^{-nTs} \tag{11.2-5}$$

Since h is very small, it can be assumed that

$$1 - \epsilon^{-hs} \approx hs \tag{11.2-6}$$

and Eq. (11.2-5) reduces to

$$X_h^*(s) = h \sum_{n=0}^{\infty} x(nT)\epsilon^{-nTs} = h\, X^*(s) \tag{11.2-7}$$

The corresponding z transform is

$$X_h(z) = h \sum_{n=0}^{\infty} x(nT)z^{-n} = h\, X(z) \tag{11.2-8}$$

Equation (11.2-8) serves as the definition of the z transform of a sequence when the pulse width is very small but the pulses cannot be represented by equivalent impulses.

When the sampler samples at instants 0, T, and multiples of T, the sampler output is given by Eq. (11.2-4), (11.2-7), or (11.2-8). However, if the sampler operates at instants $\Delta, \Delta + T, \Delta + 2T, \ldots, \Delta + kT, \ldots,$ as shown in Fig. 11.2-1, the sampler output, $x^*_\Delta(t)$, is quite different from

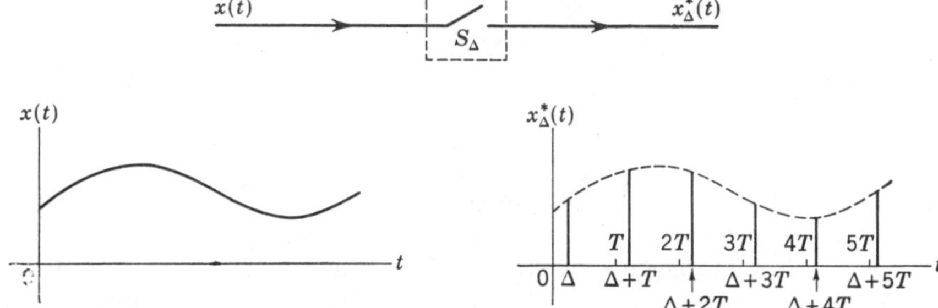

FIG. 11.2-1. Delayed ideal sampler and its output.

$x^*(t)$, which is generated when sampling is coincident with the start of the input signal $x(t)$. In Fig. 11.2-1, $x^*_\Delta(t)$ is defined as the delayed sampled output, which is produced when the sampling instants are delayed by Δ, and is given by

$$x^*_\Delta(t) = x(t)u_T(t - \Delta) \tag{11.2-9}$$

Substituting Eq. (11.2.3) into Eq. (11.2-9) and rearranging yield

$$x^*_\Delta(t) = \sum_{n=0}^{\infty} x(nT + \Delta)\{u[t - (nT + \Delta)] - u[t - (nT + \Delta + h)]\} \tag{11.2-10}$$

Taking the Laplace transform of both sides of Eq. (11.2-10) and making use of Eq. (11.2-6) yield

$$X^*(s,\Delta) = h \sum_{n=0}^{\infty} x(nT + \Delta)\epsilon^{-(nT+\Delta)s} \tag{11.2-11}$$

where h is the sampling duration which is assumed to be very small, and $X^*(s,\Delta)$ is defined as the Laplace transform of $x^*_\Delta(t)$ or the delayed transform of $x^*(t)$. By letting $z = \epsilon^{Ts}$, Eq. (11.2-11) can be written as

$$X(z,\Delta) = h \sum_{n=0}^{\infty} x(nT + \Delta)z^{-(n+\Delta/T)} \tag{11.2-12}$$

Rearranging reduces Eq. (11.2-12) to

$$X(z,\Delta) = hz^{-\Delta/T} \sum_{n=0}^{\infty} x(nT + \Delta)z^{-n} \tag{11.2-13}$$

Equation (11.2-13) defines the delayed z transform of a function.[150] Symbolically, the delayed z transform may be written as

$$X(z,\Delta) = \mathfrak{Z}\{x_\Delta^*(t)\} = \mathfrak{Z}_\Delta\{x^*(t)\} \tag{11.2-14}$$

Similarly,

$$X^*(s,\Delta) = \mathfrak{L}\{x_\Delta^*(t)\} = \mathfrak{L}_\Delta\{x^*(t)\} \tag{11.2-15}$$

is the delayed $\mathfrak{L}$ transform (starred transform) of $x^*(t)$. The above two expressions are related by

$$X^*(s,\Delta) = X(z,\Delta)\big|_{z=\epsilon^{Ts}} \tag{11.2-16}$$

TABLE 11.2-1. A SHORT TABLE OF $\mathfrak{L}$ TRANSFORMS AND DELAYED $\mathfrak{Z}$ TRANSFORMS

$\mathfrak{L}$ transform	Time function	Delayed $\mathfrak{Z}$ transform
$\dfrac{1}{s}$	$u(t)$	$\dfrac{h\,z^{-\Delta/T}}{1 - z^{-1}}$
$\dfrac{1}{s^2}$	t	$\dfrac{\Delta + (T - \Delta)z^{-1}}{(1 - z^{-1})^2}\,h\,z^{-\Delta/T}$
$\dfrac{1}{s + a}$	ϵ^{-at}	$\dfrac{h\epsilon^{-a\Delta}z^{-\Delta/T}}{1 - \epsilon^{-aT}z^{-1}}$
$\dfrac{a}{s(s + a)}$	$1 - \epsilon^{-at}$	$\dfrac{1 - \epsilon^{-a\Delta} - (\epsilon^{-a\Delta} + \epsilon^{-aT})z^{-1}}{(1 - z^{-1})(1 - \epsilon^{-aT}z^{-1})}\,h\,z^{-\Delta/T}$
$\dfrac{\omega_0}{s^2 + \omega_0^2}$	$\sin \omega_0 t$	$h\,z^{-\Delta/T}\left\{\dfrac{\sin \omega_0\Delta + z^{-1}\sin \omega_0(T - \Delta)}{1 - (2\cos \omega_0 T)z^{-1} + z^{-2}}\right\}$
$\dfrac{s}{s^2 + \omega_0^2}$	$\cos \omega_0 t$	$h\,z^{-\Delta/T}\left\{\dfrac{\cos \omega_0\Delta - z^{-1}\cos \omega_0(T - \Delta)}{1 - (2\cos \omega_0 T)z^{-1} + z^{-2}}\right\}$

Table 11.2-1 is a short table of the delayed z transforms. As an illustration of the determination of the delayed z transform of a function, two simple examples are given below.

EXAMPLE 11.2-1. Determine the delayed z transform $X(z,\Delta)$ associated with $X(s) = 1/s$.

The z transform associated with the given $X(s)$ is

$$X_h(z) = \frac{h}{1 - z^{-1}} \tag{11.2-17}$$

and the corresponding starred transform is

$$X_h^*(s) = \frac{h}{1 - \epsilon^{-Ts}} \tag{11.2-18}$$

The delayed starred transform associated with $X(s) = 1/s$ is given by

$$X^*(s,\Delta) = h \sum_{n=0}^{\infty} x(nT + \Delta)\epsilon^{-(nT+\Delta)s}$$

$$= h\epsilon^{-\Delta s} \sum_{n=0}^{\infty} \epsilon^{-nTs} \tag{11.2-19}$$

Hence,
$$X^*(s,\Delta) = \frac{h\epsilon^{-\Delta s}}{1 - \epsilon^{-Ts}} = \epsilon^{-\Delta s} X_h^*(s) \tag{11.2-20}$$

and the delayed z transform is

$$X(z,\Delta) = \frac{hz^{-\Delta/T}}{1 - z^{-1}} = z^{-\Delta/T} X_h(z) \tag{11.2-21}$$

EXAMPLE 11.2-2. Determine the delayed z transform associated with $X(s) = 1/(s + a)$.

The z transform associated with the given $X(s)$ is

$$X_h(z) = \frac{h}{1 - \epsilon^{-aT} z^{-1}} \tag{11.2-22}$$

and the corresponding starred transform is

$$X_h^*(s) = \frac{h}{1 - \epsilon^{-(s+a)T}} \tag{11.2-23}$$

Since the time function corresponding to $X(s) = 1/(s + a)$ is $x(t) = \epsilon^{-at}$, $x(nT + \Delta) = \epsilon^{-a(nT+\Delta)}$. It follows from Eq. (11.2-11) that

$$X^*(s,\Delta) = h \sum_{n=0}^{\infty} \epsilon^{-a(nT+\Delta)} \epsilon^{-(nT+\Delta)s}$$

$$= h\epsilon^{-\Delta(s+a)} \sum_{n=0}^{\infty} \epsilon^{-(s+a)nT} \tag{11.2-24}$$

Therefore,
$$X^*(s,\Delta) = \frac{h\epsilon^{-(s+a)\Delta}}{1 - \epsilon^{-(s+a)T}} = \epsilon^{-(s+a)\Delta} X_h^*(s) \tag{11.2-25}$$

and
$$X(z,\Delta) = \frac{h\epsilon^{-a\Delta} z^{-\Delta/T}}{1 - \epsilon^{-aT} z^{-1}} = \epsilon^{-a\Delta} z^{-\Delta/T} X_h(z) \tag{11.2-26}$$

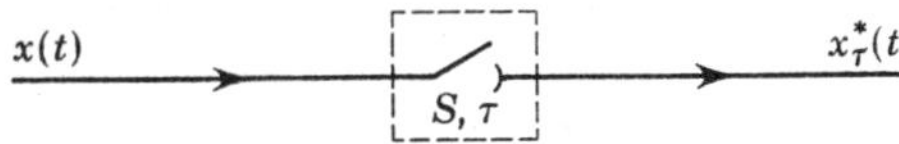

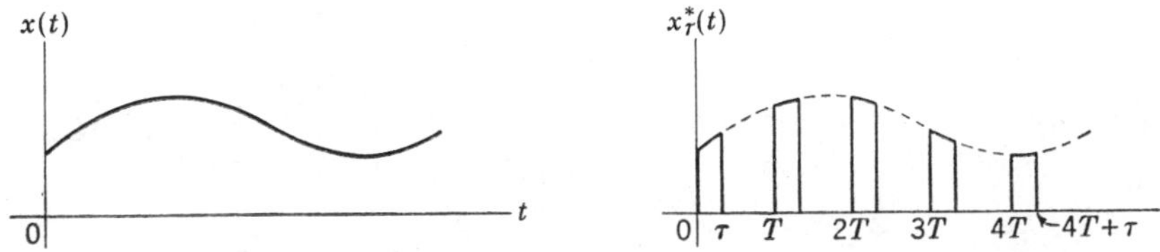

FIG. 11.3-1. Sampler with sampling duration τ and its output.

11.3. Sampler with Finite Sampling Duration and the τ Transform. The delayed z transforms described in the preceding section are now applied to the analysis of sampled-data control systems with finite sampling duration. Shown in Fig. 11.3-1 is a sampler with sampling duration τ, and

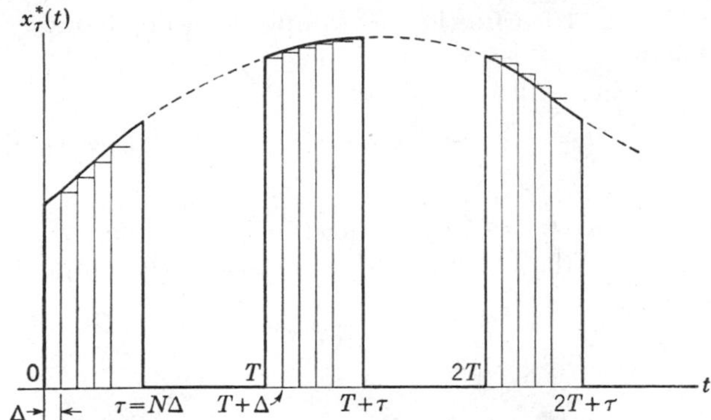

FIG. 11.3-2. Pulse of width τ is subdivided into N very narrow pulses of width Δ.

the waveforms of the input and output of the sampler. The output $x_\tau^*(t)$ is a train of amplitude-modulated pulses of finite width τ. The envelope of the output pulse train is identical to the input signal $x(t)$. Since a pulse of width τ can be considered as the resultant of N elementary pulses of

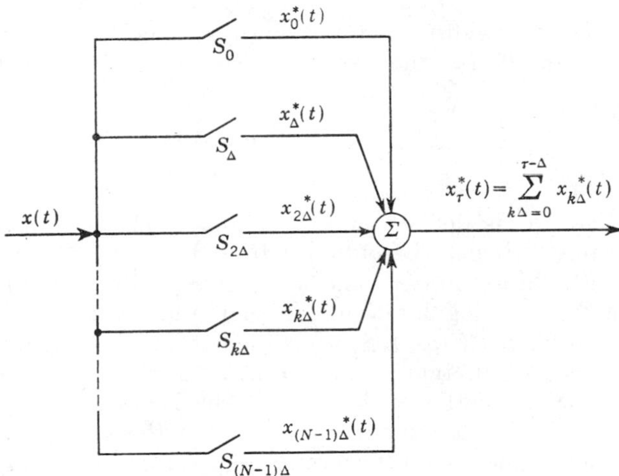

FIG. 11.3-3. Sampler with finite sampling duration is represented by a bank of N almost ideal nonsynchronized samplers.

width Δ as illustrated in Fig. 11.3-2 such that $N\Delta = \tau$, where Δ is very small, a practical sampler with sampling duration τ can be represented by N almost ideal samplers $S_0, S_\Delta, S_{2\Delta}, \ldots, S_{(N-1)}\Delta$, connected in parallel as shown in Fig. 11.3-3. The sampler S_0 samples at instants 0, T, and multiples of T; the sampler S_Δ operates at instants Δ, $\Delta + T$, $\Delta + 2T$, $\Delta + 3T$, . . . ; the sampler $S_{2\Delta}$ is actuated at instants 2Δ, $2\Delta + T$, $2\Delta + 2T$, $2\Delta + 3T$, . . . ; and the kth sampler operates at instants $k\Delta$, $k\Delta + T$, $k\Delta + 2T$, $k\Delta + 3T$, . . . ; as illustrated in Figs. 11.3-2 and 11.3-3. It is seen that the sampling instants of these samplers are successively delayed by the duration Δ. Clearly, the kth sampler can be characterized by the sampling function

$$u_{Tk}(t) = \sum_{n=0}^{\infty} \Big(u[t - (nT + k\Delta)] - u\{t - [nT + (k+1)\Delta]\}\Big) \tag{11.3-1}$$

Let $x_0^*(t)$, $x_\Delta^*(t)$, $x_{2\Delta}^*(t)$, . . . be the output of the samplers S_0, S_Δ, $S_{2\Delta}$, . . . , respectively. Then the output of the sampler with sampling duration τ is given by

$$x_\tau^*(t) = \sum_{k\Delta=0}^{\tau-\Delta} x_{k\Delta}^*(t) \tag{11.3-2}$$

in which
$$x_{k\Delta}^*(t) = x(t)u_{Tk}(t) \tag{11.3-3}$$

Substituting Eq. (11.3-1) into Eq. (11.3-3) and taking the Laplace transform yield

$$X^*(s,k\Delta) = \Delta \sum_{n=0}^{\infty} x(nT + k\Delta)\epsilon^{-(nT+k\Delta)s} \tag{11.3-4}$$

where Δ is the pulse width which is made very small.

In view of Eq. (11.3-2) the output transform of the sampler S is given by

$$X_\tau^*(s,\tau) = \sum_{k\Delta=0}^{\tau-\Delta} X^*(s,k\Delta) \tag{11.3-5}$$

in which $X^*(s,k\Delta)$ is defined in Eq. (11.3-4). The z transform of the sampler output $x_\tau^*(t)$ may be obtained from Eq. (11.3-5) by the substitution $z = \epsilon^{Ts}$. Since $X_\tau^*(s,\tau)$ and the corresponding z transform are functions of the sampling duration τ, they are referred to, for convenience, as the τ transform of $x_\tau^*(t)$. Thus, while the output of an idealized sampler is described by $X^*(s)$, that of a practical sampler is characterized by $X_\tau^*(s,\tau)$. The determination of the τ transforms is illustrated by examples.

EXAMPLE 11.3-1. If the input to a sampler with sampling duration τ is $x(t) = \epsilon^{-at}$, determine the τ transform of sampler output $x_\tau^*(t)$.

The delayed transform of $x^*(t)$ is found to be

$$X^*(s,k\Delta) = \frac{\Delta\epsilon^{-(s+a)k\Delta}}{1 - \epsilon^{-(s+a)T}} \tag{11.3-6}$$

Equation (11.3-6) can be obtained from Table 11.2-1. The τ transform of $x_\tau^*(t)$ follows immediately from Eq. (11.3-5), that is,

$$X_\tau^*(s,\tau) = \sum_{k\Delta=0}^{\tau-\Delta} \frac{\Delta\epsilon^{-(s+a)k\Delta}}{1-\epsilon^{-(s+a)T}}$$

$$= \frac{\Delta}{1-\epsilon^{-(s+a)\Delta}} \frac{1-\epsilon^{-(s+a)\tau}}{1-\epsilon^{-(s+a)T}} \tag{11.3-7}$$

By letting Δ approach zero, Eq. (11.3-7) becomes

$$X_\tau^*(s,\tau) = \frac{1}{s+a} \frac{1-\epsilon^{-(s+a)\tau}}{1-\epsilon^{-(s+a)T}} \tag{11.3-8}$$

As can readily be seen, the sampled-data system degenerates into a continuous-data system when the sampling duration of the system is equal to the sampling period. It is to be noted that if $\tau = T$, Eq. (11.3-8) reduces to

$$X_\tau^*(s,T) = \frac{1}{s+a} \tag{11.3-9}$$

which is apparently the Laplace transform of $x(t) = \epsilon^{-at}$. Thus,

$$X(s) = X_\tau^*(s,T) \tag{11.3-10}$$

and the τ transform appears to be a more general expression. Furthermore, when τ equals h, which is very small, Eq. (11.3-8) reduces to

$$X_h^*(s) = \frac{h}{1-\epsilon^{-(s+a)T}} \tag{11.3-11}$$

which is the starred transform of $x(t) = \epsilon^{-at}$, as given in Eq. (11.2-23). Thus, the starred transform or the z transform is closely related to the corresponding τ transform which is equal to the starred transform when the pulse width is very small.

EXAMPLE 11.3-2. If the input $x(t)$ to a sampler with sampling duration τ is a unit step function, determine the τ transform of the sampler output $x_\tau^*(t)$.

From Eq. (11.2-20) the delayed transform of $x^*(t)$ is found to be

$$X^*(s,k\Delta) = \frac{\Delta\epsilon^{-k\Delta s}}{1-\epsilon^{-Ts}} \tag{11.3-12}$$

Then the τ transform of $x_\tau^*(t)$ is given by

$$x_\tau^*(s,\tau) = \sum_{k\Delta=0}^{\tau-\Delta} \frac{\Delta\epsilon^{-k\Delta s}}{1-\epsilon^{-Ts}}$$

$$= \frac{\Delta}{1-\epsilon^{-\Delta s}} \frac{1-\epsilon^{-\tau s}}{1-\epsilon^{-Ts}} \tag{11.3-13}$$

By letting Δ approach zero, the above equation becomes

$$X_\tau^*(s,\tau) = \frac{1}{s}\frac{1 - \epsilon^{-\tau s}}{1 - \epsilon^{-Ts}} \tag{11.3-14}$$

which is the τ transform for a unit step function.

τ-transform Coefficients. If $X(s) = \mathcal{L}\{x(t)\}$ is a ratio of two polynomials in s with the order of the denominator higher than that of the numerator, $X(s)$ can be decomposed into partial fractions as

$$X(s) = \frac{K_0}{s} + \sum_{m=1}^{n} \frac{K_m}{s + a_m} \tag{11.3-15}$$

In Eq. (11.3-15) it is assumed that $X(s)$ contains $(n + 1)$ simple poles. Making use of Eqs. (11.3-8) and (11.3-14), one obtains the τ transform of $x_\tau^*(t)$ as

$$X_\tau^*(s,\tau) = \frac{(1 - \epsilon^{-\tau s})}{(1 - \epsilon^{-Ts})}\frac{K_0}{s} + \sum_{m=1}^{n} \frac{1 - \epsilon^{-(s+a_m)\tau}}{1 - \epsilon^{-(s+a_m)T}}\frac{K_m}{s + a_m} \tag{11.3-16}$$

Equation (11.3-16) indicates that the coefficients of K_0/s and $K_m/(s + a_m)$ terms are functions of the sampling duration τ and the complex variable s. By setting

$$\frac{1 - \epsilon^{-\tau s}}{1 - \epsilon^{-Ts}} = \gamma_0(\tau,s) \tag{11.3-17}$$

and

$$\frac{1 - \epsilon^{-(s+a_m)\tau}}{1 - \epsilon^{-(s+a_m)T}} = \gamma_m(\tau,s) \qquad m = 1, 2, \ldots, n \tag{11.3-18}$$

the τ transform of $x_\tau^*(t)$ can be written as

$$X_\tau^*(s,\tau) = \frac{K_0\gamma_0(\tau,s)}{s} + \sum_{m=1}^{n} \frac{K_m\gamma_m(\tau,s)}{s + a_m} \tag{11.3-19}$$

The coefficients $\gamma_0(\tau,s)$ and $\gamma_m(\tau,s)$ are referred to as the τ-transform coefficients.[150] When the τ-transform coefficients are multiplied to the corresponding terms of the $\mathcal{L}$ transform of a function, the τ transform of that function is obtained. Thus, the τ-transform coefficients may be considered as the conversion factors. It is to be noted that

$$\lim_{\tau \to T} \gamma_0(\tau,s) = 1 \tag{11.3-20}$$

$$\lim_{\tau \to T} \gamma_m(\tau,s) = 1 \tag{11.3-21}$$

$$\lim_{\tau \to T} X_\tau^*(s,\tau) = X(s) \tag{11.3-22}$$

The τ-transform coefficients for several basic functions are listed in Table 11.3-1.

TABLE 11.3-1. $\mathcal{L}$ TRANSFORMS AND τ-TRANSFORM COEFFICIENTS

$\mathcal{L}$ transform $F(s)$	τ-transform coefficient $\gamma(\tau,s)$
$\dfrac{1}{s}$	$\dfrac{1-\epsilon^{-s\tau}}{1-\epsilon^{-sT}}$
$\dfrac{1}{s^2}$	$\dfrac{1-(1+s\tau)\epsilon^{-s\tau}-(1-sT)\epsilon^{-sT}+[1+s(\tau-T)]\epsilon^{-(\tau+T)s}}{(1-\epsilon^{-sT})^2}$
$\dfrac{1}{s+a}$	$\dfrac{1-\epsilon^{-(s+a)\tau}}{1-\epsilon^{-(s+a)T}}$
$\dfrac{\omega_0}{s^2+\omega_0^2}$	$\dfrac{\omega_0-\epsilon^{-s\tau}(\omega_0\cos\omega_0\tau+s\sin\omega_0\tau)-\epsilon^{-sT}(\omega_0\cos\omega_0 T-s\sin\omega_0 T)+\epsilon^{-(T+\tau)}[\omega_0\cos\omega_0(T-\tau)-s\sin\omega_0(T-\tau)]}{\omega_0[1-2(\cos\omega_0 T)\epsilon^{-sT}+\epsilon^{-2sT}]}$
$\dfrac{s}{s^2+\omega_0^2}$	$\dfrac{s-\epsilon^{-s\tau}(s\cos\omega_0\tau+\omega_0\sin\omega_0\tau)-\epsilon^{-sT}(s\cos\omega_0 T-\omega_0\sin\omega_0 T)+\epsilon^{-s(T+\tau)}[s\cos\omega_0(T-\tau)-\omega_0\sin\omega_0(T-\tau)]}{s[1-2(\cos\omega_0 T)\epsilon^{-sT}+\epsilon^{-2sT}]}$

11.4. System Analysis. An open-loop sampled-data control system with finite sampling duration is shown in Fig. 11.4-1a, in which $r(t)$ is the input; $r_\tau^*(t)$, the output from the sampler S; $G(s)$, the transfer function of the

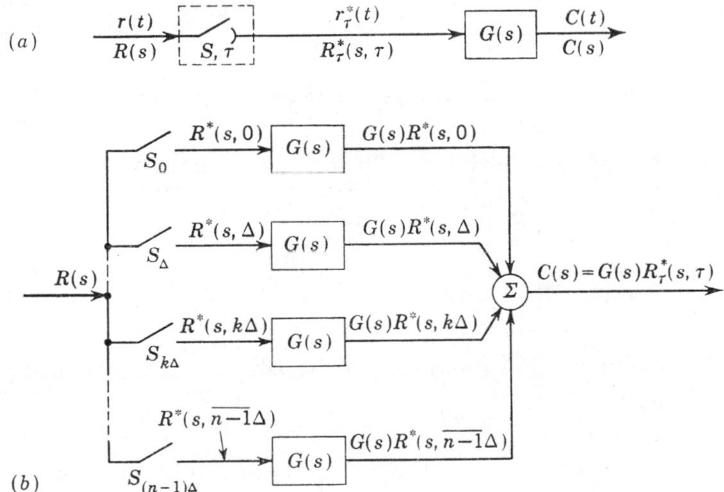

FIG. 11.4-1. (a) An open-loop sampled-data control system with sampling duration τ; (b) Equivalent block diagram of the open-loop sampled-data system of (a).

system; and $c(t)$, the system output. The open-loop sampled-data system of Fig. 11.4-1a may be described by the equivalent block diagram, as shown in Fig. 11.4-1b, with the sampler S represented by a number of almost ideal samplers connected in parallel. The sampling instants of these samplers are successively delayed by an interval Δ. If $R(s)$ is the Laplace transform of the input $r(t)$, the τ transform of the sampler output is given by

$$R_\tau^*(s,\tau) = \sum_{k\Delta=0}^{\tau-\Delta} R^*(s,k\Delta) \tag{11.4-1}$$

Inspection of Fig. 11.4-1*b* reveals that the Laplace transform of the system output is given by

$$C(s) = G(s) \sum_{k\Delta=0}^{\tau-\Delta} R^*(s,k\Delta) = G(s)R_\tau^*(s,\tau) \tag{11.4-2}$$

The transient response of this system to an input $r(t)$ can be determined by taking the inverse transform of the above equation.

However, the analysis of the sampled-data system of Fig. 11.4-1*a* may be simplified, if the sampling duration τ is much shorter than the sampling

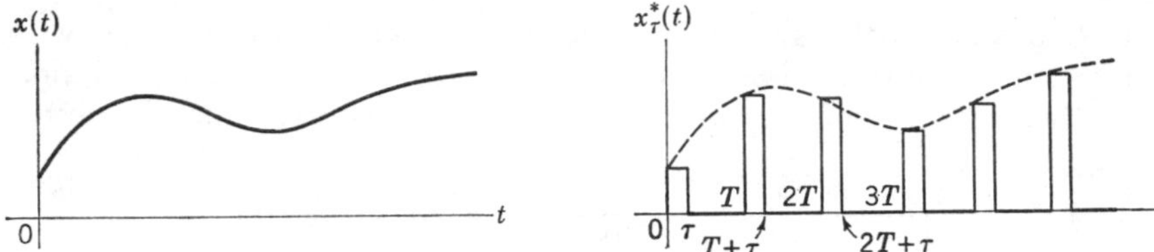

FIG. 11.4-2. Equivalent "flat-topped" pulses.

period T, or if the actual pulses can be represented by equivalent flat-topped pulses as illustrated in Fig. 11.4-2. The delayed transform $X^*(s,\Delta)$ of function $x^*(t)$, as defined in Eq. (11.2-11), is

$$X^*(s,\Delta) = h \sum_{n=0}^{\infty} x(nT + \Delta)\epsilon^{-(nT+\Delta)s} \tag{11.4-3}$$

Now, if the actual pulses are described by equivalent flat-topped pulses,

$$x(nT + k\Delta) = x(nT) \tag{11.4-4}$$

where k is a positive integer. Then Eq. (11.4-3) can be written as

$$\begin{aligned} X^*(s,\Delta) &= h\epsilon^{-\Delta s} \sum_{n=0}^{\infty} x(nT)\epsilon^{-nTs} \\ &= h\epsilon^{-\Delta s}X^*(s) \end{aligned} \tag{11.4-5}$$

In like manner, it is easy to show that

$$X^*(s,k\Delta) = h\epsilon^{-k\Delta s}X^*(s) \tag{11.4-6}$$

Thus, the τ transform of $x_\tau^*(t)$ is given by

$$X_\tau^*(s,\tau) = \sum_{k\Delta=0}^{\tau-\Delta} \Delta\epsilon^{-k\Delta s}X^*(s) \tag{11.4-7}$$

where $\Delta = h$. Rearranging and simplifying Eq. (11.4-7) yield

$$X_\tau^*(s,\tau) = \frac{(1-\epsilon^{-\tau s})\Delta}{1-\epsilon^{-\Delta s}} X^*(s) \tag{11.4-8}$$

When Δ approaches zero, $(1 - \epsilon^{-\Delta s})$ approaches Δs. Hence

$$X_\tau^*(s,\tau) = \frac{1-\epsilon^{-\tau s}}{s} X^*(s) \tag{11.4-9}$$

Equation (11.4-9) represents an approximate expression of the τ transform, when the condition of Eq. (11.4-4) is fulfilled.

Under this condition, the τ transform of the sampler output of the sampled-data system shown in Fig. 11.4-1 is given by

$$R_\tau^*(s,\tau) = \frac{1-\epsilon^{-\tau s}}{s} R^*(s) \tag{11.4-10}$$

Combining Eqs. (11.4-2) and (11.4-10) yields the Laplace transform of the system output as

$$C(s) = \frac{G(s)}{s}(1-\epsilon^{-\tau s})R^*(s) \tag{11.4-11}$$

Assuming that
$$\frac{G(s)}{s} = G_1(s) \tag{11.4-12}$$

then (11.4-11) may be written as

$$C(s) = (1-\epsilon^{-\tau s})G_1(s)R^*(s) \tag{11.4-13}$$

The output z transform of the system is given by

$$C(z) = [G_1(z) - G_1(z,1-\tau/T)]R(z) \tag{11.4-14}$$

where
$$G_1(z,1-\tau/T) = G_1(z,m)|_{m=1-\tau/T} \tag{11.4-15}$$

and $G_1(z,m)$ is the modified z transform associated with $G_1(s)$. The output sequence in response to an arbitrary input $r(t)$ can be readily evaluated from Eq. (11.4-14) through inverse z transformation.

From Eq. (11.4-13) it is obtained that the modified z transform of the system output is

$$C(z,m) = [G_1(z,m) - z_m\{\epsilon^{-\tau s}G_1(s)\}]R(z) \tag{11.4-16}$$

Evaluation of the inverse transform of Eq. (11.4-16) yields the transient response of the system to an arbitrary input $r(t)$. However, it should be pointed out that the evaluation of the inverse transform of Eq. (11.4-16) can be simplified if the procedure stated in Sec. 6.8 is followed.

A typical closed-loop sampled-data control system with finite sampling duration is shown in Fig. 11.4-3, in which $r(t)$ is the input; $e(t)$, the actu-

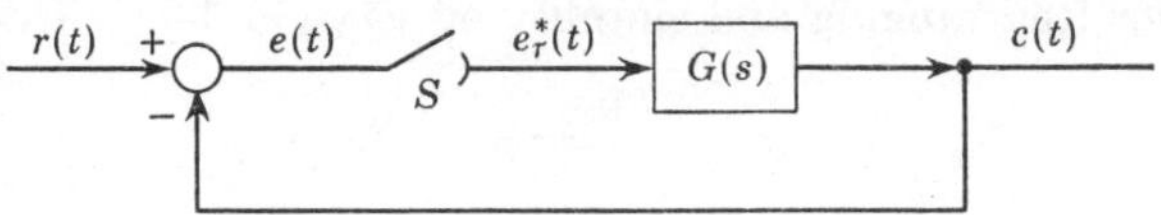

FIG. 11.4-3. A basic sampled-data feedback control system with finite sampling duration.

ating error; $e_\tau^*(t)$, the sampled error with finite pulse width; $G(s)$, the transfer function of the controlled system or plant; and $c(t)$, the system output. As can be seen, the exact analysis of closed-loop systems of this nature is quite involved. However, in most sampled-data control systems in practice the sampling duration is much shorter than the sampling period and the actual pulses may be approximated by equivalent flat-topped pulses. If this assumption is valid, closed-loop sampled-data control systems with finite sampling duration can be analyzed in a simpler manner.

In view of Eq. (11.4-9), the τ transform of the sampled error $e_\tau^*(t)$ is given by

$$E_\tau^*(s,\tau) = \frac{1 - \epsilon^{-\tau s}}{s} E^*(s) \tag{11.4-17}$$

From Fig. 11.4-3 it is seen that the system output transform is

$$C(s) = G(s)E_\tau^*(s,\tau) \tag{11.4-18}$$

Combining Eqs. (11.4-17) and (11.4-18) leads to

$$C(s) = (1 - \epsilon^{-\tau s})G_1(s)E^*(s) \tag{11.4-19}$$

where $G_1(s)$ is defined in Eq. (11.4-12). Taking the z transform of both sides of Eq. (11.4-19) yields

$$C(z) = [G_1(z) - z\{\epsilon^{-\tau s}G_1(s)\}]E(z) \tag{11.4-20}$$

or

$$C(z) = [G_1(z) - G_1(z,1 - \tau/T)]E(z) \tag{11.4-21}$$

in which $G_1(z,1 - \tau/T)$ is defined in Eq. (11.4-15). Referring to Fig. 11.4-3, it is seen that

$$E(z) = R(z) - C(z) \tag{11.4-22}$$

Eliminating $E(z)$ between Eqs. (11.4-21) and (11.4-22) and simplifying yields

$$C(z) = \frac{G_1(z) - G_1(z, 1 - \tau/T)}{1 + G_1(z) - G_1(z, 1 - \tau/T)} R(z) \tag{11.4-23}$$

It follows from the above equation that the characteristic equation of this control system is

$$1 + G_1(z) - G_1(z, 1 - \tau/T) = 0 \tag{11.4-24}$$

The location of the roots of Eq. (11.4-24) in the z plane determines the stability of the system and the modes of the transient behavior. The output sequence of this system in response to input $r(t)$ can be readily evaluated from Eq. (11.4-23) by taking the inverse transform. The synthesis procedures discussed in the preceding chapters can be applied directly to the determination of the desired compensation transfer function for this sampled-data system with finite sampling duration.

As discussed in Chap. 6, the evaluation of the complete time response of a sampled-data system to an arbitrary input is best carried out by use of the modified z-transform technique. This technique may be applied to the above problem also. It is easy to show that the modified z transform of the system output is

$$C(z,m) = \frac{(1 - z^{-\tau/T})G_1(z,m)}{1 + G_1(z) - G_1(z, 1 - \tau/T)} R(z) \tag{11.4-25}$$

Thus, the transient response of this system to input $r(t)$ is given by

$$c(nT,m) = \frac{1}{2\pi j} \oint_\Gamma \frac{(1 - z^{-\tau/T})G_1(z,m)R(z)}{1 - G_1(z) - G_1(z, 1 - \tau/T)} z^{n-1}\, dz \tag{11.4-26}$$

where the contour of integration encloses all the singularities of the integrand.

Moreover, the flat-top pulse approximation discussed above may be slightly improved, if the actual pulse is represented by an equivalent flat-topped pulse, the height of which is equal to the height of the actual pulse at the half pulse-width point, as demonstrated in Fig. 11.4-4. Based upon

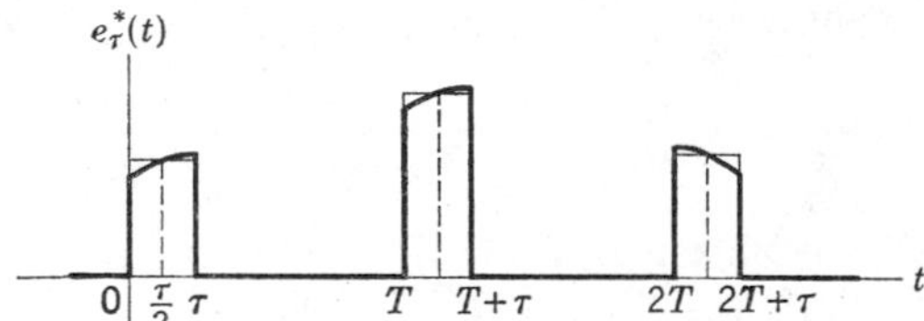

FIG. 11.4-4. Flat-top pulse approximation.

this approximation, it is easy to see that a practical sampler with sampling duration τ may be described by an idealized sampler preceded by an advance element $\epsilon^{\tau s/2}$ and followed by a partially clamped zero-order hold which clamps for a period of τ sec. The output of the partially clamped zero-order hold is a train of flat-topped pulses, which is an approximation to the actual pulse train if the pulse width τ is narrow. Following the above argument, consequently, the sampled-data system of Fig. 11.4-3 may be described by the block diagram of Fig. 11.4-5. Physically, this implies that the actuating signal $e(t)$ is advanced by half the sampling duration before it is sampled by the idealized sampler S, and that the sampled actuating signal $e^*(t)$ is then clamped for an interval of τ sec in order to generate the equivalent flat-topped pulse train. The transfer function of the partially clamped zero-order hold has been shown to be

$$G_h(s) = \frac{1 - \epsilon^{-\tau s}}{s} \tag{11.4-27}$$

It is apparent that the analysis of the equivalent system shown in Fig. 11.4-5 is fairly straightforward.

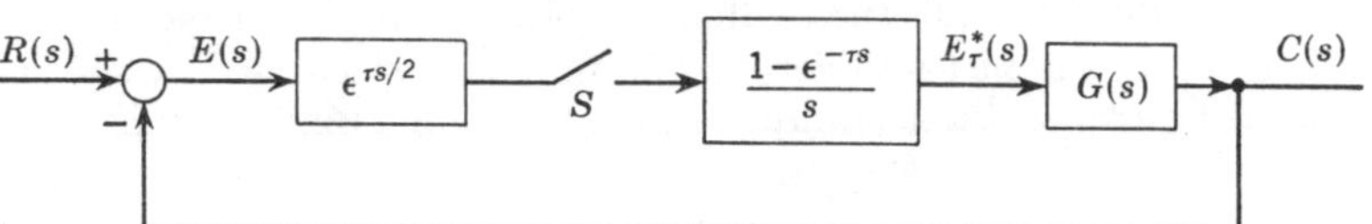

FIG. 11.4-5. Equivalent block diagram of the system of Fig. 11.4-3 (based upon the flat-top pulse approximation).

Making use of the procedures described in Sec. 6.1 it is easy to show that the z transform of the system output is given by

$$C(z) = \frac{\mathfrak{Z}\{(1 - \epsilon^{-\tau s})G_1(s)\}\mathfrak{Z}\{\epsilon^{\tau s/2}R(s)\}}{1 + \mathfrak{Z}\{\epsilon^{\tau s/2}(1 - \epsilon^{-\tau s})G_1(s)\}} \tag{11.4-28}$$

where $G_1(s) = G(s)/s$, as defined in Eq. (11.4-12). In view of the following relationships, which are discussed in Sec. 6.7,

$$\mathfrak{Z}\{\epsilon^{-\tau s}G(s)\} = G(z,m)|_{m=1-\tau/T} = G(z, 1 - \tau/T) \tag{11.4-29}$$

and

$$\mathfrak{Z}\{\epsilon^{\tau s}G(s)\} = zG(z,m)|_{m=\tau/T} = zG(z,\tau/T) \tag{11.4-30}$$

Equation (11.4-28) may be written as

$$C(z) = \frac{z[G_1(z) - G_1(z, 1 - \tau/T)]R(z,\tau/2T)}{1 + zG_1(z,\tau/2T) - G_1(z, 1 - \tau/2T)} \tag{11.4-31}$$

in which $G_1(z,\tau/2T)$ is obtained from the modified z transform associated with $G_1(s)$ by putting m equal to $\tau/2T$. It follows from Eq. (11.4-31) that the characteristic equation of the equivalent system is

$$1 + zG_1\left(z, \frac{\tau}{2T}\right) - G_1\left(z, 1 - \frac{\tau}{2T}\right) = 0 \tag{11.4-32}$$

The location of the roots of Eq. (11.4-32) in the z plane determines the stability of the system and the modes of the transient behavior. The resemblance of Eq. (11.4-32) to Eq. (11.4-24) should be noted. The evaluation of the output sequence of this system may be readily carried out by taking the inverse transform of Eq. (11.4-31). The synthesis procedures discussed in the preceding chapters may be extended to the design of sampled-data control systems with finite sampling duration, if the approximation made above is valid.

It can readily be shown that the modified z transform of the system output is

$$C(z,m) = \frac{\mathfrak{Z}_m\{(1 - \epsilon^{-\tau s})G_1(s)\}\,\mathfrak{Z}\{\epsilon^{\tau s/2}R(s)\}}{1 + \mathfrak{Z}\{\epsilon^{\tau s/2}(1 - \epsilon^{-\tau s})G_1(s)\}}$$
$$= \frac{z(1 - z^{-\tau/T})G_1(z,m)R(z,\tau/2T)}{1 + zG_1(z,\tau/2T) - G_1(z,\,1 - \tau/2T)} \qquad (11.4\text{-}33)$$

The output of this system in response to an input $r(t)$ is given by the inverse transform of Eq. (11.4-33), thus

$$c(nT,m) = \frac{1}{2\pi j}\oint_{\Gamma} \frac{z(1 - z^{-\tau/T})G_1(z,m)R(z,\tau/2T)}{1 + zG_1(z,\tau/2T) - G_1(z,\,1 - \tau/2T)}\, z^{n-1}\,dz \qquad (11.4\text{-}34)$$

The inverse transforms given in Eqs. (11.4-26) and (11.4-34) can be readily evaluated by use of the methods discussed in Chap. 5.

From the above discussion it is seen that, if the approximation of the actual pulses by equivalent flat-topped pulses is allowed, the analysis and synthesis of sampled-data control systems with finite sampling duration do not present any startling new problem nor cause any marked complexity. However, the exact analysis of sampled-data feedback control systems with finite sampling duration is more involved.

Trapezoidal-pulse Approximation. The above paragraphs present the flat-top pulse approximation, which is reasonably good if the sampling duration is relatively short. As can be easily conceived, a better solution may be obtained if the actual pulse is approximated by an equivalent trapezoidal pulse. Shown in Fig. 11.4-6 is a train of actual pulses of width τ and the corresponding trapezoidal pulses. It is observed that if the pulse shape does not change rapidly, representation of the actual pulses by trapezoidal pulses is indeed a very good approximation. In the paragraphs to follow, the analysis of sampled-data control systems with finite sampling duration is carried out on the basis of trapezoidal-pulse approximation.

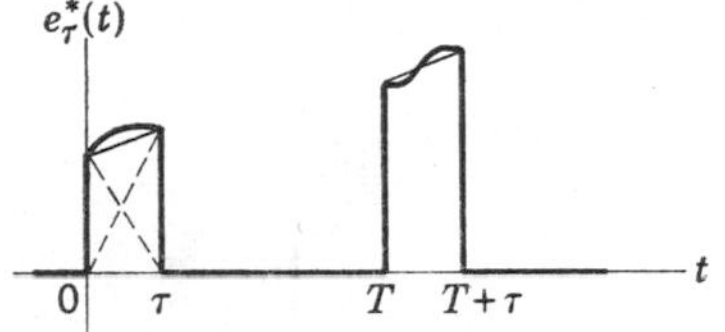

FIG. 11.4-6. Trapezoidal-pulse approximation.

When the actual pulses are approximated by equivalent trapezoidal pulses, the actual sampler of the system may be considered as being replaced by a fictitious sampler which converts a continuous signal into a train of trapezoidal pulses. A sampler of this nature may be referred to as the *trapezoidal* sampler. In order to analyze a control system containing trapezoidal samplers, the input-output relationship of a trapezoidal sampler is first established.

A trapezoidal sampler may be taken as the combination of an idealized sampler and a *polygonal* hold,† as shown in Fig. 11.4-7b. The polygonal hold converts a train of ideal pulses into a train of trapezoidal pulses. It is apparent that the polygonal hold is physically unrealizable. However,

† May also be called a *trapezoidal* hold.

for computational purposes this is immaterial. In view of the fact that a trapezoidal hold is made up of two triangles with the same base, a train of

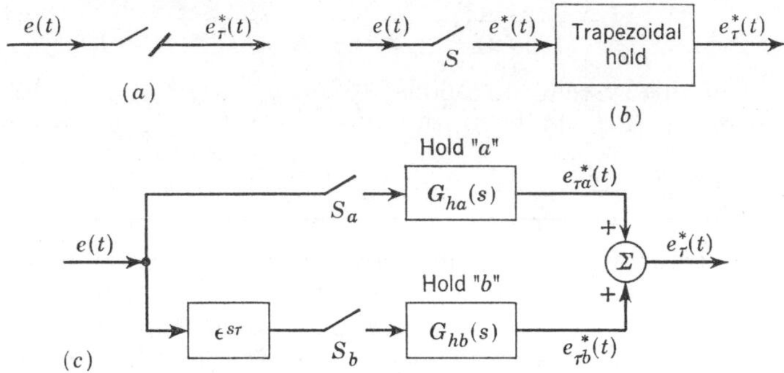

FIG. 11.4-7. The trapezoidal sampler and its equivalent representations.

trapezoidal pulses may be considered as the combination of two trains of triangular pulses, as illustrated in Fig. 11.4-8. The peaks of the triangular wave $e^*_{\tau a}(t)$ are given by the values of the input signal $e(t)$ at the beginning of the sampling operation (i.e., at the instants $t = 0, T, 2T, \ldots$); whereas the peaks of the triangular wave $e^*_{\tau b}(t)$ are determined by the values of $e(t)$ at the end of each sampling duration (i.e., at the instants $t = \tau, \tau + T, \tau + 2T, \ldots$). Based upon the above reasoning, the idealized sampler and

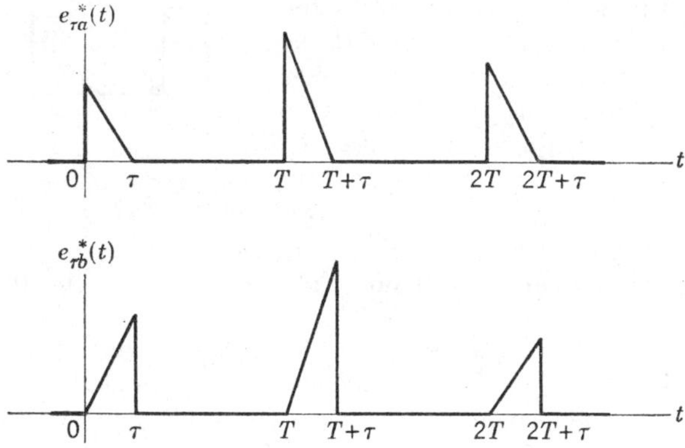

FIG. 11.4-8. Components of a trapezoidal-pulse train.

the polygonal hold shown in Fig. 11.4-7*b* may be represented by two idealized samplers and two *triangular* holds, which are connected as shown in Fig. 11.4-7*c*. The signal applied to the sampler S_b is advanced by a time interval equal to the sampling duration τ. These two samplers S_a and S_b operate in synchronism with sampling period T. In Fig. 11.4-7*c*, $G_{ha}(s)$ and $G_{hb}(s)$ denote the transfer functions of these two triangular holds, which are derived as follows:

The hold a converts a train of ideal pulses into a triangular-pulse train as shown in Fig. 11.4-8a; and the hold b converts a train of ideal pulses into a triangular-pulse train as shown in Fig. 11.4-8b. Summing these two triangular-pulse trains yields the desired trapezoidal-pulse train. Referring to Fig. 11.4-8, it is seen that the impulse responses of the triangular holds a and b are given by

$$g_{ha}(t) = \left(1 - \frac{t}{\tau}\right)[u(t) - u(t - \tau)] \tag{11.4-35}$$

and

$$g_{hb}(t) = \frac{t}{\tau}[u(t) - u(t - \tau)] \tag{11.4-36}$$

Taking the Laplace transform of both sides of Eq. (11.4-35) yields the transfer function of the triangular hold a as

$$G_{ha}(s) = \frac{1}{s} - \frac{1 - \epsilon^{-\tau s}}{\tau s^2} \tag{11.4-37}$$

In like manner, the transfer function of the triangular hold b follows from Eq. (11.4-36); that is,

$$G_{hb}(s) = \frac{1 - \epsilon^{-\tau s}}{\tau s^2} - \frac{\epsilon^{-\tau s}}{s} \tag{11.4-38}$$

Based upon the trapezoidal-pulse approximation, the sampled-data system with finite sampling duration shown in Fig. 11.4-3 may be described by the block diagram shown in Fig. 11.4-9. The z transform and the modi-

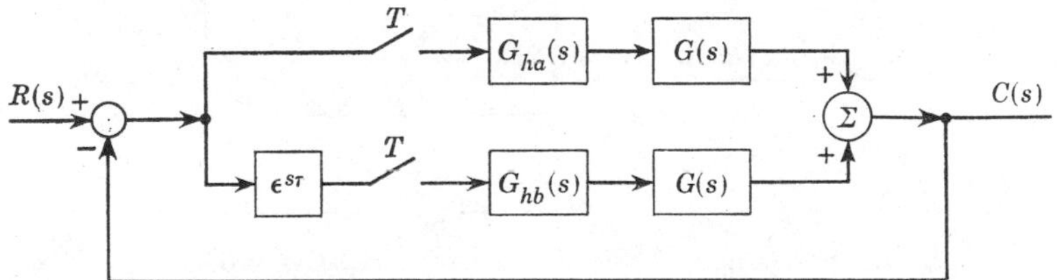

FIG. 11.4-9. Equivalent block diagram of the system of Fig. 11.4-3 (based upon the trapezoidal-pulse approximation).

fied z transform of the output of a sampled-data system of such a configuration are derived in Sec. 6.9. By defining

$$D_0(s) = 1 \qquad D_1(s) = \epsilon^{\tau s} \tag{11.4-39}$$

$$G_0(s) = G_{ha}(s)G(s) \qquad G_1(s) = G_{hb}(s)G(s) \tag{11.4-40}$$

Eqs. (6.9-16a) and (6.9-16b) may be used to determine the performance of the sampled-data control system with finite sampling duration. Although it appears that the above procedure involves much computation, the analysis can be carried out in a straightforward and systematic manner. The above discussion points out that the flat-top pulse approximation leads to a fairly simple analysis of the sampled-data system with finite sampling duration, whereas the trapezoidal-pulse approximation results in better accuracy at the expense of more computational labor.

11.5. An Alternate Approach. In the preceding sections, the analysis of sampled-data control systems by the τ-transform technique is discussed. The present section will introduce an alternate approach.[180] As will be seen, this method is quite straightforward and very easy to apply. The analysis is again based upon the fact that a pulse can be approximately represented by a number of very narrow rectangular or trapezoidal pulses, and that a practical sampler may be thought of as the combination of a number of elementary samplers with very short sampling duration. The system is then looked upon as a system containing a number of parallel branches in the path containing the sampler, and the system response at the sampling instants and during the intersampling periods is derived by applying the widely used block-diagram analysis and the z-transform and the modified z-transform techniques.

As discussed in Sec. 11.2, a pulse of width τ can be considered as consisting of n very narrow pulses of width τ/n. The sampler S of sampling duration τ sec may be represented by n samplers, S_0, S_1, S_2, . . . , S_{n-1}, of sampling duration τ/n sec, connected in parallel, each of them being delayed successively from the previous one by τ/n sec, as illustrated in Fig. 11.5-1. The sampler S_0, which operates at instants 0, T and multiples

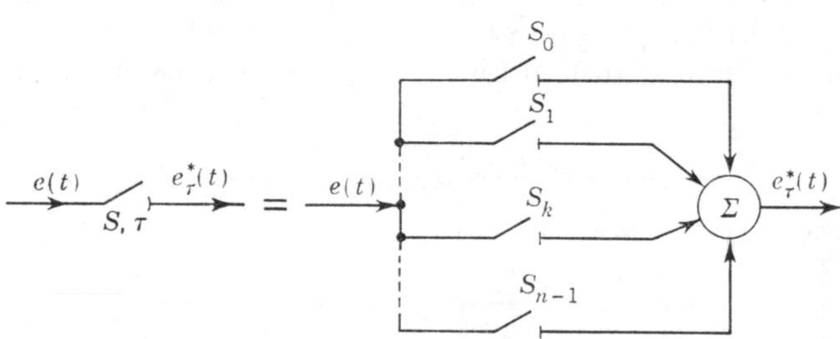

Fig. 11.5-1. A practical sampler is represented by successively delayed "flat-topped" samplers.

of T, is referred to as the basic sampler; and the samplers S_1, S_2, . . . , S_{n-1}, are referred to as the delayed samplers. Since a delayed sampler is equivalent to a basic sampler preceded by an advance element and followed by a delay element, the sampler S may be represented by n basic samplers of sampling period T and sampling duration τ/n, each of them being preceded by a proper advance element and followed by an adequate delay element, as shown in Fig. 11.5-2. For instance, the kth delayed sampler is equivalent to a basic sampler preceded by an advance element with transfer function $\epsilon^{sk\tau/n}$ and followed by a delay element with transfer function $\epsilon^{-sk\tau/n}$.

A basic sampled-data feedback control system with finite sampling duration is shown in Fig. 11.4-3. The transfer function of the controlled

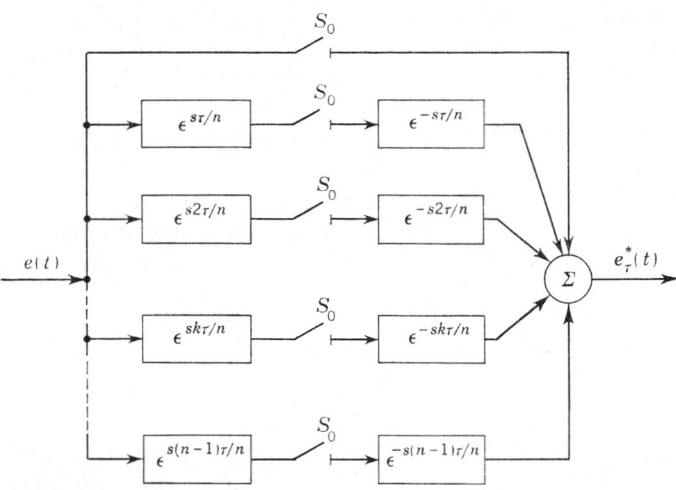

FIG. 11.5-2. Delayed samplers are represented by basic samplers together with appropriate advance and delay elements.

system is $G(s)$; the sampling period is T; and the sampling duration is τ. To analyze systems of this nature, use is made of the concept of equivalent samplers developed above and some of the results derived in Sec. 6.9. If the sampler S of the system is supplanted by its equivalent samplers, the block diagram of the system of Fig. 11.4-3 may be redrawn as shown in Fig. 11.5-3. It is observed that the block diagram of Fig. 11.5-3 resembles that of Fig. 6.9-3*b*, except that the samplers in Fig. 11.5-3 have sampling duration τ/n, whereas the samplers in Fig. 9.6-3*b* are idealized samplers.

It has been shown in the preceding section that if the sampling duration

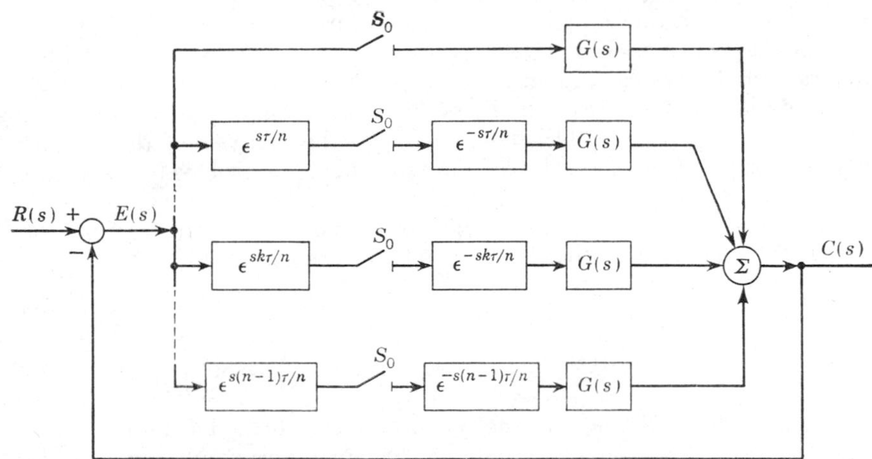

FIG. 11.5-3. Equivalent block diagram of the basic system of Fig. 11.4-3.

is much shorter than the sampling period T and the actual pulses can be represented by equivalent flat-topped pulses, the output transform of the sampler with sampling duration τ/n is given by

$$E^*_{\tau 0}(s,\tau) = \left(\frac{1 - \epsilon^{-s\tau/n}}{s}\right) E^*(s) \tag{11.5-1}$$

where $E^*(s)$ is the starred transform associated with $E(s)$. Thus, the sampler S_0 in Fig. 11.5-3 is equivalent to an idealized sampler followed by an element having transfer function $(1 - \epsilon^{-s\tau/n})/s$, as illustrated in Fig.

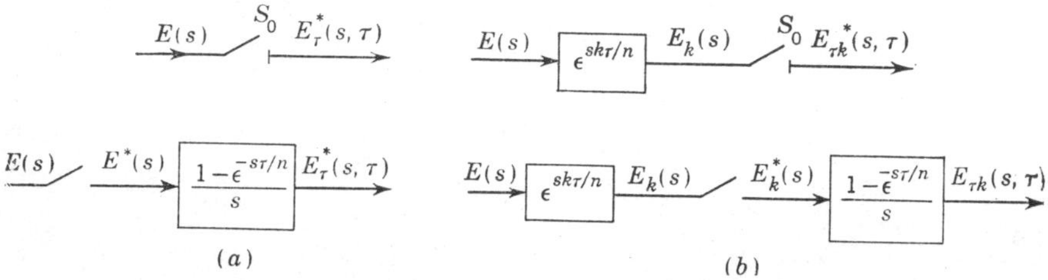

FIG. 11.5-4. Samplers with very short sampling duration represented by idealized samplers.

11.5-4. Clearly, the output transform of the kth sampler in Fig. 11.5-3 is given by

$$E^*_{\tau k}(s,\tau) = \left(\frac{1 - \epsilon^{-s\tau/n}}{s}\right) E^*_k(s) \tag{11.5-2}$$

where $E^*_k(s)$ is the starred transform associated with

$$E_k(s) = \epsilon^{+sk\tau/n} E(s) \tag{11.5-3}$$

As a result, the block diagram of Fig. 11.5-3 may be redrawn as shown in Fig. 11.5-5, with the samplers of sampling duration τ/n replaced by their equivalent shown in Fig. 11.5-4. This representation reduces the block diagram of the system of Fig. 11.5-3 to a form identical to the block diagram of Fig. 6.9-3b. As can readily be seen, this reduction allows the direct application of Eqs. (6.9-14) and (6.9-15) to the analysis of the stability and performance of the sampled-data feedback control system shown in Fig. 11.5-3.

It is to be noted that for the present system the transfer functions $D_k(s)$ and $G_k(s)$ in Eqs. (6.9-14) and (6.9-15) are given by

$$D_k(s) = \epsilon^{sk\tau/n} \tag{11.5-4}$$

and

$$G_k(s) = \epsilon^{-sk\tau/n}(1 - \epsilon^{-s\tau/n}) \frac{G(s)}{s} \tag{11.5-5}$$

Thus, when $G(s)$, T, and τ of the system are specified, the stability of the system may be determined from the system determinant given in Eq. (6.9-12). For a given input, the determinant $Q_k(z)$ in Eq. (6.9-13) can be evaluated. By substituting the functions of $B(z)$, $Q_k(z)$, and $G_k(z)$ thus derived into Eq. (6.9-14), the z transform of the system output is obtained. The modified z transform of the system output can be similarly computed from Eq. (6.9-15). It is apparent that following the above procedure the

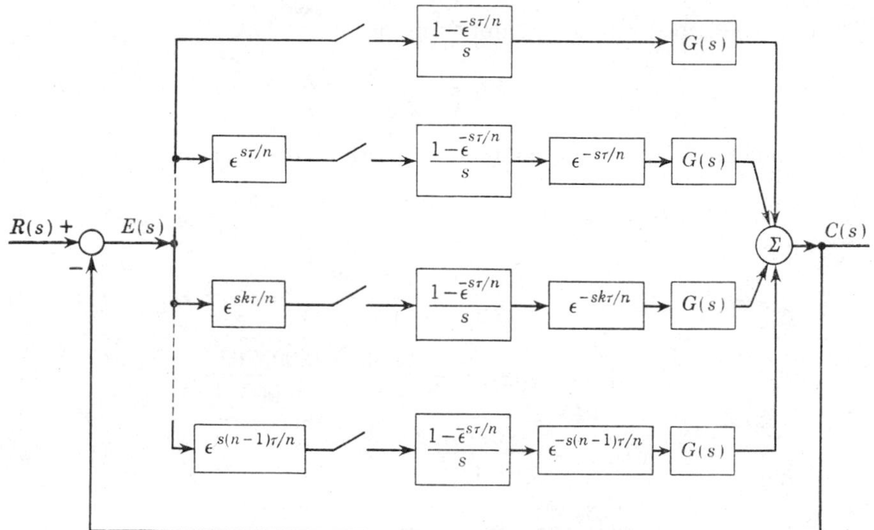

FIG. 11.5-5. Equivalent block diagram of the basic system of Fig. 11.4-3.

analysis and design of sampled-data control systems with finite sampling duration may be carried out by means of the z-transform techniques which are discussed in the preceding chapters. A numerical example is given below to illustrate the application of the method presented in this section.

EXAMPLE 11.5-1. Assume that the transfer function $G(s)$ of the system of Fig. 11.4-3 is

$$G(s) = \frac{5}{s(s+5)} \tag{11.5-6}$$

and that the sampling period T is 1 sec and the sampling duration τ is 0.2 sec. Determine the output sequence of the system in response to a unit step-function input.

As a simple illustration of the application of the above procedure, the actual pulse is approximated by two flat-topped pulses. Admittedly, this is a poor approximation. However, this can serve the purpose of illustration without involving much computation. Better approximations are obtainable at the expense of more computational labor.

From Eqs. (11.5-4) and (11.5-5) it is obtained that

$$D_0(s) = 1 \tag{11.5-7}$$

$$D_1(s) = \epsilon^{0.1s} \tag{11.5-8}$$

$$G_0(s) = \frac{5(1 - \epsilon^{-0.1s})}{s^2(s + 5)} \tag{11.5-9}$$

$$G_1(s) = \frac{5(1 - \epsilon^{-0.1s})\epsilon^{-0.1s}}{s^2(s + 5)} \tag{11.5-10}$$

The Laplace transform of the input function is

$$R(s) = \frac{1}{s} \tag{11.5-11}$$

From the above equations, the following z transforms are derived:

$$D_0G_0(z) = G_0(z) = \frac{(0.0991z + 0.0002)}{(z - 1)(z - 0.00674)} \tag{11.5-12}$$

$$D_1G_1(z) = \frac{(0.0991z + 0.0002)}{(z - 1)(z - 0.00674)} \tag{11.5-13}$$

$$D_0G_1(z) = G_1(z) = \frac{0.0986 + 0.000768}{(z - 1)(z - 0.00674)} \tag{11.5-14}$$

$$D_1G_0(z) = \frac{0.0213z(z + 3.66)}{(z - 1)(z - 0.00674)} \tag{11.5-15}$$

$$RD_0(z) = \frac{z}{z - 1} \tag{11.5-16}$$

$$RD_1(z) = \frac{z}{z - 1} \tag{11.5-17}$$

Substituting Eqs. (11.5-12) through (11.5-17) into Eq. (6.9-16) yields the z transform of the system output as

$$C(z) = \frac{0.1956z^4 - 0.1959z^3 + 0.00034z^2 + 0.00000652z}{z^5 - 2.817z^4 + 2.647z^3 - 0.843z^2 - 0.0127z - 0.000048} \tag{11.5-18}$$

By long division, Eq. (11.5-18) reduces to

$$C(z) = 0.1956z^{-1} + 0.355z^{-2} + 0.483z^{-3} + 0.585z^{-4} + 0.665z^{-5} + \cdots \tag{11.5-19}$$

The coefficients of the above power series form the output sequence of the system in response to a unit step-function input.

Although only the analysis of a basic error-sampled system is discussed in the preceding paragraphs, the techniques described above are applicable to sampled-data systems of other configurations. For instance, if the sampler is located between the compensating network $D(s)$ and the controlled system $G(s)$, as shown in Fig. 11.5-6, the transfer functions $D_k(s)$ and $G_k(s)$ in Eqs. (6.9-14) and (6.9-15) are given by

$$D_k(s) = \epsilon^{skT/n} D(s) \tag{11.5-20}$$

$$G_k(s) = \epsilon^{-sk\tau/n}(1 - \epsilon^{-s\tau/n})\frac{G(s)}{s} \tag{11.5-21}$$

respectively. The above procedure may be followed to determine the stability and performance of this system.

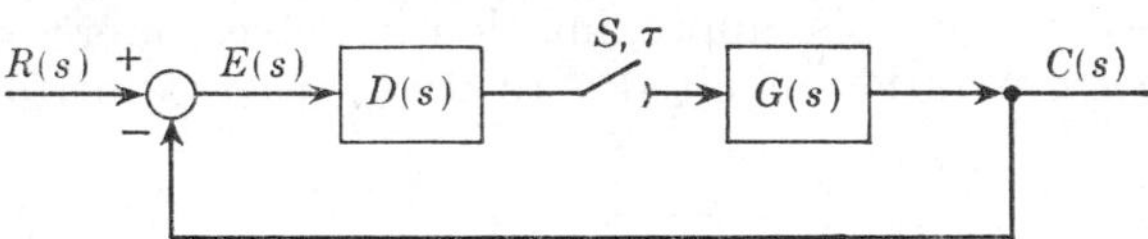

FIG. 11.5-6. System with sampler separating the controller and the controlled system.

A slight improvement in accuracy may result if the heights of the flat-topped pulses are made equal to the values of the signal at the half pulse-width points of each elementary pulse. In so doing, Eqs. (11.5-4) and (11.5-5) become

$$D_k(s) = \epsilon^{s(k+\frac{1}{2})\tau/n} \tag{11.5-22}$$

and

$$G_k(s) = \epsilon^{-s(k+\frac{1}{2})\tau/n}(1 - \epsilon^{-s\tau/n})\frac{G(s)}{s} \tag{11.5-23}$$

The procedure described in this section may then be followed to determine the system performance. Further improvement in accuracy may be obtained if the elementary pulses are represented by trapezoids instead of rectangles. With the elementary pulses approximated by trapezoids, the sampled-data system of Fig. 11.4-3 may be described by the block diagram of Fig. 11.5-7. Since this block diagram is of the same general configuration as the block diagram of Fig. 6.9-3*b*, Eqs. (6.9-14) and (6.9-15) may be applied to evaluate the performance of this system. However, as can be seen, this would involve much more computation. An improved accuracy is generally obtainable at the expense of computational labor.

11.6. Conclusion. In common practice, the sampling duration of a sampled-data control system is not infinitesimal. Apparently, without modification, the system analysis based upon the concept of impulse modulation may lead to erroneous results. In this chapter, an attempt has been made to present a concise and illuminating discussion, though brief, of the analysis of sampled-data control systems with finite sampling duration. The method of τ-transform analysis is introduced. This method may be used to carry out the exact analysis of the problem of finite sampling duration. As can be expected, the exact analysis would involve a considerable amount of computation.

However, when the sampling duration is relatively short, various approximations may be made in order to simplify the analysis. This chapter introduces the flat-top pulse approximation and the trapezoidal-pulse approximation. When the flat-top pulse approximation is valid, the finite sampling duration in sampled-data systems presents no difficult problem. The analysis and synthesis procedures, which are based upon the concept of impulse modulation and the z-transform techniques, can be readily applied to the treatment of control systems with finite sampling duration. The trapezoidal-pulse approximation generally leads to better accuracy than the flat-top pulse approximation. However, the system analysis based upon this approximation involves more computation, although the computation required is relatively easy to perform.

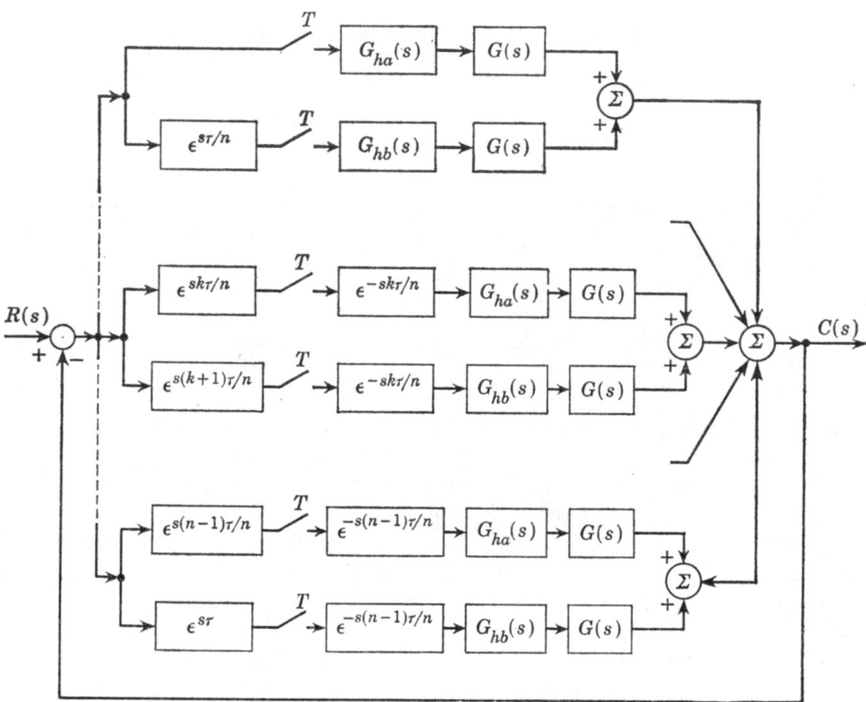

FIG. 11.5-7. Equivalent block diagram of the system of Fig. 11.4-3 when the sampling duration is appreciable.

When the sampling duration is not short compared with the sampling period, both the flat-top pulse approximation and the trapezoidal-pulse approximation become poor and perhaps are unacceptable. Under this circumstance, the actual pulse must be considered as being made up of a number of narrow rectangular or trapezoidal pulses. Based upon this approximation, the widely used z-transform techniques are directly applicable. However, because of the enormous computational labor involved in this approximate analysis, especially when a higher accuracy is desired, this approach is probably of more academic interest than of practical value. In common practice, the sampling duration of most sampled-data control systems is relatively short, and the flat-top pulse approximation and the trapezoidal-pulse approximation generally provide sufficient accuracy for most engineering applications. These two approximations lead to a simplified analysis, yield satisfactory results, and thus can be recommended for engineering design use.

APPENDIX 1
TABLE OF z TRANSFORMS AND MODIFIED z TRANSFORMS

No.	$G(s)$	$g(t)$	$G(z)$	$G(z,m)$
0.01	ϵ^{-kTs}	$\delta(t-kT)$	z^{-k}	z^{m-1-k}
0.02	1	$\delta(t)$	1 or z^{-0}	0
1.01	$\frac{1}{s}$	$u(t)$	$\frac{z}{z-1}$	$\frac{1}{z-1}$
1.02	$\frac{1}{s^2}$	t	$\frac{Tz}{(z-1)^2}$	$\frac{mT}{z-1}+\frac{T}{(z-1)^2}$
1.03	$\frac{1}{s^3}$	$\frac{1}{2!}t^2$	$\frac{T^2z(z+1)}{2(z-1)^3}$	$\frac{T^2}{2}\left[\frac{m^2}{z-1}+\frac{2m+1}{(z-1)^2}+\frac{2}{(z-1)^3}\right]$
1.04	$\frac{1}{s^4}$	$\frac{1}{3!}t^3$	$\frac{T^3z(z^2+4z+1)}{6(z-1)^4}$	$\frac{T^3}{6}\left[\frac{m^3}{z-1}+\frac{3m^2+3m+1}{(z-1)^2}+\frac{6m+6}{(z-1)^3}+\frac{6}{(z-1)^4}\right]$
1.05	$\frac{1}{s^{k+1}}$	$\frac{1}{k!}t^k$	$\lim_{a\to 0}\frac{(-1)^k}{k!}\frac{\partial^k}{\partial a^k}\left(\frac{z}{z-\epsilon^{-aT}}\right)$	$\lim_{a\to 0}\frac{(-1)^k}{k!}\frac{\partial^k}{\partial a^k}\left(\frac{\epsilon^{-amT}}{z-\epsilon^{-aT}}\right)$
2.01	$\frac{1}{s-(1/T)\ln a}$	$a^{t/T}$	$\frac{z}{z-a}$	$\frac{a^m}{z-a}$
2.02	$\frac{1}{s+a}$	ϵ^{-at}	$\frac{z}{z-\epsilon^{-aT}}$	$\frac{\epsilon^{-amT}}{z-\epsilon^{-aT}}$
2.03	$\frac{1}{(s+a)^2}$	$t\epsilon^{-at}$	$\frac{Tz\epsilon^{-aT}}{(z-\epsilon^{-aT})^2}$	$\frac{T\epsilon^{-amT}[\epsilon^{-aT}+m(z-\epsilon^{-aT})]}{(z-\epsilon^{-aT})^2}$
2.04	$\frac{1}{(s+a)^3}$	$\frac{t^2}{2}\epsilon^{-at}$	$\frac{T^2\epsilon^{-aT}z}{2(z-\epsilon^{-aT})^2}+\frac{T^2\epsilon^{-2aT}z}{(z-\epsilon^{-aT})^3}$	$\frac{T^2\epsilon^{-amT}}{2}\left[\frac{m^2}{z-\epsilon^{-aT}}+\frac{(2m+1)\epsilon^{-aT}}{(z-\epsilon^{-aT})^2}+\frac{2\epsilon^{-2aT}}{(z-\epsilon^{-aT})^3}\right]$
2.05	$\frac{1}{(s+a)^{k+1}}$	$\frac{t^k}{k!}\epsilon^{-at}$	$\frac{(-1)^k}{k!}\frac{\partial^k}{\partial a^k}\left(\frac{z}{z-\epsilon^{-aT}}\right)$	$\frac{(-1)^k}{k!}\frac{\partial^k}{\partial a^k}\left(\frac{\epsilon^{-amT}}{z-\epsilon^{-aT}}\right)$
3.01	$\frac{a}{s(s+a)}$	$1-\epsilon^{-at}$	$\frac{(1-\epsilon^{-aT})z}{(z-1)(z-\epsilon^{-aT})}$	$\frac{1}{z-1}-\frac{\epsilon^{-amT}}{z-\epsilon^{-aT}}$
3 02	$\frac{a}{s^2(s+a)}$	$t-\frac{1-\epsilon^{-at}}{a}$	$\frac{Tz}{(z-1)^2}-\frac{(1-\epsilon^{-aT})z}{a(z-1)(z-\epsilon^{-aT})}$	$\frac{T}{(z-1)^2}+\frac{mT-1/a}{z-1}+\frac{\epsilon^{-amT}}{a(z-\epsilon^{-aT})}$

Table of z Transforms and Modified z Transforms (*Continued*)

No.	$G(s)$	$g(t)$	$G(z)$	$G(z,m)$
3.03	$\dfrac{a}{s^3(s+a)}$	$\dfrac{1}{2!}\left(t^2 - \dfrac{2}{a}t + \dfrac{2}{a^2} - \dfrac{2}{a^2}\epsilon^{-at}\right)$	$\dfrac{T^2z}{(z-1)^3} + \dfrac{(aT-2)Tz}{2a(z-1)^2} + \dfrac{z}{a^2(z-1)} - \dfrac{z}{a^2(z-\epsilon^{-aT})}$	$\dfrac{T^2}{(z-1)^3} + \dfrac{T^2(m+1/2) - T/a}{(z-1)^2} + \dfrac{T^2m^2/2 - Tm/a + 1/a^2}{z-1} - \dfrac{\epsilon^{-amT}}{a^2(z-\epsilon^{-aT})}$
3.04	$\dfrac{a}{s^{k+1}(s+a)}$	$\dfrac{1}{k!}\left[t^k - \dfrac{k}{a}t^{k-1} + \dfrac{k(k-1)}{a^2}t^{k-2} - \cdots + (-1)^{k-1}\dfrac{k!}{a^k}t + (-1)^k\dfrac{k!}{a^k}\right] + (-1)^{k+1}\dfrac{\epsilon^{-at}}{a^k}$	$\dfrac{(-1)^{k+1}}{a^k}\dfrac{1}{1-\epsilon^{-aT}z^{-1}} + \dfrac{a}{k!}\lim_{x\to 0}\dfrac{\partial^k}{\partial x^k}\left[\dfrac{1}{(x+a)(1-\epsilon^{Tx}z^{-1})}\right]$	$\dfrac{(-1)^{k+1}}{a^k}\dfrac{\epsilon^{-amT}}{z-\epsilon^{-aT}} + \dfrac{a}{k!}\lim_{x\to 0}\dfrac{\partial^k}{\partial x^k}\left[\dfrac{\epsilon^{mTx}}{(x+a)(z-\epsilon^{Tx})}\right]$
4.01	$\dfrac{\omega_0}{s^2+\omega_0^2}$	$\sin \omega_0 t$	$\dfrac{z \sin \omega_0 T}{z^2 - 2z\cos\omega_0 T + 1}$	$\dfrac{z \sin m\omega_0 T + \sin(1-m)\omega_0 T}{z^2 - 2z\cos\omega_0 T + 1}$
4.02	$\dfrac{s}{s^2+\omega_0^2}$	$\cos \omega_0 t$	$\dfrac{z(z - \cos\omega_0 T)}{z^2 - 2z\cos\omega_0 T + 1}$	$\dfrac{z \cos m\omega_0 T - \cos(1-m)\omega_0 T}{z^2 - 2z\cos\omega_0 T + 1}$
4.03	$\dfrac{\omega_0}{s^2-\omega_0^2}$	$\sinh \omega_0 t$	$\dfrac{z \sinh \omega_0 T}{z^2 - 2z\cosh\omega_0 T + 1}$	$\dfrac{z \sinh m\omega_0 T + \sinh(1-m)\omega_0 T}{z^2 - 2z\cosh\omega_0 T + 1}$
4.04	$\dfrac{s}{s^2-\omega_0^2}$	$\cosh \omega_0 t$	$\dfrac{z(z - \cosh\omega_0 T)}{z^2 - 2z\cosh\omega_0 T + 1}$	$\dfrac{z \cosh m\omega_0 T - \cosh(1-m)\omega_0 T}{z^2 - 2z\cosh\omega_0 T + 1}$
4.05	$\dfrac{\omega_0^2}{s(s^2-\omega_0^2)}$	$\cosh \omega_0 t - 1$	$\dfrac{z(z - \cosh\omega_0 T)}{z^2 - 2z\cosh\omega_0 T + 1} - \dfrac{z}{z-1}$	$\dfrac{z \cosh m\omega_0 T - \cosh(1-m)\omega_0 T}{z^2 - 2z\cosh\omega_0 T + 1} - \dfrac{1}{z-1}$
4.06	$\dfrac{\omega_0^2}{s(s^2+\omega_0^2)}$	$1 - \cos \omega_0 t$	$\dfrac{z}{z-1} - \dfrac{z(z - \cos\omega_0 T)}{z^2 - 2z\cos\omega_0 T + 1}$	$\dfrac{1}{z-1} - \dfrac{z \cos m\omega_0 T - \cos(1-m)\omega_0 T}{z^2 - 2z\cos\omega_0 T + 1}$
4.07	$\dfrac{\omega_0^2(s+a)}{s(s^2+\omega_0^2)}$	$a - a\sec\theta\cos(\omega_0 t + \theta)$ where $\theta = \tan^{-1}\dfrac{\omega_0}{a}$	$\dfrac{az}{z-1} - \dfrac{az^2 - az\sec\theta\cos(\omega_0 T + \theta)}{z^2 - 2z\cos\omega_0 T + 1}$	$\dfrac{a}{z-1} - \dfrac{a\sec\theta\,\{z\cos(m\omega_0 T + \theta) - \cos[(1-m)\omega_0 T + \theta]\}}{z^2 - 2z\cos\omega_0 T + 1}$
5.01	$\dfrac{b-a}{(s+a)(s+b)}$	$\epsilon^{-at} - \epsilon^{-bt}$	$\dfrac{z}{z-\epsilon^{-aT}} - \dfrac{z}{z-\epsilon^{-bT}}$	$\dfrac{\epsilon^{-amT}}{z-\epsilon^{-aT}} - \dfrac{\epsilon^{-bmT}}{z-\epsilon^{-bT}}$
5.02	$\dfrac{(b-a)(s+c)}{(s+a)(s+b)}$	$(c-a)\epsilon^{-at} + (b-c)\epsilon^{-bt}$	$\dfrac{(c-a)z}{z-\epsilon^{-aT}} + \dfrac{(b-c)z}{z-\epsilon^{-bT}}$	$\dfrac{(c-a)\epsilon^{-amT}}{z-\epsilon^{-aT}} + \dfrac{(b-c)\epsilon^{-bmT}}{z-\epsilon^{-bT}}$
5.03	$\dfrac{ab}{s(s+a)(s+b)}$	$1 + \dfrac{b}{a-b}\epsilon^{-at} - \dfrac{a}{a-b}\epsilon^{-bt}$	$\dfrac{z}{z-1} + \dfrac{bz}{(a-b)(z-\epsilon^{-aT})} - \dfrac{az}{(a-b)(z-\epsilon^{-bT})}$	$\dfrac{1}{z-1} + \dfrac{b\epsilon^{-amT}}{(a-b)(z-\epsilon^{-aT})} - \dfrac{a\epsilon^{-bmT}}{(a-b)(z-\epsilon^{-bT})}$

5.04	$\dfrac{ab(s+c)}{s(s+a)(s+b)}$	$c+\dfrac{b(c-a)}{a-b}\epsilon^{-at}+\dfrac{a(b-c)}{a-b}\epsilon^{-bt}$	$\dfrac{cz}{z-1}+\dfrac{b(c-a)z}{(a-b)(z-\epsilon^{-aT})}+\dfrac{a(b-c)z}{(a-b)(z-\epsilon^{-bT})}$	$\dfrac{c}{z-1}+\dfrac{b(c-a)\epsilon^{-amT}}{(a-b)(z-\epsilon^{-aT})}+\dfrac{a(b-c)\epsilon^{-bmT}}{(a-b)(z-\epsilon^{-bT})}$
5.05	$\dfrac{a^2b^2}{s^2(s+a)(s+b)}$	$abt-(a+b)-\dfrac{b^2}{a-b}\epsilon^{-at}+\dfrac{a^2}{a-b}\epsilon^{-bt}$	$\dfrac{abTz}{(z-1)^2}-\dfrac{(a+b)z}{z-1}-\dfrac{b^2z}{(a-b)(z-\epsilon^{-aT})}+\dfrac{a^2z}{(a-b)(z-\epsilon^{-bT})}$	$\dfrac{abT}{(z-1)^2}+\dfrac{abmT-(a+b)}{z-1}-\dfrac{b^2\epsilon^{-amT}}{(a-b)(z-\epsilon^{-aT})}+\dfrac{a^2\epsilon^{-bmT}}{(a-b)(z-\epsilon^{-bT})}$
5.06	$\dfrac{a^2b^2(s+c)}{s^2(s+a)(s+b)}$	$abct+[ab-c(a+b)]-\dfrac{b^2(c-a)}{a-b}\epsilon^{-at}-\dfrac{a^2(b-c)}{a-b}\epsilon^{-bt}$	$\dfrac{abcTz}{(z-1)^2}+\dfrac{ab-c(a+b)z}{z-1}-\dfrac{b^2(c-a)z}{(a-b)(z-\epsilon^{-aT})}-\dfrac{a^2(b-c)z}{(a-b)(z-\epsilon^{-bT})}$	$\dfrac{abcT}{(z-1)^2}+\dfrac{ab(1+cmT)-c(a+b)}{z-1}-\dfrac{b^2(c-a)\epsilon^{-amT}}{(a-b)(z-\epsilon^{-aT})}-\dfrac{a^2(b-c)\epsilon^{-bmT}}{(a-b)(z-\epsilon^{-bT})}$
6.01	$\dfrac{1}{(s+a)(s+b)(s+c)}$	$\dfrac{\epsilon^{-at}}{(b-a)(c-a)}+\dfrac{\epsilon^{-bt}}{(a-b)(c-b)}+\dfrac{\epsilon^{-ct}}{(a-c)(b-c)}$	$\dfrac{z}{(b-a)(c-a)(z-\epsilon^{-aT})}+\dfrac{z}{(a-b)(c-b)(z-\epsilon^{-bT})}+\dfrac{z}{(a-c)(b-c)(z-\epsilon^{-cT})}$	$\dfrac{\epsilon^{-amT}}{(b-a)(c-a)(z-\epsilon^{-aT})}+\dfrac{\epsilon^{-bmT}}{(a-b)(c-b)(z-\epsilon^{-bT})}+\dfrac{\epsilon^{-cmT}}{(a-c)(b-c)(z-\epsilon^{-cT})}$
6.02	$\dfrac{s+d}{(s+a)(s+b)(s+c)}$	$\dfrac{(d-a)}{(b-a)(c-a)}\epsilon^{-at}+\dfrac{(d-b)}{(a-b)(c-b)}\epsilon^{-bt}+\dfrac{(d-c)}{(a-c)(b-c)}\epsilon^{-ct}$	$\dfrac{(d-a)z}{(b-a)(c-a)(z-\epsilon^{-aT})}+\dfrac{(d-b)z}{(a-b)(c-b)(z-\epsilon^{-bT})}+\dfrac{(d-c)z}{(a-c)(b-c)(z-\epsilon^{-cT})}$	$\dfrac{(d-a)\epsilon^{-amT}}{(b-a)(c-a)(z-\epsilon^{-aT})}+\dfrac{(d-b)\epsilon^{-bmT}}{(a-b)(c-b)(z-\epsilon^{-bT})}+\dfrac{(d-c)\epsilon^{-cmT}}{(a-c)(b-c)(z-\epsilon^{-cT})}$
6.03	$\dfrac{abc}{s(s+a)(s+b)(s+c)}$	$1-\dfrac{bc}{(b-a)(c-a)}\epsilon^{-at}-\dfrac{ca}{(c-b)(a-b)}\epsilon^{-bt}-\dfrac{ab}{(a-c)(b-c)}\epsilon^{-ct}$	$\dfrac{z}{z-1}-\dfrac{bcz}{(b-a)(c-a)(z-\epsilon^{-aT})}-\dfrac{caz}{(c-b)(a-b)(z-\epsilon^{-bT})}-\dfrac{abz}{(a-c)(b-c)(z-\epsilon^{-cT})}$	$\dfrac{1}{z-1}-\dfrac{bc\epsilon^{-amT}}{(b-a)(c-a)(z-\epsilon^{-aT})}-\dfrac{ca\epsilon^{-bmT}}{(c-b)(a-b)(z-\epsilon^{-bT})}-\dfrac{ab\epsilon^{-cmT}}{(a-c)(b-c)(z-\epsilon^{-cT})}$
6.04	$\dfrac{abc(s+d)}{s(s+a)(s+b)(s+c)}$	$d-\dfrac{bc(d-a)}{(b-a)(c-a)}\epsilon^{-at}-\dfrac{ca(d-b)}{(c-b)(a-b)}\epsilon^{-bt}-\dfrac{ab(d-c)}{(a-c)(b-c)}\epsilon^{-ct}$	$\dfrac{dz}{z-1}-\dfrac{bc(d-a)z}{(b-a)(c-a)(z-\epsilon^{-aT})}-\dfrac{ca(d-b)z}{(c-b)(a-b)(z-\epsilon^{-bT})}-\dfrac{ab(d-c)z}{(a-c)(b-c)(z-\epsilon^{-cT})}$	$\dfrac{d}{z-1}-\dfrac{bc(d-a)\epsilon^{-amT}}{(b-a)(c-a)(z-\epsilon^{-aT})}-\dfrac{ca(d-b)\epsilon^{-bmT}}{(c-b)(a-b)(z-\epsilon^{-bT})}-\dfrac{ab(d-c)\epsilon^{-cmT}}{(a-c)(b-c)(z-\epsilon^{-cT})}$
6.05	$\dfrac{(abc)^2}{s^2(s+a)(s+b)(s+c)}$	$abct-(bc+ca+ab)+\dfrac{b^2c^2}{(b-a)(c-a)}\epsilon^{-at}+\dfrac{c^2a^2}{(c-b)(a-b)}\epsilon^{-bt}+\dfrac{a^2b^2}{(a-c)(b-c)}\epsilon^{-ct}$	$\dfrac{abcTz}{(z-1)^2}-\dfrac{(bc+ca+ab)z}{z-1}+\dfrac{b^2c^2z}{(b-a)(c-a)(z-\epsilon^{-aT})}+\dfrac{c^2a^2z}{(c-b)(a-b)(z-\epsilon^{-bT})}+\dfrac{a^2b^2z}{(a-c)(b-c)(z-\epsilon^{-cT}}$	$\dfrac{abcT}{(z-1)^2}+\dfrac{abcmT-(bc+ca+ab)}{z-1}+\dfrac{b^2c^2\epsilon^{-amT}}{(b-a)(c-a)(z-\epsilon^{-aT})}+\dfrac{c^2a^2\epsilon^{-bmT}}{(c-b)(a-b)(z-\epsilon^{-bT})}+\dfrac{a^2b^2\epsilon^{-cmT}}{(a-c)(b-c)(z-\epsilon^{-cT})}$

Table of z Transforms and Modified z Transforms (*Continued*)

No.	$G(s)$	$g(t)$	$G(z)$	$G(z,m)$
6.06	$\dfrac{(abc)^2(s+d)}{s^2(s+a)(s+b)(s+c)}$	$abcdt+[abc-(bc+ca+ab)d]+\dfrac{b^2c^2(d-a)}{(b-a)(c-a)}\epsilon^{-at}$ $+\dfrac{c^2a^2(d-b)}{(c-b)(a-b)}\epsilon^{-bt}+\dfrac{a^2b^2(d-c)}{(a-c)(b-c)}\epsilon^{-ct}$	$\dfrac{abcdTz}{(z-1)^2}+\dfrac{[abc-(bc+ca+ab)d]z}{z-1}$ $+\dfrac{b^2c^2(d-a)z}{(b-a)(c-a)(z-\epsilon^{-aT})}+\dfrac{c^2a^2(d-b)z}{(c-b)(a-b)(z-\epsilon^{-bT})}$ $+\dfrac{a^2b^2(d-c)z}{(a-c)(b-c)(z-\epsilon^{-cT})}$	$\dfrac{abcdT}{(z-1)^2}+\dfrac{abc(dmT+1)-(bc+ca+ab)d}{z-1}$ $+\dfrac{b^2c^2(d-a)\epsilon^{-amT}}{(b-a)(c-a)(z-\epsilon^{-aT})}+\dfrac{c^2a^2(d-b)\epsilon^{-bmT}}{(c-b)(a-b)(z-\epsilon^{-bT})}$ $+\dfrac{a^2b^2(d-c)\epsilon^{-cmT}}{(a-c)(b-c)(z-\epsilon^{-cT})}$
7.01	$\dfrac{a^2}{s(s+a)^2}$	$1-(1+at)\epsilon^{-at}$	$\dfrac{z}{z-1}-\dfrac{z}{z-\epsilon^{-aT}}-\dfrac{aT\epsilon^{-aT}z}{(z-\epsilon^{-aT})^2}$	$\dfrac{1}{z-1}-\left[\dfrac{1+amT}{z-\epsilon^{-aT}}+\dfrac{aT\epsilon^{-aT}}{(z-\epsilon^{-aT})^2}\right]\epsilon^{-amT}$
7.02	$\dfrac{a^2(s+b)}{s(s+a)^2}$	$b-b\epsilon^{-at}+a(a-b)t\epsilon^{-at}$	$\dfrac{bz}{z-1}-\dfrac{bz}{z-\epsilon^{-aT}}+\dfrac{a(a-b)T\epsilon^{-aT}z}{(z-\epsilon^{-aT})^2}$	$\dfrac{b}{z-1}+\left[\dfrac{amT(a-b)-b}{z-\epsilon^{-aT}}+\dfrac{aT(a-b)\epsilon^{-aT}}{(z-\epsilon^{-aT})^2}\right]\epsilon^{-amT}$
7.03	$\dfrac{a^3}{s^2(s+a)^2}$	$at-2+(at+2)\epsilon^{-at}$	$\dfrac{(aT+2)z-2z^2}{(z-1)^2}+\dfrac{2z}{z-\epsilon^{-aT}}+\dfrac{aT\epsilon^{-aT}z}{(z-\epsilon^{-aT})^2}$	$\dfrac{aT}{(z-1)^2}+\dfrac{amT-2}{z-1}-\left[\dfrac{amT-2}{z-\epsilon^{-aT}}-\dfrac{aT\epsilon^{-aT}}{(z-\epsilon^{-aT})^2}\right]\epsilon^{-amT}$
7.04	$\dfrac{(a-b)^2}{(s+b)(s+a)^2}$	$\epsilon^{-bt}-\epsilon^{-at}+(a-b)t\epsilon^{-at}$	$\dfrac{z}{z-\epsilon^{-bT}}-\dfrac{z}{z-\epsilon^{-aT}}+\dfrac{(a-b)T\epsilon^{-aT}z}{(z-\epsilon^{-aT})^2}$	$\dfrac{\epsilon^{-bmT}}{z-\epsilon^{-bT}}+\left[\dfrac{mT(a-b)-1}{z-\epsilon^{-aT}}+\dfrac{(a-b)T\epsilon^{-aT}}{(z-\epsilon^{-aT})^2}\right]\epsilon^{-amT}$
7.05	$\dfrac{(a-b)^2(s+c)}{(s+b)(s+a)^2}$	$(c-b)\epsilon^{-bt}+(b-c)\epsilon^{-at}-(a-b)(c-a)t\epsilon^{-at}$	$\dfrac{(c-b)z}{z-\epsilon^{-bT}}+\dfrac{(b-c)z}{z-\epsilon^{-aT}}-\dfrac{(a-b)(c-a)T\epsilon^{-aT}z}{(z-\epsilon^{-aT})^2}$	$\dfrac{(c-b)\epsilon^{-bmT}}{z-\epsilon^{-bT}}-\left[\dfrac{mT(a-b)(c-a)-(b-c)}{z-\epsilon^{-aT}}\right.$ $\left.+\dfrac{(a-b)(c-a)T\epsilon^{-aT}}{(z-\epsilon^{-aT})^2}\right]\epsilon^{-amT}$
7.06	$\dfrac{a^2b}{s(s+b)(s+a)^2}$	$1-\dfrac{a^2}{(a-b)^2}\epsilon^{-bt}+\dfrac{ab+b(a-b)}{(a-b)^2}\epsilon^{-at}$ $+\dfrac{ab}{a-b}t\epsilon^{-at}$	$\dfrac{z}{z-1}-\dfrac{a^2z}{(a-b)^2(z-\epsilon^{-bT})}+\dfrac{[ab+b(a-b)]z}{(a-b)^2(z-\epsilon^{-aT})}$ $+\dfrac{abT\epsilon^{-aT}z}{(a-b)(z-\epsilon^{-aT})^2}$	$\dfrac{1}{z-1}-\dfrac{a^2\epsilon^{-bmT}}{(a-b)^2(z-\epsilon^{-bT})}+\left[\dfrac{b(a-b)(1+amT)+ab}{(a-b)^2(z-\epsilon^{-aT})}\right.$ $\left.+\dfrac{abT\epsilon^{-aT})}{(a-b)(z-\epsilon^{-aT})^2}\right]\epsilon^{-amT}$
7.07	$\dfrac{a^2b(s+c)}{s(s+b)(s+a)^2}$	$c+\dfrac{a^2(b-c)}{(a-b)^2}\epsilon^{-bt}+\dfrac{ab(c-a)+bc(a-b)}{(a-b)^2}\epsilon^{-at}$ $+\dfrac{ab(c-a)}{a-b}t\epsilon^{-at}$	$\dfrac{cz}{z-1}+\dfrac{a^2(b-c)z}{(a-b)^2(z-\epsilon^{-bT})}+\dfrac{[ab(c-a)+bc(a-b)]z}{(a-b)^2(z-\epsilon^{-aT})}$ $+\dfrac{ab(c-a)T\epsilon^{-aT}z}{(a-b)(z-\epsilon^{-aT})^2}$	$\dfrac{c}{z-1}+\dfrac{a^2(b-c)\epsilon^{-bmT}}{(a-b)^2(z-\epsilon^{-bT})}$ $+\left\{\dfrac{ab(c-a)[1+mT(a-b)]+bc(a-b)}{(a-b)^2(z-\epsilon^{-aT})}\right.$ $\left.+\dfrac{ab(c-a)T\epsilon^{-aT}}{(a-b)(z-\epsilon^{-aT})^2}\right\}\epsilon^{-amT}$
7.08	$\dfrac{(a^2b)^2}{s^2(s+b)(s+a)^2}$	$a^2bt-[ab+a(a+b)]+\dfrac{a^4}{(a-b)^2}\epsilon^{-bt}$ $-\dfrac{ab^2(3a-2b)}{(a-b)^2}\epsilon^{-at}-\dfrac{a^2b^2}{a-b}t\epsilon^{-at}$	$\dfrac{a^2bTz}{(z-1)^2}-\dfrac{[ab+a(a+b)]z}{z-1}+\dfrac{a^4z}{(a-b)^2(z-\epsilon^{-bT})}$ $-\dfrac{ab^2(3a-2b)z}{(a-b)^2(z-\epsilon^{-aT})}-\dfrac{a^2b^2T\epsilon^{-aT}z}{(a-b)(z-\epsilon^{-aT})^2}$	$\dfrac{a^2bT}{(z-1)^2}+\dfrac{ab(amT-2)-a^2}{z-1}+\dfrac{a^4\epsilon^{-bmT}}{(a-b)^2(z-\epsilon^{-aT})}$ $-\left[\dfrac{ab^2(a-b)(amT+2)+a^2b^2}{(a-b)^2(z-\epsilon^{-aT})}\right.$ $\left.+\dfrac{a^2b^2T\epsilon^{-aT}}{(a-b)(z-\epsilon^{-aT})^2}\right]\epsilon^{-amT}$

8.01	$\frac{\omega_0}{(s+a)^2+\omega_0^2}$	$\epsilon^{-at}\sin\omega_0 t$	$\frac{z\epsilon^{-aT}\sin\omega_0 T}{z^2-2z\epsilon^{-aT}\cos\omega_0 T+\epsilon^{-2aT}}$	$\frac{[z\sin m\omega_0 T+\epsilon^{-aT}\sin(1-m)\omega_0 T]\epsilon^{-amT}}{z^2-2z\epsilon^{-aT}\cos\omega_0 T+\epsilon^{-2aT}}$
8.02	$\frac{s+a}{(s+a)^2+\omega_0^2}$	$\epsilon^{-at}\cos\omega_0 t$	$\frac{z^2-z\epsilon^{-aT}\cos\omega_0 T}{z^2-2z\epsilon^{-aT}\cos\omega_0 T+\epsilon^{-2aT}}$	$\frac{[z\cos m\omega_0 T-\epsilon^{-aT}\cos(1-m)\omega_0 T]\epsilon^{-amT}}{z^2-2z\epsilon^{-aT}\cos\omega_0 T+\epsilon^{-2aT}}$
8.03	$\frac{(a-b)^2+\omega_0^2}{(s+b)[(s+a)^2+\omega_0^2]}$	$\epsilon^{-bt}-\epsilon^{-at}\sec\theta\cos(\omega_0 t-\theta)$ where $\theta=\tan^{-1}\frac{b-a}{\omega_0}$	$\frac{z}{z-\epsilon^{-bT}}-\frac{z^2-z\epsilon^{-aT}\sec\theta\cos(\omega_0 T-\theta)}{z^2-2z\epsilon^{-aT}\cos\omega_0 T+\epsilon^{-2aT}}$	$\frac{\epsilon^{-bmT}}{z-\epsilon^{-bT}}-\frac{\sec\theta\{z\cos(m\omega_0 T+\theta)-\epsilon^{-aT}\cos[(1-m)\omega_0 T-\theta]\}\epsilon^{-amT}}{z^2-2z\epsilon^{-aT}\cos\omega_0 T+\epsilon^{-2aT}}$
8.04	$\frac{[(a-b)^2+\omega_0^2](s+\alpha)}{(s+b)[(s+a)^2+\omega_0^2]}$	$(\alpha-b)\epsilon^{-bt}-(\alpha-b)\epsilon^{-at}\sec\theta\cos(\omega_0 t+\theta)$ where $\theta=\tan^{-1}\frac{(\alpha-a)(b-a)+\omega_0^2}{(\alpha-b)\omega_0}$	$\frac{(\alpha-b)z}{z-\epsilon^{-bT}}-\frac{(\alpha-b)[z^2-z\epsilon^{-aT}\sec\theta\cos(\omega_0 T+\theta)]}{z^2-2z\epsilon^{-aT}\cos\omega_0 T+\epsilon^{-2aT}}$	$\frac{(\alpha-b)\epsilon^{-bmT}}{z-\epsilon^{-bT}}-\frac{(\alpha-b)\sec\theta\{z\cos(m\omega_0 T+\theta)-\epsilon^{-aT}\cos[(1-m)\omega_0 T+\theta]\}\epsilon^{-amT}}{z^2-2z\epsilon^{-aT}\cos\omega_0 T+\epsilon^{-2aT}}$
8.05	$\frac{[(a-b)^2+\omega_0^2](s^2+\alpha s+\beta)}{(s+b)[(s+a)^2+\omega_0^2]}$	$(b^2-b\alpha+\beta)\epsilon^{-bt}+k^2\epsilon^{-at}\sec\theta\cos(\omega_0 t+\theta)$ where $k^2=a^2+\omega_0^2-2ab+b\alpha-\beta$ $\theta=\tan^{-1}\frac{ak^2-(a^2+\omega_0^2)(\alpha-b)+\beta(2a-b)}{\omega_0 k^2}$	$\frac{(b^2-b\alpha+\beta)z}{z-\epsilon^{-bT}}+\frac{k^2[z^2-z\epsilon^{-aT}\sec\theta\cos(\omega_0 T+\theta)]}{z^2-2z\epsilon^{-aT}\cos\omega_0 T+\epsilon^{-2aT}}$	$\frac{(b^2-b\alpha+\beta)z}{z-\epsilon^{-bT}}\quad\frac{k^2\sec\theta\{z\cos(m\omega_0 T+\theta)-\epsilon^{-aT}\cos[(1-m)\omega_0 T+\theta]\}\epsilon^{-amT}}{z^2-2z\epsilon^{-aT}\cos\omega_0 T+\epsilon^{-2aT}}$
9.01	$\frac{a^2+\omega_0^2}{s[(s+a)^2+\omega_0^2]}$	$1-\epsilon^{-at}\sec\theta\cos(\omega_0 t+\theta)$ where $\theta=\tan^{-1}-\frac{a}{\omega_0}$	$\frac{z}{z-1}-\frac{z^2-z\epsilon^{-aT}\sec\theta\cos(\omega_0 T+\theta)}{z^2-2z\epsilon^{-aT}\cos\omega_0 T+\epsilon^{-2aT}}$	$\frac{1}{z-1}-\frac{\sec\theta\{z\cos(m\omega_0 T+\theta)-\epsilon^{-aT}\cos[(1-m)\omega_0 T+\theta]\}\epsilon^{-amT}}{z^2-2z\epsilon^{-aT}\cos\omega_0 T+\epsilon^{-2aT}}$
9.02	$\frac{(a^2+\omega_0^2)(s+b)}{s[(s+a)^2+\omega_0^2]}$	$b-b\epsilon^{-at}\sec\theta\cos(\omega_0 t+\theta)$ where $\theta=\tan^{-1}\frac{a^2+\omega_0^2-ab}{b\omega_0}$	$\frac{bz}{z-1}-\frac{b[z^2-z\epsilon^{-aT}\sec\theta\cos(\omega_0 T+\theta)]}{z^2-2z\epsilon^{-aT}\cos\omega_0 T+\epsilon^{-2aT}}$	$\frac{b}{z-1}-\frac{b\sec\theta\{z\cos(m\omega_0 T+\theta)-\epsilon^{-aT}\cos[(1-m)\omega_0 T+\theta]\}\epsilon^{-amT}}{z^2-2z\epsilon^{-aT}\cos\omega_0 T+\epsilon^{-2aT}}$
9.03	$\frac{(a^2+\omega_0^2)^2}{s^2[(s+a)^2+\omega_0^2]}$	$(a^2+\omega_0^2)t-2a+2a\epsilon^{-at}\sec\theta\cos(\omega_0 t+\theta)$ where $\theta=\tan^{-1}\frac{\omega_0^2-a^2}{2a\omega_0}$	$\frac{[(a^2+\omega_0^2)T+2a]z-2az^2}{(z-1)^2}+\frac{2a[z^2-z\epsilon^{-aT}\sec\theta\cos(\omega_0 T+\theta)]}{z^2-2z\epsilon^{-aT}\cos\omega_0 T+\epsilon^{-2aT}}$	$\frac{[mT(a^2+\omega_0^2)-2a]z+(a^2+\omega_0^2)(1-m)T+2a}{(z-1)^2}+\frac{2a\sec\theta\{z\cos(m\omega_0 T+\theta)-\epsilon^{-aT}\cos[(1-m)\omega_0 T+\theta]\}\epsilon^{-amT}}{z^2-2z\epsilon^{-aT}\cos\omega_0 T+\epsilon^{-2aT}}$
9.04	$\frac{(a^2+\omega_0^2)^2(s+b)}{s^2[(s+a)^2+\omega_0^2]}$	$b(a^2+\omega_0^2)t+k^2-k^2\epsilon^{-at}\sec\theta\cos(\omega_0 t+\theta)$ where $k^2=a^2+\omega_0^2-2ab$ $\theta=\tan^{-1}-\frac{ak^2+b(a^2+\omega_0^2)}{\omega_0 k^2}$	$\frac{[bT(a^2+\omega_0^2)-k^2]z+k^2z^2}{(z-1)^2}-\frac{k^2[z^2-z\epsilon^{-aT}\sec\theta\cos(\omega_0 T+\theta)]}{z^2-2z\epsilon^{-aT}\cos\omega_0 T+\epsilon^{-2aT}}$	$\frac{[bmT(a^2+\omega_0^2)+k^2]z+(a^2+\omega_0^2)(1-m)bT-k^2}{(z-1)^2}-\frac{k^2\sec\theta z\{\cos(m\omega_0 T+\theta)-\epsilon^{-aT}\cos[(1-m)\omega_0 T+\theta]\}\epsilon^{-amT}}{z^2-2z\epsilon^{-aT}\cos\omega_0 T+\epsilon^{-2aT}}$

APPENDIX 2

REFERENCES

1945

1. MacColl, L. A.: "Fundamental Theory of Servomechanisms," chap. 10, D. Van Nostrand Company, Inc., Princeton, N. J., 1945.

1947

2. James, H. M., N. B. Nichols, and R. S. Phillips: "Theory of Servomechanisms," chap. 5, McGraw-Hill Book Company, Inc., New York, 1947.
3. Samuelson, P. A.: "Foundations of Economic Analysis," Harvard University Press, Cambridge, Mass., 1947.
4. Tustin, A.: A Method of Analyzing the Behavior of Linear Systems in Terms of Time Series, *Proc. IEE*, vol. 94, pt. IIA, pp. 130–142, 1947.
5. Goodall, W. M.: Telephony by Pulse Code Modulation, *Bell System Tech. J.*, pp. 395–409, July, 1947.

1948

6. Oldenbourg, R. C., and H. Sartorius: "The Dynamics of Automatic Control," chap. 5, American Society of Mechanical Engineers, 1948.
7. Stone, W. M.: A List of Generalized Laplace Transforms, *Iowa State Coll. J. of Sci.*, vol. 22, pp. 215–225, April, 1948.
8. Carbrey, R. L.: Decoding in PCM, *Bell Lab. Record*, pp. 451–456, November, 1948.
9. Sears, R. W.: Electron Beam Deflection Tube for Pulse Code Modulation, *Bell System Tech. J.*, vol. 27, pp. 44–57, January, 1948.
10. Bennett, W. R.: Spectra of Quantized Signals, *Bell System Tech. J.*, pp. 446–472, July, 1948.
11. Shannon, C.: The Philosophy of Pulse Code Modulation, *Proc. IRE*, vol. 36, pp. 1324–1331, November, 1948.

1949

12. Marden, M.: "The Geometry of the Zeros of a Polynomial in a Complex Variable," chap. 10, American Mathematical Society, New York, 1949.
13. Raymond, F. H.: Analyse de fonctionnement des systèmes physiques discontinus, *Ann. Télécommunication* (Paris), vol. 4, pp. 250–256, July, 1949; 307–314, August–September, 1949; 347–357, October, 1949.
14. Tsypkin, Y. Z.: Theory of Intermittent Regulation I, *Avtomat. i Telemekh.*, vol. 10, no. 3, pp. 189–224, 1949.
15. Tsypkin, Y. Z.: Theory of Intermittent Regulation II, *Avtomat. i Telemekh.*, vol. 10, no. 5, p. 342, 1949.

1950

16. Miller, K. H., and R. J. Schwarz: Analysis of Sampling Servomechanisms, *J. Appl. Phys.*, vol. 21, pp. 290–294, April, 1950.
17. Porter, A., and F. Stoneman: A New Approach to the Design of Pulse Monitored Servo Systems, *J. IEE*, vol. 97, pt. II, pp. 597–610, 1950.
18. Tsypkin, Y. Z.: Theory of Intermittent Regulation, III, *Avtomat. i Telemekh.*, vol. 11, no. 5, p. 300, 1950.

1951

19. Tsypkin, Y. Z.: "Transient and Steady-state Processes in Pulsed Networks," Moscow, 1951.
20. Lawden, D. F.: A General Theory of Sampling Servo Systems, *Proc. IEE*, vol. 98, pt. IV, pp. 31–36, October, 1951.
21. Linvill, W. K.: Sampled-data Control Systems Studied Through Comparison of Sampling with Amplitude Modulation, *Trans. AIEE*, vol. 70, pt. II, pp. 1779–1788, 1951.
22. Yaeger, R. E.: The Gray-to-binary Translator and Shift Register, in "The Transistor," pp. 611–626, Bell Telephone Laboratories, November, 1951.
23. Lippel, B.: A High-precision Analog-to-digital Converter, *Proc. Natl. Electronics Conf.*, vol. 7, pp. 206–215, 1951.

1952

24. Tustin, A. (ed.): "Automatic and Manual Control," pp. 377–407, Butterworth & Co. (Publishers) Ltd., London, 1952; (*a*) B. M. Brown, Application of Finite Difference Operators to Linear Systems; (*b*) C. H. Smith, D. F. Lawden, and A. E. Bailey, Characteristics of Sampling Servo Systems.
25. Barker, R. H.: The Pulse Transfer Function and Its Application to Sampling Servo Systems, *Proc. IEE*, vol. 99, pt. IV, pp. 302–317, December, 1952.
26. Ragazzini, J. R., and L. A. Zadeh: The Analysis of Sampled-data Systems, *Trans. AIEE*, vol. 71, pt. II, pp. 225–234, 1952.
27. Salzer, J. M.: Frequency Analysis of Digital Computers Used in Control Systems, presented at the IRE National Convention, March, 1952.
28. Salzer, J. M.: Fundamental Characteristics of Digital and Analog Units, *Proc. Natl. Electronics Conf.*, vol. 8, pp. 621–628, 1952.
29. Brown, R. G., and G. J. Murphy: An Approximate Transfer Function for the Analysis and Design of Pulsed Servos, *Trans. AIEE*, vol. 71, pp. 435–440, 1952.
30. Miller, M., B. L. Waddell, and J. Patmore: Digital-to-analog Converter, *Electronics*, vol. 25, no. 10, pp. 127–129, October, 1952.
31. Lippel, B: Interconversion of Analog and Digital Data in Systems for Measurement and Control, *Proc. Natl. Electronics Conf.*, vol. 8, pp. 636–646, 1952.
32. Follingstad, H. G., J. N. Shive, and R. E. Yaeger: A Transistor Optical Position Encoder and Digit Register, *Proc. Natl. Electronics Conf.*, vol. 8, pp. 766–775, 1952.

1953

33. Tsypkin, Y. Z.: Frequency Method of Analyzing Intermittent Regulating Systems, *Avtomat. i Telemekh.*, vol. 14, no. 1, pp. 11–33, 1953.
34. Linvill, W. K.: Use of Sampled Functions for Time Domain Synthesis, *Proc. Natl. Electronics Conf.*, vol. 9, pp. 533–542, 1953.
35. Linvill, W. K., and R. W. Sittler: Extension of Conventional Techniques to the Design of Sampled-data Systems, *IRE Conv. Rec.*, pt. I, pp. 99–104, 1953.

36. Linvill, W. K., and J. M. Salzer: Analysis of Control Systems Involving Digital Computers, *Proc. IRE*, vol. 41, pp. 901–906, July, 1953.
37. Burke, H. E.: A Survey of Analog-to-digital Converters, *Proc. IRE*, vol. 41, no. 10, pp. 1455–1462, October, 1953.
38. Gray, H. J., P. V. Levonian, and M. Rubinoff: An Analog-Digital Converter for Serial Computing Machines, *Proc. IRE*, vol. 41, no. 10, pp. 1462–1465, October, 1953.
39. Fitzpatrick, A. G.: A New Coding System for Pulse Code Modulation, *IRE Conv. Rec.*, pt. 8, p. 125, 1953.
40. Smith, B. D.: Coding by Feedback Methods, *Proc. IRE*, vol. 41, no. 8, pp. 1053–1058, August, 1953.
41. Gray, H. J.: The Organization of a Digital Real-time Simulator, *IRE Conv. Rec.*, pt. 1, pp. 85–88, 1953.
42. Slaughter, D. W.: An Analog-to-digital Converter with an Improved Linear Sweep Generator, *IRE Conv. Rec.*, pt. 7, pp. 7–12, 1953.
43. MacKnight, M. L., and P. A. Adamson: Multi-channel Analog Input-Output Systems for Digital Computers, *IRE Conv. Rec.*, pt. 7, pp. 2–6, 1953.
44. Packer, L.: Dynamic Binary Counter with Analog Read-out, *IRE Conv. Rec.*, pt. 7, pp. 13–19, 1953.
45. Lippel, B.: A Systematic Survey of Coders and Decoders, *IRE Conv. Rec.*, pt. 8, pp. 109–119, 1953.
46. Libaw, W. H., and L. J. Craig: A Photoelectric Decimal Coded Shaft Digitizer, *Trans. IRE*, vol. EC-2, no. 3, pp. 1–4, September, 1953.
47. Scarbrough, A. D.: An Analog-to-digital Converter, *Trans. IRE*, vol. EC-2, no. 3, pp. 5–7, September, 1953.
48. Sink, R., and G. M. Slocomb: The Sadic, a Precision Analog-Digital Converter, *Trans. IRE*, vol. PGI-2, pp. 48–53, June, 1953.
49. Lund, G. W.: Era Shaft-position Analog-to-digital Converter, *Trans. IRE*, vol. PGI-2, pp. 55–60, June, 1953.
50. O'Neil, S. J.: Digital-to-analog Shaft-position Transducers, *Trans. AIEE*, vol. 72, pt. I, pp. 37–41, 1953.
51. Winter, A. J.: Magnetic Shaft-position Digitizer, *Electronics*, vol. 26, no. 8, pp. 214–222, August, 1953.
52. Bennett, R. R., and H. Low: Step Switch Converter Digitizes Analog Data, *Electronics*, vol. 26, no. 11, pp. 164–165, November, 1953.
53. Raasch, F.: A Progressive Code Digital Quantizer, *Trans. AIEE*, vol. 72, pt. I, pp. 567–571, 1953.
54. Hollander, G. L.: Criteria for the Selection of Analog-to-digital Converters, *Proc. Natl. Electronics Conf.*, vol. 9, pp. 670–683, 1953.

1954

55. Tsien, H. S.: "Engineering Cybernetics," chap. 7, McGraw-Hill Book Company, Inc., New York, 1954.
56. Lago, G. V.: Additions to Sampled-data Theory, *Proc. Natl. Electronics Conf.*, vol. 10, pp. 758–766, 1954.
57. Truxal, J. G.: Numerical Analysis for Network Design, *Trans. IRE*, PGCT, vol. CT-1, no. 3, pp. 49–60, September, 1954.
58. Lago, G. V., and J. G. Truxal: The Design of Sampled-data Feedback Systems, *Trans. AIEE*, vol. 73, pt. II, pp. 247–253, November, 1954.
59. Salzer, J. M.: The Frequency Analysis of Digital Computers Operating in Real Time, *Proc. IRE*, vol. 42, no. 2, pp. 457–466, February, 1954.

60. Ragazzini, J. R., and A. R. Bergen: A Mathematical Technique for the Analysis of Linear Systems, *Proc. IRE*, vol 42, no. 11, pp. 1645–1651, November, 1954. (Also in *IRE Conv. Rec.*, pt. 2, pp. 44–51, 1954.)
61. Bergen, A. R., and J. R. Ragazzini: Sampled-data Processing Techniques for Feedback Control Systems, *Trans. AIEE*, vol. 73, pt. II, pp. 236–246, November, 1954.
62. Lindorf, D. P., and G. W. Johnson: Transient Analysis of Sampled-data Control Systems, *Trans. AIEE*, vol. 73, pt. II, pp. 147–153, July, 1954.
63. Jury, E. I.: The Analysis and Synthesis of Sampled-data Control Systems, *Trans. AIEE*, vol. 73, pt. I, pp. 332–346, September, 1954.
64. Thomasson, L. T.: Digital Servomechanisms, *Electronics*, vol. 27, pp. 134–139, August, 1954.
65. Linvill, W. K.: Some Fundamental Capabilities and Limitations of Sampled-data Systems, *National Telemetering Conference Record*, pp. 85–94, 1954.
66. Salzer, J. M.: System Compensation with a Digital Computer, *IRE Conv. Rec.*, pt. 5, pp. 179–186, 1954.
67. Margolis, M., and E. Weiss: An Experimental Digital Flight Control System, *Proc. Western Computer Conference*, pp. 23–37, April, 1954.
68. Burbeck, D. W., E. E. Bolles, W. E. Frady, and E. M. Crabbe: The Digitac Airborne Control Systems, *Proc. Western Computer Conference*, pp. 38–44, April, 1954.
69. Mergler, H. W.: A Digital-Analog Machine Tool Control System, *Proc. Western Computer Conference*, pp. 46–59, April, 1954.
70. Burns, T. J., J. D. Cloud, and J. M. Salzer: Experiments with a Digital Computer in a Simple Control System, *Proc. Western Computer Conference*, pp. 60–74, April, 1954.
71. Exner, W. L., and A. D. Scarbrough: A Digital Auto-pilot Coupler, *IRE Conv. Rec.*, pt. 5, pp. 174–178, 1954.
72. Chow, C. K.: Contactor Servomechanisms Employing Sampled Data, *Trans. AIEE*, vol. 73, pt. II, pp. 51–62, March, 1954.
73. Scott, N. R.: An Experimental Study of the Information Rate of a Digital Computer, *IRE Conv. Rec.*, pt. 4, pp. 35–39, 1954.
74. Zweizig, J. R.: A Digital Voltage Encoder, *Trans. IRE*, vol. EC-3, no. 3, pp. 25–28, September, 1954.
75. O'Neil, S. J.: Networks for Digital-to-analog Shaft-position Transducers, *Trans. AIEE*, vol. 73, pt. I, pp. 456–466, 1954.
76. Lentz, J., and R. Bennett: Automatic Measurement of Star Positions, *Electronics*, vol. 27, no. 6, pp. 158–163, June, 1954.
77. Kernahan, I. I.: A Digital Code Wheel, *Bell Lab. Record*, vol. 32, no. 4, pp. 126–131, April, 1954.
78. Gordon, B. M., M. A. Meyer, and R. N. Nicola: A Shaft-to-digital Encoder, *Proc. Western Computer Conference*, pp. 128–133, April, 1954.
79. Susskind, A. K.: Approaches to Design Problems in Conversion Equipment, *Proc. Western Computer Conference*, pp. 105–112, April, 1954.
80. Shockency, W. S.: Multi-channel Analog-Digital Conversion System for D-C Voltages, *Proc. Western Computer Conference*, pp. 113–117, April, 1954.
81. Mitchell, J. M.: A High-speed Multi-channel Analog-Digital Converter, *Proc. Western Computer Conference*, pp. 118–127, April, 1954.
82. Foss, F. A.: The Use of a Reflected Code in Digital Control Systems, *Trans. IRE*, vol. EC-3, no. 4, pp. 1–6, December, 1954.
83. Partridge, G. R.: A Transistorized Pulse Code Modulator, *Trans. IRE*, vol. EC-3, no. 4, pp. 7–12, December, 1954.

1955

84. Truxal, J. G.: "Automatic Feedback Control System Synthesis," chap. 9, McGraw-Hill Book Company, Inc., New York, 1955.
85. Richards, R. K.: "Arithmetic Operations in Digital Computers," D. Van Nostrand Book Company, Inc., Princeton, N. J., 1955.
86. Lago, G. V.: Additions to z-transformation Theory for Sampled-data Systems, *Trans. AIEE.*, vol. 74, pt. II, pp. 403–407, January, 1955.
87. Johnson, G. W., D. P. Lindorf, and C. G. A. Nordling: Extension of Continuous Data System Design Technique to Sampled-data Control Systems, *Trans. AIEE*, vol. 74, pt. II, pp. 252–263, September, 1955.
88. Sklansky, J., and J. R. Ragazzini: Analysis of Errors in Sampled-data Feedback Systems, *Trans. AIEE*, vol. 74, pt. II, pp. 65–71, May, 1955.
89. Jury, E. I.: The Effect of Pole and Zero Location on the Transient Response of Sampled-data Systems, *Trans. AIEE*, vol. 74, pt. II, pp. 41–48, March, 1955.
90. Teichmann, T.: Closed-loop Control Systems Containing a Digital Computer, *Trans. IRE*, vol. EC-4, no. 3, pp. 106–117, September, 1955.
91. Boxer, R.: Analysis of Sampled-data Systems and Digital Computers in the Frequency Domain, *IRE Conv. Rec.*, pt. 10, pp. 78–85, 1955.
92. Morris, H. N.: The Role of the Digital Computer in Processing Guided Missile Data, *IRE Conv. Rec.*, pt. 10, pp. 62–65, 1955.
93. Klein, R. C.: Analog Simulation of Sampled-data Systems, *Trans. IRE*, vol. TRC-1, no. 2, pp. 2–7, May, 1955.
94. Wadel, L. B.: Analysis of Combined Sampled-and-Continuous-Data Systems on an Electronic Analog Computer, *IRE Conv. Rec.*, pt. 4, pp. 3–7, 1955.
95. Franklin, G.: Linear Filtering of Sampled Data, *IRE Conv. Rec.*, pt. 4, pp. 119–128, 1955.
96. Lago, G. V.: A Synthesis Procedure for Sampled-data Systems, *Proc. Natl. Electronics Conf.*, vol. 11, pp. 351–360, 1955.
97. Spero, P. E.: The Effects of Digitalization on the Performance of a Feedback Control System, *Proc. Assoc. Computing Machinery*, September, 1955.
98. Karush, W.: Stability of a Method of Smoothing in a Digital Control Computer, *Trans. IRE*, vol. EC-4, no. 1, pp. 26–31, March, 1955.
99. Fletcher, T. C., and N. C. Walker: Analog Measurement and Conversion to Digits, *ISA Journal*, vol. 2, p. 345, September, 1955.
100. Lippel, B.: A Decimal Code for Analog-to-digital Conversion, *Trans. IRE*, vol. EC-4, pp. 158–159, December, 1955.
101. Ator, J. T., and L. P. Retzinger: Data Recorder for Evaluation of a Fire Control System, presented at *Western Electric Show and Convention*, San Francisco, August, 1955.

1956

102. Brillouin, L.: "Science and Information Theory," chap. 19, Academic Press Inc., New York, 1956.
103. Tsypkin and Barker in R. Oldenburger (ed.): "Frequency Response," p. 8, pp. 309–341, The Macmillan Company, New York, 1956.
104. Barker, R. H.: A Servo System for Digital Data Transmission, *Proc. IEE*, pt. B, pp. 52–64, January, 1956.
105. Graham, R. E.: Modulated Control Systems, *IRE Conv. Rec.*, pt. II, pp. 18–25, 1956.
106. Jury, E. I.: Correlation between Root Locus and Transient Response of Sampled-data Control Systems, *Trans. AIEE*, vol. 75, pt. II, pp. 427–435, January, 1956.

107. Jury, E. I.: Synthesis and Critical Study of Sampled-data Control Systems, *Trans. AIEE,* vol. 75, pt. II, pp. 141–151, July, 1956.
108. Maitra, K. K., and P. E. Sarachik: Digital Compensation of Continuous Data Feedback Control Systems, *Trans. AIEE,* vol. 75, pt. II, pp. 107–116, May, 1956.
109. Bertram, J. E.: Factors in the Design of Digital Controllers for Sampled-data Feedback Systems, *Trans. AIEE,* vol. 75, pt. II, pp. 151–159, July, 1956.
110. Tou, J.: High Accuracy Operational Digital Simulation, *Proc. Natl. Simulation Conf.,* pp. 11.1–11.6, January, 1956.
111. Tou, J.: Sampling Frequency of Digital Servomechanisms, *Proc. Assoc. Computing Machinery,* pp. 83–86, August, 1956.
112. Tou, J.: Stability Criterion for Digital Feedback Control Systems, *Proc. Natl. Electronics Conf.,* vol. 12, pp. 336–346, 1956.
113. Giloth, P. K.: A Simulator for Analysis of Sampled-data Control Systems, *Proc. Natl. Simulation Conf.,* pp. 21.1–21.21, January, 1956.
114. Sklansky, J.: Pulsed *RC* Networks for Sampled-data Systems, *IRE Conv. Rec.,* pt. 2, pp. 81–99, 1956.
115. Thaler, S., and R. Boxer: An Operational Calculus for Numerical Analysis, *IRE Conv. Rec.,* pt. 2, pp. 100–105, 1956.
116. Ryerson, J. L.: Linear Complementary Smoothing Compensation for Sampled Data Lag, *IRE Conv. Rec.,* pt. 2, pp. 106–111, 1956.
117. Lloyd, S. P., and B. McMillan: Linear Least Squares Filtering and Prediction of Sampled Signals, *Proc. Symposium on Modern Network Synthesis,* vol. 5, p. 221, Polytechnic Institute of Brooklyn, 1956.
118. Boxer, R., and S. Thaler: A Simplified Method of Solving Linear and Non-Linear Systems, *Proc. IRE,* vol. 44, no. 1, pp. 89–101, January, 1956.
119. Kalman, R. E.: Non-linear Aspects of Sampled-data Control Systems, *Proc. Symposium on Nonlinear Circuit Analysis,* vol. 6, Polytechnic Institute of Brooklyn, 1956.
120. Stewart, R. M.: Statistical Design and Evaluation of Filters for the Restoration of Sampled Data, *Proc. IRE,* vol. 44, no. 2, pp. 253–257, February, 1956.
121. Linvill, W. K.: System Theory as an Extension of Circuit Theory, *Trans. IRE,* vol. CT-3, no. 4, pp. 217–223, December, 1956.
122. Widrow, B.: A Study of Rough Amplitude Quantization by Means of Nyquist Sampling Theory, *Trans. IRE,* vol. CT-3, no. 4, pp. 266–276, December, 1956.
123. Sittler, R. W.: Systems Analysis of Discrete Markov Processes, *Trans. IRE,* vol. CT-3, no. 4, pp. 257–265, December, 1956.
124. Klein, M. L.: High-speed Analog-Digital Converters, *IRE Trans. on Instrumentation,* pp. 148–154, June, 1956.
125. Smith, B. D.: An Unusual Electronic Analog-Digital Conversion Method, *IRE Trans. on Instrumentation,* pp. 155–160, June, 1956.
126. Frank, W. L., A. B. White, and I. L. Resnick: Precision Shaft-position Encoders, *IRE Trans. on Instrumentation,* pp. 168–173, June, 1956.
127. Meyers, G. H.: Quantization of a Signal Plus Random Noise, *IRE Trans. on Instrumentation,* pp. 181–186, June, 1956.
128. Flores, I.: Reflected Number Systems, *Trans. IRE,* vol. EC-5, pp. 79–81, June, 1956.
129. Klein, M. L., F. K. Williams, and H. C. Morgan: Analog-to-digital Conversion, *Instr. and Automation,* pp. 911–917, May, 1956, and pp. 1109–1117, June, 1956.
130. Klein, M. L., F. K. Williams, and H. C. Morgan: Digital-to-analog Conversion, *Instr. and Automation,* pp. 695–697, April, 1956.
131. Tompkins, H. E.: Unit-distance Binary-decimal Codes for Two-track Commutation, *IRE Trans. on Electronic Computers,* vol. EC-5, no. 3, September, 1956.

132. Blecher, F. H.: Transistor Circuits for Analog and Digital Systems, *Bell System Tech. J.*, vol. 35, pp. 295–332, March, 1956.
133. Barker, R. H.: A Transducer for Digital Data-transmission Systems, *Proc. IEE*, pt. B, pp. 42–51, January, 1956.
134. Klein, S. I.: A Program for an Airborne Digital Control System, *IRE Trans. on Telemetry and Remote Control*, vol. TRC-2, pp. 20–22, March, 1956.
135. Lees, A. B.: Interpolation and Extrapolation of Sampled Data, *IRE Trans.* on *Information Theory*, vol. IT-2, no. 1, pp. 12–17, March, 1956.
136. Dinneen, G. P., and I. S. Reed: An Analysis of Signal Detection and Location by Digital Methods, *IRE Trans. on Information Theory*, vol. IT-2, no. 1, pp. 29–37, March, 1956.
137. Johnson, K. R.: Optimum Linear Discrete Filtering of Signals Containing a Nonrandom Component, *IRE Trans. on Information Theory*, vol. IT-2, no. 2, pp. 49–55, June, 1956.
138. Blum, M.: An Extension of the Minimum Mean Square Prediction Theory for Sampled-Input Signals, *IRE Trans. on Information Theory*, vol. IT-2, no. 3, pp. S176–S184, September, 1956.
139. Tsypkin, Y. Z.: Über die Synthese von Impulssystemen der automatischen Regelung und Steurerung, Beitrag 95, Fachtigung Regelungstechnik, Heidelberg, Germany, 1956 (unkorrigierter Vordruck mit 18 Bildern).

1957

140. Goode, H. H., and R. E. Machol: "System Engineering," pt. 4, McGraw-Hill Book Company, Inc., New York, 1957.
141. Grabbe, E. M. (ed.): "Automation in Business and Industry," chaps. 7, 9, and 16, John Wiley & Sons, Inc., New York, 1957.
142. Richards, R. K.: "Digital Computer Components and Circuits," chap. 11, D. Van Nostrand Company, Inc., Princeton, N. J., 1957.
143. Susskind, A. K. (ed.): "Notes on Analog-digital Conversion Techniques," John Wiley & Sons, Inc., New York, 1957.
144. Murphy, G. J., and R. D. Ormsby: A Survey of Techniques for the Analysis of Sampled-data Control Systems, *Trans. IRE*, vol. AC-2, pp. 79–90, February, 1957.
145. Gimpel, D. J.: Sampled-data Systems, *Control Eng.*, pp. 99–106, February, 1957.
146. Jury, E. I., and W. Schroeder: Discrete Compensation of Continuous-data Feedback Control Systems, *Trans. AIEE*, vol. 76, pt. II, pp. 317–325, January, 1957.
147. Jury, E. I.: Hidden Oscillations in Sampled-data Control Systems, *Trans. AIEE*, vol. 76, pt. II, pp. 391–394, January, 1957.
148. Friedland, B.: A Technique for the Analysis of Time-varying Sampled-data Systems, *Trans. AIEE*, vol. 76, pt. II, pp. 407–413, January, 1957.
149. Tou, J.: Digital Compensation for Control and Simulation, *Proc. IRE*, vol. 45, no. 9, pp. 1243–1248, September, 1957.
150. Tou, J.: Analysis of Sampled-data Control Systems with Finite Sampling Duration, *Proc. Natl. Electronics Conf.*, vol. 13, pp. 561–573, 1957.
151. Benningfield, L. M., and G. V. Lago: Compensation of Sampled-data Systems, *Proc. Natl. Electronics Conf.*, vol. 13, pp. 888–897, 1957.
152. Farmanfarma, G.: Analysis of Linear Sampled-data Systems with Finite Pulse Width: Open Loop, *Trans. AIEE*, vol. 76, pt. I, pp. 808–819, January, 1957.
153. Kukel, J.: Sampling in Linear and Non-linear Feedback Systems, *IRE WESCON Conv. Rec.*, pp. 43–56, 1957.
154. Ragazzini, J. R.: Digital Computers in Feedback Systems, *IRE Conv. Rec.*, pp. 33–42, 1957.

155. Braun, E. L.: Digital Computers in Continuous Control Systems, *IRE Conv. Rec.*, pp. 127–135, 1957.
156. Bauer, W. F.: Aspects of Real-time Simulation, *IRE Conv. Rec.*, pp. 142–144, 1957.
157. Susskind, A. K.: Digital Information Processing for Machine Tool Control, *IRE Conv. Rec.*, pp. 145–149, 1957.
158. Linden, D. A., and B. D. Steinberg: Synthesis of Delay Line Network, *Trans. IRE*, vol. ANE-4, pp. 34–39, March, 1957.
159. Urkowitz, H.: Analysis and Synthesis of Delay Line Periodic Filters, *Trans. IRE*, vol. CT-4, no. 2, pp. 41–53, June, 1957.
160. Kranc, G.: Compensation of an Error-sampled System by a Multi-rate Controller, *Trans. AIEE*, pt. II, pp. 149–159, 1957.
161. Mori, M.: Root-locus Method of Pulse Transfer Function for Sampled-data Control Systems, *Trans. IRE*, vol. PGAC-3, pp. 13–20, November, 1957.
162. Kranc, G. M.: Input-Output Analysis of Multi-rate Feedback Systems, *Trans. IRE*, vol. PGAC-3, pp. 21–28, November, 1957.
163. Kalman, R. E.: Optimal Non-linear Control of Saturating Systems by Intermittent Action, *IRE WESCON Conv. Rec.*, pt. 4, pp. 130–135, 1957.
164. Jury, E. I.: Additions to the Modified z-transform Method, *IRE WESCON Conv. Rec.*, pt. 4, pp. 136–156, 1957.
165. Kranc, G. M.: Additional Techniques for Sampled-data Feedback Problems, *IRE WESCON Conv. Rec.*, pt. 4, pp. 157–165, 1957.
166. Salzer, J. M.: Signal Flow Reductions in Sampled-data Systems, *IRE WESCON Conv. Rec.*, pt. 4, pp. 166–170, 1957.
167. Johnson, G. W.: Statistical Analysis of Sampled-data Systems, *IRE WESCON Conv. Rec.*, pt. 4, pp. 187–195, 1957.
168. Astrahan, M. M., B. Housman, J. F. Jacobs, R. P. Mayer, and W. H. Thomas: The Logical Design of a Digital Computer for a Large-Scale Real-Time Application, *Trans. AIEE*, vol. 76, pt. I, pp. 71–75, March, 1957.
169. Drenick, R. F., and R. A. Shahbender: Adaptive Servomechanisms, *Trans. AIEE*, vol. 76, pt. II, pp. 286–292, November, 1957.
170. Freeman, H.: Cycle and Delay Time in a Real-Time Digital Computer, *Trans. AIEE*, vol. 76, pt. I, pp. 588–593, November, 1957.
171. Stout, T. M.: A Step-by-step Method for Transient Analysis of Feedback Systems with One Non-linear Element, *Trans. AIEE*, vol. 76, pt. II, pp. 378–390, January, 1957.
172. Bower, G. G.: Analog-to-digital Converters, *Control Eng.*, pp. 107–118, April, 1957.
173. James, E. W., and A. S. Boksenbom: How to Establish the Control Problem for an On-line Computer, *Control Eng.*, pp. 148–159, September, 1957.
174. Tierney, J. W., C. J. Homan, and others: The Digital Computer as a Process Controller, *Control Eng.*, pp. 166–175, September, 1957.
175. Maze, R. O.: Converting Process Data into Controller Inputs, *Control Eng.*, pp. 176–182, September, 1957.
176. Salzer, J. M.: From Controller Output to Process Actuation, *Control Eng.*, pp. 183–189, September, 1957.

1958

177. Truxal, J. G. (ed.): "Control Engineers' Handbook," sec. 5, McGraw-Hill Book Company, Inc., New York, 1958.
178. Phister, M.: "Logical Design of Digital Computers," John Wiley & Sons, Inc., New York, 1958.

179. Tou, J.: Analysis of Sampled-data Control Systems Containing Non-linear Element, *Proc. IRE*, vol. 46, no. 5, May, 1958.
180. Tou, J.: Analysis of Sampled-data Feedback Control Systems with Finite Sampling Duration, *AIEE paper* 58-801, 1958.
181. Anderson, G. W., J. A. Aseltine, and others: A Self-adjusting System for Optimum Dynamic Performance, *IRE Conv. Rec.*, pt. 4, pp. 182–190, March, 1958.
182. Braun, E. L., and G. Post: Systems Considerations for Computers in Process Control, *IRE Conv. Rec.*, pt. 4, pp. 168–181, March, 1958.
183. Groginsky, H. L.: On the Design of Adaptive Systems, *IRE Conv. Rec.*, pt. 4, pp. 160–167, March, 1958.
184. Chang, S. S. L.: Statistical Design Theory for Strictly Digital Sampled-data Systems, *Trans. AIEE*, vol. 77, pt. I, pp. 702–709, January, 1958.
185. Freeman, H.: Stability and Physical Realizability Considerations in the Synthesis of Multiple Control Systems, *Trans. AIEE*, vol. 77, pt. II, pp. 1–5, March, 1958.
186. Farmanfarma, G.: Analysis of Multiple Sampler Systems with Finite Pulse Width: Open Loop, *Trans. AIEE*, vol. 77, pt. II, pp. 20–28, March, 1958.
187. Friedland, B.: Time Varying Analysis of a Guidance System, *Trans. AIEE*, vol. 77, pt. II, 75–81, May, 1958.
188. Taylor, C. F.: An Approach to Self-adaptive Controls, *ISA paper* ISA-FCS-1, 1958.
189. Levin, M. J.: Methods for the Realization of Self-optimizing Systems, *ISA paper* ISA-FCS-2, 1958.
190. Kalman, R. E., and R. W. Koepcke: Optimal Synthesis of Linear Sampling Control Systems Using Generalized Performance Indices, *ASME paper* 58-IRD-6, 1958.
191. Aseltine, J. A., A. R. Mancini, and C. W. Sarture: Impulse-response Self-optimization Compared with Other Criteria, *IRE paper* PGAC-101, 1958.
192. Mori, M.: Statistical Treatment of Sampled-data Control Systems for Actual Random Inputs, *Trans. ASME*, vol. 80, no. 2, pp. 444–456, February, 1958.
193. Kalman, R. E.: Design of a Self-optimizing Control System, *Trans. ASME*, vol. 80, no. 2, pp. 468–478, February, 1958.
194. Schubert, E. J.: Function Tables in Digital Control Computers, *Trans. AIEE*, vol. 77, pt. I, no. 37, pp. 316–319, July, 1958.
195. Elgerd, O. I.: An Analog Computer Study of the Transient Behavior and Stability Characteristics of Serial Type Digital Data Systems, *Trans. AIEE*, vol. 77, pt. I, no. 37, pp. 358–366, July, 1958.
196. Bertram, J. E.: The Effect of Quantization in Sampled-feedback Systems, *Trans. AIEE*, vol. 77, pt. II, pp. 177–182, September, 1958.
197. Chang, S. S. L.: Statistical Design Theory for Digital-controlled Continuous Systems, *Trans. AIEE*, vol. 77, pt. II, pp. 191–201, September, 1958.
198. Andeen, R. E.: Staggered Sampling to Improve Stability of Multiple Sampler Feedback Systems, *Trans. AIEE*, vol. 77, pt. II, pp. 399–403, 1958.
199. Hufnagel, R. E.: Analysis of Cyclic Rate Sampled-data Feedback Control Systems, *Trans. AIEE*, vol. 77, pt. II, pp. 421–423, 1958.
200. Tou, J., and E. Kinnen: Discussions of *AIEE paper* 58-803, *Trans. AIEE*, vol. 77, pt. II, pp. 424–425, 1958.
201. Torng, H. C.: A Technique for the Time-domain Synthesis of Sampled-data Systems, *AIEE paper* 58-802.
202. Mitrovic, D.: Graphical Analysis and Synthesis of Feedback Control Systems, pt. III, Sampled-data Feedback Control Systems, *Trans. AIEE*, vol. 77, pt. II, pp. 497–503, 1958.
203. Farmanfarma, G.: General Analysis and Stability Study of Finite Pulsed Feedback Systems, *Trans. AIEE*, vol. 77, pt. II, no. 37, pp. 148–162, July, 1958.

204. Mathias, R. A.: Putting Logic to Work in Distributed Program Controllers, *Control Eng.*, vol. 5, no. 9, pp. 139–145, September, 1958.
205. Mergler, H. W.: Converting Pulse and Coded Data into Usable Output Signals, *Control Eng.*, vol. 5, no. 9, pp. 146–152, September, 1958.
206. Johnson, E. C.: Interpolating between Programmed Points to Get Smooth Curves, *Control Eng.*, vol. 5, no. 9, pp. 153–157, September, 1958.
207. Knapp, C. H., E. Shapiro, and R. A. Thorpe: An Error-sampled Sweep Position Control System, *IBM J. Research Develop.* vol. 2, no. 1, January, 1958.
208. Zadoff, S. A.: Statistical Invariance of Noise in Sampled-data Systems, *IRE WESCON Conv. Rec.*, 1958.
209. Carlson, C. O.: Some Simplifying Additions to Basic Sampled-data Theory, *IRE WESCON Conv. Rec.*, 1958.
210. Cheetham, R. P., and W. A. Mulle: Enhanced Real Time Data Accuracy for Instrumentation Radars by Use of Digital Hydraulic Servos, *IRE WESCON Conv. Rec.*, 1958.

Additional References

211. Laning, J. H., and R. H. Battin: "Random Processes in Automatic Control," McGraw-Hill Book Company, Inc., New York, 1956.
212. Ragazzini, J. R., and G. F. Franklin: "Sampled-data Control Systems," McGraw-Hill Book Company, Inc., New York, 1958.
213. Fan Chun Wui: Concerning the Analysis of Sampled-data Systems, *Avtomat. i Telemekh.*, vol. 19, no. 4, pp. 296–305 (in Russian), 1958.
214. Perov, V. P.: The Synthesis of Pulse Circuits and Systems with a Pulse Feedback, *Avtomat. i Telemekh.*, vol. 18, no. 12, pp. 1081–1097, 1957 (in Russian).
215. Tsypkin, Y. Z.: Sampled-data Systems with Extrapolating Devices, *Avtomat. i Telemekh.*, vol. 19, no. 5, pp. 389–400, 1958 (in Russian).
216. Ermakov, S. S., and E. M. Esipovich: The Way of Forming Transfer Functions of Sampled-data Control Systems with Extrapolating Devices, *Avtomat. i Telemekh.*, vol. 19, no. 5, pp. 401–407, 1958 (in Russian).
217. Huskey, H. D., and D. E. Trumbo: Data Preparation for Numerical Control of Machine Tools, *IRE WESCON, Conv. Rec.*, 1958.
218. Johnson, E. C., and Y. C. Ho: Systems Design of a Numerically Controlled Machine Tool, *Proc. Eastern Joint Computer Conf.*, 1957.
219. Frady, W. E., and M. Phister: System Characteristics of a Computer-Controller for Use in the Process Industries, *Proc. Eastern Joint Computer Conf.*, 1957.
220. Leondes, C. T.: Real-time Hybrid Computers for Electronic Control Systems, *Proc. Eastern Joint Computer Conf.*, 1957.
221. Zadoff, S., and J. Rattner: Use of a Digital Computer for Airborne Guidance and Navigation, *Proc. Eastern Joint Computer Conf.*, 1957.
222. Skramstad, H. K., A. A. Ernst, and J. P. Nigro: Combined Analog-Digital Simulation of Sampled-data Systems, *Proc. Eastern Joint Computer Conf.*, 1957.
223. Blanyer, C. G., and H. Mori: Analog, Digital and Combined Analog-Digital Computers for Real Time Simulation, *Proc. Eastern Joint Computer Conf.*, 1957.
224. Robinson, A.S.: The Optimum Synthesis of Computer Limited Sampled-data Systems, *Proc. Eastern Joint Computer Conf.*, 1957.
225. Randall, J. H.: A Method of Coupling a Small Computer to Input-Output Devices without Extensive Buffers, *Proc. Eastern Joint Computer Conf.*, 1957.
226. Antista, B. A.: A High-speed Digital-to-analog Voltage Decoder, *Proc. Natl. Electronics Conf.*, 1958.
227. Boxer, R.: A Note on Numerical Transform Calculus, *Proc. IRE*, vol. 45, no. 10, pp. 1401–1406, October, 1957.

228. Towles, W. B.: Transistorized Analog-Digital Converter, *Electronics*, vol. 31, no. 31, pp. 90–93, August, 1958.
229. Robinson, A. S.: The Synthesis of Computer-limited Sampled-data Control Systems, *Proc. Computers in Control Systems Conf.*, October, 1957.
230. Stout, T. M.: System Considerations in Computer Control of Semicontinuous Chemical Process, *Proc. Computers in Control Systems Conf.*, October, 1957.
231. Helm, H. A.: Analysis of Digital Systems, *Proc. Computers in Control Systems Conf.*, October, 1957.
232. Salzer, J. M.: Signal Flow Techniques for Digital Compensation, *Proc. Computers in Control Systems Conf.*, October, 1957.
233. Mayo, J. S.: Analysis of an On-Off Digital Control System, *Proc. Computers in Control Systems Conf.*, October, 1957.
234. Kalman, R. E., and J. E. Bertram: General Synthesis Procedure for Computer Control of Single and Multiloop Linear Systems, *Proc. Computers in Control Systems Conf.*, October, 1957.
235. Chestnut, H., A. Dabul, and D. W. Leiby: Analog Computer Study of Sampled-data Systems, *Proc. Computers in Control Systems Conf.*, October, 1957.
236. Freeman, H., and O. Lowenchuss: Bibliography of Sampled-data Control Systems and *z*-transform Applications, *IRE Trans. on Automatic Control*, pp. 28–30, March, 1958.
237. Higgins, T. J., and R. W. Greer: Classified Bibliography on Feedback Control Systems, pt. I, Sampled-data Systems, *AIEE paper* 58-1269.
238. Stromer, P. R.: A Selective Bibliography on Sampled-data Systems, *IRE Trans. on Automatic Control*, pp. 112–114, December, 1958.

APPENDIX 3

PROBLEMS

Chapter 4

1. Determine the starred transform associated with

(a) $X(s) = \dfrac{s}{(s+a)(s+b)}$

(b) $X(s) = \dfrac{\omega_0^2}{(s^2+\omega_0^2)^2}$

2. Determine the starred transform of
(a) $x(t) = t\cos\omega_0 t$
(b) $x(t) = (\sin\omega_0 t)^2$

3. Given

$$G(s)H(s) = \frac{10}{s(1+0.1s)(1+0.05s)}$$

construct the approximate polar plot of $GH^*(j\omega)$. The sampling period is assumed to be 0.2 sec.

4. The block diagram of an error-sampled feedback control system is shown in Fig. P.4. A zero-order hold is used as the smoothing device. The transfer function of the controlled system is

$$G_s(s) = \frac{10\epsilon^{-T_d s}}{s(1+0.1s)(1+0.05s)}$$

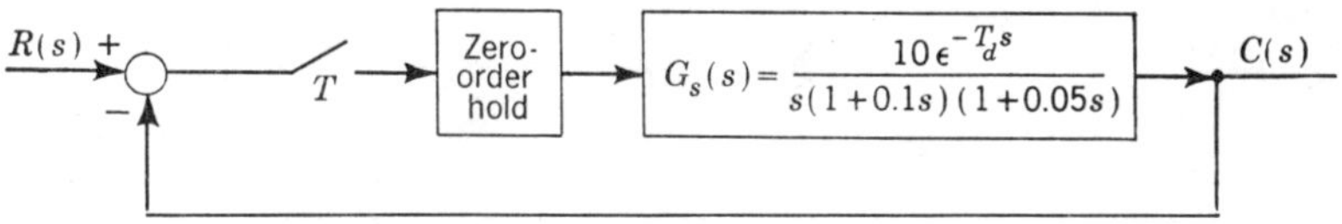

FIG. P. 4

and the sampling period is 0.2 sec. Plot the Nyquist diagram for this system with $T_d = 1.5$ sec and $T_d = 0$ sec. Discuss the effect of the transport lag T_d upon the stability of the system.

5. By making use of the concept of weighting sequence, determine the value of the output at the nth sampling instant of the open-loop sampled-data system shown in Fig. P.5, when this system is subjected to an exponential input $r(t) = \epsilon^{-at}$, where a is a constant. The sampling period is T sec.

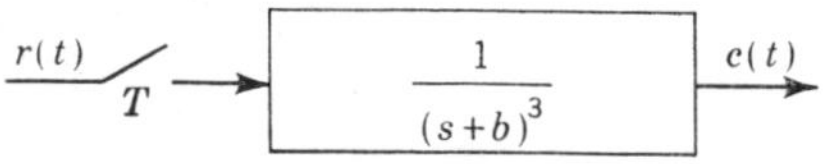

FIG. P. 5

6. The open-loop sampled-data system shown in Fig. P.6 is subjected to an exponential input $r(t) = \epsilon^{-at}$, where a is a constant. The samplers operate in synchronism with a sampling period equal to T sec. By making use of the concept of weighting sequence, evaluate the output of this system at the nth sampling instant.

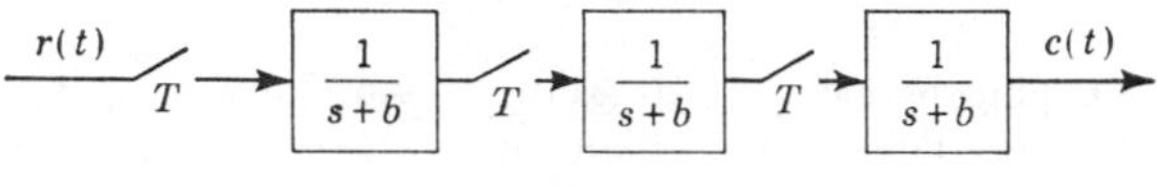

FIG. P. 6

7. (*a*) Suggest a circuitry for performing the function of the first-order hold.

(*b*) Draw a computer-program diagram for the simulation of the first-order hold on a commercial analog computer.

8. As discussed in Sec. 4.6, the frequency characteristic of a zero-order hold shows a rapid attenuation for low-frequency signals, while that of a first-order hold exhibits an overshoot. It is conceivable that better frequency characteristic may be obtained from a *fractional-order* hold. The output waveform of a zero-order hold has zero slope between two consecutive sampling instants; the output waveform of a first-order hold has a constant slope between two consecutive sampling instants, which is determined by the values of the two preceding samples; and the output waveform of a fractional-order hold has a constant slope between two consecutive sampling instants, which lie between the above two limiting values, as shown in Fig. P.8.

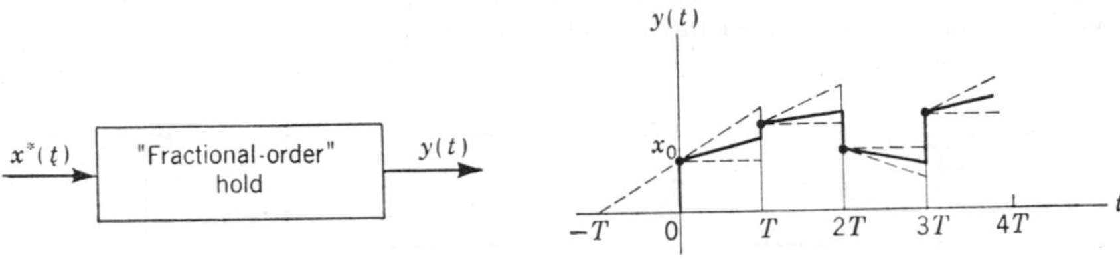

FIG. P. 8

(*a*) Show that the transfer function of a fractional-order hold is

$$G_{ha}(s) = (1 - a\epsilon^{-Ts})G_{h0}(s) + \frac{a}{T}[G_{h0}(s)]^2$$

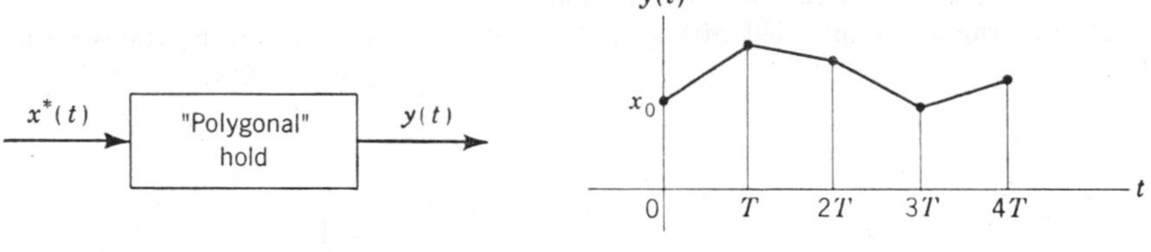

FIG. P. 9

where a is the ratio between the slope of the output waveform of the fractional-order hold to the corresponding slope of the output waveform of the first-order hold. a is equal to one for the first-order hold, zero for the zero-order hold, etc., and $G_{h0}(s)$ is the transfer function of the zero-order hold.

(*b*) Plot the frequency characteristics for $a = \frac{1}{2}, \frac{1}{3}, \frac{1}{4}$, and discuss.
(*c*) Design a circuit for performing the function of a fractional-order hold.

9. Verify that the transfer function of the *polygonal* or *trapezoidal* hold shown in Fig. P.9 is

$$G_{hp}(s) = \frac{\epsilon^{Ts}}{T}[G_{h0}(s)]^2$$

where T is the sampling period and $G_{h0}(s)$ is the transfer function of the zero-order hold.

10. By means of the Poisson summation rule evaluate the sum of the infinite series

$$\sum_{n=0}^{\infty} \frac{ab}{(n^2 + a^2)(n^2 + b^2)}$$

Chapter 5

11. Determine the z transform associated with the following transfer functions:

(*a*) $\dfrac{a}{s^3(s + a)}$ (*b*) $\dfrac{a^2}{s(s + a)^2}$

(*c*) $\dfrac{(a - b)^2 + \omega_0^2}{(s + b)[(s + a)^2 + \omega_0^2]}$ (*d*) $\dfrac{a}{s^{k+1}(s + a)}$

12. Shown in Fig. P.12 is the block diagram of a simple sampled-data feedback control system. The sampling period is 0.1 sec, the time constant is 0.05 sec, and the gain constant is 15. Is this system stable? What is the gain margin of the system? Plot the z-transform locus of the open-loop pulse-transfer function of this system.

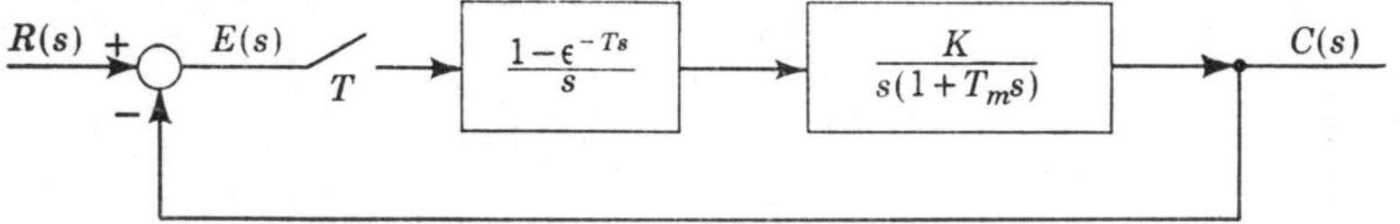

FIG. P. 12

13. Evaluate the inverse z transform of

$$G(z) = \frac{z^2(z^2 + z + 1)}{(z^2 - 0.8z + 1)(z^2 + z + 0.8)}$$

by use of (*a*) the real inversion formula; (*b*) the method of partial-fraction expansion, and (*c*) the method of power-series expansion.

14. Determine the modified z transform associated with the following transfer functions:

(*a*) $\dfrac{s}{(s + a)^2 + \omega_0^2}$ (*b*) $\dfrac{a^3}{s^2(s + a)^2}$

(*c*) $\dfrac{a^2 + \omega_0^2}{s[(s + a)^2 + \omega_0^2]}$ (*d*) $\dfrac{ab}{s^2(s + a)(s + b)}$

15. Evaluate the inverse modified z transform of

(*a*) $G(z,m) = \dfrac{[z \sin m\omega_0 T + \epsilon^{-aT} \sin (1 - m)\omega_0 T]\epsilon^{-amT}}{z^2 - 2z\epsilon^{-aT} \cos \omega_0 T + \epsilon^{-2aT}}$

(*b*) $G(z,m) = \dfrac{z\epsilon^{-amT}}{(z - 1)(z - \epsilon^{-aT})}$

16. By applying the z-transform technique solve the difference equation

$$y_{n+2} - 10y_{n+1} + 169y_n = 4^n$$

17. By means of the z-transform technique solve the difference equation

$$y_{n+2} - 3y_{n+1} - 10y_n = \epsilon^{3n}$$

18. By applying the z-transform technique find the step-function response of the continuous-data system having transfer function

$$G(s) = \frac{1}{1 + 0.1s + 0.02s^2}$$

(HINT: Approximate the given system by a sampled-data model.)

Compare the result with the actual response of the system computed by the Laplace-transform inversion method. Discuss the effect of the sampling period of the fictitious sampler upon the accuracy of the result.

19. If $g(nT,m)$ is the inverse modified z transform of $G(z,m)$, show that

$$\frac{\partial g(nT,m)}{\partial m} = \mathfrak{z}^{-1}\left\{\frac{\partial G(z,m)}{\partial m}\right\}$$

20. If $G(z,m)$ is the modified z transform associated with $G(s)$, show that the z transform associated with $G(s)G(-s)$ is equal to

$$T\overline{|G(z,m)|^2}$$

where $z = \epsilon^{j\omega T}$ and T is the sampling period.

21. If $G(z,m)$ is the modified z transform associated with $G(s)$, show that

$$\mathfrak{z}_m\{G(s + a)\} = \epsilon^{-(m-1)aT}G(z\epsilon^{aT},m)$$

$$\mathfrak{z}_m\{G(s - a)\} = \epsilon^{(m-1)aT}G(z\epsilon^{-aT},m)$$

22. Show that $\int_0^m g(nT,m)\,dm$ is equal to the inverse z transform of $\int_0^m G(z,m)\,dm$, where $g(nT,m)$ is the inverse transform of $G(z,m)$.

23. By use of the z-form technique, solve the following ordinary differential equation with variable coefficients.

$$\frac{d^2y}{dt^2} + t\frac{dy}{dt} + 2y = tu(t)$$

24. By applying the z-form technique find the step-function response of the unity-feedback, continuous-data control system having open-loop transfer function

$$G(s) = \frac{4}{s(1 + 0.1s + 0.01s^2)}$$

Chapter 6

25. Determine the z transform and the modified z transform of the output of the sampled-data system shown in Fig. P.25. All the samplers operate in synchronism with sampling period T.

26. Determine the z transform and the modified z transform of the output of the digital control system shown in Fig. P.26.

27. Derive a simplified Schur-Cohn criterion for third-order sampled-data control systems.

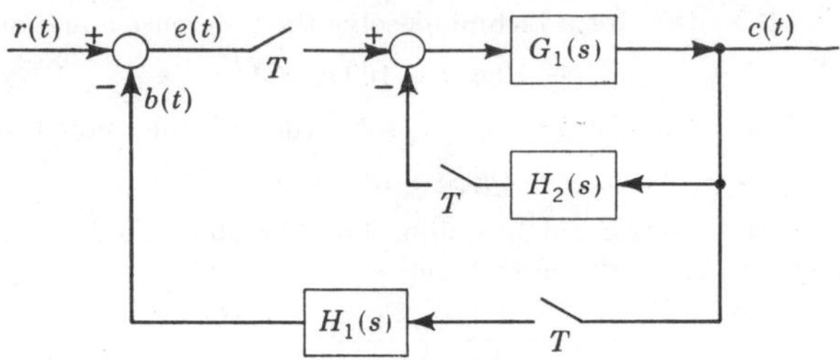

FIG. P. 25

28. For the sampled-data feedback control system shown in Fig. P.28, the sampling period is 1 sec. Determine the output sequence and the output time function in response to a unit step-function input.

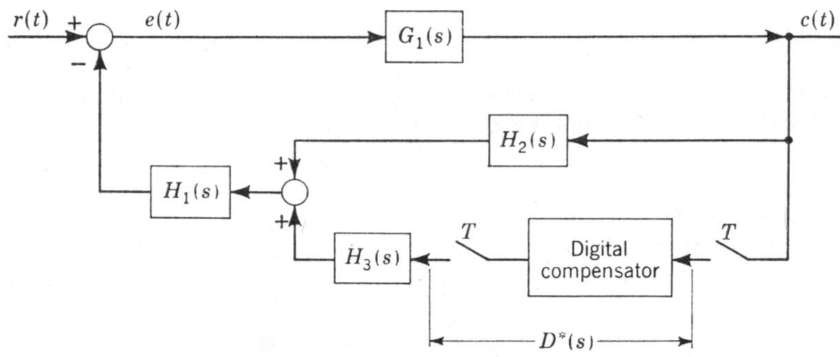

FIG. P. 26

29. By use of the z-transform technique, determine the step-function response of the unity-feedback, continuous-data control system having open-loop transfer function

$$G(s) = \frac{4}{s(1 + 0.1s + 0.01s^2)}$$

This can readily be done, if a fictitious sampler followed by a polygonal or trapezoidal hold is inserted in the feedback path. Discuss the effect of the sampling rate of the fictitious sampler upon the accuracy of the result.

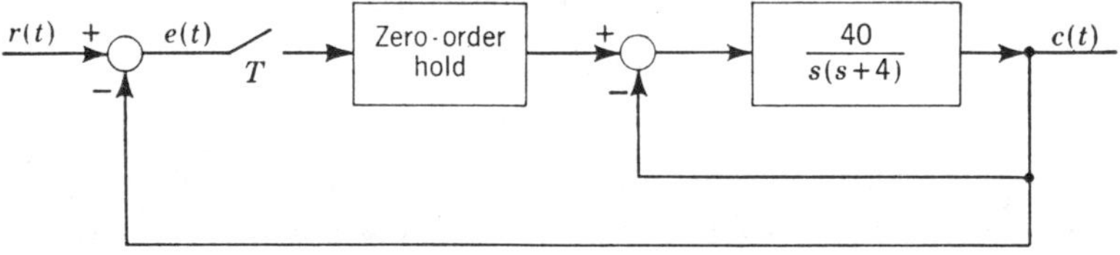

FIG. P. 28

30. Determine the error coefficients and the error series of the sampled-data feedback control system, shown in Fig. P.30, resulting from the input $r(t)$.

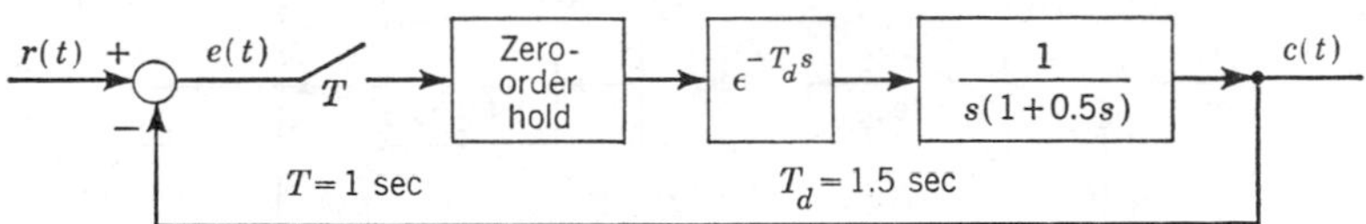

Fig. P. 30

31. Shown in Fig. P.31 is the block diagram of a sampled-data feedback control system. The sampling period is 0.2 sec. The sampling operation is assumed to be coincident with the beginning of the time function. Determine

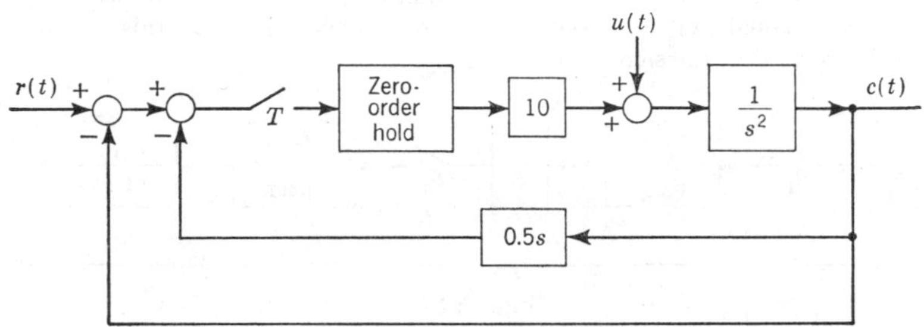

Fig. P. 31

(a) The step-function response of this system
(b) The error series resulting from an arbitrary input $r(t)$
(c) The system error $e(t)$ in steady state for an input $r(t) = 1 + t + t^2$
(d) The error series resulting from the disturbance $u(t)$

32. Figure P.32 illustrates the block diagram of an open-loop multirate sampled-data system. The sampling periods of the samplers are ½ sec and ⅓ sec, respectively. The sampling operation is assumed to be coincident with the application of the input signal.

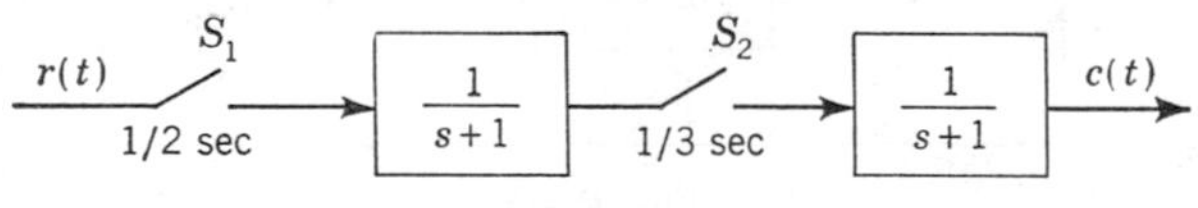

Fig. P. 32

(a) Determine the z transform of the output of the system.
(b) Evaluate the system output in response to a unit step-function input.
(c) Suppose now that the second sampler S_2 is replaced by a sampler which operates in synchronism with the sampler S_1 and at the same sampling rate. Repeat (a) and (b). Compare the results.

33. The block diagram of a multirate sampled-data feedback control system is shown in Fig. P.33. The sampling periods of the samplers are ½ sec and ⅓ sec, respectively, as indicated in the diagram. It is assumed that the sampling operation is coincident with the application of the input signal, and the samplers are synchronized. Zero-order holds are used in both the forward circuit and the feedback circuit.

(a) Determine the maximum allowable gain for stability.
(b) Evaluate the system response to a unit step-function input for $K = 1$.

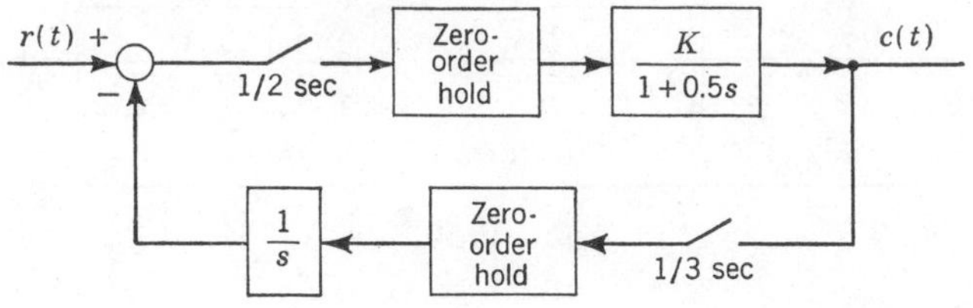

FIG. P. 33

34. The block diagram of a sampled-data feedback control system with nonsynchronized samplers is shown in Fig. P.34. The samplers S_1 and S_2 operate with the same sampling period equal to 0.5 sec, but they are not synchronized. In this system zero-order holds are used as the smoothing device.

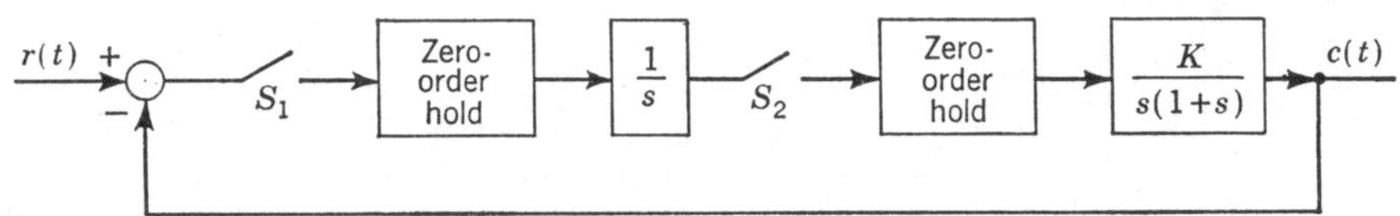

FIG. P. 34

(*a*) Determine the maximum allowable gain for stability when the slip factor of the sampler S_2 is 0.25, 0.5, 0.75.

(*b*) What is the best slip factor for system stability?

35. A sampled-data feedback control system has the configuration shown in Fig. P.35. The sampler S operates with a cyclic variable rate. It samples at the instants $t = 0$, $T/3$; T, $4T/3$; . . . kT, $(k + \frac{1}{3})T$; . . . . The period of the cycle is assumed to be 1.2 sec. Assume that the holding device is a zero-order hold.

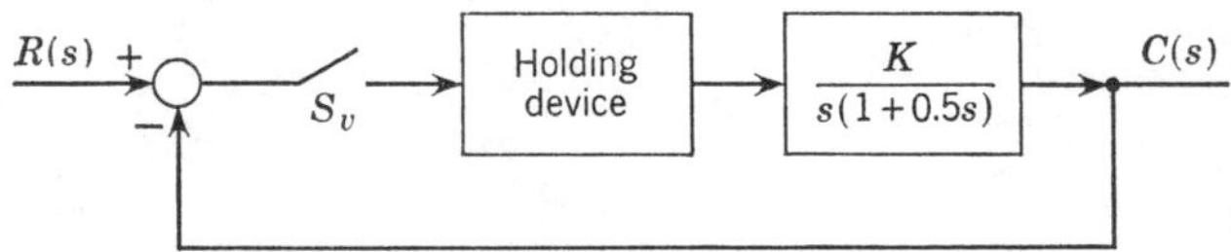

FIG. P. 35

(*a*) Investigate the stability of this system.

(*b*) For $K = 1$ evaluate the transient response of the system to a unit step-function and a unit ramp-function input.

(*c*) Suppose now that the cyclic variable-rate sampler S_v is replaced by a constant-rate sampler with sampling period equal to half the period of the variable sampler S_v. Repeat (*a*) and (*b*). Compare the results with (*a*) and (*b*).

36. In the system of Fig. P.35 assume that the holding device is a first-order hold. Repeat (*a*), (*b*), and (*c*) of Prob. 35.

37. Shown in Fig. P.37 is the block diagram of a cyclic-variable, multirate sampled-data control system. The sampler S operates at a constant rate with sampling period equal to 1 sec. The sampler S_v is a cyclic variable-rate sampler which samples at $t = 0$, $T/4$; T, $5T/4$; . . . , kT, $(k + \frac{1}{4})T$; . . . . The period of the variable sampler S_v is assumed to be 1 sec. Zero-order holds are used as the smoothing device.

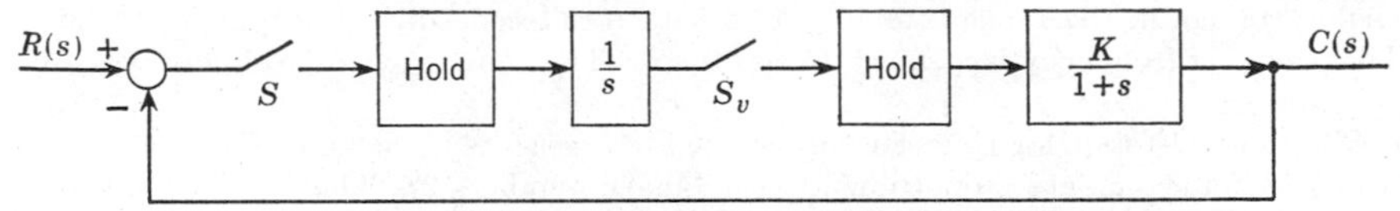

Fig. P. 37

(*a*) Investigate the stability of this system.
(*b*) For $K = 1$, compute the system output in response to a unit step-function input.

Chapter 7

38. Verify the expressions for the peak time and the maximum overshoot given in Eqs. (7.2-15) and (7.2-16), respectively.

39. If the over-all pulse-transfer function of an error-sampled unity-feedback system is

$$\frac{C(z)}{R(z)} = \frac{K \prod_{k=0}^{m} (z - z_k)}{\prod_{k=0}^{n} (z - p_k)}$$

(*a*) show that the position-error constant K_p is related to closed-loop poles and zeros by

$$K_p = \frac{\prod_{k=0}^{n} (1 - p_k)}{\prod_{k=0}^{n} (1 - p_k) - K \prod_{k=0}^{m} (1 - z_k)}$$

(*b*) if the system is of zero position error, show that velocity-error constant K_v is given by

$$\frac{1}{K_v} = \sum_{k=0}^{n} \frac{1}{p_k^{-1} - 1} - \sum_{k=0}^{m} \frac{1}{z_k^{-1} - 1} + (n - m)$$

40. Figure 7.3-6 shows the block diagram of a basic sampled-data feedback control system. The sampling period is 0.5 sec. The transfer function of the controlled system is

$$G_s(s) = \frac{1}{s(s + 1)}$$

If a first-order hold is used as the smoothing device, determine the system error resulting from the application of a unit step-function input.

41. In the sampled-data feedback control system shown in Fig. 7.4-2, if the zero-order hold is replaced by a first-order hold, determine the ripple factor k_r as a function of the sampling period T and the input frequency ω. Plot the ripple factor curve (k_r versus ω/ω_s) for $T = 0.693$ sec.

Chapter 8

42. Design a transistorized analog-to-digital converter which operates on the time-base encoding principle. It is required that the converter be capable of converting an analog voltage in the range 0 to 100 volts with a full-scale digital output of 2^{10} bits. The sampling frequency is assumed to be 20 cps. The conversion time should be kept at minimum.

43. A digital-to-analog converter using weighted resistors is shown in Fig. P.43. The resistance values R_n are proportional to the binary numbers 2^n. The switches are controlled by the relay representing the digits of a binary number. The switch is closed if the corresponding relay represents a 0 and it is open if the relay represents a 1.

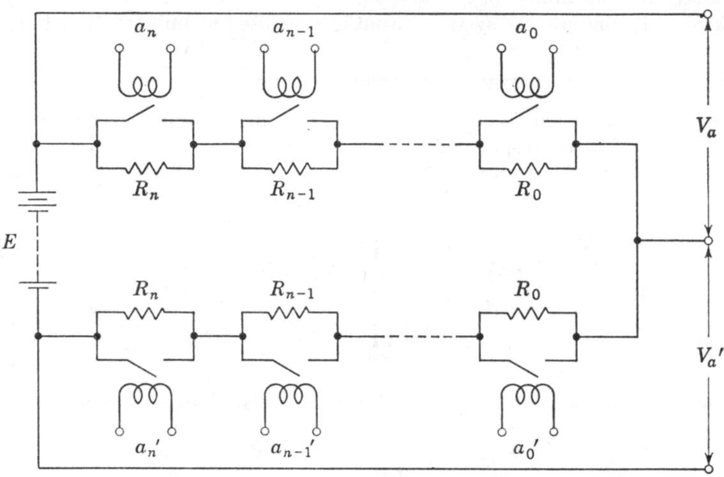

FIG. P. 43

(a) Show that V_a is a voltage proportional to the binary number input.

(b) What does V_a' represent?

44. Show that the resistance ladder network illustrated in Fig. P.44 can be used as a voltage decoder. Find the relationship between the output voltage V_a and the binary number to be decoded.

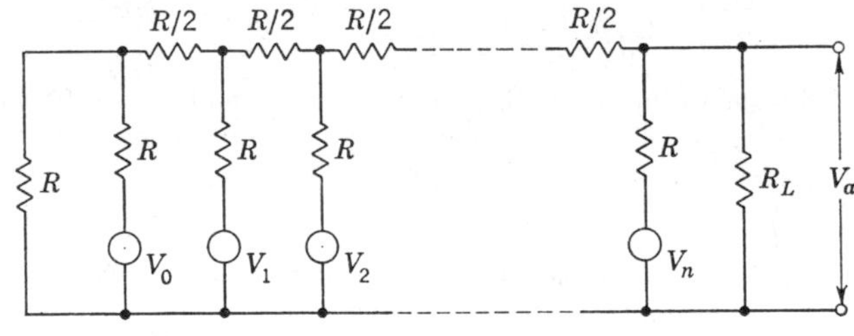

FIG. P. 44

45. A practical decoder circuit is shown in Fig. P.45. The values of the resistors are $R_k = 100{,}000$ ohms and $R = 7{,}500$ ohms. Determine the conversion factor of this decoder.

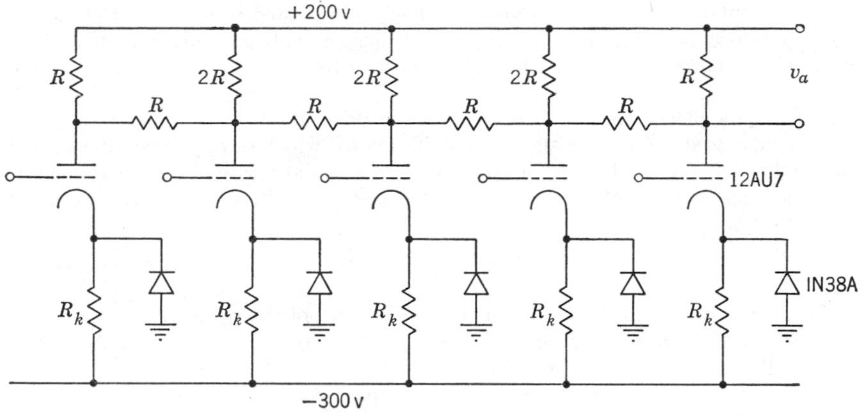

Fig. P. 45

Chapters 9 and 10

46. A multichannel drift-stabilization system is shown in simplified form in Fig. P.46. In this system, one stabilization amplifier is time shared by a group of 30 d-c amplifiers

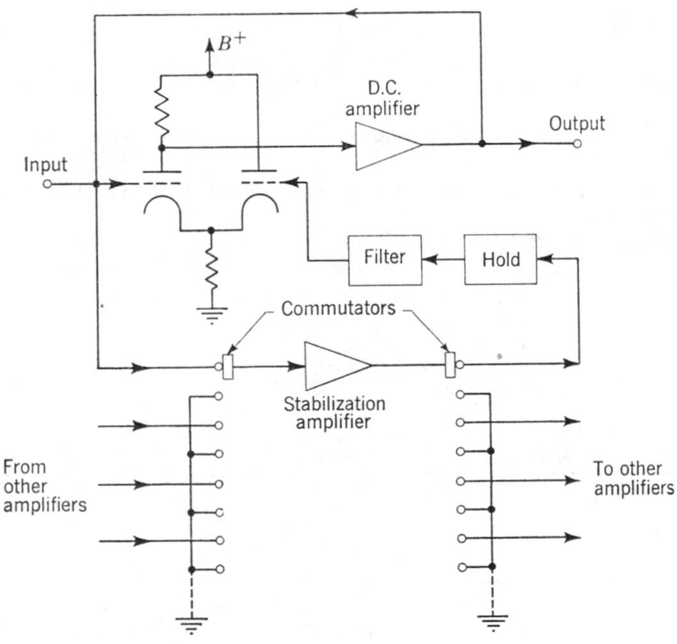

Fig. P. 46

with the aid of a commutator which samples the error-point voltage of each amplifier in turn. Any slowly varying voltage present at the error point of a particular amplifier is applied to the stabilization amplifier as a series of pulses occurring at the repetition rate of the commutator. These pluses are amplified and invested in the stabilization amplifier, and then applied to the same amplifier through a holding circuit and a smoothing filter. The stabilization amplifier is made almost drift-free by the use of intermittent feedback.

(*a*) Draw the block diagram for one channel of this drift-stabilization system.

(*b*) Assume that the gain of the d-c amplifier is K_2, which is very large, the gain of the stabilization amplifier is K_1, the commutator rotates at a rate of 5 cps, the holding circuit is of zero order, and the smoothing filter is a simple *RC* network having transfer function given by

$$G_1(s) = \frac{1}{1 + 0.2s}$$

Sketch the root-locus plot in the *z* plane for one channel of this system. Determine the gain constant K_1 so that the output sequence of the system in response to a step-function input exhibits no transient.

47. The block diagram of a sampled-data feedback control system is shown in Fig. P.47. The sampling period *T* is 1 sec.

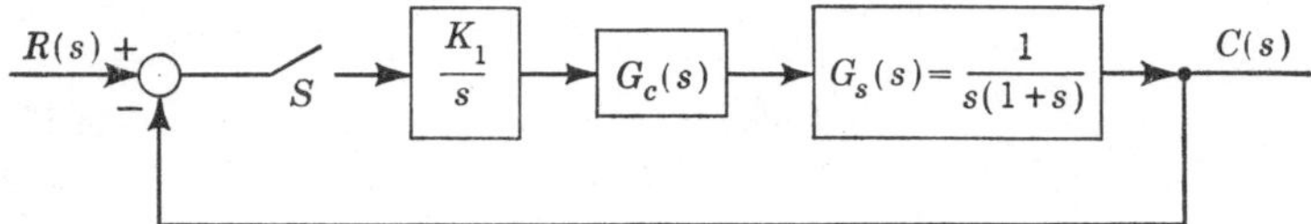

FIG. P. 47

(*a*) Design a cascade compensator between the integrator and the output member $G_s(s)$ so as to make the system response well damped and insensitive to gain changes and disturbances which occur at the output member. The zero-velocity-error feature should be retained.

(*b*) Evaluate the ripple content in the system response to a step-function input and to a ramp-function input.

(*c*) Investigate the effect of adding a zero-order hold to reduce the ripple content.

(*d*) Plot the step-function and the ramp-function response of the compensated system.

48. The sampled-data control system shown in Fig. P.48 employs feedback compensation. The controlled system has a transfer function

$$G_s(s) = \frac{K}{s(s + 1)}$$

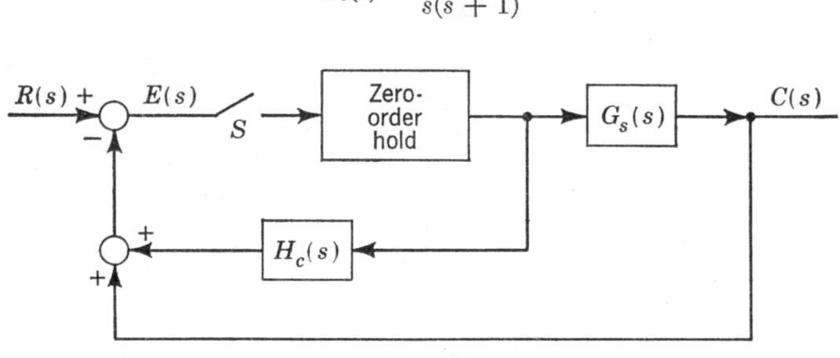

FIG. P. 48

The sampling period of this system is 1 sec. A zero-order hold is used as the smoothing device (*a*) Design the compensator $H_c(s)$ and select the gain constant K so that the system has good transient response and small steady-state error to a step-function input and to a ramp-function input.

(*b*) Plot the step-function and the ramp-function response of the compensated system.

(*c*) Evaluate the error coefficients for this system.

(*d*) Compare the use of a minor loop for compensation with the use of a pulsed-data or digital filter.

49. Shown in Fig. P.49 is the block diagram of a sampled-data control system. The sampling period of this system is 0.5 sec. A zero-order hold is used as the smoothing device.

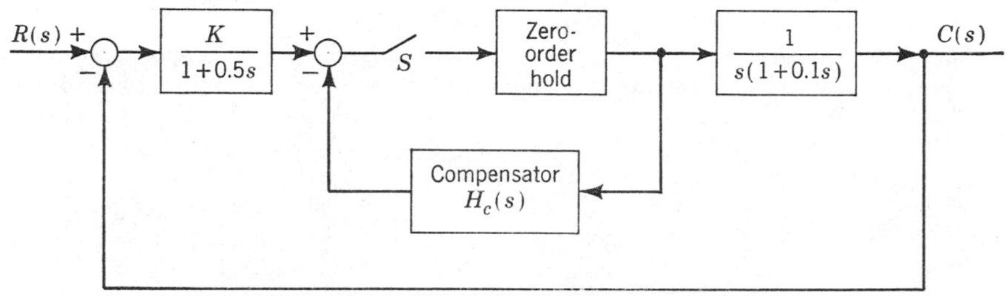

FIG. P. 49

(*a*) Determine the maximum gain for stability for the system without compensation.

(*b*) Design a feedback compensation $H_c(s)$ to meet the specifications of a velocity-error constant of at least 1.5 and a phase margin of 50°.

(*c*) Evaluate the step-function response of the compensated system.

(*d*) What are the gain margin and the bandwidth of the compensated system?

50. An error-sampled, unity-feedback control system has the forward transfer function $G(s) = G_h(s)G_s(s)$, where

$$G_h(s) = \frac{1 - \epsilon^{-Ts}}{s}$$

$$G_s(s) = \frac{K(s+3)}{s(s^2+2s+2)(s+6)}$$

The sampling period is taken as 0.5 sec.

(*a*) Sketch the root loci in the z plane as a function of K.

(*b*) Select a K which makes the relative damping ratio of the control poles equal to 0.5.

(*c*) Evaluate the response to a unit step-function input.

(*d*) When K is set at 100, design a digital compensator to meet the above damping specification, and compute the unit step-function response.

51. Synthesize a pulsed-data RC network to realize the following pulse-transfer function:

(*a*) $D(z) = 1 - 2z^{-1} + 2z^{-2}$

(*b*) $D(z) = \dfrac{1}{1 - 3z^{-1}}$

(*c*) $D(z) = \dfrac{z^{-1}(1 - 2z^{-1} + 2z^{-2})}{(1 - z^{-1})(1 - 0.9z^{-1})(1 - 2z^{-1})}$

52. A motor-driven load has a peak velocity of 2 in./sec, a peak acceleration of 5 in./sec^2 and a transfer function

$$G_s(s) = \frac{1}{s(1 + 0.04s)}$$

It is to be used as the output member of a positional servo system. Measurement of the output position must be sampled. Disturbing signals of bandwidth less than 20 radians/sec occur at the input of the motor. Because of saturation and bearing friction variations, the d-c gain of the output member can change by 30 per cent. The system is required to follow with small error a curve made up of segments of straight lines with breaks no oftener than one break per second and with slopes no steeper than 1 in./sec. Select a minimum sampling rate for this system and design a system which will behave as well as a continuous-data system would.

53. Shown in Fig. P.53 is the simplified schematic diagram of a sweep-position control system for a cathode-ray tube trace. The system is intended to position sweep traces

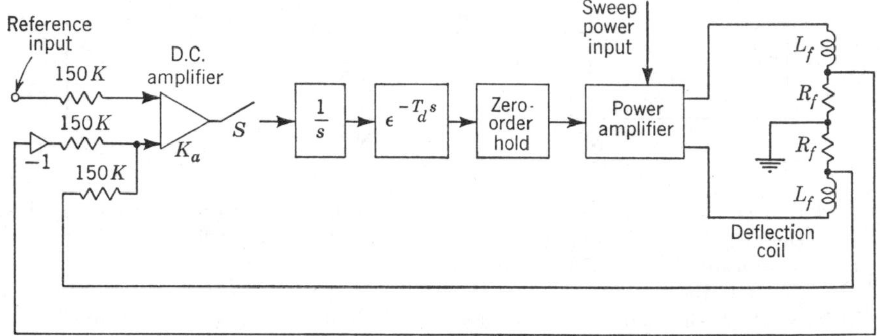

FIG. P. 53

on a cathode-ray tube presentation by comparing a voltage derived from the deflection-coil current to a reference voltage, sampling the resulting error before or during the sweep, and correcting the error before the next sweep is initiated. Because the visible trace must not be distorted, it is necessary to delay correction of error until sweep recovery time. The required accuracy is that any selected point on the trace should be correctly positioned to within 1/1000 of the tube diameter. This figure is referred to as one unit error. The feedback signal is derived from each deflection coil as a voltage across the 10-ohm series resistor. One unit error is equal to 10 mv. Maximum amplitude of the step function to which the system will be subjected is 100 mv. The sampling period of this system is 600 μsec. The circuit parameters of this system are given below:

Summing amplifier................	Gain $K_a = 50$
Transport lag....................	$T_d = 540\ \mu$sec
Deflection coil....................	$L_f = 1$ mh
Series resistor....................	$R_f = 10$ ohms

The output impedance of the power amplifier is ignored. Design a system so that the response to a step-function input settles to within 10 per cent in two sampling periods, and the response to a step-function disturbance at the load is reduced to less than 10 per cent in two sampling periods.[207]

54. For the sampled-data control system shown in Fig. 10.2-1, the sampling period is taken as 0.2 sec, the hold circuit is of zero order, and the controlled system has the transfer function

$$G_s(s) = \frac{10}{s(1 + 0.1s)(1 + 0.05s)}$$

Design a digital compensator to meet the following requirements: (1) The system response to a step-function input can have no ripples and no error in the steady state; (2) the transient must die out in the shortest possible time.

55. For the *digital-aid* system shown in Fig. P.55 the samplers operate with a sampling period equal to 1 sec, the hold circuit is of zero order, and the transfer function of the controlled system is

$$G_s(s) = \frac{10}{s(1 + s)}$$

Design a digital compensator so that the system may respond to a unit step-function input with a minimum settling time and zero steady-state error at the sampling instants.

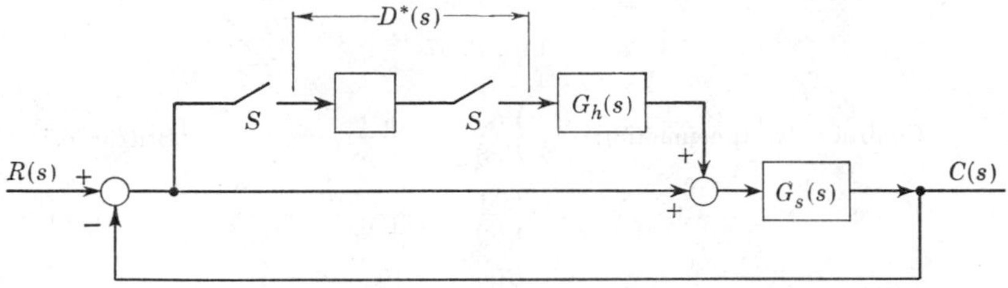

FIG. P. 55

56. Shown in Fig. P.56 is a digital-aid feedback control system. Derive the z transform of the system output, and discuss the effect of the feedforward digital control upon the system performance.

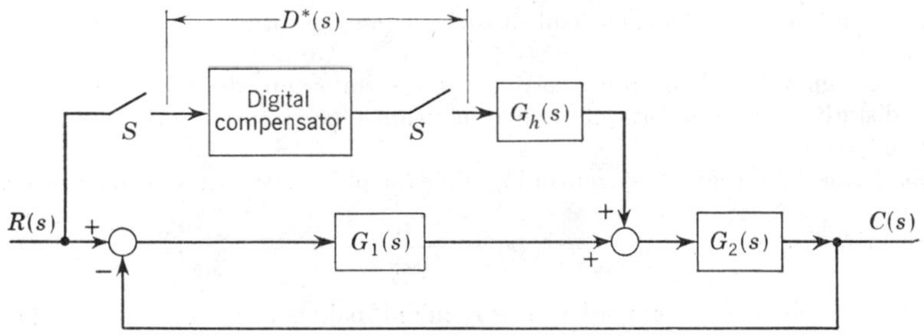

FIG. P. 56

57. In a chemical plant, the temperature of 10 identical fractionating columns must be kept constant. The accurate control of temperature is accomplished by the scheme shown in Fig. P.57. In this temperature control system, a digital controller is time shared by the 10 fractionating columns. The sampling period of this digital control system is set at 10 sec. The heating medium is steam. The temperature of the fractionating column is measured by a thermocouple which indicates 10 mv for 1°C. The transfer functions are

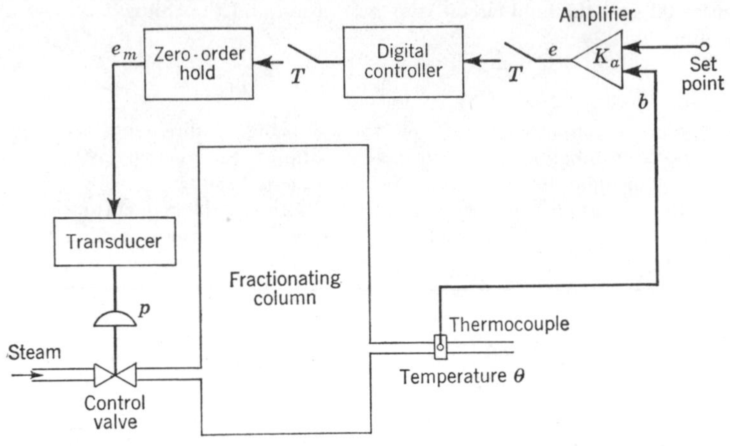

FIG. P. 57

Control valve (pneumatic):	$\dfrac{Y(s)}{P(s)} = \dfrac{5}{1 + 3s}$	Btu/hr/psi
Process:	$\dfrac{\theta(s)}{Y(s)} = \dfrac{10}{1 + 25s + 105s^2}$	°C/Btu/hr
Thermocouple:	$\dfrac{B(s)}{\theta(s)} = \dfrac{10}{1 + 8s}$	mv/°C
Transducer:	$\dfrac{P(s)}{E_m(s)} = 15$	psi/volt
Amplifier gain:	$K_a = 4$	volts/volt

(*a*) Draw a block diagram for one channel of this temperature control system for changes in both set point and load disturbance in the form of change in steam temperature.

(*b*) Design a digital controller so that the system output due to a suddenly applied load disturbance in the form of change in steam temperature decays rapidly with no overshoot.

58. In the digital control system of Fig. P.58 the plant has a transfer function given by

$$G_s(s) = \frac{10}{s(1 + s)^2}$$

and the hold circuit is of zero order. It is required to design a system which will respond

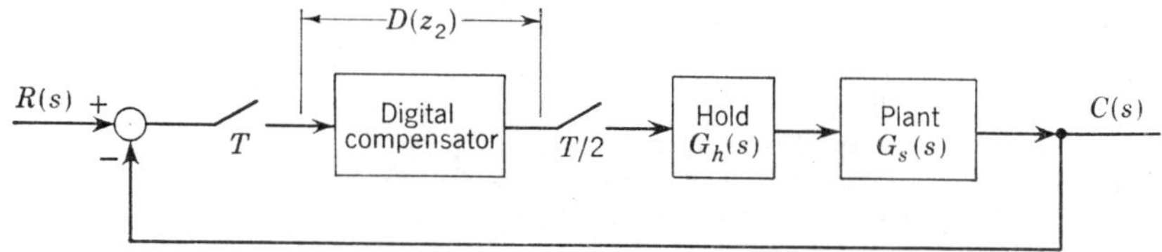

FIG. P. 58

to a unit ramp-function input with the shortest settling time and zero steady-state error at the sampling instants.

(*a*) Design a multirate digital compensator to meet the above requirement. The input to the digital compensator is sampled at a rate of one sample per second and the output from the compensator is sampled twice as fast.

(*b*) Evaluate the ramp-function response and plot.

(*c*) Design a single-rate digital compensator to meet the above requirements: (1) with the sampling period equal to 1 sec; (2) with the sampling period equal to ½ sec. Evaluate the ramp-function responses and compare with the results of part *b*.

59. For the sampled-data control system shown in Fig. P.59, the input signal $r_s(t)$ has a spectral density given by

$$\phi_{r_sr_s}(s) = \frac{-4}{s^2 - 0.04}$$

and the noise input is assumed to be zero. The sampling period is taken as 0.2 sec. The hold circuit is of zero order.

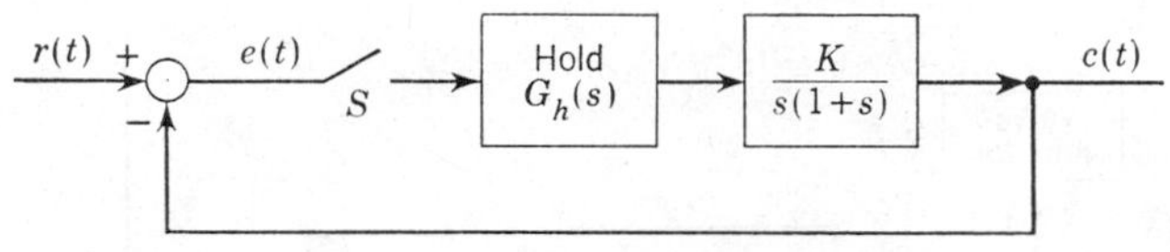

FIG. P. 59

(*a*) Select the gain constant K so that the mean-square value of the sampled error is minimum.

(*b*) Evaluate the minimum mean-square sampled error.

60. In the system of Prob. 59, assume that a noise having spectral density given by

$$\phi_{r_nr_n}(s) = 0.1$$

is present at the input. Design a digital compensator $D(z)$ that minimizes the mean-square sampled error due to the noise input.

61. A sampled-data system has the configuration shown in Fig. P.61. The transfer functions and the input signals are described by

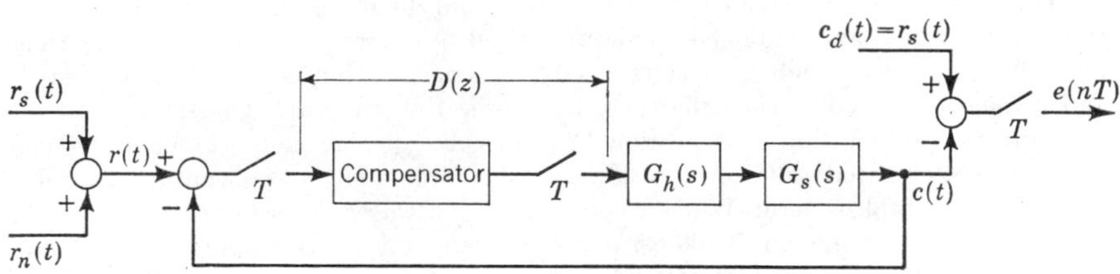

FIG. P. 61

$$G_s(s) = \frac{(1 + 0.005s)}{s\left[1 + \frac{s}{10} + \left(\frac{s}{10}\right)^2\right]}$$

$$G_h(s) = \frac{1 - \epsilon^{-Ts}}{s}$$

$$\phi_{r_sr_s}(s) = \frac{4.5}{\pi(0.25 - s^2)}$$

$$\phi_{r_nr_n}(s) = \frac{0.1}{\pi} \qquad \phi_{r_sr_n}(s) = 0$$

The sampling period is taken as 0.1 sec.

(a) Design a digital compensator $D(z)$ that minimizes the mean-square sampled error $\overline{e^2(nT)}$.

(b) Calculate the minimum value of $\overline{e^2(nT)}$.

62. In a chemical plant, a chemical process requires accurate control of the concentration of a salt solution. The control is accomplished by the scheme shown in Fig. P.62.

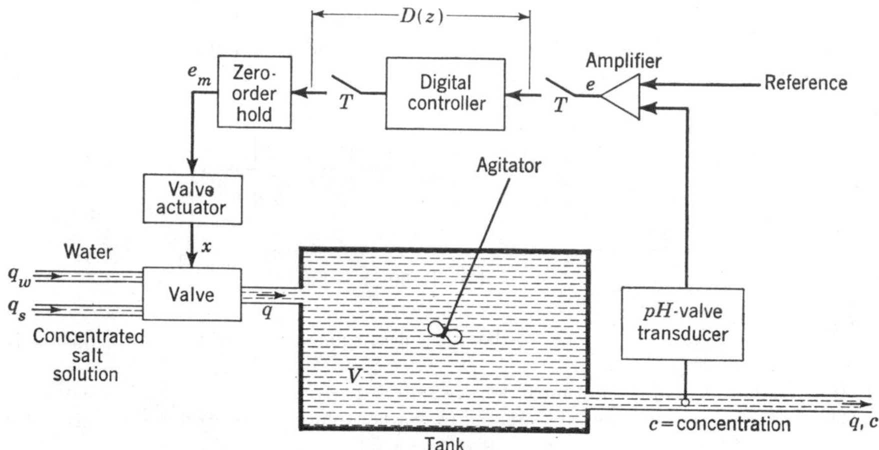

FIG. P. 62

In this concentration-control system a digital controller is time shared by a group of 10 identical tanks of salt solution. The sampling period of this digital control system is 10 sec. The concentration of the effluent is sensed by a pH-value transducer and is compared with a reference value. The deviation from the desired pH value is converted to a voltage signal and amplified, before it is used to operate the value actuator. The pH-value transducer reads zero volts when the concentration is zero (i.e., all water), and it indicates 10 volts when the concentration is 100 per cent. The inflow q_s of the concentrated salt solution is proportional to the valve displacement x. When x equals zero, no concentrated salt solution flows to the tank and the concentration of the influent to the tank is zero. When x equals 2 in., no water flows to the tank and the concentration of the influent is 100 per cent. The rate of flow q is equal to 0.1 cfs regardless of the valve position. The transfer function of the valve actuator is found to be

$$\frac{X(s)}{E_m(s)} = \frac{5}{s^2 + 4s + 16} \qquad \text{in./volt}$$

The volume of the tank is 5 cu ft. To simplify the analysis it is assumed that there is perfect mixing within the tank, that the concentration of the solution in the tank is equal to the concentration of the effluent from the tank, and that the time lag in the pH-value transducer and the quantization error may be ignored.

(a) Design a digital compensator for the system so that the system will have good transient response to a step-function input, and that the output due to load disturbance in the form of change in concentration of the incoming salt solution will decay rapidly with no overshoot.

(b) Evaluate the step-function response of the compensated system.

63. In a food processing plant, fluid A is mixed with fluid B to produce fluid C, as illustrated in Fig. P.63. The temperature of fluid C is accurately controlled by regulating

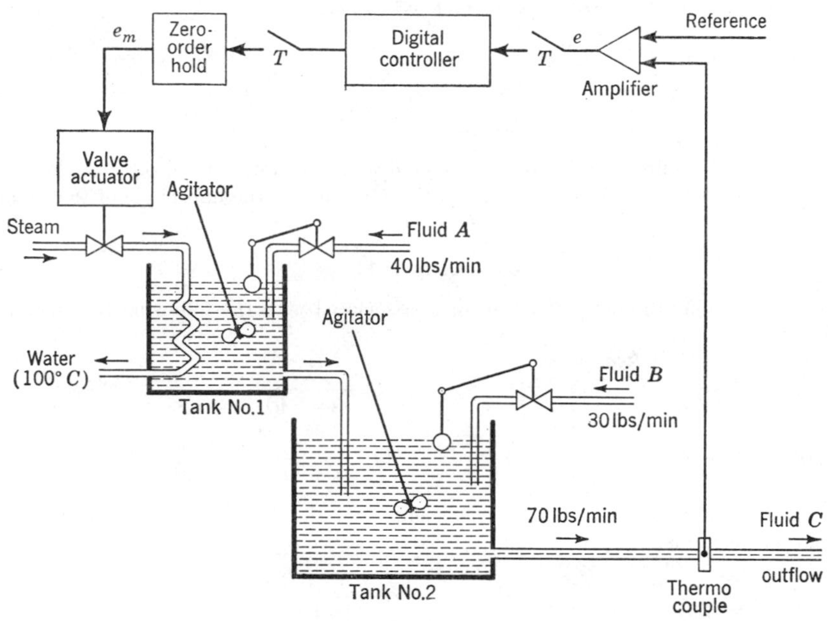

Fig. P. 63

the flow of steam for supplying heat to the food-making process. This system employs a digital controller which is time shared by 15 identical systems in the processing plant. Fluid A, which has a specific heat of 2 Btu/lb/°C and a temperature of 25 ± 5°C, is supplied to tank no. 1 at a flow rate of 40 lb/min. The temperature of fluid A may fluctuate with a period of 10 min. Fluid B, which has a specific heat of 4 Btu/lb/°C and a temperature of 45 ± 2°C, is fed to tank no. 2 at a flow rate of 30 lb/min. The temperature of fluid B may fluctuate with a period of several hours.† The temperature of fluid C is to be kept at 65 ± 0.5°C. The thermocouple, which puts out 10 mv/°C, has a time constant of 12 sec. Tank no. 1 contains 60 lb of fluid A; tank no. 2 contains 120 lb of the mixture; and the pipe from tank no. 2 to the location of the thermocouple contains 14 lb of fluid C. A voltage of 1 volt at the valve actuator moves the valve to allow an increase in steam flow by 10 lb/min. Linear variation of steam flow with the valve displacement may be assumed. The time lag in the valve actuator may be ignored. The sampling period of this digital control system is 15 sec.

Select the gain constant and design a digital controller for this temperature-control system. The system output due to load disturbance should decay rapidly.

64. If the pulse-spectral density of the input signal $x^*(t)$ to a system $G(s)$ is $\phi_{xx}(z)$

† Fluid B will be spoiled if it is heated above 85°C.

and the modified z transform associated with the system is $G(z,m)$, show that the "modified" pulse-spectral density of the output $y(t)$ of the system is given by

$$\phi_{yy}(z,m) = G(z,m)\, G(z^{-1},m)\, \phi_{xx}(z)$$

65. Show that the mean-square value of the output $y(t)$ of a system $G(s)$ subjected to a sampled input $x^*(t)$ is given by

$$\overline{y^2(t)} = \int_0^1 \overline{y^2(nT,m)}\, dm$$

where

$$\overline{y^2(nT,m)} = \frac{1}{2\pi j} \oint_\Gamma G(z,m)\, G(z^{-1},m)\, \phi_{xx}(z)\, z^{-1}\, dz$$

$G(z,m)$ is the modified z transform associated with the system $G(s)$, $\phi_{xx}(z)$ is the pulse-spectral density of the input signal, and the contour Γ is the unit circle of the z plane.

Chapter 11

66. Determine the delayed z transform associated with the following transfer functions:

(a) $\dfrac{1}{(s+a)^2}$ (b) $\dfrac{a}{s^2(s+a)}$

(c) $\dfrac{\omega_0}{s(s^2+\omega_0^2)}$ (d) $\dfrac{(a-b)^2+\omega_0^2}{(s+b)[(s+a)^2+\omega_0^2]}$

67. Determine the τ-transform coefficients and the τ transform for the following transfer functions:

(a) $\dfrac{1}{(s+a)^2}$ (b) $\dfrac{\omega_0}{(s+a)^2+\omega_0^2}$

68. For the sampled-data system shown in Fig. P.68, the controlled system has a transfer function given by

$$G_s(s) = \frac{K}{s(1+0.1s)}$$

the sampling period T is 0.1 sec and the sampling duration τ is 0.01 sec.

(a) Determine the maximum allowable gain for stability.

(b) When the gain constant K is set at 2, evaluate the unit step-function response of the system by means of the two methods of flat-top pulse approximation and the method of trapezoidal-pulse approximation. Compare the results.

(c) Discuss the effects of the sampling duration upon the system performance.

69. Referring to the block diagram of Fig. P.68, if the sampling period of the system is taken as 1 sec, the sampling duration of the sampler is in the range from 0.05 sec to 0.1 sec, and the controlled system has a transfer function given by

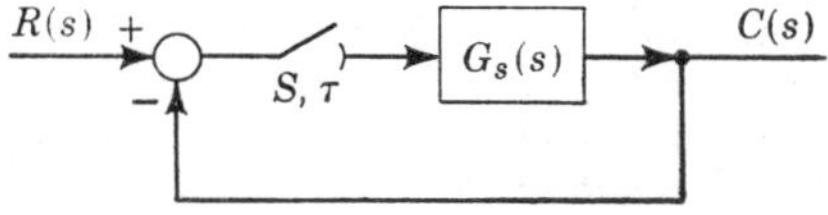

Fig. P. 68

$$G_s(s) = \frac{K}{s(1 + 0.5s)}$$

(*a*) Determine the maximum allowable gain for stability.

(*b*) Design a compensator to meet the requirements of a gain constant K equal to 10 and a damping ratio equal to 0.6.

(*c*) Evaluate the system response to a unit step-function input.

70. For the sampled-data control system with nonsynchronized samplers shown in Fig. P.70, the samplers operate with the same sampling period T equal to 1 sec. Sampler

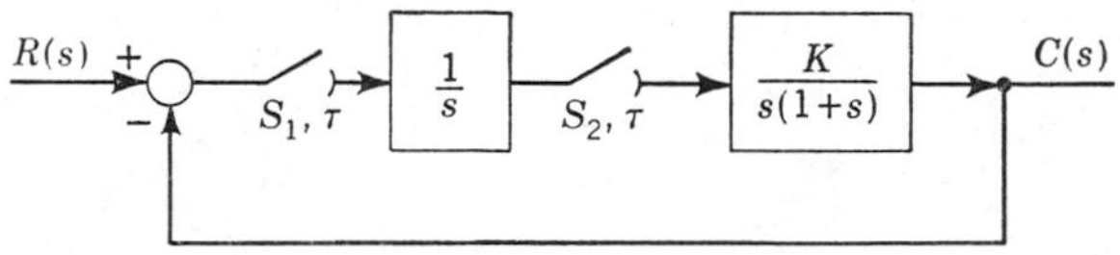

FIG. P. 70

S_1 operates at the instants 0, T, $2T$, . . . ; and sampler S_2 operates at the instants $T/2$, $3T/2$, $5T/2$, ... Both samplers have a sampling duration of 0.1 sec.

(*a*) Determine the maximum allowable gain for stability.

(*b*) Evaluate the step-function response for K equal to one-half of the maximum allowable gain.

(*c*) Repeat parts *a* and *b*, with these two samplers synchronized.

INDEX

A-c servo systems, 3, 60–68
Adaptation, 552
Adaptive control systems, 552–557
  classification of, 553
  design of, 553–557
Adaptive system, impulse-excited, 554, 555
  noise-excited, 555, 556
Airborne control systems, digital, 7
Amplifiers (*see* Operational amplifiers)
Amplitude quantization, 83–92, 112
Analog-digital conversion, requirements for, 375–377
Analog-to-digital converters, 369, 377–394
Analog simulation, 558, 559
Anderson, G. W., 555
Anodige, 378
Antiambiguity, 377
Area sampling, 92
Arithmetic in binary system, 370, 371
Aseltine, J. A., 554
Asymptotic gain plot, 31, 32, 247, 476
Asymptotic phase plot, 32–36
Automatic control, 1

Barker, R. H., 145, 185
Bilinear transformation, 244–247, 466–470
Binary code, 371
  cyclic (*see* Cyclic binary code)
Binary counter, 382
Binary encoding stage, design of, 391–394
Binary reading encoder, 383, 384
Binary-weighted resistors, 399, 400
Block diagram for sampled-data systems, 214–229
Block-diagram reduction, 17–20
  basic rules for, 18, 19
Bode-diagram technique, 31, 465–470, 475–479
Boxcar generator, 114, 134
Break frequency, 32

Calculus of variations in optimization, 549
Carrier-frequency control systems, 60–68
Cascade compensation, 40–44, 416–444
  of continuous-data systems, 40–44
  of sampled-data systems, 416–444
    by continuous-data networks, 416–430, 471–473
    by pulsed-data networks, 430–444
Cathode-ray voltage encoder, 386, 387
Characteristic equation of feedback control system, 23, 46, 125
Characteristic function, 91, 92
Characteristic roots, 46, 479
Clamping, 76–80
Closed-loop frequency response from open-loop frequency-characteristic locus, 122–125
Closed-loop multirate sampled-data systems, 281–304
Closed-loop poles and zeros related to maximum overshoot and peak time, 330–336
Code pulse, 395
Compensation of discrete-data systems, 417–444, 465–500
  cascade (*see* Cascade compensation)
  by continuous-data networks, 418–430, 471–473
  by data processing, 449–454
  by digital programming, 445–449
  feedback, 458–462, 478, 479
  pole-zero shifting, 487–491
  by pulsed-data *RC* networks, 430–444
Complementary components (*see* Complementary signals)
Complementary signals, 74, 95–97, 110, 336
Complex convolution, 99, 190
Conditional feedback systems, 528, 529

Constant-damping locus, 493–495
  in s plane, 494
  in z plane, 494, 495
Constant-M loci, 415, 416
Continuous-data network compensation, 417–430
  dual-rate sampling approximation, 421–430
  finite sum approximation, 418–421
Contours of constant maximum overshoot, 336
  computation of, 335, 336
Conversion of number systems, 371
  binary to decimal, 371
  conventional binary to cyclic binary, 375
  cyclic binary to conventional binary, 375, 387
  decimal to binary, 371
Conversion time, 376
Convolution integral, 103
Convolution summation, 105
Correlation functions, 536–540
  autocorrelation, 536
  cross-correlation, 536, 537
  properties of, 538–540
Correlation sequence, 543–549
  autocorrelation, 543, 544
  cross-correlation, 543, 544
  properties of, 546–549
Cramer's rule, 312
Cyclic binary code, 373–375
  conversation to conventional binary code, 375, 387
  properties of, 374, 375
Cyclic-to-binary translator, 387

Damping line, 53, 493
Damping spiral, 494, 495
Data signal, 62
Decimal code, 372
Decoders, parallel, 399–404
  serial, 369–399
  simulation of, 403, 404
Decrement factor, 491, 492
Delay-line networks, 444, 449–454
Delayed sampler, 580
Delayed z transform, 563–566
Design charts for sampled-data systems, 436–440
Difference equation, 328
Digital-to-analog converters, 369, 394–404
Digital code, 369
Digital compensation, 444, 502
Digital control of machine tools, 12
Digital control systems, airborne, 7
  sampled-data equivalent of, 111–113
  statistical design of, 534–551
Digital programming, 444–449
  direct, 445, 446
  iterative, 446, 447
  parallel, 447–448
Digital simulation, 558, 560
Diode matrix, 383
Direct z transformation, 177
Double-brush method, 385
Dual-rate sampled-data systems, 425–429
Dual-rate sampling approximation, 421–430
Duality between signals and impulse responses, 157

Encoders, 369, 376–394
  angle, 382
  counting-type, 378–394
  feedback, 389, 390
  reading-type, 383–387
  simulation of, 390–394
  time-base, 378–382
  voltage, binary mask, 386, 387
  weighing-type, 388, 389
Equivalent sampler, 282, 305, 313, 581
Ergodic hypothesis, 535
Error coefficients, 265, 269–281
  for continuous-data systems, 270–274
    evaluation of, 272
  for sampled-data systems, 274–281
    evaluation of, 275, 276
Error constants, 265–269
  acceleration-, 265, 269, 503
  jerk-, 503
  position-, 265, 266, 503
  velocity-, 265, 268, 473, 474, 503
Error sequence, 518
  mean-square value of, 545
Evaluation of inverse z transforms (*see* Inversion of z transforms)
External disturbance, 140–143, 527
  minimization of effect of, 527–530
  suppression of, 140–143, 527–529
Extrapolation, 127

Feedback compensation, 40, 44, 45, 458–462, 478, 479
Feedback control systems, classification of, 1–4
  definition of, 1
  nonlinear, 2, 3
Feedback encoding (*see* Encoders)
Feedforward control, 526–529
Fictitious frequency, 466
Figure of merit, 554
Final value theorem, 163, 164, 197, 364
Finite settling-time systems, 502–517, 531–534
Finite sum approximation, 418–421
First-order hold, 136–139
  frequency characteristics of, 138, 139
  transfer function of, 137, 138
Flat-top pulse approximation, 572–576
Fourier transform, 536
Frequency-characteristic locus, 117–125
  construction of, 117–120
  properties of, 120
Frequency-modulated function, 309
Frequency response, closed-loop, from open-loop frequency-characteristic locus, 122–125
  open-loop, 117–120
Frequency-response function, open-loop, 115–122
Frequency-response technique, 15, 108–117
Frequency spectrum, 72–76, 110, 111
  amplitude, 74–76
  line, 74, 75
  phase, 74
Fundamental theorem of sampling, 80–82

Gain adjustment, 39, 414–416
Gain-phase plot, 31
GCI system, 11
Gray code (*see* Cyclic binary code)

Hidden instability, 357, 359, 360, 362
Hidden oscillation, 356–366
Hold circuit, 112, 127–139
  effects of, on system performance, 139, 140
  first-order, 128, 136–139
  high-order, 128, 577
  triangular, 578, 579
  zero-order, 128, 130–136
Holding, imperfect, 136
Holding device (*see* Hold circuit)
Homeostat, 553
Homeostatic mechanisms, 553
Hurewicz, W., 145, 184

Impulse modulation, 94
Impulse response, 20, 103, 146, 357, 358, 554
Impulse-response area ratio, 554, 555
Initial-value theorem, 164, 165, 196, 364
Intermodulation, 144
Interpolation, 127, 198–200
  Newton's formula of, 199
Intersampling ripples, 336–349, 512, 513
  analysis of, 338–349
    by modified z-transform method, 348, 349
    by pulse-train response method, 338–347
  suppression of, 512, 513
Inverse modified z transformation, 194–196
Inverse z-transform integral, 177
  derivation of, 177, 178
Inversion of z transforms (*see* z transform)

Kalman, R. E., 556
Ku, Y. H., 3

Laplace transform, approximation using z forms, 208–210
  of impulse sequence, 98–102, 215
Laurent series, 208
Linearity, 161
Locus-reshaping technique, 418, 422, 430, 436–444
Logical addition, 375

M criterion, 420
Magnitude ratio, 415, 416, 420
Mathematical simulation, 558, 560
Maximum allowable gain charts, 486
Maximum overshoot, 330–336
  contours of, 336
  evaluation of, 330–332
Mean-square error, 354, 527–541
  minimization of, 527, 535–541
  in terms of spectral densities, 537, 541
Mean-square sampled error, 541
  minimization of, 549–551

Minimum settling-time system, design of, 503–512
restrictions for, 504, 508, 509
Minor-loop compensation (*see* Feedback compensation)
Modified pulse-transfer function, 189, 255
Modified z transform, 184–198, 255, 256, 284, 285
definition of, based on residue evaluation, 189–191
based on series summation, 186–189
evaluation of, 191–194
final-value theorem for, 197, 198
initial-value theorem for, 196, 197
table of, 588–592
use of, to determine pulse-transfer function of systems with delay and advance, 285, 289, 305
to determine system behavior between sampling instant and hidden oscillations, 255–265, 356–362
Modified z-transform pair, 187, 188
Modified z-transform technique, 255
Modulated control systems, 3, 4, 60–68
Modulation, pulse-amplitude, 6
pulse-code, 6
Multiar, 381
Multiple-input systems, 525–530
Multirate compensators, design of, 531–534
Multirate sampled-data systems, 281–304
closed-loop, 293–304
concept of equivalent sampler, 282, 305, 313, 581
open-loop, 282–293
reduction to equivalent single-rate sampled-data system, 282–285, 293–296

Nonlinear feedback control systems, 2
methods of analysis, 3
Nonlinearity in sampled-data systems, 143, 144, 322
Nonsynchronized sampled-data systems, 304–308
analysis of, 305–307
Number systems, 369–375
binary, 369–372
binary-coded decimal, 369, 372
cyclic-binary, 369, 373–375
decimal, 369–371
Numerical integration process, 198–207
rectangular rule, 200, 201
Simpson's one-eighth rule, 205–206
Simpson's one-third rule, 203–205
trapezoidal rule, 201–203
Weddle's rule, 206
Nyquist diagram for sampled-data control systems (*see* Frequency-characterisic locus)

One-bit coder-decoder circuit, 391
Open-loop frequency response, 117–120
Open-loop frequency-response function, 115–122
Open-loop multirate sampled-data systems, 282–293
Open-loop poles, 47, 487
imperfect cancellation of, 59, 60, 489–491
shifting of, 47–49, 487–489
Open-loop zeros, 49, 487
imperfect cancellation of, 489, 490
shifting of, 49–52, 487, 488
Operational amplifiers, 390, 403
for decoding, 403, 404
for encoding, 390–394
Optimization, 501
calculus of variations in, 549
self-, 501
Optimum control, 501, 502
Optimum pulse-transfer function, 551
Oscillation, hidden, 356–366
Output sequence, 249–255
evaluation of, 108, 249–253
Output transform, 214
derivation of, 214–229
for closed-loop systems, 218–229
for open-loop systems, 214–218
Over-all pulse-transfer function, 214

Parallel decoding circuit, 399–404
Parity, 374
Partial-fraction expansion, 179, 180
PCM signal, 395
Peak-holding system, 553
Peak time, 330
evaluation of, 330–332
relation to closed-loop poles and zeros, 332–336
Phantastron circuit, 381

Physical simulation, 558–560
Poisson summation rule, 100
Pole-zero configuration, 323–327
Polygonal hold, 577
Position value, 396
Position-value distribution curve, 396, 398
Positional notation, 370
Power-series expansion, 180–182
Primary component (*see* Primary signal)
Primary signal, 95–97, 336
Principal $\mathcal{L}$ transform, 177, 457, 472
Probability-distribution function, 535
Process-control computer, 8, 9
Programming (*see* Digital programming)
Pulse approximation, flat-top, 572–576
Pulse cross-spectral density, 543, 544, 546–549
Pulse-spectral density, 543–545
  properties of, 546–549
Pulse-transfer functions, 147–160, 531
  definition of, 147, 148, 157, 158
  evaluation of, 149–160
    based on residue evaluation, 157–160
    from weighting sequence, 150–156
  modified, 189, 255
  of multirate compensator, 531
  optimum, 551
  over-all, 214
  properties of, 166–169
  realization of, 444–464
  rules for calculating, 155, 156
  system-error, 274
  of systems with delay or advance, 285, 289, 305
Pulse value, 396
Pulse width, 562
Pulsed-data network, 430, 431
  realizability restrictions, 434, 458, 461
    on basic feedback structure, 461
    on basic series structure, 458
  stability of, 434–436
  synthesis of, from pulse-transfer functions, 444–464
Pulsed-data *RC* networks, 454–464
  basic feedback structure, 458–462
  basic series structure, 456–458
  combination of series and feedback structure, 462–464
  realizability restrictions for, 434, 458, 461

Quadrature formulas, 200
Quantization error, 7, 86–92
  mean-square value of, 86, 87, 92
  probability distribution of, 88–90
  statistical analysis of, 88–92
Quantizer, as noise generator, 112
  simulation of, 559
Quantum marks, 383

Radix, 369, 370
Radix point, 370
Ragazzini, J. R., 145, 352
Random process, stationary, 535
Real inversion integral, 178, 179, 194, 195
Real-time simulation, 558
Real translation, 161, 162
Realization restrictions for pulsed-data *RC* networks, 434, 458, 461
  basic feedback structure, 461
  basic series structure, 458
Reflected binary code (*see* Cyclic binary code)
Resistance-switching circuit, 400, 402, 404
Resistance-switching decoder, 400–404
  basic form of, 400–402
  improved version of, 402, 403
  with operational amplifiers, 403, 404
Resolution, 376
Ripple content, 129, 349
Ripple factor, 352
Ripple filter, 113
Ripple-free systems, design of, 512–518
Rms error, 349
Root locus in *z* plan, 481–499
Root-locus techniques, for continuous-data systems, 45–61
  magnitude equation, 46, 482
  phase-angle equation, 46, 482
  pole-zero shifting compensation, 59, 60, 490
  for sampled-data systems, 479–499
Routh stability criterion, 23–25

SAGE system, 11
Sampler, 93, 97
  mathematical descriptions of, 97–101
Sampling duration, 562
Sampling frequency, 72, 349
  determination of, from rms error, 349–356

Sampling process, 4, 69, 112
Scale change in z domain, 162, 163
Schmitt trigger circuit, 382
Self-optimization, 501
Serial decoding circuit, 396–399
Series compensation (*see* Cascade compensation)
Servomechanism, definition of, 1
Settling time, finite, conditions for, 503, 504
  minimum, conditions for, 504
    design for, 491, 502–512
  minimum allowable, restrictions for, 508, 509
Shaft digitizer, 384, 385
Shannon-Rack decoder, 399
Sidebands (*see* Complementary signals)
Simulation, 130, 390, 403, 557–560
  of decoders, 403, 404
  digital, 558, 560
  of encoders, 390–394
  of holding operation, 130, 131
  physical, 558–560
  of quantizer, 559
  real-time, 558
Single-bit encoding stage, 390
Sinusoidal sequence, 410–413
Sklansky, J., 352
Slip factor, 305
Smith, B. D., 390
Spatial encoding, 383–387
Spectral density, 536–540
  properties of, 538–540
Squared-error sequence, 521
  sum of, minimization of, 518–525
Stability criteria, 20–30, 230–249
  for continuous-data systems, 20–30
  for discrete-data systems, 230–249
    modified Routh, 244, 245
    Nyquist, 230–238
    Schur-Chon, 238–241
    simplified, for second-order systems, 241–244
Stability improvement through nonsynchronized sampling, 307, 308
Stabilization, by sampling, 127, 320
  by transport-lag element, 318–321
Staleness-weighting factor, 519
  determination of, 519–520
Starred transform (Laplace transform of impulse sequence), 98–102, 215
Stationary random process, 535
Statistical design of digital control systems, 534–551
Statistical sampler, 92
Steady-state error at sampling instants, conditions for zero, 503, 533
Sum of squared-error sequence, minimization of, 518–525
Suppressed-carrier amplitude-modulated a-c signal, 60
Suppression of external disturbance, 140–143, 527–529
System error, 265, 337, 518
  evaluation of, 336–349
  minimization of, 518–525
System-error pulse-transfer function, 274
System-error weighting function, 270
System response, approximate time response, 251–254
  evaluation of, 247–265
  during intersampling periods, 255–265
  at sampling instants, 249–255
Systems with multirate controller, 300–304
  design of, 531–534

Tables, of delayed z transforms, 565
  of modified z transforms, 588–592
  of output transforms of basic sampled-data systems, 224, 225
  of system-error pulse-transfer functions for minimum settling time, 505
  of τ-transform coefficients, 571
  of z forms, 209
  of z transforms, 160, 588–592
τ transform, 567–571
τ-transform coefficients, 570, 571
Taylor series, 270, 272, 273
Temporary storage, 377
Time-domain specifications, 38, 323, 329
Time encoding, 378–382
Time sharing, 7
Transfer function, 15–17
  basic forms of, 16
  of first-order hold, 137
  of triangular hold, 578, 579
  of zero-order hold, 134
Transient response of sampled-data system, 255–258, 324–327
Transport lag, 318
  effect of, 321
Trapezoidal hold, 577

Trapezoidal pulse, 577
Trapezoidal-pulse approximation, 577–580
Trapezoidal sampler, 577, 578
Triangular hold, 578, 579
Two-sided z transform, 543, 544
  definition of, 543
  inversion of, 544

Unit-distance number system, 373
Unit-sampling function, 70–72

V-scan method, 377
Variable-rate sampled-data systems, 308–318
  analysis of, 309–314
Variable-rate sampling technique, 557
Velocity-error constant in w plane, 473, 474

w plane, definition of, 244, 465, 466
  relation to z plane, 245
  velocity-error constant in, 473, 474
w transform, 244, 467
w-transform technique, 244, 465–479
Weighting function, 20, 102, 146
Weighting sequence, 104, 105, 147
Wiener-Kolmogoroff theory, 535, 541

z domain, scale change in, 162, 163
z form for integration, 207–212
  applications of, 209–212
z plane, definition of, 145, 169
  relation to s plane, 169–171
  root locus in, 481–499
z-transfer function (*see* Pulse-transfer function)
z transform, 145–149
  definition of, 145, 146
  delayed, 563–566
  evaluation of, 149–159
    based on residue evaluation, 157–159
    from weighting sequence, 150–156
  final-value theorem for, 163, 164
  for functions with dead-time delay or advance, 285, 289, 305
  initial-value theorem for, 164, 165
  inversion of, 176–180
    by contour integration, 178, 179
    by long division, 180–182
    by partial-fraction expansion, 179, 180
  modified (*see* Modified z transform)
  properties of, 166–169
  table of, 160, 588–592
  two-sided, 543, 544
z-transform loci, 169–176, 407, 408
  characteristics of, 171–175
  construction of, 169–171
z-transform technique, 145
  modified, 255
z transformation, 145–149
  inverse modified, 194–196
Zadeh, L. A., 145
Zero-order hold, 130–136
  circuits for, 130, 131
  frequency characteristics of, 135
  transfer functions of, 131–134
Zero steady-state error, 502, 532
  conditions for, at sampling instants, 503, 533
  design for, 502–512, 532–534
z_n transform, 286